LINEAR LIE GROUPS

This is Volume 35 in
PURE AND APPLIED MATHEMATICS
A Series of Monographs and Textbooks
Edited by PAUL SMITH AND SAMUEL EILENBERG
A complete list of titles in this series appears at the end of this volume

LINEAR LIE GROUPS

HANS FREUDENTHAL

Mathematisch Instituut der Rijksuniversiteit te Utrecht
Utrecht, The Netherlands

H. de VRIES

Mathematisch Instituut der Katholieke Universiteit te Nijmegen
Nijmegen, The Netherlands

ACADEMIC PRESS New York and London 1969

ACADEMIC PRESS, INC.
111 Fifth Avenue, New York, New York 10003

United Kingdom Edition published by
ACADEMIC PRESS, INC. (LONDON) LTD.
Berkeley Square House, London, W1X 6BA

LIBRARY OF CONGRESS CATALOG CARD NUMBER: 68-23479
AMS 1968 SUBJECT CLASSIFICATION 2250

PRINTED IN THE UNITED STATES OF AMERICA

CONTENTS

13–19. Solvability and Semisimplicity

20–27. Dressings and Classification of Semisimple Complex Lie Algebras

28–38. Topological and Integration Methods

39–50. The Algebraic Approach to Linear Representations

51–62. Reality in Lie Groups and Algebras and Their Linear Representations

63–67. Symmetric Spaces

68–75. Tits Geometries

76–77. Betti Numbers of Semisimple Lie Groups and Regular Subalgebras of Semisimple Lie Algebras

Appendix

Tables in the Text

Graphs

0. INTRODUCTION

0.0. Preface

Be either consequent or inconsequent, never both together. (*An unknown moralist.*)

This is not a motto. It is rather an anti-motto. The authors have tried to be both. One may still wonder whether consequential inconsequence or inconsequential consequence prevails. Purity of method has been pursued, sometimes as an ideal, sometimes as a hobby, sometimes for no reason whatsoever. Impurity of method has been allowed for pragmatic reasons or because of its charm. Group and Lie algebra methods are by turns interwoven and neatly separated. Diction vacillates between formality and looseness. Function notation has been perfected, but still the authors struggled with derivatives. Categories have not been used, even where they were badly needed. The most serious flaw, however, is that the authors stuck to our grandfathers' fields of the real and complex numbers. So neither algebraic groups nor Lie algebras over more general fields have been mentioned. In contrast, the restriction to *linear* Lie groups has been rather pragmatic.

The present work is a textbook in the sense that it aims at leading the reader more and evermore quickly to attractive results, even if this means a maze of unrelated subjects in a seemingly illogical arrangement and a lack of lengthy introductions of a highly abstract character. On the other hand, it looks like a compendium where it goes into pedantic classificatory details, summarized in so many tables (those of Section 75 included) that before long it will belong to the class of books which contain all possible tables except those one needs at the precise moment.

The reader of the present book is expected to have mastered the fundamental ideas of modern mathematics so that he may employ them with decent skill. The main subjects treated are classification of semisimple complex and real Lie algebras, their finite-dimensional linear representations and their automorphisms, the fundamental groups and Betti numbers of Lie groups, symmetric spaces, and Tits geometries. Some results and many methods are new. Deviations from traditional notations and nomenclature are justified after this preface, and an inventory of definitions is found on page 539. References are always to chapters, sections, and subsections, never to pages.

The present work has grown from gradually revised courses taught by the first author since 1931. From 1962 he has been assisted by the second author who has taken an ever increasing part in its contents and its formulation. Their cooperation has grown so close that finally the first of them does not understand how he could ever have thought to write this book alone.

Utrecht, Nijmegen

HANS FREUDENTHAL
H. DE VRIES

May 1967

0.1–7. ON NOTATION AND NOMENCLATURE

0.1. Logical Symbols

$\urcorner$ (non), $\wedge$ (or), $\vee$ (and), $\rightarrow$ (if ... then), $\leftrightarrow$ (if and only if), iff (if and only if).

$\bigvee_x$ (there is an x), $\bigwedge_x$ (all x).

Remark These notations are didactically justified by their analogy with the set theory notation.

0.2. Set Theory Symbols

$\bigcirc$ (void set).

Remark A void circle is the most intuitive symbolization of a void set. The struck out circle (or digit zero), quite usual nowadays, rather conjures the idea of a nonvoid set. This is clearly shown by the great confusion between $= \varnothing$ and $\neq \varnothing$ in the literature. During the first half-century of set theory, the void set was indicated by the same symbol as the number zero. Of course this had to be changed. A circle is a natural symbol for a void set and looks sufficiently different from a digit zero.

$\in$ (element of), $\notin$ (not element of).
$\subset$ (included in), $\supset$ (includes), $\not\subset$, $\not\supset$ (negations of the preceding).
$\cup$, $\bigcup$ (union), $\cap$, $\bigcap$ (intersection).
$(x \in A \setminus B) \leftrightarrow [(x \in A) \wedge (x \notin B)]$.
$(x \in \{a_1, \ldots, a_n\}) \leftrightarrow \bigvee_i (x = a_i)$.
$\ulcorner a, b \urcorner$ (the ordered pair of a, b).
$\ulcorner a_1, \ldots, a_n \urcorner$ (the ordered n-tuple).
$\ulcorner A, B \urcorner$ (the set of $\ulcorner a, b \urcorner$ with $a \in A$ and $b \in B$).
$\ulcorner A_1, \ldots, A_n \urcorner$ (analogously).

Remark Brackets are needed for other purposes. It is desirable to spare them.

$\uparrow_{x \in A} F(x)$ (the set of $x \in A$ with the property F).

Remark The usual notation $\{x \in A | F(x)\}$ has several disadvantages: it spills braces, which are badly needed in punctuation and in pair forming, as tools for binding variables. It indicates the binding of a variable in a rather unusual way. It has been misinterpreted and misused so often that there is no longer a clear agreement on the place of the variable that undergoes binding.

The present notation derives from B. Russell's $\hat{x}((x \in A) \wedge F(x))$. To avoid typographical troubles, the roof has been put on a pole.

$\Upsilon_x (\ldots x \ldots)$ (the expression between the parentheses as a function of x).

$\Upsilon_{x \in A} (\ldots x \ldots)$ (needs no further explanation).

Examples

$\Upsilon_x x^2$ = square of ....

$\Upsilon_x \log x = \log$.

If a group G is under discussion:

$\Upsilon_x axa^{-1}$ = the inner automorphism of G induced by a.

$\Upsilon_a \Upsilon_x axa^{-1}$ = the canonical homomorphic mapping of G onto its group of inner automorphisms.

If on the group G a set of functions is considered:

$\mathscr{R}_c \varphi = \Upsilon_a \varphi(ac)$ (right translate).

$\mathscr{R}_c = \Upsilon_\varphi \Upsilon_a \varphi(ac)$ (right translation).

$\mathscr{R} = \Upsilon_c \Upsilon_\varphi \Upsilon_a \varphi(ac)$ (representation by right translation).

Remark No doubt a symbol for function forming is badly needed. Traditional arrow notation like $x \to (\ldots x \ldots)$ would lead to clumsy expressions in the last few examples.

The historical background of the present notation is analogous to that of $\uparrow_{x \in A} F(x)$.

The composition of mappings has been denoted in the natural way rather than by a sign $\circ$.

$f|_A$ (restriction of a mapping f to a set A).

$=$ (equal), $\neq$ (unequal).

$<, >, \leqslant, \geqslant$

are used to describe various order relations besides those between cardinalities and real numbers.

inf (greatest lower bound), sup (least upper bound).

0.3. Topological Symbols

lim (limit).

$\bar{A}$ (closure of the set A; see, however, $\bar{\alpha}$ sub 0.4).

dim (topological dimension; see also dim sub 0.4).

0.4. Algebraic Symbols

The signs

$+$, $\cdot$ (often omitted), $-$, $^{-1}$, Σ, Π, 0 (sometimes boldface), 1,

are used to denote the algebraic operations of addition, multiplication, and so on, and the zero and unit elements of various algebraic systems, besides those of the field of complex numbers; 0 and 1 are also used to indicate the null and identity mappings in linear spaces.

$\beta^{-1}\alpha$ is sometimes written $\frac{\alpha}{\beta}$ or α/β.

The syggram $\pm$ means that at that spot in the context both signs are allowed. If more syggrams occur in the same context, it is usually explicitly indicated whether or not their contents vary dependently.

A sub B means that A is a substructure (not only a subset) of B.

A/B (factor group, homogeneous space of the multiplicative group A with respect to the subgroup B).

A mod B ("factor" group, or ring, of the additive group, or ring A, with respect to the subgroup, or the ideal B).

$A+B$, $A-B$, AB, A^{-1}, and so on (the set of $a+b$, $a-b$, ab, a^{-1}, with $a \in A$, $b \in B$).

A' (transpose [of a matrix]).

tr (trace [of a linear mapping]).

det (determinant [of a linear mapping]).

rank (rank [of a linear mapping]; see, however, Definitions 15.3 and 72.2).

$\otimes$ (tensoring symbol).

$(\ldots,\ldots)$, $\langle\ldots,\ldots\rangle$ (inner product).

$A^{\perp}$ (orthoplement of a set A in a linear space with an inner product, that is, the set of elements orthogonal to all of A).

$a^{\perp}$ (orthoplement of an element a).

i (imaginary unit of the field of complex numbers).

Re, Im (real, imaginary "part").

$\bar{\alpha}$ (complex conjugate of α).

$|\cdots|$ (absolute value, vector norm).

Boldface† characters usually indicate Lie algebras or elements and subsets thereof.

L, **L** type indicate certain classes of Lie groups, and Lie algebras. $\tilde{a}$, $\breve{\boldsymbol{a}}$ are the adjoints of a, $\boldsymbol{a}$ (in a Lie group or algebra).

† On the blackboard underlining is a substitute for boldface type.

0.5. Analytic Symbols

lim (limit).
e (basis of natural logarithms).
exp (exponential function).
π (half perimeter of unit circle).
Γ (gamma-function).
grad (gradient; see Key to Definitions on page 539).

0.6. Logograms

(Not all occurring combinations of logograms are listed.)

Rea: field of real numbers†
Com: field of complex numbers†
Qio: skew field of quaternions†
Spa: spaces
Lin: linear
Spa Lin: linear spaces
Spa Lin Rea: real linear spaces
Spa Lin Com: complex linear spaces
Top: topological
Hau: Hausdorff (as an adjective)
Spa Top: topological spaces
Spa Lin Top: linear topological spaces
Cls: closed
Con: connected
pc: pathwise connected
lpc: locally pathwise connected
lsc: locally simply connected
Nor: provided with a norm
Spa Lin Nor: normed linear spaces
Inp: provided with an inner product
Gru: groups
Lie: Lie (as an adjective)
Gru Lie Lin: linear Lie groups
Alg: Algebras
Alg Rea: real algebras
Alg Com: complex algebras
Alg Lin Lie: linear Lie algebras
SS: semisimple
SSS: simple semisimple
End: structure of endomorphisms (of a given structure)
Int: structure of inner automorphisms (of a given structure)
Aut: structure of automorphisms (of a given structure)
sgsa: (see Key to Definitions on page 539)
Spa Sym: symmetric spaces
Sye: elliptic symmetric spaces
Syh: hyperbolic symmetric spaces
Symi: minimal symmetric spaces
Syma: maximal symmetric spaces
Syemi, Syema: minimal, maximal elliptic symmetric spaces
Syhmi, Syhma: minimal, maximal hyperbolic symmetric spaces
rad: radical of ...
osc: oscillation
ing: integral
st: standard
un: unitary
cl: central
nst: near standard
ncl: near central
lim: (see 0.3, 0.5)
tr, det, rank, Re, Im: (see 0.4)
exp, grad: (see 0.5)

0.7. Nomenclature

A more imaginative nomenclature than one relying on overburdened terms such as "fundamental," "principal," "regular," "normal," "characteristic," "elementary," and so on is desirable. Inventors of important math-

† With their topologies.

ematical notions should give their inventions suggestive names. The disadvantage that good names might prevent the inventor's name from being immortalized as an adjective describing his invention would be more than compensated by the advantage that this honor could not possibly be bestowed on noninventors, either. This does not mean a taboo on personal names for mathematical notions, principles, and theorems; but it would be a gain if historically wrong or at least ridiculous attributions could be avoided.

The present authors have tried a few modest innovations in nomenclature, some of which have been in domestic use for many years. A few examples may be explicitly mentioned:

Trunk, instead of Cartan subalgebra and subgroup: a horticultural terminology suggested by the presence of roots and complemented by the admission of *branches*, that is, the eigenvectors belonging to the roots, and *nodes*, the commutators of branches belonging to opposite roots.

In the real case different kinds of trunks are to be distinguished, among which *maximally compact* and *minimally compact* ones play a role.

Distinguishing between *roots* and *rootforms*, that is, the restrictions of the roots to a trunk.

Primitive, instead of simple, *rootforms*: the usual terminology deviates from what is traditionally meant by simplicity and multiplicity of roots.

Investigations into semisimple Lie algebras often depend on the previous choice of a trunk, on a norming of the branches with respect to the trunk, on a partial order chosen within the trunk, and so on. To avoid a great many clumsy reiterations of definitions, the term *dressing*, with a suitable adjective, indicates such a system of previous choices; for instance, a semisimple Lie algebra $\boldsymbol{G}$ in ordered second dressing is a system consisting of $\boldsymbol{G}$, a trunk $\boldsymbol{H}$ of $\boldsymbol{G}$, a certain norming of the nodes and branches with respect to $\boldsymbol{H}$, and a certain partial order on $\boldsymbol{H}^*$; therefore, if in some proof a partial order is used, it is supposed to be that implicitly contained in the presupposed ordered second dressing.

There are first, second, and third dressings, which may be ordered, maximally compact, minimally compact, or real, and a Chevalley dressing.

Certain important expressions for semisimple Lie algebras have been named the *Weyl tool* and the *Casimir tool*. Clearly the usual "Casimir operator" no longer fits into today's terminology.

Among the automorphisms of Lie algebras some have been distinguished as the *plus-automorphism* and the *minus-automorphism*.

The real types of simple semisimple Lie algebra have been divided into *inner*, *outer*, and *twin*. Particular roles are played by the *unitary* and *standard* types. Irreducible linear representations may be *virtually real*, *antireal*, and *areal*. There *equivalent* and *contravalent* top weights are discussed.

For the important notion of the sum of the coefficients of a rootform with respect to a basis of primitive ones (a *natural basis*) the term *altitude* has been chosen; it suggests the term *altimeter* for a certain element of the trunk.

In the *numbering* of primitive rootforms (the dots of the graph) E. Cartan's system has been followed. The numbering of the fundamental weights as well as the system adopted to indicate the various *real types* of a complex simple semisimple Lie algebra depends on the numbering of the primitive rootforms.

Complex linear mappings that can be put into diagonal form are called *pure*; the usual term "semisimple" suffers from ambiguity as soon as the notion is extended to sets of linear mappings.

An element of a Lie algebra is called ad-*pure* or ad-*nilpotent* if its adjoint is pure or nilpotent.

An important operation on complex linear structures is *waiving*, that is, restricting the scalar multiplications to those by real numbers. Complex extending of a real linear structure followed by waiving is called *twinning*. In particular, if applied to real simple semisimple Lie algebras, it leads to the twin types.

To avoid ambiguities the term *covering* (with respect to topological spaces) is replaced by the more visual *wrapping*.

The usual ad $\boldsymbol{x}$, Ad x, which lead to clumsy formulas, are replaced by $\tilde{\boldsymbol{x}}$, $\tilde{x}$.

The term *gradient* (grad) is used for the differential of any differentiable mapping (not only if the image set is in Rea or Com).

Contractions: *conducible* from completely reducible,
orthoplement from orthogonal complement,
inner class from equivalence class under inner automorphisms (class of conjugate elements).

LINEAR LIE GROUPS

1–5

PRELIMINARIES

1. COMPLEX EXTENSION, REAL RESTRICTION, AND WAIVING

Linear spaces (Spa Lin) will in general be taken over the fields of real and complex numbers as scalars (Spa Lin Rea and Spa Lin Com). Algebras will be considered over the same fields (Alg Rea and Alg Com). Terminology on the relation between the real and the complex case is the subject of Section 1.†

1.1. Definition A *complex extension* of $R \in$ Spa Lin Rea is an $S \in$ Spa Lin Com which as a *real* linear space is the direct sum of R and $\mathrm{i}R$. Two complex extensions of R are canonically isomorphic. In the text R will often occur as a real subspace of a complex linear space, with $R \cap \mathrm{i}R = \{0\}$, and then the complex span of R is a complex extension of R, usually denoted by R_{Com} and referred to as *the* complex extension of R. In other cases it makes sense to reserve this notation and terminology for the complex extension of R obtained by means of the *tensor* product of R and Com.

1.2. Definition A mapping A of $R \in$ Spa Lin Com into $S \in$ Spa Lin Com is called *semilinear* if it respects addition and obeys $A(\alpha x) = \bar{\alpha} A x$ for scalar α.

1.3 R_{Com} of 1.1 possesses the involutory semilinear mapping $r + \mathrm{i}r' \to r - \mathrm{i}r'$ for $r, r' \in R$. It will be said *to belong to* the complexification from R to R_{Com}.

1.4 Under complex extension of $R \in$ Spa Lin Rea, linear subspaces S of R are passing into special ones of R_{Com} characterized by invariance under the mapping of 1.3.

1.5 Under complex extension of $R, R' \in$ Spa Lin Rea linear mappings of R into R' extend to certain linear mappings of R_{Com} into R'_{Com} characterized by their commuting with the involutory semilinear mapping of 1.3 (taken respectively on R_{Com} and on R'_{Com}).

1.6. Definition If D is an involutory semilinear mapping of $R \in$ Spa Lin Com onto itself, the *D-restriction* of R is the set of D-invariant elements of R or, equivalently, the set of $x + Dx$ with $x \in R$. It is denoted by R_D. D-restrictions in general are called *real restrictions.*

† The notions will only gradually be used in the sequel.

Note that the D-restriction of R is in Spa Lin Rea and that R is a complex extension of R_D. In fact, this yieids a one-to-one correspondence between involutory semilinear mappings and complex extensions.

1.7 Under D-, D'-restriction of R, $R' \in$ Spa Lin Com, a linear mapping A of R into R' with $D'A = AD$ is *restricted to* a linear mapping of R_D into $R'_{D'}$.

1.8. Definition By ignoring scalar multiplication with nonreals, Spa Lin Com is mapped into Spa Lin Rea. This mapping is called *waiving*.

By complex extension and real restriction the dimension is preserved; by waiving it doubles.

Under waiving in R, linear subspaces of $R \in$ Spa Lin Com subsist as real linear subspaces; under waiving in R, $R' \in$ Spa Lin Com linear mappings subsist.

1.9. Definition *Twinning*, as described hereafter, produces out of an $R \in$ Spa Lin Com a pair $\ulcorner R', D' \urcorner$ consisting of $R' \in$ Spa Lin Com and an involutory semilinear mapping D' of R' onto itself: R is mapped one-to-one by ω_+, ω_-, respectively, linearly and semilinearly onto R_+, R_-; in $R' = R_+ + R_-$ (direct sum), D' is defined by

$$D' \omega_+ x = \omega_- x, \qquad D' \omega_- x = \omega_+ x.$$

An $a \in$ End R is transferred to $a' \in$ End R' by putting

$$a' \omega_+ x = \omega_+ ax, \qquad a' \omega_- x = \omega_- ax.$$

The $a' \in$ End R' arising this way are characterized by their commuting with D'.

Evidently $\ulcorner R', D' \urcorner$ does not depend essentially on the choice of $\omega_\pm$, $R_\pm$.

Proposition Twinning R into $\ulcorner R', D' \urcorner$ can be performed by first waiving and then complex extending. D' is then the semilinear mapping belonging to this complex extending.

Proof R' obtained from R by waiving and complex extending can be considered as coming from the adjunction of a new imaginary unit j to the scalar field underlying R. The new algebra of scalars has the idempotents $\frac{1}{2}(1 \mp \mathrm{ji})$ whose product vanishes. Note that the semilinear D' belonging to the complexification of the waiving of R satisfies $D' \mathrm{i} x = \mathrm{i} D' x$, $D' \mathrm{j} x = -\mathrm{j} x$ for $x \in R$.

Now when multiplication with $\frac{1}{2}(1 \mp \mathrm{ji})$ is called $\omega_\pm$, then

$$\omega_+ \mathrm{i} x = \tfrac{1}{2}(1 - \mathrm{ji})\mathrm{i} x = \mathrm{j} \cdot \tfrac{1}{2}(1 - \mathrm{ji}) x = \mathrm{j} \omega_+ x,$$

$$\omega_- \mathrm{i} x = \tfrac{1}{2}(1 + \mathrm{ji})\mathrm{i} x = -\mathrm{j} \cdot \tfrac{1}{2}(1 + \mathrm{ji}) x = -\mathrm{j} \omega_- x,$$

which shows that ω_+ is linear and ω_- is semilinear. (Note that the imaginary unit of R' is j.)

If $R_\pm = \omega_\pm R$, then clearly $R' = R_+ + R_-$ directly. Also

$$D'\,\omega_\pm x = D'\,\tfrac{1}{2}(1 \pm \mathrm{ji})x = \tfrac{1}{2}(1 \mp \mathrm{ji})x = \omega_\mp x,$$

which shows that all conditions on twinning are fulfilled by R', D', and ω_+, ω_-.

1.10. Definition The *complex extension* of $G \in$ Alg Rea is denoted by G_{Com} or $G \otimes$ Com. It is explained by extending G as a linear space and extending multiplication on G in a natural way.

Under complex extension, subalgebras (ideals) pass into subalgebras (ideals) and homomorphisms into homomorphisms.

1.11. Definition A mapping of $G \in$ Alg Com is called a *semimorphism* if it is semilinear and respects multiplication.

The mapping of 1.3 (in algebras) is a semimorphism.

C-restriction (by means of an involutory semimorphism C) and waiving applied to $G \in$ Alg Com create real algebras. Twinning (by means of isomorphic and semimorphic ω_+, ω_-) applied to $G \in$ Alg Com creates a direct sum $G' = G_+ + G_-$ of algebras $G_\pm = \omega_\pm G$.

1.12. Proposition Twinning $G \in$ Alg Com into $\ulcorner G, C' \urcorner$ can be performed by first waiving and then complex extending. C' is then the semimorphism belonging to the extending.

Proof The proof of 1.9 is extended by showing that $\omega_\pm$ respects the product, and that the sum $G_+ + G_-$ is direct; thus $G_+ \cdot G_- = \{0\}$. These facts rest on the idempotency of $\frac{1}{2}(1 \pm \mathrm{ji})$: $\omega_\pm(ab) = \omega_\pm^2(ab) = (\omega_\pm a)(\omega_\pm b)$ and on $(1 - \mathrm{ji})(1 + \mathrm{ji}) = 0$.

2. THE EXPONENTIAL

2.1 Often in what follows, particularly in 2.2–6, R means a topological linear space (Spa Lin Top) over Rea or Com (scalars are indicated by Greek letters). Its topology is supposed to stem from a norm in the usual way. If employed for the purpose of a convenient description of the topology, such a norm is indicated by $|\ldots|$.

Mostly $\dim R < \infty$, and then without impoverishing the structure of R, one may forget its topology. All norms are then topologically equivalent.

2.2 End R means the set of (continuous) endomorphisms of R.
End $R \in$ Spa Lin by means of the definition

$$(A+B)x = Ax + Bx, \qquad (\alpha A)x = \alpha(Ax) \quad \text{for all} \quad x \in R,$$

if $A, B \in$ End R. Moreover, End $R \in$ Spa Lin Nor by

$$|A| = \sup_{|x| \leqslant 1} |Ax|.$$

In fact, $|A| < \infty$ because by continuity there is a δ-neighborhood of $0 \in R$ where $|Ax| \leqslant 1$. But then $|Ax| < \delta^{-1}$ if $|x| \leqslant 1$. Furthermore, one can easily prove

$$|A| = 0 \leftrightarrow A = 0, \qquad |A+B| \leqslant |A| + |B|, \qquad |\alpha A| = |\alpha| \cdot |A|.$$

With AB defined by

$$AB = \curlyvee_x ABx,$$

$$|AB| \leqslant |A| \cdot |B|$$

because $|ABx| \leqslant |A| \cdot |Bx| \leqslant |A| \cdot |B| \cdot |x|$; hence $\sup_{|x| \leqslant 1} |ABx| \leqslant |A| \cdot |B|$.

Hence:

$$\text{End } R \in \text{Alg Nor}.$$

Suppose that R is complete. Then End R is complete, and $A \in$ End R can be substituted into polynomials and even into power series such as

$$\exp A = \sum_{m=0}^{\infty} (1/m!) A^m,$$

the *exponential* of A, also written e^A.

If the numerical power series $\sum_{m=0}^{\infty} |\alpha_m| \gamma^m$ converges and $A \in$ End R, $|A| \leqslant \gamma$, then $\sum_{m=0}^{\infty} \alpha_m A^m$ also converges. Indeed,

$$|A^m| = |AA^{m-1}| \leqslant |A| \cdot |A^{m-1}| \leqslant \ldots \leqslant \gamma^m$$

implies that

$$\left| \sum_{m=p+1}^{p+k} \alpha_m A^m \right| \leqslant \sum_{m=p+1}^{p+k} |\alpha_m| \cdot |A^m| \leqslant \sum_{m=p+1}^{p+k} |\alpha_m| \gamma^m$$

becomes arbitrarily small for all sufficiently large p.

This convergence criterion justifies the definition of the exponential.

Let the numerical functions f, g, h be given by power series

$$f(x) = \sum \alpha_i x^i, \qquad g(x) = \sum \beta_i x^i, \qquad h(x) = \sum \gamma_i x^i$$

such that h has arisen by substitution of f into g. Define for $X \in$ End R

$$f(X) = \sum \alpha_i X^i, \qquad g(X) = \sum \beta_i X^i, \qquad h(X) = \sum \gamma_i X^i,$$

if convergent. Then, obviously, $h(A) = g(f(A))$ as long as the underlying series converge in the norm.

Define the *logarithm* by

$$\log(1 + A) = \sum_{1}^{\infty} [(-1)^{n-1}/n]\, A^n$$

as far as convergence in the norm prevails. Then by the foregoing

$$\exp \log X = \log \exp X = X$$

as long as convergence in the norm prevails.

2.3 In topological linear spaces it makes sense to speak of curves, tangent vectors, and so on.

Definition A k-times continuously differentiable mapping of an open connected set of real or complex numbers into R is called a real or complex C^k-*curve* on R.

A C^1-curve is simply called a *curve*.

If x is a curve one defines

$$\left(\frac{d}{dt}x\right)(t) = \lim_{\tau=0} \tau^{-1}(x(t+\tau) - x(t))$$

wherever this limit exists.

$$\left(\frac{d}{dt}x\right)(t), \quad \text{also written} \quad \frac{dx(t)}{dt} \quad \text{or} \quad \frac{d}{dt}x(t),$$

is called its *tangent vector at t*, or *at* $x(t)$.

Analogs of well-known rules are

$$\frac{d}{dt}(x(t) + y(t)) = \frac{d}{dt}x(t) + \frac{d}{dt}y(t),$$

and if $A(t)$, $B(t)$ are continuous linear mappings of R into R, depending differentiably on t,

2.3.1 $$\frac{d}{dt}(A(t)\,x(t)) = \left(\frac{d}{dt}A(t)\right) x(t) + A(t)\frac{d}{dt}x(t),$$

2.3.2 $$\frac{d}{dt}(A(t)\,B(t)) = \left(\frac{d}{dt}A(t)\right) B(t) + A(t)\frac{d}{dt}B(t).$$

If $A(t)^{-1}$ exists, it is easily seen to be differentiable with respect to t and its derivative can be found by differentiating $A(t)\,A(t)^{-1} = 1$:

$$\left(\frac{d}{dt}A(t)\right)(A(t))^{-1} + A(t)\frac{d}{dt}(A(t))^{-1} = 0;$$

thus,

2.3.3 $$\frac{d}{dt}(A(t)^{-1}) = -A(t)^{-1}\left(\frac{d}{dt}A(t)\right) A(t)^{-1}.$$

2.4 It follows from the definition of exp that

2.4.1 $$\frac{d}{dt}\exp tA = A\exp tA = (\exp tA)A.$$

For commuting continuous linear mappings A, B

$$\exp(A+B) = \exp A \cdot \exp B.$$

This results from the same principle used at the end of 2.2. It is worthwhile, however, to prove it by a method that will be applied in the sequel in a more profound way:

First 2.4.1 is generalized.

2.4.2 For $AB = BA$, $(d/dt)e^{tA+B} = Ae^{tA+B}$

Indeed,

$$\frac{d}{dt}((tA+B)^m = m(tA+B)^{m-1}\frac{d}{dt}(tA+B)$$

because all things commute. Therefore,

$$\frac{d}{dt}\sum\frac{1}{m!}(tA+B)^m = A\sum\frac{1}{(m-1)!}(tA+B)^{m-1},$$

which proves 2.4.2.

Now

$$\frac{d}{dt}(e^{-tA}\,e^{tA+B}) = -Ae^{-tA}\,e^{tA+B} + e^{-tA}\,Ae^{tA+B} = 0$$

because factors commute. So

$$C = e^{-tA}\,e^{tA+B}$$

is constant. Substituting $t = 0$, one gets

$$C = e^B.$$

Substituting $t = 1$:

2.4.3 $$e^{-A}\,e^{A+B} = e^B,$$

and, more particularly, for $B = 0$

$$e^{-A}\,e^A = 1;$$

thus,

$$e^{-A} = (e^A)^{-1}.$$

Multiplying 2.4.3 by e^A, one finally gets

2.4.4 $$\exp(A+B) = \exp A \cdot \exp B \quad \text{for commuting} \quad A, B.$$

2.5 A consequence of 2.4.4 is

$$\exp(\tau_1 + \tau_2)A = \exp \tau_1 A \cdot \exp \tau_2 A.$$

This means that

$$\curlyvee_t \exp tA$$

is a homomorphic mapping of the addition group of scalars. It is a continuous and even a differentiable homomorphism:

$$\frac{d}{dt} \exp tA = A \exp tA.$$

2.6† Any $A(t)$ as a function of t with $A(0) = 1$ may be interpreted as a *flow* in R: the particle that was in a at time 0 will be in $A(t)a$ at time t. In this sense $(d/dt)A(t)$ is the velocity field of the flow at time t.

If the flow is of the special kind $A(t) = \exp tA$, the particle that was in a at $t = 0$, and consequently in $b = (\exp tA)a$ at time t, will show there the velocity $A(\exp tA)a = Ab$ at time t. This means that the velocity at any time depends on the spatial spot only, not on time. Particles passing through a given spot b will have the same velocity there. This kind of flow is called *stationary*.

$\curlyvee_t \exp tA$ yields a stationary flow with the velocity field

$$A = \left(\frac{d}{dt} \exp tA\right)_{t=0}.$$

It is clear that in a stationary flow all particles passing through b will arrive at some other spot in the same lapse of time τ so that $A(t + \tau) \cdot a$ will not depend on t, provided $A(t)a = b$. In other words, $A(t + \tau)A(t)^{-1}$ does not depend on t, thus equals $A(\tau)$ which just restates the homomorphic character of $\curlyvee_t A(t)$.

2.7–10. Examples

2.7 Suppose that $\dim R = n < \infty$. Assume an ordered basis in R. Then a linear mapping is described by a matrix.

Let A be triangular with zeros below the main diagonal. Then A^m is also triangular and so is $\exp A$. To every diagonal element λ of A corresponds e^λ of $\exp A$. Thus,

2.7.1 $$\det \exp A = \exp \operatorname{tr} A.$$

In particular,

† This section will not be used in the sequel.

2.7.2 $$\text{if} \quad \operatorname{tr} A = 0, \quad \text{then } \det \exp A = 1.$$

These formulas are generally valid because over the complex field and on a suitable basis, a linear mapping of R ($\dim R < \infty$) takes the triangular form.

2.7.3 $$\det \exp A \neq 0 \quad \text{for all} \quad A.$$

2.8. Suppose

$$\dim R = 2, \qquad A = \begin{pmatrix} 0 & 1 \\ 0 & 0 \end{pmatrix}.$$

Then

$$\exp \tau A = \begin{pmatrix} 1 & \tau \\ 0 & 1 \end{pmatrix}.$$

Generalization: let A be n-dimensional triangular with a vanishing main diagonal. Then in A^2 all elements just above the main diagonal also vanish and so on; finally, $A^n = 0$. Thus $\exp \tau A$ is a polynomial in τ of degree $\leqslant n - 1$.

2.9 Suppose that A is skew. With A' the transpose of A,

$$A' = -A;$$

thus,

$$(A^m)' = (-A)^m,$$

$$(\exp A)' = \left(\sum \frac{1}{m!} A^m\right)' = \sum \frac{1}{m!} (-A)^m = \exp(-A),$$

$$(\exp A)' \exp A = 1.$$

Therefore, if A is skew, $\exp A$ is orthogonal.

In the same way one proves the following.

If A is hermitean skew, then $\exp A$ is unitary. (*Hermitean skew* means that $A^* = -A$, where A^* is the conjugate transpose of A; *unitary* means that $A^*A = 1$.)

2.10† The importance of the exponential is illustrated in a quite informal way by the next example.

Let R be the linear space of functions of a real variable in $[-\infty, \infty]$. The substitution $\xi \to \xi + t$ in the argument produces a mapping T_t of R onto itself:

$$(T_t \varphi)(\xi) = \varphi(\xi + t);$$

T_t transfers the graph of φ over a distance t to the left; T_t is linear, and, because of

$$(T_s T_t \varphi)(\xi) = \varphi(\xi + t + s) = (T_{s+t} \varphi)(\xi),$$

† This section is not used in the sequel.

$\Upsilon_t T_t$ maps the addition group of real numbers homomorphically. One might expect it to be a stationary flow. Differentiating, one gets

$$\left(\left(\frac{d}{dt}T_t\right)\varphi\right)(\xi)=\frac{d}{dt}\varphi(\xi+t)=D\varphi(\xi+t)=(T_t\,D\varphi)(\xi),$$

where D is the differentiation operator,

$$(D\varphi)(\xi)=\frac{d}{d\xi}\varphi(\xi).$$

Thus,

$$\frac{d}{dt}T_t=T_t D=DT_t.$$

D is the velocity field of the flow. (Note that it is restricted to the subspace of differentiable functions.)

Analogy suggests that

$$T_t=\exp tD,$$

which means that

$$T_t=\sum_0^\infty \frac{t^m}{m!}D^m,$$

$$\varphi(\xi+t)=(T_t\,\varphi)=\sum_0^\infty \frac{t^m}{m!}(D^m\varphi)(\xi);$$

that is, Taylor's formula. Because of its restricted validity, the analogy is merely formal.

By a Fourier transformation of this example, another develops:

$$(Z\varphi)(\eta)=(2\pi)^{-1/2}\int_{-\infty}^{\infty}e^{-i\xi\eta}\,\varphi(\xi)\,d\xi$$

defines the Fourier transform $Z\varphi$ of φ in a certain subspace of R. It is invertible there:

$$(Z^{-1}\varphi^*)(\xi)=(2\pi)^{-1/2}\int_{-\infty}^{\infty}e^{i\xi\eta}\,\varphi^*(\eta)\,d\eta.$$

Translating T_t from the "φ-language" into the "φ^*-language," one gets

$$P_t=ZT_tZ^{-1}.$$

Now

$$\begin{aligned}(Z^{-1}P_t\,\varphi^*)(\xi)=(T_tZ^{-1}\varphi^*)(\xi)&=(2\pi)^{-1/2}\int_{-\infty}^{\infty}e^{i\eta(\xi+t)}\,\varphi^*(\eta)\,d\eta\\&=(2\pi)^{-1/2}\int_{-\infty}^{\infty}e^{i\xi\eta}\,e^{i\eta t}\,\varphi^*(\eta)\,d\eta,\end{aligned}$$

thus,

$$(P_t\,\varphi^*)(\eta)=e^{i\eta t}\,\varphi^*(\eta).$$

Again,

$$P_{s+t} = P_s P_t.$$

$\Upsilon_t P_t$ maps the addition group of real numbers homomorphically. For the velocity field A of this flow one finds

$$(A\varphi^*)(\eta) = \left(\left(\frac{d}{dt}P_t\right)_{t=0}\varphi^*\right)(\eta) = \left(\frac{d}{dt}\mathrm{e}^{\mathrm{i}\eta t}\,\varphi^*(\eta)\right)_{t=0} = \mathrm{i}\eta\varphi^*(\eta);$$

A is the multiplication by i times the argument. Again formally,

$$P_t = \mathrm{e}^{tA}.$$

3. SOME LIE GROUPS

The groups that appeared in Section 2 were homomorphic images of the addition group of real or complex numbers. This section is a preliminary exploration of groups in which the general element depends on more parameters.

3.1 The multiplication group of n–n-matrices with determinant $\neq 0$ (or the group of automorphisms of linear n-space). The element a depends on n^2 parameters, the matrix coefficients $\alpha_{ij}(a)$.

3.2 The subgroup of 3.1 singled out by the condition $\det a = 1$. The group element a now depends on $n^2 - 1$ parameters, one matrix coefficient being redundant: a_0 has some matrix coefficient $\alpha_{ij}(a_0)$ with nonvanishing minor; near a_0 the equation $\det a = 1$ can be solved with respect to α_{ij}, and a is fully described by the remaining matrix coefficients as parameters. The validity of this parameter system is merely local; it breaks down as soon as the minor vanishes.

3.3 The subgroup of 3.2 consisting of orthogonal a; thus $a'a = 1$. Later on it will be shown that a depends on $\frac{1}{2}n(n-1)$ parameters.

3.4 The group of complex n–n-matrices a with $a^*a = 1$ (unitary matrices). The number of (real) parameters is n^2.

3.5 The group of matrices $\begin{pmatrix}1 & \alpha\\ 0 & \beta\end{pmatrix}$ with real α, β and $\beta > 0$; two parameters.

3.6 The group of matrices

$$\begin{pmatrix}\mathrm{e}^{2\pi\mathrm{i}s} & 0\\ 0 & \mathrm{e}^{2\pi\mathrm{i}t}\end{pmatrix}, \qquad s, t \text{ real.}$$

There are two parameters s, t. The pairs $\ulcorner s_1, t_1 \urcorner$, $\ulcorner s_2, t_2 \urcorner$ produce the same element iff $s_2 - s_1$ and $t_2 - t_1$ are integers. The topology of this group is that of the torus; a model is the square defined by $0 \leqslant s \leqslant 1$, $0 \leqslant t \leqslant 1$, with identification of opposite sides.

3.7 The subgroup of 3.6 defined by

$$s = \alpha\tau, \qquad t = \beta\tau, \qquad \alpha, \beta \text{ fixed}, \qquad \beta \neq 0, \qquad \tau \text{ variable.}$$

There is one parameter τ. In the model of 3.6 the subgroup shows up as a straight line in the $\ulcorner s, t \urcorner$-plane brought back piecewise into the square by reduction mod 1. Two cases are to be distinguished:

3.7.1 α/β rational. Then $\alpha\tau$, $\beta\tau$ are both integers for some τ, and a finite τ-interval suffices to describe the subgroup.

3.7.2 α/β irrational. Different τ furnish different group elements. The group 3.7.2 is dense in 3.6.

In 3.7.2 one can distinguish two topologies, one borrowed from 3.6 but pathological for 3.7.2 and the other that of the straight line, which is more adapted to 3.7.2.

This phenomenon explains some precautions which will be taken in the fundamental definition of Section 6.

3.8 The group consisting of the (real or complex) upper triangular n–n-matrices (those of the form $\triangledown$ with 1's in the main diagonal); the number of parameters is $\frac{1}{2}n(n-1)$.

4. TOPOLOGICAL GROUPS

4.1–7. Group Topology

4.1. Definition A *topological group* (Gru Top) is a set with a group structure and a topology such that multiplication and inversion are continuous operations in the given topology.

It suffices to suppose that

ab is a continuous function of $\ulcorner a, b \urcorner$ at $\ulcorner 1, 1 \urcorner$;
a^{-1} is a continuous function of a at 1; and
ab is a continuous function of a as well as of b.

Then the continuity of $\curlyvee_a a^{-1}$ at x is proved by considering $x^{-1}(ax^{-1})^{-1}$ for fixed x and that of $\curlyvee_{\ulcorner a,b \urcorner}\, ab$ at $\ulcorner x,y \urcorner$ by considering $x(x^{-1}a)(by^{-1})y$ for fixed x, y.

4.2 In groups, AB means the set of ab with $a \in A$, $b \in B$; A^{-1} means the set of a^{-1} with $a \in A$.

4.3 The continuity of group operations at 1 can be expressed as follows: for every 1-neighborhood U there is a 1-neighborhood V such that $V^{-1} \subset U$, $VV \subset U$.

4.4 In a topological group, left (right) multiplication with a fixed element and inversion carry open sets into open sets.

4.5 In a topological group the 1-component is a closed normal subgroup.

4.6.1 If $A \subset G \in$ Gru Top, then the intersection of all UA with U ranging over the set of the 1-neighborhoods in G equals the closure $\bar{A}$ of A.

Indeed

$$x \in \bar{A} \leftrightarrow \bigwedge_U U^{-1}x \cap A \neq \bigcirc \leftrightarrow x \in \bigcap_U UA.$$

4.6.2 $\bar{V} \subset VV$ for any 1-neighborhood V in $G \in$ Gru Top.

This follows from 4.6.1.

4.6.3 Any T_1-group is Hausdorff and even regular.

Indeed, given a 1-neighborhood U, there is a 1-neighborhood V such that $VV \subset U$, but then $\bar{V} \subset U$. This property carries over to any point by left multiplication.

4.6.4 Any open subgroup of $G \in$ Gru Top is closed.

This follows from 4.6.2 applied to an open subgroup V.

4.6.5 A connected topological group (Gru Top Con) is generated by any nonvoid open subset.

Indeed, the set generates an open subgroup which by 4.6.4 is closed; since the group is connected, it is identical with the whole group.

4.7 A discrete normal subgroup N of a connected topological group G lies in the center of G.

Indeed, the set of axa^{-1} $(a \in G)$ is connected for $x \in G$, and discrete for $x \in N$ whence consisting of one point, which by taking $a = 1$ is identified as x. So $axa^{-1} = x$ for all $a \in G$ and $x \in N$.

4.8. Coset Spaces†

4.8.1 If H is a subgroup of the topological group G, the topology of G is transferred to the left coset space G/H by the convention that the open sets in G/H are just the images of open sets in G under the canonical mapping.

The Hausdorff property and many others are preserved under this transition if H is closed.

4.8.2 Under the canonical mapping of G onto G/H, the image of a connected set is connected; the inverse image of a connected set is connected if H is connected.

In particular, if both G/H and H are connected, then G is connected.

(Indeed, $\Upsilon_a aH$ maps open subsets of G onto open subsets of G/H even when restricted to some CH as a subspace of G.)

∴ If H is the 1-component of G then G/H is totally disconnected.

4.8.3. Definition A (continuous) *representation* f of $G \in$ Gru Top in $R \in$ Spa Top is a homomorphic mapping of G into the group of auto-homeomorphisms of R (notation: $f = \Upsilon_{a\in G} f_a$) such that, in addition to the requirement that $f_a f_b = f_{ab}$ for $a, b \in G$,

$$\Upsilon_{\ulcorner a,x \urcorner \in \ulcorner G,R \urcorner} f_a x \quad \text{is continuous.}$$

The *stability group* of $x_0 \in R$ consists of the $a \in G$ with $f_a x_0 = x_0$.

For any $A \subset G$, $f_A x$ means the set of $f_a x$ with $a \in A$.

f is called *transitive* if for all $x, y \in R$ there is an $a \in G$ with $f_a x = y$.

4.8.4 Clearly, if f is transitive, then the stability groups of all points are conjugate in G. If H is the stability group of x_0, then

$$\Upsilon_{aH} f_{aH} x_0$$

maps G/H one-to-one and continuously into R. If f is transitive, this mapping is even onto.

Proposition Let G be a locally compact Hausdorff group that satisfies the second countability axiom and let R be a locally compact Hausdorff space. Let G be transitively, continuously represented in R by f and let H be the stability group of x_0. Then

$$\Upsilon_{aH} f_{aH} x_0$$

is a homeomorphic mapping of G/H onto R.

† The results obtained in this section will only incidentally be used in the sequel.

Proof It suffices to prove that there are "arbitrarily small" open 1-neighborhoods U in G such that $f_U x_0$ is again open.

Let a 1-neighborhood U_3 in G be prescribed. Choose a compact 1-neighborhood U in G such that

$$U^{-1}U^{-1}UU \subset U_3.$$

Suppose that $f_U x_0$ has no interior. Then $f_{aU} x_0 = f_a f_U x_0$ has no interior either. Now every point of G is interior to some aU $(a \in G)$; hence by second countability there is a sequence $\ulcorner a_i \urcorner_{i=1}^{\infty}$ in G such that $\bigcup_i a_i U = G$. Put $A_i = f_{a_i U} x_0$. Then

$$A_i \text{ is compact,} \qquad A_i \text{ has no interior,} \qquad \bigcup A_i = R.$$

A decreasing sequence of $V_i \subset R$ will be defined such that

$$V_i \text{ compact,} \qquad V_i \text{ has an interior,} \qquad V_{i+1} \cap A_i = \bigcirc:$$

V_1 may be arbitrarily chosen to satisfy the first two requirements, and if V_i has been determined then on the one hand V_i has an interior, whereas A_i has not, so, since A_i is closed, one finds in $V_i \diagdown A_i$ an interior point with a closed neighborhood V_{i+1} also contained in $V_i \diagdown A_i$.

Now $\bigcap_i V_i$ has a void intersection with all A_j, hence with R, whereas on the other hand it is nonvoid because of the compactness of the V_i. This contradiction shows that $f_U x_0$ has an interior. Take an open U_0 with $U \subset U_0 \subset UU$. Then

$$f_{U_0} x_0 \text{ has a nonvoid interior } W.$$

$$U_1 = U_0 \cap \uparrow_{a \in G}(f_a x_0 \in W) \text{ is open, and}$$

$$f_{U_1} x_0 = W \text{ is open.}$$

Finally, $U_2 = U_1^{-1} U_1$ is an open 1-neighborhood in G, contained in $U_0^{-1} U_0$, thus in the prescribed U_3, and $f_{U_2} x_0 = f_{U_1^{-1}} f_{U_1} x_0 = f_{U_1^{-1}} W$ is still open. So U_2 is the required "arbitrarily small" open 1-neighborhood with open $f_{U_2} x_0$.

4.8.5. Note More general theorems are found in H. Freudenthal, *Ann. Math.* **37**, 46–56 (1936).

4.8.6. Corollary Under the conditions in 4.8.4, if both R and H are connected, then G is connected. (See 4.8.2.)

4.8.7. Corollary Let φ be a (continuous) homomorphism of the locally compact Hausdorff group G with second countability axiom onto the locally compact Hausdorff group G', with H its kernel. Then G/H and G' are topologically isomorphic in a natural way.

Indeed, putting $f_a = \curlyvee_{x \in G'} (\varphi a)x$ for $a \in G$, one gets a transitive representation f of G in G' with H as the stability group at the unit element of G' to which 4.8.4 applies.

4.9–11. Local Groups

Let $G \in$ Gru Top.

4.9. Definition Two subsets of G are called *locally identical* if they coincide in some 1-neighborhood in G (thus in every sufficiently small one).

This notion will sometimes also be applied to subsets of *different* topological groups.

The next definition is concerned with local subgroups of G. A tentative definition would read: H is a local subgroup of G if it is locally identical with H^{-1} and with HH in a nontrivial way; that is,

there is a 1-neighborhood U in G with

$$1 \in H \cap U = H^{-1} \cap U = HH \cap U.$$

Clearly nothing is lost if the requirement $U = U^{-1}$ is added. Further, if H is replaced by its local equivalent $H_1 = H \cap U$, then

$$H_1 = H_1^{-1} \subset U, \qquad H_1 H_1 \cap U = H_1.$$

This consideration leads to a more practical definition:

4.10. Definition H is called a *local subgroup* of G if:

$1 \in H = H^{-1}$;

H is contained in some open $U = U^{-1}$, such that

$HH \cap U = H.$

Moreover, such an H is called a *closed* local subgroup of G if it is closed in U.

(It will be seen that the condition of closedness does not depend on the choice of U.)

A great many properties of topological groups extend to local subgroups H. For instance, the group operations as far as defined in H are continuous. There is a 1-neighborhood H_0 in H with $H_0^{-1} = H_0$, $H_0 H_0 \subset H$. For any $a \in H$ there is a 1-neighborhood H_1 in H with $aH_1 \subset H$. If P is open in H and $aP(Pa) \subset H$, then $aP(Pa)$ is open in H, and so on.

4.11. Proposition A subset H of G is a closed local subgroup of G if and only if $1 \in H = H^{-1}$ and H is open in the closure $\overline{HH}$ of HH.

Proof If: Let H be open in $\overline{HH}$. Then $U = G \setminus (\overline{HH} \setminus H)$ is open; if $1 \in H$, U is a 1-neighborhood, and, if $H = H^{-1}$, then $U = U^{-1}$. In any case, $H \subset U$, and $HH \cap U = H$, which shows that H is a closed local subgroup as soon as all conditions on H are satisfied.

Only if: Let $U=U^{-1}$ be open, $1\in H$, $H=H^{-1}$ closed in U, and $HH\cap U=H$. Then, with $A=G\setminus U$,

$$HH=H\cup(HH\cap A),$$

$$\overline{HH}\subset\bar{H}\cup\overline{HH\cap A}\subset\bar{H}\cup A;$$

intersecting with U,

$$\overline{HH}\cap U\subset\bar{H}\cap U=H,$$

which proves that H is open in $\overline{HH}$.

4.12–13. Expanding Local Groups

4.12 The local subgroup H of G will now be expanded into a topological group $\hat{H}$ in a natural and unique way.

As a group, $\hat{H}$ will be the subgroup of G generated by H. The topology of $\hat{H}$, however, is required to extend that of H in the following sense.

Definition The topology of $\hat{H}$ is said to *extend* that of H if H is open in $\hat{H}$ and H is a subspace of $\hat{H}$; in other words, if the following applies:

4.12.1 Every set open in H is open in $\hat{H}$.

4.12.2 Every set open in $\hat{H}$ intersects H in an open set.

Suppose that such a topology exists. Then by 4.12.1 every aP ($a\in\hat{H}$, P open in H) is open in $\hat{H}$ and so is every union of such sets. Call $\mathscr{T}$ the set of unions of aP ($a\in\hat{H}$, P open in H). Then any member of $\mathscr{T}$ is open in $\hat{H}$. Conversely, let Q be any open set in $\hat{H}$, and c any point of Q. Then $c^{-1}Q$ is open in $\hat{H}$ and, by 4.12.2, $Q'=c^{-1}Q\cap H$ open in H. So cQ' belongs to $\mathscr{T}$, and, since $1\in Q'$, $c\in cQ'\subset Q$, there is a member cQ' of $\mathscr{T}$ containing c and contained in Q. This shows Q as a union of members of $\mathscr{T}$, and therefore $Q\in\mathscr{T}$. Thus, if it exists, the topology of $\hat{H}$ is described by $\mathscr{T}$ as its set of open sets.

Its existence is guaranteed as soon as the intersection of any two members of $\mathscr{T}$ (defined as above) belongs to $\mathscr{T}$. Set theory distributivity allows restriction to the case of aP and $a'P'$, where $a,a'\in\hat{H}$, P, P' open in H. Without loss of generality, one may even suppose that $a'=1$ and $P'=H$. Let

$$c\in aP\cap H.$$

One then has to find a neighborhood Q of c in $aP\cap H$. One knows

$$c\in H\qquad\text{and}\qquad a^{-1}c\in P\subset H.$$

Because of the continuity of left multiplication with a^{-1} in H, one gets a c-neighborhood Q in H with $a^{-1}Q$ still $\subset P$; hence $Q \subset aP$. So $c \in Q \subset aP \cap H$, which proves the existence of the required topology of $\hat{H}$.

With this topology $\hat{H}$ appears to be a topological group:

First, multiplication and inversion are continuous at 1, because they are so in H. Left multiplication is continuous because it leaves $\mathscr{T}$ invariant. The continuity of right multiplication requires Pb to be open for any open P in $\hat{H}$ and $b \in \hat{H}$. To prove this one may assume that $b \in H$ (which generates $\hat{H}$) and furthermore that P is open in H. Given $c \in Pb$, c has to be proved an interior point of Pb. Now $b^{-1} \in c^{-1}P \cap H$, which is open in H; thus there is a 1-neighborhood Q in H such that $Qb^{-1} \subset c^{-1}P \cap H$; hence $c \in cQ \subset Pb$, which shows the continuity of right multiplication.

This proves the following proposition.

Proposition If H is a local subgroup of G, then $\hat{H}$, generated by H and provided with the unique topology that extends that of H, is a topological group. If H is connected, then $\hat{H}$ is also connected.

4.13 Note that the topology of $\hat{H}$ may differ from that induced by G. This is illustrated by 3.7.2, in which $|\tau| < \omega$ defines a local subgroup H of the topological group G of 3.6. Its $\hat{H}$ is essentially the addition group of real numbers with the ordinary topology. As a dense subgroup of G, however, it bears another topology.

Yet the following is true.

Proposition If H is a closed local subgroup of G and $\hat{H}$ bears the topology of subspace of G, then $\hat{H}$ has to be closed. If G is locally compact and satisfies the second axiom of countability, the converse still holds: if $\hat{H}$ is closed as a subset of G, it bears the topology of subspace of G.

Proof Let $\hat{H}$ bear the topology of subspace of G. Since H is open in $\hat{H}$, one finds a U open in G with $\hat{H} \cap U = H$ and H closed in U. Let a belong to the closure of $\hat{H}$. There is then some $b \in \hat{H} \cap aU$. Now $a^{-1}b$ belongs to U and to the closure of $\hat{H}$, so that it belongs even to the closure in U of $\hat{H} \cap U = H$, hence to H (and $\hat{H}$), since H is closed in U. From $a^{-1}b \in \hat{H}$ and $b \in \hat{H}$ it follows that $a \in \hat{H}$. Consequently, $\hat{H}$ is closed. Conversely, if G is locally compact, the closed subspace $\hat{H}$ is also locally compact, and 4.8.7 applies; namely, the identity mapping of $\hat{H}$ into G is homeomorphic and therefore the topology of $\hat{H}$ coincides with that induced by G in $\hat{H}$.

Remark There is no real need of the Hausdorff property, for the assertions are not influenced by the factoring out of the closure of $\{1\}$ in G.

4.14–15. Local Coset Spaces†

4.14. Definition If $G \in$ Gru Top and H is a closed local subgroup of G, then for any sufficiently small 1-neighborhood $V = V^{-1}$ in G the *local coset space* V/H is defined as the set of the $aH \cap V$ with $a \in V$, topologized by calling the subsets of V/H open whose unions are open in V.

To justify this definition, one has to find a V such that the sets $aH \cap V$ constitute a partition of V:

4.14.1 $$[a \in V \wedge b \in (aH \cap V)] \rightarrow [aH \cap V = bH \cap V].$$

This is achieved as follows.

As in 4.10, take an open 1-neighborhood $U = U^{-1}$ in G such that

$$HH \cap U = H \qquad \text{closed in } U.$$

Take a 1-neighborhood H_1 in H such that

$$H_1 H_1 \subset H$$

and a 1-neighborhood $V = V^{-1}$ in G such that

$$VV \subset U \qquad \text{and} \qquad H \cap VV \subset H_1.$$

To verify 4.14.1 for $a \in V$, take

$$b_i \in aH \cap V \qquad (i = 1, 2).$$

Then

$$a^{-1} b_i \in H \cap a^{-1} V \subset H \cap VV \subset H_1;$$

hence

$$b_1^{-1} b_2 = (a^{-1} b_1)^{-1} (a^{-1} b_2) \in H_1 H_1 \subset H,$$

$$b_2 \in b_1 H,$$

and likewise

$$b_1 \in b_2 H,$$

which proves 4.14.1.

Proposition If $G \in$ Gru Top and H and H' are closed local subgroups of G which coincide locally and such that $H \subset H'$, then for sufficiently small 1-neighborhoods V both V/H and V/H' make sense and coincide.

Moreover, if H is a closed subgroup of G, then for open or compact V, V/H is topologically a subspace of G/H.

† The results of 4.14–15 will be used only incidentally.

Proof Clearly V can be chosen so that V/H as well as V/H' are well defined, so one has only to make sure that $(aH' \cap V = bH' \cap V) \to (aH \cap V = bH \cap V)$, in other words, $b \in aH' \cap V \to b \in aH \cap V$; but this is evident as soon as V is so small that H and H' coincide in VV.

The remainder of the proposition is evident.

4.15. Proposition As defined in 4.14, V/H is Hausdorff and even regular.

Proof With U and V as above and $a \in V$, H is closed in U, so that $H \cap a^{-1}V$ is closed in $U \cap a^{-1}V$. Now $a^{-1}V \subset VV \subset U$, $U \cap a^{-1}V = a^{-1}V$; hence $H \cap a^{-1}V$ is closed in $a^{-1}V$, $aH \cap V$ is closed in V, which proves V/H to be a T_1-space.

A neighborhood of $aH \cap V$ in V/H can be given in such a form that its union is $Wa \cap V$, where W is a 1-neighborhood in G. Let another neighborhood of $aH \cap V$ have as its union $W_1 a \cap V$, where W_1 is now a 1-neighborhood in G with $W_1^{-1}W_1 \subset W$. To ensure regularity the union of the closure of the latter neighborhood in V/H must be shown to be contained in $Wa \cap V$.

Indeed, let $bH \cap V$ belong to this closure, with $b \in V$. Then $W_1 bH \cap V$, representing a neighborhood of $bH \cap V$ in V/H, has a nonvoid intersection with $W_1 a \cap V$. This shows that $bh \in W_1^{-1}W_1 a \subset Wa$ for some $h \in H$, whence $bH \cap V \subset Wa \cap V$.

4.16–17. Locally Connected Sets

4.16. Proposition Let G be a topological group satisfying the second countability axiom, H a closed local subgroup of G, and $\hat{H}$ defined as in 4.12. Let the subset A of $\hat{H}$ be locally connected in the topology of G. Then the topologies induced on A by G and by $\hat{H}$ coincide.

Proof For given $a \in A$ it suffices to find a neighborhood W of a in A according to the topology of G such that on W both topologies coincide. As a matter of convenience one may suppose that $a = 1$.

As in 4.14, V is constructed on the evidence of H. Moreover, V is assumed to be open and V/H is defined as in 4.14. Note that V, H, and V/H fulfill the second countability axiom. It is easily verified that the same is true of $\hat{H}$.

4.16.1 $$\curlyvee_c (cH \cap V)$$

maps $A \cap V$ continuously onto a subset A' of V/H. In the $\hat{H}$-topology the different $cH \cap V = c(H \cap c^{-1}V)$ with $c \in A \cap V$ are open and pairwise disjoint (see 4.15). Therefore, since $\hat{H}$ fulfills the second countability axiom, their number is countable. Consequently, A' is countable.

Since V/H is regular (see 4.15), it may be presumed to be equipped with a metric. Its restriction to A' assumes a countable number of values. From this it follows easily that A' is of dimension 0. Therefore the components of A' are single points.

Since A is locally connected, $A \cap V$ contains a connected 1-neighborhood W (in the sense of G). Its image according to 4.16.1 is connected, thus a component of A', and thus a point, which must be $H \cap V$. This shows $W \subset H \cap V \subset H$; but by the construction of $\hat{H}$ its topology coincides with that of G on H, hence on W. This proves the assertion.

4.17 The foregoing proposition will be applied later to make sure that a curve of G lying on $\hat{H}$ is also a curve on $\hat{H}$.

5. DIFFERENTIABLE MAPPINGS

$E, F \in$ Spa Lin Top, dim E, dim $F < \infty$.

5.1. Definition If f maps an open part of E into F and f admits of a linear mapping A of E into F such that

$$f(x') - f(x) = A(x' - x) + |x' - x|\,\varepsilon(x \to x_0, x' \to x_0)$$

(i.e., ε goes to 0 if x and x' go to x_0), then A is called the gradient mapping or the *gradient* of f at x_0,

$$A = \text{grad}_{x_0} f.$$

If it exists, A is unique. It exists as soon as f possesses continuous partial derivatives at x_0 on some basis. AE is called *the tangent space of the mapping at* x_0 or, if confusion is unlikely, *the tangent space at* $f(x_0)$.

f is called of *class* $C^k(C^\infty;\ C^{an})$ if it possesses continuous kth-order derivatives (if it possesses derivatives of any order; if it is analytic).

In statements involving C^k it is understood that ∞ and *an* are values of k. The inequality $k < \infty < an$ is assumed.

In the case of complex E, F it is known that $C^k = C^{an}$ for $k \geqslant 1$. In this case by means of a semilinear K, one defines semi-$C^k = K \cdot C^k$.

5.2 If gf makes sense and if f has the gradient A at x_0, and g has the gradient B at $f(x_0)$, then gf has the gradient BA at x_0.

If f^{-1} makes sense, and if f and f^{-1} have gradients, A, B at $x_0, f(x_0)$, respectively, then $B = A^{-1}$.

If dim $E =$ dim $F =$ rank $\text{grad}_{x_0} f$, then f maps a neighborhood of x_0 *onto* a neighborhood of $f(x_0)$, and then f^{-1} exists locally near $f(x_0)$, and $\text{grad}_{f(x_0)} f^{-1} = (\text{grad}_{x_0} f)^{-1}$.

If dim $E =$ rank $\text{grad}_{x_0} f$, then f is one-to-one near x_0.

5.3 Manifolds will mostly occur smoothly embedded in finite-dimensional linear spaces. The next definitions concern such manifolds. For a more abstract definition, see 5.6.

Definition A C_r^k*-piece* in F is the image M of an open ball S in E, $\dim E = r$, by means of a mapping f, which is (a) homeomorphic, (b) of class C^k, and (c) provided with a nondegenerate $\operatorname{grad}_x f$ for all $x \in S$ or, equivalently, provided with an r-dimensional tangent space at $f(x)$ for all $x \in S$. The pair $\ulcorner E, f \urcorner$ is called the *presentation* of the C_r^k-piece M. The piece M is endowed with the topology induced by F.

The notion of C^l-curve for $l \leqslant k$ on M, the notion of a C^l-mapping and semi-C^l-mapping of M, the notion of gradient of such a mapping, are explained in terms of E by means of the presentation of M. (They do not depend on the choice of the presentation.)

Note that the tangent space of M at p depends continuously on p.

Near p any affine projection of M on its tangent space is a C^k-mapping with an identity gradient.

Definition A C_r^k*-manifold* M in F is a connected topological space with the following properties: (a) M is a subset of F, (b) M is the union of a countable number of C_r^k-pieces M_j, such that (c) any M_j is a subspace of M, and (d) any M_j is open in M.

If $\ulcorner E, f \urcorner$ is the presentation of a C_r^k-piece contained in M and f maps the open ball S in E such that its center is mapped into p, then f is called a *local presentation* of M near p.

The foregoing remarks on tangent spaces, curves, mappings, and gradients extend to M.

Note that the topology of M need not coincide with that induced by F.

Whether a piece or a manifold is called real or complex depends on the underlying field of E.

5.4. Definition An *infinitesimal measure* m on the real C_r^1-manifold M is an assignment of a nondegenerate r-linear skew functional m_p to the tangent space at p, depending continuously on $p \in M$.

An infinitesimal measure m on M can be integrated into a measure either directly by lifting the infinitesimal measure from the tangent spaces into M by means of affine projection and forming Riemann sums or indirectly by choosing a parallelepiped P in E (a sequence of r vectors), such that

$$m_x((\operatorname{grad}_x f)(P)) > 0,$$

and putting

$$\mu(U) = \int_{f^{-1}U} m_x((\operatorname{grad}_x f)(P))\, d\nu(x)$$

where ν is the ordinary measure in E, gauged by $\nu(P) = 1$.

The result does not depend on the presentation of M. This follows from a formula known in calculus as "transformation of multiple integrals."

5.5. Definition G is called a *C_r^k-group* if it is a topological group, its space is a C_r^k-manifold, and its group operations are C^k-mappings with respect to the C_r^k-structure of the manifold G.

The examples in 3.1–8 are C^{an}-groups. For Aut R (3.1) it follows directly from the analyticity of matrix multiplication and inversion; for the others, it is less obvious but it will formally be proved in 11.3.5.

Under left and right multiplication and inversion, the tangent spaces of a C_r^1-group are mapped by nondegenerate mappings (see 5.1).

5.6† Sometimes more abstract notions of C_r^k-manifolds and -groups are needed. They are described by the following.

Definition A *C_r^k-manifold* consists of a pathwise connected topological space M and a set Φ of mappings with the properties:

5.6.1 Any $\varphi \in \Phi$ is a homeomorphic mapping of an open ball of an r-dimensional $E \in$ Spa Lin Top into M.

5.6.2 The images of some countable number of $\varphi \in \Phi$ cover M.

5.6.3 For $\varphi_i \in \Phi$, $\varphi_2^{-1}\varphi_1$, as far as it is defined, is a C^k-mapping with nowhere-degenerate gradient.

It can be useful to add the following assumption.

5.6.4 Φ is maximal with respect to 5.6.1–3.

C_r^k-mappings and local presentations of such manifolds are defined in an obvious way. (The $\varphi \in \Phi$ are local presentations of the defined manifold.)

To define the tangent space of $\ulcorner M,\Phi \urcorner$ at some $p \in M$ ($p = \varphi a$, where φ is some local presentation near a and a belongs to a ball S) an *auxiliary tangent* space of S at a is introduced:

The set of C^1-curves χ in S with $\chi(0) = a, [d/d\tau\, \chi(\tau)]_{\tau=0} = c$, is called the auxiliary tangent vector σc of S at a. The σc form the auxiliary tangent space of S at a, with that structure of linear space in which σ becomes a linear mapping.

The φ-image of an auxiliary tangent vector σc is the set of C^1-curves ϑ on $\ulcorner M,\Phi \urcorner$ such that $\vartheta(0) = p$ and ϑ coincides with some $\varphi\chi$ ($\chi \in \sigma c$) in a 0-neighborhood; $\varphi\sigma c$ is called a tangent vector of $\ulcorner M,\Phi \urcorner$ at p; these tangent vectors form the tangent space at p with that structure of linear space in which φ becomes a linear mapping.

The union over p of the tangent spaces at $p \in M$ of $\ulcorner M,\Phi \urcorner$ is gifted with a structure of C_{2r}^k-manifold in an obvious way.

†The definitions of this section will only be used incidentally.

6–12

THE CONNECTION BETWEEN LOCAL LINEAR LIE GROUPS AND LIE ALGEBRAS

6. DEFINITION OF LOCAL AND GLOBAL LINEAR LIE GROUPS

$R \in$ Spa Lin Top, $E \in$ Spa Lin Top, dim $R = n < \infty$, dim $E = r < \infty$.

6.1. Definition G is called an *r-dimensional local linear Lie group* (Gru Lie Loc Lin) in R if it is a local subgroup of Aut R, and a C^2-piece (in some $\ulcorner E, f \urcorner$-presentation).

G is called an r-dimensional (global) *linear Lie group* (Gru Lie Lin) in R if it is the extension according to 4.12 of an r-dimensional local linear Lie group in R.

According to the field underlying E, a local G and its global extension are called *real* or *complex*. If R is real, then E is supposed to be real as well; if R is complex, then E is either real or complex. (Gru Lie Loc Lin Rea or Com; Gru Lie Lin Rea or Com.)

Real restriction and *waiving in G* are understood to be induced by the same operations in E if they again lead to (local) linear Lie groups. (Of course, a real restriction of the domain ball of f must again be a ball in the restriction of E.) Both are to be distinguished from real restriction and waiving in R (and consequently in Aut R), which may or may not accompany the corresponding operations in G.

Complex extension of G, which must be some converse of real restriction, is explained in 10.6.

6.2 The examples in 3.1–8 will reveal themselves as linear Lie groups (see 11.3.5). Every linear Lie group will prove to be a C^{an}-group (see 8.3). Meanwhile, a weaker assertion can be proved:

6.3. Proposition A linear Lie group is a C^2-group.

Proof Let G be the underlying local group; $\hat{G}$, according to 4.12, is a connected topological group. The aG ($a \in \hat{G}$) are C^2-pieces because of the analyticity of left multiplication in Aut R and the nondegeneracy of the gradients. An everywhere dense countable subset A of G generates an everywhere dense countable subset B of $\hat{G}$. The bG ($b \in B$) form a countable system of C^2-pieces covering $\hat{G}$ and are open subspaces of $\hat{G}$ according to its construction. The

C^2-character of group operations in G follows from the analyticity of those in Aut R.

6.4 Incidentally it will be useful to consider a group G_1 that is locally the isomorphic image of a given linear Lie group G. This means that by a certain φ a 1-neighborhood U in G is homeomorphically mapped onto a 1-neighborhood U_1 in G_1 such that $\varphi(ab) = \varphi a \cdot \varphi b$ as far as it is defined. Such a G_1 may possess several components, which, necessarily, are isolated. If such a G_1 is connected, it shares with G the same simply connected wrapping, as will be shown in Section 29.

By means of the local presentations $a\varphi f$ ($a \in G_1$, f as in 6.1) every component of G_1 is to be considered as a C^2-manifold [even a C^{an}-manifold (see 6.2)], though not an embedded one. The 1-component then is a C^2-group (even a C^{an}-group).

6.5. Historical Note Local Lie groups are due to Sophus Lie (1842–1899). The adjective "linear" means the restriction to groups whose elements are linear mappings of some linear space. This restriction is pragmatic. An exact definition of general local Lie groups would be long-winded. The present methods are such that they can easily be adapted to general local Lie groups.

Hilbert's Fifth Problem asked for an elimination of differentiability assumptions from the definition of Lie groups. Its complete solution was reached in numerous steps from 1929 to 1952. (See D. Montgomery and L. Zippin, *Topological Transformation Groups*, Wiley (Interscience), New York, 1955; 3rd ed., 1965.)

Its solution for local linear Lie groups is expounded in Section 11.

7. THE INFINITESIMAL ALGEBRA OF A LOCAL LINEAR LIE GROUP

$G \in$ Gru Lie Loc Lin, dim $G = r$, $G \subset$ Aut R, in $\ulcorner E, f \urcorner$-presentation.

7.1. Definition The tangent space of G at 1 is called $\boldsymbol{G}$. Its elements are called the *infinitesimal elements* of G.

Another way of looking at $\boldsymbol{G}$ will be useful: take a curve $\curlyvee_t a_t$ on G with $a_0 = 1$ and the tangent vector

$$\boldsymbol{a} = \left(\frac{d}{dt} a_t\right)_{t=0}.$$

$\boldsymbol{G}$ consists of all $\boldsymbol{a}$.

$\boldsymbol{G}$ is an r-dimensional linear subspace of End R. In 7.5 the following is proved.

Proposition $\boldsymbol{a}, \boldsymbol{b} \in \boldsymbol{G} \rightarrow \boldsymbol{ab} - \boldsymbol{ba} \in \boldsymbol{G}$.

7.2 The expression $\boldsymbol{ab} - \boldsymbol{ba}$ is the keynote of the Lie theory. It is called the (infinitesimal) *commutator* of $\boldsymbol{a}, \boldsymbol{b}$.

Definition For linear mappings $\boldsymbol{a}, \boldsymbol{b}$ of a linear space into itself, one writes

$$[\boldsymbol{a}, \boldsymbol{b}] = \boldsymbol{ab} - \boldsymbol{ba}.$$

It is called the *commutator* of $\boldsymbol{a}$ and $\boldsymbol{b}$.

[..., ...] is *anticommutative*,

$$[\boldsymbol{a}, \boldsymbol{b}] + [\boldsymbol{b}, \boldsymbol{a}] = \boldsymbol{0},$$

and *Jacobi-associative*,

$$[[\boldsymbol{a}, \boldsymbol{b}], \boldsymbol{c}] + [[\boldsymbol{b}, \boldsymbol{c}], \boldsymbol{a}] + [[\boldsymbol{c}, \boldsymbol{a}], \boldsymbol{b}] = \boldsymbol{0}.$$

The first is obvious; the second results from simple computation.

Furthermore,

[...,...] is *bilinear*.

With [...,...] interpreted as a product, $\boldsymbol{G}$ becomes an algebra, the *infinitesimal algebra* of G.

7.3 Disregarding the particular origin of the elements and the products [...,...], a general definition is given:

Definition An algebra with the product operation [...,...] is called a *Lie algebra* (Alg Lie, Rea or Com) if it fulfills

anticommutativity, $[\boldsymbol{a}, \boldsymbol{b}] + [\boldsymbol{b}, \boldsymbol{a}] = \boldsymbol{0},$

and

Jacobi-associativity, $[[\boldsymbol{a}, \boldsymbol{b}], \boldsymbol{c}] + [[\boldsymbol{b}, \boldsymbol{c}], \boldsymbol{a}] + [[\boldsymbol{c}, \boldsymbol{a}], \boldsymbol{b}] = \boldsymbol{0}.$

Complex extension, real restriction (if it leads to an algebra), and *waiving* in Lie algebras again lead to Lie algebras.

From any associative algebra a Lie algebra is derived by putting

$$[\boldsymbol{a}, \boldsymbol{b}] = \boldsymbol{ab} - \boldsymbol{ba}.$$

In fact, any finite-dimensional Lie algebra can be derived this way up to isomorphy, even as a linear Lie algebra as defined in 7.4. This is known as Ado's theorem [see *Trans. Amer. Math. Soc. Transl.* **2** (1949)], which is not proved in this book.

7.4. Definition A *linear Lie algebra* (Alg Lie Lin) in R is a Lie algebra contained in End R, with $[\ldots,\ldots]$ defined by $[\boldsymbol{a},\boldsymbol{b}] = \boldsymbol{ab} - \boldsymbol{ba}$.

R acted on by a complex linear Lie algebra $\boldsymbol{G}$ has to be complex; R acted on by a real linear Lie algebra $\boldsymbol{G}$ may be real or complex.

Complex extension, real restriction, and *waiving* with respect to $\boldsymbol{G}$ are to be distinguished from the same kind of processes with respect to R, though in some applications they can go together.

Proposition 7.1 can now be stated as follows.

Theorem The tangent space of G at 1 is an r-dimensional linear Lie algebra $\boldsymbol{G}$, the *infinitesimal algebra* of G.

Remarks (1) The term "infinitesimal algebra of G" is also used with global linear groups. (2) Infinitesimal elements and algebras, and subsets thereof, are usually indicated by boldface type. If a (local) group is identified by some capital letter, its boldface counterpart usually indicates the infinitesimal algebra. (3) The converse of the theorem, that is, the unique existence of $G \in$ Gru Lie Lin with a given infinitesimal algebra $\boldsymbol{G} \in$ Alg Lie Lin, is proved in Sections 8 and 10.1. It justifies the use of italic and boldface counterparts for related Lie groups and algebras.

7.5 *Proof* of Proposition 7.1. As a paradigm of future procedures, the fact that $\boldsymbol{G}$ is an r-dimensional linear space is restated in 7.5.1–3.

7.5.1
$$\boldsymbol{a} \in \boldsymbol{G} \to \alpha\boldsymbol{a} \in \boldsymbol{G} \qquad (\alpha \text{ scalar}).$$

Proof There is a curve $\Upsilon_t a_t$ on G with $a_0 = 1$, $\boldsymbol{a} = [(d/dt)a_t]_{t=0}$. The curve $\Upsilon_t a_{\alpha t}$ lies at least partly on G. Its tangent vector at $t = 0$ is $[(d/dt)a_{\alpha t}]_{t=0} = \alpha[(d/dt)a_t]_{t=0} = \alpha\boldsymbol{a}$. Hence $\alpha\boldsymbol{a} \in \boldsymbol{G}$.

7.5.2
$$\boldsymbol{a},\boldsymbol{b} \in \boldsymbol{G} \to \boldsymbol{a}+\boldsymbol{b} \in \boldsymbol{G}.$$

Proof There are curves $\Upsilon_t a_t$, $\Upsilon_t b_t$ on G with $a_0 = b_0 = 1$, $\boldsymbol{a} = [(d/dt)a_t]_{t=0}$, $\boldsymbol{b} = [(d/dt)b_t]_{t=0}$. By $c_t = a_t b_t$ for small t, a curve on G is defined, and

$$\frac{d}{dt}c_t = \left(\frac{d}{dt}a_t\right)b_t + a_t\frac{d}{dt}b_t,$$

$$\left(\frac{d}{dt}c_t\right)_{t=0} = \left(\frac{d}{dt}a_t\right)_{t=0}\cdot 1 + 1\cdot\left(\frac{d}{dt}b_t\right)_{t=0} = \boldsymbol{a}+\boldsymbol{b},$$

which proves $\boldsymbol{a}+\boldsymbol{b} \in \boldsymbol{G}$.

7.5.3 $\dim \boldsymbol{G} = r.$

Proof It may be assumed that $f0 = 1$ in the $\ulcorner E, f \urcorner$-presentation of G. On a basis of E curves on G can be expressed by

$$a_t = f\ulcorner \varphi_1(t), \ldots, \varphi_r(t)\urcorner,$$

with continuously differentiable φ_j and $\varphi_j(0) = 0$. In particular,

$$\varphi_j(t) = t, \qquad \varphi_k(t) = 0 \qquad \text{for} \quad k \neq j$$

defines a curve $\curlyvee_t a_j(t)$ on G with

$$\boldsymbol{a}_j = \left[\frac{d}{dt} a_j(t)\right]_{t=0} = \left[\frac{\partial f(\tau_1, \ldots, \tau_r)}{\partial \tau_j}\right]_{\tau_1 = \cdots = \tau_r = 0} \in \boldsymbol{G}.$$

The $\boldsymbol{a}_j$ are the images of the basis vectors in E under $\mathrm{grad}_0 f$, which is of rank r, and are linearly independent.

Any $\boldsymbol{a} \in \boldsymbol{G}$ is the tangent vector at 1 of some curve defined by

$$a_t = f\ulcorner \varphi_1(t), \ldots, \varphi_r(t)\urcorner;$$

hence,

$$\boldsymbol{a} = \left(\frac{d}{dt} a_t\right)_{t=0} = \sum_j \left[\frac{\partial f(\tau_1, \ldots, \tau_r)}{\partial \tau_j}\right]_{\tau_1 = \cdots = \tau_r = 0} \left[\frac{d}{dt} \varphi_j(t)\right]_{t=0}$$

is linearly dependent on $\boldsymbol{a}_1, \ldots, \boldsymbol{a}_r$, which consequently form a basis of $\boldsymbol{G}$.

Remark Every $\boldsymbol{a} \in \boldsymbol{G}$ is a tangent vector of a C^2-curve on G. Indeed, if u is the $\mathrm{grad}_0 f$-original of $\boldsymbol{a}$, then $\curlyvee_t f(tu)$ has the required property.

7.5.4 $\boldsymbol{a}, \boldsymbol{b} \in \boldsymbol{G} \to [\boldsymbol{a}, \boldsymbol{b}] \in \boldsymbol{G}.$

Proof According to the preceding remark, C^2-curves $\curlyvee_t a_t$, $\curlyvee_t b_t$ can be found with $a_0 = b_0 = 1$,

$$\boldsymbol{a} = \left(\frac{d}{dt} a_t\right)_{t=0}, \qquad \boldsymbol{b} = \left(\frac{d}{dt} b_t\right)_{t=0}.$$

The finite commutators for small t,

$$c_t = a_t b_t a_t^{-1} b_t^{-1},$$

define a curve $\curlyvee_t c_t$ on G with $c_0 = 1$.

7.5.4.1 $$\frac{d}{dt}(a_t a_t^{-1}) = \left(\frac{d}{dt} a_t\right) a_t^{-1} + a_t \left(\frac{d}{dt} a_t^{-1}\right);$$

hence,

7.5.4.2 $$\left(\frac{d}{dt} a_t\right)_{t=0} = -\left(\frac{d}{dt} a_t^{-1}\right)_{t=0}.$$

Also

7.5.4.3
$$\left(\frac{d}{dt}b_t\right)_{t=0} = -\left(\frac{d}{dt}b_t^{-1}\right)_{t=0}.$$

Differentiating 7.5.4.1 once more, putting $t = 0$, and using 7.5.4.2 one obtains

$$\left(\frac{d^2}{dt^2}a_t\right)a_t^{-1} + 2\left(\frac{d}{dt}a_t\right)\left(\frac{d}{dt}a_t^{-1}\right) + a_t\left(\frac{d^2}{dt^2}a_t^{-1}\right) = \mathbf{0}.$$

7.5.4.4
$$\left(\frac{d^2}{dt^2}a_t\right)_{t=0} + \left(\frac{d^2}{dt^2}a_t^{-1}\right)_{t=0} = 2\boldsymbol{a}^2.$$

7.5.4.5
$$\left(\frac{d^2}{dt^2}b_t\right)_{t=0} + \left(\frac{d^2}{dt^2}b_t^{-1}\right)_{t=0} = 2\boldsymbol{b}^2.$$

Differentiating $\curlyvee_t c_t$, one gets

$$\frac{d}{dt}c_t = \left(\frac{d}{dt}a_t\right)b_t a_t^{-1}b_t^{-1} + a_t\left(\frac{d}{dt}b_t\right)a_t^{-1}b_t^{-1}$$
$$+ a_t b_t\left(\frac{d}{dt}a_t^{-1}\right)b_t^{-1} + a_t b_t a_t^{-1}\left(\frac{d}{dt}b_t^{-1}\right),$$

which because of 7.5.4.2–3 shows

$$\left(\frac{d}{dt}c_t\right)_{t=0} = \mathbf{0}.$$

Differentiating once more, putting $t = 0$, and using 7.5.4.2–3, one gets

$$\left(\frac{d^2}{dt^2}c_t\right)_{t=0} = 2\boldsymbol{ab} - 2\boldsymbol{a}^2 - 2\boldsymbol{ab} - 2\boldsymbol{ba} - 2\boldsymbol{b}^2 + 2\boldsymbol{ab} + 2\boldsymbol{a}^2 + 2\boldsymbol{b}^2$$
$$= 2(\boldsymbol{ab} - \boldsymbol{ba}).$$

The statement 7.5.4. now follows from the following lemma.

7.5.5. Lemma If $\curlyvee_t c_t$ is a C^2-curve on $G \in$ Gru Lie Loc Lin, and $c_0 = 1$, $(dc/dt)_{t=0} = \mathbf{0}$, then $(d^2 c/dt^2)_{t=0} \in \boldsymbol{G}$.

Proof $\curlyvee_t c_\tau^{-1} c_{t+\tau}$ is a C^2-curve on G for any small τ. Its tangent vector for $t = 0$ is

$$\boldsymbol{c}_\tau = c_\tau^{-1}\left(\frac{d}{dt}c_{t+\tau}\right)_{t=0} \in \boldsymbol{G}.$$

Since $\boldsymbol{G}$ is a closed set, $(d/d\tau)\boldsymbol{c}_\tau \in \boldsymbol{G}$ too, but

$$\left(\frac{d}{d\tau}\boldsymbol{c}_\tau\right)_{\tau=0} = \left(\frac{d^2}{dt^2}c_t\right)_{t=0}.$$

7.6. Examples Though the Lie character of the groups G of 3.1–8 has not yet been formally discussed, it is possible to compute $\boldsymbol{G}$:

ad 3.1 Clearly $\boldsymbol{G} \subset \operatorname{End} R$. Let $\boldsymbol{a} \in \operatorname{End} R$. If $a_t = \exp t\boldsymbol{a}$ then $\det a_t \neq 0$ and $\curlyvee_t a_t$ is a curve on G with

$$\left(\frac{d}{dt} a_t\right)_{t=0} = \boldsymbol{a};$$

hence $\boldsymbol{G} = \operatorname{End} R$.

ad 3.2 If $a_t \in G$, $\det a_t = 1$, then $d/dt \det a_t = 0$. On an ordered basis a_t is presented by a matrix $\ulcorner \alpha_{ij}(t) \urcorner_{i,j=1}^n$ and $\det a_t$ is a sum of terms $\pm\alpha_{1j_1} \dots \alpha_{nj_n}$. For $t = 0, \alpha_{ij} = 0$, unless $i = j$. Every summand other than $\alpha_{11} \dots \alpha_{nn}$ possesses at least two nondiagonal factors. Therefore after differentiation of $\det a_t$ at $t = 0$ the only remaining contribution is

$$\left(\frac{d}{dt} \det a_t\right)_{t=0} = \left[\frac{d}{dt}(\alpha_{11}(t) \dots \alpha_{nn}(t))\right]_{t=0}$$

$$= \left[\sum_j \frac{d}{dt} \alpha_{jj}(t)\right]_{t=0}$$

$$= \operatorname{tr}\left(\frac{d}{dt} a_t\right)_{t=0}.$$

Thus $\boldsymbol{a} \in \boldsymbol{G} \rightarrow \operatorname{tr} \boldsymbol{a} = 0$.

Conversely, from 2.7.1, one learns that if $\operatorname{tr} \boldsymbol{a} = 0$ then $\det \exp t\boldsymbol{a} = 1$. Then $a_t = \exp t\boldsymbol{a}$ defines a curve on G with $[(d/dt)a_t]_{t=0} = \boldsymbol{a}$.

Consequently, $\boldsymbol{a} \in \boldsymbol{G} \leftrightarrow [\boldsymbol{a} \in \operatorname{End} R \wedge \operatorname{tr} \boldsymbol{a} = 0]$.

ad 3.3 If $a_t \in G$, $\boldsymbol{a} = [(d/dt)a_t]_{t=0}$, then $a_t' a_t = 1$; hence

$$\left(\frac{d}{dt} a_t\right)' a_t + a_t' \left(\frac{d}{dt} a_t\right) = \boldsymbol{0},$$

$$\boldsymbol{a}' + \boldsymbol{a} = \boldsymbol{0}.$$

Thus $\boldsymbol{a}$ is skew.

Conversely, if $\boldsymbol{a}$ is skew, $a_t = \exp t\boldsymbol{a}$ is orthogonal (see 2.9) and $[(d/dt)a_t]_{t=0} = \boldsymbol{a}$. Consequently, $\boldsymbol{G}$ consists of the skew matrices of $\operatorname{End} R$.

The skew matrices are also called *infinitesimal rotations*. The case of $n = 3$ is particularly interesting. Then with

$$\boldsymbol{a} = \begin{pmatrix} 0 & -\omega_3 & \omega_2 \\ \omega_3 & 0 & -\omega_1 \\ -\omega_2 & \omega_1 & 0 \end{pmatrix}$$

one gets $\boldsymbol{a}x = [u, x]$, where $u = \ulcorner \omega_1, \omega_2, \omega_3 \urcorner$ and $[\ldots, \ldots]$ denotes the vector product; u is the axis of the infinitesimal rotation $\boldsymbol{a}$ and the rotations exp $t\boldsymbol{a}$. (Note that $\boldsymbol{a}u = 0$.)

ad 3.4 $\boldsymbol{G}$ consists of the hermitean skew matrices $\boldsymbol{a}$ of End R, $\boldsymbol{a}^* + \boldsymbol{a} = \boldsymbol{0}$.

ad 3.5 $\boldsymbol{G}$ consists of the matrices $\begin{pmatrix} 0 & \rho \\ 0 & \sigma \end{pmatrix}$.

ad 3.6 $\boldsymbol{G}$ consists of the matrices $\begin{pmatrix} \alpha & 0 \\ 0 & \beta \end{pmatrix}$ with imaginary α, β.

ad 3.7 $\boldsymbol{G}$ consists of the real multiples of $\begin{pmatrix} i\alpha & 0 \\ 0 & i\beta \end{pmatrix}$.

ad 3.8 $\boldsymbol{G}$ consists of the triangular matrices of the form $\bigtriangledown$ with zeros in the main diagonal.

Thanks to the nilpotency of $a - 1$ for $a \in G$, the power series of $\log a = \log(1 + (a - 1))$ converges (see 2.2). So log exists as the inverse of exp all over G and $\boldsymbol{G}$, respectively; hence

exp maps $\boldsymbol{G}$ homeomorphically onto G.

In all cases 3.1–8 one easily verifies directly that $\boldsymbol{G}$ is a Lie algebra. In particular, 3.2 states that the commutator of two matrices with vanishing trace again has vanishing trace. This is true even of any pair $A = \ulcorner \alpha_{ij} \urcorner_{i,j=1}^n$, $B = \ulcorner \beta_{ij} \urcorner_{i,j=1}^n$ of n–n-matrices because tr $AB = \sum \alpha_{ij}\beta_{ji}$ is symmetric in A, B.

In 3.3 the case of $n = 3$ is again of particular interest. Given $\boldsymbol{a}, \boldsymbol{b} \in \boldsymbol{G}$, there are vectors u, v such that, for all x,

$$\boldsymbol{a}x = [u, x],$$

$$\boldsymbol{b}x = [v, x].$$

Then

$$\boldsymbol{ab}x = [u,[v, x]],$$
$$\boldsymbol{ba}x = [v,[u,x]].$$

Computing the commutator of the matrices $\boldsymbol{a}, \boldsymbol{b}$, one finds

$$[\boldsymbol{a},\boldsymbol{b}]x = [[u,v],x];$$

thus,

$$[u,[v,x]] - [v,[u,x]] = [[u,v],x],$$

which is a well-known property of the vector product, closely related to Jacobi-associativity.

Lie algebras of linear mappings in function spaces play a role in quantum mechanics. Let Q, P, and I be defined by

$$(Q\varphi)(\xi) = \xi\varphi(\xi),$$
$$(P\varphi)(\xi) = \frac{d}{d\xi}\varphi(\xi),$$
$$I\varphi = \varphi.$$

Then

$$[P,I] = [Q,I] = 0.$$
$$[P,Q] = I,$$

The linear combinations $\alpha I + \beta P + \gamma Q$ with scalar α, β, γ form a Lie algebra.

7.7 Real restriction and waiving in (local) linear Lie groups induce the same kind of processes in their infinitesimal algebras.

7.8. Historical Note Commutators and Jacobi-associativity first appeared in Jacobi's study of partial differential operators.

8. THE EXPONENTIAL PRESENTATION

$G \in$ Gru Lie Lin, $G \subset$ Aut R, G locally presented as $\ulcorner E, f \urcorner$, $f0 = 1$, $\boldsymbol{G}$ its infinitesimal algebra.

8.1. Proposition The tangent space of G at a_0 is $a_0\boldsymbol{G}$.

Proof By left multiplication with a_0^{-1} a curve $\curlyvee_t a_t$ through a_0 on G is mapped into a curve $\curlyvee_t b_t$ on G through 1,

$$b_t = a_0^{-1}\, a_t.$$

The tangent space of G at a_0 is made up of the

$$\left(\frac{d}{dt}a_t\right)_{t=0} = \left(\frac{d}{dt}(a_0\, b_t)\right)_{t=0} = a_0\left(\frac{d}{dt}b_t\right)_{t=0},$$

which belong to $a_0\mathbf{G}$.

8.2 How does one reconstruct G from $\mathbf{G}$? The examples 7.6 suggest that it could be done by the exponential. Indeed, local coincidence of G and $\exp \mathbf{G}$ will be shown. The first step is the following proposition.

Proposition $\mathbf{a} \in \mathbf{G} \to \exp t\mathbf{a} \in G$.

Proof $c_t = \exp t\mathbf{a}$ as a function of t is characterized by the differential equation

8.2.1 $$\frac{d}{dt}c_t = c_t\,\mathbf{a},$$

with the initial condition

8.2.2 $$c_0 = 1.$$

The solution to 8.2.1–2 in End R is unique. If it can be shown that for small t 8.2.1–2 can already be solved on G, the uniqueness of the solution will guarantee $\exp t\mathbf{a} \in G$ for small t and so for all t because the $\exp t\mathbf{a}$ form a group.

According to 8.1, $c\mathbf{a}$ belongs to the tangent space of G at $c \in G$. Marking the vector $c\mathbf{a}$ at any point $c \in G$, one gets a continuous vector field on G. By integrating it† one obtains a curve $\curlyvee_t a_t$ for small t, with $a_t \in G$, $a_0 = 1$, and such that for any t its tangent vector is just the prescribed $a_t\mathbf{a}$. Therefore the curve fulfills 8.2.1–2, which consequently can be solved on G. This proves the assertion.

† It is done by translating the problem into E through f^{-1}, where the resulting differential equation has to be solved.

8.3 The previous proposition shows: exp $\boldsymbol{G} \subset G$. By the equality of dimensions and by the fact that grad_0 exp is the identity mapping of $\boldsymbol{G}$, it follows from Proposition 4.16 that exp maps a sufficiently small open $\mathbf{0}$-neighborhood of $\boldsymbol{G}$ homeomorphically and nondegenerately onto an open 1-neighborhood of G.

This yields a new presentation of G near 1, E being replaced by $\boldsymbol{G}$ (as a linear space) and f by exp. The new presentation has the advantage of being intrinsic and analytic (because exp is so). By left multiplication this presentation is transferred to any point of G, which shows that G is analytic.

This suggests the following definition.

Definition The $\ulcorner E,f \urcorner$*-presentation* of G near 1 is called *exponential* if $E = \boldsymbol{G}$ (as a linear space) and f is the restriction of exp to an open ball around $\mathbf{0}$ in $\boldsymbol{G}$.

The following has been proved:

Theorem A linear Lie group may be considered as an analytic group. Near 1 it admits an exponential presentation.

8.4. Definition An open ball $\boldsymbol{N}$ around $\mathbf{0}$ in $\boldsymbol{G} \in$ Alg Lie Lin (according to some norm in $\boldsymbol{G}$) is called a *smooth ball* if, in the closure of $\boldsymbol{N}$, exp is one-to-one and grad exp is nondegenerate. By exp the notion of smooth ball is carried to G, if $\boldsymbol{G}$ is the infinitesimal algebra of G.

The existence of smooth balls follows from $\text{grad}_0 \exp = 1$ and the continuity of $\curlyvee_{\boldsymbol{a}} \text{grad}_{\boldsymbol{a}} \exp$.

Note that if $\boldsymbol{N}$ is a smooth ball then exp $\boldsymbol{N}$ is a C^{an}-piece.

Proposition If $\boldsymbol{N}$ is a smooth ball in $\boldsymbol{G} \in$ Alg Lie Lin and $\boldsymbol{N}'$ is a smaller concentric open ball in $\boldsymbol{G}$ such that

$$\exp \boldsymbol{N}' \cdot \exp \boldsymbol{N}' \subset \exp \boldsymbol{N},$$

then exp $\boldsymbol{N}'$ is a closed local subgroup of Aut R, as well as a local linear Lie group.

This follows from 4.11.

Proposition For the infinitesimal algebra $\boldsymbol{G}$ of the linear Lie group G, sets $\boldsymbol{N}$, $\boldsymbol{N}'$ as introduced in the preceding proposition exist and then exp $\boldsymbol{N}'$ is locally identical with G.

8.5 The exp-image of a straight line through $\mathbf{0}$ as far as contained in $\boldsymbol{N}'$ (see 8.4) is a one-dimensional local linear Lie group. This leads to the following theorem.

Theorem A 1-neighborhood in G is covered by a smooth system of one-dimensional local linear Lie groups, intersecting in 1 only.

8.6 Globally things might be less smooth. The torus group 3.6 admits an infinity of one-dimensional subgroups through every one of its points.

On the other hand, it may happen that G is not exhausted by exp $\boldsymbol{G}$. As an example, take the group G of 2–2-matrices with complex coefficients and unit determinant. Then $\boldsymbol{G}$ consists of the 2–2-matrices $\boldsymbol{a}$ with tr $\boldsymbol{a} = 0$. There is no basis on which

$$a = \begin{pmatrix} -1 & 1 \\ 0 & -1 \end{pmatrix} \in G$$

appears in diagonal form. The same can be said of $\boldsymbol{a}$ if exp $\boldsymbol{a} = a$. Consequently, $\boldsymbol{a}$ should have two equal eigenvalues. Since tr $\boldsymbol{a} = 0$, both must vanish and those of a should be 1, whereas in fact they are -1. This shows $a \notin \exp \boldsymbol{G}$.

8.7. Proposition Let K_i $(i = 1,\ldots,k)$ be C^1-pieces in G, passing through 1 and with the respective tangent spaces $\boldsymbol{K}_i$ at 1. Let $\boldsymbol{G} = \sum \boldsymbol{K}_i$ directly as linear spaces. Then there are C^1-pieces $K_i' \subset K_i$ with the same tangent spaces at 1 such that

$$\curlyvee_{\ulcorner a_1, a_2, \ldots, a_k \urcorner} a_1 \cdot a_2 \cdot \cdots \cdot a_k$$

maps $\ulcorner K_1', K_2', \ldots, K_k' \urcorner$ homeomorphically onto a 1-neighborhood in G. In particular, $K_1 \cdot K_2 \cdot \cdots \cdot K_k$ contains 1 in its interior with respect to G.

Proof The K_i may be assumed in $\ulcorner E_i, f_i \urcorner$-presentations with $f_i t_i$ defined for $t_i \in S_i$ and S_i open balls around 0 in E_i $(i = 1,\ldots,k)$; the E_i may be assumed to be direct summands of $E = \sum E_i$. Put

$$f(\textstyle\sum t_i) = f_1(t_1) \cdot f_2(t_2) \cdot \cdots \cdot f_k(t_k).$$

Then f is a C^1-mapping into G and

$$(\mathrm{grad}_0 f)(\textstyle\sum t_i) = \sum (\mathrm{grad}_0 f_i) t_i,$$

$$\det(\mathrm{grad}_0 f) = \prod \det(\mathrm{grad}_0 f_i) \neq 0.$$

So f maps a small 0-neighborhood in E homeomorphically onto a 1-neighborhood in G, which proves the assertions.

8.8 The special case in which U is a small 1-neighborhood in G and

$$K_i = (\exp \boldsymbol{K}_i) \cap U,$$

leads to the following.

Definition Let $\boldsymbol{G} = \boldsymbol{K}_1 + \boldsymbol{K}_2 + \cdots + \boldsymbol{K}_k$ directly as linear spaces and let ω_i be the natural projection of $\boldsymbol{G}$ onto $\boldsymbol{K}_i$. Then $\ulcorner E, f \urcorner$ is called a *generalized exponential presentation* of G near 1, induced by the aforementioned direct splitting, if $E = \boldsymbol{G}$,

$$f\boldsymbol{a} = \exp \omega_1 \boldsymbol{a} \cdot \exp \omega_2 \boldsymbol{a} \cdot \ \cdots \ \cdot \exp \omega_k \boldsymbol{a}.$$

The existence of such presentations has just been proved.

9. HOMOMORPHISMS, AUTOMORPHISMS, AND DERIVATIONS

9.1. Local Homomorphisms $G, H \in$ Gru Lie Lin.

Definition Θ is called a *local homomorphism* of G into H if it maps a 1-neighborhood in G continuously into H such that

$$\Theta(ab) = \Theta a \cdot \Theta b$$

as far as $\Theta a, \Theta b, \Theta(ab)$ are defined. Two local homomorphisms coinciding in some 1-neighborhood in G are considered identical. If such a Θ maps every sufficiently small 1-neighborhood of G onto a 1-neighborhood in H, it is called a local epimorphism. The terms local endo-, iso-, and automorphism apply in an obvious way. It is also clear what is meant by a *local C^2-homomorphism* and a *local semi-C^2-homomorphism* (see 5.1, 5.3).

A local *C^2-homomorphism* Θ of G into H induces a linear mapping, also called Θ (instead of $\operatorname{grad}_1 \Theta$), of their infinitesimal algebras $\boldsymbol{G}$ into $\boldsymbol{H}$ such that if

$$\boldsymbol{a} = \left(\frac{d}{dt} a_t\right)_{t=0} \in \boldsymbol{G},$$

then

$$\Theta \boldsymbol{a} = \left(\frac{d}{dt} \Theta a_t\right)_{t=0} \in \boldsymbol{H}.$$

If for C^2-curves $\curlyvee_t a_t, \curlyvee_t b_t$,

$$\boldsymbol{a} = \left(\frac{d}{dt} a_t\right)_{t=0}, \qquad \boldsymbol{b} = \left(\frac{d}{dt} b_t\right)_{t=0} \in \boldsymbol{G},$$

then (see 7.5)

$$[\boldsymbol{a}, \boldsymbol{b}] = \frac{1}{2}\left[\frac{d^2}{dt^2}(a_t b_t a_t^{-1} b_t^{-1})\right]_{t=0},$$

$$\Theta[\boldsymbol{a}, \boldsymbol{b}] = \frac{1}{2}\left[\frac{d^2}{dt^2}\Theta(a_t\, b_t\, a_t^{-1}\, b_t^{-1})\right]_{t=0}$$

$$= \frac{1}{2}\left[\frac{d^2}{dt^2}(\Theta a_t \cdot \Theta b_t \cdot (\Theta a_t)^{-1} \cdot (\Theta b_t)^{-1}))\right]_{t=0}$$

$$= [\Theta \boldsymbol{a},\ \Theta \boldsymbol{b}].$$

This proves the following proposition.

Proposition A local C^2-homomorphism of linear Lie groups induces a homomorphism of their infinitesimal algebras.

In 10.4 the converse will be proved. In fact exp and Θ will be shown to commute. As a consequence, the validity of the prefixes epi, endo, iso, and auto, with respect to local groups and their infinitesimal algebras, will imply each other.

It is clear how the proposition is to be stated for local semi-C^2-homomorphisms.

9.2–4. Derivations

9.2 The automorphisms of a Lie algebra $\boldsymbol{G}$ form a linear group, denoted by Aut $\boldsymbol{G}$. Though the Lie character of Aut $\boldsymbol{G}$ still has to be established (see 11.3.4), the Lie group notions can be applied to Aut $\boldsymbol{G}$ in a heuristic approach.

Definition Ω is called an *infinitesimal automorphism* of $\boldsymbol{G}$ if

$$\Omega = \left(\frac{d}{dt}\Theta_t\right)_{t=0}$$

for some curve $\Upsilon_t\, \Theta_t$ in Aut $\boldsymbol{G}$ with $\Theta_0 = 1$.

With the notation of this definition one gets $\Theta_t[\boldsymbol{a}, \boldsymbol{b}] = [\Theta_t \boldsymbol{a}, \Theta_t \boldsymbol{b}]$; hence by differentiation at $t = 0$

$$\Omega[\boldsymbol{a}, \boldsymbol{b}] = [\Omega \boldsymbol{a}, \boldsymbol{b}] \dotplus [\boldsymbol{a}, \Omega \boldsymbol{b}].$$

Clearly Ω is linear.

This suggests the following.

9.3. Definition A linear mapping Ω of $\boldsymbol{G}$ into itself is called a *derivation* of $\boldsymbol{G}$ if

$$\Omega[\boldsymbol{a}, \boldsymbol{b}] = [\Omega \boldsymbol{a}, \boldsymbol{b}] + [\boldsymbol{a}, \Omega \boldsymbol{b}].$$

It has been shown that an infinitesimal automorphism is a derivation. The converse is also true:

Proposition The notions of infinitesimal automorphism and derivation of a Lie algebra $\boldsymbol{G}$ coincide. If Ω is a derivation, exp Ω is an automorphism.

Proof Let Ω be a derivation of $\boldsymbol{G}$. Put $\boldsymbol{c}_t = [(\exp t\Omega)\,\boldsymbol{a}, (\exp t\Omega)\,\boldsymbol{b}]$. Then

$$\begin{aligned}\frac{d}{dt}\boldsymbol{c}_t &= [\Omega(\exp t\Omega)\boldsymbol{a}, (\exp t\Omega)\boldsymbol{b}] + [(\exp t\Omega)\boldsymbol{a}, \Omega(\exp t\Omega)\boldsymbol{b}] \\ &= \Omega[(\exp t\Omega)\boldsymbol{a}, (\exp t\Omega)\boldsymbol{b}] \\ &= \Omega\boldsymbol{c}_t.\end{aligned}$$

The differential equation

$$\frac{d}{dt}\boldsymbol{c}_t = \Omega\boldsymbol{c}_t, \qquad \boldsymbol{c}_0 = [\boldsymbol{a}, \boldsymbol{b}]$$

admits the unique solution

$$\boldsymbol{c}_t = (\exp t\Omega)\,[\boldsymbol{a}, \boldsymbol{b}].$$

This proves $\exp t\Omega \in \operatorname{Aut} \boldsymbol{G}$. Because of

$$\left(\frac{d}{dt}\exp t\Omega\right)_{t=0} = \Omega,$$

Ω is an infinitesimal automorphism.

9.4. Proposition The derivations of a Lie algebra $\boldsymbol{G}$ form a linear Lie algebra.

Proof Clearly they form a linear space. Let Ω_1, Ω_2 be two derivations of $\boldsymbol{G}$.

$$\Omega_1\Omega_2[\boldsymbol{a}, \boldsymbol{b}] = [\Omega_1\Omega_2\,\boldsymbol{a}, \boldsymbol{b}] + [\Omega_1\,\boldsymbol{a},\ \Omega_2\,\boldsymbol{b}] + [\Omega_2\,\boldsymbol{a},\ \Omega_1\,\boldsymbol{b}] + [\boldsymbol{a},\ \Omega_1\Omega_2\,\boldsymbol{b}].$$

$$\begin{aligned}[\Omega_1, \Omega_2]\,[\boldsymbol{a}, \boldsymbol{b}] &= \Omega_1\Omega_2[\boldsymbol{a}, \boldsymbol{b}] - \Omega_2\Omega_1[\boldsymbol{a}, \boldsymbol{b}] \\ &= [(\Omega_1\Omega_2 - \Omega_2\Omega_1)\,\boldsymbol{a}, \boldsymbol{b}] + [\boldsymbol{a}, (\Omega_1\Omega_2 - \Omega_2\Omega_1)\,\boldsymbol{b}] \\ &= [[\Omega_1, \Omega_2]\,\boldsymbol{a}, \boldsymbol{b}] + [\boldsymbol{a}, [\Omega_1, \Omega_2]\,\boldsymbol{b}],\end{aligned}$$

which proves that $[\Omega_1, \Omega_2]$ is again a derivation of $\boldsymbol{G}$.

9.5–7. Inner Automorphisms

9.5 Any group G possesses a special kind of automorphisms called *inner*, which again form a group, denoted by Int G.

Definition For $c \in G$

$$\tilde{c} = \Upsilon_{a \in G}\, cac^{-1}.$$

The group of $\tilde{c}$ with $c \in G$, with the composition of mappings as the group product, is called the group Int G of *inner automorphisms* of G.

Indeed, Int G is a group because

$$\tilde{c}_1(\tilde{c}_2 a) = c_1 c_2 a c_2^{-1} c_1^{-1} = c_1 c_2 a (c_1 c_2)^{-1} = \widetilde{c_1 c_2}\, a,$$

$$\tilde{c}_1 \tilde{c}_1^{-1} a = \widetilde{c_1 c_1^{-1}}\, a = a.$$

This also shows the following.

Proposition $\Upsilon_c \tilde{c}$ is a homomorphism of G onto Int G. Its kernel consists of those c that fulfill $cac^{-1} = a$ for all $a \in G$. This is the *center* of G.

9.6 If, moreover, $G \in$ Gru Lie Lin, then according to 9.1, $\tilde{c}$ induces an automorphism of $\boldsymbol{G}$, mapping

$$\boldsymbol{a} = \left(\frac{d}{dt} a_t\right)_{t=0}$$

into

$$\tilde{c}\boldsymbol{a} = \left(\frac{d}{dt} c a_t c^{-1}\right)_{t=0} = c \left(\frac{d}{dt} a_t\right)_{t=0} c^{-1} = c\boldsymbol{a}c^{-1}.$$

It can be directly verified that $\tilde{c}$ is an automorphism of $\boldsymbol{G}$: the linearity is evident and $c[\boldsymbol{a},\boldsymbol{b}]c^{-1} = c(\boldsymbol{ab} - \boldsymbol{ba})c^{-1} = c\boldsymbol{a}c^{-1} \cdot c\boldsymbol{b}c^{-1} - c\boldsymbol{b}c^{-1} \cdot c\boldsymbol{a}c^{-1} = [c\boldsymbol{a}c^{-1}, c\boldsymbol{b}c^{-1}]$.

Moreover,

$$\tilde{c}_1(\tilde{c}_2 \boldsymbol{a}) = c_1 c_2 \boldsymbol{a} c_2^{-1} c_1^{-1} = c_1 c_2 \boldsymbol{a} (c_1 c_2)^{-1} = \widetilde{c_1 c_2}\, \boldsymbol{a}.$$

This leads to the following.

Definition The *adjoint group* $\tilde{G}$ of $G \in$ Gru Lie Lin is the group of linear mappings $\tilde{c} = \Upsilon_{\boldsymbol{a} \in \boldsymbol{G}}\, c\boldsymbol{a}c^{-1}$ of $\boldsymbol{G}$ onto itself with $c \in G$.

The following has been shown.

Proposition $\Upsilon_c \tilde{c}$ is a linear representation of G in $\boldsymbol{G}$.

$\tilde{G}$ is a linear group. In 9.11 it is proved to be a linear Lie group.

9.7 The representation in 9.6 of G by $\tilde{G}$ in $\boldsymbol{G}$ may fail to be faithful just as much as the representation in 9.5 of G by Int G. It may be asked how they are related. Their actions are connected by exp:

$$\tilde{c} \exp \boldsymbol{a} = c(\exp \boldsymbol{a}) c^{-1} = \sum c \frac{1}{j!} \boldsymbol{a}^j c^{-1} = \sum \frac{1}{j!} (c\boldsymbol{a}c^{-1})^j$$

$$= \sum \frac{1}{j!} (\tilde{c}\boldsymbol{a})^j = \exp \tilde{c}\boldsymbol{a}.$$

One notes that in the case of an automorphism Θ of the form $\tilde{c}$ it is evident that Θ and exp commute (see end of 9.1).

Therefore, if $\tilde{c}_1, \tilde{c}_2$ coincide in $\boldsymbol{G}$, they do so near 1 in G, but because they are homomorphisms and any 1-neighborhood in G generates G, the same is true all over G.

This shows:

Proposition If $G \in$ Gru Lie Lin, then $\tilde{G}$ and Int G are isomorphically related by the mapping exp of the spaces $\boldsymbol{G}$ into G, on which $\tilde{G}$ and Int G act, respectively.

9.8–11. Inner Derivations and Automorphisms

9.8 Since $\tilde{G} \subset$ Aut $\boldsymbol{G}$, the notions of 9.2 apply to $\tilde{G}$ if Θ is specialized to $\tilde{c}$.

Taking, as usual, a curve $\curlyvee_t c_t$ on G with $c_0 = 1$ and putting

$$\tilde{\boldsymbol{c}} = \left(\frac{d}{dt}\tilde{c}_t\right)_{t=0},$$

one obtains an infinitesimal automorphism of $\boldsymbol{G}$, hence a derivation.

$$\tilde{\boldsymbol{c}}\boldsymbol{a} = \left(\frac{d}{dt}\tilde{c}_t\right)_{t=0}\boldsymbol{a} = \left(\frac{d}{dt}(c_t\,\boldsymbol{a}c_t^{-1})\right)_{t=0} = \boldsymbol{ca} - \boldsymbol{ac}.$$

This definition of $\tilde{\boldsymbol{c}}$ makes sense if $\boldsymbol{G}$ is a general (not necessarily linear) Lie algebra:

$$\tilde{\boldsymbol{c}}\boldsymbol{a} = [\boldsymbol{c}, \boldsymbol{a}].$$

$\tilde{\boldsymbol{c}}$ is a derivation, since $\tilde{\boldsymbol{c}}$ is linear and

$$\tilde{\boldsymbol{c}}[\boldsymbol{a}, \boldsymbol{b}] = [\boldsymbol{c}, [\boldsymbol{a}, \boldsymbol{b}]] = [[\boldsymbol{c}, \boldsymbol{a}], \boldsymbol{b}] + [\boldsymbol{a}, [\boldsymbol{c}, \boldsymbol{b}]]$$

by anticommutativity and Jacobi-associativity.

Notation For $\boldsymbol{G} \in$ Alg Lie and $\boldsymbol{c} \in \boldsymbol{G}$

$$\tilde{\boldsymbol{c}} = \curlyvee_{\boldsymbol{a} \in \boldsymbol{G}} [\boldsymbol{c}, \boldsymbol{a}]$$

or, if $\boldsymbol{G}$ has to be mentioned explicitly,

$$\mathrm{ad}_{\boldsymbol{G}}\, \boldsymbol{c} = \curlyvee_{\boldsymbol{a} \in \boldsymbol{G}} [\boldsymbol{c}, \boldsymbol{a}].$$

For any $\boldsymbol{N} \subset \boldsymbol{G}$, $\tilde{\boldsymbol{N}}$, or $\mathrm{ad}_{\boldsymbol{G}} \boldsymbol{N}$, means the set of $\tilde{\boldsymbol{c}}$ with $\boldsymbol{c} \in \boldsymbol{N}$.

Definition For $\boldsymbol{G} \in$ Alg Lie the $\tilde{\boldsymbol{c}}$ with $\boldsymbol{c} \in \boldsymbol{G}$ are called the *inner derivations* of $\boldsymbol{G}$. The linear Lie algebra made up of these $\tilde{\boldsymbol{c}}$ (see next proposition) is called the *adjoint algebra* $\tilde{\boldsymbol{G}}$ of $\boldsymbol{G}$.

Proposition For finite-dimensional $\boldsymbol{G} \in$ Alg Lie: (1) $\tilde{\boldsymbol{G}} \in$ Alg Lie Lin; (2) $\Upsilon_{\boldsymbol{a}}\, \tilde{\boldsymbol{a}}$ maps $\boldsymbol{G}$ homomorphically onto $\tilde{\boldsymbol{G}}$.

Proof

$$(\alpha\tilde{\boldsymbol{c}})\boldsymbol{a} = \alpha(\tilde{\boldsymbol{c}}\boldsymbol{a}) = \alpha[\boldsymbol{c},\boldsymbol{a}] = [\alpha\boldsymbol{c},\boldsymbol{a}] = \widetilde{\alpha\boldsymbol{c}}\ \boldsymbol{a},$$

$$(\tilde{\boldsymbol{c}}_1 + \tilde{\boldsymbol{c}}_2)\boldsymbol{a} = \tilde{\boldsymbol{c}}_1\boldsymbol{a} + \tilde{\boldsymbol{c}}_2\boldsymbol{a} = [\boldsymbol{c}_1,\boldsymbol{a}] + [\boldsymbol{c}_2,\boldsymbol{a}] = [\boldsymbol{c}_1 + \boldsymbol{c}_2,\boldsymbol{a}] = \widetilde{\boldsymbol{c}_1 + \boldsymbol{c}_2}\,\boldsymbol{a},$$

$$[\tilde{\boldsymbol{c}}_1,\tilde{\boldsymbol{c}}_2]\boldsymbol{a} = \tilde{\boldsymbol{c}}_1\tilde{\boldsymbol{c}}_2\boldsymbol{a} - \tilde{\boldsymbol{c}}_2\tilde{\boldsymbol{c}}_1\boldsymbol{a} = [\boldsymbol{c}_1,[\boldsymbol{c}_2,\boldsymbol{a}]] - [\boldsymbol{c}_2,[\boldsymbol{c}_1,\boldsymbol{a}]] = [[\boldsymbol{c}_1,\boldsymbol{c}_2],\boldsymbol{a}] = \widetilde{[\boldsymbol{c}_1,\boldsymbol{c}_2]}\boldsymbol{a},$$

by using anticommutativity and Jacobi-associativity.

9.9 Pursuing the application of 9.3 to finite-dimensional $\boldsymbol{G} \in$ Alg Lie, one notes that exp $\tilde{\boldsymbol{c}}$ is an automorphism of $\boldsymbol{G}$, which could be called inner. It is not yet clear, however, whether these mappings generate a linear Lie group and whether this is $\tilde{G}$. This is proved in 10.3. Meanwhile there is no objection to expressing the following definition.

Definition If $\tilde{\boldsymbol{G}}$ is the infinitesimal algebra of a linear Lie group, this group is called Int $\boldsymbol{G}$.

Meanwhile one can go farther if it is assumed that $\boldsymbol{G} \in$ Alg Lie Lin or even that $\boldsymbol{G}$ is the infinitesimal algebra of some $G \in$ Gru Lie Lin. This is done in 9.10–11.

9.10. Proposition If $\boldsymbol{G} \in$ Alg Lie Lin, then

$$(\exp\tilde{\boldsymbol{c}})\,\boldsymbol{a} = \exp\boldsymbol{c}\cdot\boldsymbol{a}\cdot\exp(-\boldsymbol{c}).$$

Proof The differential equation

$$\frac{d}{dt}\boldsymbol{a}_t = \tilde{\boldsymbol{c}}\boldsymbol{a}_t, \qquad \boldsymbol{a}_0 = \boldsymbol{a},$$

is solved by

$$\boldsymbol{a}_t = (\exp t\tilde{\boldsymbol{c}})\,\boldsymbol{a}$$

as well as by

$$\boldsymbol{a}_t = \exp t\boldsymbol{c}\cdot\boldsymbol{a}\cdot\exp(-t\boldsymbol{c}).$$

The uniqueness of the solution proves the assertion.

9.11. Proposition If $G \in$ Gru Lie Lin and $\boldsymbol{G}$ is its infinitesimal algebra, then Int $\boldsymbol{G}$ exists and equals $\tilde{G}$.

Proof Under the present condition the result of 9.10 may be written

$$(\exp \tilde{\boldsymbol{c}})\, \boldsymbol{a} = \widetilde{\exp \boldsymbol{c}}\, \boldsymbol{a},$$

or, for short,

9.11.1 $$\exp \tilde{\boldsymbol{c}} = \widetilde{\exp \boldsymbol{c}}.$$

Now a local linear Lie group of which $\tilde{\boldsymbol{G}}$ is the infinitesimal algebra is found by the following construction:

Take a smooth ball $\boldsymbol{N}$ in $\boldsymbol{G}$ (see 8.4). Then, by 8.4, an open ball $\boldsymbol{N}'$ in $\boldsymbol{G}$ around $\boldsymbol{0}$ can be found such that

$$\exp \boldsymbol{N}' \cdot \exp \boldsymbol{N}' \subset \exp \boldsymbol{N}.$$

By 9.11.1 the mapping $\curlyvee_c \tilde{c}$ yields

$$\exp \tilde{\boldsymbol{N}}' \cdot \exp \tilde{\boldsymbol{N}}' \subset \exp \tilde{\boldsymbol{N}}.$$

If $\boldsymbol{N}$ has been chosen so small that $\tilde{\boldsymbol{N}}$ is still a smooth ball with respect to $\tilde{\boldsymbol{G}}$, then from this relation it follows (by 8.4) that $\exp \tilde{\boldsymbol{N}}'$ is a local linear Lie group whose infinitesimal algebra is $\tilde{\boldsymbol{G}}$. Consequently, Int $\boldsymbol{G}$, as introduced in Definition 9.9, exists as the global extension of $\exp \tilde{\boldsymbol{N}}'$. By 9.10 it coincides with $\tilde{G}$.

9.12–13. The Topology of Int G

9.12 One should first be inclined to topologize Int G as a set of mappings of G onto itself, preferably by means of compact convergence (i.e., a sequence of mappings converges if it does so on any compact subset). If Int G and $\tilde{G}$ are identified according to Proposition 9.7, this topology of Int G would coincide with that of $\tilde{G}$ as a subgroup of the general linear group of the linear space $\boldsymbol{G}$. This, however, need not be the topology that is borne by $\tilde{G}$ as a linear Lie group. Of course, both topologies coincide as soon as $\tilde{G}$ is closed. With a view to a later application, one is advised to express the following:

Definition $\boldsymbol{G} \in$ Alg Lie is called ad-*closed* if Int $\boldsymbol{G}$ is closed in the general linear group of the linear space $\boldsymbol{G}$. $G \in$ Gru Lie Lin is called ad-*closed* if its infinitesimal algebra $\boldsymbol{G}$ is ad-closed.

For ad-closed G the topology borne by Int G as a set of mappings of G coincides with the linear Lie group topology of $\tilde{G}$.

9.13 Another obvious topology to impose on Int G of $G \in$ Gru Lie Lin would be that of the coset space G/Z, where Z is the center of G. It will soon become clear (see 12.14) that this topology coincides with that borne by $\tilde{G}$ as a linear Lie group (after due identification of $\tilde{G}$ and Int G).

10. EXPANDING LINEAR LIE ALGEBRAS AND THEIR HOMOMORPHISMS INTO LINEAR LIE GROUPS AND THEIR LOCAL HOMOMORPHISMS

$\boldsymbol{G} \in$ Alg Lie Lin.

10.1. Theorem Gru Lie Lin is one-to-one mapped onto Alg Lie Lin by the functor "infinitesimal algebra of... ."

This was announced in 7.4, Remark 3. In Section 8, the functor mapping of $\boldsymbol{G}$ into G was inverted by means of the exponential. What is still left to prove can be formulated as the following theorem.

Theorem $\boldsymbol{G}$ is the infinitesimal algebra of some (uniquely determined) $G \in$ Gru Lie Lin.

Proof According to 6.1, a local construction of G is sufficient; according to 8.3, one may expect exp $\boldsymbol{G}$ to do the job.

Let $\boldsymbol{N}$ be a smooth ball in $\boldsymbol{G}$. The first step is to show that at any point exp $\boldsymbol{c}_0$ ($\boldsymbol{c}_0 \in \boldsymbol{N}$) the tangent space of exp $\boldsymbol{N}$ is (exp $\boldsymbol{c}_0$) $\boldsymbol{G}$, as might be expected from 8.1. A curve on exp $\boldsymbol{N}$ is given by Υ_t exp $\boldsymbol{c}_t$, where $\Upsilon_t \boldsymbol{c}_t$ is a curve on $\boldsymbol{N}$. It is proved that

$$\left(\frac{d}{dt}\exp \boldsymbol{c}_t\right)_{t=0} \in (\exp \boldsymbol{c}_0)\,\boldsymbol{G};$$

then, because of the nondegeneracy of grad exp in $\boldsymbol{N}$, it is evident that the tangent vectors at exp $\boldsymbol{c}_0$ exhaust (exp $\boldsymbol{c}_0$) $\boldsymbol{G}$. Put

10.1.1 $$y(t, s) = \exp(-s\boldsymbol{c}_t)\cdot\frac{\partial}{\partial t}\exp s\boldsymbol{c}_t.$$

Differentiating with regard to s and interchanging differentiations in s and t, one obtains

$$\begin{aligned}\frac{\partial}{\partial s}y(t,s) &= -\exp(-s\boldsymbol{c}_t)\cdot\boldsymbol{c}_t\frac{\partial}{\partial t}\exp s\boldsymbol{c}_t + \exp(-s\boldsymbol{c}_t)\cdot\frac{\partial}{\partial t}(\boldsymbol{c}_t\exp s\boldsymbol{c}_t)\\ &= \exp(-s\boldsymbol{c}_t)\cdot\frac{d}{dt}\boldsymbol{c}_t\cdot\exp s\boldsymbol{c}_t.\end{aligned}$$

which belongs to $\boldsymbol{G}$ because of 9.9–10. Integrating in s yields

10.1.2 $$y(t,1) = \int_0^1 \exp(-s\boldsymbol{c}_t)\cdot \frac{d}{dt}\boldsymbol{c}_t \cdot \exp s\boldsymbol{c}_t \cdot ds \in \boldsymbol{G}.$$

According to the definition of y, this means

$$\left(\frac{d}{dt}\exp \boldsymbol{c}_t\right)_{t=0} \in (\exp \boldsymbol{c}_0)\,\boldsymbol{G}.$$

This proves that $(\exp \boldsymbol{c}_0)\boldsymbol{G}$ is the tangent space of $\exp \boldsymbol{N}$ at $\exp \boldsymbol{c}_0$. To complete the proof a smaller concentric open ball $\boldsymbol{N}'$ is constructed such that

$$\exp \boldsymbol{N}'\cdot \exp \boldsymbol{N}' \subset \exp \boldsymbol{N}.$$

Then by 8.4 $\exp \boldsymbol{N}'$ is a local linear Lie group with the infinitesimal algebra $\boldsymbol{G}$.

To find such an $\boldsymbol{N}'$ one considers

$$c_t = \exp \boldsymbol{a}\cdot \exp t\boldsymbol{b}$$

for $\boldsymbol{a} \in \boldsymbol{N}$ and $\boldsymbol{b} \in \boldsymbol{G}$. The curve $\Upsilon_t c_t$ is characterized by the differential equation

$$\frac{d}{dt}c_t = c_t\,\boldsymbol{b}, \qquad c_0 = \exp \boldsymbol{a}.$$

The solution can also be obtained by integrating the field of vectors $(\exp \boldsymbol{a})\boldsymbol{b}$ ($\boldsymbol{b}$ fixed $\in \boldsymbol{G}$), which have been shown to lie in the tangent space of $\exp \boldsymbol{N}$ at $\exp \boldsymbol{a}$. By the same reasoning as in 8.2 the solution is found within $\exp \boldsymbol{N}$ for small t. So, for small $\boldsymbol{b}$ and $0 \leqslant t \leqslant 1$, $c_t \in \exp \boldsymbol{N}$. Because the solution depends continuously on $\boldsymbol{a}$ and $\boldsymbol{b}$, this means that

$$\exp \boldsymbol{a}\cdot \exp \boldsymbol{b} \in \exp \boldsymbol{N}$$

for small $\boldsymbol{a}, \boldsymbol{b}$, say, in a ball $\boldsymbol{N}'$ around $\boldsymbol{0}$. This proves the assertion.

10.2 In the preceding proof, when putting

$$\boldsymbol{c}_t = \boldsymbol{c}_0 + t\boldsymbol{b} \qquad (\boldsymbol{b} \in \boldsymbol{G}),$$

one obtains from 10.1.1–2

$$\exp(-\boldsymbol{c}_0)\left(\frac{d}{dt}\exp \boldsymbol{c}_t\right)_{t=0} = y(0,1) = \int_0^1 \exp(-s\boldsymbol{c}_0)\cdot \boldsymbol{b}\cdot \exp s\boldsymbol{c}_0\cdot ds$$
$$= \int_0^1 \exp(-s\tilde{\boldsymbol{c}}_0)\cdot \boldsymbol{b}\cdot ds.$$

For later use

$$k_{\boldsymbol{c}_0} = \int_0^1 \exp(-s\tilde{\boldsymbol{c}}_0)\,ds = 1 - \frac{1}{2!}\tilde{\boldsymbol{c}}_0 + \frac{1}{3!}\tilde{\boldsymbol{c}}_0{}^2 - \dots$$

is defined as a linear mapping of $\boldsymbol{G}$ into itself. Then

$$\exp(-\boldsymbol{c}_0)\left(\frac{d}{dt}\exp \boldsymbol{c}_t\right)_{t=0} = k_{\boldsymbol{c}_0}\,\boldsymbol{b}.$$

Theorem If $\boldsymbol{c}_t = \boldsymbol{c}_0 + t\boldsymbol{b}$, then

$$\exp(-\boldsymbol{c}_0)\left(\frac{d}{dt}\exp \boldsymbol{c}_t\right)_{t=0} = k_{\boldsymbol{c}_0}\boldsymbol{b},$$

where

$$k_{\boldsymbol{c}} = \int_0^1 \exp(-s\tilde{\boldsymbol{c}})\,ds = \frac{1-\exp(-\tilde{\boldsymbol{c}})}{\tilde{\boldsymbol{c}}}$$

(this fraction with its degenerate denominator has to be understood as a power series).

In other words,

$$\operatorname{grad}_{\boldsymbol{c}} \exp = (\exp \boldsymbol{c})k_{\boldsymbol{c}}.$$

This shows that exp maps $\boldsymbol{G}$ onto a C^{an}-manifold, as long as exp is one-to-one and $\det k_{\boldsymbol{c}} \neq 0$.

Furthermore, if $\boldsymbol{H}$ is a linear subspace of $\boldsymbol{G}$, the tangent space of $\exp(\boldsymbol{c}+\boldsymbol{H})$ at $\exp \boldsymbol{c}$ will coincide with $(\exp \boldsymbol{c})k_{\boldsymbol{c}}\boldsymbol{H}$ as long as $\det k_{\boldsymbol{c}} \neq 0$.

Proposition $k_{\boldsymbol{c}}$ as defined before can degenerate only if $\tilde{\boldsymbol{c}}$ has some eigenvalue that is a nonvanishing integral multiple of $2\pi\mathrm{i}$.

Indeed, these are the only zeros of the numerical function $\curlyvee_x(1-\mathrm{e}^{-x})/x$.

10.3 The next theorem, which was mentioned in 9.9, is an immediate consequence of 10.1.

Theorem For any Lie algebra $\boldsymbol{G}$, Int $\boldsymbol{G}$ exists as a linear Lie group.

10.4 By a simple artifice the converse of Proposition 9.1 is derived from Theorem 10.1.

Theorem Let $G, H \in$ Gru Lie Lin. Then a homomorphism Θ of their infinitesimal algebras $\boldsymbol{G}$ into $\boldsymbol{H}$ extends to a local one of G into H, namely, by means of $\Theta \exp \boldsymbol{a} = \exp(\Theta\boldsymbol{a})$.

Remark It is clear how the theorem is to be stated for a semimorphism Θ.

Proof With $\boldsymbol{G} \subset \operatorname{End} R$, $\boldsymbol{H} \subset \operatorname{End} S$, a new linear Lie algebra $\boldsymbol{F} \subset \operatorname{End} T$ is built up, where T is the direct sum $R + S$. For $\boldsymbol{a} \in \boldsymbol{G}$, $\boldsymbol{a}^* \in \operatorname{End} T$ is defined by

$$\boldsymbol{a}^* x = \boldsymbol{a}x \qquad \text{for} \quad x \in R,$$

$$\boldsymbol{a}^* y = (\Theta\boldsymbol{a})y \qquad \text{for} \quad y \in S.$$

By definition $\boldsymbol{F}$ is the set of $\boldsymbol{a}^*$ with $\boldsymbol{a} \in \boldsymbol{G}$. Using bases of R and S and their union as a basis of T, one can write $\boldsymbol{a}^*$ as a matrix:

$$\boldsymbol{a}^* = \begin{pmatrix} \boldsymbol{a} & \mathbf{0} \\ \mathbf{0} & \Theta\boldsymbol{a} \end{pmatrix}.$$

The linearity of Θ implies that $\boldsymbol{F}$ is a linear space and $\Theta[\boldsymbol{a},\boldsymbol{b}] = [\Theta\boldsymbol{a}, \Theta\boldsymbol{b}]$ implies

$$[\boldsymbol{a}^*, \boldsymbol{b}^*] = \begin{pmatrix} [\boldsymbol{a},\boldsymbol{b}] & \mathbf{0} \\ \mathbf{0} & [\Theta\boldsymbol{a}, \Theta\boldsymbol{b}] \end{pmatrix} = \begin{pmatrix} [\boldsymbol{a},\boldsymbol{b}] & \mathbf{0} \\ \mathbf{0} & \Theta[\boldsymbol{a},\boldsymbol{b}] \end{pmatrix} = [\boldsymbol{a},\boldsymbol{b}]^*.$$

So $\boldsymbol{F} \in$ Alg Lie Lin. By Theorem 10.1 $\boldsymbol{F}$ extends to an $F \in$ Gru Lie Loc Lin, the elements of which are

$$\exp\begin{pmatrix} \boldsymbol{a} & \mathbf{0} \\ \mathbf{0} & \Theta\boldsymbol{a} \end{pmatrix} = \begin{pmatrix} \exp \boldsymbol{a} & 0 \\ 0 & \exp \Theta\boldsymbol{a} \end{pmatrix} \qquad \text{for small } \boldsymbol{a}.$$

For small $\boldsymbol{a}, \boldsymbol{b}$

$$\begin{pmatrix} \exp \boldsymbol{a} & 0 \\ 0 & \exp \Theta\boldsymbol{a} \end{pmatrix} \begin{pmatrix} \exp \boldsymbol{b} & 0 \\ 0 & \exp \Theta\boldsymbol{b} \end{pmatrix}$$

is some

$$\begin{pmatrix} \exp \boldsymbol{c} & 0 \\ 0 & \exp \Theta\boldsymbol{c} \end{pmatrix} \in F,$$

hence,

$$\Theta(\exp \boldsymbol{a} \cdot \exp \boldsymbol{b}) = \Theta \exp \boldsymbol{a} \cdot \Theta \exp \boldsymbol{b},$$

which proves the assertion.

10.5 It is now evident that local C^2-homomorphisms of linear Lie groups and their infinitesimal algebras induce each other locally. Globally, this assertion may fail to be valid. The addition group of real numbers, expressed as a linear group by the matrix

$$\begin{pmatrix} 1 & t \\ 0 & 1 \end{pmatrix}$$

and the multiplication group of complex numbers of absolute value 1,

$$(\mathrm{e}^{\mathrm{i}t}),$$

have isomorphic infinitesimal algebras. They are locally but not globally isomorphic.

10.6 The functor "infinitesimal algebra of..." clearly maps the set of real restrictions of G and the waiving of G onto those of $\boldsymbol{G}$.

This suggests defining *complex extension* of G via $\boldsymbol{G}$ so that the functors "infinitesimal algebra of..." and "complex extension of..." commute.

10.7. Historical Note The proof in 10.1 is a modern adaptation of ideas of F. Schur, *Math. Ann.* **33**, 49–60 (1889), **35**, 161–197 (1890), **38**, 263–286 (1893), **41**, 509–538 (1893). See also H. Kneser, *Jahresber. Deutsche Math. Ver.* **39**, 72–78 (1930), and H. Freudenthal, *Jahresber. Deutsche Math. Ver.* **43**, 26–39 (1933). It has been formulated so to remain valid for nonlinear Lie groups.

11. DROPPING DIFFERENTIABILITY ASSUMPTIONS

$R \in$ Spa Lin, dim $R < \infty$.

11.1–3. Closed Local Groups

11.1. Definition A closed local linear group (Gru Cls Loc Lin) in R is a closed local subgroup (see 4.10) of Aut R.

Notice that Gru Lie Loc Lin $\subset$ Gru Cls Loc Lin.

11.2. Theorem Every closed local linear group G coincides locally with a real local linear Lie group.

Remark Differentiability assumptions have been replaced by the topological assumption of closedness.

Proof Put $F = \text{Aut } R$, consider F as a real linear Lie group (if needed after waiving), and denote its infinitesimal algebra by $\boldsymbol{F}$. Let $\boldsymbol{N}$ be a smooth ball in $\boldsymbol{F}$ and $N = \exp \boldsymbol{N}$. Replacing given G, if needed, by $G \cap N$, one may suppose that

11.2.1 $$1 \in G \subset N, \qquad GG \cap N \subset G, \qquad G^{-1} = G$$

(see 4.10). Now a set $\boldsymbol{G} \subset \boldsymbol{F}$ is defined as follows: $\boldsymbol{a} \in \boldsymbol{G}$ if there is a sequence of $\boldsymbol{a}_j \in \boldsymbol{N}$ such that

11.2.2 $$a_j = \exp \boldsymbol{a}_j \in G \qquad \text{and} \qquad \lim a_j = 1$$

and a sequence of positive numbers α_j such that

11.2.3 $$\lim \alpha_j \boldsymbol{a}_j = \boldsymbol{a}.$$

Note that 11.2.2 implies $\lim \boldsymbol{a}_j = \boldsymbol{0}$. From 11.2.3 it follows that if $\boldsymbol{a} \neq \boldsymbol{0}$ then $\lim \alpha_j = \infty$.

$\boldsymbol{G}$ will turn out to be a linear Lie algebra; to be more precise, that of the local linear Lie group coinciding locally with G.

In the definition of $\boldsymbol{G}$ the positive numbers α_j could be replaced by positive *integers* p_j. Indeed, if p_j is the integral part of α_j and $\boldsymbol{a} \neq \boldsymbol{0}$, then $\lim p_j \boldsymbol{a}_j = \lim \alpha_j \boldsymbol{a}_j - \lim (\alpha_j - p_j) \boldsymbol{a}_j = \lim \alpha_j \boldsymbol{a}_j$, so that nothing is lost by that restriction.

It will be proved that

11.2.4 $$\boldsymbol{a} \in \boldsymbol{G} \cap N \rightarrow \exp \boldsymbol{a} \in G.$$

It may be supposed that $\boldsymbol{a} \neq \boldsymbol{0}$. By definition there are $\boldsymbol{a}_j \in \boldsymbol{G}$ and natural numbers p_j such that

11.2.5 $$\exp \boldsymbol{a}_j \in G, \qquad \boldsymbol{a} = \lim p_j \boldsymbol{a}_j.$$

Since $\boldsymbol{a} \in N$, one may assume that all $p_j \boldsymbol{a}_j \in N$ and, since N is a ball around $\boldsymbol{0}$,

11.2.6 $$p\,\boldsymbol{a}_j \in N \quad \text{for all nonnegative integers } p \leqslant p_j.$$

So

11.2.7 $$(\exp \boldsymbol{a}_j)^p = \exp p\boldsymbol{a}_j \in \exp N = N \quad \text{for the same } p.$$

Induction shows that

11.2.8 $$(\exp \boldsymbol{a}_j)^p \in G \quad \text{for all nonnegative integers } p \leqslant p_j.$$

Indeed this is true for $p = 0$. If it is true for some $p \leqslant p_j - 1$, then $\exp \boldsymbol{a}_j$, $(\exp \boldsymbol{a}_j)^p \in G$, $\exp \boldsymbol{a}_j \cdot (\exp \boldsymbol{a}_j)^p \in N$ by 11.2.7, hence an element of G by 11.2.1, which settles the induction.

In particular,

$$\exp p_j \boldsymbol{a}_j = (\exp \boldsymbol{a}_j)^{p_j} \in G;$$

thus, since G is closed in N,

$$\exp \boldsymbol{a} \in G.$$

This proves 11.2.4.

The next step is to prove the following.

11.2.9 If $c_t \in G$ is differentiable in the real variable t and $c_0 = 1$, then

$$\left(\frac{d}{dt} c_t\right)_{t=0} \in \boldsymbol{G}.$$

c_t may be assumed to be in the form $\exp \boldsymbol{c}_t$, where $\boldsymbol{c}_t \in N$ is differentiable and $\boldsymbol{c}_0 = \boldsymbol{0}$. Now

$$\left(\frac{d}{dt} c_t\right)_{t=0} = \left(\frac{d}{dt} \boldsymbol{c}_t\right)_{t=0} = \lim j\boldsymbol{c}_{1/j},$$

where j runs through the positive integers and $\lim j = \infty$. By definition this limit belongs to $\boldsymbol{G}$, which proves 11.2.9.

The following step is to ascertain that

11.2.10 $\qquad \boldsymbol{G} \in \text{Alg Lie Rea}.$

Evidently for positive α

$$\boldsymbol{a} \in \boldsymbol{G} \to \alpha\boldsymbol{a} \in \boldsymbol{G}.$$

Replacing $\boldsymbol{a}_j$ in 11.2.2 by $-\boldsymbol{a}_j$ one finds the same for $\alpha = -1$, and so it may be asserted for all real α. Suppose that $\boldsymbol{a}, \boldsymbol{b} \in \boldsymbol{G}$; then by 11.2.4 and 11.2.1 for small t

$$\exp t\boldsymbol{a}, \quad \exp t\boldsymbol{b}, \quad c_t = \exp t\boldsymbol{a} \cdot \exp t\boldsymbol{b} \in G.$$

By 11.2.9,

$$\boldsymbol{a} + \boldsymbol{b} = \left(\frac{d}{dt} c_t\right)_{t=0} \in \boldsymbol{G}.$$

Applying the same kind of argument to

$$k_s = \exp t\boldsymbol{a} \cdot \exp t\boldsymbol{b} \cdot \exp(-t\boldsymbol{a}) \cdot \exp(-t\boldsymbol{b}) \quad \text{with} \quad s = t^2,$$

one gets

$$[\boldsymbol{a}, \boldsymbol{b}] \in \boldsymbol{G}.$$

This proves 11.2.10.

Finally it is shown that

11.2.11 $\qquad \exp \boldsymbol{G} \cap \boldsymbol{N}$ coincides locally with G.

Let $\boldsymbol{K}$ be a linear complement of $\boldsymbol{G}$ in $\boldsymbol{F}$ (defined in the beginning of the proof). The direct splitting of linear spaces $\boldsymbol{F} = \boldsymbol{G} + \boldsymbol{K}$ induces a generalized exponential presentation of F near 1 (see 8.8) which shows that

$$\Upsilon_{\ulcorner \boldsymbol{b}, \boldsymbol{c} \urcorner} \exp \boldsymbol{b} \cdot \exp \boldsymbol{c}$$

maps homeomorphically a $\boldsymbol{0}$-neighborhood in $\boldsymbol{F}$ onto a 1-neighborhood in F.

Suppose that 11.2.11 is false. Then there is a sequence of

$$a_j \in G \setminus \exp(\boldsymbol{G} \cap \boldsymbol{N}) \qquad \text{with} \quad \lim a_j = 1.$$

It may be assumed by the foregoing that

$$a_j = \exp \boldsymbol{b}_j \cdot \exp \boldsymbol{c}_j$$

with suitable

$$\boldsymbol{b}_j \in \boldsymbol{G} \cap \boldsymbol{N}, \qquad \boldsymbol{c}_j \in \boldsymbol{K} \cap \boldsymbol{N},$$

and

$$\lim \boldsymbol{b}_j = \lim \boldsymbol{c}_j = \mathbf{0},$$

though $\boldsymbol{c}_j \neq \mathbf{0}$. All a_j belong to G and so do all exp $\boldsymbol{b}_j$ by 11.2.4; hence almost all exp $\boldsymbol{c}_j$ belong to G. Let α_j be the largest integer such that $\alpha_j \boldsymbol{c}_j \in N$, thus near the boundary of N for large j. Then the $\alpha_j \boldsymbol{c}_j$ may be assumed to converge to some $\boldsymbol{c} \neq \mathbf{0}$, which contradicts the definition of $\boldsymbol{G}$. This proves 11.2.11 and therefore the theorem.

11.3.1. Proposition Let G be a *connected* closed local linear group. Then the expansion $\hat{G}$ of G, according to 4.12, is a real linear Lie group.

Proof By 11.2 there is an open 1-neighborhood $V \subset \text{Aut } R$ such that $H = G \cap V$ is a local linear Lie group. The global expansion of H is $\hat{H}$. Clearly $\hat{H} \subset \hat{G}$ and every open set of $\hat{H}$ is also open in $\hat{G}$. So $\hat{H}$ is open in $\hat{G}$; but, since G is connected, $\hat{G}$ is also connected so that it coincides with $\hat{H}$ which is a linear Lie group.

11.3.2 An immediate consequence is the following.

Proposition A connected closed linear group is a real linear Lie group.

11.3.3. Proposition Let G be a closed linear group. Its 1-component G_0 is then a real linear Lie group; G_0 is isolated in G and so are all other components.

Indeed, by 11.2 $G \cap U \in$ Gru Lie Loc Lin for some 1-neighborhood U of Aut R. Then $G \cap U$ is connected, hence contained in G_0. So G_0 contains a 1-neighborhood of G, whence G_0 is open in G. This is the assertion that had to be proved.

11.3.4. Proposition Let $\boldsymbol{G} \in$ Alg Lie. The 1-component $(\text{Aut } \boldsymbol{G})_0$ of Aut $\boldsymbol{G}$ is then a linear Lie group, with the algebra of the derivations of $\boldsymbol{G}$ as its infinitesimal algebra.

Since Aut $\boldsymbol{G}$ is closed, this follows from 11.3.3 and 9.2–4 if $\boldsymbol{G}$ is real. If $\boldsymbol{G}$ is complex, one gets a *real* linear Lie group. Its infinitesimal elements are again the derivations of $\boldsymbol{G}$, its infinitesimal algebra can be provided with the complex structure of the algebra of the derivations of $\boldsymbol{G}$, and this can be used to give $(\text{Aut } \boldsymbol{G})_0$ a structure of complex linear Lie group as desired.

11.3.5 It is now easy to provide the overdue proof of the statement:

The examples 3.1–3.8 are linear Lie groups.

For 3.5–8 this needs no proof. In all other cases proceed by induction: consider the closed subgroup H, which fixes the first basis vector: G is transitive on its orbit S under G. Both G and S are locally compact Hausdorff spaces that satisfy the second countability axiom. So 4.8.6 can be applied, since by induction H is seen to be connected and S is also connected. Hence G itself is connected. Since G is closed, 11.3.2 can be applied, with the result that G is a real linear Lie group, which in the case of complex scalars even bears a complex structure.

Clearly the infinitesimal algebras of G are those computed in 7.6.

11.4. Continuous Homomorphisms By the same trick as used in 10.4 the notion of homomorphism can be freed of differentiability assumptions. (The continuity assumption will always be included in the notion of homomorphism.)

Theorem A local homomorphism Θ of real linear Lie groups G into H is analytic (in the usual analytic structure of G and H) and induced by a homomorphism of their infinitesimal algebras $\boldsymbol{G}$ into $\boldsymbol{H}$.

Remark Note that for complex linear Lie groups such a theorem could be stated only after waiving.

Proof G, H may be replaced by local linear Lie groups acting on $R, S \in$ Spa Lin, where bases are introduced. Let F be the set of

$$a^* = \begin{pmatrix} a & 0 \\ 0 & \Theta a \end{pmatrix}, \qquad \text{with} \quad a \in G.$$

Since Θ is a homomorphism,

$$(a_1 a_2)^* = a_1{}^* a_2{}^*$$

is locally valid. After open 1-neighborhoods $U = U^{-1}$, $V = V^{-1}$ have been chosen in Aut R, Aut S, such that

$$1 \in G = G^{-1}, \qquad G \subset U, \qquad GG \cap U = G,$$

$$1 \in H = H^{-1}, \qquad H \subset V, \qquad HH \cap V = H,$$

one defines $W = UV \subset \operatorname{Aut}(R + S)$. Then

$$1 \in F = F^{-1}, \qquad F \subset W, \qquad FF \cap W = F.$$

So F is a local subgroup of $\operatorname{Aut}(R + S)$. F is closed in W. Indeed,

$$\begin{pmatrix} a_j & 0 \\ 0 & \Theta a_j \end{pmatrix} \in F, \qquad \lim \begin{pmatrix} a_j & 0 \\ 0 & \Theta a_j \end{pmatrix} = \begin{pmatrix} a & 0 \\ 0 & b \end{pmatrix} \in W$$

implies $\lim \Theta a_j = b$. Since Θ is continuous, however, $\lim \Theta a_j = \Theta \lim a_j = \Theta a$. This shows $b = \Theta a$; hence

$$\begin{pmatrix} a & 0 \\ 0 & b \end{pmatrix} \in F.$$

By 11.2 F possesses an infinitesimal algebra $\boldsymbol{F}$ (sub $\boldsymbol{G} + \boldsymbol{H}$), the elements of which have the form

$$\boldsymbol{c}^* = \begin{pmatrix} \boldsymbol{a} & \boldsymbol{0} \\ \boldsymbol{0} & \boldsymbol{b} \end{pmatrix} \qquad (\boldsymbol{a} \in \boldsymbol{G}, \boldsymbol{b} \in \boldsymbol{H}).$$

For small $\boldsymbol{c}^* \in \boldsymbol{F}$, $\exp \boldsymbol{c}^* \in F$. Therefore, if $\boldsymbol{a} = \boldsymbol{0}$, then $\boldsymbol{b} = \boldsymbol{0}$. Since $\boldsymbol{F}$ intersects $\boldsymbol{G}$ trivially, it induces a linear mapping Θ of $\boldsymbol{G}$ into $\boldsymbol{H}$ such that

$$\boldsymbol{b} = \Theta \boldsymbol{a} \leftrightarrow \begin{pmatrix} \boldsymbol{a} & \boldsymbol{0} \\ \boldsymbol{0} & \boldsymbol{b} \end{pmatrix} \in \boldsymbol{F}.$$

Furthermore, since $\boldsymbol{F} \in$ Alg Lie Lin,

$$\begin{pmatrix} [\boldsymbol{a}_1, \boldsymbol{a}_2] & \boldsymbol{0} \\ \boldsymbol{0} & [\Theta \boldsymbol{a}_1, \Theta \boldsymbol{a}_2] \end{pmatrix} = \begin{pmatrix} \boldsymbol{a}_1 & \boldsymbol{0} \\ \boldsymbol{0} & \Theta \boldsymbol{a}_1 \end{pmatrix} \begin{pmatrix} \boldsymbol{a}_2 & \boldsymbol{0} \\ \boldsymbol{0} & \Theta \boldsymbol{a}_2 \end{pmatrix} - \begin{pmatrix} \boldsymbol{a}_2 & \boldsymbol{0} \\ \boldsymbol{0} & \Theta \boldsymbol{a}_2 \end{pmatrix} \begin{pmatrix} \boldsymbol{a}_1 & \boldsymbol{0} \\ \boldsymbol{0} & \Theta \boldsymbol{a}_1 \end{pmatrix}$$
$$= \begin{pmatrix} [\boldsymbol{a}_1, \boldsymbol{a}_2] & \boldsymbol{0} \\ \boldsymbol{0} & \Theta [\boldsymbol{a}_1, \boldsymbol{a}_2] \end{pmatrix}.$$

Thus Θ is an algebra homomorphism. It clearly induces the given one, which consequently is analytic.

11.7. C^2-Connected Subgroups

Definition A subset G of a C^2-manifold M is called *C^2-connected* if for every $a, b \in G$ there is a C^2-curve in G containing a and b.

Note that for complex M the C^2-curve containing a and b is understood in the complex sense.

Though it is not obvious whether complex M itself is C^2-connected, it is easily seen that any linear Lie group G is C^2-connected. Indeed, the C^2-curves through 1 in G cover a neighborhood of 1, and by 4.7 the product of such curves, which are C^2-curves also, cover all G.

Theorem A C^2-connected subgroup G of Aut R ($R \in$ Spa Lin) is a linear Lie group.

Proof Let $\boldsymbol{H}$ be the set of tangent vectors at 1 of C^2-curves in G. The method of 7.5 shows that $\boldsymbol{H}$ is a linear Lie algebra (check, in particular, the argument of 7.5.5). Its Lie group is denoted by H.

If $\Upsilon_t c_t$ is a C^2-curve on G, then $\Upsilon_t c_{t_0}^{-1} c_t$ has the same property. Its tangent vector for $t = t_0$ belongs to $\boldsymbol{H}$. Thus,

$$c_t^{-1} \frac{d}{dt} c_t \in \boldsymbol{H}.$$

By the method of 8.2 it follows that the whole curve lies on H as soon as one of its points. Therefore $G \subset H$.

Let $\boldsymbol{a}_1, \ldots, \boldsymbol{a}_r$ form a basis of $\boldsymbol{H}$. There are C^2-curves $\Upsilon_t c_t^{(j)}$ with tangent vectors $\boldsymbol{a}_j$ at 1. From 8.7 it follows that the $c_{\tau_1}^{(1)} \cdot c_{\tau_2}^{(2)} \cdot \cdots \cdot c_{\tau_r}^{(r)}$ cover a 1-neighborhood in H. Together with $G \subset H$ this proves that G and H coincide.

11.8. Historical Note Dropping the differentiability assumptions in the definition of linear Lie groups and their homomorphisms is due to J. von Neumann [*Math. Z.* **30**, 3–42 (1929), Collected Works I, No. 22]. The theorem in Section 11.7 was proved by H. Freudenthal [*Ann. Math.* **42**, 1051–1074 (1941)]

12. SUBGROUPS AND SUBALGEBRAS, NORMAL SUBGROUPS AND IDEALS

12.1–3. Closed Local Subgroups

12.1. Definition If G is a (local) linear Lie group, the term (local) Lie subgroup and the notation H sub G is reserved for H which are (local) subgroups of G and at the same time (local) linear Lie groups over the same field (Rea or Com) as is G.

Clearly:

Proposition If H sub G, then $\boldsymbol{H}$ sub $\boldsymbol{G}$ for the infinitesimal algebras $\boldsymbol{H}, \boldsymbol{G}$ of H, G. Conversely, if $\boldsymbol{H}$ sub $\boldsymbol{G}$, then $\boldsymbol{H}$ is the infinitesimal algebra of some H sub G.

Notation The relation between H sub G and $\boldsymbol{H}$ sub $\boldsymbol{G}$ is called the sgsa-*relation* (subgroup-subalgebra-relation).

12.2 Not too much is lost by the restriction of the class of subgroups to that of Lie subgroups:

Proposition Any closed (local) subgroup H of $G \in$ Gru Lie Rea (Loc) Lin is locally a linear Lie group.

Proof Let G be in Aut R and let U be a smooth ball in G. Put $H_1 = H \cap U$. The closure of H_1 in G is compact and so is the closure of $H_1 H_1$. Thus it does not change if taken in Aut R. According to 4.11, H_1 is also a closed local subgroup of Aut R, and by 11.2 it coincides locally with a local linear Lie group.

12.3 For $G \in$ Gru Lie Rea Lin the following analogies of 11.3.2–3 can be stated as consequences of 12.2.

Proposition The expansion, according to 4.12, of a connected closed local subgroup of G is a linear Lie group. A connected closed subgroup of G is a linear Lie group. The components of a closed subgroup of G are isolated.

Note that in the complex case a connected closed subgroup need not be a *Lie* subgroup. Even the closure of a Lie subgroup H of $G \in$ Gru Lie Lin Com need not be a Lie subgroup, as is shown by the following.

Counterexample Let G be the addition group of pairs of complex numbers modulo the integers (which can easily be turned into a complex linear Lie group). Let H be the subgroup of the pairs $\ulcorner \alpha, \sqrt{2}\,\alpha \urcorner$. Its closure is a real linear Lie group but not a complex one.

12.4–13 $G \in$ Gru Lie Lin, acting on $R \in$ Spa Lin, $\boldsymbol{G}$ its infinitesimal algebra if no other assumption is made.

12.4. Normal Subgroups and Ideals

Definition A local subgroup of G is called *normal* if it is locally identical to any of its conjugates.

Let H be a normal local Lie subgroup of G, and $\boldsymbol{H}$ its infinitesimal algebra; $\boldsymbol{H}$ is invariant under the adjoint of $G, \tilde{a}\boldsymbol{H} \subset \boldsymbol{H}$ for $a \in G$. Consequently, it is also invariant under $\tilde{\boldsymbol{G}}$. This means that

12.4.1 $$\tilde{\boldsymbol{a}}\boldsymbol{H} \subset \boldsymbol{H} \quad \text{for} \quad \boldsymbol{a} \in \boldsymbol{G},$$

in other words,

12.4.2 $$[\boldsymbol{G}, \boldsymbol{H}] \subset \boldsymbol{H}.$$

Conversely, if 12.4.2 is satisfied for a subalgebra $\boldsymbol{H}$ of $\boldsymbol{G}$, the same is true of 12.4.1; hence,

$$(\exp \tilde{\boldsymbol{a}})\,\boldsymbol{H} \subset \boldsymbol{H} \quad \text{for} \quad \boldsymbol{a} \in \boldsymbol{G},$$

$$aHa^{-1} \subset H$$

for $a \in G$ near 1, thus for all $a \in G$, and finally

$$a(\exp \boldsymbol{H})a^{-1} \subset \exp \boldsymbol{H},$$

which shows that $\boldsymbol{H}$ gives rise to a normal local subgroup of G.

In the language of algebras 12.4.2 reads: the linear subspace $\boldsymbol{H}$ is an *ideal* of $\boldsymbol{G}$; so it has been proved:

Proposition Under the sgsa-relation normal local Lie subgroups and ideals correspond to each other.

Furthermore:

Proposition A linear subspace of $\boldsymbol{G} \in$ Alg Lie is an ideal if and only if it is invariant under Int $\boldsymbol{G}$.

12.5–6. Abelian Subgroups and Algebras

12.5 A center element of G is characterized by invariance under all inner automorphisms. The center of G is closed in G. Its infinitesimal algebra $\boldsymbol{Z}$ generates a Lie subgroup Z of G. Though Z need not exhaust the center, it is open and closed in the center (12.2). The full center consists of isolated cosets of Z.

If $\boldsymbol{z} \in \boldsymbol{Z}$, then $\boldsymbol{z} = [(d/dt)z_t]_{t=0}$ for some curve $\curlyvee_t z_t$ on Z; hence $\tilde{z}_t \boldsymbol{a} = \boldsymbol{a}$ for all $\boldsymbol{a} \in \boldsymbol{G}$, and after differentiation in $t = 0$: $\tilde{\boldsymbol{z}}\boldsymbol{a} = \boldsymbol{0}$. Thus $\tilde{\boldsymbol{z}}\boldsymbol{G} = \{\boldsymbol{0}\}$.

Conversely, if $\boldsymbol{z} \in \boldsymbol{G}$, $\tilde{\boldsymbol{z}}\boldsymbol{G} = \{\boldsymbol{0}\}$, then $\exp t\tilde{\boldsymbol{z}}$ is the identity on $\boldsymbol{G}$, hence on G. Thus $\exp t\boldsymbol{z} \in Z$.

Definition The *center* of a Lie algebra $\boldsymbol{G}$ is the set of $\boldsymbol{z} \in \boldsymbol{G}$ with $[\boldsymbol{z}, \boldsymbol{G}] = \{\boldsymbol{0}\}$.

It is evident that the center is an ideal. The following has been proved.

Proposition Under the sgsa-relation the 1-component of the center corresponds to the center.

12.6 An abelian (or commutative) group is characterized as being its own center. So if G is abelian, then $[\boldsymbol{G}, \boldsymbol{G}] = \{\boldsymbol{0}\}$ and conversely.

Definition A Lie algebra $\boldsymbol{G}$ is called *abelian* if $[\boldsymbol{G}, \boldsymbol{G}] = \{\boldsymbol{0}\}$.

Proposition Under the sgsa-relation abelian local subgroups and abelian subalgebras correspond to each other.

If $\boldsymbol{G}$ is abelian, every subset $\boldsymbol{a}_1, \ldots, \boldsymbol{a}_k$ of $\boldsymbol{G}$ linearly spans a subalgebra. So abelian G has local Lie subgroups of any dimension $\leqslant \dim G$.

If $\mathbf{G}$ is abelian and $\mathbf{a}_1, \ldots, \mathbf{a}_r$ form a basis of $\mathbf{G}$, then $\mathbf{G}$ is the direct sum of r one-dimensional ideals generated by the $\mathbf{a}_j$. Passing from $\mathbf{G}$ to G, one sees that abelian G is locally a direct product of r one-dimensional local Lie subgroups:

$$\exp(\alpha_1 \mathbf{a}_1 + \cdots + \alpha_r \mathbf{a}_r) = \exp \alpha_1 \mathbf{a}_1 \cdots \exp \alpha_r \mathbf{a}_r.$$

Proposition An abelian G is locally (isomorphic to) a direct product of one-dimensional local Lie subgroups. All r-dimensional abelian linear Lie groups are locally isomorphic.

Globally there is a greater variety, though the first assertion is still true. In 30.5 it will be seen that there are two kinds of one-dimensional real abelian Lie groups, those that are isomorphic to the multiplication group of positive numbers and those that are isomorphic to the unit norm complex numbers. Real abelian Lie groups are isomorphic to direct products of factors of one or both kinds.

Definition Direct products with the first kind of factors only are called *flat* abelian groups; direct products with the second kind of factors only are called *torus* groups.

12.7. Direct Products and Sums The anticipated localization of the notion of direct product has still to be sanctioned.

Definition $G \in$ Gru Top is the *direct product* of G_1, G_2, sub G, if G_1, G_2 are closed normal, and $\curlyvee_{\ulcorner g_1, g_2 \urcorner \in \ulcorner G_1, G_2 \urcorner} g_1 g_2$ maps homeomorphically onto G.

$G \in$ Gru Top is locally the direct product of its local subgroups G_1, G_2, if G_1, G_2 are closed normal, and $\curlyvee_{\ulcorner g_1, g_2 \urcorner \in \ulcorner G_1, G_2 \urcorner} g_1 g_2$ maps homeomorphically onto a 1-neighborhood in G. In this case G is also said to be locally the direct product of the subgroups generated by G_1, G_2 according to 4.12. Similarly, any local subgroup of G coinciding locally with G is said to be locally the direct product of the above G_1, G_2.

If $G \in$ Gru Lie Lin, the (local) direct factors may also be assumed to be the Lie kind.

For a Lie algebra $\mathbf{G}$ the notion of direct sum is understood in the algebra sense: $\mathbf{G} = \mathbf{G}_1 + \mathbf{G}_2$, where, of course, the $\mathbf{G}_i$ are ideals, $\mathbf{G}_1 \cap \mathbf{G}_2 = \{\mathbf{0}\}$; thus $[\mathbf{G}_1, \mathbf{G}_2] = \{\mathbf{0}\}$.

Let $\mathbf{G}$ and $\mathbf{G}_1, \mathbf{G}_2$ sub $\mathbf{G}$, respectively, be the infinitesimal algebras of G and G_1, G_2. If G is locally the direct product of G_1, G_2, one may assume $G_1 \cap G_2 = \{1\}$; since, generally, $\mathbf{G}_1 \cap \mathbf{G}_2$ is the infinitesimal algebra of $G_1 \cap G_2$, this implies $\mathbf{G}_1 \cap \mathbf{G}_2 = \{\mathbf{0}\}$ and, finally, that $\mathbf{G}$ is the direct sum of $\mathbf{G}_1$ and $\mathbf{G}_2$. The converse is proved by applying Proposition 8.7 to the (elementwise commuting) pieces $\exp(\mathbf{G}_i \cap \mathbf{U})$, where $\mathbf{U}$ is an open ball in $\mathbf{G}$ around $\mathbf{0}$.

Proposition Under the sgsa-relation local direct products and direct algebraic sums correspond to each other.

12.8–9. Commutator Group and Ideal

12.8. Definition The group generated by the commutators $aba^{-1}b^{-1}$ with $a,b \in G$ is called the *commutator group* $C(G)$ of G. The algebra generated by the $[\boldsymbol{a},\boldsymbol{b}]$ with $\boldsymbol{a},\boldsymbol{b} \in \boldsymbol{G}$ is called the *commutator algebra* $C(\boldsymbol{G})$ of $\boldsymbol{G}$.

Since the notion of commutator is invariant under inner automorphisms, $C(G)$ is normal in G. Because $[\boldsymbol{G},[\boldsymbol{G},\boldsymbol{G}]] \subset [\boldsymbol{G},\boldsymbol{G}]$, $C(\boldsymbol{G})$ is also an ideal of $\boldsymbol{G}$. Note that both are invariant under all (not only inner) automorphisms. Note also that $G/C(G)$ and $\boldsymbol{G}$ mod $C(\boldsymbol{G})$ are abelian.

Proposition If G is a linear Lie group, then $C(G)$ is a linear Lie group and its infinitesimal algebra is $C(\boldsymbol{G})$.

Proof If a and $b \in G$ are C^2-connected with 1 by curves $\curlyvee_t a_t$, $\curlyvee_t b_t$, then so is $aba^{-1}b^{-1}$ by $\curlyvee_t a_t b_t a_t^{-1} b_t^{-1}$. Multiplying these curves, one notes that $C(G)$ is C^2-connected. By 11.7 it has an infinitesimal algebra, say $\boldsymbol{H}$. The proof in 7.5.4 shows that

12.8.1 $$C(\boldsymbol{G}) \subset \boldsymbol{H}.$$

To prove

12.8.2 $$\boldsymbol{H} \subset C(\boldsymbol{G}),$$

the first step is

12.8.3 $$(a \in G) \wedge (\boldsymbol{b} \in \boldsymbol{G}) \to a\boldsymbol{b}a^{-1} - \boldsymbol{b} \in C(\boldsymbol{G}).$$

For $a = \exp \boldsymbol{a}$ $(\boldsymbol{a} \in \boldsymbol{G})$ this follows from

$$(\exp \tilde{\boldsymbol{a}})\boldsymbol{b} = \boldsymbol{b} + \tilde{\boldsymbol{a}}\boldsymbol{b} + \tfrac{1}{2}\tilde{\boldsymbol{a}}^2\boldsymbol{b} + \cdots = \boldsymbol{b} + [\boldsymbol{a},\boldsymbol{b}] + \tfrac{1}{2}[\boldsymbol{a},[\boldsymbol{a},\boldsymbol{b}]] + \cdots.$$

An arbitrary $a \in G$ can be written as

$$a = a_k a_{k-1} \cdots a_2 a_1 \quad \text{with} \quad a_\nu = \exp \boldsymbol{a}_\nu, \quad \boldsymbol{a}_\nu \in \boldsymbol{G}.$$

Putting

$$\boldsymbol{b}_0 = \boldsymbol{b}$$

$$\boldsymbol{b}_{\nu-1} = a_{\nu-1}\boldsymbol{b}_{\nu-2}a_{\nu-1}^{-1} \qquad \text{for} \quad \nu = 2,\ldots,k,$$

one gets

$$aba^{-1} - \boldsymbol{b} = \sum_{1}^{k} (a_\nu \boldsymbol{b}_{\nu-1} a_\nu^{-1} - \boldsymbol{b}_{\nu-1}) \in C(\boldsymbol{G}),$$

which proves 12.8.3.

For differentiable $\Upsilon_t a_t$, $\Upsilon_t b_t$ on G put

$$\frac{d}{dt} a_t = a_t \boldsymbol{a}_t, \qquad \frac{d}{dt} b_t = b_t \boldsymbol{b}_t \qquad \text{with} \quad \boldsymbol{a}_t, \boldsymbol{b}_t \in \boldsymbol{G}.$$

Then

$$\frac{d}{dt} a_t^{-1} = -\boldsymbol{a}_t a_t^{-1}, \qquad \frac{d}{dt} b_t = \boldsymbol{b}_t b_t^{-1}.$$

By differentiating

$$c_t = a_t b_t a_t^{-1} b_t^{-1}$$

and dropping the subscripts t, one gets

$$\begin{aligned}\frac{dc}{dt} &= a\boldsymbol{a}ba^{-1}b^{-1} + ab\boldsymbol{b}a^{-1}b^{-1} - ab\boldsymbol{a}a^{-1}b^{-1} - aba^{-1}\boldsymbol{b}b^{-1}\\ &= aba^{-1}b^{-1}((bab^{-1})\,\boldsymbol{a}(bab^{-1})^{-1} + (ba)\,\boldsymbol{b}(ba)^{-1} - (ba)\,\boldsymbol{a}(ba)^{-1} - b\boldsymbol{b}\,b^{-1})\\ &= c_t\,\boldsymbol{c}_t,\end{aligned}$$

with $\boldsymbol{c}_t \in C(\boldsymbol{G})$ because of 12.8.3.

By known methods (8.2) this implies that c_t lies on the Lie group generated by $C(\boldsymbol{G})$, which consequently contains $C(G)$. So $C(\boldsymbol{G})$ contains the infinitesimal algebra of $C(G)$, which is $\boldsymbol{H}$. This proves 12.8.2.

12.9 The next propositions are methodically related to the preceding one.

12.9.1. Proposition Let G be a linear Lie group, $1 \in H \subset G$, $K \subset G$, and H C^2-connected (e.g., H is a Lie subgroup). Then the group L generated by the $hkh^{-1}k^{-1}$ ($h \in H$, $k \in K$) is a Lie subgroup.

Indeed, as in the proof of 12.8.1 one shows that L is C^2-connected.

12.9.2. Proposition Let G be a linear Lie group, and H a normal subgroup that is its own commutator group. Then H is a Lie subgroup.

This follows from the foregoing proposition with G and H instead of H and K; the group generated by $ghg^{-1}h^{-1}$ ($g \in G$, $h \in H$) coincides with H.

12.9.3. Proposition A normal subgroup H of $G \in$ Gru Lie Lin, not contained in the center of G, contains a normal Lie subgroup of G of positive dimension.

Proof If $a \in H$ is not in the center of G and $\curlyvee_t c_t$ is a suitable C^2-curve on G, then $\curlyvee_t c_t a c_t^{-1}$ appears to be a nonconstant C^2-curve on H. The set of all $c \in H$, C^2-connected in H with 1, is a normal Lie subgroup of G of positive dimension.

12.9.4. Proposition A discrete normal subgroup of $G \in$ Gru Lie Lin is in the center of G.

A more general statement has already been proved in 4.7.

12.10. Simple Groups and Ideals

Definition $G \neq \{1\}$ is called *locally simple* if its only normal Lie subgroups are $\{1\}$ or G; $\mathbf{G} \neq \{\mathbf{0}\}$ is called *simple* of its ideals are $\{\mathbf{0}\}$ or $\mathbf{G}$.

12.10.1. Proposition G is locally simple if and only if $\mathbf{G}$ is simple.

12.10.2. Proposition If $G \in$ Gru Lie Lin is locally simple, its normal subgroups are in the center of G, which is a discrete subgroup, or G.

This follows from Proposition 12.9.4.

12.11–12. Coset Spaces†

12.11 Let H be a local Lie subgroup of G. The local coset space G/H can then be described more easily than in 4.14–15, provided H is sufficiently small:

Let $\mathbf{K}$ be a linear complement of $\mathbf{H}$ in $\mathbf{G}$, and let $\mathbf{U}$ and $\mathbf{V}$ be open balls around $\mathbf{0}$, respectively, in $\mathbf{K}$ and $\mathbf{H}$. Thus, by 8.7–8, if $\mathbf{U}$ and $\mathbf{V}$ are sufficiently small and

$$K_1 = \exp \mathbf{U},$$

$$H_1 = \exp \mathbf{V},$$

then

$$G_1 = K_1 H_1$$

is a 1-neighborhood in G and G_1/H_1 is a homeomorphic image

$$\text{of } K_1 \text{ by } \curlyvee_a aH_1, \qquad \text{and of } \mathbf{U} \text{ by } \curlyvee_{\mathbf{a}} (\exp \mathbf{a})\, H_1.$$

This leads to the following definition.

† The contents of these sections will only be used incidentally.

Definition If H_1 is a small local Lie subgroup of G, $\boldsymbol{K}$ a linear complement of $\boldsymbol{H}_1$ in $\boldsymbol{G}$, G_1 a suitable open connected 1-neighborhood in G, a *natural* homeomorphic mapping of a $\boldsymbol{0}$-neighborhood $\boldsymbol{U}$ in $\boldsymbol{K}$ onto G_1/H_1 is defined by

$$\nu = \Upsilon_{\boldsymbol{a} \in \boldsymbol{U}} (\exp \boldsymbol{a})\, H_1 ;$$

G_1/H_1 is interpreted as a C^{an}-manifold according to 5.6 by means of the presentation $\ulcorner \boldsymbol{K}, \nu \urcorner$.

Clearly this analytic structure does not depend on the choice of $\boldsymbol{K}$. Moreover:

Proposition As far as defined, the action of G on G_1/H_1 by left multiplication is analytic.

12.12 Let H be a closed subgroup of G. Then G/H makes sense as a topological space. Let H_1 and G_1 be 1-neighborhoods in H and G, respectively, to which Definition 12.11 applies. Then by 4.14 an H_1-neighborhood in G_1/H_1 is homeomorphically mapped into G/H by the inclusion map, denoted by j.

Definition G/H is provided with a structure of C^{an}-manifold (according to 5.6) by considering $j\nu$, as far as defined, homeomorphic and nondegenerate, as a local presentation near H and transferring it by left multiplication to other points of G/H.

This definition is justified by Proposition 12.11. It is easily seen that the C^{an}-structure does not depend on the choice of H_1.

12.13–14. Factor and Mod Reduction

12.13 The case in which H is a normal local Lie subgroup of G merits a special discussion. In the realm of Lie algebras its counterpart is $\boldsymbol{H}$, an ideal of $\boldsymbol{G}$.

Definition If $\boldsymbol{H}$ is an ideal in $\boldsymbol{G}$, then $\boldsymbol{G}$ mod $\boldsymbol{H}$ refers to the Lie algebra on the linear space $\boldsymbol{G}$ mod $\boldsymbol{H}$ with $[\boldsymbol{a}+\boldsymbol{H}, \boldsymbol{b}+\boldsymbol{H}]$ defined by $[\boldsymbol{a},\boldsymbol{b}]+\boldsymbol{H}$.

Clearly this is a Lie algebra and $\Upsilon_{\boldsymbol{a}} (\boldsymbol{a}+\boldsymbol{H})$ is a homomorphism of $\boldsymbol{G}$ onto $\boldsymbol{G}$ mod $\boldsymbol{H}$ (the canonical one).

If, moreover, $\boldsymbol{G}, \boldsymbol{H}$ are the infinitesimal algebras of $G, H \in$ Gru Lie Lin, one would guess that $\boldsymbol{G}$ mod $\boldsymbol{H}$ is the algebra of G/H. Bear in mind, however, that G/H does not exist as a *linear* Lie group, so under the present restriction to linear Lie groups the infinitesimal algebra of G/H is not defined.

Of course, G_1/H_1 can still be defined as in 12.11 and it even bears something like a local group structure, though in a wider sense than that of Definition 4.10, in which only local *sub*groups of given groups were considered.

Within the frame of the present discussion, however, some refinement of 12.11 is still possible if H is normal:

Proposition Let H be a normal local Lie subgroup of G. For a suitable $\mathbf{0}$-neighborhood $\boldsymbol{U}$ in $\boldsymbol{G}$, and for every $\boldsymbol{a} \in \boldsymbol{U}$, there is a $\mathbf{0}$-neighborhood $\boldsymbol{H}_0$ in $\boldsymbol{H}$ and a 1-neighborhood H_1 in H such that $\exp(\boldsymbol{a} + \boldsymbol{H}_0)$ and $(\exp \boldsymbol{a}) H_1$ coincide.

Proof Choose an open ball $\boldsymbol{U}$ such that $k_{\boldsymbol{c}}$, as defined in 10.2, is nondegenerate and note that $k_{\boldsymbol{c}}\boldsymbol{H} \subset \boldsymbol{H}$, since $\tilde{\boldsymbol{c}}\boldsymbol{H} \subset \boldsymbol{H}$. As long as $\boldsymbol{c} \in \boldsymbol{U}$, at $\exp \boldsymbol{c}$ the tangent space of $\exp(\boldsymbol{c} + \boldsymbol{H})$ coincides with $(\exp \boldsymbol{c}) k_{\boldsymbol{c}} \boldsymbol{H} = (\exp \boldsymbol{c}) \boldsymbol{H}$, which is also the tangent space of the coset $(\exp \boldsymbol{c}) H$ at $\exp \boldsymbol{c}$. With the usual techniques of differential equations (see 8.2), one concludes that for any $\boldsymbol{a} \in \boldsymbol{U}$ the manifolds $\exp(\boldsymbol{a} + \boldsymbol{H})$ and $(\exp \boldsymbol{a}) H$ coincide near $\exp \boldsymbol{a}$.

12.14 One can go further if there is no doubt about the linear Lie character of G/H or $\boldsymbol{G} \bmod \boldsymbol{H}$:

Proposition Let $G, G' \in$ Gru Lie Lin. Then a local epimorphism of G onto G' with the (local) kernel H induces the epimorphism of $\boldsymbol{G}$ onto $\boldsymbol{G}'$ with the kernel $\boldsymbol{H}$ for the corresponding infinitesimal algebras.

Let $\boldsymbol{G}, \boldsymbol{G}' \in$ Alg Lie Lin. Then an epimorphism of $\boldsymbol{G}$ onto $\boldsymbol{G}'$ with the kernel $\boldsymbol{H}$ induces a local epimorphism of G onto G' with the local kernel H.

Locally G' bears the topology of G/H. If the epimorphism is global, G' bears the topology of G/H globally. An immediate consequence (see 9.13):

If Z is the center of $G \in$ Gru Lie Lin, the topological groups $\tilde{G}$ and G/Z are isomorphic.

12.15. Centerfree Groups

12.15.1 Let G be a linear Lie group and $\boldsymbol{G}$ its infinitesimal algebra. Even if $\boldsymbol{G}$ is *centerfree* (i.e., $\tilde{\boldsymbol{a}} = \mathbf{0} \to \boldsymbol{a} = \mathbf{0}$), it can happen that G has a nontrivial center (is not *centerfree*). This is not the case, however, if $\boldsymbol{G}$ is the adjoint of a centerfree algebra. Indeed:

Proposition If $\boldsymbol{G} \in$ Alg Lie and $\boldsymbol{G}$ is centerfree, then Int $\boldsymbol{G}$ is centerfree.

Proof $\tilde{\boldsymbol{G}}$ as acting on $\boldsymbol{G}$ is the infinitesimal algebra of Int $\boldsymbol{G}$ (see 9.9 and 10.3). Similarly, $\tilde{\tilde{\boldsymbol{G}}}$, acting on $\tilde{\boldsymbol{G}}$, is that of Int $\tilde{\boldsymbol{G}}$. Since $\boldsymbol{G}$ is centerfree and $\tilde{\boldsymbol{G}}$, as its isomorphic image, is also centerfree, φ defined by

$$\varphi \tilde{\boldsymbol{a}} = \tilde{\tilde{\boldsymbol{a}}}$$

maps $\tilde{\boldsymbol{G}}$ isomorphically onto $\tilde{\tilde{\boldsymbol{G}}}$; $\tilde{\boldsymbol{G}}$ and $\tilde{\tilde{\boldsymbol{G}}}$, however, are not only isomorphic, they are also equivalent as linear algebras by means of ϑ defined by

$$\vartheta \boldsymbol{a} = \tilde{\boldsymbol{a}}$$

(i.e., identifying the linear spaces $\boldsymbol{G}$ and $\tilde{\boldsymbol{G}}$ by ϑ causes $\tilde{\boldsymbol{G}}$ and $\tilde{\tilde{\boldsymbol{G}}}$ to coincide):

$$\varphi \tilde{\boldsymbol{a}} = \vartheta \tilde{\boldsymbol{a}} \vartheta^{-1}$$

(ϑ^{-1} exists because $\boldsymbol{G}$ is centerfree).

$$\begin{array}{ccc} & \tilde{\boldsymbol{a}} & \\ \boldsymbol{G} & \rightarrow & \boldsymbol{G} \\ \vartheta\downarrow & & \downarrow\vartheta \\ \tilde{\boldsymbol{G}} & \rightarrow & \tilde{\boldsymbol{G}} \\ & \tilde{\tilde{\boldsymbol{a}}} & \end{array}$$

This extends to $\tilde{a} \in \mathrm{Int}\,\boldsymbol{G}$, $\tilde{\tilde{a}} \in \widetilde{\mathrm{Int}\,\boldsymbol{G}}$:

$$\tilde{\tilde{a}} = \varphi \tilde{a} = \vartheta \tilde{a}\, \vartheta^{-1}.$$

Now, if $\tilde{a}$ belongs to the center of Int $\boldsymbol{G}$, then $\tilde{\tilde{a}} = 1$; hence $\vartheta \tilde{a} \vartheta^{-1} = 1$, whence $\tilde{a}=1$.

12.15.2. Corollary If $G \in$ Gru Lie Lin and $\boldsymbol{G}$ is centerfree, then G is centerfree if and only if G is isomorphic to Int $\boldsymbol{G}$.

12.15.3 If $\boldsymbol{G} \in$ Alg Lie Lin Rea, then because of the natural embedding of Int $\boldsymbol{G}$ into Int $\boldsymbol{G}_{\mathrm{Com}}$ the following applies:

Proposition $G \in$ Gru Lie Lin Rea is centerfree if and only if it is isomorphic to a real restriction of some centerfree complex linear Lie group.

12.16.† ad-Closed Groups Let $G \in$ Gru Lin Lie act on $R \in$ Spa Lin. The closure of G in the topology of Aut R is a linear Lie group F. Let $\boldsymbol{G}$, $\boldsymbol{F}$ be the infinitesimal algebras of G, F; $\boldsymbol{G}$ is invariant under $\curlyvee_{\boldsymbol{g}} a\boldsymbol{g}a^{-1}$ for $a \in G$ and thus for $a \in F$ as well. As a consequence, $\boldsymbol{G}$ is an ideal of $\boldsymbol{F}$.

Every $\curlyvee_{\boldsymbol{g}} a\boldsymbol{g}a^{-1}$ ($a \in F$) belongs to the closure of Int $\boldsymbol{G}$. Hence, if G is ad-closed (see 9.12) and Z is the center of F, then $F = GZ$.

With the same notation one has the following.

Proposition If G is ad-closed, the center Z_G of G is dense in the center Z_F of F in the topology of Aut R. Moreover, if Z_G is compact, then G is closed in the topology of Aut R.

† This will not essentially be used in the sequel.

Proof Let $z \in Z_F$. There is a sequence of $g_n \in G$ such that $\lim g_n = z$ in the topology of Aut R. Then $\lim \tilde{g}_n = 1$; hence by 12.14 $\lim g_n Z_G = Z_G$. Thus there is a sequence of $z_n \in Z_G$ such that $\lim z_n^{-1} g_n = 1$ in the topology of G, hence in that of Aut R, which shows $\lim z_n = z$ in the topology of Aut R and proves the first part. If Z_G is compact, then $Z_F = Z_G$; thus $F = G$, which proves G to be closed.

Remark For ad-closed G the compactness of the center is also required for G to be closed in all larger groups. (Without proof.)

12.17. Historical Note 12.15.1 seems to be due to H. Freudenthal; 12.16 is a special case of problems dealt with by M. Gotô, Faithful representations of Lie Groups I, *Math. Japonicae* **1**, 107–119 (1948), and particularly by W. T. van Est, Dense imbeddings of Lie groups [*Proc. Kon. Ned. Akad. Wet.* **A54**, 321–328 (1951); **A55**, 255–266, 267–274 (1952) = *Indagationes Math.* **13** (1951), **14** (1952)].

13–19

SOLVABILITY AND SEMISIMPLICITY

13. SOLVABLE GROUPS AND SOLVABLE LIE ALGEBRAS

$G \in$ Gru Lie Lin, $\boldsymbol{G} \in$ Alg Lie, dim $\boldsymbol{G} = r < \infty$.
Read first the definition of 13.2 and Theorems 13.9, 13.10, and 13.12.

13.1.1. Proposition If F_1 is normal Lie sub G and F_2 is Lie sub G, then $F_1 F_2$ is Lie sub G. If $\boldsymbol{F}_1$ is ideal sub $\boldsymbol{G}$ and $\boldsymbol{F}_2$ is sub $\boldsymbol{G}$, then $\boldsymbol{F}_1 + \boldsymbol{F}_2$ is sub $\boldsymbol{G}$. Moreover, if G, F_1, F_2 correspond to $\boldsymbol{G}$, $\boldsymbol{F}_1$, $\boldsymbol{F}_2$ under sgsa, then $F_1 F_2$ corresponds to $\boldsymbol{F}_1 + \boldsymbol{F}_2$.

13.1.2. Proposition If F_1, F_2 are normal Lie sub G, then $F_1 F_2$ is normal Lie sub G. If $\boldsymbol{F}_1, \boldsymbol{F}_2$ are ideals sub $\boldsymbol{G}$, then $\boldsymbol{F}_1 + \boldsymbol{F}_2$ is ideal sub $\boldsymbol{G}$.

13.1.3. Proposition If F is normal Lie sub G, the commutator group $C(F)$ is normal sub G. If $\boldsymbol{F}$ is an ideal sub $\boldsymbol{G}$, the commutator algebra $C(\boldsymbol{F})$ is an ideal sub $\boldsymbol{G}$.

13.1.4. Proposition If F_1 is normal sub G and F_2 is sub G, then

$$C(F_1 F_2) \subset F_1 C(F_2).$$

If $\boldsymbol{F}_1$ is an ideal sub $\boldsymbol{G}$ and $\boldsymbol{F}_2$ is sub $\boldsymbol{G}$, then

$$C(\boldsymbol{F}_1 + \boldsymbol{F}_2) \subset \boldsymbol{F}_1 + C(\boldsymbol{F}_2).$$

These propositions are self-evident. The last assertion of Proposition 13.1.3 follows from Jacobi-associativity,

$$[\boldsymbol{G}, [\boldsymbol{F}, \boldsymbol{F}]] \subset [[\boldsymbol{G}, \boldsymbol{F}], \boldsymbol{F}] + [\boldsymbol{F}, [\boldsymbol{G}, \boldsymbol{F}]] \subset [\boldsymbol{F}, \boldsymbol{F}] \subset C(\boldsymbol{F});$$

thus $[\boldsymbol{G}, C(\boldsymbol{F})] \subset C(\boldsymbol{F})$.

13.1.5. Proposition If F sub G, then for the topological closures $C(\bar{F}) \subset \overline{C(F)}$.

This is self-evident.

13.2 Iterating the process of forming the commutator group (algebra), one descends along the *commutator sequence* of the given group (algebra).

Definition A group (Lie algebra) is called *solvable* if its commutator sequence stops descending after a finite number of steps at $\{1\}$ ($\{\mathbf{0}\}$).

By sgsa and 12.8 it follows:

13.2.1. Proposition A linear Lie group is solvable if and only if its infinitesimal algebra is solvable.

13.2.2. Proposition Solvability is preserved by taking subgroups (subalgebras) and by mapping homomorphically. The (topological) closure of a solvable subgroup is solvable.

13.2.3. Proposition If $\boldsymbol{H}$ is a solvable ideal of $\boldsymbol{G}$ and $\boldsymbol{G}$ mod $\boldsymbol{H}$ is solvable, then $\boldsymbol{G}$ is solvable. If $\tilde{\boldsymbol{G}}$ is solvable, then $\boldsymbol{G}$ is solvable. If $C(\boldsymbol{G})$ is solvable, then $\boldsymbol{G}$ is solvable.

Proof $C^k(\boldsymbol{G} \bmod \boldsymbol{H}) = \{\mathbf{0}\}$ means $C^k(\boldsymbol{G}) \subset \boldsymbol{H}$. If, moreover, $C^m(\boldsymbol{H}) = \{\mathbf{0}\}$, then $C^{k+m}(\boldsymbol{G}) = \{\mathbf{0}\}$. The remainder is self-evident.

13.3 It follows from 13.1.1–4 that if F_1, F_2 are solvable normal Lie sub G ($\boldsymbol{F}_1, \boldsymbol{F}_2$ are solvable ideals sub $\boldsymbol{G}$), then $F_1 F_2$ ($\boldsymbol{F}_1 + \boldsymbol{F}_2$) has the same property. This fact guarantees the existence of a unique maximal one.

Definition The maximal solvable normal Lie subgroup of G is called the *radical* of G (rad G). The maximal solvable ideal of $\boldsymbol{G}$ is called the *radical* of $\boldsymbol{G}$ (rad $\boldsymbol{G}$).

Note that as a consequence of Proposition 13.1.5 the following subgroups of G are closed (if existent):

Any maximal solvable subgroup.
The maximal solvable normal subgroup.
Any maximal solvable connected subgroup.
The maximal solvable connected normal subgroup.
Any maximal solvable Lie subgroup.
The maximal solvable normal Lie subgroup.

Note also that the Lie character of subgroups need not be preserved if one passes to the closure. (See 12.3.) Therefore, to verify the last two statements in the complex case one must recur to Lie algebras and use the fact that solvability is preserved under complex extension.

Proposition The infinitesimal algebra of the radical of a linear Lie group is the radical of its infinitesimal algebra.

13.4. Definition A linear Lie group (Lie algebra) is called *semisimple* if its radical is $\{1\}$ ($\{\mathbf{0}\}$).

Proposition A linear Lie group is semisimple if and only if its infinitesimal algebra is semisimple.

Proposition $G/\text{rad } G$ (if in Gru Lie Lin) is semisimple; $\boldsymbol{G}$ mod rad $\boldsymbol{G}$ is semisimple.

Since solvability is preserved under closure (see 13.2.2), one has the following:

Proposition A linear Lie group is semisimple if and only if it has no solvable closed normal subgroup of positive dimension.

Note that discrete solvable normal subgroups are allowed.

A locally simple linear Lie group (Lie algebra) that is not semisimple must be its own radical, thus solvable, thus abelian, and thus of dimension 1.

Proposition A locally simple linear Lie group (simple Lie algebra) of dimension > 1 is semisimple.

This explains the term "semisimple" historically.

The last nontrivial term in the commutator sequence of the radical of G ($\boldsymbol{G}$), if it exists, is abelian, and by 13.1.3 normal (an ideal). Thus:

Proposition A linear Lie group (Lie algebra) is semisimple if and only if it has no abelian normal Lie subgroup (abelian ideal) $\neq \{1\}$ ($\{\mathbf{0}\}$).

13.5. Definition If $R \in$ Spa Lin, then $K \subset \text{End } R$ is called *reducible* if there is a nontrivial proper S sub R ($S \neq \{0\}, \neq R$) which is invariant under K, that is, $KS \subset S$. Otherwise K is called *irreducible*.

The invariance of linear subspaces under a linear Lie group and under its infinitesimal algebra imply each other. The same is true with respect to irreducibility.

In the sequel $R \in$ Spa Lin Com, $\dim R < \infty$.

If $\dim R > 0$, there is an S sub R with $\dim S > 0$ on which G ($\boldsymbol{G}$) acts irreducibly.

13.6. Proposition Let $R \in$ Spa Lin Com, $0 < \dim R < \infty$, $K \subset \text{End } R$, and let the elements of K commute with each other. Then, if K acts irreducibly, $\dim R = 1$. In other words, without the supposition of irreducibility: K possesses a simultaneous eigenvector x, that is, an $x \neq 0$, $x \in R$ such that for all $a \in K$ and suitable λ_a:

$$ax = \lambda_a x.$$

Proof Suppose irreducibility. For $a \in K$ there is a scalar λ, and $x \in R$, $x \neq 0$ such that $ax = \lambda x$. Let S be the set of all $x \in R$ such that

$$ax = \lambda x.$$

Then S sub R, $S \neq \{0\}$, and, for any $b \in K$,

$$abx = bax = \lambda bx,$$

thus $bx \in S$. This shows that S is K-invariant, thus $S = R$, and a behaves like a scalar multiplier on R. Hence, every T sub R is invariant under a. This is true of any $a \in K$. Thus dim $R = 1$.

13.7. Proposition Let $R \in$ Spa Lin Com, dim $R < \infty$, $G \in$ Gru Lie Lin ($\boldsymbol{G} \in$ Alg Lie Lin), $G \subset$ Aut R ($\boldsymbol{G} \subset$ End R), G ($\boldsymbol{G}$) *irreducible*. Suppose that A normal Lie sub G ($\boldsymbol{A}$ ideal sub $\boldsymbol{G}$) possesses a simultaneous eigenvector. Then A ($\boldsymbol{A}$) consists of scalar multiplications.

Remark Independent proofs are given for the group and the algebra case, though the statements imply each other under sgsa. The proof for algebras is more involved than that for groups. The proof for groups does not use analytic properties of the Lie group G but only the fact that G is connected, hence also connected in the topology induced by Aut R.

Proof for groups The given simultaneous eigenvector of A belongs to an eigenvalue λ_a ($a \in A$). Lef S be the set of x such that

$$ax = \lambda_a x \qquad \text{for} \quad a \in A.$$

Then S sub R. Again it is shown that $GS \subset S$.

For $x \in S$, $g \in G$, $a \in A$ one gets $g^{-1}ag \in A$; thus,

$$agx = g(g^{-1}ag)x = g\lambda_{g^{-1}ag}x = \lambda_{g^{-1}ag}gx;$$

a and $g^{-1}ag$ have the same set of eigenvalues but $\lambda_a, \lambda_{g^{-1}ag}$ could be different. However, they will turn out to be equal.

Indeed, $\curlyvee_{g \in G} \lambda_{g^{-1}ag}$ is continuous, with values in the finite set of eigenvalues of a, whence constant because G is connected. This proves

$$gx \in S \qquad \text{for} \quad g \in G.$$

Because of the irreducibility and of $S \neq \{0\}$, it appears that $S = R$. This proves that A consists of scalar multiplications.

Proof for algebras The given simultaneous eigenvector belongs to an eigenvalue $\lambda_{\boldsymbol{a}}$ ($\boldsymbol{a} \in \boldsymbol{A}$). Define S_p as the set of x with

13.7.1 $$(\boldsymbol{a} - \lambda_a)^p x = 0 \qquad \text{for all} \quad \boldsymbol{a} \in \boldsymbol{A}.$$

Then S_p sub $R, S_p \neq \{0\}$. Further

13.7.2 $$S_p \subset S_{p+1},$$

13.7.3 $$(\boldsymbol{a} - \lambda_a) z \in S_{p-1} \qquad \text{for all} \quad \boldsymbol{a} \in \boldsymbol{A} \leftrightarrow z \in S_p.$$

By induction it will be shown that

13.7.4 $$\boldsymbol{g} S_{p-1} \subset S_p \qquad \text{for} \quad \boldsymbol{g} \in \boldsymbol{G}.$$

Assuming 13.7.4, the subscript p can be raised by a unit: For $x \in S_p$, $\boldsymbol{g} \in \boldsymbol{G}$, $\boldsymbol{a} \in \boldsymbol{A}$,

13.7.5 $$(\boldsymbol{a} - \lambda_a)\boldsymbol{g}x = \boldsymbol{g}(\boldsymbol{a} - \lambda_a)x + [\boldsymbol{a}, \boldsymbol{g}]x.$$

Now $(\boldsymbol{a} - \lambda_a)x \in S_{p-1}$ by 13.7.3; thus by 13.7.4

$$\boldsymbol{g}(\boldsymbol{a} - \lambda_a)x \in S_p.$$

Further $[\boldsymbol{a}, \boldsymbol{g}] \in \boldsymbol{A}$; thus by 13.7.3

$$[\boldsymbol{a}, \boldsymbol{g}]x = \lambda_{[\boldsymbol{a},\boldsymbol{g}]} x \bmod S_{p-1};$$

thus in 13.7.5

$$(\boldsymbol{a} - \lambda_a)\boldsymbol{g}x \in S_p \qquad \text{for all} \quad \boldsymbol{a} \in \boldsymbol{A},$$

which proves $\boldsymbol{g}x \in S_{p+1}$, and therefore

$$\boldsymbol{g} S_p \subset S_{p+1},$$

which settles the induction.

From 13.7.4 it follows that the union of the S_p is $\boldsymbol{G}$-invariant and thus equals R. This shows that with a suitable p 13.7.1 prevails for *all* $x \in R$. Therefore all eigenvalues of $\boldsymbol{a} \in \boldsymbol{A}$ are the same; $[\boldsymbol{a}, \boldsymbol{g}]$, for $\boldsymbol{a} \in \boldsymbol{A}$, $\boldsymbol{g} \in \boldsymbol{G}$, is in $\boldsymbol{A}$ and as a commutator it has 0-trace. Therefore its eigenvalues vanish:

$$\lambda_{[\boldsymbol{a},\boldsymbol{g}]} = 0.$$

For $x \in S_1$ by 13.7.1

$$[\boldsymbol{a}, \boldsymbol{g}]x = \lambda_{[\boldsymbol{a},\boldsymbol{g}]} x = 0.$$

Supposing that $x \in S_1$ in 13.7.5, it turns out that $\boldsymbol{g}x \in S_1$; thus S_1 is invariant under $\boldsymbol{G}$ and $S_1 = R$,

$$\boldsymbol{a}x = \lambda_a x \qquad \text{for all} \quad x \in R, \quad \boldsymbol{a} \in \boldsymbol{A},$$

which proves the assertion.

13.8 The following is an immediate consequence of 13.7:

Proposition If $G \in$ Gru Lie Lin ($\boldsymbol{G} \in$ Alg Lie Lin) acting on a complex linear space is irreducible and $\det g = 1$ for $g \in G$ ($\operatorname{tr} \boldsymbol{g} = 0$ for $\boldsymbol{g} \in \boldsymbol{G}$), then G ($\boldsymbol{G}$) is semisimple.

Indeed, if this were not true, the last proposition of 13.4 would provide an abelian normal $A \neq \{1\}$ (an abelian ideal $\boldsymbol{A} \neq \{\boldsymbol{0}\}$) with a simultaneous eigenvector according to 13.6. Then 13.7 would apply to the effect that A ($\boldsymbol{A}$) consists of scalar multiplications, hence of 1 ($\boldsymbol{0}$) only.

13.9 If from $\boldsymbol{a} \in \operatorname{End} R$ one subtracts the scalar multiplication by $(\dim R)^{-1} \operatorname{tr} \boldsymbol{a}$, one gets a certain $\varphi\boldsymbol{a} \in \operatorname{End} R$ with $\operatorname{tr} \varphi\boldsymbol{a} = 0$. Obviously φ maps the Lie algebra End R endomorphically. If φ is applied to irreducible $\boldsymbol{G} \subset$ End R, a $\boldsymbol{G}' \in$ Alg Lie Lin is obtained that is still irreducible and, by 13.8, semisimple.

Suppose, moreover, that $\boldsymbol{G}$ is solvable. Then by 13.2 $\boldsymbol{G}'$ is also solvable. It was shown to be semisimple; therefore it is $\{\boldsymbol{0}\}$ and $\boldsymbol{G}$ itself is abelian; hence by Proposition 13.6 $\dim R = 1$ as soon as $\boldsymbol{G} \neq \{\boldsymbol{0}\}$. This proves that 13.6 still prevails if K is presumed solvable instead of abelian. This fact is known as:

Lie's Theorem Let $R \in$ Spa Lin Com, $0 < \dim R < \infty$. If solvable $G \in$ Gru Lie Lin ($\boldsymbol{G} \in$ Alg Lie Lin) acts irreducibly on R, then $\dim R = 1$. In other words, without supposing irreducibility, G ($\boldsymbol{G}$) possesses a simultaneous eigenvector.

This has been proved for algebras and by sgsa is still valid for groups. The group part, however, could easily have been proved independently.

13.10 Thanks to Lie's theorem, a concretization of 13.7 is obtained:

Theorem Let $R \in$ Spa Lin Com, $\dim R < \infty$. If $G \in$ Gru Lie Lin ($\boldsymbol{G} \in$ Alg Lie Lin) acts irreducibly on R, then rad G (rad $\boldsymbol{G}$) consists of scalar multiplications.

In 19.14 this statement is strengthened to the effect that rad G is even a local direct factor (rad $\boldsymbol{G}$ a direct summand).

13.11 If G is a solvable linear Lie group ($\boldsymbol{G}$ is a solvable linear Lie algebra) as before and x_1 is a simultaneous eigenvector, then Lie's theorem applies anew to $R \bmod x_1$ where G ($\boldsymbol{G}$) again acts as a solvable linear Lie group (solvable linear Lie algebra) and an eigenvector mod x_1 is obtained. This process continues. One gets vectors $x_1, \ldots, x_k$ that span a linear subspace S_k of R and an $x_{k+1} \notin S_k$ such that

$$ax_{k+1} = \lambda_a^{(k+1)} x_{k+1} \bmod S_k \qquad \text{for} \quad a \in G$$

$$\text{(respectively, } \boldsymbol{a}x_{k+1} = \lambda_{\boldsymbol{a}}^{(k+1)} x_{k+1} \bmod S_k \qquad \text{for} \quad \boldsymbol{a} \in \boldsymbol{G}\text{).}$$

On the basis $x_1, \ldots, x_n$ ($n = \dim R$) the elements a ($\boldsymbol{a}$) of G ($\boldsymbol{G}$) take the simultaneous triangular form ∇, the diagonal coefficients being $\lambda_a^{(k)}$ ($\lambda_{\boldsymbol{a}}^{(k)}$).

Triangle Theorem A linear Lie group (algebra) acting linearly in complex R is solvable if and only if it is triangular on a suitable basis.

"Only if" has just been proved. "If" follows from the next proposition:

Proposition Let G ($\boldsymbol{G}$) be the group of all complex n–n–∇-matrices with nonvanishing determinants (the Lie algebra of all complex n–n–∇-matrices). Then G ($\boldsymbol{G}$) is solvable.

(Remember that solvability is preserved when passing to subgroups and subalgebras.)

Proof Let $\boldsymbol{G}_i$ be the set of $\boldsymbol{a} \in \boldsymbol{G}$ with zeros in the main diagonal and in the first $i-1$ parallels above the main diagonal ($i = 0, 1, \ldots$). For the matrix coefficients α_{pq} of $\boldsymbol{a}$ this means

$$\boldsymbol{a} \in \boldsymbol{G}_i \leftrightarrow \alpha_{pq} = 0 \qquad \text{for} \quad q \leqslant p + i - 1,$$

$$\boldsymbol{G}_0 = \boldsymbol{G}.$$

Then

$$[\boldsymbol{G}_i, \boldsymbol{G}_j] \subset \boldsymbol{G}_{i+j}, \qquad [\boldsymbol{G}_0, \boldsymbol{G}_0] \subset \boldsymbol{G}_1,$$

which shows that $\boldsymbol{G}$ is solvable.

Let G_i be the set of $1 + \boldsymbol{a}$ with $\boldsymbol{a} \in \boldsymbol{G}_i$, for $i \geqslant 1$, and $G_0 = G$. Then G_i is a normal subgroup of G_{i-1}. For $\boldsymbol{a} \in \boldsymbol{G}_i$, $\boldsymbol{b} \in \boldsymbol{G}_j$, $a = 1 + \boldsymbol{a}$, $b = 1 + \boldsymbol{b}$,

$$aba^{-1}b^{-1} = (1 + \boldsymbol{a})(1 + \boldsymbol{b})(1 - \boldsymbol{a} + \boldsymbol{a}^2 - \cdots)(1 - \boldsymbol{b} + \boldsymbol{b}^2 - \cdots)$$

$$= 1 + (\boldsymbol{ab} - \boldsymbol{ba}) + \cdots \in G_{i+j},$$

and, for $i = j = 0$,

$$aba^{-1}b^{-1} \in G_1.$$

(Note that some positive power of $\boldsymbol{a} \in \boldsymbol{G}_i$ ($i > 0$) vanishes.)

This proves the proposition.

13.12 According to 13.2.3, solvability is preserved in the passage from $\boldsymbol{G}$ to $\tilde{\boldsymbol{G}}$. By applying the triangle theorem to $\tilde{\boldsymbol{G}}$ for complex $\boldsymbol{G}$ one finds a basis $\boldsymbol{x}_1, \ldots, \boldsymbol{x}_r$ of $\boldsymbol{G}$ such that, for $\boldsymbol{a} \in \boldsymbol{G}$,

$$\tilde{\boldsymbol{a}}\boldsymbol{x}_{k+1} = \lambda_{\tilde{\boldsymbol{a}}}\boldsymbol{x}_{k+1} \bmod \boldsymbol{x}_1, \ldots, \boldsymbol{x}_k.$$

Let $\boldsymbol{G}_k$ be the subspace linearly spanned by $\boldsymbol{x}_1, \ldots, \boldsymbol{x}_k$. Then

$$[\boldsymbol{G}, \boldsymbol{G}_k] \subset \boldsymbol{G}_k.$$

Thus $\boldsymbol{G}_k$ is an ideal in $\boldsymbol{G}$.

This shows:

Theorem In a complex solvable Lie algebra $\boldsymbol{G}$ of dimension r there is a sequence of ideals $\boldsymbol{G}_k$ ($k = 1, \ldots, r$) such that $\boldsymbol{G}_k \subset \boldsymbol{G}_{k+1}$ and $\dim \boldsymbol{G}_k = k$.

13.13 Clearly, solvability is preserved under complex extension, real restriction, and waiving. Lie's theorem and some of its consequences, however, cease to be true in the real case.

14. INVARIANTS OF LINEAR LIE GROUPS AND ALGEBRAS

$R \in \text{Spa Lin Top}$, $\dim R < \infty$.

14.1 Let φ be a function defined in an open part of R. Under $a \in \text{End } R$, φ goes into

$$S_a \varphi = \curlyvee_x \varphi(ax).$$

If

$$\left(\frac{d}{dt} a_t\right)_{t=0} = \boldsymbol{a}, \qquad a_t \in \text{End } R, \qquad a_0 = 1,$$

one may define

$$S_{\boldsymbol{a}} \varphi = \left(\frac{d}{dt} S_{a_t} \varphi\right)_{t=0}$$

whenever φ is continuously differentiable. Then

$$(S_{\boldsymbol{a}} \varphi)(x) = \left(\frac{d}{dt} \varphi(a_t x)\right)_{t=0} = \left(\frac{d}{dt} \varphi(x + t\boldsymbol{a}x + \cdots)\right)_{t=0} = (\text{grad}_x \varphi)(\boldsymbol{a}x),$$

or

$$S_{\boldsymbol{a}} \varphi = (\text{grad } \varphi)\, \boldsymbol{a}.$$

If φ is invariant under S_{a_t}, then $S_{\boldsymbol{a}} \varphi = 0$.

These notions apply to Lie groups of linear mappings of R. They lead to the following definition:

Definition A C^1-function φ on R (or part of R) is called *(infinitesimally) invariant* under $\boldsymbol{a} \in \boldsymbol{G} \in \text{Alg Lie Lin}$ in R if

$$(\text{grad } \varphi)\, \boldsymbol{a} = 0;$$

φ is called *(infinitesimally) invariant* under $\boldsymbol{G}$ if this equality holds for all $\boldsymbol{a} \in \boldsymbol{G}$.

Since no confusion is likely, the term "infinitesimally" is usually omitted.

Proposition Let $G \in$ Gru Lie Lin in R. Then a C^1-function φ defined on R is invariant under G if and only if it is invariant under $\boldsymbol{G}$.

Proof "Only if" is known. Let $S_{\boldsymbol{a}}\varphi = 0$ for all $\boldsymbol{a} \in \boldsymbol{G}$. Then for a C^1-curve $\curlyvee_t a_t$ on G and $b_t = a_t a_{t0}^{-1}$, $[(d/dt)b_t]_{t=0} = \boldsymbol{b}$, one gets $\boldsymbol{b} \in \boldsymbol{G}$; thus

$$\left(\left(\frac{d}{dt} S_{a_t}\varphi\right)_{t=t0}\right)(x) = \left(\left(\frac{d}{dt} S_{a_{t_0}} S_{b_t}\varphi\right)_{t=0}\right)(x) = ((\operatorname{grad}_{a_{t_0}x}\varphi)\,\boldsymbol{b})(a_{t_0}x) = 0,$$

which proves "if."

14.2 In particular, φ may be a form of degree p that arises from a p-linear form B:

$$\varphi(x) = B(x, \ldots, x).$$

Then

$$\begin{aligned}(\operatorname{grad}_x \varphi)\,h &= \left(\frac{d}{dt} B(x + th, \ldots, x + th)\right)_{t=0} \\ &= B(h, x, \ldots, x) + \cdots + B(x, \ldots, x, h).\end{aligned}$$

Invariance of φ under $\boldsymbol{G}$ then reads

$$B(\boldsymbol{a}x, x, \ldots, x) + \cdots + B(x, \ldots, x, \boldsymbol{a}x) = 0.$$

14.3 $\boldsymbol{G} \in$ Alg Lie, hence $\tilde{\boldsymbol{G}} \in$ Alg Lie Lin, dim $\boldsymbol{G} = r$. By 10.3 the adjoint group $\tilde{G}$ exists. By 11.3.4 the 1-component $(\text{Aut } \boldsymbol{G})_0$ of Aut $\boldsymbol{G}$ is a linear Lie group; its infinitesimal algebra consists of the derivations of $\boldsymbol{G}$.

Important invariants are introduced:

Proposition The $\curlyvee_{\boldsymbol{a}} \operatorname{tr}(\tilde{\boldsymbol{a}}^p)$ (p positive integral) are invariant under the automorphisms of $\boldsymbol{G}$ and infinitesimally invariant under the derivations of $\boldsymbol{G}$. So are the coefficients φ_ν of the polynomial in λ defined by

14.3.1
$$\det(\tilde{\boldsymbol{a}} - \lambda) = \sum_{j=0}^{r} \varphi_{r-j}(\boldsymbol{a})(-\lambda)^j,$$

which are νth degree polynomial functions on $\boldsymbol{G}$.

Proof Let A be an automorphism of $\boldsymbol{G}$; thus $[A\boldsymbol{x}, A\boldsymbol{y}] = A[\boldsymbol{x}, \boldsymbol{y}]$, which can be rewritten as $\widetilde{A\boldsymbol{x}} = A\tilde{\boldsymbol{x}}A^{-1}$; this proves the statement on automorphisms. The statement on derivations is an immediate consequence. A direct proof runs as follows:

Let Ω be a derivation of $\boldsymbol{G}$; thus

$$[\Omega\boldsymbol{x}, \boldsymbol{y}] + [\boldsymbol{x}, \Omega\boldsymbol{y}] = \Omega[\boldsymbol{x}, \boldsymbol{y}],$$

which can be rewritten as

$$\widetilde{\Omega \boldsymbol{x}} = \Omega \tilde{\boldsymbol{x}} - \tilde{\boldsymbol{x}}\Omega.$$

Applying Ω infinitesimally to $\Upsilon_{\boldsymbol{a}} \operatorname{tr}(\tilde{\boldsymbol{a}}^p)$, one gets

$$(\operatorname{grad}_{\boldsymbol{x}} \Upsilon_{\boldsymbol{x}} \operatorname{tr}(\tilde{\boldsymbol{x}}^p))\Omega \boldsymbol{x} = \sum_{j+k+1=p} \operatorname{tr}(\tilde{\boldsymbol{x}}^j \cdot \widetilde{\Omega \boldsymbol{x}} \cdot \tilde{\boldsymbol{x}}^k),$$

which vanishes because $\operatorname{tr}(AB) = \operatorname{tr}(BA)$ for any two linear mappings A, B. This proves the statement on $\Upsilon_{\boldsymbol{a}} \operatorname{tr}(\tilde{\boldsymbol{a}}^p)$.

The $\varphi_\nu(\boldsymbol{a})$ are the values of the elementary symmetric functions for the λ-roots of $\det(\tilde{\boldsymbol{a}} - \lambda) = 0$; the pth powers of the roots are the eigenvalues of $\tilde{\boldsymbol{a}}^p$ and $\operatorname{tr}(\tilde{\boldsymbol{a}}^p)$ is their sum. A well-known universal formula expresses one kind of symmetric functions by the other. This completes the proof.

Remark The statement still holds if semimorphisms instead of automorphisms are allowed.

14.4. Definition $\Upsilon_{\boldsymbol{a}} \operatorname{tr}(\tilde{\boldsymbol{a}}^2)$ is called the *Killing form* of $\boldsymbol{G}$. The corresponding symmetric bilinear form is indicated by ψ_G (the subscript is usually omitted).

Thus

$$\psi(\boldsymbol{a}, \boldsymbol{b}) = \operatorname{tr} \tilde{\boldsymbol{a}}\tilde{\boldsymbol{b}} = \operatorname{tr} \tilde{\boldsymbol{b}}\tilde{\boldsymbol{a}}.$$

Self-explanatory subscripts C and Com are attached to ψ to indicate restrictions and extensions corresponding to real restrictions and complex extensions of $\boldsymbol{G}$.

The invariance of ψ yields

14.4.1 $$\psi(\tilde{\boldsymbol{c}}\boldsymbol{a}, \boldsymbol{b}) + \psi(\boldsymbol{a}, \tilde{\boldsymbol{c}}\boldsymbol{b}) = 0.$$

14.5 Note that

$$\varphi_1(\boldsymbol{a}) = \operatorname{tr} \tilde{\boldsymbol{a}},$$

$$2\varphi_2(\boldsymbol{a}) = (\operatorname{tr} \tilde{\boldsymbol{a}})^2 - \operatorname{tr} \tilde{\boldsymbol{a}}^2,$$

$$\varphi_r(\boldsymbol{a}) = \det \tilde{\boldsymbol{a}} = 0,$$

because $\tilde{\boldsymbol{a}}\boldsymbol{a} = [\boldsymbol{a}, \boldsymbol{a}] = \boldsymbol{0}$ makes $\tilde{\boldsymbol{a}}$ degenerate.

14.6 Under complex extension and real restriction the forms undergo the corresponding processes. Under waiving they are replaced by forms on the resulting real spaces.

15. ROOTS AND RANK

$G \in$ Alg Lie Com, dim $G = r$.

15.1. Definition The roots of $\det(\tilde{a} - \lambda) = 0$ or, equivalently, the eigenvalues of $\tilde{a} \in \tilde{G}$ are called the *roots* of $a \in G$.

Proposition There is a connected open dense subset $S \subset G$ such that in a neighborhood of any $a \in S$ the roots can be considered as analytic functions.

Proof Let $\mathscr{P}$ be the ring of polynomial functions on G, and $\mathscr{P}[\lambda]$ the ring of polynomials in λ over $\mathscr{P}$. As an element of $\mathscr{P}[\lambda]$, $\det(\tilde{a} - \lambda)$ splits into irreducible elements $f_j(a; \lambda)$ of $\mathscr{P}[\lambda]$; in $f_j(a; \lambda)$ the highest λ-power coefficient is assumed to be scalar. The irreducibility of f_j guarantees that f_j and $\partial f_j / \partial \lambda$ have no nontrivial common factor in $\mathscr{P}[\lambda]$. Thus there are $u_j, v_j \in \mathscr{P}[\lambda]$, $w_j \in \mathscr{P}$, $w_j \neq 0$ such that

$$u_j f_j + v_j \frac{\partial f_j}{\partial \lambda} = w_j.$$

Let N_j be the set of $a \in G$ such that $f_j(a; \lambda) = 0$, $(\partial f_j / \partial \lambda)(a; \lambda) = 0$ have some common λ-root. Thus $w_j(a) = 0$ for $a \in N_j$, which shows that N_j is nowhere dense. The same is true of $N = \bigcup N_j$. Take S as the complement of N. Then S is open and dense in G, and for $a \in S$ the equations $f_j(a; \lambda) = 0$ and $(\partial / \partial \lambda) f_j(a; \lambda) = 0$ have no common λ-root. Thus the λ-roots of $f_j(a; \lambda) = 0$ and consequently those of $\det(\tilde{a} - \lambda) = 0$ are analytic functions near every point of S. (Of course, they might become multivalued by analytic continuation.)

If $a, b \in G$, then $w_j((1 - \tau) a + \tau b)$ as a polynomial in τ has a finite number of zeros unless it vanishes identically. So $a, b \in S$ can be connected by a curve $\curlyvee_t((1 - \tau_t) a + \tau_t b)$ (t real) avoiding the zeros of the various w_j. Hence S is connected.

15.2 Notice that S, as defined in the proof of 15.1, is invariant under Int G and $\tilde{G}$; by 14.3, so are the roots as (multivalued) functions on S.

15.3 Let the mappings Φ and Λ_U be defined by

$$\Phi a = \ulcorner \varphi_1(a), \ldots, \varphi_r(a) \urcorner \qquad (a \in G),$$

where

$$\det(\tilde{a} - \lambda) = \sum_{j=0}^{r} \varphi_{r-j}(a)(-\lambda)^j,$$

and by

$$\Lambda_U a = \ulcorner \lambda_1(a), \ldots, \lambda_r(a) \urcorner \qquad (a \in U),$$

where U is an open connected set in which the roots $\lambda_1, \ldots, \lambda_r$ of $\det(\tilde{a} - \lambda) = 0$ ($a \in U$) are defined as analytic functions.

The mapping Γ is defined by

$$\Gamma \ulcorner \lambda_1, \ldots, \lambda_r \urcorner = \ulcorner \varepsilon_1, \ldots, \varepsilon_r \urcorner,$$

where ε_ν is the value of the νth elementary symmetric function for the arguments $\lambda_1, \ldots, \lambda_r$. Then

15.3.1 $$\Phi a = \Gamma \Lambda_U a \quad \text{for} \quad a \in U.$$

Definition The *rank* of $G \in$ Alg Lie Com, usually indicated by l, is the maximal rank of grad Φ or, equivalently, the maximal rank of grad Λ_U (for all admissible U).

In other words, it is the maximal number of functionally independent coefficients of $\det(\tilde{a} - \lambda)$ or, equivalently, zeros of $\det(\tilde{a} - \lambda)$. To justify the definition both parts must be shown to be equivalent.

Let the rank of grad Φ be maximal at a_0. It is the same in a neighborhood of a_0, which by 15.1 contains a point of S. Thus $a_0 \in S$ may be supposed. a_0 possesses an open neighborhood U_0 such that Λ_{U_0} makes sense. Then by 15.3.1

$$\text{rank grad}_{a_0} \Phi \leqslant \text{rank grad}_{a_0} \Lambda_{U_0} \leqslant \max_U \text{rank grad } \Lambda_U.$$

In general, it is assumed that the neighborhoods U for Λ_U are chosen such that rank $\text{grad}_a \Lambda_U$ does not depend on $a \in U$; then rank grad Λ_U has the obvious meaning.

Conversely, let rank grad $\Lambda_{U_1} = \max_U$ rank grad Λ_U. Let a_1 be chosen in U_1 such that the number of different roots of $a \in U_1$ is maximal for $a = a_1$. Let α be the minimum of the positive ones among the numbers $|\lambda_i(a_1) - \lambda_j(a_1)|$. Let V be open such that $a_1 \in V \subset U_1$, $|\lambda_j(a) - \lambda_j(a_1)| < \frac{1}{2}\alpha$ for $a \in V$ and all j, and such that Λ_{U_1} maps V onto an analytic piece of dimension rank grad Λ_{U_1}. Then the root systems of $a, b \in V$ cannot be equivalent with each other under permutation unless $\lambda_j(a) = \lambda_j(b)$ for all j. Though, in general, Γ is one-to-one only up to root permutations, it is actually one-to-one on $\Lambda_{U_1} V$. Then $\Lambda_{U_1} V$ must contain an element $\Lambda_{U_1} a_2$ for some $a_2 \in V$ such that Γ restricted to $\Lambda_{U_1} V$ is nondegenerate in $\Lambda_{U_1} a_2$. Then, by 15.3.1,

$$\text{rank grad}_{a_2} \Phi = \text{rank grad}_{a_2} \Lambda_{U_1} = \max_U \text{rank grad } \Lambda_U,$$

whence

$$\max_a \text{rank grad}_a \Phi \geqslant \max_U \text{rank grad } \Lambda_U,$$

which proves the equivalence of both definitions.

15.4. Definition The *nullity* of $a \in G$ is the multiplicity of its root 0. The *nullity* of G is the minimal nullity of all $a \in G$; equivalently, it is the largest integer k such that $\det(\tilde{a} - \lambda)$ as a polynomial contains a factor λ^k. An element of G is called *regular* if its nullity equals that of G.

Note that rank of $G = 0$ if and only if nullity of $G =$ dimension of G.

Proposition The set of regular elements of G is open, dense, and connected.

Indeed, the set of nonregular elements of G is defined by $\varphi_{r-k-1}(a) = 0$, where k is the nullity of G (see 14.3.1). It is closed and does not contain an interior point because otherwise φ_{r-k-1} would vanish identically. Its connectedness is shown by the argument at the end of 15.1.

15.5. Theorem Nullity of $G \geqslant$ rank of G.

Proof Let l be the rank of G and rank grad Φ at a be l. It is constant near a so by 15.4 a may be supposed to be regular. The solutions of

$$\varphi_j(x) = \varphi_j(a) \qquad (j = 1, \ldots, r)$$

form a C^{an}_{r-l}-piece M near a. Because of the invariance of the φ_j under Int G, one gets

$$(\exp \tilde{c})\, a \in M \qquad \text{for small } c.$$

The tangent space of M at a, of dimension $r - l$, contains all $\tilde{c}a$, hence $\tilde{G}a$. Because of $\tilde{c}a = -\tilde{a}c$, it coincides with $\tilde{a}G$; thus

$$\dim \tilde{a}G \leqslant r - l.$$

As $\dim G = r$, the kernel of $\tilde{a}$ has dimension $\geqslant l$, which proves the assertion.

15.6 The *nullity* of a *real* Lie algebra is defined in the same way as that of a complex one. For the *rank* of a real Lie algebra the first part of the definition in 15.3 is taken. Then nullity and rank remain unchanged under complex extension.

15.7 Remark As a consequence of 14.3, expressions and properties depending on the coefficients of $\det(\tilde{a} - \lambda)$ are invariant under automorphisms. Such is the nullity of an element and its regularity.

16. IMPORTANT CLASSES OF COMPLEX LIE ALGEBRAS

16.1. Notation In the following sections light face sans serif types like G with or without subscripts are used to indicate entire classes of locally isomorphic linear Lie groups and bold face sans serif types like **G** to indicate entire classes of isomorphic Lie algebras; **G** contains the infinitesimal algebras of groups belonging to G.

The introduction of $\mathbf{A}_l$, $\mathbf{B}_l$, $\mathbf{C}_l$, $\mathbf{D}_l$ is made by representatives. They are complex linear Lie algebras. Under every letter, first a group and then its infinitesimal algebra is mentioned; $R_n \in$ Spa Lin Com, dim $R_n = n$. When needed, a basis in R_n is chosen.

These groups also admit a *projective* interpretation if viewed as acting on the projective derivative of R_n. The projective interpretation is locally an isomorphism, its kernel consisting of the scalar multipliers.

$\mathbf{A}_l$ ($l \geqslant 1$). The subgroup of Aut R_{l+1} characterized by det $= 1$. The Lie subalgebra of $\boldsymbol{a} \in$ End R_{l+1}, characterized by tr $\boldsymbol{a} = 0$.

$\mathbf{B}_l$ ($l \geqslant 1$). The subgroup of Aut R_{2l+1} characterized by det $= 1$ and the invariance of a nondegenerate quadratic form $s = s'$ (in matrix notation). The Lie subalgebra of $\boldsymbol{a} \in$ End R_{2l+1} characterized by $\boldsymbol{a}'s + s\boldsymbol{a} = 0$.

$\mathbf{C}_l$ ($l \geqslant 1$). The subgroup of Aut R_{2l} characterized by the invariance of a nondegenerate skew bilinear form, in matrix notation $s = -s'$. The Lie subalgebra of $\boldsymbol{a} \in$ End R_{2l}, characterized by $\boldsymbol{a}'s + s\boldsymbol{a} = 0$.

$\mathbf{D}_l$ ($l \geqslant 2$). As $\mathbf{B}_l$, with $2l$ instead of $2l + 1$.

These groups belonging to $\mathbf{A}_l$, $\mathbf{B}_l$, $\mathbf{C}_l$, and $\mathbf{D}_l$ are also called the

special $(l + 1)$-linear group,
special $(2l + 1)$-orthogonal group,
$2l$-symplectic group,
special $2l$-orthogonal group.

The dimensions are

$\mathbf{A}_l$: $(l + 1)^2 - 1$;
$\mathbf{B}_l$ and $\mathbf{C}_l$: $l(2l + 1)$;
$\mathbf{D}_l$: $l(2l - 1)$.

The representatives with which these classes of groups have been introduced are linear Lie groups. For a few of them it has been proved in 11.3.4 and for the others the proof is analogous.

16.2 $G \in \mathbf{A}_l$. Let H be the (maximal abelian) subalgebra consisting of the diagonal matrices with trace 0. The diagonal coefficients in due order are functions defined on H, denoted by $\omega_1, \ldots, \omega_{l+1}$, with $\sum \omega_j(\boldsymbol{h}) = 0$ for $\boldsymbol{h} \in \boldsymbol{H}$

or, for short, $\sum \omega_i = 0$. The elements $\boldsymbol{e}_{ij}$ $(i \neq j)$ are defined as bearing 1 on the i-jth place and 0 elsewhere. Together with a basis of $\boldsymbol{H}$, they form one of $\boldsymbol{G}$. The structure of $\boldsymbol{G}$ is described by the commutator relations:

$$\begin{aligned}
&\boldsymbol{H} \text{ abelian,} \\
&[\boldsymbol{h}, \boldsymbol{e}_{ij}] = (\omega_i(\boldsymbol{h}) - \omega_j(\boldsymbol{h}))\,\boldsymbol{e}_{ij}, \qquad \text{for} \quad \boldsymbol{h} \in \boldsymbol{H}, \\
&[\boldsymbol{e}_{ij}, \boldsymbol{e}_{pq}] = \boldsymbol{0} \qquad \text{for} \quad i \neq q, \quad p \neq j, \\
&[\boldsymbol{e}_{ij}, \boldsymbol{e}_{jk}] = \boldsymbol{e}_{ik} \qquad \text{for} \quad i \neq k, \\
&[\boldsymbol{e}_{ij}, \boldsymbol{e}_{ki}] = -\boldsymbol{e}_{kj} \qquad \text{for} \quad j \neq k, \\
&[\boldsymbol{e}_{ij}, \boldsymbol{e}_{ji}] = \boldsymbol{h}_{ij} \in \boldsymbol{H}
\end{aligned}$$

where $\omega_p(\boldsymbol{h}_{ij}) = 1$ for $p = i$, $= -1$ for $p = j$, $= 0$ for $p \neq i, j$.

$\boldsymbol{H}$ is no ideal in a larger subalgebra of $\boldsymbol{G}$. Anticipating a more general terminology, H is called a *trunk* of $\boldsymbol{G}$.

$$\begin{aligned}
&\tilde{\boldsymbol{h}}\boldsymbol{e}_{ij} = (\omega_i - \omega_j)(\boldsymbol{h})\,\boldsymbol{e}_{ij}, \\
&\tilde{\boldsymbol{h}}\boldsymbol{h}_0 = \boldsymbol{0} \qquad \text{for} \quad \boldsymbol{h}_0 \in \boldsymbol{H},
\end{aligned}$$

for $\boldsymbol{h} \in \boldsymbol{H}$, show that the roots of $\boldsymbol{h}$ are $(\omega_i - \omega_j)(\boldsymbol{h})$ and l-fold 0, with simultaneous eigenvectors of $\tilde{\boldsymbol{h}}$: $\boldsymbol{e}_{ij}$ and nonvanishing elements of $\boldsymbol{H}$.

The restrictions of the roots to $\boldsymbol{H}$ are called the *rootforms* (with respect to $\boldsymbol{H}$). They are linear functions on $\boldsymbol{H}$, and are simple, except 0, which is l-fold. Among them there are l linearly independent ones:

$$\omega_1 - \omega_2,\ \omega_2 - \omega_3,\ \ldots,\ \omega_l - \omega_{l+1}.$$

Every rootform is a linear combination of this subset with integral coefficients, all $\geqslant 0$ or all $\leqslant 0$.

l = number of linearly independent rootforms
= number of functionally independent rootforms
$\leqslant$ number of functionally independent roots
= rank of $\boldsymbol{G}$ (see 15.3)
$\leqslant$ nullity of $\boldsymbol{G}$ (see 15.5)
$\leqslant$ multiplicity of rootform 0
$= l$.

This shows that

$$\text{rank } \boldsymbol{G} = l.$$

The negative of every rootform is again a rootform.

The eigenvector $\boldsymbol{e}_{ij}$ (determined up to a scalar factor) of the rootform $\omega_i - \omega_j$ is called the *branch* (with respect to $\boldsymbol{H}$) belonging to the rootform

$\omega_i - \omega_j$. The commutator of branches belonging to opposite rootforms is called the *node* belonging to them (determined up to a scalar factor); $\boldsymbol{h}_{ij}$ is the node belonging to $\omega_i - \omega_j$.

For $\boldsymbol{h} \in \boldsymbol{H}$

$$\operatorname{tr} \tilde{\boldsymbol{h}} = 0, \qquad \operatorname{tr} \tilde{\boldsymbol{h}}^2 = 2 \sum_{i<j} (\omega_i - \omega_j)^2 (\boldsymbol{h}).$$

It is easy to see that

$$\operatorname{tr} \tilde{\boldsymbol{h}} \, \tilde{\boldsymbol{e}}_{ij} = 0,$$

$$\operatorname{tr} \tilde{\boldsymbol{e}}_{ij} \, \tilde{\boldsymbol{e}}_{pq} = 0, \qquad \text{for} \quad \ulcorner p,q \urcorner \neq \ulcorner j,i \urcorner,$$

and

$$\operatorname{tr} \tilde{\boldsymbol{e}}_{ij} \, \tilde{\boldsymbol{e}}_{ji} = 2(l+1),$$

which is computed as follows:

$$\tilde{\boldsymbol{e}}_{ij} \, \tilde{\boldsymbol{e}}_{ji} \, \boldsymbol{h} = (\omega_i - \omega_j)(\boldsymbol{h}) \, \boldsymbol{h}_{ij}$$

shows that $\boldsymbol{h}_{ij}$ is an eigenvector of $\tilde{\boldsymbol{e}}_{ij}\tilde{\boldsymbol{e}}_{ji}$ wth the eigenvalue $(\omega_i - \omega_j)(\boldsymbol{h}_{ij}) = 2$, and thus the subspace of $\boldsymbol{H}$ defined by $(\omega_i - \omega_j)(\boldsymbol{h}) = 0$ is the $(\dim \boldsymbol{H} - 1)$-dimensional eigenspace of the eigenvalue 0 within $\boldsymbol{H}$. Other contributions to $\operatorname{tr} \tilde{\boldsymbol{e}}_{ij}\tilde{\boldsymbol{e}}_{ji}$ are furnished by

$$\tilde{\boldsymbol{e}}_{ij} \tilde{\boldsymbol{e}}_{ji} \boldsymbol{e}_{pq},$$

namely, 1 for $p = i, q \neq j$, and for $p \neq i, q = j$, and 2 for $p = i, q = j$. Together

$$2 + (l-1) + (l-1) + 2 = 2(l+1).$$

With these data the Killing form is determined. It is nondegenerate.

16.3 $G \in \mathbf{D}_l$. On the most convenient basis the quadratic invariant is

$$2\xi_1 \xi_{l+1} + 2\xi_2 \xi_{l+2} + \cdots 2\xi_l \xi_{2l}$$

in coordinates $\xi_1, \ldots, \xi_{2l}$, with the matrix

$$\begin{pmatrix} 0 & 1 \\ 1 & 0 \end{pmatrix},$$

where 0 and 1 represent l–l-matrices. Analogously, by writing $\boldsymbol{a} \in \boldsymbol{G}$ as

$$\boldsymbol{a} = \begin{pmatrix} \boldsymbol{a}_1 & \boldsymbol{a}_2 \\ \boldsymbol{a}_3 & \boldsymbol{a}_4 \end{pmatrix},$$

the defining equality

$$\boldsymbol{a}' s + s \boldsymbol{a} = 0$$

becomes

$$\boldsymbol{a}_2 + \boldsymbol{a}_2' = \boldsymbol{a}_3 + \boldsymbol{a}_3' = \boldsymbol{a}_1 + \boldsymbol{a}_4' = 0.$$

A trunk $\boldsymbol{H}$ is the (maximal abelian) subalgebra of diagonal matrices, where in the diagonal the values of

$$\omega_1, \omega_2, \ldots, \omega_l, -\omega_1, -\omega_2, \ldots, -\omega_l$$

are found. There are three kinds of branches, for $1 \leqslant i, j \leqslant l, i \neq j$:

$$\begin{array}{lll} \boldsymbol{e}_{ij}: & 1 \text{ on } i, j; & -1 \text{ on } j+l,\, i+l; \\ \boldsymbol{e}_{i,j+l}: & 1 \text{ on } i, j+l; & -1 \text{ on } j, i+l; \\ \boldsymbol{e}_{i+l,j}: & 1 \text{ on } i+l, j; & -1 \text{ on } j+l, i; \end{array}$$

0 on all others. These branches belong to the rootforms

$$\omega_i - \omega_j, \qquad \omega_i + \omega_j, \qquad -\omega_i - \omega_j,$$

which are simple, whereas 0 is l-fold. As a basis of the rootforms, one can take

$$\omega_1 - \omega_2, \omega_2 - \omega_3, \ldots, \omega_{l-1} - \omega_l, \omega_{l-1} + \omega_l,$$

from which every rootform can be built by linear combination with integral coefficients, all $\geqslant 0$ or all $\leqslant 0$. The negative of every rootform is a rootform. The rank is again l. The commutator relations are somewhat involved. The following general principle is useful:

If $\boldsymbol{e}, \boldsymbol{e}'$ belong to the rootforms α, α', then $[\boldsymbol{e}, \boldsymbol{e}']$ either belongs to the rootform $\alpha + \alpha'$ or vanishes.

Indeed, from

$$[\boldsymbol{h}, \boldsymbol{e}] = \alpha(\boldsymbol{h})\, \boldsymbol{e}, \qquad [\boldsymbol{h}, \boldsymbol{e}'] = \alpha'(\boldsymbol{h})\, \boldsymbol{e}',$$

one obtains by Jacobi-associativity

$$[\boldsymbol{h}, [\boldsymbol{e}, \boldsymbol{e}']] = [[\boldsymbol{h}, \boldsymbol{e}], \boldsymbol{e}'] + [\boldsymbol{e}, [\boldsymbol{h}, \boldsymbol{e}']] = (\alpha + \alpha')(\boldsymbol{h})\, [\boldsymbol{e}, \boldsymbol{e}'].$$

From this it follows that $[\boldsymbol{e}, \boldsymbol{e}'] \in \boldsymbol{H}$ as soon as $\alpha + \alpha' = 0$ because $\boldsymbol{H}$ is maximal abelian. Furthermore, for any $\boldsymbol{e}, \boldsymbol{e}'$ chosen from the set of branches $\boldsymbol{e}_{ij}$,

$$[\boldsymbol{e}, \boldsymbol{e}'] = \text{scalar multiple of } \boldsymbol{e}'', \qquad \operatorname{tr} \tilde{\boldsymbol{e}}\tilde{\boldsymbol{e}}' = 0,$$

if $\alpha + \alpha' \neq 0$ is a rootform and $\boldsymbol{e}''$ its branch.

Let $1 \leqslant i, j \leqslant l, i \neq j$. The pairs $\boldsymbol{e}_{ij}$, $\boldsymbol{e}_{ji}$ and $\boldsymbol{e}_{i,j+l}$, $\boldsymbol{e}_{j+l,i}$ belong to opposite rootforms and their nodes are $\boldsymbol{h}_{ij} \in \boldsymbol{H}$ with 1 on the ith and $(j+l)$th places, -1 on the jth and $(i+l)$th places, and $\boldsymbol{h}_{i,j+l} \in \boldsymbol{H}$ with 1 on the ith and jth places, and -1 on the $(i+l)$th and $(j+l)$th places.

On $\boldsymbol{H}$ the Killing form

$$\operatorname{tr} \tilde{\boldsymbol{h}}^2 = 4(l-1) \sum \omega_j(\boldsymbol{h})^2$$

is nondegenerate and so is the total ψ, which can be shown by a somewhat longer computation.

16.4 $G \in \mathbf{B}_l$. The quadratic invariant is assumed to be

$$\xi_0^2 + 2\xi_1 \xi_{l+1} + \cdots + 2\xi_l \xi_{2l},$$

with the matrix

$$s = \begin{pmatrix} 1 & 0 & 0 \\ 0 & 0 & 1 \\ 0 & 1 & 0 \end{pmatrix},$$

a horizontal and a vertical line being added to the s of 16.3. The elements of $\boldsymbol{G}$ have the form

$$\boldsymbol{a} = \begin{pmatrix} 0 & -a_2' & -a_1' \\ a_1 & \boldsymbol{a}_1 & \boldsymbol{a}_2 \\ a_2 & \boldsymbol{a}_3 & -\boldsymbol{a}_1' \end{pmatrix},$$

with $\boldsymbol{a}_2 + \boldsymbol{a}_2' = \boldsymbol{a}_3 + \boldsymbol{a}_3' = \mathbf{0}$.

A trunk $\boldsymbol{H}$ is again the set of diagonal matrices with the values of

$$0, \omega_1, \ldots, \omega_l, -\omega_1, \ldots, -\omega_l$$

as diagonal coefficients.

To the branches of $\mathbf{D}_l$ are added

$$\boldsymbol{e}_{0i} \quad (1 \leqslant i \leqslant l) \text{ with } 1 \text{ on } 0, i; -1 \text{ on } i+l, 0,$$
$$\boldsymbol{e}_{i0} \quad (1 \leqslant i \leqslant l) \text{ with } 1 \text{ on } i, 0; -1 \text{ on } 0, i+l.$$

They belong to the rootforms $-\omega_i, \omega_i$ so that

$$\pm\omega_i, \pm\omega_i \pm \omega_j \ (i \neq j, \pm \text{ independent}) \text{ and } l\text{-fold } 0$$

are all rootforms. A basis with the old properties is provided by

$$\omega_1 - \omega_2, \omega_2 - \omega_3, \ldots, \omega_{l-1} - \omega_l, \omega_l.$$

The rank is l and all the other properties reappear.

16.5 $G \in \mathbf{C}_l$. The skew bilinear invariant has the matrix

$$s = \begin{pmatrix} 0 & 1 \\ -1 & 0 \end{pmatrix},$$

where 0, 1, -1 represent l–l-matrices. From

$$\boldsymbol{a} = \begin{pmatrix} \boldsymbol{a}_1 & \boldsymbol{a}_2 \\ \boldsymbol{a}_3 & \boldsymbol{a}_4 \end{pmatrix}$$

and

$$\boldsymbol{a}' s + s\boldsymbol{a} = 0$$

one gets

$$a_2 = a_2', \qquad a_3 = a_3', \qquad a_1 + a_4' = 0;$$

a_2 and a_3 are symmetric instead of skew, as they were in $\mathbf{D}_l$. After the usual choice of a trunk H, this means branches and rootforms like those of $\mathbf{D}_l$, though in the second and third kind the matrix coefficient -1 should be changed to 1; furthermore the branches

$$e_{i,i+l} \quad \text{with 1 on } i, i+l, \qquad e_{i+l,i} \quad \text{with 1 on } i+l, i,$$

and zeros elsewhere, with the rootforms $2\omega_i$, $-2\omega_i$, must be added. All rootforms are

$$\pm 2\omega_i, \pm\omega_i \pm \omega_j \ (i \neq j, \pm \text{ independent}) \text{ and } l\text{-fold } 0.$$

A basis with the usual properties is provided by

$$\omega_1 - \omega_2, \omega_2 - \omega_3, \ldots, \omega_{l-1} - \omega_l, 2\omega_l.$$

The usual properties can be verified again.

16.6 The properties displayed in these examples are common to the important class of complex semisimple Lie algebras. Their study is pursued in Sections 20–27.

17. SOLVABLE SUBALGEBRAS

$G \in$ Alg Lie (generally Com, sometimes Rea), dim $G = r < \infty$; $R \in$ Spa Lin Com, dim $R = n < \infty$.

17.1–3. Nilpotency

17.1. Definition An element a of End R is called *nilpotent* if $a^p = 0$ for some positive integral p. A subset A of End R is called *nilpotent* if $A^p = 0$ for some natural p. (Here A^p is defined inductively by $A^1 = A$, $A^{q+1} = AA^q$.)

Evidently an element is nilpotent iff all its eigenvalues are zero.

If G_i is defined as the set of complex n–n-matrices with zeros under and in the main diagonal and in the first $i-1$ parallels above the main diagonal ($i = 0, 1, \ldots$), then

$$G_i\, G_j \subset G_{i+j}$$

(see 13.11, Proof). Thus

$$G_1 \text{ is nilpotent.}$$

Definition $a \in G$ ($A \subset G$) is called ad-*nilpotent* if $\tilde{a}$ ($\tilde{A}$) is nilpotent. An element is ad-nilpotent iff all its roots vanish. All elements of G are ad-nilpotent iff G is of rank 0.

Proposition Let $G \subset \mathrm{End}\, R$ be a complex linear Lie algebra. If every element of G is nilpotent, then G is solvable and even nilpotent.

Proof The statement is supposed by induction to be true for any R' instead of R and any G' ($\subset \mathrm{End}\, R'$) instead of G as soon as either $\dim G' < \dim G$ or $\dim R' < \dim R$.

Let H be a maximal proper subalgebra of G. Then every element of H is nilpotent, so by induction H is solvable. According to Lie's theorem (13.9) take $x \in R$ as a simultaneous eigenvector of H. Because of the nilpotency of the elements of G

17.1.1 $$Hx = \{0\}.$$

Let K be the maximal subalgebra of G such that $Kx = \{0\}$. Then $K = G$ or $= H$. If $Gx = \{0\}$, then G acts upon $R' = R \bmod x$ as an algebra G' which by induction is nilpotent; this implies the nilpotency of G.

If $K = H$ then $ax \neq 0$ for all $a \in G \setminus H$.

H is invariant under $\tilde{h}$ with $h \in H$. Thus h induces a linear mapping $\vartheta(h)$ of $G \bmod H$ into itself; ϑ is a homomorphism; $\vartheta(H)$, as a homomorphic image of H, is solvable. According to Lie's theorem there is a simultaneous eigenvector of $\vartheta(H)$. Thus for some $a \in G$, $a \notin H$,

17.1.2 $$\tilde{h}a = \alpha(h)\, a \bmod H \qquad \text{for all} \quad h \in H.$$

Now

$$\begin{aligned} hax &= [h, a]\, x + ahx \\ &= \alpha(h)\, ax \end{aligned}$$

because of 17.1.1–2. The nilpotency of h requires $\alpha(h) = 0$, which by 17.1.2 shows that the algebra spanned by H, a, hence G, is solvable. It may be assumed to be triangular, but then it has zeros in the main diagonal and so it is nilpotent.

Corollary A complex linear Lie algebra has rank 0 if and only if its adjoint is nilpotent.

17.2 A solvable linear Lie algebra need not be nilpotent. Its commutator algebra, however, is nilpotent because the diagonal of the commutator of triangular matrices vanishes.

Proposition A complex linear Lie algebra is solvable iff its commutator algebra is nilpotent.

17.3 If G is a Lie algebra, the preceding propositions can be applied to the linear Lie algebra $\tilde{G}$.

First Criterion on Solvability The complex Lie algebra G is solvablė iff its commutator algebra $C(G)$ is of rank 0 (ad-nilpotent).

Proof If G is solvable, then by 17.2, for any $a \in C(G)$, all eigenvalues of $\tilde{a}$ vanish and, in particular, all roots of a as element of $C(G)$. Conversely, if rank $C(G)=0$, its adjoint is nilpotent, and therefore solvable, and so are $C(G)$ and G. (See 13.2.3.)

17.4–12. Trunks

17.4 Let $G \in$ Alg Lie Com, $h_0 \in G$. According to the *different* roots of h_0, G as a linear space splits directly into linear subspaces G_α such that

$$(\tilde{h}_0 - \alpha)^{\dim G_\alpha} G_\alpha = \{0\}.$$

Proposition $[G_\alpha, G_\beta] \subset G_{\alpha+\beta}$ or $= \{0\}$ (if $\alpha+\beta$ is no root of h_0).

Proof For $x \in G_\alpha$, $y \in G_\beta$, and some i, j

$$(\tilde{h}_0 - \alpha)^i x = (\tilde{h}_0 - \beta)^j y = 0.$$

Now

$$(\tilde{h}_0 - \alpha - \beta)[x, y] = [(\tilde{h}_0 - \alpha)x, y] + [x, (\tilde{h}_0 - \beta)y].$$

Iterating this, one gets

$$(\tilde{h}_0 - \alpha - \beta)^{i+j-1}[x, y] = \text{a sum of} \quad [(\tilde{h}_0 - \alpha)^p x, (\tilde{h}_0 - \beta)^q y],$$

with $p+q=i+j-1$, hence $p \geqslant i$ or $q \geqslant j$. This means that all summands vanish and proves the assertion.

17.5 In particular, $[G_0, G_0] \subset G_0$, which shows that G_0 is a subalgebra.

17.6. Definition For any *regular* $h_0 \in G$ the set of all $x \in G$ such that

$$\tilde{h}_0^p x = 0 \qquad \text{for some } p$$

is called the *trunk* of h_0. The letter H usually denotes a trunk.

Theorem A trunk H of $G \in$ Alg Lie Com is a solvable subalgebra of rank 0; H is the trunk of all its G-regular elements and contains all simultaneous eigenvectors of $\tilde{h}$ $(h \in H)$ for the eigenvalue 0. It is an ideal in no larger subalgebra of G.

Proof H, the trunk of regular h_0, called G_0 in 17.5, is an algebra and therefore invariant under $\tilde{h}$ with $h \in H$. The multiplicity of the eigenvalue 0 of $\tilde{\boldsymbol{h}}$, as acting on $\boldsymbol{H}$ and $\boldsymbol{G}$ mod $\boldsymbol{H}$, is denoted by $n_{\boldsymbol{H}}(\boldsymbol{h})$ and $n_{\text{mod}\,\boldsymbol{H}}(\boldsymbol{h})$, respectively. Continuity prevents $n_{\text{mod}\,\boldsymbol{H}}(\boldsymbol{h})$ from increasing near $\boldsymbol{h}_0$; regularity prevents the nullity of $\boldsymbol{h}$, that is, $n_{\boldsymbol{H}}(\boldsymbol{h}) + n_{\text{mod}\,\boldsymbol{H}}(\boldsymbol{h})$, from decreasing. Therefore $n_{\boldsymbol{H}}(\boldsymbol{h}) \geqslant n_{\boldsymbol{H}}(\boldsymbol{h}_0)$ for $\boldsymbol{h}$ near $\boldsymbol{h}_0$. Hence

$$\tilde{\boldsymbol{h}}^p \boldsymbol{x} = \boldsymbol{0} \qquad \text{for} \quad \boldsymbol{x} \in \boldsymbol{H} \text{ and some } p$$

and for all $\boldsymbol{h} \in \boldsymbol{H}$ near $\boldsymbol{h}_0$, but because of the analyticity of $\tilde{\boldsymbol{h}}^p \boldsymbol{x}$ as a function of $\boldsymbol{h}$ this holds good for all $\boldsymbol{h} \in \boldsymbol{H}$. All $\boldsymbol{h} \in \boldsymbol{H}$ are ad-nilpotent as elements of the subalgebra $\boldsymbol{H}$; by 17.1 the same is true of $\boldsymbol{H}$, which, again by 17.1, is also solvable.

The trunk of any regular $\boldsymbol{h} \in \boldsymbol{H}$ is at least $\boldsymbol{H}$. It cannot be larger because this would enlarge the nullity of $\boldsymbol{h}$.

The third assertion of the theorem is a mere consequence of the definition of trunk.

If $\boldsymbol{H}$ were a proper ideal of some subalgebra of $\boldsymbol{G}$, there would be some $\boldsymbol{a} \notin \boldsymbol{H}$ such that $\tilde{\boldsymbol{h}}\boldsymbol{a} \in \boldsymbol{H}$ for all $\boldsymbol{h} \in \boldsymbol{H}$ and $\tilde{\boldsymbol{h}}^{p+1}\boldsymbol{a} = \boldsymbol{0}$ for some p, which would produce the contradiction $\boldsymbol{a} \in \boldsymbol{H}$.

17.7 A converse of 17.6 is proved in 17.11:

Theorem Let A be a subalgebra of rank 0 of the complex Lie algebra $\boldsymbol{G}$ and let A be ideal of no larger subalgebra of $\boldsymbol{G}$. Then A is a trunk of $\boldsymbol{G}$.

17.8† Under automorphisms of $\boldsymbol{G}$ a trunk goes into trunks. In 17.11 it will be proved:

Conjugacy Theorem Two trunks of complex $\boldsymbol{G}$ are equivalent under the action of Int $\boldsymbol{G}$.

17.9 The proofs are prepared by means of the next propositions.

Proposition Let $\boldsymbol{G} \in$ Alg Lie Rea or Com, $\boldsymbol{A}$ a linear subspace of $\boldsymbol{G}$, $\boldsymbol{a}_0 \in \boldsymbol{A}$ such that $\tilde{\boldsymbol{a}}_0 \boldsymbol{A} \subset \boldsymbol{A}$ and the mapping induced by $\tilde{\boldsymbol{a}}_0$ in the linear space $\boldsymbol{G}$ mod $\boldsymbol{A}$ is nondegenerate. Then the $(\exp \tilde{\boldsymbol{b}})\boldsymbol{A}$ with $\boldsymbol{b}$ from a $\boldsymbol{0}$-neighborhood in $\boldsymbol{G}$ cover a neighborhood of $\boldsymbol{a}_0$. If, moreover, $\boldsymbol{G} \in$ Alg Lie Com, then $\boldsymbol{A}$ contains a regular element of $\boldsymbol{G}$.

Proof As a linear space, $\boldsymbol{G}$ is the direct sum of $\boldsymbol{A}$ and a linear subspace $\boldsymbol{B}$. The mapping ϑ defined by

$$\vartheta \ulcorner \boldsymbol{a}, \boldsymbol{b} \urcorner = (\exp \tilde{\boldsymbol{b}})(\boldsymbol{a}_0 + \boldsymbol{a}) \qquad \text{for} \quad \boldsymbol{a} \in \boldsymbol{A}, \boldsymbol{b} \in \boldsymbol{B}$$

† 17.8–12 will not essentially be used for some time.

has at $\ulcorner \mathbf{0}, \mathbf{0} \urcorner$

$$(\text{grad}\, \vartheta)\, \ulcorner \boldsymbol{a}, \boldsymbol{b} \urcorner = \boldsymbol{a} + [\boldsymbol{b}, \boldsymbol{a}_0] = \boldsymbol{a} - \tilde{\boldsymbol{a}}_0 \boldsymbol{b}.$$

Now $\boldsymbol{a} - \tilde{\boldsymbol{a}}_0 \boldsymbol{b} = \mathbf{0}$ would mean $\tilde{\boldsymbol{a}}_0 \boldsymbol{b} = \mathbf{0} \bmod \boldsymbol{A}$, which by the supposition on nondegeneracy implies $\boldsymbol{b} = \mathbf{0}$, hence $\boldsymbol{a} = \mathbf{0}$. Therefore grad ϑ at $\ulcorner \mathbf{0},\mathbf{0} \urcorner$ is nondegenerate and ϑ maps a neighborhood of $\ulcorner \mathbf{0}, \mathbf{0} \urcorner$ onto a neighborhood of $\boldsymbol{a}_0$. This proves the first assertion. The set of regular elements is dense, so the neighborhood of $\boldsymbol{a}_0$ covered by the $(\exp \tilde{\boldsymbol{b}})\boldsymbol{A}$ $(\boldsymbol{b} \in \boldsymbol{B})$ contains a regular element. Since $(\exp \tilde{\boldsymbol{b}})\boldsymbol{A}$ possesses a regular element for some $\boldsymbol{b}$, and the notion of regular element is Int$\boldsymbol{G}$-invariant (see 15.7), $\boldsymbol{A}$ has the same property.

17.10. Proposition Let $\boldsymbol{G} \in$ Alg Lie Com, $\boldsymbol{A}$ sub $\boldsymbol{G}$, rank $\boldsymbol{A} = 0$. Let the mapping induced by $\tilde{\boldsymbol{a}}$ $(\boldsymbol{a} \in \boldsymbol{A})$ in the linear space $\boldsymbol{G}$ mod $\boldsymbol{A}$ have an identically vanishing eigenvalue. Then $\boldsymbol{A}$ is an ideal in a larger subalgebra of $\boldsymbol{G}$.

Proof Let $\boldsymbol{h}_0 \in \boldsymbol{A}$ be chosen with a minimal nullity in $\boldsymbol{G}$ among elements of $\boldsymbol{A}$. As in 17.4, $\boldsymbol{G}_\alpha$ is defined with respect to $\boldsymbol{h}_0$. Then, since rank $\boldsymbol{A} = 0$, $\boldsymbol{A} \subset \boldsymbol{G}_0$. The postulated behavior of $\tilde{\boldsymbol{h}}_0$ in $\boldsymbol{G}$ mod $\boldsymbol{A}$ implies the existence of $\boldsymbol{x} \in \boldsymbol{G} \setminus \boldsymbol{A}$ such that $\tilde{\boldsymbol{h}}_0 \boldsymbol{x} \in \boldsymbol{A}$, hence $\boldsymbol{x} \in \boldsymbol{G}_0$ and $\boldsymbol{G}_0 \neq \boldsymbol{A}$. By 17.4 $\boldsymbol{G}_0$ is invariant under $\tilde{\boldsymbol{h}}_0$. The restriction of $\tilde{\boldsymbol{h}}_0$ to $\boldsymbol{G}_0$ is nilpotent, and the same reasoning used in 17.6 shows that this property remains true for all $\boldsymbol{h} \in \boldsymbol{A}$ because of the minimal nullity of $\boldsymbol{h}_0$. So $\boldsymbol{A}$ is represented nilpotently in $\boldsymbol{G}_0$ by $\Upsilon_{\boldsymbol{h} \in \boldsymbol{A}} \tilde{\boldsymbol{h}}$, and so it is in $\boldsymbol{G}_0$ mod $\boldsymbol{A}$. Let $\boldsymbol{x} + \boldsymbol{A} \in \boldsymbol{G}_0$ mod $\boldsymbol{A}$ be an eigenvector of this representation (with the eigenvalue 0). Then the linear subspace spanned by $\boldsymbol{A}$ and $\boldsymbol{x}$ is a subalgebra properly containing $\boldsymbol{A}$ as an ideal.

17.11 *Proof* of Theorem 17.7–8. Let $\boldsymbol{A}$ be assumed as in 17.7. Then by 17.10 no identically vanishing eigenvalue of the mapping induced by $\tilde{\boldsymbol{a}}$ $(\boldsymbol{a} \in \boldsymbol{A})$ in $\boldsymbol{G}$ mod $\boldsymbol{A}$ exists. By 17.9 $\boldsymbol{A}$ possesses a regular element $\boldsymbol{h}_0$ of $\boldsymbol{G}$, the trunk of which is called $\boldsymbol{H}$. Since rank $\boldsymbol{A} = 0$, the restriction of $\tilde{\boldsymbol{h}}_0$ to $\boldsymbol{A}$ is nilpotent, and since $\boldsymbol{H}$ itself is the maximal linear subspace with this property, $\boldsymbol{A}$ is contained in $\boldsymbol{H}$. If $\boldsymbol{A} \neq \boldsymbol{H}$, then $\tilde{\boldsymbol{A}}$, acting nilpotently on $\boldsymbol{H}$ mod $\boldsymbol{A}$, has an eigenvector belonging to the eigenvalue 0. Hence there is some $\boldsymbol{x} \in \boldsymbol{H} \setminus \boldsymbol{A}$ such that $\tilde{\boldsymbol{A}}\boldsymbol{x} = \{\mathbf{0}\}$. The subalgebra spanned by $\boldsymbol{A}$ and $\boldsymbol{x}$ contains $\boldsymbol{A}$ as an ideal. This contradiction shows that $\boldsymbol{A} = \boldsymbol{H}$, hence that $\boldsymbol{A}$ is a trunk.

For any trunk $\boldsymbol{H}$ let $\Phi(\boldsymbol{H})$ be the set of regular elements of (Int $\boldsymbol{G}$)$\boldsymbol{H}$. By 17.9 (which applies because of 17.10) $\Phi(\boldsymbol{H})$ is open, and by the same reason every regular element belongs to some $\Phi(\boldsymbol{H})$. If there were several $\Phi(\boldsymbol{H})$, the set of regular elements, which is connected (15.4), would split into $\Phi(\boldsymbol{H}_0)$ and a union of certain $\Phi(\boldsymbol{H})$, which are both open. This contradiction proves 17.8.

17.12. Theorem Let φ be a homomorphism of $\boldsymbol{G} \in$ Alg Lie Com onto $\boldsymbol{G}' \in$ Alg Lie Com. By φ the regular elements of $\boldsymbol{G}$ are mapped into regular elements of $\boldsymbol{G}'$, and the trunks of $\boldsymbol{G}'$ are the images of the trunks of $\boldsymbol{G}$.

Proof Let N be the kernel of φ; $\boldsymbol{G}'$ is canonically isomorphic with $\boldsymbol{G}$ mod N. If $\boldsymbol{h}_0$ is a regular element of $\boldsymbol{G}$, then $\varphi(\boldsymbol{h}_0)$ is one of $\boldsymbol{G}'$ because the regular elements of $\boldsymbol{G}'$ are dense in $\boldsymbol{G}'$ and a slight variation of $\boldsymbol{h}_0$ does not change its nullity on N, thus cannot decrease its nullity on $\boldsymbol{G}$ mod N. It is clear then that the trunk $\boldsymbol{H}$ associated with a regular element $\boldsymbol{h}_0$ of $\boldsymbol{G}$ is mapped onto the trunk $\boldsymbol{H}'$ associated with $\varphi(\boldsymbol{h}_0)$. Any other trunk of $\boldsymbol{G}'$ is of the form $\psi'\boldsymbol{H}'$ for some $\psi' \in \text{Int}\,\boldsymbol{G}'$. Now $\text{Int}\,\boldsymbol{G}'$ is canonically the image of $\text{Int}\,\boldsymbol{G}$, and, if $\psi \in \text{Int}\,\boldsymbol{G}$ is mapped into ψ', then $\psi\boldsymbol{H}$ is a trunk of $\boldsymbol{G}$ mapped onto $\psi'\boldsymbol{H}'$ by φ.

17.13–15. Rootforms and Nodes

17.13.1 Definition Let $\boldsymbol{H}$ be a trunk of $\boldsymbol{G} \in$ Alg Lie Com. The restrictions of the roots to $\boldsymbol{H}$ are called the *rootforms* (with respect to $\boldsymbol{H}$). The system of rootforms, with due multiplicities, is denoted by W or, more precisely, $W(\boldsymbol{G},\boldsymbol{H})$.

Since $\boldsymbol{H}$ is solvable, its respresentation by $\Upsilon_{\boldsymbol{h}}\tilde{\boldsymbol{h}}$ may be considered triangular, with the rootforms in the diagonal. Thus:

Theorem The rootforms are linear functions on the trunk.

17.13.2 The set of $\boldsymbol{h} \in \boldsymbol{H}$ such that $\alpha(\boldsymbol{h}) = \beta(\boldsymbol{h})$ for some couple α, β of *different* rootforms is nowhere dense in $\boldsymbol{H}$. One can choose some $\boldsymbol{h}_0 \in \boldsymbol{H}$ such that for any couple α, β of rootforms $\alpha(\boldsymbol{h}_0) \neq \beta(\boldsymbol{h}_0)$ unless $\alpha = \beta$. Splitting $\boldsymbol{G}$ into $\boldsymbol{G}_\alpha$ (see 17.4) with respect to $\boldsymbol{h}_0$, one obtains

$$(\tilde{\boldsymbol{h}}_0 - \alpha(\boldsymbol{h}_0))^{\dim G_\alpha} \boldsymbol{G}_\alpha = \{0\}.$$

Because of 17.4, $\boldsymbol{G}_\alpha$ is invariant under $\tilde{\boldsymbol{h}}$ ($\boldsymbol{h} \in \boldsymbol{H}$). The restriction of $\tilde{\boldsymbol{h}}_0$ to $\boldsymbol{G}_\alpha$ has one eigenvalue only. With a view to the choice of $\boldsymbol{h}_0$, it appears that this property belongs to all $\boldsymbol{h} \in \boldsymbol{H}$. Hence:

Theorem Let $\boldsymbol{H}$ be a trunk of $\boldsymbol{G} \in$ Alg Lie Com. Then $\boldsymbol{G}$ splits as a direct sum of subspaces $\boldsymbol{G}_\alpha$ corresponding to the different members α of W such that

$$(\tilde{\boldsymbol{h}} - \alpha(\boldsymbol{h}))^{\dim G_\alpha} \boldsymbol{G}_\alpha = \{0\} \qquad \text{for} \quad \boldsymbol{h} \in \boldsymbol{H};$$

$[\boldsymbol{G}_\alpha, \boldsymbol{G}_\beta] \subset \boldsymbol{G}_{\alpha+\beta}$ or $\{0\}$ (if $\alpha + \beta$ is no rootform). $\boldsymbol{G}_0$ is the same as $\boldsymbol{H}$.

17.14 By 17.8, $W(\boldsymbol{G},\boldsymbol{H})$ is essentially the same for all trunks $\boldsymbol{H}$ of $\boldsymbol{G}$. Any functional dependency among roots causes a dependency among the corresponding rootforms, and conversely any dependency among rootforms is raised to a dependency among roots by the action of Int $\boldsymbol{G}$. Functional dependency among rootforms coincides with linear dependency. Therefore:

Theorem The rank of $\boldsymbol{G}$ equals the number of linearly independent rootforms.

The last-mentioned number does not exceed dim $\boldsymbol{H}$, which is the nullity of $\boldsymbol{G}$. This confirms Theorem 15.5.

17.15. Definition If α and $-\alpha$ belong to W, the nonvanishing elements of $[\boldsymbol{G}_\alpha, \boldsymbol{G}_{-\alpha}]$ are called the *α-nodes* (with respect to $\boldsymbol{H}$).

Of course, the α-nodes belong to $\boldsymbol{H}$.

Theorem For any α-node $\boldsymbol{h}$ and any rootform μ, $\mu(\boldsymbol{h})$ is a rational multiple of $\alpha(\boldsymbol{h})$, where the factor does not depend on $\boldsymbol{h}$ (though it may depend on α and μ).

Proof Let $\boldsymbol{h} = [\boldsymbol{f}_+, \boldsymbol{f}_-]$ where $\boldsymbol{f}_+ \in \boldsymbol{G}_\alpha$, $\boldsymbol{f}_- \in \boldsymbol{G}_{-\alpha}$. Then

$$\tilde{\boldsymbol{f}}_+ \boldsymbol{G}_\nu \subset \boldsymbol{G}_{\nu+\alpha}, \qquad \tilde{\boldsymbol{f}}_- \boldsymbol{G}_\nu \subset \boldsymbol{G}_{\nu-\alpha}$$

as far as existent. Put

$$\boldsymbol{F} = \sum_{j \text{ integer}} \boldsymbol{G}_{\mu+j\alpha};$$

$\boldsymbol{F}$ is invariant under $\tilde{\boldsymbol{f}}_+, \tilde{\boldsymbol{f}}_-$, thus under $\tilde{\boldsymbol{h}}$. Since $\tilde{\boldsymbol{h}}$ is a commutator of elements preserving $\boldsymbol{F}$, $\text{tr}_{\boldsymbol{F}} \tilde{\boldsymbol{h}} = 0$; however, $\text{tr}_{\boldsymbol{F}} \tilde{\boldsymbol{h}} = \sum_j \text{tr}_{\boldsymbol{G}_{\mu+j\alpha}} \tilde{\boldsymbol{h}}$. In $\boldsymbol{G}_{\mu+j\alpha}$ the only eigenvalue of $\tilde{\boldsymbol{h}}$ is $(\mu + j\alpha)(\boldsymbol{h})$ with multiplicity dim $\boldsymbol{G}_{\mu+j\alpha}$. Thus,

$$\sum_j \dim \boldsymbol{G}_{\mu+j\alpha} \cdot (\mu + j\alpha)(\boldsymbol{h}) = 0.$$

This proves the assertion.

17.16–17. The Killing Form and Solvability

17.16 If $\boldsymbol{E}$ sub $\boldsymbol{G}$ one can restrict the Killing form to $\boldsymbol{E}$ and then distinguish between

$$\psi_{\boldsymbol{E}}(\boldsymbol{x}, \boldsymbol{y}) = \text{tr}_{\boldsymbol{E}} \tilde{\boldsymbol{x}} \tilde{\boldsymbol{y}} \qquad (\boldsymbol{x}, \boldsymbol{y} \in \boldsymbol{E})$$

and

$$\psi_{\boldsymbol{G}}(\boldsymbol{x}, \boldsymbol{y}) = \text{tr}_{\boldsymbol{G}} \tilde{\boldsymbol{x}} \tilde{\boldsymbol{y}} \qquad (\boldsymbol{x}, \boldsymbol{y} \in \boldsymbol{E}),$$

which in general will be different. However:

Proposition If $\boldsymbol{E}$ is an ideal in $\boldsymbol{G} \in$ Alg Lie, then

$$\psi_{\boldsymbol{E}}(\boldsymbol{x}, \boldsymbol{y}) = \psi_{\boldsymbol{G}}(\boldsymbol{x}, \boldsymbol{y}) \qquad \text{for} \quad \boldsymbol{x}, \boldsymbol{y} \in \boldsymbol{E}.$$

Indeed, if $\boldsymbol{E}$ is an ideal, then $\tilde{\boldsymbol{x}}\tilde{\boldsymbol{y}}\boldsymbol{z} \in \boldsymbol{E}$ for $\boldsymbol{x}, \boldsymbol{y} \in \boldsymbol{E}$, even if $\boldsymbol{z} \notin \boldsymbol{E}$. So contributions to the trace come from $\boldsymbol{z} \in \boldsymbol{E}$ only.

17.17 If $\boldsymbol{G} \in$ Alg Lie Com is solvable, then, according to the first criterion on solvability (17.3), all roots of elements of $C(\boldsymbol{G})$ vanish [not only on $C(\boldsymbol{G})$ but also on $\boldsymbol{G}$ because $C(\boldsymbol{G})$ is an ideal]. As the sum of the squares of the eigenvalues of $\tilde{\boldsymbol{x}}$, $\psi(\boldsymbol{x}, \boldsymbol{x})$ then vanishes for all $\boldsymbol{x} \in C(\boldsymbol{G})$. The converse is also valid:

Second Criterion on Solvability $\boldsymbol{G} \in$ Alg Lie Com is solvable if and only if $\psi(\boldsymbol{x}, \boldsymbol{x}) = 0$ for all $\boldsymbol{x} \in C(\boldsymbol{G})$.

Proof One still has to show that if $\psi(\boldsymbol{x}, \boldsymbol{x}) = 0$ for all $\boldsymbol{x} \in C(\boldsymbol{G})$ then $\boldsymbol{G}$ is solvable. By 17.16 the supposition implies

$$\mathrm{tr}_{\boldsymbol{E}}\, \tilde{\boldsymbol{x}}^2 = 0 \qquad \text{for} \quad \boldsymbol{x} \in \boldsymbol{E},$$

where $\boldsymbol{E} = C(\boldsymbol{E})$ is the last member of the commutator sequence of $\boldsymbol{G}$. It has to be shown that $\boldsymbol{E} = \{\boldsymbol{0}\}$.

Suppose that $\boldsymbol{E} \neq \{\boldsymbol{0}\}$ and choose a trunk $\boldsymbol{H}$ of $\boldsymbol{E}$. Then $\boldsymbol{H} \neq \{\boldsymbol{0}\}$. As a trunk $\boldsymbol{H}$ is solvable, whereas $\boldsymbol{E} = C(\boldsymbol{E})$ is not, and so there exists a rootform $\beta \neq 0$ with respect to $\boldsymbol{H}$. Since $\boldsymbol{E} = C(\boldsymbol{E})$, the trunk $\boldsymbol{H}$ is spanned by the nodes; therefore there is a node $\boldsymbol{h}_\alpha$ of some α such that $\beta(\boldsymbol{h}_\alpha) \neq 0$. Then, according to 17.15,

$$0 = \psi(\boldsymbol{h}_\alpha, \boldsymbol{h}_\alpha) = \sum_\mu \dim \boldsymbol{G}_\mu\, \mu(\boldsymbol{h}_\alpha)^2 = \kappa\alpha(\boldsymbol{h}_\alpha)^2$$

with $\kappa \neq 0$. Therefore $\alpha(\boldsymbol{h}_\alpha) = 0$ and again, by 17.15, $\mu(\boldsymbol{h}_\alpha) = 0$ for any rootform μ, in particular for β, which is a contradiction.

17.18. The Real Aspect By 13.13 and 14.6 the notions of solvability, commutator algebra, and vanishing Killing form are invariant under complex extension, real restriction, and waiving. These properties are also shared by the notion of being of rank 0. The two solvability criteria remain valid in $\boldsymbol{G} \in$ Alg Lie Rea.

17.19. Historical Note Theorem 17.12 is due to H. de Vries.

18. CLEAVING

18.1 $R \in$ Spa Lin Com, $\dim R = n < \infty$.

Definition A subset and in particular, an element of End R is called *pure* if it takes the diagonal form on a suitable basis.

Definition If $\boldsymbol{h} \in \operatorname{End} R$, the splitting $\boldsymbol{h} = \boldsymbol{a} + \boldsymbol{e}$ is called a *cleaving* if $\boldsymbol{a} \in \operatorname{End} R$ is pure, $\boldsymbol{e} \in \operatorname{End} R$ is nilpotent and $\boldsymbol{ae} = \boldsymbol{ea}$.

18.1.1. Proposition $\boldsymbol{h} \in \operatorname{End} R$ admits one and only one cleaving. The cleaving components are scalar linear combinations of the powers of $\boldsymbol{h}$ with positive integral exponents.

As a consequence: Every $\boldsymbol{u} \in \operatorname{End} R$ commuting with $\boldsymbol{h}$ also commutes with the cleaving components. Every linear subspace invariant under $\boldsymbol{h}$ is invariant under the cleaving components. Even: if S, T sub R and $\boldsymbol{h}S \subset T \subset S$, then $\boldsymbol{a}S \subset T$, $\boldsymbol{e}S \subset T$.

Proof R splits directly into subspaces R_i corresponding to the different eigenvalues $\lambda_1, \ldots, \lambda_p$ of $\boldsymbol{h}$. In every R_i choose a basis on which the restriction of $\boldsymbol{h}$ to R_i is triangular. Take the union of these bases as one for R. The diagonal part of $\boldsymbol{h}$ is taken as $\boldsymbol{a}$, the remainder as $\boldsymbol{e}$. Obviously this is a cleaving.

Conversely, if the cleaving $\boldsymbol{h} = \boldsymbol{a} + \boldsymbol{e}$ is given and λ_i are the different eigenvalues of $\boldsymbol{a}$ with eigenspaces R_i,

$$(\boldsymbol{a} - \lambda_i) R_i = \{0\},$$

then

$$(\boldsymbol{h} - \lambda_i)^n R_i = ((\boldsymbol{a} - \lambda_i) + \boldsymbol{e})^n R_i,$$

which by the binomial formula and by $\boldsymbol{e}^n = \boldsymbol{0}$ turns out to be $\{0\}$. This shows that the λ_i are the eigenvalues of $\boldsymbol{h}$ and the R_i the corresponding subspaces, and that the cleaving coincides with the previous one.

Further define a polynomial $\varphi(z)$ such that for $\varphi(z)$ and its derivatives

$$\varphi(0) = 0, \qquad \varphi(\lambda_i) = \lambda_i, \qquad \varphi'(\lambda_i) = \cdots = \varphi^{(n-1)}(\lambda_i) = 0 \quad \text{for} \quad i = 1, \ldots, p.$$

The polynomial $\varphi(z) - \lambda_i$ then has a factor $(z - \lambda_i)^n$. Substituting $\boldsymbol{h} = \boldsymbol{a} + \boldsymbol{e}$ into φ, one gets $\varphi(\boldsymbol{h}) = \boldsymbol{a}$. This is a linear combination of $\boldsymbol{h}^i$ $(i \geqslant 1)$ as required.

18.1.2† Cleaving as defined in End R has a multiplicative analog in Aut R.

Proposition $h \in \operatorname{Aut} R$ can be split uniquely as $h = au$ where a is pure, u is unipotent (i.e., all its eigenvalues are 1), and $au = ua$.

This follows from the cleaving $h = a + \boldsymbol{e}$ with pure a, nilpotent $\boldsymbol{e}$, and $\boldsymbol{ae} = \boldsymbol{ea}$ by putting $u = 1 + a^{-1}\boldsymbol{e}$.

18.1.3 Let $\boldsymbol{D}$ be the set of $\boldsymbol{h} \in \operatorname{End} R$ such that all eigenvalues λ of $\boldsymbol{h}$ satisfy

$$-\pi < \operatorname{Im} \lambda < \pi,$$

and $\boldsymbol{D}_p$ the subset of pure elements of $\boldsymbol{D}$. Then exp is one-to-one on $\boldsymbol{D}_p$.

† 18.1.2–5 will not be used before Section 38.

exp maps the (additive) cleaving of $\boldsymbol{h} \in \operatorname{End} R$ on the multiplicative one of $\exp \boldsymbol{h}$; moreover, it maps the set of nilpotents onto the set of unipotents, since exp is inverted by log. Therefore

$$\exp \text{ maps } \boldsymbol{D} \text{ one-to-one.}$$

18.1.4 Now interpret End R as a linear Lie algebra $\boldsymbol{G}$. The kernel of the trace in End R is a member $\boldsymbol{G}_0$ of $\mathbf{A}_{n-1}$. For $\boldsymbol{a} \in \boldsymbol{G}$ let $\boldsymbol{a}_0$ be such that $\boldsymbol{a} - \boldsymbol{a}_0$ is a scalar multiplier. The eigenvalues of $\tilde{\boldsymbol{a}}$ or, equivalently, of $\tilde{\boldsymbol{a}}_0$ are the roots of $\boldsymbol{a}_0$, hence are differences of the eigenvalues of $\boldsymbol{a}_0$ or, equivalently, of $\boldsymbol{a}$ if $\boldsymbol{a}_0$ belongs to a trunk of $\boldsymbol{G}_0$. Hence by a continuity argument this, however, holds in general.

So for $\boldsymbol{a} \in \boldsymbol{D}$ and all roots α

$$-2\pi < \operatorname{Im} \alpha(\boldsymbol{a}) < 2\pi;$$

hence, by 10.2, $\operatorname{grad}_{\boldsymbol{a}} \exp$ is nondegenerate. Together with 18.1.3 this yields the following.

Theorem exp maps $\boldsymbol{D}$ homeomorphically and with nowhere degenerate gradient onto an open subset of Aut R, which is an analytic manifold.

18.1.5 An application.

Proposition If $\boldsymbol{G}$ is the linear Lie algebra of the real n–n-triangular matrices of the form ∇, then $\exp \boldsymbol{G}$ coincides with the group infinitesimally generated by $\boldsymbol{G}$ (which, in fact, is the group of real n–$\dot{n}$-triangular matrices with positive eigenvalues), and exp is a homeomorphism of $\boldsymbol{G}$ onto $\exp \boldsymbol{G}$. The same holds for subalgebras of $\boldsymbol{G}$ as well.

18.2 The foregoing is applied to the adjoint $\tilde{\boldsymbol{G}}$ of $\boldsymbol{G} \in$ Alg Lie Com. Consider the splitting of $\boldsymbol{G}$ into $\boldsymbol{G}_\alpha$ under some $\boldsymbol{h} \in \boldsymbol{G}$, as introduced in 17.4. Then

$$(\tilde{\boldsymbol{h}} - \alpha)^{\dim \boldsymbol{G}_\alpha} \boldsymbol{G}_\alpha = \{\boldsymbol{0}\}, \qquad [\boldsymbol{G}_\alpha, \boldsymbol{G}_\beta] \subset \boldsymbol{G}_{\alpha+\beta} \quad \text{or} \quad \{\boldsymbol{0}\}.$$

Define a linear mapping ϑ of $\boldsymbol{G}$ into itself by $\vartheta \boldsymbol{x} = \alpha \boldsymbol{x}$ for $\boldsymbol{x} \in \boldsymbol{G}_\alpha$. Then ϑ is a derivation of $\boldsymbol{G}$, for

$$\text{if} \quad \boldsymbol{x} \in \boldsymbol{G}_\alpha, \quad \boldsymbol{y} \in \boldsymbol{G}_\beta, \qquad \text{then} \quad [\boldsymbol{x}, \boldsymbol{y}] \in \boldsymbol{G}_{\alpha+\beta} \quad \text{or} \quad \boldsymbol{0};$$

hence

$$\vartheta[\boldsymbol{x}, \boldsymbol{y}] = (\alpha + \beta)[\boldsymbol{x}, \boldsymbol{y}] = [\alpha \boldsymbol{x}, \boldsymbol{y}] + [\boldsymbol{x}, \beta \boldsymbol{y}] = [\vartheta \boldsymbol{x}, \boldsymbol{y}] + [\boldsymbol{x}, \vartheta \boldsymbol{y}]$$

or $\boldsymbol{0}$ in the first and last members.

Since ϑ is the first component of the cleaving of $\tilde{\boldsymbol{h}}$, one is led to the following.

Proposition If $G \in$ Alg Lie Com, the cleaving components of $\tilde{\boldsymbol{h}}$ ($\boldsymbol{h} \in \boldsymbol{G}$) are derivations of $\boldsymbol{G}$.

18.3 A stronger assertion can be made if $\boldsymbol{G}$ is centerfree and all its derivations are inner. (Such is the case for the semisimple algebras to be studied later on.)

Definition $\boldsymbol{h} \in \boldsymbol{G} \in$ Alg Lie Com is called ad-*pure* if $\tilde{\boldsymbol{h}}$ is pure. A subset $\boldsymbol{A}$ of $\boldsymbol{G}$ is called ad-*pure* if the set of $\tilde{\boldsymbol{a}}$ with $\boldsymbol{a} \in \boldsymbol{A}$ is pure.

Definition For $\boldsymbol{h} \in \boldsymbol{G} \in$ Alg Lie Com, $\boldsymbol{h} = \boldsymbol{a} + \boldsymbol{e}$ is called an ad-*cleaving* if $\boldsymbol{a}, \boldsymbol{e} \in \boldsymbol{G}$, $\boldsymbol{a}$ is ad-pure, $\boldsymbol{e}$ is ad-nilpotent, and $[\boldsymbol{a}, \boldsymbol{e}] = \boldsymbol{0}$.

Theorem Let $\boldsymbol{G} \in$ Alg Lie Com such that $\boldsymbol{G}$ is centerfree and has inner derivations only. Then every element $\boldsymbol{h}$ of $\boldsymbol{G}$ admits unique ad-cleaving. If $\boldsymbol{h}$ belongs to the trunk $\boldsymbol{H}$, then the same is true of its ad-cleaving components.

Proof According to 18.2, the cleaving components of $\tilde{\boldsymbol{h}}$ are derivations and thus inner derivations of the form $\tilde{\boldsymbol{a}}, \tilde{\boldsymbol{e}}$ with $[\tilde{\boldsymbol{a}}, \tilde{\boldsymbol{e}}] = \tilde{\boldsymbol{0}}$. Then $\widetilde{[\boldsymbol{a}, \boldsymbol{e}]} = \tilde{\boldsymbol{0}}$, hence $[\boldsymbol{a}, \boldsymbol{e}] = \boldsymbol{0}$ because $\boldsymbol{G}$ is centerfree. This proves the first part. If $\boldsymbol{h} \in \boldsymbol{H}$, $\tilde{\boldsymbol{h}}$ leaves $\boldsymbol{H}$ invariant; by 18.1.1 the same is true of its ad-cleaving components; by the last remark of Theorem 17.6 their ad-originals belong to $\boldsymbol{H}$.

18.4. Proposition If cleaving is possible in $\tilde{\boldsymbol{G}}$ and the trunk $\boldsymbol{H}$ does not possess ad-nilpotents $\neq \boldsymbol{0}$, all elements of $\boldsymbol{H}$ are ad-pure.

A direct consequence of the proof of 18.3.

18.5† Suppose that $R \in$ Spa Lin Com, dim $R = n < \infty$, $A \subset$ End R, A pure. Then the linear span of A is also pure.

Call R_α the subspace belonging to the eigenvalue α (as a function on A).

Suppose that S sub R is invariant under A. Then the following is easily shown by the method of 18.1.

18.5.1 S is the direct sum of the $S \cap R_\alpha$.

18.5.2 The restriction of A to S is still pure.

18.6. Proposition If $R \in$ Spa Lin Com, $A \cup B \subset$ End R, $A \cup B$ abelian and both A and B are pure, then $A \cup B$ is pure.

Proof R_α is again defined with respect to A. Since $A \cup B$ is abelian, R_α is B-invariant. The restriction of B to R_α is still pure. For every α take a basis of

† 18.5 will not be used for some time.

R_α on which B is diagonal and combine them. This provides one on which $A \cup B$ is diagonal.

18.7. Historical Note The importance of cleaving in semisimple Lie algebras was discovered by F. Gantmakher, *Mat. Sbornik* **5**, (47), 101–144 (1939).

19. SEMISIMPLICITY

First read the criteria and theorems.
$\mathbf{G} \in$ Alg Lie, dim $\mathbf{G} = r < \infty$.

19.1–13. Criteria

19.1 Repetition of parts of Section 13.

Definitions The maximal solvable ideal of $\mathbf{G}$ is called the *radical*, rad $\mathbf{G}$, of $\mathbf{G}$. $\mathbf{G}$ is called *semisimple* if rad $\mathbf{G} = \{\mathbf{0}\}$, equivalently, if $\mathbf{G}$ has no abelian ideal except $\{\mathbf{0}\}$.

Notation If $\mathbf{G}$ is semisimple: $\mathbf{G} \in$ Alg Lie SS. If $\mathbf{G}$ is semisimple and simple: $\mathbf{G} \in$ Alg Lie SSS. If $G \in$ Gru Lie Lin the predicates SS and SSS indicate that $\mathbf{G} \in$ Alg Lie SS and SSS, respectively.

It has been proved that if $\mathbf{G}$ is simple and dim $\mathbf{G} > 1$, then $\mathbf{G} \in$ Alg Lie SSS.

$\mathbf{G}$ mod rad $\mathbf{G} \in$ Alg Lie SS.

19.2 The Killing form of $\mathbf{G}$ is denoted by ψ. This is a $\tilde{\mathbf{G}}$-invariant (see 14.4.1).

Notation For $\mathbf{K} \subset \mathbf{G}$ the ψ-orthoplement of $\mathbf{K}$ is written $\mathbf{K}^\perp$; thus,

$$\boldsymbol{a} \in \mathbf{K}^\perp \leftrightarrow \psi(\boldsymbol{a}, \mathbf{K}) = \{0\}.$$

19.5 From

19.5.1
$$\psi(\tilde{\mathfrak{z}}\boldsymbol{x}, \boldsymbol{y}) + \psi(\boldsymbol{x}, \tilde{\mathfrak{z}}\boldsymbol{y}) = 0$$

it follows:

Proposition If $\mathbf{F}$ is an ideal in $\mathbf{G}$, the orthoplement $\mathbf{F}^\perp$ of $\mathbf{F}$ with respect to ψ, defined by

$$\boldsymbol{y} \in \mathbf{F}^\perp \leftrightarrow \bigwedge_{\boldsymbol{x} \in \mathbf{F}} \psi(\boldsymbol{x}, \boldsymbol{y}) = 0,$$

is again an ideal of $\mathbf{G}$.

19.6 In particular, the set $G^{\perp}$ of all y such that

$$\psi(x,y) = 0 \quad \text{for all} \quad x \in G$$

is an ideal. By 17.16 $\psi(x,x) = \psi_{G^{\perp}}(x,x)$ for $x \in G^{\perp}$, and by the second criterion on solvability $G^{\perp}$ is a solvable ideal of G.

Therefore, if G is semisimple, the only solution of

$$\psi(x,y) = 0 \qquad \text{for all} \quad x \in G$$

is $y = 0$, which means that ψ is nondegenerate.

If, however, G is not semisimple and $F \neq \{0\}$ is an abelian ideal of G, then

$$\tilde{x}\tilde{y}z = [x,[y,z]] \in F \qquad \text{for} \quad x, z \in G, \quad y \in F.$$

If z contributes to tr $\tilde{x}\tilde{y}$, then $z \in F$, but then $[y,z] = 0$; thus $\tilde{x}\tilde{y}z = 0$. Consequently, tr $\tilde{x}\tilde{y} = 0$,

$$\psi(x,y) = 0 \qquad \text{for} \quad x \in G, y \in F,$$

which means that ψ degenerates as soon as G is not semisimple.

This yields the:

First Criterion on Semisimplicity G is semisimple iff its Killing form is nondegenerate.

19.7 Let F be an ideal of G and let $F^{\perp}$ be defined as in 19.5. If dim $G = r$ and $x_1, \ldots, x_s$ form a basis of F, then $F^{\perp}$ is the intersection of the linear subspaces L_j of at least $(r-1)$ dimensions, defined by

$$y \in L_j \leftrightarrow \psi(x_j, y) = 0.$$

This makes dim $F^{\perp} \geqslant r - s$,

$$\dim F + \dim F^{\perp} \geqslant \dim G;$$

$F \cap F^{\perp}$ is an ideal of G and is solvable because of 17.16 and the vanishing of ψ on $F \cap F^{\perp}$.

19.8 Applying this result to a semisimple ideal F of G, one gets the ideal $F^{\perp}$ (see 19.5) with $F \cap F^{\perp} = \{0\}$ and $F + F^{\perp} = G$.

Theorem If a semisimple Lie algebra is an ideal in a larger one, it is so in a trivial way, that is, as a direct summand.

If a semisimple linear Lie group is a normal subgroup in a larger one, it is so in a locally trivial way, that is, as a local direct factor.

19.9 A consequence of 19.8:

Theorem All derivations of semisimple $\boldsymbol{F}$ are inner.

Proof Let $\boldsymbol{G}$ be the linear Lie algebra of derivations of semisimple $\boldsymbol{F}$ and let $\tilde{\boldsymbol{F}}$ be that of the inner derivations; $\tilde{\boldsymbol{F}}$ is an ideal in $\boldsymbol{G}$ since, for $\Phi \in \boldsymbol{G}$; $[\Phi, \tilde{\boldsymbol{a}}]\boldsymbol{x} = \Phi\tilde{\boldsymbol{a}}\boldsymbol{x} - \tilde{\boldsymbol{a}}\Phi\boldsymbol{x} = \Phi[\boldsymbol{a},\boldsymbol{x}] - [\boldsymbol{a},\Phi\boldsymbol{x}] = [\Phi\boldsymbol{a},\boldsymbol{x}] + [\boldsymbol{a},\Phi\boldsymbol{x}] - [\boldsymbol{a},\Phi\boldsymbol{x}] = \widetilde{\Phi\boldsymbol{a}}\boldsymbol{x}$; hence:

19.9.1 $[\Phi,\tilde{\boldsymbol{a}}] = \widetilde{\Phi\boldsymbol{a}}$, thus $[\Phi,\tilde{\boldsymbol{F}}] \subset \tilde{\boldsymbol{F}}$.

Since $\boldsymbol{F}$ is semisimple, its center is $\{\boldsymbol{0}\}$ and $\tilde{\boldsymbol{F}}$ is isomorphic to $\boldsymbol{F}$; consequently, it is semisimple. By 19.8 $\boldsymbol{G}$ is the direct sum of $\tilde{\boldsymbol{F}}$ and $\tilde{\boldsymbol{F}}^{\perp}$. For $\Phi \in \tilde{\boldsymbol{F}}^{\perp}$ it follows from 19.9.1 that $\tilde{\boldsymbol{0}} = [\Phi,\tilde{\boldsymbol{a}}] = \widetilde{\Phi\boldsymbol{a}}$; thus $\Phi\boldsymbol{a} = \boldsymbol{0}$ for all $\boldsymbol{a} \in \boldsymbol{F}$. Hence $\Phi = \tilde{\boldsymbol{0}}$ and $\boldsymbol{G} = \tilde{\boldsymbol{F}}$.

Corollary For any $\boldsymbol{x} \in \boldsymbol{G} \in$ Alg Lie Com SS cleaving of $\tilde{\boldsymbol{x}}$ is possible within $\tilde{\boldsymbol{G}}$. (See 18.3.)

19.10. Theorem The 1-component of Aut $\boldsymbol{F}$ of semisimple $\boldsymbol{F}$ is Int $\boldsymbol{F}$. Both are closed in the group of linear space automorphisms of $\boldsymbol{F}$.

Indeed, by 11.3.4, the infinitesimal algebra of the 1-component of Aut $\boldsymbol{F}$ consists of the derivations of $\boldsymbol{F}$, which by 19.9 are all inner and infinitesimally generate Int $\boldsymbol{F}$. The closedness of Aut $\boldsymbol{F}$ is obvious and implies that of Int $\boldsymbol{F}$.

Remark In 38.5 it will be shown that any $G \in$ Gru Lie Lin SS acting in $R \in$ Spa Lin is closed in Aut R.

19.11 A consequence by means of 9.1 is the following.

Theorem The automorphisms of $G \in$ Gru Lie Lin SS in the 1-component (even the local ones) are inner; Aut G/Int G is discrete.

19.12 Now apply 19.7 to the case of a semisimple $\boldsymbol{G}$ and an ideal $\boldsymbol{F}$. Again $\boldsymbol{F} \cap \boldsymbol{F}^{\perp}$ as a solvable ideal of $\boldsymbol{G}$ is $\{\boldsymbol{0}\}$ and $\boldsymbol{G}$ is a direct sum of $\boldsymbol{F}$ and $\boldsymbol{F}^{\perp}$, which are again semisimple. Repeating this process, one obtains the following:

Second Criterion on Semisimplicity $\boldsymbol{G}$ is semisimple iff it is a direct sum of nonabelian simple Lie algebras.

The sufficiency is obvious.

Note that the splitting of semisimple $\boldsymbol{G}$ is uniquely determined.

Indeed, any simple ideal other than the summands would have zero-intersection with each of them and therefore would commute with each of them elementwise; thus it would be contained in the center, which is $\{\boldsymbol{0}\}$.

Globally:

Theorem $G \in$ Gru Lie Lin is semisimple iff it is locally isomorphic to a direct product of locally simple nonabelian linear Lie groups.

19.13 From 19.12 it is evident that any ideal and any homomorphic image of semisimple $\boldsymbol{G}$ is semisimple.

Proposition If $\boldsymbol{G}'$ is an ideal sub $\boldsymbol{G}$, then rad $\boldsymbol{G}'$ is still an ideal sub $\boldsymbol{G}$.

Proof This follows most easily by observing that any $\varphi \in$ Int $\boldsymbol{G}$ induces an automorphism of $\boldsymbol{G}'$, which consequently maps rad $\boldsymbol{G}'$ onto itself. In a purely algebraic fashion from the semisimplicity of $\boldsymbol{G}$ mod rad $\boldsymbol{G}$ one draws the conclusion that $\boldsymbol{G}'$ mod $\boldsymbol{G}' \cap$ rad $\boldsymbol{G}$, isomorphic to an ideal of the former, is also semisimple; thus rad $\boldsymbol{G}' \subset \boldsymbol{G}' \cap$ rad $\boldsymbol{G}$, which is a solvable ideal of $\boldsymbol{G}'$, hence equals rad $\boldsymbol{G}'$.

19.14–16. Irreducible Algebras

19.14 Because of 19.12 semisimple $\boldsymbol{G}$ is clearly its own commutator algebra. Thus, on $\boldsymbol{G} \in$ Alg Lie Lin SS the trace function vanishes.

Theorem Let $R \in$ Spa Lin Com, dim $R < \infty$. If $\boldsymbol{G} \in$ Alg Lie Lin acts irreducibly on R, it splits directly as a sum of a semisimple ideal $\boldsymbol{G}_0$ and a Lie algebra of scalar multiplications.

This re-enforces 13.10.

Proof Let $\boldsymbol{G}_0$ be the set of $\boldsymbol{g} \in \boldsymbol{G}$ with tr $\boldsymbol{g} = 0$. Then $\boldsymbol{G}_0$ is an ideal of $\boldsymbol{G}$. By 19.13 the same is true of rad $\boldsymbol{G}_0$, which according to 13.10 consists of scalar multiplications. Since tr$(\boldsymbol{G}_0) = \{0\}$, it follows that rad $\boldsymbol{G}_0 = \{\boldsymbol{0}\}$ and that $\boldsymbol{G}_0$ is semisimple. According to 19.8, $\boldsymbol{G} \in \boldsymbol{G}_0 + \boldsymbol{A}$ as a direct sum. The commutator algebra of $\boldsymbol{G}$ is in the kernel of the trace, thus in $\boldsymbol{G}_0$, from which it follows that $\boldsymbol{A}$ is abelian, and thus by 13.10 consists of scalar multiplications.

19.15 The following is an extension of 19.14:

Theorem Let $R \in$ Spa Lin Com, dim $R < \infty$, be the direct sum of R_j sub R. If $\boldsymbol{G} \in$ Alg Lie Lin acts on R, leaves the R_j invariant, and acts irreducibly on each R_j, then $\boldsymbol{G}$ is a direct sum of simple Lie algebras.

Proof The restriction of $\boldsymbol{G}$ to R_j is a linear Lie algebra $\boldsymbol{G}_j$, homomorphic image of $\boldsymbol{G}$ by means of canonical ζ_j. The kernels $\boldsymbol{F}_j$ of ζ_j have intersection $\{\boldsymbol{0}\}$. Let $\boldsymbol{G}'$ and $\boldsymbol{G}_j'$ be the commutator algebras of $\boldsymbol{G}, \boldsymbol{G}_j$. Then $\zeta_j \boldsymbol{G}' = \boldsymbol{G}_j'$. By 19.14 $\boldsymbol{G}_j'$ is semisimple, ζ_j rad $\boldsymbol{G}' \subset$ rad $\boldsymbol{G}_j' = \{\boldsymbol{0}\}$. Thus rad $\boldsymbol{G}' = \{\boldsymbol{0}\}$, $\boldsymbol{G}'$ is semisimple,

$G = G' + A$ as a direct sum and, because of 19.8, A abelian. This proves the assertion.

19.16. Theorem All $G \in \mathbf{A}_l$, $\mathbf{B}_l$, $\mathbf{C}_l$, $\mathbf{D}_l$ of Section 16 are semisimple.

Because of 13.8 it has only to be shown that the representatives G are irreducible. Since an invariant linear subspace would also be invariant under the associative algebra with unit element generated by G, it suffices to show that the latter is irreducible, that is, the full matrix algebra of complex d-space on which G acts. The trunk of G, together with the unit matrix, generates all diagonal matrices, and by multiplying the diagonal matrices $\ulcorner 0, \ldots, 0, 1, 0, \ldots 0 \urcorner$ by branches of G one gets all branches of $\mathbf{A}_d$. In this way the full matrix algebra of complex d-space is produced.

19.17. The Real Aspect

Because of the validity of the solvability criteria for real Lie algebras the results of Section 19 prevail for real as well as complex Lie algebras. This is especially true of the semisimplicity criteria.

Semisimplicity is preserved under complex extension, real restriction, and waiving.

With a slight modification 19.14–15 can be extended to the case of real R. Then, of course, G has to be real. To tackle 19.14 one passes to the complex extension R_{Com} of R, which as a matter of fact can become reducible. Together with $S \neq \{0\}$, R, its conjugate DS is invariant sub R_{Com}. The real restrictions of $S \cap DS$ and $S + DS$ are invariant sub R, and thus $= \{0\}$ and R, respectively, which shows that $R_{\mathrm{Com}} = S + DS$. To this situation, however, the method of 19.15 readily applies.

In the formulation of 19.14 for real R the scalar multiplications must still be allowed over the complex field.

19.18–22. Purity and Cleaving

19.18 If $G \in$ Alg Lie is centerfree, then $\tilde{G}$ is isomorphic to G. Then, up to isomorphy, G may be assumed to be linear. This remark applies in particular to semisimple G.

19.19†. Theorem Let $G \in$ Alg Lie Com Lin. Then every pure element of G is ad-pure and every nilpotent element of G is ad-nilpotent; in particular, if G admits cleaving, G also admits ad-cleaving; therefore if G is centerfree and admits cleaving, then for elements of G the notions of purity, nilpotence, and cleaving coincide with those of ad-purity, ad-nilpotence, and ad-cleaving.

† 19.19–22 will not necessarily be used for some time.

Proof $\boldsymbol{G} \subset \text{End } V$ with $V \in \text{Spa Lin Com}$.

$(\text{End } V)_0$ is the kernel of the trace of End V. One may suppose that $\dim V > 1$.

First assume that $\boldsymbol{G} = (\text{End } V)_0$. Then by 19.16, $\boldsymbol{G}$ is semisimple. Since the cleaving components of a linear mapping with trace 0 also have trace 0, $\boldsymbol{G}$ admits cleaving. From 16.2 it is easily seen that $\boldsymbol{G}$ contains a pure trunk; in fact, every pure element of $\boldsymbol{G}$ is in a trunk of $\boldsymbol{G}$. The elements of the given trunk are ad-pure; hence the elements of any trunk are ad-pure because the trunks are conjugate under $\tilde{G}$ (if G is the group of linear mappings with determinant 1) and $\tilde{G}$ preserves ad-purity. By putting a nilpotent element of $\boldsymbol{G}$ in triangular form it is also easily verified that each nilpotent element of $\boldsymbol{G}$ is ad-nilpotent. Hence a cleaving in $\boldsymbol{G}$ is also an ad-cleaving. Thus the notions of cleaving, purity, and nilpotence coincide with those of ad-cleaving, ad-purity, and ad-nilpotence, respectively. (Note that ad-cleaving is unique because $\boldsymbol{G}$ is centerfree.)

Next assume that $\boldsymbol{G}$ sub $(\text{End } V)_0$, that is, all elements of $\boldsymbol{G}$ have trace 0. Now observe that an element of $\boldsymbol{G}$, which is ad-pure as an element of $(\text{End } V)_0$, is also ad-pure as an element of $\boldsymbol{G}$ and the same applies to ad-nilpotence. From this, and the above special case, the same assertions follow.

If not all elements of $\boldsymbol{G}$ have trace 0, let $\boldsymbol{G}$ act on a vector space V' spanned by V and an element w not in V, by

$$\boldsymbol{g}(v + \alpha w) = \boldsymbol{g}v - \alpha \operatorname{tr} \boldsymbol{g} \cdot w, \qquad \text{for } v \in V, \quad \boldsymbol{g} \in \boldsymbol{G}, \quad \alpha \text{ a complex number.}$$

It is easily seen that this yields a faithful representation of $\boldsymbol{G}$ which does not alter the notions of purity and nilpotence; the theorem also follows in this case.

19.20. Theorem Let $\boldsymbol{G} \in \text{Alg Lie Com Lin}$ admit cleaving, and let $\boldsymbol{A}$ be a maximal pure subspace of $\boldsymbol{G}$, with $\boldsymbol{H}$ as its idealizer. Then:

19.20.1 $\boldsymbol{H}$ is a trunk of $\boldsymbol{G}$.

19.20.2 $\boldsymbol{A}$ consists of the pure elements of $\boldsymbol{H}$.

19.20.3 $\boldsymbol{H} = \boldsymbol{A} + \boldsymbol{N}$ is a direct sum of Lie algebras in which $\boldsymbol{N}$ consists of the nilpotent elements of $\boldsymbol{H}$.

19.20.4 $\boldsymbol{N} \subset \text{rad } \boldsymbol{G}$, even $\psi(\boldsymbol{N}, \boldsymbol{G}) = \{0\}$.

Proof By the same device used in the proof of Theorem 19.19 one may suppose that $\boldsymbol{G} \subset (\text{End } V)_0$. By 19.19 one may substitute ad-cleaving for cleaving, and so on, ad-cleaving, ad-pure and ad-nilpotence being meant in the sense of $(\text{End } V)_0$.

As in 17.4, $\boldsymbol{G}$ splits into subspaces $\boldsymbol{G}_\alpha \neq \{\boldsymbol{0}\}$ with respect to the adjoint image of $\boldsymbol{A}$, but now $\tilde{\boldsymbol{a}}$ acts on $\boldsymbol{G}_\alpha$ as a scalar multiplication by $\alpha(\boldsymbol{a})$ because of its purity; the α's are elements of the linear dual of $\boldsymbol{A}$. Obviously

$$[\boldsymbol{A}, \boldsymbol{G}_0] = \{\boldsymbol{0}\}, \qquad \boldsymbol{A} \subset \boldsymbol{G}_0 = \boldsymbol{H}.$$

The ad-pure elements of $\boldsymbol{G}_0$, like all elements of $\boldsymbol{G}_0$, commute with every element of $\boldsymbol{A}$, hence are in $\boldsymbol{A}$ because of the maximality of $\boldsymbol{A}$; this proves 19.20.2. The commutator of an element of $\boldsymbol{A}$ in which all α are different from 0, with an element not in $\boldsymbol{G}_0$, still is not in $\boldsymbol{G}_0$. This implies that $\boldsymbol{H}$ is its own idealizer in $\boldsymbol{G}$. The last assertion of Proposition 18.1.1 applied with $S = T = \boldsymbol{H}$ implies that the ad-cleaving components of an element of $\boldsymbol{H}$, being also in $\boldsymbol{G}$, are even in $\boldsymbol{H}$. Since $\boldsymbol{A}$ is in the center of $\boldsymbol{H}$ it follows that $\boldsymbol{H}$ has rank 0, and $\boldsymbol{H}$ is a trunk of $\boldsymbol{G}$. Then $\boldsymbol{H} = \boldsymbol{A} + \boldsymbol{N}$ as asserted in 19.20.3, since the ad-nilpotent elements of the solvable Lie algebra $\boldsymbol{H}$ form an ideal of $\boldsymbol{H}$.

Obviously $[\boldsymbol{G}_\alpha, \boldsymbol{G}_\beta] \subset \boldsymbol{G}_{\alpha+\beta}$ or $= \{\boldsymbol{0}\}$. From this it easily follows that:

$$\psi(\boldsymbol{G}_\alpha, \boldsymbol{G}_\beta) = \{0\} \qquad \text{if} \quad \alpha + \beta \neq 0.$$

Putting the image of $\boldsymbol{H}$ in the adjoint of $\boldsymbol{G}$ in triangular form, one sees that

$$\psi(\boldsymbol{H}, \boldsymbol{N}) = \{0\}.$$

Hence,

$$\psi(\boldsymbol{G}, \boldsymbol{N}) = \{0\}.$$

So by 19.6 $\boldsymbol{N}$ is a solvable ideal of $\boldsymbol{G}$, from which $\boldsymbol{N} \subset \operatorname{rad} \boldsymbol{G}$.

19.21. Theorem If $\boldsymbol{G} \in$ Alg Lie Com Lin admits cleaving, the maximal pure subspaces of $\boldsymbol{G}$ are equivalent under Int $\boldsymbol{G}$, that is, conjugate under G, where G is the group infinitesimally generated by $\boldsymbol{G}$.

Proof Indeed, trunks of $\boldsymbol{G}$ are conjugate under G, and the elements of $\tilde{G}$ preserve purity; the assertion follows from 19.20.

19.22. Theorem If $\boldsymbol{G} \in$ Alg Lie Com SS, the trunks of $\boldsymbol{G}$ are the maximal ad-pure subspaces of $\boldsymbol{G}$; in particular, they are abelian.

Proof The assertion follows from 18.3 and 19.20 applied to the adjoint action.

19.23. Historical Note Theorems 19.19–21 are due to H. de Vries, though partly anticipated by S. Tôgô [*Math. Z.* **75**, 305–324 (1961); *J. Sci. Hiroshima Univ.* **A-I**, **25**, 63–93 (1961)]. They are closely connected to results of C. Chevalley (*Théorie des groupes de Lie*, Vol. III, p. 230, 1955).

20–27

DRESSINGS AND CLASSIFICATION OF SEMISIMPLE COMPLEX LIE ALGEBRAS

20. THE FIRST DRESSING OF COMPLEX SEMISIMPLE LIE ALGEBRAS

$\boldsymbol{G} \in$ Alg Lie Com SS, dim $G = r$, ψ is the Killing form of $\boldsymbol{G}$, and $\boldsymbol{H}$ is a trunk of $\boldsymbol{G}$. The $\boldsymbol{G}_\alpha$ of 17.13.2 are defined with respect to $\boldsymbol{H}$.

20.1–4. The Trunk

20.1 From 17.13.2 it follows that

$$\psi(\boldsymbol{x}, \boldsymbol{y}) = \operatorname{tr} \tilde{\boldsymbol{x}}\tilde{\boldsymbol{y}} = 0$$

for

$$\boldsymbol{x} \in \boldsymbol{H}, \qquad \boldsymbol{y} \in \boldsymbol{G}_\alpha \qquad (\alpha \neq 0),$$

$$\boldsymbol{x} \in \boldsymbol{G}_\alpha, \qquad \boldsymbol{y} \in \boldsymbol{G}_\beta \qquad (\alpha \neq -\beta).$$

Exploiting the first criterion of semisimplicity one gets for any $\boldsymbol{h} \in \boldsymbol{H}$, $\boldsymbol{h} \neq \boldsymbol{0}$ the existence of $\boldsymbol{h}_1 \in \boldsymbol{H}$ with

20.1.1 $$\psi(\boldsymbol{h}, \boldsymbol{h}_1) \neq 0;$$

and for any $\alpha \in W$, $\alpha \neq 0$, $\boldsymbol{f}_+ \in \boldsymbol{G}_\alpha$, $\boldsymbol{f}_+ \neq \boldsymbol{0}$ the existence of an $\boldsymbol{f}_- \in \boldsymbol{G}_{-\alpha}$ with

20.1.2 $$\psi(\boldsymbol{f}_+, \boldsymbol{f}_-) \neq 0.$$

20.2 If $[\boldsymbol{f}_+, \boldsymbol{f}_-] = \boldsymbol{0}$, then $\boldsymbol{f}_+, \boldsymbol{f}_-$ generate an abelian, hence solvable algebra; taking $\tilde{\boldsymbol{f}}_+, \tilde{\boldsymbol{f}}_-$ simultaneously triangular and noting that all eigenvalues of $\tilde{\boldsymbol{f}}_+, \tilde{\boldsymbol{f}}_-$ vanish (because of $\tilde{\boldsymbol{f}}_+ \boldsymbol{G}_\mu \subset \boldsymbol{G}_{\mu+\alpha}$), one gets $\psi(\boldsymbol{f}_+, \boldsymbol{f}_-) = \operatorname{tr} \tilde{\boldsymbol{f}}_+ \tilde{\boldsymbol{f}}_- = 0$, which contradicts 20.1.2. Therefore in the case of 20.1.2 one may conclude that $[\boldsymbol{f}_+, \boldsymbol{f}_-] \neq \boldsymbol{0}$. Thus,

20.2.1 $$[\boldsymbol{G}_\alpha, \boldsymbol{G}_{-\alpha}] \neq \{\boldsymbol{0}\} \qquad \text{for} \quad \alpha \in W, \alpha \neq 0.$$

In other words, there are α-nodes for $\alpha \neq 0$.

20.3 The solvability of $\boldsymbol{H}$ can be used to put $\tilde{\boldsymbol{h}}, \tilde{\boldsymbol{h}}_1$ simultaneously into triangular form. Then

$$\psi(\boldsymbol{h}, \boldsymbol{h}_1) = \sum_{\mu \in W} \dim \boldsymbol{G}_\mu \cdot \mu(\boldsymbol{h})\, \mu(\boldsymbol{h}_1).$$

Hence by 20.1.1:

20.3.1 If $\boldsymbol{h} \in \boldsymbol{H}$ and $\mu(\boldsymbol{h}) = 0$ for all $\mu \in W$, then $\boldsymbol{h} = \boldsymbol{0}$.

This proves again that $\boldsymbol{H}$ has no ad-nilpotents $\neq \boldsymbol{0}$. Consequently, by 18.4:

20.3.2 All elements of $\boldsymbol{H}$ are ad-pure.

20.4 If $\boldsymbol{h} \in \boldsymbol{H}$ is linearly spanned by α-nodes, 17.15 can be applied which means that $\mu(\boldsymbol{h}) = 0$ as soon as $\alpha(\boldsymbol{h}) = 0$. Then 20.3.1 becomes:

20.4.1 If $\boldsymbol{h}$ is spanned by α-nodes and $\alpha(\boldsymbol{h}) = 0$, then $\boldsymbol{h} = \boldsymbol{0}$.

Applied to $\alpha = 0$, this yields that every 0-node vanishes; thus it is shown anew (cf. 19.22) that

20.4.2 $\boldsymbol{H}$ is abelian.

If, however, $\alpha \neq 0$, then by 20.4.1 the homomorphism α maps the linear space spanned by $[\boldsymbol{G}_\alpha, \boldsymbol{G}_{-\alpha}]$ in such a manner that the kernel of the mapping is $\{\boldsymbol{0}\}$. Thus its dimension is $\leqslant 1$, whereas by 20.2.1 it is > 0. Hence

20.4.3 $\dim[\boldsymbol{G}_\alpha, \boldsymbol{G}_{-\alpha}] = 1 \quad \text{if} \quad \alpha \neq 0.$

In other words, the α-node ($\alpha \neq 0$) is unique up to a scalar factor. Let $\boldsymbol{h}_\alpha$ be some α-node.

Since $\boldsymbol{h}_\alpha \neq \boldsymbol{0}$, 20.4.1 shows

20.4.4 $\alpha(\boldsymbol{h}_\alpha) \neq 0 \quad \text{for} \quad \alpha \neq 0.$

By 20.3.1 the number of linearly independent members of W cannot fall short of $\dim \boldsymbol{H}$. Combined with 17.14 this shows that

20.4.5 $\dim \boldsymbol{H} = \operatorname{rank} \boldsymbol{G}.$

20.5 Ladders

Choose $\boldsymbol{f}_+ \in \boldsymbol{G}_\alpha$ ($\alpha \neq 0$) as a simultaneous eigenvector of the $\curlyvee_{\boldsymbol{h}} \tilde{\boldsymbol{h}}$-representation of $\boldsymbol{H}$. Thus

20.5.1 $$[h, f_+] = \alpha(h)\, f_+ \qquad \text{for all} \quad h \in H.$$

Choose $f_- \in G_{-\alpha}$ such that $\psi(f_+, f_-) \neq 0$ (see 20.1.2). Thus $[f_+, f_-]$ (see 20.2) is an α-node, denoted by h_α:

20.5.2 $$[f_+, f_-] = h_\alpha \neq 0.$$

Choose $\mu \neq 0$, $\mu \in W$, and $x \in G_\mu$, $x \neq 0$ such that

20.5.3 $$\tilde{h}x = \mu(h)\, x \qquad \text{for all} \quad h \in H$$

and

20.5.4 $$\tilde{f}_- x = 0.$$

(Note that if $\mu - \alpha \notin W$ then 20.5.4 is a mere consequence of $x \in G_\mu$; therefore, if μ is chosen to imply $\mu - \alpha \notin W$, 20.5.4 is fulfilled.)

An "α-*ladder*" $x_0, x_1, \ldots$ is defined by

20.5.5 $$x_j = \tilde{f}_+^j x, \qquad j \text{ integer} \geqslant 0.$$

Then $x_j \in G_{\mu + j\alpha}$ or $= 0$.

By induction it is verified anew that

20.5.6 $$\tilde{h}_\alpha x_j = (\mu + j\alpha)(h_\alpha)\, x_j:$$

$$\begin{aligned} \tilde{h}_\alpha x_{j+1} &= \tilde{h}_\alpha \tilde{f}_+ x_j = \tilde{f}_+ \tilde{h}_\alpha x_j + [\tilde{h}_\alpha, \tilde{f}_+]\, x_j \\ &= (\mu + j\alpha)(h_\alpha)\, x_{j+1} + \alpha(h_\alpha)\, x_{j+1}, \end{aligned}$$

where 20.5.5, 20.5.1, and 20.5.6 (inductively) have been used.

By an analogous induction,

20.5.7 $$\tilde{f}_- x_j = \rho_{j-1}\, x_{j-1}$$

with certain scalar ρ_j:

$$\begin{aligned} \tilde{f}_- x_{j+1} &= \tilde{f}_- \tilde{f}_+ x_j = \tilde{f}_+ \tilde{f}_- x_j - [\tilde{f}_+, \tilde{f}_-]\, x_j \\ &= \rho_{j-1} \tilde{f}_+ x_{j-1} - \tilde{h}_\alpha x_j \\ &= \rho_{j-1}\, x_j - (\mu + j\alpha)(h_\alpha)\, x_j, \end{aligned}$$

where 20.5.5, 20.5.7 (inductively), 20.5.2, and 20.5.6 have been used, the basis of the induction being 20.5.4, provided x_{-1} is understood as 0 and ρ_{-1} as 0. Moreover,

20.5.8 $$\rho_j = \rho_{j-1} - (\mu + j\alpha)(h_\alpha).$$

Adding up over $j = 0, 1, \ldots, i$, it turns out that

20.5.9 $$\rho_i = -\sum_{j=0}^{i} (\mu + j\alpha)(\boldsymbol{h}_\alpha).$$

Since the number of spaces $\boldsymbol{G}_\alpha$ is finite, there is a p such that

$$\boldsymbol{x}_p \neq \boldsymbol{0},$$
$$\boldsymbol{x}_{p+1} = \boldsymbol{0}.$$

This makes $\rho_p = 0$; hence

$$\sum_{j=0}^{p} (\mu + j\alpha)(\boldsymbol{h}_\alpha) = 0,$$
$$(p+1)\,\mu(\boldsymbol{h}_\alpha) + \tfrac{1}{2}p(p+1)\,\alpha(\boldsymbol{h}_\alpha) = 0,$$

20.5.10 $$p = -2\,\frac{\mu(\boldsymbol{h}_\alpha)}{\alpha(\boldsymbol{h}_\alpha)}$$

is the length of the ladder, counting intervals rather than rungs. Again one notes that $\mu(\boldsymbol{h}_\alpha)$ is a rational multiple of $\alpha(\boldsymbol{h}_\alpha)$ (see 17.15). The midpoint of the corresponding rootform sequence is

20.5.11 $$\mu - \frac{\mu(\boldsymbol{h}_\alpha)}{\alpha(\boldsymbol{h}_\alpha)}\,\alpha = \lambda - \frac{\lambda(\boldsymbol{h}_\alpha)}{\alpha(\boldsymbol{h}_\alpha)}\,\alpha$$

if

$$\lambda = \mu + \xi\alpha$$

with an arbitrary real scalar ξ. Thus all sequences of rootforms corresponding to α-ladders and lying on the straight line $\mu + \xi\alpha$ (ξ variable) have the same midpoint.

Rewriting 20.5.9 by means of 20.5.10 one finds

$$\rho_i = -\sum_{j=0}^{i} (-\tfrac{1}{2}p + j)\,\alpha(\boldsymbol{h}_\alpha)$$
$$= \tfrac{1}{2}(i+1)(p-i)\,\alpha(\boldsymbol{h}_\alpha).$$

Hence by 20.5.7

20.5.12 $$\tilde{\boldsymbol{f}}_-\tilde{\boldsymbol{f}}_+\boldsymbol{x}_j = \tfrac{1}{2}(j+1)(p-j)\,\alpha(\boldsymbol{h}_\alpha)\,\boldsymbol{x}_j \neq \boldsymbol{0} \qquad \text{for} \quad j = 0, 1, \ldots, p-1,$$

which can be memorized by noting that $j+1$ is the rank number of $\boldsymbol{x}_j$ in its α-ladder and $p-j$ is the number of elements above $\boldsymbol{x}_j$ in its ladder.

Thus by inverting an α-ladder one gets (up to scalar factors $\neq 0$) a $(-\alpha)$-ladder.

20.6–7. Branches

20.6 It is now proved that dim $\boldsymbol{G}_\alpha = 1$ for $\alpha \neq 0$.

$\boldsymbol{f}_+, \boldsymbol{f}_-, \boldsymbol{h}_\alpha$ are defined as in 20.5. Suppose that dim $\boldsymbol{G}_\alpha > 1$. Then, since $\tilde{\boldsymbol{h}}_\alpha$ is pure (20.3.2), there is a $\boldsymbol{y} \in \boldsymbol{G}_\alpha$, not linearly dependent on $\boldsymbol{f}_+$, with

20.6.1 $$\tilde{\boldsymbol{h}}_\alpha \boldsymbol{y} = \alpha(\boldsymbol{h}_\alpha)\boldsymbol{y}.$$

Since $\tilde{\boldsymbol{f}}_- \boldsymbol{y}$ is an α-node, it is some multiple of $\boldsymbol{h}_\alpha$ because of 20.4.3. Therefore in $\boldsymbol{x} = \boldsymbol{y} + \sigma \boldsymbol{f}_+$ the scalar σ may be chosen to make

20.6.2 $$\tilde{\boldsymbol{f}}_- \boldsymbol{x} = \boldsymbol{0}.$$

The conditions in 20.5.1–4 are fulfilled with α instead of μ. Hence, according to 20.5.10, the α-ladder initiated by $\boldsymbol{x}$ should have length -2, which is not possible. The supposition dim $\boldsymbol{G}_\alpha > 1$ must be wrong. This proves that

20.6.3 $$\dim \boldsymbol{G}_\alpha = 1 \qquad \text{for} \quad \alpha \neq 0.$$

20.7. Definition The elements $\neq \boldsymbol{0}$ of $\boldsymbol{G}_\alpha$ for $\alpha \neq 0$ are called *α-branches.* Later on they are indicated by $\boldsymbol{e}_\alpha$.

It has been proved that the α-branch is uniquely determined up to a scalar factor.

20.8–12. Ladders of Rootforms

20.8. Definition For $\alpha \in W$, $\alpha \neq 0$, the $\mu_0, \ldots, \mu_p$ form an *α-ladder* of rootforms if $\mu_{j+1} - \mu_j = \alpha$ and for $\boldsymbol{f}_\pm \in \boldsymbol{G}_{\pm\alpha}$

20.8.1 $$\tilde{\boldsymbol{f}}_- \boldsymbol{G}_{\mu_0} = \{\boldsymbol{0}\} = \tilde{\boldsymbol{f}}_+ \boldsymbol{G}_{\mu_p},$$

20.8.2 $$\tilde{\boldsymbol{f}}_+ \boldsymbol{G}_{\mu_j} \neq \{\boldsymbol{0}\} \qquad \text{for} \quad j = 0, \ldots, p-1.$$

Let $\mu \in W$ and $\boldsymbol{x} \in \boldsymbol{G}_\mu$. Then $\boldsymbol{y} = \tilde{\boldsymbol{f}}_-^{\,q}\boldsymbol{x} \neq \boldsymbol{0}$, $\tilde{\boldsymbol{f}}_-^{\,q+1}\boldsymbol{x} = \boldsymbol{0}$ for some positive integer q. By 20.5.11–12, $\tilde{\boldsymbol{f}}_+^{\,q}\boldsymbol{y} \neq \boldsymbol{0}$. So μ belongs to an α-ladder which by 20.5.11, 20.6.3 is unique. By 20.5.7 the inverse of an α-ladder is a $(-\alpha)$-ladder. By 20.5.11 it happens that all $(\pm\alpha)$-ladders on the real straight line $\mu + \xi\alpha$ (ξ variable) have the same midpoint. Therefore the α-ladder $\mu_0, \ldots, \mu_p$ contains all $\mu \in W$ with $\mu \equiv \mu_0 \bmod \alpha$.

20.8.3 $$\tilde{\boldsymbol{f}}_+ \boldsymbol{G}_\mu \neq \{\boldsymbol{0}\} \quad \text{if} \quad \boldsymbol{f}_+ \in \boldsymbol{G}_\alpha, \quad \boldsymbol{f}_+ \neq 0, \quad \alpha \neq 0, \quad \alpha, \mu, \mu + \alpha \in W.$$

20.9 If $\mu_0, \ldots, \mu_p$ is an α-ladder, then by 20.5.10

$$p = -2\,\frac{\mu_0(\boldsymbol{h}_\alpha)}{\alpha(\boldsymbol{h}_\alpha)}.$$

For $\mu_j = \mu_0 + j\alpha$

$$-2\frac{\mu_j(\boldsymbol{h}_\alpha)}{\alpha(\boldsymbol{h}_\alpha)} = p - 2j.$$

Since any rootform is a member of some α-ladder, this shows that

20.9.1 $$-2\frac{\mu(\boldsymbol{h}_\alpha)}{\alpha(\boldsymbol{h}_\alpha)} \text{ is an integer for any } \mu \in W.$$

Defining

$$S_\alpha \mu = \mu - 2\frac{\mu(\boldsymbol{h}_\alpha)}{\alpha(\boldsymbol{h}_\alpha)}\alpha,$$

one gets

$$S_\alpha \mu_j = \mu_{p-j}.$$

This shows that S_α manages to invert the α-ladders. Since every rootform belongs to some α-ladder, S_α maps W onto W.

The definition of S_α can be extended. The rootforms are special linear functions on $\boldsymbol{H}$. One is led to define S_α for all linear functions on $\boldsymbol{H}$.

20.10. Definition $\boldsymbol{H}^*$ is the dual space of $\boldsymbol{H}$ (i.e., the linear space of complex linear functions on $\boldsymbol{H}$). For $\alpha \in W$, $\alpha \neq 0$, S_α is the linear mapping of $\boldsymbol{H}^*$ onto itself, defined by

$$S_\alpha \xi = \xi - 2\frac{\xi(\boldsymbol{h}_\alpha)}{\alpha(\boldsymbol{h}_\alpha)}\alpha.$$

It was shown that S_α maps W onto itself; S_α leaves the subspace of ξ with $\xi(\boldsymbol{h}_\alpha) = 0$ invariant, and it changes α into $-\alpha$. Thus it is a kind of *reflection*. In any case, $S_\alpha{}^2 = 1$.

20.11 If λ, $\mu \in W$ and $\mu = t\lambda \neq 0$ with a scalar t, then $t = \pm 1$.

This is shown as follows: One may suppose $|t| \geqq 1$.

$$2\frac{\mu(\boldsymbol{h}_\lambda)}{\lambda(\boldsymbol{h}_\lambda)} = 2t \qquad \text{and} \qquad 2\frac{\lambda(\boldsymbol{h}_\mu)}{\mu(\boldsymbol{h}_\mu)} = \frac{2}{t}$$

are integers by 20.9.1. Hence $t = \pm 1$ or ± 2. In the case $t = \pm 2$ a λ-ladder is formed by $-2\lambda, -\lambda, 0, \lambda, 2\lambda$. With $\boldsymbol{f}_+ \in \boldsymbol{G}_\lambda$, $\boldsymbol{x}_0 \in \boldsymbol{G}_{-2\lambda}$, $\boldsymbol{x}_0 \neq \boldsymbol{0}$, $\boldsymbol{x}_j = \tilde{\boldsymbol{f}}_+^j \boldsymbol{x}_0 \neq \boldsymbol{0}$ for $j = 0, 1, 2, 3, 4$, one would get

$$\boldsymbol{x}_0 \in \boldsymbol{G}_{-2\lambda}, \quad \boldsymbol{x}_1 \in \boldsymbol{G}_{-\lambda}, \quad \boldsymbol{x}_2 \in \boldsymbol{G}_0, \quad \boldsymbol{x}_3 \in \boldsymbol{G}_\lambda, \quad \boldsymbol{x}_4 \in \boldsymbol{G}_{2\lambda},$$

where $\boldsymbol{x}_3$ would be a scalar multiple of $\boldsymbol{f}_+$; therefore $\boldsymbol{x}_4 = \tilde{\boldsymbol{f}}_+ \boldsymbol{x}_3 = \boldsymbol{0}$, which is a contradiction. Thus $t = \pm 1$.

Note that all ladders through 0 have the form $-\alpha, 0, \alpha$.

20.12 By means of 20.5.12 the trace of $\tilde{\boldsymbol{f}}_-\tilde{\boldsymbol{f}}_+$ in $\sum_{j=0}^{p} \boldsymbol{G}_{\mu+j\alpha}$ can be computed as the sum of the ρ_j; thus

$$\tfrac{1}{2}\sum_{j=0}^{p-1}(j+1)(p-j)\,\alpha(\boldsymbol{h}_\alpha).$$

By elementary algebra (e.g., induction on p) this turns out to be

$$\tfrac{1}{12}p(p+1)(p+2)\,\alpha(\boldsymbol{h}_\alpha).$$

Hence

20.12.1 $$\operatorname{tr}\tilde{\boldsymbol{f}}_-\tilde{\boldsymbol{f}}_+ = \tfrac{1}{12}\sum p(p+1)(p+2)\,\alpha(\boldsymbol{h}_\alpha),$$

where the sum runs over the set of all α-ladders and p is their respective length.

20.13. First Dressing The results are collected in a definition and a theorem.

Definition $\boldsymbol{G} \in$ Alg Lie Com SS is said to be in *first dressing* with respect to a trunk $\boldsymbol{H}$ if the branches $\boldsymbol{e}_\alpha$ and the nodes $\boldsymbol{h}_\alpha$ have been normed such that $[\boldsymbol{e}_\alpha, \boldsymbol{e}_{-\alpha}] = \boldsymbol{h}_\alpha$.

First Dressing Theorem on the complex semisimple Lie algebra $\boldsymbol{G}$ of rank l with the trunk $\boldsymbol{H}$, its dual $\boldsymbol{H}^*$, the Killing form ψ, and the rootform system W.

$$\boldsymbol{H} \text{ is abelian, } \dim \boldsymbol{H} = l,$$

the rootform 0 is l-fold, and all others are simple.

Among the rootforms there are l independent and no more.

If $\alpha \in W$, then $-\alpha \in W$, and no other multiple $\neq 0$ of α belongs to W.

To every $\alpha \in W$, $\alpha \neq 0$, there is a branch $\boldsymbol{e}_\alpha$, unique up to a scalar factor, such that

$$\begin{aligned}
[\boldsymbol{h}, \boldsymbol{e}_\alpha] &= \alpha(\boldsymbol{h})\,\boldsymbol{e}_\alpha && \text{for } \boldsymbol{h} \in \boldsymbol{H},\\
[\boldsymbol{e}_\alpha, \boldsymbol{e}_{-\alpha}] &= \boldsymbol{h}_\alpha \in \boldsymbol{H},\\
[\boldsymbol{e}_\alpha, \boldsymbol{e}_\beta] &= N_{\alpha,\beta}\,\boldsymbol{e}_{\alpha+\beta} \neq \boldsymbol{0} && \text{if } \alpha+\beta \neq 0, \quad \alpha+\beta \in W,\\
&= \boldsymbol{0} && \text{if } \alpha+\beta \notin W.
\end{aligned}$$

The nodes $\boldsymbol{h}_\alpha$ span $\boldsymbol{H}$ linearly; $\boldsymbol{G}$ is spanned by $\boldsymbol{H}$ and the branches $\boldsymbol{e}_\alpha$, which are a basis of a linear complement of $\boldsymbol{H}$.

$$\alpha(\boldsymbol{h}_\alpha) \neq 0 \qquad \text{for } \alpha \in W, \quad \alpha \neq 0.$$

$$-2[\lambda(\boldsymbol{h}_\alpha)/\alpha(\boldsymbol{h}_\alpha)] \text{ is an integer for } \alpha, \lambda \in W,\ \alpha \neq 0.$$

S_α (see 20.10) maps $\boldsymbol{H}^*$ onto $\boldsymbol{H}^*$, W onto W, and inverts the α-ladders of rootforms.

If $\alpha, \lambda \in W$, $\alpha \neq 0$, then any $\mu \in \boldsymbol{H}^*$ which is congruent to λ mod α and is situated between λ and $S_\alpha \lambda$, belongs to W.

If $\alpha, \lambda \in W$, $\lambda - \alpha \notin W$, any rootform that is congruent to λ mod α belongs to the α-ladder from λ to $S_\alpha \lambda$. The length of the ladder is $-2[\lambda(\boldsymbol{h}_\alpha)/\alpha[\boldsymbol{h}_\alpha)]$.

ψ is nondegenerate on $\boldsymbol{G}$, and on $\boldsymbol{H}$.

For $\boldsymbol{h}, \boldsymbol{h}' \in \boldsymbol{H}$: $\psi(\boldsymbol{h}, \boldsymbol{h}') = \sum_{\mu \in W} \mu(\boldsymbol{h}) \mu(\boldsymbol{h}')$.

For $\boldsymbol{h} \in \boldsymbol{H}$: $\psi(\boldsymbol{h}, \boldsymbol{e}_\alpha) = 0$.

For $\alpha, \beta \in W$, $\alpha \neq 0$, $\beta \neq 0$, $\alpha + \beta \neq 0$: $\psi(\boldsymbol{e}_\alpha, \boldsymbol{e}_\beta) = 0$.

$$\psi(\boldsymbol{e}_\alpha, \boldsymbol{e}_{-\alpha}) = \tfrac{1}{12} \sum p(p+1)(p+2)\, \alpha(\boldsymbol{h}_\alpha) = N_\alpha,$$

the sum running over all α-ladders, p being their respective length.

If in its α-ladder γ is the $(j+1)$th element with $p-j$ elements following, then

$$\tilde{\boldsymbol{e}}_{-\alpha} \tilde{\boldsymbol{e}}_\alpha \boldsymbol{e}_\gamma = \tfrac{1}{2}(j+1)(p-j)\, \alpha(\boldsymbol{h}_\alpha)\, \boldsymbol{e}_\gamma,$$

where for $\gamma = 0$ the role of $\boldsymbol{e}_\gamma$ is played by $\boldsymbol{h}_\alpha$.

Definition N_α and $N_{\alpha,\beta}$ are defined by their occurrence in the first dressing theorem. Moreover, $N_{\alpha,\beta} = 0$ if $\alpha, \beta \in W$, $\alpha, \beta \neq 0$, $\alpha + \beta \notin W$.

20.14. Historical Note The preceding analysis of semisimple Lie algebras and most of the notions on which it depends are due to W. Killing and E. Cartan (see 26.25). Killing's work exhibits some gaps and errors, yet by no means enough to justify the tradition, going back to S. Lie himself, of belittling or ignoring Killing's part.

20.15–16.† Semisimple Subalgebras

20.15. Proposition Let $\boldsymbol{G} \in$ Alg Lie Com SS, let $\boldsymbol{H}$ be a trunk of $\boldsymbol{G}$, and let $\boldsymbol{F}$ sub $\boldsymbol{G}$, $\boldsymbol{H} \subset \boldsymbol{F}$. Then $\boldsymbol{F}$ is linearly spanned by $\boldsymbol{H}$ and some branches of $\boldsymbol{G}$ with respect to $\boldsymbol{H}$. If, moreover, $\boldsymbol{e}_\alpha \in \boldsymbol{F}$ implies $\boldsymbol{e}_{-\alpha} \in \boldsymbol{F}$ ($\alpha \in W$), then $\boldsymbol{F}$ is the direct sum of a subalgebra $\boldsymbol{H}_1$ of $\boldsymbol{H}$ and of a semisimple $\boldsymbol{F}_1$.

Proof $\boldsymbol{H}$ being ad-pure, $\boldsymbol{G}$ as a linear space splits under the $\tilde{\boldsymbol{h}}$ ($\boldsymbol{h} \in \boldsymbol{H}$) into $\boldsymbol{H}$ and uniquely determined one-dimensional linear subspaces, each spanned by a branch. The splitting of $\boldsymbol{F}$ is part of the splitting of $\boldsymbol{G}$, which proves the first assertion. Further, let V be the set of $\alpha \in W$ with $\boldsymbol{e}_\alpha \in \boldsymbol{F}$, let $\boldsymbol{H}_1$ be the intersection of the kernels of the $\alpha \in V$, and let $\boldsymbol{F}_1$ be the linear span of the $\boldsymbol{e}_\alpha$ and $\boldsymbol{h}_\alpha$ with $\alpha \in V$. Then $\boldsymbol{F}_1$ sub $\boldsymbol{F}$, $[\boldsymbol{H}_1, \boldsymbol{F}_1] = \{\boldsymbol{0}\}$ and $\boldsymbol{H}_1 + \boldsymbol{F}_1 = \boldsymbol{F}$.

To show that $\boldsymbol{F}_1$ is semisimple, think of $\psi_{\boldsymbol{F}_1}$ as being degenerate. Then $\psi_{\boldsymbol{F}_1}(\boldsymbol{e}_\alpha, \boldsymbol{e}_{-\alpha}) = 0$ for some $\alpha \in V$, from which it would follow that $\psi_{\boldsymbol{F}_1}(\boldsymbol{e}_\alpha, \boldsymbol{F}_1) = \psi_{\boldsymbol{F}_1}(\boldsymbol{F}_1, \boldsymbol{e}_{-\alpha}) = \{0\}$; thus $\boldsymbol{e}_\alpha, \boldsymbol{e}_{-\alpha} \in \operatorname{rad} \boldsymbol{F}_1$. This, however, contradicts $\boldsymbol{e}_\alpha, \boldsymbol{e}_{-\alpha}$, $\boldsymbol{h}_\alpha$ spanning a semisimple subalgebra of $\boldsymbol{F}_1$.

† The contents of 20.15–16 will not be used for some time.

20.16 Remark If F is a subalgebra of the real Lie algebra obtained from $G \in$ Alg Lie Com SS by waiving, and F contains a trunk of G, then F is even a (complex) subalgebra of G.

21. THE FIRST WEYL NORMING AND THE SECOND DRESSING OF COMPLEX SEMISIMPLE LIE ALGEBRAS

$G \in$ Alg Lie Com SS. The notation is that of 20.13.

21.1. Norming the Branches By applying the $\tilde{G}$-invariance of ψ (19.5.1) with the derivation $\tilde{e}_{-\mu}$ to $\psi(h_\lambda, e_\mu)$ one gets

$$\psi(\tilde{e}_{-\mu} h_\lambda, e_\mu) + \psi(h_\lambda, \tilde{e}_{-\mu} e_\mu) = 0.$$

Since

$$\tilde{e}_{-\mu} h_\lambda = -[h_\lambda, e_{-\mu}] = \mu(h_\lambda) e_{-\mu},$$
$$\tilde{e}_{-\mu} e_\mu = -[e_\mu, e_{-\mu}] = -h_\mu,$$

this becomes

21.1.1 $$\mu(h_\lambda) N_\mu = \psi(h_\lambda, h_\mu).$$

Replacing the e_α by appropriate scalar multiples, one can make

21.1.2 $$N_\alpha = \psi(e_\alpha, e_{-\alpha}) = 1.$$

This is called a first Weyl norming, which in the sequel is assumed to have been carried out. Note that the nodes no longer depend on the choice of norming as long as the norming has been carried out according to 21.1.2. Now 21.1.1 reads

21.1.3 $$\mu(h_\lambda) = \psi(h_\lambda, h_\mu).$$

Consider, for μ fixed, the linear function on H

$$\curlyvee_h(\mu(h) - \psi(h, h_\mu)).$$

It vanishes for all nodes h_λ, but since they span H it vanishes on all H:

21.1.4 $$\mu(h) = \psi(h, h_\mu) \qquad \text{for} \quad h \in H.$$

This suggests the following.

Definition of the (canonical) *mapping* ζ of H onto H^*:

$$\zeta = \curlyvee_{h'} \curlyvee_h \psi(h, h'),$$

in other words

21.1.5 $$(\zeta(\boldsymbol{h}'))(\boldsymbol{h}) = \psi(\boldsymbol{h}, \boldsymbol{h}') \qquad \text{for} \quad \boldsymbol{h}, \boldsymbol{h}' \in \boldsymbol{H}.$$

ζ is linear and one-to-one because of the nondegeneracy of ψ.

21.1.6 $$\zeta \boldsymbol{h}_\mu = \mu$$

because of 21.1.3.

ψ can be interpreted as an inner product on $\boldsymbol{H}$. It induces an inner product on $\boldsymbol{H}^*$, written $(\ldots, \ldots)$:

Definition

21.1.7 $$(\zeta \boldsymbol{h}, \zeta \boldsymbol{h}') = \psi(\boldsymbol{h}, \boldsymbol{h}').$$

Note that the definition of the inner product on $\boldsymbol{H}^*$ does not depend on the norming.

With the use of this inner product, 21.1.3 reads

21.1.8 $$\mu(\boldsymbol{h}_\lambda) = (\lambda, \mu).$$

By means of 21.1.8 formulas like those of the ladders' length and of S_α can be rewritten,

$$p = -2\frac{(\mu, \alpha)}{(\alpha, \alpha)}, \qquad S_\alpha \xi = \xi - 2\frac{(\xi, \alpha)}{(\alpha, \alpha)}\alpha.$$

The inner product on $\boldsymbol{H}^*$ like that on $\boldsymbol{H}$ is nondegenerate, but since $\boldsymbol{H}^*$ is a complex space there is no question of definiteness of the inner product.

By the first dressing theorem

$$\psi(\boldsymbol{h}_\lambda, \boldsymbol{h}_\mu) = \sum_{\alpha \in W} \alpha(\boldsymbol{h}_\lambda)\, \alpha(\boldsymbol{h}_\mu),$$

which now becomes

21.1.9 $$(\lambda, \mu) = \sum_{\alpha \in W} (\lambda, \alpha)(\mu, \alpha),$$

a remarkable formula, which remains true if λ and μ are replaced by arbitrary linear combinations of rootforms and thus by arbitrary elements of $\boldsymbol{H}^*$.

From $N_\alpha = 1$ (and the formula for $N_\alpha = \psi(\boldsymbol{e}_\alpha, \boldsymbol{e}_{-\alpha})$ in 20.13) it follows that all (α, α) $(\alpha \in W)$ are rational. Since all $-2[(\beta, \alpha)/(\alpha, \alpha)]$ $(\alpha, \beta \in W, \alpha \neq 0)$ are integers, it follows that

21.1.10 all (α, β) are rational $\qquad (\alpha, \beta \in W)$.

On a basis of $\boldsymbol{H}^*$ consisting of rootforms $\mu_1, \ldots, \mu_l$ every rootform μ is presented as

$$\mu = \sum r_j \mu_j.$$

From

$$(\mu, \mu_i) = \sum_j r_j(\mu_j, \mu_i)$$

the r_j, if computed by Cramer's rule, turn out to be rational.

Therefore all rootforms are rational-linearly dependent on l among them. Correspondingly, by 21.1.6 the nodes are rational-linearly dependent on l among them.

21.2. The Standard Trunk

Definition After norming $N_\alpha = 1$, $\boldsymbol{H}_{\text{st}}$ resp. $\boldsymbol{H}^*_{\text{st}}$ is the *real* linear space spanned by the nodes $\boldsymbol{h}_\mu$ resp. by the rootforms.

They do no depend on the choice of norming $N_\alpha = 1$; $\boldsymbol{H}_{\text{st}}$ is called the *standard trunk* belonging to $\boldsymbol{H}$ for reasons made clear later on.

Obviously

$$\zeta \boldsymbol{H}_{\text{st}} = \boldsymbol{H}^*_{\text{st}},$$
$$\dim \boldsymbol{H}_{\text{st}} = \dim \boldsymbol{H}^*_{\text{st}} = l.$$

$\boldsymbol{H}, \boldsymbol{H}^*$ are the complex extensions of $\boldsymbol{H}_{\text{st}}, \boldsymbol{H}^*_{\text{st}}$.

$\boldsymbol{H}_{\text{st}}$ can also be characterized as the maximal subset of $\boldsymbol{H}$ on which all rootforms are real.

There is a nondegenerate inner product on $\boldsymbol{H}^*_{\text{st}}$ by restriction. By 21.1.10 it is real-valued. By 21.1.9

$$(\xi, \eta) = \sum_{\alpha \in W} (\xi, \alpha)(\eta, \alpha) \qquad \text{for} \quad \xi, \eta \in \boldsymbol{H}^*_{\text{st}},$$

and by 21.1.10

$$(\xi, \xi) \geqslant 0,$$

which shows the positive definiteness of the inner product on $\boldsymbol{H}^*_{\text{st}}$.

Correspondingly, the inner product on $\boldsymbol{H}_{\text{st}}$ by restriction of $\psi(\ldots, \ldots)$ is positive definite.

On any linear space spanned by real linear combinations of nodes (over any subfield of Com), ψ is nondegenerate.

21.3. The Reflections Thanks to 20.10 S_α is a kind of *reflection*; because

$$S_\alpha \alpha = -\alpha,$$
$$S_\alpha \xi = \xi \qquad \text{for} \quad (\xi, \alpha) = 0,$$

S_α is even orthogonal with respect to the inner product on $\boldsymbol{H}^*$.

S_α maps W onto itself and consequently $\boldsymbol{H}^*_{\text{st}}$ onto itself. Its restriction to $\boldsymbol{H}^*_{\text{st}}$ (also called S_α) turns out to be the orthogonal reflection in the orthoplement of α with respect to the inner product on $\boldsymbol{H}^*_{\text{st}}$.

By means of ζ^{-1} the reflection S_α can be transferred to $\boldsymbol{H}_{st}$. It is again called S_α (instead of $\zeta^{-1} S_\alpha \zeta$). In $\boldsymbol{H}_{st}$ it is the reflection in the kernel of α.

21.4. Second Dressing The results are collected in a definition and a theorem:

Definition $G \in$ Alg Lie Com SS in first dressing is said to be in *second dressing* if the branches have been normed according to the *first Weyl norming*, that is, such that

$$N_\alpha = \psi(\boldsymbol{e}_\alpha, \boldsymbol{e}_{-\alpha}) = 1,$$

and consequently the nodes such that

$$\mu(\boldsymbol{h}_\lambda) = \psi(\boldsymbol{h}_\lambda, \boldsymbol{h}_\mu) \qquad \text{for} \quad \lambda, \mu \in W, \quad \lambda, \mu \neq 0,$$

and an inner product $(\ldots, \ldots)$ has been introduced in $\boldsymbol{H}^*$ such that

$$(\lambda, \mu) = \psi(\boldsymbol{h}_\lambda, \boldsymbol{h}_\mu) \qquad \text{for} \quad \lambda, \mu \in W, \quad \lambda, \mu \neq 0.$$

Second dressing is always possible.

Second Dressing Theorem on the complex semisimple Lie algebra $\boldsymbol{G}$ (see 20.13).

Under second dressing one obtains for $\lambda, \mu \in W$, $\lambda, \mu \neq 0$,

$$\mu(\boldsymbol{h}_\lambda) = (\lambda, \mu) = \psi(\boldsymbol{h}_\lambda, \boldsymbol{h}_\mu) = \sum_{\alpha \in W} (\lambda, \alpha)(\mu, \alpha),$$

and, more generally,

$$(\xi, \eta) = \sum_{\alpha \in W} (\xi, \alpha)(\eta, \alpha) \qquad \text{for} \quad \xi, \eta \in \boldsymbol{H}^*.$$

Furthermore,

$$(\lambda, \mu) \text{ rational} \qquad \text{for} \quad \lambda, \mu \in W,$$

$$(\lambda, \lambda) > 0 \qquad \text{for} \quad \lambda \in W, \quad \lambda \neq 0.$$

On any basis of rootforms all rootforms have rational coordinates.

The second dressing nodes and the inner product on $\boldsymbol{H}^*$ do not depend on the choice of the norming.

On the real linear space $\boldsymbol{H}_{st}^*$ spanned by W the inner product is real-valued and positive definite; the same is true of ψ on the real linear space $\boldsymbol{H}_{st}$ spanned by the nodes $\boldsymbol{h}_\alpha$.

On any linear space spanned by the nodes (over any subfield of Com) ψ is nondegenerate.

S_α is a reflection in the sense of the inner product.

Notation If by means of ζ endomorphisms (and semiendomorphisms) of $\boldsymbol{H}$ and $\boldsymbol{H}_{st}$ are carried to $\boldsymbol{H}^*$ and $\boldsymbol{H}^*_{st}$, respectively, and conversely, they are indicated by the same symbols.

An immediate consequence is the following:

Proposition If T is an endomorphism of $\boldsymbol{H}$ and T' is its transpose with respect to ψ, then

$$\xi(T\boldsymbol{h}) = (T'\,\xi)(\boldsymbol{h});$$

in particular, if T is orthogonal with respect to ψ,

$$\xi(T\boldsymbol{h}) = (T^{-1}\,\xi)(\boldsymbol{h}).$$

21.5. Gordon Brown's Formula A remarkable conclusion derived from 21.1.9 is

$$\sum_{\alpha\in W} (\alpha, \alpha) = l \qquad (= \text{rank } \boldsymbol{G}).$$

Proof Considering the symmetric matrix M of (λ, μ) $(\lambda, \mu \in W, \lambda, \mu \neq 0)$, one can read 21.1.9 as

$$M^2 = M.$$

Clearly rank $M = l$. Thus $\sum_{\alpha\in W} (\alpha, \alpha) = \text{tr } M = \text{rank } M = l$, since for idempotent matrices trace and rank are equal.

21.6. Historical Note The norming $N_\alpha = 1$ (actually -1) was introduced by H. Weyl in *Math. Z.* **24** (1926); see *Selecta*, 338–342 (1956). Notwithstanding its great theoretical importance, it suffers from the large denominators in the rational numbers $\psi(h_\alpha, h_\beta)$ which make it less practicable for computations in Lie algebras. This is the reason for not identifying $\boldsymbol{H}$ and $\boldsymbol{H}^*$ in this exposition, contrary to common usage.

Gordon Brown's formula is found in *Proc. Amer. Math. Soc.* **15**, 518 (1964).

22. G DETERMINED BY W^*

$\boldsymbol{G} \in$ Alg Lie Com SS in second dressing. The notations are those of Sections 20–21.

22.1 By 17.8 the adjoint group Int $\boldsymbol{G}$ acts transitively on the set of trunks. By this action the $W(\boldsymbol{G}, \boldsymbol{H})$ of different $\boldsymbol{H}$ are related. The structure of W does not depend on the choice of $\boldsymbol{H}$.

Definition W^* is the subset of W consisting of the rootforms $\neq 0$. W^* possesses:

22.1.1 the *strong* structure of a system of vectors in an l-dimensional linear space with nondegenerate inner product, and

22.1.2 the *weak* structure of a system of things α, β, γ, ..., related by abstract relations $\alpha+\beta=0$ and $\alpha+\beta+\gamma=0$.

22.1.3. Proposition The strong structure of W^* is fixed by the weak structure.

Proof Given the weak structure, one can subsequently determine the ladders, their lengths, the mappings S_α as far as they act on W^* (namely, inverting the ladders), the (α,α) by formula 20.13 for $N_\alpha = \psi(\boldsymbol{e}_\alpha, \boldsymbol{e}_{-\alpha}) = 1$, the (α,β) by the ladder length formula, all linear relations among the rootforms by the values of (α,β) because of the nondegeneracy of the inner product, the rank as the number of independent ones, and the embedding of W^* in $\boldsymbol{H}^*_{\mathrm{st}}$ up to orthogonal mappings.

22.1.4 The influence of the choice of $\boldsymbol{H}$ on the structure of $W(\boldsymbol{G})$ was eliminated by the adjoint group. This appeal to Int $\boldsymbol{G}$ can be avoided. With a continuous change of $\boldsymbol{H}$, the branches, after suitable norming, change continuously. So do the $\psi(\boldsymbol{e}_\alpha, \boldsymbol{e}_{-\alpha})$, and therefore the norming factors needed for second dressing may be assumed to be continuous. Then the second dressing nodes depend continuously on $\boldsymbol{H}$. Since, by the end of 21.1 they are *rational*-linearly dependent on l among them, the rational-linear, hence the real relations among the nodes and, consequently, among the rootforms are invariant under a continuous change of $\boldsymbol{H}$. This shows anew that the weak, and consequently the strong, structure $W(\boldsymbol{G},\boldsymbol{H})$ does not depend on $\boldsymbol{H}$.

22.2. Theorem W^* determines $\boldsymbol{G}$ up to isomorphy. For two complex semisimple Lie algebras $\boldsymbol{G},\boldsymbol{G}'$, with trunks $\boldsymbol{H},\boldsymbol{H}'$, any isomorphism of $W^*(\boldsymbol{G},\boldsymbol{H})$ to $W^*(\boldsymbol{G}',\boldsymbol{H}')$ is induced by some isomorphism of $\boldsymbol{G}$ onto $\boldsymbol{G}'$, thus relating $\boldsymbol{H}$ to $\boldsymbol{H}'$ and mapping nodes into nodes and branches into branches after suitable norming in second dressing.

The theorem is proved in 22.3–5.

22.3 $W^*(\boldsymbol{G},\boldsymbol{H})$ and $W^*(\boldsymbol{G}',\boldsymbol{H}')$ are identified according to the given isomorphisms; notation W^*.

$\boldsymbol{G},\boldsymbol{G}'$ are assumed in second dressing with respect to $\boldsymbol{H},\boldsymbol{H}'$. Thus $N_\alpha(\boldsymbol{G},\boldsymbol{H}) = N_\alpha(\boldsymbol{G}',\boldsymbol{H}') = 1$.

The normed α-branches and α-nodes are called e_α, e'_α, h_α, h'_α.

h'_α is made to correspond to h_α. This correspondence is extended by 21.1.6 to a linear mapping of H onto H'.

A scalar multiple of e'_α is to be assigned to e_α as its image. Independent of the choice of this multiple, the relation

$$[h, e_\alpha] = \alpha(h)\, e_\alpha \qquad (h \in H),$$

remains valid if h, e_α are replaced by their images.

Rather than mapping e_α into a multiple of e'_α, it is advisable to renorm the e'_α. In doing so, one has to keep $N_\alpha(G', H') = 1$. Thus renorming means multiplying e'_α, $e'_{-\alpha}$ by reciprocal factors. Then $\psi(e'_\alpha, e'_{-\alpha})$, as well as $h'_\alpha = [e'_\alpha, e'_{-\alpha}]$, is preserved.

To settle the isomorphy of G and G', one has to renorm the e'_α such that

$$[e'_\alpha, e'_\beta] = [e_\alpha, e_\beta]'.$$

(Of course, for any scalar κ, $(\kappa e_\lambda)'$ means $\kappa e'_\lambda$.)

22.4 Suppose $\alpha, \beta, \gamma \in W^*$, $\alpha + \beta + \gamma = 0$. If

$$[e'_\alpha, e'_\beta] = [e_\alpha, e_\beta]',$$

then

$$[e'_\beta, e'_\gamma] = [e_\beta, e_\gamma]'.$$

Proof In

$$[[e_\alpha, e_\beta], e_\gamma] + [[e_\beta, e_\gamma], e_\alpha] + [[e_\gamma, e_\alpha], e_\beta] = 0$$

and

$$[[e'_\alpha, e'_\beta], e'_\gamma] + [[e'_\beta, e'_\gamma], e'_\alpha] + [[e'_\gamma, e'_\alpha], e'_\beta] = 0$$

the first summands are the same multiples of h_γ and h'_γ, respectively, the other summands are multiples of h_α, h_β and h'_α, h'_β, respectively. There is essentially one relation between them:

$$h_\gamma + h_\alpha + h_\beta = 0,$$
$$h'_\gamma + h'_\alpha + h'_\beta = 0$$

(see 21.1.6 and 20.11). Thus the last two summands are the same multiples of h_α, h_β respectively h'_α, h'_β, and consequently $[e_\beta, e_\gamma]$, $[e'_\beta, e'_\gamma]$ are the same multiples of $e_{-\alpha}$ and $e'_{-\alpha}$. This proves the assertion.

22.5 On an ordered basis of H^*_{st} the elements of W are lexicographically ordered with respect to their coordinates. The order relation is denoted by $>$.

For $\rho > 0$, $\rho \in W^*$ the set of all $\mu \in W^*$ such that $-\rho < \mu < \rho$ is called W_ρ. Suppose that renorming of the e'_μ has been achieved within W_ρ:

22.5.1 $[e'_\lambda, e'_\mu] = [e_\lambda, e_\mu]'$ for $\lambda, \mu, \lambda + \mu \in W_\rho$.

It is expanded to

$$W_\rho \cup \{\rho\} \cup \{-\rho\}.$$

This means that by renorming $e'_\rho, e'_{-\rho}$ one has to satisfy

22.5.2 $[e'_\lambda, e'_\mu] = [e_\lambda, e_\mu]'$ for $\lambda, \mu \in W_\rho$, $\lambda + \mu = \pm\rho$,

22.5.3 $[e'_{\pm\rho}, e'_\lambda] = [e_{\pm\rho}, e_\lambda]'$ for $\lambda, \lambda \pm \rho \in W_\rho$,

22.5.4 $[e'_\rho, e'_{-\rho}] = [e_\rho, e_{-\rho}]'$.

If $\rho \neq \lambda + \mu$ for all $\lambda, \mu \in W_\rho$, then the same is true of $-\rho$, and $\lambda + \rho \notin W_\rho$. Then 22.5.2–3 are void, whereas 22.5.4 is fulfilled in advance.

Thus suppose

$$\rho = \alpha + \beta \qquad \text{for some} \quad \alpha, \beta \in W_\rho.$$

e'_ρ is some multiple of $[e'_\alpha, e'_\beta]$. It is renormed by requiring that it be the same multiple of $[e'_\alpha, e'_\beta]$ as e_ρ is of $[e_\alpha, e_\beta]$. Then

22.5.5 $$[e'_\alpha, e'_\beta] = [e_\alpha, e_\beta]'$$

is fulfilled. Likewise one can make

22.5.6 $$[e'_{-\alpha}, e'_{-\beta}] = [e_{-\alpha}, e_{-\beta}]'.$$

The norming $N_\rho = 1$, however, might now be lost. Moreover, the definition of $e'_{\pm\rho}$ seemingly depends on the choice of α, β in $\rho = \alpha + \beta$. Let γ, δ, with $\rho = \gamma + \delta$, also be a choice ($\gamma, \delta \in W_\rho$). It must be shown that 22.5.5 remains true with γ, δ instead of α, β. (This implies that $e'_{\pm\rho}$ do not depend on the choice of α, β.)

By Jacobi-associativity

22.5.7 $[[e'_\alpha, e'_\beta], e'_{-\gamma}] + [[e'_\beta, e'_{-\gamma}], e'_\alpha] + [[e'_{-\gamma}, e'_\alpha], e'_\beta] = \mathbf{0}$.

Now $\beta < \rho$, hence $\rho = \alpha + \beta < \alpha + \rho$, hence $0 < \alpha$; thus $0 < \alpha < \rho$. Likewise $0 < \beta < \rho$, $0 < \gamma < \rho$, $0 < \delta < \rho$, hence

$$-\rho < \alpha - \gamma < \rho, \qquad -\rho < \beta - \gamma < \rho;$$

if $\alpha - \gamma$, $\beta - \gamma$ are rootforms, they belong to W_ρ. Finally, $\delta = \alpha + \beta - \gamma \in W_\rho$.

Consequently the second and third summands of 22.5.7 are constructed within W_ρ. There one may pull the dashes out of the brackets. But then it is also allowed in the first summand

22.5.8 $$[[e'_\alpha, e'_\beta], e'_{-\gamma}].$$

This permission extends to the case $\gamma = \alpha$, hence to the expression

$$[[[e'_\alpha, e'_\beta], e'_{-\alpha}], e'_{-\beta}],$$

and likewise to

$$[[[e'_\alpha, e'_\beta], e'_{-\beta}], e'_{-\alpha}],$$

thus by Jacobi-associativity to

$$[[e'_\alpha, e'_\beta], [e'_{-\alpha} e'_{-\beta}]],$$

and by 22.5.6 to

$$[[e_\alpha, e_\beta]', [e_{-\alpha}, e_{-\beta}]'],$$

and consequently to

$$[e'_\rho, e'_{-\rho}].$$

Now 22.5.4 is satisfied and so is the norming $N_\rho = 1$. It is possible to apply 22.4.

From 22.5.8 it follows that

$$[e'_\rho, e'_{-\gamma}] = [e_\rho, e_{-\gamma}]',$$

thus half of 22.5.3. Thanks to 22.4, this proves the validity of

$$[e'_{-\gamma}, e'_{-\delta}] = [e_{-\gamma}, e_{-\delta}]',$$

which is half of 22.5.2. The other halves are obtained by interchanging ρ and $-\rho$.

23. THE SECOND WEYL NORMING AND THE THIRD DRESSING OF COMPLEX SEMISIMPLE LIE ALGEBRAS

$\boldsymbol{G} \in$ Alg Lie Com SS in second dressing. The notations are those of 20.13.

23.1 The mapping $\alpha \to -\alpha$ is an automorphism of W^*. According to 22.2, it is induced by an automorphism M of $\boldsymbol{G}$ with

$$M\boldsymbol{h}_\alpha = \boldsymbol{h}_{-\alpha}, \qquad \text{hence} \quad M\boldsymbol{h} = -\boldsymbol{h} \quad \text{for} \quad \boldsymbol{h} \in \boldsymbol{H},$$

$$M\boldsymbol{e}_\alpha = \nu_\alpha \boldsymbol{e}_{-\alpha}$$

with scalar ν_α. Because of

$$M\boldsymbol{h}_\alpha = M[\boldsymbol{e}_\alpha, \boldsymbol{e}_{-\alpha}] = [M\boldsymbol{e}_\alpha, M\boldsymbol{e}_{-\alpha}] = \nu_\alpha \nu_{-\alpha} [\boldsymbol{e}_{-\alpha}, \boldsymbol{e}_\alpha] = \nu_\alpha \nu_{-\alpha} \boldsymbol{h}_{-\alpha},$$

one obtains

23.1.1 $$\nu_\alpha \nu_{-\alpha} = 1.$$

For all $\alpha \in W^*$, e_α is replaced by

$$e'_\alpha = \sqrt{\nu_{-\alpha}}\, e_\alpha,$$

where because of 23.1.1 the square roots can be chosen to arrive at

$$\sqrt{\nu_\alpha}\,\sqrt{\nu_{-\alpha}} = 1.$$

This norming retains $N_\alpha = 1$.

23.1.2 $$Me'_\alpha = \sqrt{\nu_{-\alpha}}\, Me_\alpha = \sqrt{\nu_{-\alpha}}\,\nu_\alpha e_{-\alpha} = \sqrt{\nu_\alpha}\, e_{-\alpha} = e'_{-\alpha}.$$

The process just carried out is called *second Weyl norming*. It brings G into its *third dressing*. More precisely:

Definition An automorphism of $G \in$ Alg Lie Com SS is called a *minus-automorphism* with respect to a trunk H (and generally indicated by M) if it preserves H and behaves on H as the scalar multiplier -1.

Note that M is not uniquely determined by H. Any element of $(\exp \tilde{H})M$ satisfies as well. The converse holds too (see 33.9).

Proposition $M^2 = 1$.

This follows from 23.1.2.

Definition $G \in$ Alg Lie Com SS is said to be in *third dressing* if a pair $\ulcorner H, M \urcorner$ has been chosen consisting of a trunk H of G in second dressing and a minus-automorphism M with respect to H, which are connected by the requirement

$$Me_\alpha = e_{-\alpha} \qquad (\alpha \in W,\ \alpha \neq 0).$$

Third Dressing Theorem Third dressing is always possible, namely by a readjustment of the branches which preserves second dressing.

Note that this readjustment depends on the choice of M, but even if M were fixed the ambiguity of the $\sqrt{\nu_\alpha}$ would allow for changing $\ulcorner e_\alpha, e_{-\alpha} \urcorner$ into $\ulcorner -e_\alpha, -e_{-\alpha} \urcorner$ for any set of $\alpha \in W^*$. This, however, is the only indeterminacy left.

23.2 Assume that G is in third dressing.

The structure of G is settled by the knowledge of the $N_{\alpha,\beta}$ in

$$[e_\alpha, e_\beta] = N_{\alpha,\beta}\, e_{\alpha+\beta} \qquad (\beta \neq -\alpha).$$

By applying M, one gets

$$[\boldsymbol{e}_{-\alpha}, \boldsymbol{e}_{-\beta}] = N_{\alpha,\beta}\, \boldsymbol{e}_{-\alpha-\beta};$$

hence

23.2.1 $$N_{\alpha,\beta} = N_{-\alpha,-\beta}.$$

According to 20.5.12,

$$\tilde{\boldsymbol{e}}_{-\alpha}\tilde{\boldsymbol{e}}_{\alpha}\,\boldsymbol{e}_{\beta} = \tfrac{1}{2}(j+1)(p-j)(\alpha,\alpha)\,\boldsymbol{e}_{\beta}$$

if β is the $(j+1)$th element in its α-ladder of length p. Now

$$\tilde{\boldsymbol{e}}_{-\alpha}\tilde{\boldsymbol{e}}_{\alpha}\,\boldsymbol{e}_{\beta} = N_{-\alpha,\alpha+\beta}\,N_{\alpha,\beta}\,\boldsymbol{e}_{\beta},$$

hence

$$N_{-\alpha,\alpha+\beta}\,N_{\alpha,\beta} = \tfrac{1}{2}(j+1)(p-j)(\alpha,\alpha).$$

By Jacobi-associativity applied to $\boldsymbol{e}_{-\alpha}$, $\boldsymbol{e}_{-\beta}$, $\boldsymbol{e}_{\alpha+\beta}$ one obtains

$$N_{-\alpha,-\beta}\,\boldsymbol{h}_{-\alpha-\beta} + N_{-\beta,\alpha+\beta}\,\boldsymbol{h}_{\alpha} + N_{\alpha+\beta,-\alpha}\,\boldsymbol{h}_{\beta} = \boldsymbol{0}.$$

Thus, because of $\boldsymbol{h}_{-\alpha-\beta} + \boldsymbol{h}_{\alpha} + \boldsymbol{h}_{\beta} = \boldsymbol{0}$ and the independence of $\boldsymbol{h}_{\alpha}, \boldsymbol{h}_{\beta}$ for $\beta \neq -\alpha$, α $(\neq 0)$, all N in that equation are equal. Hence

$$N_{\alpha,\beta}\,N_{-\alpha,-\beta} = -\tfrac{1}{2}(j+1)(p-j)(\alpha,\alpha)$$

and by 23.2.1

$$N_{\alpha,\beta} = \pm i\sqrt{(\tfrac{1}{2}(j+1)(p-j)(\alpha,\alpha))}.$$

This proves the following:

Theorem In third dressing, if β is the $(j+1)$th element in its α-ladder (of length p),

$$N_{\alpha,\beta} = \pm i\sqrt{(\tfrac{1}{2}(j+1)(p-j)(\alpha,\alpha))} = N_{-\alpha,-\beta},$$

thus purely imaginary.

23.3 In third dressing the $N_{\alpha,\beta}$ are uniquely determined up to factors ± 1.

24. THE UNITARY AND STANDARD RESTRICTIONS OF A SEMISIMPLE LIE ALGEBRA

$G \in$ Alg Lie Com SS in third dressing. The notation is the same as that preceding.

24.1–4. Standard and Unitary Semimorphism

24.1. Definition The semilinear (see 1.2) mappings C_{st} and C_{un} of $\boldsymbol{G}$ in third dressing onto itself are defined by

$$C_{st}\,\boldsymbol{h} = \boldsymbol{h} \quad \text{for} \quad \boldsymbol{h} \in \boldsymbol{H}_{st}, \quad C_{st}\,\boldsymbol{e}_\alpha = -\boldsymbol{e}_\alpha.$$
$$C_{un} = MC_{st} = C_{st}\,M;$$

hence

$$C_{un}\,\boldsymbol{h} = -\boldsymbol{h} \quad \text{for} \quad \boldsymbol{h} \in \boldsymbol{H}_{st}, \quad C_{un}\boldsymbol{e}_\alpha = -\boldsymbol{e}_{-\alpha}.$$

Proposition C_{st} and C_{un} are involutory semimorphisms (see 1.6, 1.11) of $\boldsymbol{G}$.

Proof It suffices to show that

$$C_{st}[\boldsymbol{x}, \boldsymbol{y}] = [C_{st}\,\boldsymbol{x}, C_{st}\,\boldsymbol{y}]$$

where $\boldsymbol{x}$, $\boldsymbol{y}$ may be restricted to $\boldsymbol{h} \in \boldsymbol{H}_{st}$ and $\boldsymbol{e}_\alpha$.

$$C_{st}[\boldsymbol{h}, \boldsymbol{e}_\alpha] = C_{st}\,\alpha(\boldsymbol{h})\,\boldsymbol{e}_\alpha = \alpha(\boldsymbol{h})\,C_{st}\,\boldsymbol{e}_\alpha = -\alpha(\boldsymbol{h})\,\boldsymbol{e}_\alpha = [\boldsymbol{h}, -\boldsymbol{e}_\alpha] = [C_{st}\,\boldsymbol{h}, C_{st}\,\boldsymbol{e}_\alpha]$$

since $\alpha(\boldsymbol{h})$ is real for $\boldsymbol{h} \in \boldsymbol{H}_{st}$;

$$C_{st}[\boldsymbol{e}_\alpha, \boldsymbol{e}_{-\alpha}] = C_{st}\,\boldsymbol{h}_\alpha = \boldsymbol{h}_\alpha = [-\boldsymbol{e}_\alpha, -\boldsymbol{e}_{-\alpha}] = [C_{st}\,\boldsymbol{e}_\alpha, C_{st}\,\boldsymbol{e}_{-\alpha}],$$
$$C_{st}[\boldsymbol{e}_\alpha, \boldsymbol{e}_\beta] = C_{st}\,N_{\alpha,\beta}\,\boldsymbol{e}_{\alpha+\beta} = -N_{\alpha,\beta}\,C_{st}\,\boldsymbol{e}_{\alpha+\beta} = N_{\alpha,\beta}\,\boldsymbol{e}_{\alpha+\beta}$$
$$= [\boldsymbol{e}_\alpha, \boldsymbol{e}_\beta] = [C_{st}\,\boldsymbol{e}_\alpha, C_{st}\,\boldsymbol{e}_\beta]$$

since $N_{\alpha,\beta}$ is purely imaginary (23.2).

24.2. Definition C_{st} and C_{un} are called the *standard* and the *unitary semimorphisms* of $\boldsymbol{G}$ in third dressing (with respect to $\boldsymbol{H}$); the C_{st}- and C_{un}-restrictions of $\boldsymbol{G}$ (see 1.6) are called the *standard* and *unitary restrictions*: $\boldsymbol{G}_{st}$ and $\boldsymbol{G}_{un}$.

The *standard* and *unitary trunks* (in $\boldsymbol{H}$) are $\boldsymbol{H}_{st} = \boldsymbol{H} \cap \boldsymbol{G}_{st}$ and $\boldsymbol{H}_{un} = \boldsymbol{H} \cap \boldsymbol{G}_{un}$, and ψ_{st}, ψ_{un} are the restrictions of ψ to $\boldsymbol{G}_{st}$, $\boldsymbol{G}_{un}$. Their signatures are called the *signatures of* $\boldsymbol{G}_{st}$, $\boldsymbol{G}_{un}$, respectively.

If $\boldsymbol{G}$ is given as a linear Lie algebra, then G_{st}, G_{un}, H_{st}, H_{un} are the linear Lie groups infinitesimally generated by $\boldsymbol{G}_{st}$, $\boldsymbol{G}_{un}$, $\boldsymbol{H}_{st}$, $\boldsymbol{H}_{un}$.

More generally, if C is an involutory semimorphism of $\boldsymbol{G}$ and $\boldsymbol{H}$ is a C-invariant trunk of $\boldsymbol{G}$, then $\boldsymbol{H} \cap \boldsymbol{G}_C$ is called a *C-trunk of* $\boldsymbol{G}$ or a *trunk of* $\boldsymbol{G}_C$. The *signature of* $\boldsymbol{G}_C$ is the signature of ψ_C.

By Definition 1.6 the C-restriction consists of the $\boldsymbol{a} = C\boldsymbol{a}$ or, equivalently, the $\boldsymbol{a} + C\boldsymbol{a}$. This means that

$\boldsymbol{G}_{\text{st}}$ is the real linear space spanned by $\boldsymbol{H}_{\text{st}}$ and the $\mathrm{i}\boldsymbol{e}_\alpha$,

$\boldsymbol{G}_{\text{un}}$ is the set of $\mathrm{i}\boldsymbol{h} + \sum_{\alpha \in W^*} \tau_\alpha \boldsymbol{e}_\alpha$ with $\boldsymbol{h} \in \boldsymbol{H}_{\text{st}}$ and $\tau_\alpha + \bar{\tau}_{-\alpha} = 0$ ($\bar{\tau}$ the conjugate of τ).

$\boldsymbol{H}_{\text{un}} = \mathrm{i}\boldsymbol{H}_{\text{st}}$.

Note that $\boldsymbol{H}_{\text{st}}$ and $\boldsymbol{H}_{\text{un}}$ do not depend on the choice of M and that C_{st}, C_{un}, $\boldsymbol{G}_{\text{st}}$, $\boldsymbol{G}_{\text{un}}$ depend on $\boldsymbol{H}$ and M only (not on the choice of the signs in the $\boldsymbol{e}_\alpha$).

In 33.13 it is shown that a unitary semimorphism is a unitary semimorphism with respect to any trunk left invariant by it.

24.3. Theorem $\boldsymbol{G}_{\text{st}}$ and $\boldsymbol{G}_{\text{un}}$ are real Lie algebras with the complex extension $\boldsymbol{G}$. The signature of $\boldsymbol{G}_{\text{st}}$ is rank $\boldsymbol{G}$, that of $\boldsymbol{G}_{\text{un}}$ is $-\dim \boldsymbol{G}$; ψ_{un} is negative definite.

Proof The first assertion follows from the general principle of Section 1.

$$\psi_{\text{st}} \text{ is positive definite on } \boldsymbol{H}_{\text{st}} \text{ (21.2)},$$

$$\psi_{\text{st}}(\boldsymbol{h}, \boldsymbol{e}_\alpha) = 0 \qquad \text{for} \quad \boldsymbol{h} \in \boldsymbol{H}_{\text{st}},$$

$$\psi_{\text{st}}\left(\sum \tau_\alpha \mathrm{i}\boldsymbol{e}_\alpha, \sum \tau_\alpha \mathrm{i}\boldsymbol{e}_\alpha\right) = -\sum \tau_\alpha \tau_{-\alpha},$$

which shows that signature $\psi_{\text{st}} = \dim \boldsymbol{H}_{\text{st}} = \text{rank } \boldsymbol{G}$.

$$\psi_{\text{un}} \text{ is negative definite on } \boldsymbol{H}_{\text{un}} = \mathrm{i}\boldsymbol{H}_{\text{st}},$$

$$\psi_{\text{un}}(\mathrm{i}\boldsymbol{h}, \tau_\alpha \boldsymbol{e}_\alpha - \bar{\tau}_\alpha \boldsymbol{e}_{-\alpha}) = 0,$$

$$\psi_{\text{un}}\Big(\sum_{\alpha>0} (\tau_\alpha \boldsymbol{e}_\alpha - \bar{\tau}_\alpha \boldsymbol{e}_{-\alpha}), \sum_{\alpha>0} (\tau_\alpha \boldsymbol{e}_\alpha - \bar{\tau}_\alpha \boldsymbol{e}_{-\alpha})\Big) = -2 \sum_{\alpha > 0} \tau_\alpha \bar{\tau}_\alpha,$$

which shows that ψ_{un} is negative definite.

24.4 Together with an orthonormal basis of $\boldsymbol{H}_{\text{un}}$ for ψ_{un} the elements

$$\sqrt{\tfrac{1}{2}}(\boldsymbol{e}_\alpha - \boldsymbol{e}_{-\alpha}), \quad \mathrm{i}\sqrt{\tfrac{1}{2}}(\boldsymbol{e}_\alpha + \boldsymbol{e}_{-\alpha}), \qquad \text{with} \quad \alpha > 0,$$

form an orthonormal basis of $\boldsymbol{G}_{\text{un}}$ for $-\psi_{\text{un}}$; Int$(\boldsymbol{G}_{\text{un}})$ leaves ψ_{un} invariant. Therefore, being connected, it is a group of rotations and, as such, is bounded. By Theorem 19.10 it is closed, hence compact.

Theorem Int $\boldsymbol{G}_{\text{un}}$ is compact.

This fact explains the particular importance of the unitary restriction. In 32.2.4 G_{un} itself is proved to be compact (if $\boldsymbol{G}$ is linear).

The standard restriction arises in numerous geometric contexts. In general, there are more real restrictions than the unitary and standard ones.

24.5. Historical Note Though the unitary restriction was already known in any particular case, H. Weyl first recognized its importance and proved its existence by a method which is essentially that of Sections 22–23 [*Math. Z.* **24** (1926); see *Selecta*, 342–346 (1956)], though he took its compactness for granted.

24.6–7. Examples

24.6 In 19.14 it was shown that the

$$\boldsymbol{G} \in \mathbf{A}_l,\ \mathbf{B}_l,\ \mathbf{C}_l,\ \mathbf{D}_l$$

of Section 16 are semisimple. It is worthwhile to find out what standard and unitary restrictions mean in these examples.

It is easily seen by means of 17.7 that the subalgebra $\boldsymbol{H}$ of $\boldsymbol{G}$ indicated in Section 16 as a trunk *is* a trunk. The branches $\boldsymbol{e}_\alpha, \boldsymbol{e}_{-\alpha}$ were chosen with real matrix coefficients and were transposes of each other. They do not obey the first Weyl norming. However, by computing

$$[[\boldsymbol{e}_\alpha, \boldsymbol{e}_{-\alpha}], \boldsymbol{e}_\alpha]$$

in the particular cases, one can verify that

$$\alpha(\boldsymbol{h}_\alpha) > 0$$

(this result could be used for another proof of the semisimplicity of $\boldsymbol{G}$). Now, by 20.12.1 it turns out that

$$N_\alpha > 0.$$

The first Weyl norming can be performed by multiplying $\boldsymbol{e}_\alpha, \boldsymbol{e}_{-\alpha}$ by equal real factors. After this norming $\boldsymbol{e}_\alpha, \boldsymbol{e}_{-\alpha}$ are still real and are still transposes of each other; $\boldsymbol{h}_\alpha$ is also still real and consequently $\boldsymbol{H}_{\mathrm{st}}$ consists of *real* diagonal matrices.

For matrix groups $\Upsilon_a a'^{-1}$ is an isomorphism. So is

$$\eta = \Upsilon_a(-\boldsymbol{a}')$$

for Lie algebras of matrices.

For $\boldsymbol{G} \in \mathbf{A}_l$, $\mathbf{B}_l$, $\mathbf{C}_l$, $\mathbf{D}_l$, as presented in Section 16, η is even an automorphism: in $\mathbf{A}_l$ because $\operatorname{tr} \boldsymbol{a} = 0$ implies $\operatorname{tr}(-\boldsymbol{a}') = 0$; in the others because the defining relation $\boldsymbol{a}'s + s\boldsymbol{a} = \boldsymbol{0}$ remains true if $\boldsymbol{a}$ is replaced by $-\boldsymbol{a}'$ (note that $s = s^{-1}$). Now

$$\eta \boldsymbol{h} = -\boldsymbol{h} \qquad \text{for} \quad \boldsymbol{h} \in \boldsymbol{H},$$

$$\eta \boldsymbol{e}_\alpha = -\boldsymbol{e}_{-\alpha},$$

which shows (see 23.1) that one may put

$$\eta = M$$

and that the second Weyl norming can be performed

by replacing $\boldsymbol{e}_\alpha, \boldsymbol{e}_{-\alpha}$ by $\mathrm{i}\boldsymbol{e}_\alpha, -\mathrm{i}\boldsymbol{e}_{-\alpha}$,

where α runs through a set X such that $X \cap (-X) = \bigcirc$ and $X \cup (-X) = W^*$.

The standard restriction is really spanned by $\boldsymbol{H}_{\mathrm{st}}$ and by the new branches with factors $\pm\mathrm{i}$, that is, by the old branches.

Thus the standard restriction consists of the matrices defined in Section 16, interpreted with *real* matrix coefficients. For this very reason it was called the standard restriction.

The unitary restriction means that opposite branches must have opposite conjugate coefficients. This requirement is not influenced by the factors i, –i at $\boldsymbol{e}_\alpha, \boldsymbol{e}_{-\alpha}$. Further, $\boldsymbol{G}_{\mathrm{un}}$ has $\mathrm{i}\boldsymbol{H}_{\mathrm{st}}$ as its trunk, which makes the diagonal coefficients purely imaginary. Since $\boldsymbol{e}_\alpha, \boldsymbol{e}_{-\alpha}$ were transposes of each other, the unitary restriction in the matrix representation consists of matrices satisfying

$$\boldsymbol{a} + \overline{\boldsymbol{a}'} = \boldsymbol{0}.$$

This equation characterizes the infinitesimal algebra of the group of unitary matrices with determinant 1, which explains the term unitary restriction. The result can be formulated as follows:

Theorem For $\boldsymbol{G} \in \mathbf{A}_l, \mathbf{B}_l, \mathbf{C}_l, \mathbf{D}_l$, as introduced in Section 16, the standard restriction is obtained by restricting the matrix coefficients to real values; the unitary restriction is obtained as the intersection with the infinitesimal algebra of the group of unitary matrices.

The latter property is extended in Theorem 38.4.

24.7. Proposition On a suitable basis $\boldsymbol{G}_{\mathrm{un}}$ of $\boldsymbol{G} \in \mathbf{B}_l, \mathbf{D}_l$, as defined in Section 16, is the infinitesimal algebra of the ordinary real rotation group in $(2l+1)$- and $2l$-space.

Proof for $\mathbf{D}_l$ (the case $\mathbf{B}_l$ is much the same).

Let $e_1, \ldots, e_{2l}$ be the ordered basis with respect to which the quadratic form is described, that is, has matrix s. Now the unitary restriction of this member of $\mathbf{D}_l$ consists of those endomorphisms that leave both the quadratic form and the canonical positive definite hermitean form (with matrix 1 on $e_1, \ldots, e_{2l}$) infinitesimally invariant. Take as the elements of a new basis

$$b_j = \tfrac{1}{2}(1+\mathrm{i})\,e_j + \tfrac{1}{2}(1-\mathrm{i})\,e_{j+l}, \qquad j = 1, \ldots, l,$$
$$b_{j+l} = \tfrac{1}{2}(1-\mathrm{i})\,e_j + \tfrac{1}{2}(1+\mathrm{i})\,e_{j+l}, \qquad j = 1, \ldots, l.$$

This new basis is orthonormal with respect to both the quadratic and the hermitean form. Hence the matrices on this basis of the elements of the unitary restriction of this member of $\mathbf{D}_l$ are those that are both skew and hermitean-skew, that is, real and skew. This proves the assertion.

25. G DETERMINED BY W^{++}

$G \in$ Alg Lie Com SS, if needed in second dressing on a trunk $\boldsymbol{H}$.

25.1. Angles of Rootforms

The notation remains the same. For independent $\lambda, \mu \in W^*$ under the angle $\sphericalangle(\lambda, \mu)$ (according to the inner product in $\boldsymbol{H}_{\mathrm{st}}^*$)

25.1.1
$$-2\frac{(\lambda, \mu)}{(\lambda, \lambda)} \cdot -2\frac{(\lambda, \mu)}{(\mu, \mu)}$$

is an integer (20.13),

$$4\cos^2 \sphericalangle (\lambda, \mu) < 4;$$

hence

$$\cos \sphericalangle (\lambda, \mu) = 0, \qquad \pm\tfrac{1}{2}\sqrt{1}, \qquad \pm\tfrac{1}{2}\sqrt{2}, \qquad \pm\tfrac{1}{2}\sqrt{3},$$

$$\sphericalangle (\lambda, \mu) = 90°, 60°, 120°, 45°, 135°, 30°, 150°,$$

$$2 \sphericalangle (\lambda, \mu) = \frac{2\pi}{m}, \qquad m = 2, 3, 4, 6.$$

If $(\lambda, \mu) \neq 0$, then at least one of the factors in 25.1.1 has absolute value 1, say

$$-2\frac{(\lambda, \mu)}{(\lambda, \lambda)} = \mp 1,$$

the other being allowed the values

$$-2\frac{(\lambda, \mu)}{(\mu, \mu)} = \mp 1, \mp 2, \mp 3.$$

This excludes ladders longer than 3. By $2(\lambda, \mu) = \pm(\lambda, \lambda)$ one gets

$$4\cos^2 \sphericalangle (\lambda, \mu) = \frac{(\lambda, \lambda)}{(\mu, \mu)},$$

which settles the length ratio of nonorthogonal (independent) λ, μ. It can be

$$\sqrt{1}, \quad \sqrt{2}, \quad \sqrt{3}.$$

Summarizing:

Theorem For $\lambda, \mu \in W^*$, $\lambda \neq \pm\mu$, one gets

$$\cos \sphericalangle (\lambda, \mu) = \pm\tfrac{1}{2}\sqrt{j} \qquad (j = 0, 1, 2, 3),$$

and, if $(\lambda,\mu)\neq 0$, $(\lambda,\lambda)\geqslant(\mu,\mu)$, then

$$2\frac{(\lambda,\mu)}{(\mu,\mu)}=\pm j\neq 0,$$
$$\frac{(\lambda,\lambda)}{(\mu,\mu)}=j.$$

Ladder lengths are $\leqslant 3$.

25.2. Natural Bases and Ordered Dressing

25.2.1. Definition A subset Z of W^* is called a *natural basis* if its elements are linearly independent and every element of W is a linear combination of elements of Z with integral coefficients, all $\geqslant 0$ or all $\leqslant 0$.

Clearly, such a Z is a basis of $\boldsymbol{H}_{\mathrm{st}}^*$ and $\boldsymbol{H}^*$.

Natural bases occurred in Section 16 for the cases $\mathbf{A}_l$, $\mathbf{B}_l$, $\mathbf{C}_l$, $\mathbf{D}_l$. Their existence is proved for all $\boldsymbol{G}\in$ Alg Lie Com SS in 25.2.5.

25.2.2. Definition A *partial order on* $\boldsymbol{H}_{\mathrm{st}}^*$ is a binary transitive irreflexive relation $<$ on $\boldsymbol{H}_{\mathrm{st}}^*$ (with the inverse $>$) fulfilling the requirements

$$(\xi>0\wedge p>0)\rightarrow p\xi>0 \qquad \text{for}\quad \xi\in\boldsymbol{H}_{\mathrm{st}}^*,\quad p \text{ real},$$
$$\xi_1<\xi_2\rightarrow\xi_1+\eta<\xi_2+\eta \quad \text{for}\quad \xi_1,\xi_2,\eta\in\boldsymbol{H}_{\mathrm{st}}^*,$$
$$\alpha\in W^*\rightarrow(\alpha>0\vee\alpha<0).$$

With respect to such an order,

$$W^+=\text{set of }\xi\in W^* \qquad \text{with}\quad \xi>0,$$
$$W^-=\text{set of }\xi\in W^* \qquad \text{with}\quad \xi<0,$$
$$W^{++}=W^+\diagdown(W^++W^+).$$

The elements of W^{++} are called *primitive rootforms* (with respect to the given partial order). They are usually indicated by ρ with subscripts.

A partial order on $\boldsymbol{H}_{\mathrm{st}}^*$ is called *minimal* if the set of $\ulcorner\xi,\eta\urcorner$ with $\xi<\eta$ is minimal.

If a partial order on $\boldsymbol{H}_{\mathrm{st}}^*$ is total as an order, it is called a *total order* on $\boldsymbol{H}_{\mathrm{st}}^*$.

Note that if $\xi>0$ then $0>-\xi$, hence $W^+\cap W^-=\bigcirc$, and $W^-=-W^+$. Furthermore, $(W^++W^+)\cap W\subset W^+$.

Proposition Every $\boldsymbol{h}_0\in\boldsymbol{H}_{\mathrm{st}}$ with $\alpha(\boldsymbol{h}_0)=0$ for no $\alpha\in W^*$ determines a partial order on $\boldsymbol{H}_{\mathrm{st}}^*$ by the requirement that

$$\xi<\eta\leftrightarrow\xi(\boldsymbol{h}_0)<\eta(\boldsymbol{h}_0).$$

This is obvious.

25.2.3. Proposition For any partial order on $\boldsymbol{H}_{\mathrm{st}}^*$ any natural basis contained in W^+ is contained even in W^{++}.

Remark Later on such a basis turns out to coincide with W^{++}.

Proof Let Z be such a natural basis contained in W^+. If $Z \not\subset W^{++}$, then $\alpha+\beta \in Z$ for some $\alpha, \beta \in W^+$. Both would be sums of elements of Z, which would imply a nontrivial linear relation between elements of Z. So $Z \subset W^{++}$.

25.2.4. Proposition $(\rho, \sigma) \leqslant 0$ for different $\rho, \sigma \in W^{++}$.

Proof Assume $\rho, \sigma \in W^{++}$ different with $(\rho, \sigma) > 0$. Then, by 20.13, $\rho-\sigma$ and $\sigma-\rho \in W^*$. Now $\rho-\sigma \in W^+$ or $\sigma-\rho \in W^+$, hence $\rho \in \sigma+W^+ \subset W^+ + W^+$ or $\sigma \in \rho + W^+ \subset W^+ + W^+$, which contradicts $\rho, \sigma \in W^{++}$.

25.2.5. Theorem For any given $\boldsymbol{G} \in$ Alg Lie Com SS with the trunk $\boldsymbol{H}$ there is a natural basis, namely, W^{++}, constructed by means of an arbitrary partial order on $\boldsymbol{H}_{\mathrm{st}}^*$. Conversely, every natural basis can be obtained this way and even by the use of a minimal partial order. In this way minimal partial orders on $\boldsymbol{H}_{\mathrm{st}}^*$ and natural bases are one-to-one related.

Proof Assume a partial order on $\boldsymbol{H}_{\mathrm{st}}^*$ (its existence was proved in 25.2.2). To prove the linear independence of the elements of W^{++} suppose that the relation

$$\sum r_i \rho_i = \sum r'_j \rho'_j$$

exists between the elements ρ_i, ρ'_j of W^{++}, all different, with $r_i, r'_j > 0$. Since $(\rho_i, \rho'_j) \leqslant 0$ (25.2.4),

$$(\sum r_i \rho_i, \sum r'_j \rho'_j) \leqslant 0,$$

whereas the positive definiteness of $(\ldots, \ldots)$ shows

$$(\sum r_i \rho_i, \sum r_i \rho_i) \geqslant 0.$$

Thus $\sum r_i \rho_i = \sum r'_j \rho'_j = 0$. On the other hand, $r_i, r'_j > 0$, $\rho_i, \rho'_j > 0$; hence $\sum r_i \rho_i > 0$ or $\sum r'_j \rho'_j > 0$ if the given relation is nonvoid, which would be contradictory.

If $\alpha \in W^+$, then either $\alpha \in W^{++}$ or $\alpha \in W^+ + W^+$, whence $\alpha = \beta + \gamma$ with suitable $\beta, \gamma \in W^+$, and $\beta < \alpha$, $\gamma < \alpha$. This splitting continues until α is written as a sum of primitive rootforms, with possible repetitions.

Conversely, let a natural basis Z be given. Put $\xi < \eta$ if and only if $\eta - \xi$ is a linear combination out of Z with positive coefficients. Clearly, this defines a partial order on $\boldsymbol{H}_{\mathrm{st}}^*$ and even a minimal one. Furthermore, $Z \subset W^+$. From 25.2.3 it follows that $Z \subset W^{++}$; hence $Z = W^{++}$.

The last assertion is obvious.

25.2.6. Proposition Every natural basis can also be obtained as W^{++} belonging to a partial order as defined in Proposition 25.2.2.

Proof Let the given natural basis Z consist of $\rho_1, \ldots, \rho_l$. Choose a basis $\boldsymbol{h}_1, \ldots, \boldsymbol{h}_l$ of $\boldsymbol{H}_{st}$ and define T by

$$T\boldsymbol{h} = \sum \rho_i(\boldsymbol{h})\,\boldsymbol{h}_i \quad \text{for all} \quad \boldsymbol{h} \in \boldsymbol{H}_{st}.$$

Then T is a nondegenerate linear mapping of $\boldsymbol{H}_{st}$ onto itself, so

$$\boldsymbol{h}_0 = T^{-1} \sum \boldsymbol{h}_i$$

makes sense, and

$$\rho_i(\boldsymbol{h}_0) = 1 > 0 \quad \text{for} \quad i = 1, \ldots, l.$$

In the order defined by $\boldsymbol{h}_0$ according to Proposition 25.2.2, all $\rho_i > 0$, hence $\rho_i \in W^+, Z \subset W^+$. From Proposition 25.2.3 it follows that $Z \subset W^{++}$, hence $Z = W^{++}$.

25.2.7. Proposition Every natural basis Z can be obtained as W^{++} belonging to a total order on $\boldsymbol{H}_{st}^*$.

Proof First order Z, and then $\boldsymbol{H}_{st}^*$ lexicographically with respect to Z as an ordered basis.

25.2.8 In the sequel a minimal partial order on $\boldsymbol{H}_{st}^*$ is mostly sufficient. Therefore the adjectives "minimal" and "partial" will be omitted. As soon as a total order on $\boldsymbol{H}_{st}^*$ is needed, it will be explicitly mentioned.

Definition $G \in$ Alg Lie Com SS is said to be "*in ordered dressing*" with respect to the trunk $\boldsymbol{H}$ if a minimal partial order has been assigned to $\boldsymbol{H}_{st}^*$ or, equivalently, if a natural basis has been fixed on $\boldsymbol{H}_{st}^*$. If needed, the order and the natural basis are transferred to $\boldsymbol{H}_{st}$ by means of ζ^{-1} (see 21.1.5). In this sense $\boldsymbol{H}_{st}$, and $\boldsymbol{H}$, for short, is called an *ordered trunk* of $\boldsymbol{G}$.

The meaning of *ordered second* (*third*) *dressing* is clear.

25.3. The Graph The essentials of the structure of W^{++} are recorded in a graph.

Definition The elements of W^{++} are accounted for by dots. Two dots ρ, σ are joined by a j-fold bond ($j = 1, 2, 3$) if

$$\cos \measuredangle (\rho, \sigma) = -\tfrac{1}{2}\sqrt{j}.$$

If $j = 2, 3$, an arrow is to point in the direction from the longest to the smallest rootform. This constitutes the *graph of* W^{++}, again denoted by W^{++}. It is also called the *graph of* $\boldsymbol{G}$ (with respect to an ordered $\boldsymbol{H}^*_{\text{st}}$).

Thus a j-fold bond (with an arrow pointing from ρ to σ for $j = 2, 3$) means

25.3.1 $$(\sigma,\sigma):(\rho,\sigma):(\rho,\rho) = 1:-\tfrac{1}{2}j:j.$$

Theorem Up to isomorphy $\boldsymbol{G}$ is determined by W^{++} ($\boldsymbol{G}$ in ordered second dressing).

To reduce this assertion to that of 22.2, W^+ must be built from a given W^{++}. This is done in 25.4.

The converse of the present theorem, which would mean that the structure of W^{++} is determined by $\boldsymbol{G}$, independent of the order chosen in $\boldsymbol{H}^*_{\text{st}}$, is verified in 33.5.

25.4. Building W^+ from W^{++}

Proposition By successively applying the following rule, W^+ can be rebuilt from W^{++}: if in the course of rebuilding $\alpha \in W^+$ has been secured and $\rho \in W^{++}$ is such that $(\alpha,\rho) < 0$, then $S_\rho\alpha$ is added. The decision of whether the process continues, and if so in which way, can be made on the knowledge of W^{++}.

(This proposition implies Theorem 25.3.)

Proof Suppose

$$W^{++} \subset Z \subset W^+, \qquad Z \neq W^+.$$

First the existence of $\alpha \in Z$, $\rho \in W^{++}$ with $(\alpha,\rho) < 0$ and $S_\rho\alpha \notin Z$ is shown.

Let β be such that all lower elements of W^+ are already in Z. Then

$$\beta = \sum r_j\rho_j, \qquad r_j \text{ integer} > 0, \qquad \rho_j \in W^{++}.$$

Now

$$(\beta, \sum r_j\rho_j) = (\beta,\beta) > 0;$$

thus for some j

$$(\beta, r_j\rho_j) > 0,$$

$$m = 2\frac{(\beta,\rho_j)}{(\rho_j,\rho_j)} > 0,$$

$$\alpha = S_{\rho_j}\beta = \beta - m\rho_j \in W.$$

$\beta \notin W^{++}$, so, on the basis W^{++}, it has at least two positive coordinates and α has at least one; hence $\alpha \in W^+$ though $\alpha < \beta$. Since β was a lowest element outside Z it follows $\alpha \in Z$.

$$S_{\rho_j}\alpha = \beta = \alpha + m\rho_j,$$

since S_{ρ_j} is involutory; thus

$$-2\frac{(\alpha,\rho_j)}{(\rho_j,\rho_j)} = m > 0;$$

hence $(\alpha,\rho_j) < 0$.

This proves the existence of α, ρ (namely, ρ_j), as required.

The value (α,ρ) is determined by the presentation of α as a sum of elements of W^{++} and by the values of (ρ,σ) for $\rho,\sigma \in W^{++}$. This settles the remainder of the proposition.

25.4.1. Proposition The coefficients of $\alpha \in W^+$ on the basis W^{++} have no common divisor (except 1).

Indeed, the assertion is evident for primitive rootforms and is preserved in the building up of W^+ from W^{++}, since (in the preceding proof) any common divisor of the coefficients of β reappears in m, hence in the coefficients of $\alpha = \beta - m\rho$.

25.4.2 An immediate consequence of the construction of W^+ from W^{++} is the following:

Proposition G is generated by the $e_\rho, e_{-\rho}$ with $\rho \in W^{++}$.

25.5. Direct Splittings

Definition A splitting of W^* into mutually orthogonal sets is called *direct*. A splitting of W^{++} into mutually orthogonal sets or, equivalently, into subsets with no bond from one to another is called *direct*.

Theorem Direct splittings of G, W^*, and W^{++} go together and induce each other.

Proof Let $G = G_1 + G_2$ be a direct sum. If H_1, H_2 are trunks of G_1, G_2, then $H = H_1 + H_2$ is a trunk of G, and all trunks of G are obtained this way, thanks to the equivalence of trunks under the adjoint group. Branches of G_1, G_2 commute with each other because $[G_1, G_2] = \{0\}$. Therefore rootforms from G_1, G_2 are orthogonal; this is particularly true of rootforms in W^{++}, which consequently splits according to the assertion.

Conversely, if W^{++} splits into nonconnected and consequently orthogonal subsets W_j^{++}, rebuilding W^* by 25.4 only creates sums for every W_j^{++} separately. They form orthogonal W_j^+, which constitute W^+. Adding the opposite rootforms produces W_j^*. For $\alpha_j \in W_j^*$ ($j = i, k, i \neq k$) one gets $(\alpha_i, \alpha_k) = 0$ as well as $\alpha_i + \alpha_k \notin W$, hence

$$[h_{\alpha i}, h_{\alpha k}] = [h_{\alpha i}, e_{\alpha k}] = [e_{\alpha i}, e_{\alpha k}] = 0,$$

which make G a direct sum of the G_j corresponding to W_j^{++}.

Corollary G is simple if and only if W^{++} is connected.

25.6. The Top Rootform

Proposition $G \in$ Alg Lie Com SSS (i.e., simple G) in ordered dressing has *one* maximal rootform (i.e., exceeding all other rootforms).

Proof Let α and β be maximal rootforms, $\alpha \neq \beta$,

$$\beta = \sum b_j \rho_j \qquad (\rho_j \in W^{++}).$$

Of course, $\alpha, \beta \in W^+$, $b_j \geqslant 0$. Now $\alpha - \beta \notin W^+$ because β is maximal and $\beta - \alpha \notin W^+$ because α is maximal. Therefore $\alpha - \beta \notin W$, whence $(\alpha, \beta) = 0$,

$$\sum b_j(\alpha, \rho_j) = 0.$$

The maximality of α implies $(\alpha, \rho_j) \geqslant 0$ for all j; thus

$$(\alpha, \rho_j) \neq 0 \to b_j = 0.$$

Because of $\alpha \neq 0$, there is a j with $(\alpha, \rho_j) \neq 0$ and consequently with $b_j = 0$. The graph of G is connected. Therefore there is some $\rho \in W^{++}$ with a neighbor $\sigma \in W^{++}$ and such that ρ occurs in β with a coefficient > 0, whereas σ does not. Thus $(\beta, \sigma) < 0$, $\beta + \sigma \in W^+$, which contradicts the maximality of β.

Definition If there is a unique maximal rootform, it is called the *top rootform*.

Note that the existence of the top rootform is equivalent to the simplicity of G.

25.7–8. Examples

25.7 In Section 16 natural bases of W^* were found for $G \in \mathbf{A}_l, \mathbf{B}_l, \mathbf{C}_l, \mathbf{D}_l$. The corresponding graphs are:

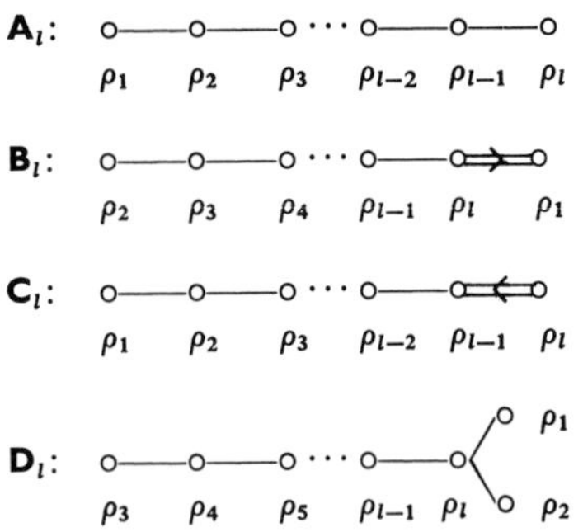

	dimension
$\mathbf{A}_l$	$(l+1)^2 - 1$
$\mathbf{B}_l$	$l(2l+1)$
$\mathbf{C}_l$	$l(2l+1)$
$\mathbf{D}_l$	$l(2l-1)$

The primitive rootforms have been linearly arranged as in Section 16,

$\mathbf{A}_l$: $\rho_j = \omega_j - \omega_{j+1}$,

$\mathbf{B}_l$: $\rho_j = \omega_{j-1} - \omega_j$ for $j > 1$, $\rho_1 = \omega_l$,

$\mathbf{C}_l$: $\rho_j = \omega_j - \omega_{j+1}$ for $j < l$, $\rho_l = 2\omega_l$,

$\mathbf{D}_l$: $\rho_j = \omega_{j-2} - \omega_{j-1}$ for $j \geqslant 3$, $\rho_1 = \omega_{l-1} - \omega_l$, $\rho_2 = \omega_{l-1} + \omega_l$.

It is easily verified that no other bonds than those appearing in the diagrams are possible; for example, $\omega_1 - \omega_2$ and $\omega_3 - \omega_4$ are not joined because $(\omega_1 - \omega_2) + (\omega_3 - \omega_4)$ is not a rootform; $\omega_1 - \omega_2$ and $\omega_2 - \omega_3$ are simply joined because $(\omega_1 - \omega_2) + (\omega_2 - \omega_3) = \omega_1 - \omega_3$ is a rootform, whereas neither $(\omega_1 - \omega_2) + 2(\omega_2 - \omega_3)$ nor $2(\omega_1 - \omega_2) + (\omega_2 - \omega_3)$ is a rootform. In the case of $G \in \mathbf{B}_l$ there are rootforms $(\omega_{l-1} - \omega_l) + j\omega_l$ for $j = 0, 1, 2$; hence

$$-2\frac{(\omega_{l-1} - \omega_l, \omega_l)}{(\omega_l, \omega_l)} = 2$$

and (see 25.1)

$$-2\frac{(\omega_{l-1} - \omega_l, \omega_l)}{(\omega_{l-1} - \omega_l, \omega_{l-1} - \omega_l)} = 1;$$

thus

$$(\omega_l, \omega_l) < (\omega_{l-1} - \omega_l, \omega_{l-1} - \omega_l),$$

which settles the direction of the arrow. For $G \in \mathbf{C}_l$ it points the other way.

25.8 The graphs disclose a few isomorphies:

25.8.1
$$\mathbf{A}_1 = \mathbf{B}_1 = \mathbf{C}_1$$

($\mathbf{D}_1$ was not defined).

25.8.2
$$\mathbf{B}_2 = \mathbf{C}_2.$$

25.8.3
$$\mathbf{D}_2 = \mathbf{A}_1 + \mathbf{A}_1$$

(which is a way of saying that a member of $\mathbf{D}_2$ is the direct sum of two of $\mathbf{A}_1$).

25.8.4
$$\mathbf{A}_3 = \mathbf{D}_3.$$

These isomorphies can be proved directly. The proofs are sketched.

25.8.1′ By definition, $\mathbf{A}_1 = \mathbf{C}_1$ is trivial; $\mathbf{A}_1 = \mathbf{B}_1$ reflects the well-known local isomorphism between the projective group of the complex projective line (function theory sphere) and the rotation group in 3-space by means of the stereographic projection between plane and sphere.

25.8.4′ $\mathbf{A}_3 = \mathbf{D}_3$. Linear mappings with unit determinants in 4-space, defined by

(a) $$\xi'_{i'} = \sum_i \alpha_{i'i}\, \xi_i,$$

induce mappings in the 6-space of skew tensors of degree 2:

$$\pi'_{i'j'} = \sum_{i<j} (\alpha_{i'i}\,\alpha_{j'j} - \alpha_{j'i}\,\alpha_{i'j})\, \pi_{ij}.$$

This leads to a representation G' of $G \in \mathsf{A}_3$ in 6-space. The variety of bivectors with coordinates

(b) $$\pi_{ij} = \begin{vmatrix} \xi_i & \xi_j \\ \eta_i & \eta_j \end{vmatrix},$$

where $\ulcorner \xi_1, \xi_2, \xi_3, \xi_4 \urcorner$, $\ulcorner \eta_1, \eta_2, \eta_3, \eta_4 \urcorner$ are points of 4-space transformed according to (a), is invariant under this representation of G'. The bivectors are characterized by the identity

(c) $$\pi_{12}\pi_{34} + \pi_{13}\pi_{42} + \pi_{14}\pi_{23} = 0,$$

which originates from developing

$$\begin{vmatrix} \xi_1 & \xi_2 & \xi_3 & \xi_4 \\ \eta_1 & \eta_2 & \eta_3 & \eta_4 \\ \xi_1 & \xi_2 & \xi_3 & \xi_4 \\ \eta_1 & \eta_2 & \eta_3 & \eta_4 \end{vmatrix} = 0.$$

This suggests that the quadratic form in the first member of (c) is invariant under G', hence G' contained in a member of D_3. By comparing dimensions one can show that G' *is* a member of $\mathbf{D}_3$.

The preceding notions admit of a projective interpretation. From a projective point of view (a) describes the projectivities of 3-space. Up to a scalar factor (b) is determined by the line joining the two points ξ, η (Plücker coordinates). The manifold (c) in projective 5-space is the image of the set of lines in 3-space.

25.8.2′ $\mathbf{B}_2 = \mathbf{C}_2$. With the same notation, $G \in \mathsf{C}_2$ is the group of transformations (a) leaving the skew bilinear form

$$\sum \sigma_{ij}\, \xi_j \eta_j$$

on 4-space invariant. In 6-space this implies invariance under G' of a linear form:

$$\sum \sigma_{ij}\, \pi_{ij}$$

(for bivectors $\ulcorner \pi_{ij} \urcorner$, thus for all skew tensors $\ulcorner \pi_{ij} \urcorner$ by linear combination). The nullspace of this form is a 5-subspace invariant under G'. Its intersection with

(c) is a quadric in 5-space and is again invariant. Consequently G' belongs to B_2.

In projective geometry $\sum \sigma_{ij}\xi_i\eta_j=0$ defines a so-called complex; $\sum \sigma_{ij}\pi_{ij}=0$ gives the lines lying on the complex.

25.8.3′ $\mathbf{D}_2 = \mathbf{A}_1 + \mathbf{A}_1$. The projectivities of 3-space leaving a quadric invariant also leave invariant or interchange the two families of straight lines on the quadric. The second kind may be disregarded. The projectivities leaving every line of one family invariant form a subgroup that is essentially the projective group of a projective line. The whole group is the direct product of the two subgroups belonging to the two families. This verifies the assertion.

An alternative argument: the rotations of 4-space can be presented by quaternion multiplications $D_{p,q}$,

$$D_{p,q}x = pxq^{-1} \qquad (|p| = |q| = 1).$$

The same is true of rotations B_p of 3-space:

$$B_p x = pxp^{-1} \qquad (\operatorname{Re} x = 0,\ |p| = 1).$$

The assignment of the pair $\ulcorner B_p, B_q \urcorner$ to $D_{p,q}$ produces a homomorphism of $G \in \mathsf{D}_2$ onto $G' \in \ulcorner \mathsf{B}_1, \mathsf{B}_1 \urcorner$ with the kernel consisting of $D_{1,1}$ and $D_{1,-1}$. It is a local isomorphism that induces an isomorphism of $\boldsymbol{G}$ and $\boldsymbol{G}'$.

26. CLASSIFICATION OF SEMISIMPLE COMPLEX LIE ALGEBRAS UP TO ISOMORPHISM

26.1 Because of the second criterion on semisimplicity, $\boldsymbol{G}$ is supposed simple of rank $\geqslant 1$.

26.2 All systems W^{++} must be determined. At present the lengths of their elements are not taken into account. The elements are normed as unit vectors.

One has to solve the following problem:

Problem To find the class $\mathscr{P}$ of nonvoid systems P of vectors in Euclidean space such that

26.2.1 $$\alpha \in P \rightarrow |\alpha| = 1,$$

26.2.2 the elements of P are linearly independent,

26.2.3 for $\alpha, \beta \in P$, $\alpha \neq \beta$, $(\alpha, \beta) = -\frac{1}{2}\sqrt{s}$ with $s = 0, 1, 2, 3$,

26.2.4 P is not a union of mutually orthogonal proper subsystems.

26.3 With the notation of 26.2.3, α, β are called s-fold joined if $s \neq 0$, unjoined if $s = 0$. The graph of P is connected because of 26.2.4.

26.4 $[P \in \mathscr{P} \wedge P' \subset P \wedge \text{graph } P' \text{ connected}] \to P' \in \mathscr{P}$.

26.5 The graph of $P \in \mathscr{P}$ is not a "circle."

Proof Suppose that P consists of different $\alpha_1, \ldots, \alpha_m$, with $(\alpha_j, \alpha_{j+1}) \neq 0$ for $j = 1, \ldots, m \bmod m$. Then

$$|\Sigma\, \alpha_j|^2 = \sum_j |\alpha_j|^2 + \sum_{i \neq j} (\alpha_i, \alpha_j) \leqslant m + 2\,\Sigma(\alpha_j, \alpha_{j+1}) \leqslant 0,$$

which cannot happen because of 26.2.2.

26.6 From 26.4–5 it follows that the graph cannot contain a circle. By 26.3 it is a "tree."

26.7 If $\alpha \in P$ is joined to exactly k elements of P, it is called k-sided. If $P \in \mathscr{P}$ and α is k-sided, then $P \setminus \{\alpha\}$ breaks into k nonvoid subsystems belonging to $\mathscr{P}$, called the arms of α.

26.8 If P is some set of vectors, $L(P)$ denotes the linear space spanned by P.

26.9 For $P \in \mathscr{P}$ and $\alpha \in P$, define

$$\varphi(P, \alpha) = \text{square of distance } \alpha, L(P \setminus \{\alpha\}).$$

Then

$$0 < \varphi(P, \alpha) \leqslant 1,$$

and, for $\alpha \in P' \subset P$, $P, P' \in \mathscr{P}$

$$\varphi(P', \alpha) \geqslant \varphi(P, \alpha).$$

26.10 For some $\alpha \in P \in \mathscr{P}$, let P_j signify the different arms of α in P. Let $\alpha_j \in P_j$ be s_j-fold joined to α (according to 26.6, these vectors and numbers are uniquely determined). Put

$$a_j = \varphi(P_j, \alpha_j), \qquad a = \varphi(P, \alpha).$$

Then

$$a \leqslant 1 - \sum_j \frac{s_j}{4a_j}.$$

This formula is the principal tool in this section.

Proof By definition there are

$$\gamma_j \in L(P_j \setminus \{\alpha_j\}),$$

with

$$|\alpha_j - \gamma_j|^2 = a_j.$$

The elements of different arms are orthogonal to each other; hence

$$(\alpha_i - \gamma_i, \alpha_j - \gamma_j) = 0 \quad \text{for} \quad i \neq j.$$

Moreover,

$$(\alpha, \alpha_j - \gamma_j) = (\alpha, \alpha_j) = -\tfrac{1}{2}\sqrt{s_j}.$$

Put

$$\beta = \alpha - \sum x_j(\alpha_j - \gamma_j)$$

and determine the scalars x_j such that

$$|\beta|^2 = 1 + \sum \sqrt{s_j}\, x_j + \sum a_j x_j^2$$

becomes minimal. This means

$$x_j = -\frac{\sqrt{s_j}}{2a_j}, \qquad |\beta|^2 = 1 - \sum \frac{s_j}{4a_j},$$

which proves the assertion.

26.11 At most, $\alpha \in P \in \mathscr{P}$ can be three-sided, for in the sum of 26.10 all summands are $\geqslant \frac{1}{4}$, whereas $a > 0$. If it is three-sided, its joins are simple, if it is two-sided, one of its joins is simple and the other may be simple or twofold.

26.12 If $P, P_i \in \mathscr{P}$ $(i = 1,2)$, $P_1 \cup P_2 = P$, $P_1 \cap P_2 = \{\alpha\}$, and $\varphi(P_1, \alpha) \leqslant \frac{1}{2}$, then $\varphi(P, \beta) \leqslant \frac{1}{2}$ for any $\beta \in P_2$.

Proof For $P_2 = \{\alpha, \beta\}$ this is a consequence of 26.10 because

$$\varphi(P, \beta) \leqslant 1 - \frac{1}{4 \cdot \frac{1}{2}} = \tfrac{1}{2}.$$

Induction on the number of steps needed to reach β from α and application of 26.9 complete the proof.

26.13 If $\alpha \in P \in \mathscr{P}$ is at least two-sided, then $\varphi(P, \alpha) \leqslant \frac{1}{2}$.

Proof Let α be joined to α_1, α_2. It suffices to prove the assertion for the system $\{\alpha_1, \alpha, \alpha_2\}$:

$$\varphi(P, \alpha) \leqslant 1 - \frac{1}{4 \cdot 1} - \frac{1}{4 \cdot 1} = \tfrac{1}{2}.$$

26.14 If $\beta \in P \in \mathscr{P}$ is three-sided, then $\varphi(P,\alpha) \leqslant \frac{1}{2}$ for any $\alpha \in P$.

Proof Thanks to 26.13, the case $\alpha = \beta$ may be waived. Suppose that α is in the arm P' of β and put $P'' = P \setminus P'$. Then $\beta \in P'' \in \mathscr{P}$. In P'', β is at least two-sided; hence, by 26.13, $\varphi(P'',\beta) \leqslant \frac{1}{2}$ and by 26.12, $\varphi(P,\alpha) \leqslant \frac{1}{2}$.

26.15 $P \in \mathscr{P}$ can have at most one three-sided element.

Proof Assume that α, β are three-sided. Let P_j $(j = 1, 2, 3)$ be the arms of α, and $\alpha_j \in P_j$ joined to α. Assume that $\beta \in P_1$. Then $\varphi(P_j,\alpha_j) \leqslant 1$ and by 26.14 $\varphi(P_1,\alpha_1) \leqslant \frac{1}{2}$. Now

$$\varphi(P,\alpha) \leqslant 1 - \frac{1}{4\cdot\frac{1}{2}} - \frac{1}{4\cdot 1} - \frac{1}{4\cdot 1} = 0,$$

which is not allowed by 26.2.2.

26.16 No $P \in \mathscr{P}$ with more than two elements has a threefold join.

Proof It suffices to refute $P = \{\alpha, \beta, \gamma\}$ with a threefold join between α and β and a join between β and γ. This is contained in 26.11.

26.17 If $P \in \mathscr{P}$ has a twofold join, then $\varphi(P,\gamma) \leqslant \frac{1}{2}$ for all $\gamma \in P$.

Proof By 26.12 it suffices to prove 26.17 for $P = \{\alpha, \beta\}$:

$$\varphi(P,\beta) \leqslant 1 - \frac{2}{4\cdot 1} = \tfrac{1}{2}.$$

26.18 No $P \in \mathscr{P}$ possesses both a three-sided element and a twofold join.

Proof Suppose that $\alpha \in P$ is three-sided and β, γ are twofold joined. They may be arranged so that an arm P' of γ contains α, β. If $\alpha \neq \beta$, then α is three-sided in P'; hence, by 26.14, $\varphi(P',\beta) \leqslant \frac{1}{2}$. If $\alpha = \beta$, the same follows from 26.11. Now by 26.10

$$\varphi(P' \cup \{\gamma\}, \gamma) \leqslant 1 - \frac{2}{4\cdot\frac{1}{2}} = 0.$$

26.19 No $P \in \mathscr{P}$ has more than one twofold join.

Proof Assume twofold joins between α and β and between γ and δ. They may be arranged so that an arm P' of δ contains α, β, γ. By 26.17 $\varphi(P', \gamma) \leqslant \frac{1}{2}$; hence

$$\varphi(P' \cup \{\delta\}, \delta) \leqslant 1 - \frac{2}{4\cdot\frac{1}{2}} = 0.$$

26.20 A $P \in \mathscr{P}$ with a twofold join has a linearly arranged graph according to 26.18. If P has more than four elements, then the twofold join can stand at one of its ends only.

Proof Consider P consisting of different $\alpha_1, \alpha_2, \alpha_3, \alpha_4, \alpha_5$, with α_i, α_{i+1} joined and α_2, α_3 twofold joined. Put $P_j = \{\alpha_1, \ldots, \alpha_j\}$.

$$\varphi(P_2, \alpha_2) \leqslant 1 - \frac{1}{4\cdot 1} = \tfrac{3}{4},$$

$$\varphi(P_3, \alpha_3) \leqslant 1 - \frac{2}{4\cdot\frac{3}{4}} = \tfrac{1}{3},$$

$$\varphi(P_4, \alpha_4) \leqslant 1 - \frac{1}{4\cdot\frac{1}{3}} = \tfrac{1}{4},$$

$$\varphi(P_5, \alpha_5) \leqslant 1 - \frac{1}{4\cdot\frac{1}{4}} = 0.$$

26.21 Let $K_q \in \mathscr{P}$ be the system of different $\alpha_1, \ldots, \alpha_q$, with α_j, α_{j+1} simply joined. Then

$$\varphi(K_q, \alpha_q) \leqslant \frac{q+1}{2q}.$$

Proof Obvious for $q = 1$. Induction:

$$\varphi(K_{q+1}, \alpha_{q+1}) \leqslant 1 - \left(4\cdot\frac{q+1}{2q}\right)^{-1} = \frac{q+2}{2(q+1)}.$$

26.22 Let $\delta \in P \in \mathscr{P}$ be three-sided. By 26.15 and 26.18 the arms of δ have the form K_p, K_q, K_r (see 26.21). Hence

$$\varphi(P, \delta) \leqslant 1 - \frac{p}{2(p+1)} - \frac{q}{2(q+1)} - \frac{r}{2(r+1)}.$$

From a function table for $y = x/(2(x+1))$,

$$x = 1, 2, 3, 4, 5, \ldots,$$
$$y = \tfrac{1}{4}, \tfrac{1}{3}, \tfrac{3}{8}, \tfrac{2}{5}, \tfrac{5}{12}, \ldots, \text{ increasing},$$

it follows for p, q, r that

not all of them are $\geqslant 2$,

no two of them $\geqslant 3$.

Suppose that $p \leqslant q \leqslant r$. Then the only admissible p, q, r are

$p = q = 1$, r arbitrary,

$p = 1, q = 2$, $r \leqslant 4$.

26.23 In addition to the known connected graphs belonging to

$$\mathbf{A}_l\ (l \geqslant 1), \qquad \mathbf{B}_l\ (l \geqslant 3), \qquad \mathbf{C}_l\ (l \geqslant 2), \qquad \mathbf{D}_l\ (l \geqslant 4),$$

the only possible ones are:

		dimension (see Table B)
$\mathbf{G}_2$:	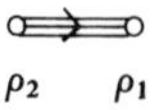	14
$\mathbf{F}_4$:	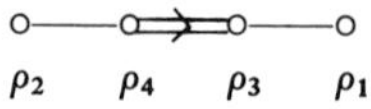	52
$\mathbf{E}_6$:	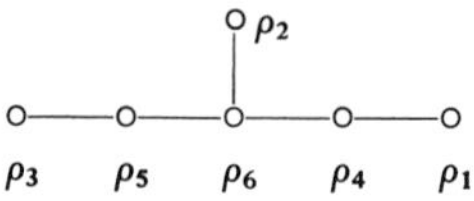	78
$\mathbf{E}_7$:	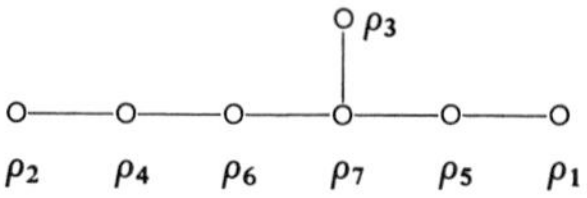	133
$\mathbf{E}_8$:	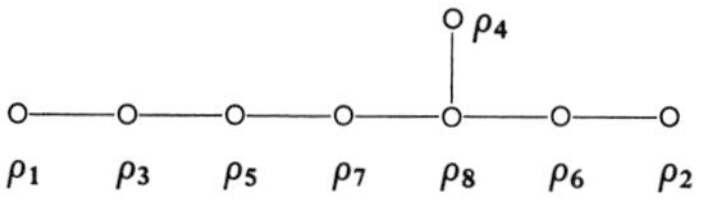	248

Indeed, according to 26.16, the systems with threefold joins are exhausted by $\mathbf{G}_2$. According to 26.18, 26.19, and 26.20, the systems with twofold joins are exhausted by $\mathbf{B}_l$, $\mathbf{C}_l$, $\mathbf{F}_4$. According to 26.15 and 26.22 those with three-sided elements are exhausted by $\mathbf{D}_l$, $\mathbf{E}_6$, $\mathbf{E}_7$, $\mathbf{E}_8$.

By these graphs the vector lengths in W^{++} are settled as well. An essential choice of how to point the arrow exists in the cases $\mathbf{B}_l$, $\mathbf{C}_l$ $(l > 2)$ only.

26.24 Complex Classification Theorem The isomorphism classes of simple semisimple complex Lie algebras are given by

$$\mathbf{A}_l\ (l \geqslant 1), \qquad \mathbf{B}_l\ (l \geqslant 3), \qquad \mathbf{C}_l\ (l \geqslant 2), \qquad \mathbf{D}_l\ (l \geqslant 4),$$
$$\mathbf{G}_2, \quad \mathbf{F}_4, \quad \mathbf{E}_6, \quad \mathbf{E}_7, \quad \mathbf{E}_8.$$

Actually, the existence of the five *exceptional* Lie algebras has not been proved here. In 27.1 it is done for $\mathbf{G}_2$. (See also 26.25.)

Likewise, it has not yet been proved that all of these classes are different. This depends on the proof that the order chosen in H^*_{st} does not exert any influence on the structure of W^{++} (see 25.3 and 33.5).

By the procedure in 25.4, W^+ can be built up from W^{++}. This also yields the dimension of the corresponding Lie algebra. The results of these computations are to be found in Table B. The top rootforms are collected in Table D. The construction of $W^+(\mathbf{F}_4)$ is shown in 27.2.

26.25 Historical Note The classification goes back to W. Killing, *Math. Ann.* **31** (1888), **33** (1889), **34** (1889), **36** (1890) and E. Cartan (Thèse, 1894). B. L. van der Waerden simplified it by using the second Weyl norming [*Math. Z.* **37**, 446–462 (1933)]. As a new tool, E. Dynkin introduced the notions of order and of natural basis, and the graph [*Uspehi Mat. Nauk N.S.* **2**, 59–127 (1947)], though graphs like these had already been used by L. Schläfli and H. S. M. Coxeter in similar situations. The present method was published by H. Freudenthal [*Proc. Kon. Akad. Wet. Amsterdam* **61**, 379–383 (1958)].

The exhibited numbering of the primitive rootforms corresponds to Cartan's of the fundamental weights (see *Œuvres* I, **1**, 355–398), which is the most natural (except in the case $\mathbf{E}_6$, in which it contains an inconsistency). Though it has become a habit for every author to use his own numbering, it would be better to stick to Cartan's as has been done here.

In E. Cartan's thesis the existence of the simple Lie algebras occurring in the complex classification theorem has been ascertained by individual construction. A general, though cumbersome, construction was devised by Harish-Chandra (*Trans. Amer. Math. Soc.* **70**, 28–96 (1951). Another, still involved, has been designed by J. Tits (unpublished). According to H. de Vries (unpublished), the case of simple bonds only can be dealt with by a rather easy method.

The exceptional Lie algebras have been extensively studied in the last 15 years. The literature on this subject can be found in part in the bibliography in H. Freudenthal, "Lie Groups in Geometry," *Advan. Math.* **1**, 145–190 (1965). A general formula for the construction of all five exceptional Lie algebras has been given by J. Tits (*Publ. Math. I.H.E.S.* **31**, 525–562 (1966); see also R. D. Schafer, *Proc. Kon. Akad. Wet. Amsterdam* **A69**, 64–69 (1966) (*Indagationes* **28**).

27. $\mathbf{G}_2$ AND $\mathbf{F}_4$. THE CHEVALLEY DRESSING

27.1–2 $\mathbf{G}_2$ and $\mathbf{F}_4$

27.1 $G \in \mathbf{G}_2$.

$$(\rho_1, \rho_1) = c, \qquad (\rho_1, \rho_2) = -\tfrac{3}{2} c, \qquad (\rho_2, \rho_2) = 3c,$$

with some c yet to be determined. Because of

$$-2\frac{(\rho_1, \rho_2)}{(\rho_1, \rho_1)} = 3,$$

there is a ρ_1-ladder of length 3 from ρ_2. This gives the rootforms

$$\rho_2+\rho_1, \qquad \rho_2+2\rho_1, \qquad \rho_2+3\rho_1.$$

Because of

$$-2\frac{(\rho_2+3\rho_1,\rho_2)}{(\rho_2,\rho_2)}=1,$$

there is still a rootform

$$2\rho_2+3\rho_1.$$

Furthermore, there are the opposite rootforms and twofold 0. Hence

$$\dim \boldsymbol{G}=14.$$

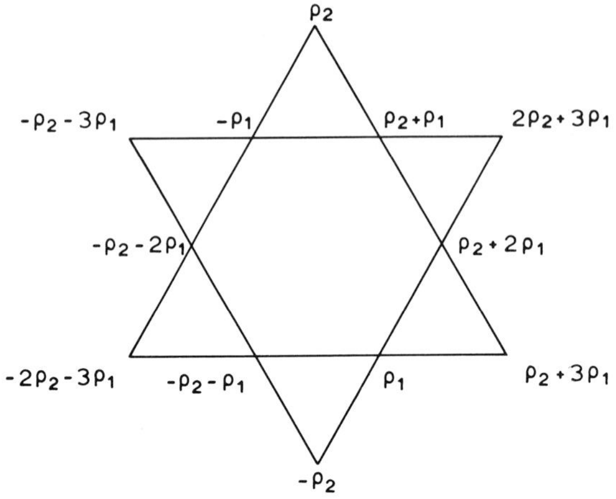

FIG. 1.

There are

$$\left.\begin{array}{ll}1 & \rho_1\text{-ladder of length } 2\\ 2 & \rho_1\text{-ladders of length } 3\end{array}\right\} N_{\rho 1}=12(\rho_1,\rho_1),$$

$$\left.\begin{array}{ll}1 & \rho_2\text{-ladder of length } 2\\ 4 & \rho_2\text{-ladders of length } 1\end{array}\right\} N_{\rho 2}=4(\rho_2,\rho_2).$$

(The $N_{\rho 1}, N_{\rho 2}$ have been computed by 20.13.)

Since $N_{\rho i}=1$, $c=\frac{1}{12}$. To compute $N_{\alpha,\beta}$ the formula in Theorem 23.2 is used. Then (with $\varepsilon=\pm 1$)

$$N_{\rho 1,\rho 2}=i\varepsilon_1\sqrt{\tfrac{1}{8}},$$

$$N_{\rho 1,\rho 1+\rho 2}=i\varepsilon_2\sqrt{\tfrac{1}{6}},$$

$$N_{\rho 1,2\rho 1+\rho 2}=i\varepsilon_3\sqrt{\tfrac{1}{8}},$$

$$N_{\rho 2,3\rho 1+\rho 2}=i\varepsilon_4\sqrt{\tfrac{1}{8}},$$

$$N_{\rho 1+\rho 2,2\rho 1+\rho 2}=i\varepsilon_5\sqrt{\tfrac{1}{8}},$$

with the relation

$$\varepsilon_1 \varepsilon_3 + \varepsilon_4 \varepsilon_5 = 0$$

by Jacobi-associativity. These $N_{\alpha,\beta}$ determine the others.

27.2 The method in 25.4 produces the rootforms of $G \in \mathbf{F}_4$ (Fig. 2).

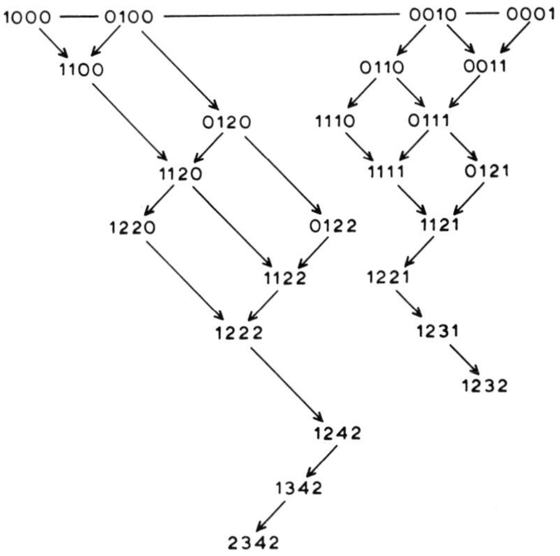

FIG. 2.

Here the primitive rootforms have been arranged according to their appearance in the graph. So 2342 means $2\rho_2 + 3\rho_4 + 4\rho_3 + 2\rho_1$.

27.3.† The Chevalley Dressing

$G \in$ Alg Lie Com SS in third dressing on $\boldsymbol{H}$ with branches $\boldsymbol{e}_\alpha$ and nodes $\boldsymbol{h}_\alpha$.

27.3.1. Theorem The branches $\boldsymbol{e}_\alpha$ can be renormed into branches $\boldsymbol{e}'_\alpha$ such that

(a) all $N'_{\alpha,\beta}$ in $[\boldsymbol{e}'_\alpha, \boldsymbol{e}'_\beta] = N'_{\alpha,\beta}\boldsymbol{e}'_{\alpha+\beta}$ are integral;
(b) linear M defined by $M\boldsymbol{h} = -\boldsymbol{h}$ ($\boldsymbol{h} \in \boldsymbol{H}$) and $M\boldsymbol{e}'_\alpha = \boldsymbol{e}'_{-\alpha}$ ($\alpha \in W^*$) is still an automorphism of $\boldsymbol{G}$;
(c) the nodes $\boldsymbol{h}'_\alpha = [\boldsymbol{e}'_\alpha, \boldsymbol{e}'_{-\alpha}]$ are

$$\boldsymbol{h}'_\alpha = -\frac{2}{(\alpha, \alpha)}\boldsymbol{h}_\alpha \qquad (\alpha \in W^*).$$

Of course, by such a renorming the third dressing will be destroyed.

† The contents of 27.3 will not be used in the sequel.

27.3.2. Definition A first dressing with respect to a trunk $\boldsymbol{H}$, branches $\boldsymbol{e}'_\alpha$, and nodes $\boldsymbol{h}'_\alpha$ is called a *Chevalley* or *integral* dressing if the $\boldsymbol{e}'_\alpha$ and $\boldsymbol{h}'_\alpha$ have the properties (a), (b), (c) enunciated in Theorem 27.3.1.

The existence of Chevalley dressings follows from Theorem 27.3.1. Clearly, every Chevalley dressing can be derived from a third dressing by renorming the branches and adjusting the nodes.

27.3.3. *Proof of the theorem* The new nodes $\boldsymbol{h}'_\alpha$ are defined by

$$\text{(d)} \qquad \boldsymbol{h}'_\alpha = -\frac{2}{(\alpha, \alpha)} \boldsymbol{h}_\alpha \qquad (\alpha \in W^*).$$

In view of (d), the fact that the $N_{\alpha,\beta}$ are purely imaginary, and (b), one is led to put

$$\text{(e)} \qquad \boldsymbol{e}'_\alpha = \mathrm{i} \left(\frac{2}{(\alpha, \alpha)}\right)^{1/2} \boldsymbol{e}_\alpha .$$

Then

$$N'^2_{\alpha,\beta} = N^2_{\alpha,\beta} \cdot \frac{-2}{(\alpha, \alpha)} \cdot \frac{-2}{(\beta, \beta)} \cdot \frac{-(\alpha+\beta, \alpha+\beta)}{2},$$

from which by 23.2

$$\text{(f)} \qquad N'^2_{\alpha,\beta} = (j+1)(p-j) \frac{(\alpha+\beta, \alpha+\beta)}{(\beta, \beta)}$$

if β is the $(j+1)$th element in an α-ladder of length p. Only the case $\alpha + \beta \in W^*$ is relevant. Then

$$\text{(g)} \qquad j < p.$$

If $(\alpha, \beta) = 0$, then $p = 2j$, hence $p = 2, j = 1$; moreover

$$(\alpha+\beta, \alpha+\beta) > (\beta, \beta), \qquad -2\frac{(\alpha+\beta, \beta)}{(\beta, \beta)} = -2,$$

whence by 25.1

$$\frac{(\alpha+\beta, \alpha+\beta)}{(\beta, \beta)} = 2,$$

thus,

$$\text{(h)} \qquad \text{if } (\alpha, \beta) = 0 \text{ then } N'^2_{\alpha,\beta} = 4.$$

Now let $(\alpha, \beta) \neq 0$. Because $N'_{\alpha,\beta} = -N'_{\beta,\alpha}$, it suffices to investigate the case

$$(\alpha, \alpha) \leqslant (\beta, \beta).$$

Then, again by 25.1, it follows from

$$-2\frac{(\alpha,\beta)}{(\alpha,\alpha)}=p-2j$$

that

$$\frac{(\beta,\beta)}{(\alpha,\alpha)}=|p-2j|.$$

Substituting these results into (f) one gets

$$\text{(i)} \qquad N'^2_{\alpha,\beta}=(j+1)(p-j)\left(1+\frac{1-p+2j}{|p-2j|}\right) \qquad \text{if} \quad (\alpha,\beta)\neq 0.$$

Substituting the possible values $p=1,2,3$ and $j=0,1,\ldots,p-1$, one obtains from (g), (h), and (i)

$$|N'_{\alpha,\beta}|=j+1 \quad \text{(or 0)}.$$

This proves the theorem.

Proposition In Chevalley dressing the $|N'_{\alpha,\beta}|$ are $j+1$ if β is the $(j+1)$th (but not the last) element in its α-ladder.

This has been proved under the assumption $(\alpha,\alpha)\leqslant(\beta,\beta)$. If $(\alpha,\alpha)<(\beta,\beta)$, then necessarily $j=0$, $p=2,3$ so β is the first element in its α-ladder of length >1. Then, however, α is also the first element in its β-ladder (of length 1), and j remains unchanged if α,β are interchanged. This shows that the condition $(\alpha,\alpha)\leqslant(\beta,\beta)$ can be dismissed.

The assertion is true for any Chevalley dressing, which follows from the fact that apart from signs there is really no other choice for e'_α in (e).

27.3.4. Historical Note Integral dressing, introduced by C. Chevalley in *Tôhoku Math. J.* 7 (2), 14–66 (1955), proves its importance in algebraic groups.

28–38

TOPOLOGICAL AND INTEGRATION METHODS

28. HOMOTOPY AND WRAPPING

G is supposed to be a Hausdorff space (Spa Top Hau), G is pathwise connected (pc) from 28.7 on, locally pathwise connected (lpc) from 28.8 on, and locally simply connected (lsc) from 28.13 on.

28.1 A *path* on a topological space G is a continuous mapping of $\uparrow_\tau(0 \leqslant \tau \leqslant 1)$. The set of paths on G is called $\mathscr{W}(G)$ or, for short, $\mathscr{W}$.

For $w, w' \in \mathscr{W}$, with $w(1) = w'(0)$, a product

$$w'' = w \circ w' \in \mathscr{W}$$

is defined by

$$\begin{aligned} w''(\tau) &= w(2\tau) \qquad &\text{for} \quad 0 \leqslant \tau \leqslant \tfrac{1}{2}, \\ &= w'(2\tau - 1) \qquad &\text{for} \quad \tfrac{1}{2} \leqslant \tau \leqslant 1. \end{aligned}$$

For $A, B \subset G$, by $\mathscr{W}_A{}^B$ is meant the set of $w \in \mathscr{W}$ with

$$w(0) \in A, \qquad w(1) \in B.$$

If A or B consists of a single point, its name is used in the notation $\mathscr{W}_A{}^B$.

28.2 Two paths w_0, w_1 are called *A-B-homotopic*, if there is a system of paths w_σ depending on a parameter σ $(0 \leqslant \sigma \leqslant 1)$ such that $w_\sigma \in \mathscr{W}_A{}^B$ and $\curlyvee_{\ulcorner \sigma, \tau \urcorner} w_\sigma(\tau)$ is continuous.

Clearly A-B-homotopy is an equivalence relation.

If A or B consists of a single point, its name is used in the term A-B-homotopy.

w_0, w_1 are called *homotopic* (without specification) if they are a-b-homotopic with $a = w_0(0) = w_1(0)$, $b = w_0(1) = w_1(1)$.

The homotopy class of w is denoted by $[w]$. The set of all homotopy classes in G is denoted by $[\mathscr{W}(G)]$ or, for short, $[\mathscr{W}]$.

28.3 Every $w_0 \in \mathscr{W}_A{}^G$ is A-G-homotopic with a constant path w_1; that is, $w_1(\tau) = a$ for some a and all τ.

Indeed, put

$$\begin{aligned} w_\sigma(\tau) &= w_0(\tau) \qquad &\text{for} \quad \tau \leqslant 1 - \sigma, \\ &= w_0(1 - \sigma) \qquad &\text{for} \quad \tau \geqslant 1 - \sigma. \end{aligned}$$

28.4 From w_0 homotopic w_1, w_0' homotopic w_1', it follows $w_0 \circ w_0'$ homotopic $w_1 \circ w_1'$ (if defined). This induces a product of classes:

$$[w] \circ [w'] = [w \circ w'].$$

28.5 This product is associative. See Fig. 3; the nonhorizontal lines are

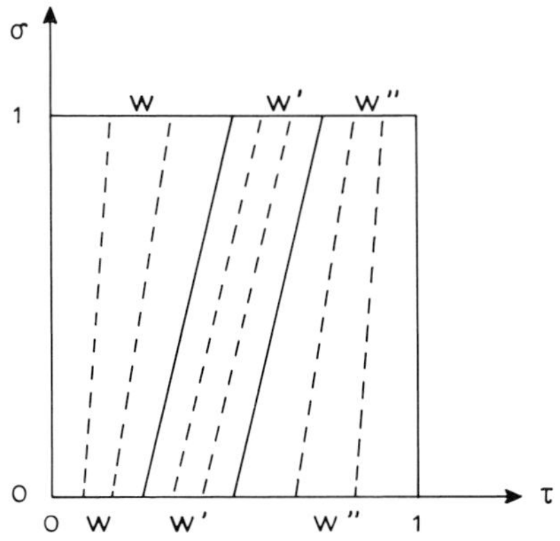

FIG. 3.

mapped into points, the horizontal lines are mapped according to the functions shown by letters; formally

$$\begin{aligned} w_\sigma'''(\tau) &= w\left(\frac{4\tau}{\sigma+1}\right) && \text{for } 0 \leqslant 4\tau \leqslant \sigma+1, \\ &= w'(4\tau-\sigma-1) && \text{for } \sigma+1 \leqslant 4\tau \leqslant \sigma+2, \\ &= w''\left(\frac{4\tau-\sigma-2}{2-\sigma}\right) && \text{for } \sigma+2 \leqslant 4\tau \leqslant 4. \end{aligned}$$

Thus

$$w_0''' = (w \circ w') \circ w'' \qquad \text{and} \qquad w_1''' = w \circ (w' \circ w'')$$

are homotopic.

28.6 With respect to this product $[w] \in [\mathscr{W}^\frown]$ possesses one right unit (containing the constant path $u = \curlyvee_\tau w(1)$), one left unit (containing the constant path $\Upsilon_\tau w(0)$), and a right and left inverse (containing the inverted path $z = \Upsilon_\tau w(1-\tau)$). (See Figs. 4 and 5.)

$[\mathscr{W}]$ is a *groupoid.*

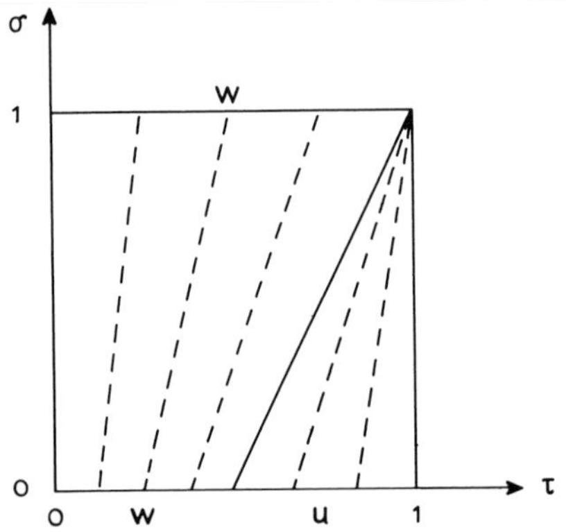

FIG. 4.

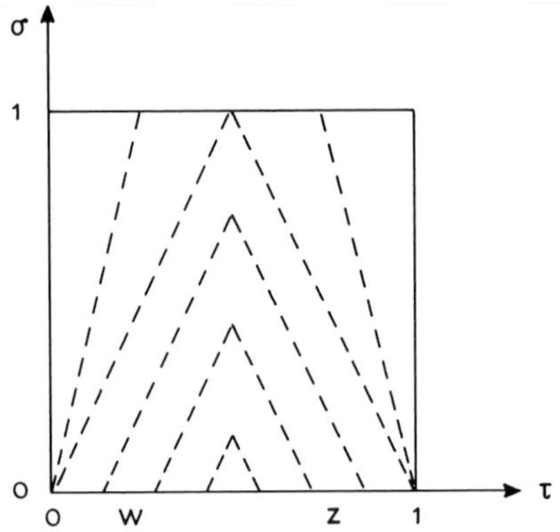

FIG. 5.

28.7 The $[w]$ with $w \in \mathscr{W}_p{}^p$ form even a *group* denoted by Φ_p.

From now on G is supposed to be *pathwise connected* (pc).

Then, for two points $p,q \in G$, Φ_p and Φ_q are isomorphic by means of a mapping f defined by choosing some fixed $u \in \mathscr{W}_p{}^q$ and putting

$$f[w] = [u]^{-1} \circ [w] \circ [u].$$

Often the subscript p of Φ_p is dropped. Φ is called the *fundamental group* of G.

G is called *simply connected* (sc) if Φ consists of the unit only. Then any path w with $w(0) = w(1)$ is homotopic with a constant path and any pair of paths w_0, w_1, with $w_0(0) = w_1(0)$, $w_0(1) = w_1(1)$, is homotopic, since $[w_0] = [w_0 \circ w_1^{-1} \circ w_1] = [w_1]$.

28.8 G is called *locally pathwise connected* (lpc) if every point of G has arbitrary small open neighborhoods that are pathwise connected.

From now on G is assumed to be lpc.

The set of $[w] \in [\mathscr{W}]$ with $w \in \mathscr{W}_p{}^G$ is called $\hat{G}_p$ or simply $\hat{G}$. The set $\hat{G}$ is going to be *topologized* and the result is called the *universal wrapping* of G.

Let U be a pc open set in G and let K be a maximal set of p-U-homotopic paths. The set of all $[w] \subset K$ is called a *sheet* $\hat{U}$ over U. Two different sheets over U are disjoint.

Let U_1 be another pc open set in G, and $\hat{U}_1$ a sheet over U_1. Now $U \cap U_1$ as an open set in a lpc space is the union of disjoint pc open sets. From this it follows that $\hat{U} \cap \hat{U}_1$ is a union of sheets (over those components of $U \cap U_1$).

A set in $\hat{G}$ is called *open* if it is a union of sheets.

From the last paragraph it follows that $\hat{G}$ has become a topological space. The method used in 28.7 shows that its structure does not depend on p up to homeomorphy.

28.9 The mapping π defined by

$$\pi[w] = w(1)$$

maps $\hat{G}$ onto G, since G is pc. It is called the *projection*.

π maps a sheet over U onto U.

To prove this take some $[w] \in \hat{U}$ (then $w(1) \in U$) and connect $w(1)$ with an arbitrary $q \in U$ by a path v within U. Then, according to 28.3 applied to U instead of G, v is $w(1)$-U-homotopic with a constant path; therefore $w \circ v$ is p-U-homotopic with w and consequently contained in an element of $\hat{U}$. So $q = \pi[w \circ v]$ belongs to $\pi\hat{U}$.

28.10 The π-original of a pc open U is the union of the sheets over U, hence open. Thus π *is continuous.* According to 28.9, π even maps open sets *onto* open sets.

28.11 A system of paths w_σ is said to depend continuously on the parameter σ if $\Upsilon_{\ulcorner \sigma,\tau \urcorner} w_\sigma(\tau)$ is continuous.

Let the paths w_σ depend continuously on σ ($0 \leqslant \sigma \leqslant 1$) and put

$$v_i = \Upsilon_\sigma\, w_\sigma(i) \quad \text{for} \quad i = 0, 1.$$

Then $v_0 \circ w_1$ is homotopic with $w_0 \circ v_1$ and with $\Upsilon_\sigma\, w_\sigma(\sigma)$. (See Fig. 6.)

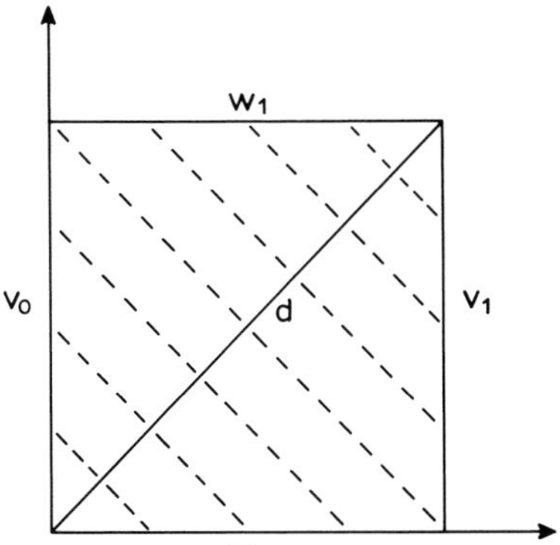

FIG. 6.

Conversely, if for some paths v_0, v_1, w_0, w_1, $v_0 \circ w_1$ is homotopic with $w_0 \circ v_1$, then there is a system of paths w_σ depending continuously on σ $(0 \leqslant \sigma \leqslant 1)$ such that $v_i = \curlyvee_\sigma w_\sigma(i)$ for $i = 0, 1$.

28.12 Let A be a line segment or a square and $w_\alpha \in \mathscr{W}_p{}^G$ depend continuously on $\alpha \in A$. Then $[w_\alpha]$ depends continuously on α.

Proof As a neighborhood of $[w_{\alpha_0}]$ take a sheet $\hat{U}$ (over U). Then $w_{\alpha_0}(1) \in U$ and still $w_\alpha(1) \in U$ for α in some line segment or square neighborhood A_0 of α_0. Thus w_{α_0}, w_α are p-U-homotopic by means of some subsystem of the w_β $(\beta \in A_0)$. In any case $[w_\alpha] \in \hat{U}$ for $\alpha \in A_0$, which proves the assertion.

28.13 G is called *locally simply connected* (lsc) if every point of G possesses arbitrarily small simply connected open neighborhoods.

From now on G is assumed to be lsc.

Then π is *locally topological.*

According to 28.9–10 it suffices to prove:

Let $\hat{U}$ be a sheet over sc open $U \subset G$. Then π maps $\hat{U}$ one-to-one.

Proof Take $[w_0], [w_1] \in \hat{U}$; hence w_0, w_1 are p-U-homotopic. Suppose $\pi[w_0] = \pi[w_1] = q$, that is $w_0(1) = w_1(1) = q$ in addition to $w_0(0) = w_1(0) = p$. There is a system of w_σ depending continuously on σ $(0 \leqslant \sigma \leqslant 1)$ such that

$$w_\sigma(0) = p, \qquad w_\sigma(1) \in U.$$

By 28.11 w_1 is homotopic with $w_0 \circ \curlyvee_\sigma w_\sigma(1)$. Since U is sc, the second factor is homotopic with $\curlyvee_\sigma q$, which proves the assertion.

28.14 For a path $w \in \mathscr{W}_p{}^G$ define $\hat{w}$ by putting

$$w_\sigma(\tau) = w(\sigma\tau), \qquad [w_\sigma] = \hat{w}(\sigma).$$

By 28.12 $\hat{w}$ is a path on $\hat{G}$. The process by which it was obtained is called *stretching*.

If $w_\gamma \in \mathscr{W}_p{}^G$ depends continuously on γ $(0 \leqslant \gamma \leqslant 1)$, then $\hat{w}_\gamma$ has the same property.

This follows from 28.12 if applied with $\ulcorner \gamma, \sigma \urcorner$ instead of α.

28.15 *Projection* and *stretching* are inverses of each other.

Proof It is obvious that $\pi\hat{w} = w$. Conversely, let a path on $\hat{G}$ be given by

$$z = \curlyvee_\sigma[\curlyvee_\tau w_\sigma(\tau)], \qquad [w_0] = [\curlyvee_\tau p]$$

where $w_\sigma \in \mathscr{W}_p{}^G$ for each σ $(0 \leqslant \sigma \leqslant 1)$. The set of $z(\sigma)$ is covered by a finite number of sheets $\hat{U}_i$ (over sc U_i) of which it can be assumed that there are σ_i, $i = 0, \ldots, m$, such that $\sigma_0 = 0$, $\sigma_m = 1$, $\sigma_i < \sigma_{i+1}$, $z(\sigma) \in \hat{U}_{i+1}$ for $\sigma_i \leqslant \sigma \leqslant \sigma_{i+1}$, $z(\sigma_i) \in \hat{U}_i \cap \hat{U}_{i+1}$. Since $z(\sigma_i)$, $z(\sigma_{i+1}) \in \hat{U}_{i+1}$, it follows that w_{σ_i} and $w_{\sigma_{i+1}}$ are p-U_{i+1}-homotopic. So there are paths $v_\alpha{}^i$ depending continuously on α $(0 \leqslant \alpha \leqslant 1)$ such that $v_\alpha{}^i(0) = p$, $v_\alpha{}^i(1) \in U_{i+1}$, $v_0{}^i = w_{\sigma_i}$, $v_1{}^i = w_{\sigma_{i+1}}$. Define $y_i = \Upsilon_\alpha v_\alpha{}^i(1)$. Then by 28.11 $w_{\sigma_{i+1}} (= v_1{}^i)$ is homotopic with $w_{\sigma_i} \circ y_i$ $(= v_0{}^i \circ y_i)$. In turn, since U_{i+1} is sc, y_i is homotopic with x_i arising by reparametrization from $\Upsilon_{\sigma_i \leqslant \sigma \leqslant \sigma_{i+1}} w_\sigma(1) = \pi \Upsilon_{\sigma_i \leqslant \sigma \leqslant \sigma_{i+1}} z(\sigma)$. So $w_{\sigma_{i+1}}$ is homotopic with $w_{\sigma_i} \circ x_i$. From this it follows easily that w_γ is homotopic with $w_0 \circ \Upsilon_\sigma w_{\gamma\sigma}(1)$. Putting

$$\Upsilon_\sigma w_\sigma(1) = w'$$

and remembering that $[w_0] = [\Upsilon_\tau p]$, one obtains

$$z(\gamma) = [w_\gamma] = [\Upsilon_\sigma w'(\gamma\sigma)] \quad \text{for} \quad 0 \leqslant \gamma \leqslant 1;$$

now

$$z = \hat{w}'$$

$$\pi z = w',$$

which proves the assertion.

28.16 $\hat{G}$ is (pathwise and) simply connected.

Proof Let $[w]$ be a point of $\hat{G}$. Then $\hat{w}$ is a path from $[\Upsilon_\tau p]$ to $[w]$, which shows that $\hat{G}$ is pc. Let z be a path on $\hat{G}$ with start and finish at $[\Upsilon_\tau p]$. There is a path w in G such that $z = \hat{w}$. Since $[w] = \hat{w}(1) = [\Upsilon_\tau p]$,

$$w \text{ homotopic with } \Upsilon_\tau p.$$

By 28.14 this homotopy is transferred to the stretching results so that

$$\hat{w} \text{ homotopic with } \Upsilon_\sigma [\Upsilon_\tau p],$$

which is homotopically trivial.

28.17 Besides G a space G' is considered; G' is continuously mapped onto G by λ.

G' is called a *wrapping* of G (by means of λ), if the following holds:

28.17.1 G' is pc,

28.17.2 λ is locally topological,

28.17.3 $w'(\tau) \in G'$ depending continuously on τ for $0 \leqslant \tau < 1$ extends continuously into $\tau = 1$ as soon as $\curlyvee_\tau \lambda\, w'(\tau)$ does so.

From 28.14–16 it follows that the universal wrapping *is* a wrapping (by means of π).

The foregoing conditions readily imply the following:

28.17.4 Every path w on G has a uniquely determined λ-original-path w' on G' such that $w'(0)$ is a prescribed λ-original of $w(0)$.

The uniqueness follows easily from 28.17.2. Then, using 28.17.2 in a neighborhood of the prescribed λ-original of $w(0)$, one finds the existence of a maximal σ with $0 < \sigma \leqslant 1$ such that $w'(\tau)$ can be defined for $0 \leqslant \tau < \sigma$. By 28.17.3 $w'(\sigma)$ can be defined as well, and by 28.17.2 w' could even be defined beyond σ if σ were less than 1. So $\sigma = 1$ and the result follows.

28.18 One can *dismiss the condition* in 28.17.3 as soon as it is known that the λ-original of any compact set of G is again compact.

Indeed, then for $\alpha < 1$,

$\lambda^{-1} w(\uparrow_\tau \tau \geqslant \alpha)$ is compact,

closure of $w'(\uparrow_\tau \tau \geqslant \alpha)$ is compact, nonvoid, and connected,

$\bigcap_\alpha$ closure of $w'(\uparrow_\tau \tau \geqslant \alpha)$ is nonvoid and connected,

but on the other hand contained in $\lambda^{-1} w(1)$, thus finite, thus consisting of one point, which is $\lim_{\tau=1} w'(\tau)$.

28.19 Let G' be a wrapping of G by λ. Then, if the paths w'_σ on G' are such that $w'_\sigma(0)$ and $w_\sigma = \lambda w'_\sigma$ depend continuously on σ, then w'_σ depends continuously on σ.

Proof Consider some σ_0. The set of $w'_{\sigma_0}(\tau)$ is compact. It is covered by a finite number of open U'_i mapped topologically onto U_i. Let $w'_{\sigma_0}(\tau) \in U'_i$ for $\tau_{i-1} \leqslant \tau \leqslant \tau_i$. Then $w_{\sigma_0}(\tau) \in U_i$ for $\tau_{i-1} \leqslant \tau \leqslant \tau_i$.

Because of the continuity of $\curlyvee_{\ulcorner \sigma, \tau \urcorner}\, w_\sigma(\tau)$, there is a $\delta > 0$ such that

$$w_\sigma(\tau) \in U_i \quad \text{for} \quad \tau_{i-1} \leqslant \tau \leqslant \tau_i, \quad |\sigma - \sigma_0| < \delta.$$

If for some i it is known that

$$w'_\sigma(\tau_{i-1}) \in U'_i \quad \text{for} \quad |\sigma - \sigma_0| < \delta,$$

then by 28.17.4 it may be concluded that

$$w'_\sigma(\tau) \in U'_i \quad \text{for} \quad \tau_{i-1} \leqslant \tau \leqslant \tau_i \quad \text{and} \quad |\sigma - \sigma_0| < \delta.$$

It may also be assumed that $w'_\sigma(0) \in U_1$ for $|\sigma - \sigma_0| < \delta$. Hence by induction this is true for all i. Using the topological nature of λ in any U'_i, the continuity of $\curlyvee_{\ulcorner\sigma,\tau\urcorner} w'_\sigma(\tau)$ is derived from that of $\curlyvee_{\ulcorner\sigma,\tau\urcorner} w_\sigma(\tau)$.

28.20 Let G' be a wrapping of G by λ. Let A be sc, lpc, and continuously mapped by ρ into G such that $\rho q = p$. Then for a given $p' \in G'$ with $\lambda p' = p$ there is a unique continuous mapping ρ' of A into G' with $\rho' q = p'$ such that

$$\lambda\rho' = \rho.$$

(*The mapping into G can be "lifted" to G'.*)

To construct $\rho'(x)$ for any $x \in A$, q is joined to x by a path v on A. Then to $\rho v = w$ on G the path w' on G' is constructed such that $\lambda w' = w$, $w'(0) = p'$. Finally $\rho'(x)$ is put $w'(1)$. Any other choice of v is homotopic with this one, since A is sc. It leads to a homotopically equivalent w, hence by 28.19 to the same $w'(1)$. The continuity of ρ' also follows from 28.19, and $\lambda\rho' = \rho$ is obvious by construction. So is the uniqueness of ρ'.

28.21 In 21.7 Φ was defined as the set of homotopy classes of paths in G with $w(0) = w(1) = p$. Moreover, Φ possesses a group structure.

Alternatively, Φ may be said to consist of the π-originals of p. If $\pi[w_1] = \pi[w_2]$, then $[w_2] \circ [w_1]^{-1} \in \Phi$; hence $[w_2] \in \Phi \circ [w_1]$.

If $\pi\hat{x} = x$, then $\Phi \circ \hat{x}$ is the entire π-original set of x.

The elements of Φ act by left multiplication on $\hat{G}$. They permute the sheets over an open pc U and operate continuously on $\hat{G}$.

28.22 Let G' be a wrapping of G by λ; $\lambda p' = p$.

If 28.20 is applied with the universal wrapping $\hat{G}$ instead of A, and π instead of ρ, and $\pi\hat{p} = p$, one obtains a continuous mapping π' of $\hat{G}$ onto G' such that $\lambda\pi' = \pi$ and $\pi'\hat{p} = p'$.

It is easily seen that the universal wrapping of G' can be identified with $\hat{G}$, π' being the corresponding projection. Then the π'-originals of p' form a subgroup Φ' of Φ. The π'-originals of some x' form a set $\Phi' \circ \hat{x}$.

Conversely, given a subgroup Φ' of Φ, one can define a G' as the set of all $\Phi' \circ \hat{x}$, a mapping π' of $\hat{G}$ onto G' by $\pi'(\hat{x}) = \Phi' \circ \hat{x}$, and a mapping λ of G' onto G by $\lambda(\Phi \circ \hat{x}) = \pi\hat{x}$; one can also introduce a topology in G' by calling the π'-images of open sets of $\hat{G}$ open. Then G' appears to be a wrapping of G by means of λ; the λ-original of $\pi\hat{x}$ consists of the $\Phi \circ \hat{y}$ contained in $\Phi \circ \hat{x}$.

The pairs $\ulcorner G', p'\urcorner$, where G' wraps G by means of λ and $\lambda p' = p$, are divided into equivalence classes: If G'_i wraps G by means of λ_i, then $\ulcorner G'_1, p'_1\urcorner$ is equivalent to $\ulcorner G'_2, p'_2\urcorner$ if, and only if, there is a homeomorphism ϑ of G'_2 onto G'_1 such that $\lambda_1\vartheta = \lambda_2$ and $\vartheta p'_2 = p'_1$.

The foregoing can be summarized as follows:

The equivalence classes of $\ulcorner G', p' \urcorner$ *where* G' *wraps* G *and* p' *lies above* p *are one-to-one related to the subgroups* Φ' *of the fundamental group* Φ_p *of* G*; a representative* $\ulcorner G', p' \urcorner$ *of the class belonging to* Φ' (sub Φ) *is obtained from the universal wrapping by identifying points that proceed from each other by the action of* Φ' *and taking for* p' *the image of the homotopy class of the constant path* ($=p$). *The fundamental group* $\Phi_{p'}(G')$ *of such a* G' *is essentially* Φ'.

If the wrapping G' *of* G *by means of* λ *is given and* p' *is allowed to change* ($\lambda p' = p$), *the subgroups* Φ *corresponding to the pairs* $\ulcorner G', p' \urcorner$ *run through a class of conjugate subgroups of* Φ.

29. FUNDAMENTAL GROUPS AND WRAPPINGS OF TOPOLOGICAL GROUPS

The results of Section 28 are applied to topological groups; p is taken to be the group unit.

$G \in$ Gru Top Hau pc lsc.

29.1 The group multiplication induces a new multiplication on $\mathscr{W}_p$:

$$w'' = ww' \qquad \text{means} \qquad w''(\tau) = w(\tau)\, w'(\tau).$$

If w_0, w_1 are homotopic by means of w_σ, and w_0', w_1' by means of w_σ', then $w_0 w_0'$, $w_1 w_1'$ are homotopic by means of $w_\sigma w_\sigma'$. This produces a multiplication of homotopy classes,

$$[w][w'] = [ww'].$$

By this definition the universal wrapping becomes a group that is easily recognized as topological.

π is now a homomorphism because of

$$\pi[ww'] = (ww')(1) = w(1)\, w'(1) = \pi[w]\, \pi[w'].$$

The kernel of π consists of all $[w]$ with $\pi[w] = w(1) = p$, hence all of Φ. As a subgroup of $\hat{G}$, it is isomorphic to Φ; this means that for $w(0) = w(1) = w'(0) = w'(1) = p$

$$[w] \circ [w'] = [w][w'];$$

in other words

$$w \circ w' \text{ and } ww' \text{ are homotopic.}$$

To prove it consider the square of $\ulcorner\alpha,\beta\urcorner$, with $0\leqslant\alpha\leqslant 1$, $0\leqslant\beta\leqslant 1$ (see Fig. 7) mapped by

$$\curlyvee_{\ulcorner\alpha,\beta\urcorner}\, w(\alpha)\, w'(\beta),$$

and apply 28.11.

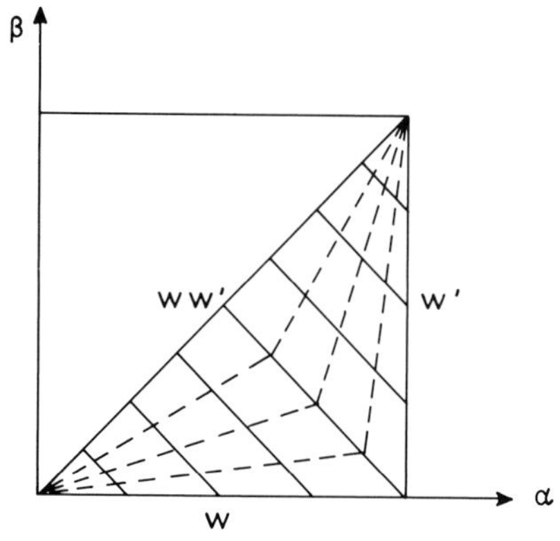

FIG. 7

With a view on the other half of the square, it appears that $w\circ w'$, $w'\circ w$ are homotopic. Thus Φ is commutative.

This is not new, however; 4.7 states that Φ considered as a (discrete) normal subgroup of (connected) $\hat{G}$ is in the center of $\hat{G}$.

Summarizing the results, one obtains the following theorem:

Theorem Let G be a pc lsc Hausdorff group. Its universal wrapping $\hat{G}$ is also a pc lsc Hausdorff group, the projection π of $\hat{G}$ onto G being a continuous homomorphism that maps open sets onto open sets; $\hat{G}$ is simply connected. The fundamental group Φ of G is a subgroup of $\hat{G}$ and lies in its center; G is topologically isomorphic with $\hat{G}/\Phi$. If Φ' sub Φ and G' is the wrapping of G by means of λ, characterized by Φ' (i.e., obtained from $\hat{G}$ by identifying points that proceed from one another by the action of Φ'), then G' bears a natural structure of a topological group and λ is a continuous homomorphism that maps open sets onto open sets. The universal wrapping of G' is essentially $\hat{G}$. If π' is the projection of $\hat{G}$ onto G', then $\Phi'\subset\Phi$ and $\pi=\lambda\pi'$.

29.2 In a neighborhood of the group unit G and $\hat{G}$ are topologically isomorphic (they are locally isomorphic). A converse:

Theorem If $G, G'\in$ Gru Top Hau pc lsc are locally topologically isomorphic, they possess a common wrapping; thus they have topologically isomorphic universal wrappings. The local isomorphism extends to a global one of the universal wrappings.

Proof Suppose that the 1-neighborhood U_1 in G_1 by a topological isomorphism f is mapped onto the 1-neighborhood U_2 in G_2. Form the direct product G of G_1 and G_2 with the natural projections ω_i of G on G_i. Take an open pc 1-neighborhood $V_1 = V_1^{-1}$ in G_1 such that $V_1 V_1 \subset U_1$ and define $V \subset G$ as the set of

$$\ulcorner a, fa \urcorner \qquad \text{with} \quad a \in V_1.$$

Then

$$VV \cap \ulcorner V_1, fV_1 \urcorner \subset V,$$

which shows that V is a local subgroup of G.

By the method of 4.12 V expands to a connected and even pc topological group G_3 such that cV is open in G_3 for any $c \in G_3$. This G_3 is easily seen to wrap G_i by the restriction of ω_i $(i = 1,2)$.

This proves the first statement. If applied to universal wrappings, it proves the second.

30. COMPACTNESS ASPECTS OF SEMISIMPLE AND ABELIAN GROUPS

30.1 For $\boldsymbol{G} \in$ Alg Lie Lin SS acting on $R \in$ Spa Lin it was seen in 19.10 that Int $\boldsymbol{G}$ is closed in the group of linear space automorphisms of $\boldsymbol{G}$. In 38.5 G infinitesimally generated by $\boldsymbol{G}$ itself will be shown to be closed in Aut R.

If, moreover, $\boldsymbol{G}$ is a *unitary restriction*, then by 24.4 Int $\boldsymbol{G}$ is compact; in 32.2.4 G itself will be shown to be compact.

The following proposition, though not used in the sequel, shows the degree to which noncompactness pervades a noncompact semisimple group.

30.4.† Compact Inner Classes

Proposition If centerfree $G \in$ Gru Lin Lie SSS has a relatively compact *inner class* (i.e., class of conjugate elements) $\neq \{1\}$, it is itself compact.

Proof The first step is the construction of a relatively compact 1-neighborhood, invariant under Int G.

Let the inner class of x be denoted by $[x]$ and let $[c]$ be relatively compact, $c \neq 1$. Then $[c^{-1}] = [c]^{-1}$ is also relatively compact, as is any repeated product of $[c]$ and $[c^{-1}]$ with a finite number of factors.

Since c is not a center element of G, there is a $\boldsymbol{u} \in \boldsymbol{G}$ with $\tilde{c}\boldsymbol{u} \neq \boldsymbol{u}$. Take $\curlyvee_t u_t$ on G with $u_0 = 1$ and $((d/dt)u_t)_{t=0} = \boldsymbol{u}$ and define

$$a_t = u_t c u_t^{-1} c^{-1}.$$

† The contents of 30.4 will not be used in the sequel.

Then

$$a_0 = 1, \qquad \boldsymbol{a} = \left(\frac{d}{dt}a_t\right)_{t=0} = \boldsymbol{u} - \tilde{c}\boldsymbol{u} \neq \boldsymbol{0}.$$

Note that

30.4.1 $$[a_t] \subset [c][c^{-1}].$$

Because $\boldsymbol{G}$ is simple, $\tilde{G}$ acts irreducibly on $\boldsymbol{G}$ (see 12.4). Thus $\boldsymbol{G}$ is linearly spanned by the $\tilde{v}\boldsymbol{a}$ ($v \in G$), hence by a finite linearly independent set among them, $\tilde{v}_1\boldsymbol{a}, \ldots, \tilde{v}_r\boldsymbol{a}$.

Put

$$a_t^{(i)} = \tilde{v}_i a_t,$$

form the inner classes of the $a_t^{(i)}$ and the union of products

$$N = \bigcup_{|t_1{}^2|+\cdots+|t_r{}^2|<\varepsilon^2} [a_{t_1}^{(1)}] \cdots [a_{t_r}^{(r)}];$$

N is invariant under $\tilde{G}$ and, by 30.4.1, relatively compact.

On the other hand,

$$\curlyvee_{\ulcorner t_1,\ldots,t_r \urcorner}\, a_{t_1}^{(1)} \cdots a_{t_r}^{(r)}$$

maps $\ulcorner 0, \ldots, 0 \urcorner$ into 1 and the ε-ball around 0 in r-space into N. Its gradient at $\ulcorner 0, \ldots, 0 \urcorner$ maps the ith basis vector into $\tilde{v}_i\boldsymbol{a}$; because of their independence the gradient is nondegenerate. Consequently, 1 is an inner point of the image and therefore of N.

So N is a relatively compact, Int G-invariant 1-neighborhood.

To prove the proposition it suffices according to 30.1 to show that $\tilde{G}$ is bounded. Now suppose $\tilde{G}$ were not bounded. Then $\tilde{G}\boldsymbol{x}$ would be unbounded for some $\boldsymbol{x} \in \boldsymbol{G}$, and it would be possible to find $\boldsymbol{x}_j \in \boldsymbol{G}$, $g_j \in G$ such that

$$\lim \boldsymbol{x}_j = \boldsymbol{0}, \qquad \lim \tilde{g}_j\boldsymbol{x}_j = \boldsymbol{y} \neq \boldsymbol{0}.$$

The characteristic polynomials of the $\boldsymbol{x}_j$ converge to $\lambda^{\dim G}$. So do those of $\tilde{g}_j\boldsymbol{x}_j$. Thus all eigenvalues of $\boldsymbol{y}$ vanish and $\boldsymbol{y}$ is nilpotent.

On the other hand,

$$\lim \tilde{g}_j \exp t\boldsymbol{x}_j = \lim \exp t(\tilde{g}_j\boldsymbol{x}_j) = \exp t\boldsymbol{y}.$$

Obviously, $\exp t\boldsymbol{x}_j \in N$ for almost all j if t is given. Because of the Int G-invariance of N, the same is true of $\tilde{g}_j \exp t\boldsymbol{x}_j$. Thus $\exp t\boldsymbol{y} \in \bar{N}$ for all t. From 2.8 it follows that $\exp t\boldsymbol{y}$ is a nonconstant polynomial in t and therefore unbounded. This contradicts the compactness of $\bar{N}$.

30.5. The Global Structure of Abelian Linear Lie Groups This structure becomes clear as a consequence of the ideas of Section 29.

Theorem If $G \in$ Gru Lin Lie Rea is abelian, then up to isomorphy it is the direct product of copies of the multiplication group of the positive numbers and of that of the unit norm complex numbers; that is, it is the direct product of a flat abelian and a torus group (see 12.6).

Proof G is locally isomorphic to a direct sum $\hat{G}$ of r copies G_i of the addition group of the real numbers (see 12.6); $\hat{G}$ is simply connected. Theorem 29.2 allows one to consider $\hat{G}$ as the universal wrapping of G, and therefore G as $\hat{G}$ mod a discrete subgroup M. It is well known that M has a finite number of linearly independent generators $a_1, \ldots, a_p$. Now $\hat{G}$ can be rewritten as a direct sum of G_i' $(i = 1, 2, \ldots, r)$ with $a_i \in G_i'$ for $i = 1, \ldots, p$. If G_i'' arises from G_i' by reduction mod the multiples of a_i, and $G_i'' = G_i'$ for $i > p$, then G turns out to be isomorphic to the direct sum of the G_i'' which up to isomorphy are addition groups of the real numbers, maybe mod 1.

30.8. Historical Note Proposition 30.4 seems to be due to H. Freudenthal, *Arch. Math.* **15**, 161–165 (1964).

31. THE CONJUGACY THEOREM FOR CENTERFREE UNITARILY RESTRICTED SEMISIMPLE LIE GROUPS

31.1 Trunks have until now mostly been considered for Lie algebras. By exp they are transferred to linear Lie groups.

Definition If $\boldsymbol{H}$ $(\boldsymbol{H}_C)$ is a trunk of $\boldsymbol{G}$ $(\boldsymbol{G}_C)$, then $H = \exp \boldsymbol{H}$ $(H_C = \exp \boldsymbol{H}_C)$ is called a *trunk of* G (G_C).

This definition is presently applied to $\boldsymbol{G} \in$ Alg Lie Lin Com SS; G is the group generated by it.

31.2. Proposition H (H_C) is a closed abelian linear Lie group.

Proof Because $\boldsymbol{H}$ is abelian, H is an abelian group. The closure of H in G is also abelian; it has an abelian infinitesimal algebra, which by 17.6 coincides with $\boldsymbol{H}$. Thus H is closed. Clearly this implies the closedness of H_C.

31.3 Until further notice the groups to be discussed are centerfree, unitarily restricted, and semisimple; such a group is denoted by G, one of its trunks is H, and the respective infinitesimal algebras are $\boldsymbol{G}, \boldsymbol{H}$. It is supposed that $\boldsymbol{G}$ is derived from $\boldsymbol{G}_{\text{Com}}$ in ordered third dressing with respect to the trunk $\boldsymbol{H}_{\text{Com}}$, and that G_{Com}, infinitesimally generated by $\boldsymbol{G}_{\text{Com}}$, is centerfree (see 12.15.3). It is often convenient to represent them as adjoint groups and algebras. Note that such a representation is faithful.

Proposition A trunk of a centerfree, unitarily restricted, semisimple, linear Lie group of rank l is an l-dimensional torus group, which after ordered dressing is coordinatized by the sequence of $\exp \rho_i$ (ρ_i the different primitive rootforms).

Proof On a suitable basis $\boldsymbol{H}$ consists of diagonal matrices $\boldsymbol{h}$ carrying the purely imaginary $\alpha(\boldsymbol{h})$ ($\alpha \in W$) in the main diagonal. $\exp \boldsymbol{h}$, which is the general element of H, carries the $\exp \alpha(\boldsymbol{h})$ ($\alpha \in W$) in the main diagonal. In ordered dressing one may use the $\exp \rho(\boldsymbol{h})$ ($\rho \in W^{++}$) as coordinates in H, all other diagonal coefficients being power products of these ones with integral exponents. These coordinates range independently over the unit circle. This makes H a direct product of l circles.

31.4. Definition In the trunk $\boldsymbol{H}$ of $\boldsymbol{G}$ (as before) the *principal domain* $\boldsymbol{D}$ is defined by

$$\boldsymbol{h} \in \boldsymbol{D} \text{ if and only if } \boldsymbol{h} \in \boldsymbol{H}, \text{ and } 0 < \operatorname{Im} \alpha(\boldsymbol{h}) < 2\pi \text{ for all } \alpha \in W^+;$$

D means $\exp \boldsymbol{D}$. For $h \in D$ the uniquely determined $\boldsymbol{h} \in \boldsymbol{D}$ with $\exp \boldsymbol{h} = h$ is called $\log h$. The closure of $\boldsymbol{D}$ is $\bar{\boldsymbol{D}}$.

A straight path in $\bar{\boldsymbol{D}}$ is a uniform motion ($0 \leqslant t \leqslant 1$) of a point in $\bar{\boldsymbol{D}}$ over a straight line segment. By exp this terminology is carried over to $\exp \bar{\boldsymbol{D}}$.

Note that $\boldsymbol{D}$ depends on the chosen order.

31.5 It is a well-known fact that on a suitable orthonormal basis a unitary matrix takes the diagonal form. An analogous fact for unitarily restricted groups is enunciated in the following theorem:

Conjugacy Theorem for centerfree unitarily restricted semisimple G:

All trunks of G are conjugate in G; all trunks of $\boldsymbol{G}$ are equivalent under $\tilde{G}$. Every element of G is conjugate to some element of the closed principal domain of a given ordered trunk of G and thus is a member of some trunk.

Remark For complex G the first part still holds (see 17.8), but the second part is disproved by the existence of nonpure linear mappings; thus not all elements belong to trunks. For nonunitary real G both assertions can be refuted. In the unitary case the condition of center-freedom will be dropped in 32.9.

The proof of this theorem in 31.9 rests on 31.6–8.

31.6 Let, $G, H, \boldsymbol{G}, \boldsymbol{H}$ be as before; $\boldsymbol{G}_{\text{Com}}$ in ordered third dressing, $\boldsymbol{e}_\alpha$ the branches of $\boldsymbol{G}_{\text{Com}}$; $\boldsymbol{E}$ the set of all $\sum \tau_\alpha \boldsymbol{e}_\alpha \in \boldsymbol{G}$; and $\boldsymbol{E}_i$ small balls in $\boldsymbol{E}$ around $\boldsymbol{0}$, $\exp \boldsymbol{E}_i = E_i$.

Proposition If $\boldsymbol{E}_0$ is small enough, then

31.6.1 $$\curlyvee \ulcorner g,h \urcorner\, gh$$

maps $\ulcorner E_0, H \urcorner$ homeomorphically onto an H-neighborhood in G.

Proof Since $\boldsymbol{H} \cap \boldsymbol{E} = \{\boldsymbol{0}\}$, $\boldsymbol{H} + \boldsymbol{E} = \boldsymbol{G}$, there are 1-neighborhoods E_1, H^0 in E, H such that 31.6.1 maps $\ulcorner E_1, H^0 \urcorner$ homeomorphically onto a 1-neighborhood in G. Choose $\boldsymbol{E}_0 \subset \boldsymbol{E}_1$ such that $E_0^{-1} E_0 \cap H \subset H^0$. Then even

$$E_0^{-1} E_0 \cap H = \{1\},$$

since $g_i \in E_0$, $g_1^{-1} g_2 \in H$ implies that $g_1^{-1} g_2 \in H^0$, which shows that $\ulcorner g_1, g_1^{-1} g_2 \urcorner$ and $\ulcorner g_2, 1 \urcorner$ coincide since they have the same image under 31.6.1 and lie in $\ulcorner E_1, H^0 \urcorner$; hence $g_1^{-1} g_2 = 1$.

$E_0 H^0$ is still a 1-neighborhood, so $E_0 H = E_0 H^0 H$ is an H-neighborhood. From $\ulcorner g_i, h_i \urcorner \in \ulcorner E_0, H \urcorner$ and $g_1 h_1 = g_2 h_2$, it follows that $g_1^{-1} g_2 \in E_0^{-1} E_0 \cap H = \{1\}$, which proves that 31.6.1 maps $\ulcorner E_0, H \urcorner$ homeomorphically.

Definition The mapping φ of a neighborhood of H is defined by

$$\varphi(gh) = \tilde{g}h$$

for $g = \exp \boldsymbol{g}$ with small $\boldsymbol{g} \in \boldsymbol{E}$ and $h \in H$.

The gradient of φ at $h_0 = \exp \boldsymbol{h}_0$ ($\boldsymbol{h}_0 \in \boldsymbol{H}$), computed by putting

$$g = \exp t \sum \tau_\alpha \boldsymbol{e}_\alpha, \qquad h = h_0 \exp t\boldsymbol{h} \qquad (\boldsymbol{h} \in \boldsymbol{H})$$

and differentiating on t at $t = 0$, maps

$$\sum \tau_\alpha \boldsymbol{e}_\alpha h_0 + h_0 \boldsymbol{h} \quad \text{into} \quad h_0 \boldsymbol{h} + [\sum \tau_\alpha \boldsymbol{e}_\alpha, h_0].$$

Transferring the tangent space at h_0 into that at 1 by right multiplication by h_0^{-1}, one gets a linear mapping that carries

$$\sum \tau_\alpha \boldsymbol{e}_\alpha + \boldsymbol{h} \quad \text{into} \quad \boldsymbol{h} + (1 - \tilde{h}_0) \sum \tau_\alpha \boldsymbol{e}_\alpha.$$

It is the identity on $\boldsymbol{H}$ and it multiplies

$$\boldsymbol{e}_\alpha \text{ by } 1 - \exp \alpha(\boldsymbol{h}_0)$$

because $\tilde{h}_0 \boldsymbol{e}_\alpha = (\exp \tilde{\boldsymbol{h}}_0) \boldsymbol{e}_\alpha = (\exp \alpha(\boldsymbol{h}_0)) \boldsymbol{e}_\alpha$. This proves:

Theorem det grad φ at $h_0 = \exp \boldsymbol{h}_0$ equals

$$\prod_{\alpha \in W^*} (1 - \exp \alpha(\boldsymbol{h}_0)).$$

31.7. Definition $F = \bigcup_{a \in G} \tilde{a} D$; $F_* = \bigcup_{a \in G} \tilde{a}(\bar{D} \setminus D)$.

Proposition F is open in G.

Proof For $h_0 \in D$, as before, det grad $\varphi \neq 0$ because $\alpha(h_0) \neq 0$, $\neq 2\pi\mathrm{i}$. Thus the image of φ covers a neighborhood of h_0, and every $h_0 \in D$ is interior point of F; the same is true of its conjugates.

31.8 In order to study the conjugation class of an arbitrary $\boldsymbol{h} \in \boldsymbol{H}$, consider the centralizer $Y(\boldsymbol{h}_0)$ of $\exp \boldsymbol{h}_0 = h_0$. It is closed in G; the 1-component has an infinitesimal algebra $\boldsymbol{Y}(\boldsymbol{h}_0)$. From

$$\tilde{h}_0 \boldsymbol{e}_\alpha = (\exp \tilde{\boldsymbol{h}}_0)\boldsymbol{e}_\alpha = (\exp \alpha(\boldsymbol{h}_0))\boldsymbol{e}_\alpha$$

it follows that $\boldsymbol{Y}(\boldsymbol{h}_0)$ is spanned by $\boldsymbol{H}$ and the $\tau_\alpha \boldsymbol{e}_\alpha - \bar{\tau}_\alpha \boldsymbol{e}_{-\alpha}$ with $\alpha(\boldsymbol{h}_0) = 0 \bmod 2\pi\mathrm{i}$.

In particular, $\boldsymbol{Y}(\boldsymbol{h}_0) = \boldsymbol{H}$ for $\boldsymbol{h}_0 \in \boldsymbol{D}$.

Furthermore, consider the set $\boldsymbol{E}(\boldsymbol{h}_0)$ of $\sum \tau_\alpha \boldsymbol{e}_\alpha \in \boldsymbol{G}$ with $\alpha(\boldsymbol{h}_0) \neq 0 \bmod 2\pi\mathrm{i}$. Then $\boldsymbol{G} = \boldsymbol{E}(\boldsymbol{h}_0) + \boldsymbol{Y}(\boldsymbol{h}_0)$.

Finally, let $\boldsymbol{D}(\boldsymbol{h}_0)$ be the set of $\boldsymbol{h} \in \bar{\boldsymbol{D}}$ with $[\alpha(\boldsymbol{h}) = 0 \leftrightarrow \alpha(\boldsymbol{h}_0) = 0] \wedge [\alpha(\boldsymbol{h}) = 2\pi\mathrm{i} \leftrightarrow \alpha(\boldsymbol{h}_0) = 2\pi\mathrm{i}]$; $D(\boldsymbol{h}_0) = \exp \boldsymbol{D}(\boldsymbol{h}_0)$. Then $\boldsymbol{Y}(\boldsymbol{h})$ and $\boldsymbol{E}(\boldsymbol{h})$ are constant for $\boldsymbol{h} \in \boldsymbol{D}(\boldsymbol{h}_0)$. There is a finite number of different $\boldsymbol{D}(\boldsymbol{h}_0)$, which together form $\bar{\boldsymbol{D}}$.

In 31.6 $\varphi(gh)$ was defined for $g = \exp \boldsymbol{g}$ with small $\boldsymbol{g} \in \boldsymbol{E}$ and $h \in H$. Let it now be restricted to $\boldsymbol{g} \in \boldsymbol{E}(\boldsymbol{h}_0)$ and $h \in D(\boldsymbol{h}_0)$. Then $\mathrm{grad}_h\, \varphi$ is again nondegenerate for $h \in D(\boldsymbol{h}_0)$. For any $h \in D(\boldsymbol{h}_0)$ there is an $\boldsymbol{E}(\boldsymbol{h}_0)$-neighborhood $\boldsymbol{E}_h(\boldsymbol{h}_0)$ of $\boldsymbol{0}$ and a $D(\boldsymbol{h}_0)$-neighborhood $A(h)$ of h such that φ maps $(\exp \boldsymbol{E}_h(\boldsymbol{h}_0))\,A(h)$ onto a C^{an}-piece, say $Q(h)$.

$\exp \boldsymbol{E}_h(\boldsymbol{h}_0) \cdot \exp \boldsymbol{Y}(\boldsymbol{h}_0)$ contains a G-neighborhood $U(h)$ of 1. Since $\tilde{a}$ is the identity on $A(h)$ for $a \in \exp \boldsymbol{Y}(\boldsymbol{h}_0)$, it follows that $Q(h)$ contains $\bigcup_{g \in U(h)} \tilde{g}A(h)$ for a suitable G-neighborhood $U(h)$ of 1. So, by the compactness of G,

$$\bigcup_{g \in G} \tilde{g}A(h)$$

is covered by a finite number of C^{an}-pieces, conjugates of $Q(h)$, and

$$\bigcup_{g \in G} \tilde{g}D(\boldsymbol{h}_0)$$

is covered by a countable number of C^{an}-pieces.

Now suppose that $\boldsymbol{h}_0 \in \bar{\boldsymbol{D}} \setminus \boldsymbol{D}$. Then the codimension of $\boldsymbol{D}(\boldsymbol{h}_0)$ in $\boldsymbol{H}$ is $\geqslant 1$, that of $\boldsymbol{E}(\boldsymbol{h}_0)$ in $\boldsymbol{E}$ is $\geqslant 2$, and consequently, that of the above C^{an}-pieces is $\geqslant 3$. There is a finite number of different $D(\boldsymbol{h}_0)$. Hence:

Proposition F_* is a countable union of C^{an}-pieces of codimension $\geqslant 3$ in G.

Remark The constituent C^{an}-pieces may be assumed such that their closures are still contained in C^{an}-pieces of the same dimension.

31.9 F_* is contained in the boundary $\bar{F} \setminus F$ of open F. Conversely, if $c \in \bar{F} \setminus F$, then $c = \lim c_n$ with some $c_n \in F$, hence with $c_n = \tilde{a}_n h_n$ $(a_n \in G, h_n \in D)$. Because of the compactness of G, one may assume $\lim a_n = a \in G$, $\lim h_n = h \in \bar{D}$. Then $c = \tilde{a}h \in F_*$, which proves that $\bar{F} \setminus F \subset F_*$; thus

$$F_* = \bar{F} \setminus F.$$

According to dimension theory codim $F_* \geqslant 3$. Thus the boundary of F has codimension $\geqslant 3$. In a manifold the complement of a closed set of codimension $\geqslant 2$ is connected. Therefore $G \setminus (\bar{F} \setminus F) = F \cup (G \setminus \bar{F})$ is connected. Since both summands are open and their intersection is void, this means that $G \setminus \bar{F}$ is void, hence $G = \bar{F}$.

This proves that every element of G is conjugate to some element of $\bar{D}$.

Let H' be some other trunk of G. In H' take an element h' which generates a dense subgroup of H'. Then $h' = \tilde{a}h$ with suitable $h \in \bar{D}$, $a \in G$; obviously even $h \in D$. Now $\tilde{a}^{-1} H'$ is a trunk in the centralizer of h. Since the 1-component of the centralizer of $h \in D$ coincides with H, it follows that $\tilde{a}H' = H$, which proves the remainder of Theorem 31.5.

31.10 It is overdone to use dimension theory because F_* is a rather elementary set to which elementary methods apply. This is done by the following

Device Let P be a finite polytope of dimension p in real s-space S, and Q a closed subset in a q-dimensional linear subspace R' of real r-space R, with $p + q < r$. Let f be a continuous mapping of P into R. Then arbitrarily close to f there is a continuous f^* such that f^*P does not meet Q; f^* may even be chosen to agree with f on a given closed subset P_0 of P such that $fP_0 \cap Q$ is void.

Proof fP_0 and Q have a positive distance α. Choose a finite subpolytope P_1 (of a subdivision of P), which does not meet P_0 and which contains the f-original of the $\frac{1}{2}\alpha$-neighborhood of Q. Choose another finite subpolytope P_2 of P, which does not meet P_0 either and which contains P_1 in its interior. Then $f(P_2 \setminus P_1)$ has a distance $\geqslant \frac{1}{2}\alpha$ from Q. Choose a continuous real function σ such that $\sigma(x) = 0$ for $x \in P \setminus P_2$, $\sigma(x) = 1$ for $x \in P_1$, and $0 \leqslant \sigma(x) \leqslant 1$ for $x \in P_2 \setminus P_1$.

A simplicial mapping f_0 of P_2 into R is defined such that $f_0 x = fx$ in the vertices x of $P_2 \setminus P_1$ and such that for any set of $m + 1$ vertices $a_0, \ldots, a_m$ $(m \leqslant p)$ of P_1 the plane through $f_0 a_i$ $(i = 0, \ldots, m)$ does not meet R' (which is q-dimensional). Then $f_0 P_1$ will not meet Q.

With a fine enough subdivision of P and with $f_0 x$ near fx in the vertices, one can make sure that f_0 is an ε-approximation of f for a given $\varepsilon > 0$. Finally one defines $f^* x = \sigma f_0 x + (1 - \sigma) f^* x$ for $x \in P_2$ and $f^* x = fx$ for $x \in P \setminus P_2$. Then f^* is still an ε-approximation of f. Furthermore, $f^* P_1 = f_0 P_1$ does not meet Q, nor does $f^*(P_2 \setminus P_1)$, as soon as $\varepsilon < \frac{1}{2}\alpha$.

31.11. Proposition Let Q_i ($i = 1,2, \ldots$) be compact subsets of C^{an}-pieces of codimension $\geqslant 3$ in G, and f a continuous mapping of a finite polytope T of dimension $\leqslant 2$ into G. Then there is an arbitrarily close continuous approximation f^* of f such that fT does not meet $\cup_i Q_i$; f^* may even be required to agree with f on a closed subset of T whose f-image does not meet $\cup_i Q_i$.

Proof This statement is proved first for one summand, denoted by Q.

It is allowable to interpret Q and a suitable open neighborhood B of it as lying in real r-space R, with $r = \dim G$, where B is an open ball, and Q is a subset of a linear subspace R' of R with codimension $\geqslant 3$. Take a smaller open ball B' that still contains Q. Form a finite subpolytope P of T such that fP is contained in B and P contains the f-original of B'. Then, according to 31.10, f restricted to P is approximated by an f^* such that f^*P does not meet Q, and agrees with f on the f-original of $B \diagdown B'$, and finally f^* is extended to the remainder of T, where the same agreement is required.

This proves the statement for the case of one summand.

A metric is assumed in G. Let $\varepsilon > 0$ be given. Suppose a $(1 - 2^{-n})\,\varepsilon$-approximation f_n of f has been constructed and a closed neighborhood S_i has been assigned to Q_i ($i = 1, \ldots, n$) such that $f_n T$ does not meet $\cup_{i=1}^n S_i$. Then $\delta > 0$ is chosen smaller than $2^{-n-1}\,\varepsilon$ and smaller than the distance between fT and $\cup_{i=1}^n S_i$; according to the first part of the proof, a δ-approximation f_{n+1} of f_n is constructed such that $f_{n+1}T$ does not meet Q_{n+1}. Finally, a closed neighborhood S_{n+1} of Q_{n+1} is chosen such that S_{n+1} is not met by fT.

$f^* = \lim f_n$ fulfills the main requirements of the statement for a given $\varepsilon > 0$. The supplementary one is easily satisfied.

Remark If $\cup_i Q_i$ is closed, the induction actually stops after a finite number of steps. This phenomenon can easily be accounted for in the proof.

31.12 What matters in the proof of 31.9 is the knowledge that $G \diagdown F_*$ is connected. This is now derived from 31.11.

If $x, y \in G \diagdown F_*$, the connectedness of G guarantees the existence of a continuous mapping of the unit interval T into G with $f(0) = x$, $f(1) = y$. According to 31.11, applied to F_* (see 31.8), f is changed into a continuous mapping f^* of T with $f^*(0) = x, f^*(1) = y$ such that fT does not meet F_*. This shows that $G \diagdown F_*$ is connected.

Proposition Let $p \in F$, U open in G. Then a path in G starting at p and finishing in U is p-U-homotopic with one in F. Two such paths contained in F, if p-U-homotopic in G, are also p-U-homotopic in F.

Actually, as to the first part it has been proved only that in an ε-neighborhood of a given $w_0 \in \mathscr{W}_p{}^U$ there is a $w_1 \in \mathscr{W}_p{}^U$ such that $w_1(\tau) \in F$ for all τ. This, however, is easily turned into a homotopy, for example by putting

$$w_\sigma(\tau) = (\exp \sigma \boldsymbol{a}_\tau)\, w_0(\tau),$$

where $\boldsymbol{a}_\tau$, continuously depending on τ, has been chosen such that

$$\exp \boldsymbol{a}_\tau = w_1(\tau)\; w_0(\tau)^{-1},$$

which is possible for small $\varepsilon > 0$.

To prove the second part the former argument must be applied to a unit square rather than a unit interval.

This proposition is used in the next section.

31.13. Historical Note The methods and results in this section are essentially H. Weyl's in *Math. Z.* **24** (1926) = *Selecta*, 348–352.

32. THE FUNDAMENTAL GROUP OF CENTERFREE UNITARILY RESTRICTED SEMISIMPLE GROUPS

$G \in$ Gru Lie Lin SS, centerfree (in 32.1–6), unitarily restricted. Other notations as in Section 31.

It is shown that the fundamental group is finite. The fundamental group is computed in all relevant cases, although a simpler method will become available in Section 46.

32.1 As the set of left cosets aH of H in G, G/H bears a natural topology (see 4.8.1): the UH with U open in G are the open sets of G/H; by 12.12 G/H inherits a C^{an}-manifold structure from G, compatible with this topology.

The $q \in G/H$ map H by

$$qh = \tilde{g}h \qquad \text{if} \quad g \in q.$$

It is obvious that this definition is unambiguous.

Proposition $\ulcorner G/H, D \urcorner$ is a wrapping of F by means of $\curlyvee_{\ulcorner q,h \urcorner} qh$.

Actually it is the universal wrapping; that is, G/H is simply connected. This is proved in Proposition 32.11.

Proof Since G/H is compact, 28.17.3 merits no attention (see 28.18), and it suffices to verify 28.17.2. According to 31.6–7,

$$\curlyvee_{\ulcorner g,h \urcorner} gh$$

is locally topological at $\ulcorner 1, h_0 \urcorner$ for $h_0 \in D$ as a mapping of $\ulcorner E_0, D \urcorner$ into G (it maps a neighborhood of $\ulcorner 1, h_0 \urcorner$ topologically onto one of h_0).

$$\curlyvee_g gH$$

being topological at 1 as a mapping of E_0 into G/H, the preceding sentence may be restated as follows:

32.1.1 $\curlyvee_{\ulcorner q,h \urcorner} qh$ ($q \in G/H$, $h \in D$) is locally topological at $\ulcorner H, h_0 \urcorner$ for $h_0 \in D$.

The proposition states that even

32.1.2 $\curlyvee_{\ulcorner q,h \urcorner} qh$ ($q \in G/H$, $h \in D$) is locally topological at $\ulcorner q_0, h_0 \urcorner$ for $q_0 \in G/H$, $h_0 \in D$.

This assertion follows from the fact that by left multiplication G acts transitively as a group of homeomorphisms on G/H:

If $q_0 = g_0 H$, then left multiplication by g_0^{-1} in the first component, followed by $\curlyvee_{\ulcorner q,h \urcorner} qh$ and by conjugation by means of g_0 in G, sends $\ulcorner q_0, h_0 \urcorner$ in this succession into

$$\ulcorner H, h_0 \urcorner, \quad h_0, \quad \text{and} \quad g_0 h_0 g_0^{-1} = q_0 h_0.$$

All three mappings are at least locally topological in corresponding points; their composite is $\curlyvee_{\ulcorner q,h \urcorner} qh$.

32.2 In the metric induced on $\boldsymbol{G}$ by $-\psi$ (the opposite of the Killing form) every open ball is invariant under $\tilde{G}$, since the Killing form is itself invariant under $\tilde{G}$.

Now take in this metric

32.2.1 a smooth ball $\boldsymbol{U}$ around $\boldsymbol{0}$ (see Definition 8.4). In particular, $\boldsymbol{U}$ is invariant under $\tilde{G}$, exp maps $\boldsymbol{U}$ homomorphically onto exp $\boldsymbol{U} = U$, and $\tau \boldsymbol{U} \subset \boldsymbol{U}$ for any real τ with $|\tau| \leqslant 1$.

$\boldsymbol{U}$ is simply connected, and so is U.

A *straight path* on U is meant as the exp-image of a rectilinear motion in $\boldsymbol{U}$.

With the notation of 32.1, $q(D \cap U) \subset U$ for $q \in G/H$.

In the sequel p is a fixed point in D.

32.2.2. Proposition $w \in \mathscr{W}_p^U$ is p-U-homotopic with a path on D.

Proof By 31.12 it may be assumed that $w(\tau) \in F$. After extending w, if needed, one may suppose that $w(1) \in D$. By 32.1 the equation

$$w(\tau) = q(\tau) h(\tau)$$

can be solved by a path q on G/H and a path h on D with $q(0) = H$ and $h(0) = w(0) = p$. Now put

$$w_\sigma(\tau) = q(\sigma) h(\tau).$$

By 28.11

$$w \text{ is homotopic with } q(0)h \circ qh(1);$$

$h(1)$ is a conjugate of $w(1)$ by $w(1) = q(1)h(1)$. By 32.2.1 it follows from $w(1) \in U$ that $h(1) \in U$, and for the same reason $q(\tau)h(1) \in U$. Consequently, $qh(1)$ is $h(1)$-U-homotopic with a constant path. Furthermore $q(0)h = h$, since $q(0) = H$.

This shows that

$$w \text{ is } p\text{-}U\text{-homotopic with } h,$$

which is situated on D as required by the proposition.

32.2.3. Proposition If $w_0, w_1 \in \mathscr{W}_p^U$, lying on D, are p-U-homotopic in G, they are so in D.

Proof By 31.12 the p-U-homotopy of w_0, w_1 is already realized within F:

$$w_\sigma(\tau) \in F, \qquad w_0(\tau), w_1(\tau) \in D, \qquad w_\sigma(0) = p, \qquad w_\sigma(1) \in U.$$

By 32.1 and 28.19 the equation

$$w_\sigma(\tau) = q_\sigma(\tau) h_\sigma(\tau)$$

may be solved by $q_\sigma(\tau) \in G/H$, $h_\sigma(\tau) \in D$, depending continuously on $\ulcorner \sigma, \tau \urcorner$, with $q_\sigma(0) = H$, $h_\sigma(0) = w_\sigma(0) = p$. The solution is unique, hence

$$h_0 = w_0, \qquad h_1 = w_1.$$

Finally $h_\sigma(1) \in U$ as a conjugate of $w_\sigma(1)$. So $\curlyvee_\sigma h_\sigma$ meets the requirements for the p-U-homotopy of w_0, w_1 within D.

32.2.4. Definition $\boldsymbol{Z}$ is the set of $\boldsymbol{h} \in \bar{\boldsymbol{D}}$ with $\exp \boldsymbol{h} = 1$; $\boldsymbol{Z}$ consists of the distinct points $\mathbf{0} = z_0, z_1, \ldots, z_k$.

Let C_i be a component of $D \cap U$ which accumulates at 1 (actually all of them do if U is small enough, but this does not matter). $\boldsymbol{C}_i = \log C_i$ makes sense (see 31.4). It accumulates at some element of $\boldsymbol{Z}$ and every element of $\boldsymbol{Z}$ occurs in this quality once and only once. If, moreover, U is small enough, $\boldsymbol{C}_i$ has only one accumulation point in $\boldsymbol{Z}$. (Actually U is small enough.) So the $\boldsymbol{C}_i$ may be numbered such that

$$z_i \text{ is the only accumulation point of } \boldsymbol{C}_i \text{ in } \boldsymbol{Z}.$$

Now let a path $w \in \mathscr{W}_1^{\,1}$ be given. After a homotopic change (if necessary), one may assume that $w = w_1 \circ w_2$ with $w_1(1) = p$. Furthermore w_1 may be supposed to be straight in $\bar{D}$, from 1 to p. By p-U-homotopy w_2 is changed into w_3 lying on D (see 32.2.2) by means of w_σ $(2 \leqslant \sigma \leqslant 3)$. Straight paths u_σ $(2 \leqslant \sigma \leqslant 3)$ within U, with $u_\sigma(0) = w_\sigma(1)$, $u_\sigma(1) = 1$, are attached to w_σ. Then $w_1 \circ w_\sigma \circ u_\sigma$ $(2 \leqslant \sigma \leqslant 3)$ describes a homotopical change of given w into $w' \in \mathscr{W}_1^{\,1}$ such that

$$w'(0) = w'(1) = 1, \qquad w'(\tau) \in D \qquad \text{for} \quad 0 < \tau < 1;$$

$\boldsymbol{w}'$ is defined by

$$\boldsymbol{w}'(\tau) = \log w'(\tau) \qquad \text{for} \quad 0 < \tau < 1,$$

$$\boldsymbol{w}'(0) = \mathbf{0},$$

$$\boldsymbol{w}'(1) = \lim_{\tau = 1} \log w'(\tau).$$

$\boldsymbol{w}'$ is a path on $\bar{\boldsymbol{D}}$, starting at $\mathbf{0}$ and ending at some $z_j \in \boldsymbol{Z}$. It is homotopic on $\bar{\boldsymbol{D}}$ to a straight path from $\mathbf{0}$ to z_j, called $\boldsymbol{h}_j$. Then w', and consequently w, is homotopic with $\exp \boldsymbol{h}_j$.

So the $\exp \boldsymbol{h}_j$ represent the homotopy classes. It remains to show that they represent every homotopy class once. Suppose that $\exp \boldsymbol{h}_i, \exp \boldsymbol{h}_j$ are homotopic in G. Let $\boldsymbol{u}$ be a straight path in $\bar{\boldsymbol{D}}$, starting at $\log p$ and finishing at $\mathbf{0}$. Put $\boldsymbol{v}_i = \boldsymbol{u} \circ \boldsymbol{h}_i$ and $\boldsymbol{v}_j = \boldsymbol{u} \circ \boldsymbol{h}_j$. Then $\exp \boldsymbol{v}_i$, $\exp \boldsymbol{v}_j$ are p-1-homotopic and therefore p-U-homotopic; $\boldsymbol{v}_i, \boldsymbol{v}_j$ can be slightly changed into $\boldsymbol{w}_i, \boldsymbol{w}_j$, such that $\boldsymbol{w}_i(0) = \boldsymbol{w}_j(0) = \log p$, and both are completely contained in $\boldsymbol{D}$. As $\boldsymbol{v}_i(1) = \boldsymbol{h}_i(1) = z_i$, $\boldsymbol{v}_j(1) = \boldsymbol{h}_j(1) = z_j$, still $\boldsymbol{w}_i(1) \in \boldsymbol{C}_i$, $\boldsymbol{w}_j(1) \in \boldsymbol{C}_j$. Now $\exp \boldsymbol{w}_i$, $\exp \boldsymbol{w}_j$ are p-U-homotopic in G. By 32.2.3 they are already so within D. The endpoints of $\exp \boldsymbol{w}_i$, $\exp \boldsymbol{w}_j$ are in C_i, C_j. During the homotopic transition they stay in U and in D. Therefore they stay in a component of $D \cap U$. Consequently $C_i = C_j$, whence $i = j$, which was asserted.

The results are stated in the following theorem:

Theorem Let G be a centerfree unitarily restricted semisimple group. The fundamental group of G is finite; its universal wrapping (and any wrapping whatsoever) is compact. Let $\boldsymbol{D}$ be a principal domain of $\boldsymbol{G}$, and $\boldsymbol{Z}$ the set of $\boldsymbol{h} \in \bar{\boldsymbol{D}}$ with $\exp \boldsymbol{h} = 1$. For any $z_i \in \boldsymbol{Z}$ let $\boldsymbol{h}_i$ be the straight path from $\mathbf{0}$ to z_i. The $\exp \boldsymbol{h}_i$ form a representative system of the $\mathscr{W}_1{}^1$-homotopy classes.

Since a unitary restriction of a complex semisimple linear Lie group wraps a unitary restriction of its adjoint, it follows that the unitary restriction of any complex semisimple linear Lie group is compact.

32.3 To know the fundamental group Φ of G explicitly more information is needed. Using $\boldsymbol{h}_j$ rather than $\exp \boldsymbol{h}_j$ to indicate an element of Φ, one is advised to describe the group operation as an addition rather than a multiplication. By 29.1 it is known that $\exp \boldsymbol{h}_i \circ \exp \boldsymbol{h}_j$ is homotopic with $(\exp \boldsymbol{h}_i)(\exp \boldsymbol{h}_j) = \exp(\boldsymbol{h}_i + \boldsymbol{h}_j)$. One must compute $\boldsymbol{h}_i + \boldsymbol{h}_j$. Unfortunately, it need not belong to $\bar{\boldsymbol{D}}$. This difficulty can be overcome by the use of the reflections S_α (see 20.10). In 33.1 it will be shown that S_α is induced by an inner automorphism of G. Inner automorphisms do not change the homotopy class of a path $w \in \mathscr{W}_1{}^1$, since w and $\tilde{c}_1 w$ are homotopic by $\curlyvee_\sigma \tilde{c}_\sigma w$ if $\curlyvee_\sigma c_\sigma$ is a path from 1 to c_1.

To study the action of such an automorphism on $\boldsymbol{H}$, a basis $\boldsymbol{a}_1, \ldots, \boldsymbol{a}_l$ of $\boldsymbol{H}$ is chosen such that

$$\rho_k(\boldsymbol{a}_j) = 0 \quad \text{for} \quad k \neq j,$$

$$= \mathrm{i} \quad \text{for} \quad k = j,$$

where $\rho_1, \ldots, \rho_l$ are the elements of W^{++}.

$$S_\rho(\xi) = \xi - 2\frac{(\xi, \rho)}{(\rho, \rho)}\rho$$

describes the action of S_ρ in $\boldsymbol{H}^*$;

$$\rho_p(S_{\rho_k}\boldsymbol{a}_j) = (S_{\rho_k}\rho_p)(\boldsymbol{a}_j) = \rho_p(\boldsymbol{a}_j) - 2\frac{(\rho_p, \rho_k)}{(\rho_k, \rho_k)}\rho_k(\boldsymbol{a}_j).$$

Put

$$a_{p,k} = -2\frac{(\rho_p, \rho_k)}{(\rho_k, \rho_k)}.$$

Then

$$(S_{\rho_k} - 1)\,\boldsymbol{a}_j = \sum_p a_{p,k}\,\boldsymbol{a}_p \quad \text{for} \quad k = j,$$

$$= \boldsymbol{0} \qquad\qquad \text{for} \quad k \neq j.$$

Let $\boldsymbol{v}_j$ be the straight path from $\boldsymbol{0}$ to $2\pi\boldsymbol{a}_j$. (The paths $\boldsymbol{h}_i$ with $i \neq 0$ form a subset of the set of $\boldsymbol{v}_j$.) Then $\exp \boldsymbol{v}_j \in \mathscr{W}_1{}^1$. Since $\exp \boldsymbol{v}_j$ and $\exp S_{\rho_j}\boldsymbol{v}_j$ are homotopic, one recognizes that $\exp \boldsymbol{u}_j$, with

$$\boldsymbol{u}_j = \sum_p a_{p,j}\,\boldsymbol{v}_p,$$

is homotopic with the constant path.

For $G_{\text{Com}} \in \mathbf{A}_l$ this produces the homotopically trivial paths $\exp \boldsymbol{u}_j$, with

$$\boldsymbol{u}_1 = -2\boldsymbol{v}_1 + \boldsymbol{v}_2, \ldots, \boldsymbol{u}_j = \boldsymbol{v}_{j-1} - 2\boldsymbol{v}_j + \boldsymbol{v}_{j+1}, \ldots, \boldsymbol{u}_l = \boldsymbol{v}_{l-1} - 2\boldsymbol{v}_l.$$

A simple computation shows:

$$\exp \boldsymbol{v}_j \text{ is homotopic with } \exp j\boldsymbol{v}_1,$$

$$\exp(l+1)\boldsymbol{v}_1 \text{ is homotopically trivial.}$$

For $G_{\text{Com}} \in \mathbf{D}_l$ one finds the homotopically trivial

$$\boldsymbol{u}_1 = -2\boldsymbol{v}_1 + \boldsymbol{v}_l, \qquad \boldsymbol{u}_2 = -2\boldsymbol{v}_2 + \boldsymbol{v}_l, \qquad \boldsymbol{u}_3 = -2\boldsymbol{v}_3 + \boldsymbol{v}_4, \ldots,$$

$$\boldsymbol{u}_j = \boldsymbol{v}_{j-1} - 2\boldsymbol{v}_j + \boldsymbol{v}_{j+1}, \ldots, \boldsymbol{u}_l = \boldsymbol{v}_1 + \boldsymbol{v}_2 + \boldsymbol{v}_{l-1} - 2\boldsymbol{v}_l,$$

which shows that

$$\exp 2\boldsymbol{v}_1, \quad \exp 2\boldsymbol{v}_2, \quad \exp(l-2)\boldsymbol{v}_3, \quad \exp(\boldsymbol{v}_1 + \boldsymbol{v}_2 + \boldsymbol{v}_3)$$

are homotopically equivalent.

32.4 The fundamental group of a Cartesian product equals the direct product of those of the factors. To find the fundamental group of G, one may restrict oneself to the case of simple G.

Then by 25.6 there is a top rootform which surpasses or equals all others in all coordinates. This shows:

Proposition If G is simple and μ is its top rootform, a principal domain is given by

$$\operatorname{Im} \rho_j > 0 \quad (j = 1, \ldots, l), \qquad \operatorname{Im} \mu < 2\pi;$$

$\boldsymbol{D}$ is bounded in $\boldsymbol{H}$ by hyperplanes and $\boldsymbol{Z}$ consists of all points $\boldsymbol{h}$ with

$$\rho_j(\boldsymbol{h}) = 0 \bmod 2\pi\mathrm{i}, \qquad \operatorname{Im} \rho_j(\boldsymbol{h}) \geqslant 0, \qquad \operatorname{Im} \mu(\boldsymbol{h}) \leqslant 2\pi,$$

that is, apart from $\mathbf{0}$, one point for each primitive rootform occurring with multiplicity 1 in the top rootform.

Using the top rootforms in Table E, one gets the following list for $\boldsymbol{Z}$, in which the elements of $\boldsymbol{Z}$ are indicated by their ρ_j-values as coordinates, omitting a factor $2\pi\mathrm{i}$

32.5

A_l: $\ulcorner 0, 0, \ldots, 0, 0 \urcorner$
$\ulcorner 1, 0, \ldots, 0, 0 \urcorner$
$\ulcorner 0, 1, \ldots, 0, 0 \urcorner$
$\vdots$
$\ulcorner 0, 0, \ldots, 1, 0 \urcorner$
$\ulcorner 0, 0, \ldots, 0, 1 \urcorner$

B_l: $\ulcorner 0, 0, \ldots, 0, 0 \urcorner$
$\ulcorner 0, 1, \ldots, 0, 0 \urcorner$

C_l: $\ulcorner 0, 0, \ldots, 0, 0 \urcorner$
$\ulcorner 0, 0, \ldots, 0, 1 \urcorner$

D_l: $\ulcorner 0, 0, 0, \ldots, 0, 0 \urcorner$
$\ulcorner 1, 0, 0, \ldots, 0, 0 \urcorner$
$\ulcorner 0, 1, 0, \ldots, 0, 0 \urcorner$
$\ulcorner 0, 0, 1, \ldots, 0, 0 \urcorner$

E_6: $\ulcorner 0, 0, 0, 0, 0, 0 \urcorner$
$\ulcorner 1, 0, 0, 0, 0, 0 \urcorner$
$\ulcorner 0, 0, 1, 0, 0, 0 \urcorner$

E_7: $\ulcorner 0, 0, 0, 0, 0, 0, 0 \urcorner$
$\ulcorner 0, 1, 0, 0, 0, 0, 0 \urcorner$

E_8: $\ulcorner 0, 0, 0, 0, 0, 0, 0, 0 \urcorner$

F_4: $\ulcorner 0, 0, 0, 0 \urcorner$

G_2: $\ulcorner 0, 0 \urcorner$.

32.6 For A_l the computation in 32.3 shows that the fundamental group is $(l+1)$-cyclic. For D_l the only nontrivial elements are $\exp \boldsymbol{v}_1$, $\exp \boldsymbol{v}_2$, $\exp \boldsymbol{v}_3$, all of order 2 if l is even, whereas for odd l, $\exp \boldsymbol{v}_1$ is of order 4. This shows:

Theorem Let G be a centerfree unitarily restricted simple semisimple Lie group. It is simply connected if $G_{\mathrm{Com}} \in \mathsf{G}_2, \mathsf{F}_4, \mathsf{E}_8$. The fundamental group of G is two-cyclic for $G_{\mathrm{Com}} \in \mathsf{B}_l, \mathsf{C}_l, \mathsf{E}_7$, three-cyclic for $G_{\mathrm{Com}} \in \mathsf{E}_6$, and $(l+1)$-cyclic for $G_{\mathrm{Com}} \in \mathsf{A}_l$. It is four-cyclic for $G_{\mathrm{Com}} \in \mathsf{D}_l$ (l odd) and noncyclic of order 4 for $G_{\mathrm{Com}} \in \mathsf{D}_l$ (l even).

32.7. Theorem Let G be a unitarily restricted semisimple linear Lie group. The center of G is contained in any trunk of G.

Proof $\boldsymbol{G}$ and $\tilde{\boldsymbol{G}}$ are isomorphic, and G and $\tilde{G}$ are locally isomorphic. As $\tilde{G}$ is centerfree, G wraps $\tilde{G}$ by means of a homomorphism λ. If $\boldsymbol{H}$ (H) is a trunk of $\boldsymbol{G}$ (G), $\lambda\boldsymbol{H}$ (λH) is a trunk of $\tilde{\boldsymbol{G}}$ $(\tilde{G})$.

Let w be a path in G leading from 1 to some center element. Then λw is a path in $\tilde{G}$ with $(\lambda w)(0) = (\lambda w)(1) = 1$. By 32.2 it is homotopic with a path

$\curlyvee_\tau \exp \tilde{h}(\tau)$ with $\tilde{h}(\tau) \in \tilde{H}$. Here $\curlyvee_\tau h(\tau)$ may be assumed to be continuous. Now by 28.19, $\curlyvee_\tau \exp h(\tau)$, which is mapped by λ into $\curlyvee_\tau \exp \tilde{h}(\tau)$, is homotopic with w in G. It finishes at $w(1)$ which is contained in H. This proves the assertion.

32.8. An immediate consequence:

Proposition Let G be a unitarily restricted semisimple linear Lie group. Then under the adjoint mapping the original of a trunk is again a trunk.

32.9. Another consequence:

Conjugacy Theorem 31.5 remains valid for arbitrary unitarily restricted semisimple linear Lie groups.

32.10. Proposition The one-dimensional connected locally closed subgroups of a unitarily restricted semisimple linear Lie group G cover G.

Indeed, a trunk of G is covered in this way, and by the conjugacy theorem this property is extended to G itself.

32.11. Proposition G/H is simply connected.

Remark This result was announced in 32.1. It suffices to prove it for centerfree G, since the center is anyhow factored out according to 32.7.

Proof Let U be as in 32.2.1, and C_i as in 32.2.4. Since U is $\tilde{G}$-invariant, $\ulcorner G/H, D \cap U \urcorner$ is the original of $U \cap F$ under the wrapping of F by $\ulcorner G/H, D \urcorner$. The $\ulcorner G/H, C_i \urcorner$ are the different components of $\ulcorner G/H, D \cap U \urcorner$. Since $U \setminus F$ has codimension 3 in U, $U \cap F$ is still simply connected. Hence each $\ulcorner G/H, C_i \urcorner$ wraps $U \cap F$ homeomorphically. Consequently the number of points above a point of F equals the number of the C_i, which is the cardinality of the fundamental group. So $\ulcorner G/H, D \urcorner$, and G/H as well, is simply connected.

32.12. Historical Note The preceding approach to the fundamental group is H. Weyl's, *Math. Z.* **24** (1926) = *Selecta* 348–352, though the actual computation of the fundamental group was performed by E. Cartan, *Ann. Mat.* **4**, 209–256 (1927) = *Œuvres* I, **2**, 793–840.

33. THE AUTOMORPHISMS OF SEMISIMPLE LIE GROUPS

G is assumed to be semisimple in ordered third dressing, complex or unitarily restricted, and sometimes centerfree or simply connected. Other notations as usual.

33.1. Reflections as Automorphisms

A (continuous) automorphism of G leaving the trunk H invariant, induces an automorphism of W^*. Conversely, any automorphism of W^* is induced by one of $\boldsymbol{G}$, which extends to a local one of G, to a global one of the universal wrapping, and (by factoring out the center) to a global one of the adjoint group.

A special automorphism of W^* is known as S_α ($\alpha \in W^*$; see 20.10).

Proposition S_α is induced by an *inner* automorphism of $\boldsymbol{G}$ (unitary or complex), which interchanges $\boldsymbol{e}_\alpha$ and $\boldsymbol{e}_{-\alpha}$.

Proof For $\alpha \in W^*$ put

$$\boldsymbol{p}_\alpha = \boldsymbol{e}_\alpha + \boldsymbol{e}_{-\alpha},$$
$$\boldsymbol{q}_\alpha = \boldsymbol{h}_\alpha + (\tfrac{1}{2}(\alpha, \alpha))^{1/2} (\boldsymbol{e}_\alpha - \boldsymbol{e}_{-\alpha}),$$
$$\boldsymbol{r}_\alpha = \boldsymbol{h}_\alpha - (\tfrac{1}{2}(\alpha, \alpha))^{1/2} (\boldsymbol{e}_\alpha - \boldsymbol{e}_{-\alpha}).$$

Then

$$\tilde{\boldsymbol{p}}_\alpha \boldsymbol{q}_\alpha = -(2(\alpha, \alpha))^{1/2} \boldsymbol{q}_\alpha,$$
$$\tilde{\boldsymbol{p}}_\alpha \boldsymbol{r}_\alpha = +(2(\alpha, \alpha))^{1/2} \boldsymbol{r}_\alpha,$$
$$\tilde{\boldsymbol{p}}_\alpha \boldsymbol{h} = \boldsymbol{0} \quad \text{for all} \quad \boldsymbol{h} \in \boldsymbol{H} \quad \text{with} \quad \alpha(\boldsymbol{h}) = 0.$$

With $\tau = \pi \mathrm{i}(2(\alpha, \alpha))^{-\frac{1}{2}}$,

$$\tau\tilde{\boldsymbol{p}}_\alpha \boldsymbol{q}_\alpha = -\pi \mathrm{i} \boldsymbol{q}_\alpha,$$
$$\tau\tilde{\boldsymbol{p}}_\alpha \boldsymbol{r}_\alpha = \pi \mathrm{i} \boldsymbol{r}_\alpha,$$
$$\tau\tilde{\boldsymbol{p}}_\alpha \boldsymbol{h} = \boldsymbol{0} \quad \text{for} \quad \boldsymbol{h} \in \boldsymbol{H} \quad \text{with} \quad \alpha(\boldsymbol{h}) = 0;$$

hence

$$(\exp \tau\tilde{\boldsymbol{p}}_\alpha) \boldsymbol{q}_\alpha = -\boldsymbol{q}_\alpha,$$
$$(\exp \tau\tilde{\boldsymbol{p}}_\alpha) \boldsymbol{r}_\alpha = -\boldsymbol{r}_\alpha,$$
$$(\exp \tau\tilde{\boldsymbol{p}}_\alpha) \boldsymbol{h} = \boldsymbol{h} \quad \text{for} \quad \boldsymbol{h} \in \boldsymbol{H} \text{ with } \alpha(\boldsymbol{h}) = 0.$$

Since $2\boldsymbol{h}_\alpha = \boldsymbol{q}_\alpha + \boldsymbol{r}_\alpha$,

$$(\exp \tau\tilde{\boldsymbol{p}}_\alpha) \boldsymbol{h}_\alpha = -\boldsymbol{h}_\alpha.$$

Therefore $\exp \tau\tilde{\boldsymbol{p}}_\alpha$ maps

$$\boldsymbol{h} \quad \text{into} \quad \boldsymbol{h} - 2\frac{\alpha(\boldsymbol{h})}{\alpha(\boldsymbol{h}_\alpha)} \boldsymbol{h}_\alpha,$$

which mapping in fact induces S_α. It also interchanges $\boldsymbol{e}_\alpha$ and $\boldsymbol{e}_{-\alpha}$.

$\exp \tau\tilde{\boldsymbol{p}}_\alpha$ is an inner automorphism of complex $\boldsymbol{G}$. Because of third dressing, it is even an inner automorphism of unitarily restricted $\boldsymbol{G}$, since τ is purely imaginary.

Definition $\exp(\pi i(2(\alpha,\alpha))^{-\frac{1}{2}}(\tilde{\boldsymbol{e}}_\alpha+\tilde{\boldsymbol{e}}_{-\alpha}))$, as an extension of S_α, is also denoted by S_α.

33.2–3. The Automorphisms of W^*

33.2.1. Definition Aut W^* is the *group of automorphisms* of W^*; also if linearly extended to $\boldsymbol{H}^*$ or $\boldsymbol{H}^*_{\text{st}}$ and if transferred to $\boldsymbol{H}$ and $\boldsymbol{H}_{\text{st}}$. The subgroup generated by the reflections S_α ($\alpha \in W^*$), considered as mappings of W^*, or $\boldsymbol{H}^*$, $\boldsymbol{H}^*_{\text{st}}$, or $\boldsymbol{H}$, $\boldsymbol{H}_{\text{st}}$, is called the *kaleidoscope group* or group of *inner automorphisms of* W^*, indicated by Int W^*. The group of *automorphisms of the graph* W^{++} is denoted by Aut W^{++}; also if linearly extended to $\boldsymbol{H}^*$ or $\boldsymbol{H}^*_{\text{st}}$ or transferred to $\boldsymbol{H}$ and $\boldsymbol{H}_{\text{st}}$.

As a permutation group of W^*, Aut W^* is finite. Int W^* is normal in Aut W^*. Aut W^* preserves the inner product in $\boldsymbol{H}^*_{\text{st}}$.

33.2.2. Proposition Int W^* is generated by the reflections S_ρ with $\rho \in W^{++}$.

Proof By 25.4 every $\alpha \in W^+$ can be obtained as a $T\rho_0$, where $\rho_0 \in W^{++}$ and T is a product of reflections S_ρ, with $\rho \in W^{++}$. Obviously $S_\alpha = TS_{\rho_0}T^{-1}$, which proves the statement.

33.2.3. Proposition Under Int W^* every element of W^* is equivalent to one of W^{++}.

This follows as well from 25.4.

33.2.4. Proposition If $\boldsymbol{G}$ is simple, then Int W^* acts transitively in each of the (at most two) sets of nonzero rootforms with equal lengths.

Proof By 33.2.3 it suffices to show that primitive rootforms of the same length are Int W^*-equivalent. Inspection of the graphs shows that the subgraphs of primitive rootforms with the same length are connected. Now, if ρ, σ are adjacent primitive rootforms with the same length, then $S_\rho S_\sigma \rho = \sigma$. This proves the proposition.

33.3 Every $A \in$ Aut W^{++} somehow extends to complex $\boldsymbol{G}$, say

$$A\boldsymbol{e}_\alpha = \nu_\alpha \boldsymbol{e}_{A\alpha}.$$

Using an $\boldsymbol{h} \in \boldsymbol{H}$ with $\rho(\boldsymbol{h}) = \log \nu_\rho$ for all $\rho \in W^{++}$ and arbitrary log-values, one can replace A by $A\tilde{h}^{-1}$ with $h = \exp \boldsymbol{h}$, in this way reducing all ν_ρ ($\rho \in W^{++}$) to 1.

33.3.1. Definition An extension of $A \in \operatorname{Aut} W^{++}$ to $\boldsymbol{G}$ is called *straight* if $A\boldsymbol{e}_\rho = \boldsymbol{e}_{A\rho}$ for all $\rho \in W^{++}$.

Proposition $A \in \operatorname{Aut} W^{++}$ possesses a straight extension to $\boldsymbol{G}$. Because of 25.4.2, it is unique (after ordered third dressing). It commutes with C_{un}, C_{st}, M. It leaves the unitary restriction invariant.

The straight extensions of the elements of Aut W^{++} to $\boldsymbol{G}$ clearly form a group.

33.3.2. Definition The group consisting of the straight extensions of Aut W^{++} to $\boldsymbol{G}$ is denoted by $\operatorname{Aut}^{\boldsymbol{G}}(W^{++})$.

It is a subgroup of Aut $\boldsymbol{G}$.

An automorphism of $\boldsymbol{G}$ need not be induced by one of G.

33.3.3. Definition The subgroup of Aut G consisting of the automorphisms inducing elements of $\operatorname{Aut}^{\boldsymbol{G}}(W^{++})$ is denoted by $\operatorname{Aut}^{G}(W^{++})$.

If G is centerfree or simply connected, any automorphism of $\boldsymbol{G}$ is induced by one of G and therefore all of $\operatorname{Aut}^{\boldsymbol{G}}(W^{++})$ is induced by $\operatorname{Aut}^{G}(W^{++})$. Therefore they are isomorphic.

33.3.4 Aut W^{++} interchanges the components of W^{++}. For simple $\boldsymbol{G}$, that is, connected W^{++}, it is trivial in most cases. The exceptions are

$\mathbf{A}_l$ $(l > 1)$: inverting the graph,

$\mathbf{D}_l$ $(l > 4)$: permuting ρ_1, ρ_2,

$\mathbf{D}_4$: permuting ρ_1, ρ_2, ρ_3,

$\mathbf{E}_6$: simultaneously permuting ρ_1 and ρ_3, ρ_4 and ρ_5.

Comparing these data with those on the fundamental group (32.5), one notes that nontrivial elements of Aut W^{++} induce nontrivial automorphisms of the fundamental group of centerfree G_{un}. On the other hand, Int G_{un} always acts trivially on the fundamental group. So nontrivial elements of Aut W^{++} cannot be induced by elements of Int G_{un}, whereas all Int W^* is induced by elements of Int G_{un} (see 33.1). This proves:

Proposition Int $W^* \cap \operatorname{Aut} W^{++} = \{1\}$.

In 33.8 this is proved in a more elementary way by avoiding the fundamental group.

33.4–5. Chambers

33.4. Definition The open convex domains in which H^*_{st} is divided by the orthoplanes $\alpha^\perp$ of the rootforms $\alpha \neq 0$ are called *chambers*.

Evidently Aut W^* permutes the chambers.

Any natural basis Z (see 25.2) defines a chamber $C(Z)$:

33.4.1 $$\xi \in C(Z) \leftrightarrow (\xi, \rho) > 0 \quad \text{for all} \quad \rho \in Z.$$

Indeed, any α combines from Z with all coefficients nonnegative or nonpositive; therefore $(\xi, \alpha) = 0$ for no $\alpha \in W^*$ as long as $\xi \in C(Z)$, and thus no plane $\alpha^\perp$ enters $C(Z)$.

Definition $\xi \in H^*_{st}$ is called *dominant* if, in the given order, it is surpassed by no other Int W^*-equivalent element of H^*_{st}. A *dominant chamber* is one with a dominant element.

If ξ is in some chamber, then any maximal element of the set (Int $W^*)\xi$ is dominant and again in a chamber. Therefore there is at least one dominant chamber.

33.4.2 $$(\xi, \rho) \geqslant 0 \quad \text{for all} \quad \rho \in W^{++}$$

is necessary to make ξ dominant, for, if $(\xi, \rho) < 0$, then $S_\rho \xi = \xi - 2((\xi, \rho)/(\rho, \rho))\rho$ is higher than ξ.

The system of inequalities 33.4.2 describes the closure of $C(W^{++})$, as defined by 33.4.1. Therefore every dominant element is in $\overline{C(W^{++})}$ and every dominant element that is in some chamber is in $C(W^{++})$. Consequently there is only one dominant chamber, namely, $C(W^{++})$.

If C_1 is some chamber, then for $\xi \in C_1$ any dominant equivalent of ξ is contained in (Int $W^*)\xi \cap C(W^{++})$. Therefore (Int $W^*)C_1 \cap C(W^{++})$ is nonvoid, as is $C_1 \cap$ (Int $W^*)C(W^{++})$. This shows that in every chamber (Int $W^*)C(W^{++})$ has some point, and, since Int W^* permutes the chambers, the following obtains:

33.4.3 Int W^* is transitive on the set of chambers.

Now consider an element of Aut W^* that preserves the dominant chamber C. It interchanges the walls, and thus the elements of W^{++}, while preserving the angles, and so it preserves the structure of the graph W^{++}. It belongs to Aut W^{++}. By the proposition of 33.3.4 an element of Int W^* preserving C must be 1. Hence:

33.4.4 Int W^* is *simply transitive* on the set of chambers.

33.4.5 A consequence: Different points of a chamber can never be Int W^*-equivalent. In 33.8.1 this is extended to closed chambers.

Another consequence: No element of Int W^*, except the identity, can have a fixed point in a chamber. So if $S \in \text{Int } W^*$ is a reflection, its reflecting plane cannot cross any chamber. Hence:

Proposition Any reflection belonging to Int W^* has the form S_α with some $\alpha \in W^*$.

33.4.7 The foregoing results are expressed in the following theorem:

Theorem Int W^* is generated by the S_ρ ($\rho \in W^{++}$) and is simply transitive on the set of chambers. A complete representative system of Aut W^*/Int W^* is furnished by Aut W^{++}. Any element of Int W^* is induced by some inner automorphism of $\boldsymbol{G}$ leaving $\boldsymbol{H}$ and $\boldsymbol{G}_{\text{un}}$ invariant, but no element $\neq 1$ of Aut W^{++} is induced by an inner automorphism of $\boldsymbol{G}$. Any element of Aut W^* is induced by some automorphism of $\boldsymbol{G}$ leaving $\boldsymbol{H}$ and $\boldsymbol{G}_{\text{un}}$ invariant.

The last assertion is easily verified: if $A \in \text{Aut } W^*$, then $A = A_1 A_2$ with $A_1 \in \text{Aut } W^{++}$, $A_2 \in \text{Int } W^*$, where the extensions of A_1, A_2 are achieved as in 33.3.1 and 33.1.

33.5. Proposition If Z is a natural basis of W^*, the intersection of the halfspaces $\uparrow_\xi (\xi, \rho) > 0$ with $\rho \in Z$ is a chamber. By this construction natural bases and chambers are one-to-one related. Under a suitable order of $\boldsymbol{H}_{\text{st}}^*$ any chamber may play the role of dominant chamber. The structure of the graph of $\boldsymbol{G}$ does not depend on the choice of the order in $\boldsymbol{H}_{\text{st}}^*$.

Proof The first assertion was proved in 33.4.1. Int W^* preserves the notions of natural basis and chamber. It is transitive on the set of chambers. Therefore every chamber is produced by a natural basis. It is evident that this relation is one-to-one. According to 25.2.5, any natural basis can be obtained as a W^{++} under a suitable order. In this way any chamber can appear as the dominant one. All chambers are congruent, and thus all possible graphs are isomorphic.

Remark The last sentence of the proposition fills the gap indicated in 25.3 and 26.24.

33.6–8. An Alternative Approach

33.6. Proposition If $\alpha, \beta \in W^*$ and $2 \sphericalangle(\alpha, \beta) = 2\pi/m_{\alpha,\beta}$, then $S_\alpha S_\beta$ is a rotation of order $m_{\alpha,\beta}$ around the intersection of $\alpha^\perp$ and $\beta^\perp$ as the axis. In particular, $S_\alpha S_\beta = S_\beta S_\alpha$ if and only if $\alpha = \pm\beta$ or $(\alpha, \beta) = 0$.

If $\alpha \neq \pm\beta$, the only possible values of $m_{\alpha,\beta}$ are 2, 3, 4, and 6.

The proposition is obvious. Actually, the relations

$$S_\rho^{\,2} = 1, \qquad (S_\rho S_\sigma)^{m_{\rho,\sigma}} = 1 \qquad (\rho \neq \sigma),$$

between the generators S_τ ($\tau \in W^{++}$) of Int W^* characterize Int W^* as an abstract group. (Without proof.)

33.7. Proposition Let B be the intersection of the two half-spaces $\uparrow_\xi(\xi,\rho) > 0$, $\uparrow_\xi(\xi,\sigma) > 0$ ($\rho,\sigma \in W^{++}$, $\rho \neq \sigma$) and let $K_{\rho,\sigma}$ be the group generated by S_ρ, S_σ. The interior angle of B is $\pi/m_{\rho,\sigma}$ (see 33.6), and the $K_{\rho,\sigma}$-images of B do not meet each other.

Proof The first assertion follows from the fact that $\measuredangle(\rho,\sigma) = \pi(1-(m_{\rho,\sigma})^{-1})$, $\measuredangle(\rho,\sigma)$ being obtuse, and the second from the first and Proposition 33.6 because this proposition implies that the orbits of B and $S_\rho B$ under $S_\rho S_\sigma$ each consist of $m_{\rho,\sigma}$ elements, all mutually disjoint.

33.8 In the proof of the proposition of 33.3.4, on which part of Theorem 33.4.7 rests, the fundamental group has been used. A much more elementary proof is possible. Eventually one has to show that different points of the dominant chamber C cannot be Int W^*-equivalent. Even more will be proved:

33.8.1. Proposition Different points of $\bar{C}$ cannot be Int W^*-equivalent.
In other words, 33.4.2 is also sufficient for ξ to be dominant.

33.8.2. Proposition If $\xi \in \bar{C}$, then ξ surpasses all its other Int W^*-equivalents.

33.8.3 *Derivation* of 33.8.1 from 33.8.2. Suppose 33.8.2 and both ξ and $S\xi$ in $\bar{C}$ (some $S \in$ Int W^*); then, by 33.8.2, $\xi \geqslant S\xi$ as well as $S\xi \geqslant S^{-1}S\xi$, which proves 33.8.1.

33.8.4 If $\xi, \eta \in \boldsymbol{H}_{\mathrm{st}}^*$ are Int W^*-equivalent, they can be joined by a chain $\xi = \xi_0, \xi_1, \ldots, \xi_p = \eta$ such that for every $j = 1, \ldots, p$: $\xi_j \neq \xi_{j-1}$, and $\xi_j = S_\rho \xi_{j-1}$ for some $\rho \in W^{++}$. In all but one W^{++}-coordinate ξ_{j-1} and ξ_j agree. Only the coordinate corresponding to ρ may decrease or increase from ξ_{j-1} to ξ_j. It will be shown:

Proposition If $\xi_0 \in \bar{C}$, then increases can be avoided.
(It is evident that this proposition implies 33.8.2.)

Proof For the needs of the proof assume a total order on $\boldsymbol{H}_{\mathrm{st}}^*$, extending the given one (see 25.2.7).

Since $(\xi,\rho) \geqslant 0$ for all $\rho \in W^{++}$, no $S_\rho\xi$ is higher than ξ; thus ξ_1 is definitely lower than ξ_0. If the chain $\xi_0, \xi_1, \ldots, \xi_p$ shows some increase, then there must be a reversal-ξ_j, which means a ξ_j such that $\xi_{j-1} > \xi_j < \xi_{j+1}$. Suppose that the chain between ξ and η has been chosen such that the lowest reversal-ξ_j is as high as possible. This will lead to a contradiction.

Let ξ_j be the lowest reversal,

$$\xi_j = S_\rho \xi_{j-1}, \qquad \xi_{j+1} = S_\sigma \xi_j, \quad \text{with} \quad \rho, \sigma \in W^{++},$$

$$(\xi_j, \rho) < 0, \qquad (\xi_j, \sigma) < 0.$$

Put

$$\vartheta_0 = \xi_j,$$

$$\vartheta_{i+1} = S_\rho \vartheta_i \qquad \text{for even} \quad i,$$

$$\vartheta_{i+1} = S_\sigma \vartheta_i \qquad \text{for odd} \quad i,$$

up to

$$\vartheta_{2m_{\rho,\sigma}} = \vartheta_0,$$

with $m_{\rho,\sigma}$ defined as in 33.7. The intersection of $\uparrow_\xi(\xi, \rho) > 0$ and $\uparrow_\xi(\xi, \sigma) > 0$ is called B as in 33.7. In the ϑ-sequence a reversal from decrease to increase could take place only at $\vartheta_i \in -B$. Since the $K_{\rho,\sigma}$-images of B do not overlap (see 33.7), no $\vartheta_i \in -B$ except ϑ_0. Thus there is no such reversal in the ϑ-sequence.

The ξ-sequence is now modified by traveling from ξ_{i-1} to ξ_{i+1} the other way around the intersection of $\rho^\perp$ and $\sigma^\perp$, that is, through $\xi_{j-1} = \vartheta_1, \vartheta_2, \ldots, \vartheta_{2m_{\rho,\sigma}-1} = \xi_{j+1}$. The lowest reversal-$\xi_j$ has been removed, while no lower reversals have been created. The lowest reversal has been raised, which proves the proposition by contradiction.

33.8.5 A consequence of 33.2.4 and 33.8.1 is the following:

Proposition If $\mathbf{G}$ is simple, then among the rootforms of the same (non-vanishing) length there is only one dominant one.

This is also confirmed by Table E.

33.9. Automorphisms of $\mathbf{G}$ and G

Definition

$\mathrm{Aut}(\mathbf{G}, \mathbf{H})$ is the group of automorphisms of $\mathbf{G}$ leaving $\mathbf{H}$ invariant,
$\mathrm{Aut}(G, H)$ is the group of automorphisms of G leaving H invariant,
$\mathrm{Int}(\mathbf{G}, \mathbf{H})$ is the group of inner automorphisms of $\mathbf{G}$ leaving $\mathbf{H}$ invariant,
$\mathrm{Int}(G, H)$ is the group of inner automorphisms of G leaving H invariant;

$\tilde{H}$ is used for both the subgroup of Aut $\mathbf{G}$ as well as that of Aut G constituted by the exp $\tilde{\mathbf{h}}$ with $\mathbf{h} \in \mathbf{H}$.

Theorem For complex or unitarily restricted $\boldsymbol{G}$:

(1) Int $\boldsymbol{G}$ is transitive on the set of trunks of $\boldsymbol{G}$,
(2) $\tilde{\boldsymbol{H}}$ equals the group of automorphisms of $\boldsymbol{G}$, leaving $\boldsymbol{H}$ elementwise invariant,
(3) $\mathrm{Aut}(\boldsymbol{G},\boldsymbol{H})/\tilde{\boldsymbol{H}} \simeq \mathrm{Aut}\, W^*$ in a natural way,
(4) $\mathrm{Int}(\boldsymbol{G},\boldsymbol{H})/\tilde{\boldsymbol{H}} \simeq \mathrm{Int}\, W^*$ by restriction of the preceding mapping,
(5) $\mathrm{Aut}(\boldsymbol{G},\boldsymbol{H}) = \mathrm{Aut}^{\boldsymbol{G}}(W^{++})\cdot\mathrm{Int}(\boldsymbol{G},\boldsymbol{H})$,
(6) $\mathrm{Aut}\,\boldsymbol{G} = \mathrm{Aut}^{\boldsymbol{G}}(W^{++})\cdot\mathrm{Int}\,\boldsymbol{G}$,
with trivial intersections of the factors.

Furthermore the following statements hold:

(i') ($i = 1,2,4,5,6$), obtained by replacing $\boldsymbol{G},\boldsymbol{H}$ by G,H in the statement i, and
(3′) $\mathrm{Aut}(G,H)/\tilde{H}$ is isomorphic to a subgroup of Aut W^*, which in the case of centerfree or simply connected G again coincides with Aut W^*.

Proof (1), (1′). See the conjugacy theorems 17.8, 31.5, 32.9.
(2), (2′). It suffices to consider an automorphism f of $\boldsymbol{G}$ with $f\boldsymbol{a} = \boldsymbol{a}$ for all $\boldsymbol{a} \in \boldsymbol{H}$ and to find an $\boldsymbol{h} \in \boldsymbol{H}$ such that $f = \exp \tilde{\boldsymbol{h}}$. Clearly, for some ν_α

$$f\boldsymbol{e}_\alpha = \nu_\alpha \boldsymbol{e}_\alpha.$$

From the commutator relations it follows that

$$\text{(a)} \qquad \nu_\alpha \nu_{-\alpha} = 1, \qquad \nu_\alpha \nu_\beta = \nu_{\alpha+\beta} \qquad (\alpha, \beta,\ \alpha + \beta \in W^*).$$

For $\boldsymbol{h} \in \boldsymbol{H}$

$$\tilde{\boldsymbol{h}}\boldsymbol{e}_\alpha = \alpha(\boldsymbol{h})\,\boldsymbol{e}_\alpha,$$

$$(\exp \tilde{\boldsymbol{h}})\,\boldsymbol{e}_\alpha = (\exp \alpha(\boldsymbol{h}))\,\boldsymbol{e}_\alpha.$$

To prove the assertion one must determine $\boldsymbol{h} \in \boldsymbol{H}$ such that

$$\text{(b)} \qquad \exp \alpha(\boldsymbol{h}) = \nu_\alpha.$$

There is an $\boldsymbol{h} \in \boldsymbol{H}$ that fulfills (b) for all $\alpha \in W^{++}$. Then by (a) it fulfills (b) for all $\alpha \in W^*$, since the $\boldsymbol{e}_{\pm\alpha}$ ($\alpha \in W^{++}$) generate $\boldsymbol{G}$ (see 25.4.2).

In the unitary case one must take care that $\boldsymbol{h} \in \mathrm{i}\boldsymbol{H}_{\mathrm{st}}$, but in that case f respects the unitary restriction, which means

$$\nu_\alpha \boldsymbol{e}_\alpha = f\boldsymbol{e}_\alpha = C_{\mathrm{un}}\, fC_{\mathrm{un}}\; \boldsymbol{e}_\alpha = -C_{\mathrm{un}}\, f\boldsymbol{e}_{-\alpha} = -C_{\mathrm{un}}\; \nu_{-\alpha}\, \boldsymbol{e}_{-\alpha}$$
$$= -\bar{\nu}_{-\alpha}\, C_{\mathrm{un}}\; \boldsymbol{e}_{-\alpha} = \bar{\nu}_{-\alpha}\, \boldsymbol{e}_\alpha,$$

hence

$$\nu_\alpha = \bar{\nu}_{-\alpha} = \bar{\nu}_\alpha^{-1}.$$

Now, since $|\nu_\alpha| = 1$, all $\alpha(\boldsymbol{h})$ are purely imaginary for $\boldsymbol{h}$ fulfilling (b). So $\boldsymbol{h} \in \mathrm{i}\boldsymbol{H}_{\mathrm{st}} = \boldsymbol{H}_{\mathrm{un}}$.

(3)(4)(3′)(4′). $f \in \mathrm{Aut}(\boldsymbol{G},\boldsymbol{H})$ or $\in \mathrm{Aut}(G,H)$ induces an element Θf of Aut W^*. This inducement Θ is a homomorphism. Its kernel consists of the f that induce the identity on W^*, hence on $\boldsymbol{H}$. By (2) this is just $\tilde{H}$. Conversely, by 33.4.7 any element of Aut W^* (Int W^*) is induced by some of $\mathrm{Aut}(\boldsymbol{G},\boldsymbol{H})$ $(\mathrm{Int}(\boldsymbol{G},\boldsymbol{H}))$ (whether $\boldsymbol{G}$ is complex or unitarily restricted), and this is again induced by some of $\mathrm{Aut}(G,H)$ $(\mathrm{Int}(G,H))$ if G is centerfree or simply connected (see 33.1).

(5)(5′). The image of $\mathrm{Aut}(\boldsymbol{G},\boldsymbol{H})$ or $\mathrm{Aut}(G,H)$ under the inducement Θ contains Int W^* and is contained in Aut W^*. By 33.4.7 the splitting Aut W^* $=$ Aut $W^{++}\cdot$Int W^* is lifted to $\mathrm{Aut}(\boldsymbol{G},\boldsymbol{H})$, where, according to 33.3.2–3, the first factor can be assumed to be in $\mathrm{Aut}^{\boldsymbol{G}} W^{++}$. By this procedure Θf can be lifted into $f' = f_1 f_2$ with some $f_1 \in \mathrm{Aut}^{\boldsymbol{G}}(W^{++})$, $f_2 \in \mathrm{Int}(\boldsymbol{G},\boldsymbol{H})$ or $f_1 \in \mathrm{Aut}^{G}(W^{++})$, $f_2 \in \mathrm{Int}(G,H)$. Now $\Theta f' = \Theta f$; hence by (2) $f \in f'\tilde{H}$. Therefore $f \in f_1\, \mathrm{Int}(\boldsymbol{G},\boldsymbol{H})$, respectively, $\in f_1\, \mathrm{Int}(G,H)$, which proves the assertions.

(6)(6′). Given $f \in \mathrm{Aut}\,\boldsymbol{G}$ or $\in \mathrm{Aut}\,G$, there is, according to (1), some $g \in \mathrm{Int}\,\boldsymbol{G}$, respectively, Int G, which carries $\boldsymbol{H}$ (H) into the trunk $f\boldsymbol{H}$ (fH). By (5)(5′) $g^{-1}f \in \mathrm{Aut}^{\boldsymbol{G}}(W^{++})\cdot\mathrm{Int}\,\boldsymbol{G}$, respectively, $\mathrm{Aut}^{G}(W^{++})\cdot\mathrm{Int}\,G$, which proves the statement about f.

The statement on the intersection of the factors is obvious.

33.10. Automorphisms and the Fundamental Group

Proposition An automorphism of centerfree G is inner if, and only if it acts trivially on the fundamental group of G (the unitary restriction).

Proof The automorphism f may be assumed to leave the trunk H invariant and even to preserve the dominant chamber, thus to induce an element of Aut W^{++}. If it is outer, then 33.3.4 states that it acts nontrivially on the fundamental group. If it is inner, it acts trivially according to 32.3.

33.11. Plus-Automorphism In the case of simple $\boldsymbol{G}$ (see 33.3.4), with the exception of $\mathbf{D}_4$, there is at most one nontrivial element of Aut W^{++}, which extends to dressed $\boldsymbol{G}$ as a straight automorphism according to 33.3. For later use it is convenient to have the following:

Definition The *plus-automorphism* P is determined after ordered third dressing as the straight extension of P defined on $\boldsymbol{H}^*$ by

$\mathbf{A}_l$ $(l > 1)$: $P\rho_j = \rho_{l+1-j}$,

$\mathbf{D}_l$ $(l \geqslant 4)$: $P\rho_1 = \rho_2, P\rho_2 = \rho_1, P\rho_j = \rho_j\ (j \neq 1, 2)$,

$\mathbf{E}_6$: $P\rho_1 = \rho_3, P\rho_3 = \rho_1, P\rho_4 = \rho_5, P\rho_5 = \rho_4, P\rho_2 = \rho_2, P\rho_6 = \rho_6$.

P is involutory; it commutes with the minus-automorphism M, with C_{un} and C_{st}, and, except for $\mathbf{D}_4$, is uniquely determined.

33.12–13. Minus-Automorphism

33.12. Proposition For simple $\boldsymbol{G}$ the minus-automorphism M is inner, except in the cases $\mathbf{A}_l$ $(l > 1)$, $\mathbf{D}_l$ (l odd), $\mathbf{E}_6$, where it is outer. M preserves the simple summands of semisimple $\boldsymbol{G}$.

Proof M maps an element of the fundamental group of centerfree unitary G into its inverse. By 33.10 and 32.6 the assertion is obvious.

33.13 As mentioned in 23.1, the given third dressing is not uniquely determined by its trunk $\boldsymbol{H}$.

Assume that M' is an involutory automorphism of $\boldsymbol{G}$ acting on the trunk $\boldsymbol{H}$ as the scalar multiplication by -1. Then by Theorem 33.9

$$M' = \tilde{h}_1 M \quad \text{for some} \quad h_1 \in H,$$

which can also be written as

$$M' = \tilde{h} M \tilde{h}^{-1} = \tilde{h}^2 M,$$

where h is some (existent) square root of h_1 in H.

Putting

$$\boldsymbol{e}'_\alpha = \tilde{h}\boldsymbol{e}_\alpha \qquad (\alpha \in W^*),$$

one gets

$$M' \boldsymbol{e}'_\alpha = \tilde{h} M \tilde{h}^{-1} \cdot \tilde{h}\boldsymbol{e}_\alpha = \tilde{h}\boldsymbol{e}_{-\alpha} = \boldsymbol{e}'_{-\alpha},$$

$$\psi(\tilde{h}\boldsymbol{e}_\alpha, \tilde{h}\boldsymbol{e}_{-\alpha}) = \psi(\boldsymbol{e}_\alpha, \boldsymbol{e}_{-\alpha}) = 1.$$

In other words, a new third dressing on $\boldsymbol{H}$ is obtained with M' as its minus-automorphism; its unitary semimorphism is $\tilde{h} C_{\text{un}} \tilde{h}^{-1}$, since $\tilde{h} C_{\text{un}} \tilde{h}^{-1} \boldsymbol{e}'_\alpha = \tilde{h} C_{\text{un}} \tilde{h}^{-1} \cdot \tilde{h}\boldsymbol{e}_\alpha = -\tilde{h}\boldsymbol{e}_{-\alpha} = -\boldsymbol{e}'_{-\alpha}$, and its unitary restriction is $\tilde{h}\boldsymbol{G}_{\text{un}}$.

More generally, let M' be an involutory automorphism of $\boldsymbol{G}$ acting on *some* trunk $\boldsymbol{H}'$ of $\boldsymbol{G}$ as the scalar multiplication by -1. Since trunks are conjugate, there is an $a \in G$ such that $\boldsymbol{H}' = \tilde{a}\boldsymbol{H}$. Then $\tilde{a}^{-1} M' \tilde{a}$ is as in the first situation, and $\tilde{a}^{-1} M' \tilde{a} = \tilde{h} M \tilde{h}^{-1}$ for some $h \in H$. In the same way as above it is shown that M' is the minus-automorphism of a third dressing on $\boldsymbol{H}'$ with branches $\tilde{a}\tilde{h}\boldsymbol{e}_\alpha$ $(\alpha \in W^*)$, unitary semimorphism $\tilde{a}\tilde{h} C_{\text{un}} \tilde{h}^{-1} \tilde{a}^{-1}$, and unitary restriction $\tilde{a}\tilde{h}\boldsymbol{G}_{\text{un}}$.

It follows:

Theorem The unitary restrictions and unitary semimorphisms of $\boldsymbol{G}$ with respect to the various third dressings form a conjugacy class under Int $\boldsymbol{G}$ and so do the minus-automorphisms. The possible minus-automorphisms are the involutory automorphisms of $\boldsymbol{G}$ that act as scalar multiplications by -1 on *some* trunk.

Remark An involutory automorphism and a trunk, as mentioned in the theorem, determine a unitary restriction, but an involutory automorphism alone does not. Different involutory automorphisms with the same trunk may yield the same unitary restriction.

Proposition A unitary semimorphism of $\boldsymbol{G}$ is a unitary semimorphism with respect to any trunk left invariant by it.

Proof It may be assumed that the unitary semimorphism is the given one C_{un} defined with respect to $\boldsymbol{H}$. Let $\boldsymbol{H}'$ be another trunk, $C_{\mathrm{un}}\boldsymbol{H}' = \boldsymbol{H}'$. By 32.9 there is an element $a \in G_{\mathrm{un}}$ such that $\boldsymbol{H}' = \tilde{a}\boldsymbol{H}$. Then, if M is the minus-automorphism of the given third dressing, the involutory automorphism $\tilde{a}M\tilde{a}^{-1}$ defines a third dressing on $\boldsymbol{H}'$ with unitary semimorphism $\tilde{a}C_{\mathrm{un}}\tilde{a}^{-1} = C_{\mathrm{un}}$.

33.14. The Corner Lattice

33.14.1 The notion of principal domain (31.4) can be generalized:

Definition The trunk $\boldsymbol{H}_{\mathrm{un}}$ is divided into domains called *fundamental*, by means of the hyperplanes defined by $\alpha = 0 \bmod 2\pi\mathrm{i}$ ($\alpha \in W^*$).

The fundamental domains are bounded and convex, and one of them is the principal domain. The notion of fundamental domain is carried over to H_{un} by exp.

33.14.2 The chambers are one-to-one related to the fundamental domains with a corner $\mathbf{0}$ (namely, by multiplication by i and inclusion); Int W^* is simply transitive on the set of chambers (33.4.4).

33.14.3. Definition The *corner lattice* consists of the points $\boldsymbol{h} \in \boldsymbol{H}_{\mathrm{un}}$ with $\alpha(\boldsymbol{h}) = 0 \bmod 2\pi\mathrm{i}$ for all $\alpha \in W^*$ (it suffices to require it for $\alpha \in W^{++}$).

33.14.4. Definition The group generated by Int W^* (acting on $\boldsymbol{H}_{\mathrm{un}}$) and the translations of the corner lattice is denoted by Int mod W^*.

33.14.5. Definition $S_{\alpha,m}$ is the reflection in the hyperplane $\alpha = m \cdot 2\pi\mathrm{i}$ (m integral, $\alpha \in W^*$). The group generated by the $S_{\alpha,m}$ is denoted by Int′ mod W^*.

33.14.6 Int mod W^* interchanges the fundamental domains. It contains the $S_{\alpha,m}$; thus Int′ mod W^* sub Int mod W^*.

Proposition Int′ mod W^* acts transitively on the set of fundamental domains.

Proof Let $\boldsymbol{D}'$ be a fundamental domain, $\boldsymbol{h} \in \boldsymbol{D}'$, and w a path from $\mathbf{0}$ to $\boldsymbol{h}$ in $\boldsymbol{H}_{\text{un}}$. After a slight modification, it may be assumed that if w leaves a fundamental domain it will pass *through* the interior of a face and *into* an adjacent domain. Let the faces successively crossed by w lie in the hyperplanes $\alpha_k = m_k \cdot 2\pi\mathrm{i}$ ($\alpha_k \in W^*$, where $k = 1, \ldots, q$). Then $\boldsymbol{D}'' = S_{\alpha 1, m_1} \cdots S_{\alpha_q, m_q} \boldsymbol{D}'$ is a fundamental domain with a corner $\mathbf{0}$. By 33.14.2 there is an $S \in \text{Int } W^*$ such that $S\boldsymbol{D}'' = \boldsymbol{D}$. This proves the assertion.

Remark One can show that Int′ mod W^* is even *simply* transitive on the set of fundamental domains.

33.14.7 The parallelepiped $\boldsymbol{Q} \subset \boldsymbol{H}_{\text{un}}$ defined by

$$\boldsymbol{h} \in \boldsymbol{Q} \leftrightarrow 0 < \operatorname{Im} \rho(\boldsymbol{h}) < 2\pi \qquad \text{for all} \quad \rho \in W^{++}$$

is mapped one-to-one into H_{un} by exp; its closure is mapped onto H_{un}. The division of $\boldsymbol{Q}$ into fundamental domains is transferred to H_{un}. By exp an element of Int mod W^* is mapped into one induced by an element of $\tilde{G}_{\text{un}}$, since this is true for the elements of Int W^* and since the translations in Int mod W^* are mapped trivially. Hence:

Proposition H_{un} is divided into sets equivalent to $\bar{D}$ under $\tilde{G}_{\text{un}}$ such that two of them meet in boundary points only.

33.16. Kaleidoscope Groups

A$_l$, **B**$_l$, **C**$_l$, **D**$_l$. The terminology on $\boldsymbol{H}$, as introduced in Section 16 (see also Table C), is used.

A$_l$:
$$S_{\rho i}\omega_j = \omega_j \qquad \text{for} \quad j \neq i, i+1,$$
$$S_{\rho i}\omega_i = \omega_{i+1},$$
$$S_{\rho i}\omega_{i+1} = \omega_i.$$

The reflections generate the symmetric group of $l+1$ permutands.

$\mathbf{B}_l$ $S_{\rho_1}\omega_i = \omega_i$ for $i \neq l$,

$S_{\rho_1}\omega_l = -\omega_l$,

S_{ρ_i} $(i \neq 1)$ as $S_{\rho_{i-1}}$ in $\mathbf{A}_{l-1}$.

The general element of Int W^* is a permutation of $\omega_1, \ldots, \omega_l$ combined with a mapping $\omega_1 \to \pm\omega_1, \ldots, \omega_l \to \pm\omega_l$, the signs being independent of each other.

$\mathbf{C}_l$: S_{ρ_i} $(i \neq l)$ as in $\mathbf{A}_l$,

$S_{\rho_l}\omega_i = \omega_i$ for $i \neq l$,

$S_{\rho_l}\omega_l = -\omega_l$.

The same Int W^* as in $\mathbf{B}_l$.

$\mathbf{D}_l$: S_{ρ_i} $(i \neq 1,2)$ as $S_{\rho_{i-2}}$ in $\mathbf{A}_{l-2}$,

$S_{\rho_1}\omega_i = S_{\rho_2}\omega_i = \omega_i$ for $i \leqslant l-2$,

$S_{\rho_2}\omega_{l-1} = -\omega_l$,

$S_{\rho_2}\omega_l = -\omega_{l-1}$,

$S_{\rho_1}\omega_{l-1} = \omega_l$,

$S_{\rho_1}\omega_l = \omega_{l-1}$.

The general element of Int W^* is a permutation of $\omega_1, \ldots, \omega_l$ combined with a mapping $\omega_1 \to \pm\omega_1, \ldots, \omega_l \to \pm\omega_l$, with independent signs such that the number of minus signs is even.

The case of the exceptional groups is more involved. Without proof: the orders of Int W^* are

$$\mathbf{G}_2: 12, \quad \mathbf{F}_4: 1152, \quad \mathbf{E}_6: 72\cdot 6!, \quad \mathbf{E}_7: 56\cdot 72\cdot 6!, \quad \mathbf{E}_8: 240\cdot 56\cdot 72\cdot 6!$$

33.17. Historical Note Though implicitly used by E. Cartan, the explicit introduction of the kaleidoscope group is due to H. Weyl, *Math. Z.* **24** (1926) = *Selecta*, 338. The kaleidoscope groups of the exceptional groups were more closely studied by E. Cartan, *Amer. J. Math.* **18**, 1–61 (1896); *Œuvres* I **1**, 293–353. Another method is expounded in: H. Freudenthal, *Proc. Kon. Akad. Wet.* **A57**, 487–491 (1954) = *Indagationes Math.* **16**.

34. INTEGRATION IN COMPACT GROUPS

34.1–2. Measure in Groups

34.1 In a real linear Lie group G an infinitesimal measure (see 5.4) assigned to the tangent space at 1 can be transferred by multiplication on the right to any point of G. Such an infinitesimal measure is invariant under multiplication on the right, as is the measure arising from it by integration.

It is important to know whether this measure is invariant under left multiplication as well. This is the case if and only if $\tilde{a}$ $(a \in G)$ preserves the infinitesimal measure at 1 or, equivalently, if and only if $\det \tilde{a} = 1$ for all $\boldsymbol{a} \in G$.

If G is semisimple, this condition is fulfilled, for then $\operatorname{tr} \tilde{\boldsymbol{a}} = 0$ for $\boldsymbol{a} \in \boldsymbol{G}$.

It is also fulfilled if $\tilde{G}$ is compact because then det maps $\tilde{G}$ onto a bounded connected subgroup of the multiplication group of reals, which can consist of 1 only.

34.2 Without proof it may be mentioned that a one-sided invariant measure exists in any locally compact group (*Haar measure*); if the group is compact, it is two-sided invariant and the total measure is finite.

A short proof is given of the existence of such a measure in compact groups G, or rather of the existence of an invariant average $\mathscr{M}$ of continuous functions on G.

34.3. Measure in Compact Groups

Let G be a compact group, and Φ the linear space of real continuous functions of G topologized by means of the norm $|\ldots|$ defined by

$$|f| = \sup_{x \in G} |f(x)|.$$

Linear mappings $\mathscr{R}_a, \mathscr{L}_a$ $(a \in G)$ of Φ onto Φ are defined by

$$\mathscr{R}_a = \curlyvee_f \curlyvee_x f(xa), \qquad \mathscr{L}_a = \curlyvee_f \curlyvee_x f(a^{-1} x).$$

Note that $\curlyvee_a \mathscr{R}_a$ and $\curlyvee_a \mathscr{L}_a$ are homomorphisms of G.

$\mathscr{R}_G f$, respectively $\mathscr{L}_G f$, is the set of $\mathscr{R}_a f, \mathscr{L}_a f$ $(a \in G)$. The closure of the convex envelope of $\mathscr{R}_G f, \mathscr{L}_G f$ is denoted by $C\mathscr{R}_G f, C\mathscr{L}_G f$.

Because of the uniform continuity of continuous f,

$$C\mathscr{R}_G f,\ C\mathscr{L}_G f \text{ are compact.}$$

Furthermore, they are

$$\text{convex}$$

and invariant under all $\mathscr{R}_a$, respectively $\mathscr{L}_a$;

$$\operatorname{osc} = \max - \min$$

is a continuous functional on Φ.

If there exists anything like a continuous invariant average on Φ, it has to be the same for all $\mathscr{R}_a f$, hence for all elements of $C\mathscr{R}_G f$. If a constant function can be found in $C\mathscr{R}_G f$, its value should be the average of f. To find such a constant one looks for the function with the smallest oscillation and proves that its oscillation vanishes.

Put

$$\inf_{g \in C\mathscr{R}_G f} \operatorname{osc} g = \gamma.$$

Because of the compactness of $C\mathscr{R}_G f$, there is a $g \in C\mathscr{R}_G f$ with

$$\operatorname{osc} g = \gamma.$$

Given some $\varepsilon > 0$, because of the compactness of $C\mathscr{R}_G g$, there are

$$a_1, \ldots, a_m \in G$$

such that for every $a \in G$ there is a j with

$$|g(xa) - g(xa_j)| < \varepsilon \quad \text{for all} \quad x \in G.$$

Putting

$$h = (1/m) \sum_k \mathscr{R}_{a_k} g,$$

one obtains

$$\operatorname{osc} h \leqslant \operatorname{osc} g.$$

On the other hand, $h \in C\mathscr{R}_G f$; hence

$$\operatorname{osc} h \geqslant \operatorname{osc} g.$$

Thus

$$\operatorname{osc} h = \operatorname{osc} g.$$

Further,

$$\min g \leqslant \min h \leqslant \max h \leqslant \max g;$$

hence

$$\max h = \max g.$$

Now take x_0 such that $h(x_0) = \max h$. Then

$$g(x_0 a_k) = \max g \qquad \text{for} \quad k = 1, \ldots, m.$$

For $a \in G$ there is a j with

$$|g(x_0 a) - g(x_0 a_j)| < \varepsilon,$$

and thus

$$g(x_0 a) > \max g - \varepsilon \qquad \text{for every} \quad a \in G.$$

This is true for every $\varepsilon > 0$. Therefore g is constant.

The same reasoning applies to $C\mathscr{L}_G f$.

The value of a constant function in $C\mathscr{R}_G f$, $C\mathscr{L}_G f$ is called a *right*, respectively, a *left*, *average of* f.

Let A, B be right and left averages of f. Then

$$|\Sigma\ \alpha_j f(xa_j) - A| < \tfrac{1}{2}\varepsilon,$$

$$|\Sigma\ \beta_k f(b_k^{-1} x) - B| < \tfrac{1}{2}\varepsilon,$$

for a suitable choice of $a_j, b_k \in G$ and real $\alpha_1, \ldots, \alpha_m$, $\beta_1, \ldots, \beta_n$ such that $\alpha_j \geqslant 0$, $\beta_k \geqslant 0$, $\Sigma\ \alpha_j = 1$, $\Sigma\ \beta_k = 1$. Replacing x in the first equality by $b_k^{-1} x$, multiplying by β_k, and summing up, one obtains

$$|\Sigma\ \beta_k \alpha_j f(b_k^{-1} xa_j) - A| < \tfrac{1}{2}\varepsilon,$$

and likewise

$$|\Sigma\ \beta_k \alpha_j f(b_k^{-1} xa_j) - B| < \tfrac{1}{2}\varepsilon.$$

From this it follows that every right average of f equals every left average of f, and therefore all are equal.

Similarly, it can be shown that the average $\mathscr{M}$ is a continuous linear functional on Φ.

Obviously $\mathscr{M}$ is invariant under $\mathscr{R}_a$ and $\mathscr{L}_a$ because $C\mathscr{R}_G f$ and $C\mathscr{L}_G f$ are invariant under $\mathscr{R}_a$ and $\mathscr{L}_a$, respectively.

Furthermore,

$$\text{if } f(x) \geqslant 0 \text{ for all } x, \text{ then } \mathscr{M}f \geqslant 0.$$

Even more can be proved:

$$\text{if } f(x) \geqslant 0 \text{ for all } x \text{ and } f(x) \neq 0 \text{ for some } x, \text{ then } \mathscr{M}f > 0.$$

Indeed, in this case there is an open $U \subset G$ on which $f(x) > \delta$ for some $\delta > 0$; G is covered by a finite number of Ua, say $Ua_1, \ldots, Ua_m$.

$$\begin{aligned} (\mathscr{R}_{a_k^{-1}} f)(x) &> \delta \qquad \text{for} \quad x \in Ua_k \\ &\geqslant 0 \qquad \text{elsewhere}; \end{aligned}$$

hence, if

$$g = (1/m)\ \Sigma\ \mathscr{R}_{a_k^{-1}} f,$$

then

$$\mathscr{M}g = \mathscr{M}f,$$

and

$$g(x) > (1/m)\ \delta \quad \text{for all} \quad x \in G.$$

Finally,

$$\mathscr{M}g = \mathscr{M}\ (g - (1/m)\ \delta) + \mathscr{M}\ (1/m)\ \delta \geqslant (1/m)\ \delta > 0.$$

Theorem On a compact group G there exists an average $\mathscr{M}$(or $\mathscr{M}_G$) of continuous functions with the following properties.

34.3.1 $\mathscr{M}$ is linear.

34.3.2 $$\mathscr{M}\mathscr{R}_a = \mathscr{M}\mathscr{L}_a = \mathscr{M} \quad \text{for} \quad a \in G,$$

34.3.3 $$\mathscr{M}1 = 1,$$

34.3.4 If $f(x) \geqslant 0$ for all $x \in G$ and $f(x) \neq 0$ for some $x \in G$, then $\mathscr{M}f > 0$.

34.3.5 $\mathscr{M}$ is continuous.

The properties 34.3.1, 34.3.2, 34.3.3, 34.3.5 characterize $\mathscr{M}$. So do 34.3.1, 34.3.2, 34.3.3, 34.3.4, even if the last one is weakened to

34.3.4′ $$f(x) \geqslant 0 \rightarrow \mathscr{M}f \geqslant 0.$$

The last remark is easily proved by observing that 34.3.4′ can be generalized by 34.3.1 and 34.3.3 to

$$-\varepsilon \leqslant f(x) \leqslant \varepsilon \rightarrow -\varepsilon \leqslant \mathscr{M}f \leqslant \varepsilon.$$

Using this characterization of the average, one can easily prove an analog of Fubini's theorem for continuous functions f defined on $\ulcorner G, G \urcorner$:

34.3.6 $$\mathscr{M} \curlyvee_a \mathscr{M} \curlyvee_b f(a, b) = \mathscr{M}f = \mathscr{M} \curlyvee_b \mathscr{M} \curlyvee_a f(a, b).$$

The average $\mathscr{M}$ extends in an obvious way to complex functions and finite-dimensional linear-space-valued functions. Then, if φ maps the finite-dimensional linear spaces R into R' linearly,

34.3.7 $$\mathscr{M}(\varphi f) = \varphi \mathscr{M}f$$

for linear functions from G to R.

The above characterization shows that if μ is an invariant measure on G, gauged by $\mu(G) = 1$, then for continuous f

34.3.8 $$\mathscr{M}f = \int f \, d\mu;$$

conversely such an invariant measure can easily be recovered from the average.

34.4. Historical Note The preceding construction of the average in compact groups is due to J. von Neumann (*Compositio Math.* **1**, 106–114 (1934)). Haar's measure dates from 1933 (*Ann. Math.* **34**, 147–169). Simpler constructions are extant (see, e.g., S. Banach in S. Saks, *Theory of the Integral*, 1937; A. Weil, *L'intégration dans les groupes topologiques et ses applications*, Hermann, Paris, 1940, 1951).

35. THE CONDUCIBILITY THEOREM

35.1–2. An Invariant Inner Product

35.1. Theorem Suppose $R \in$ Spa Lin Rea or Com, dim $R < \infty$, G sub Aut R. If G is compact, then R can be endowed with a definite hermitean inner product, invariant under G (which then becomes a group of unitary mappings).

Proof Starting with some definite hermitean inner product $(\ldots, \ldots)$ in R, define a^* for $a \in$ End R by

$$(ax, y) = (x, a^* y) \qquad \text{for all} \quad x, y \in R;$$

a^* depends continuously on a, and so does $a^* a$.

$$s = \mathcal{M}_G \curlyvee_{a \in G} a^* a$$

makes sense as an element of End R. Furthermore, $s^* = s$,

$$(sx, x) = \mathcal{M}_G \curlyvee_{a \in G}(a^* ax, x)$$
$$= \mathcal{M}_G \curlyvee_{a \in G}(ax, ax),$$

which vanishes only if $(ax, ax) = 0$ for all a, hence if $(x, x) = 0$. Therefore $(x, y)' = (sx, y)$ may be used as a new definite hermitean inner product on R. Moreover,

$$(cx, cy)' = (scx, cy) = (c^* scx, y),$$

and, using the invariance property of $\mathcal{M}$ for $c \in G$,

$$s = \mathcal{M}_G \mathcal{R}_c \curlyvee_{a \in G} a^* a = \mathcal{M}_G \curlyvee_{a \in G}(ac)^* (ac) = \mathcal{M}_G\, c^* (\curlyvee_{a \in G} a^* a)\, c = c^* sc,$$

which proves the invariance of the new inner product.

35.2. Proposition Suppose $R \in$ Spa Lin Rea or Com Inp, G sub Aut R. Then for every complete G-invariant linear subspace S of R there is a G-invariant linear subspace T of R, such that $R = S + T$ is a direct sum, namely the orthoplement of S in R.

The proof is obvious.

Note that the completeness of S implies that its orthoplement is a linear complement in R even if R is not complete.

35.3–4. Conducibility

35.3. Definition Suppose $R \in$ Spa Lin, $0 < \dim R < \infty$ and G sub Aut R; G is called *conducible*† if to every G-invariant subspace S of R there belongs a G-invariant subspace T of R such that $R = S + T$ as a direct sum.

† "Conducible" is a shortening of the usual term "completely reducible."

The definition is analogous for linear Lie algebras $\boldsymbol{G} \subset \text{End } R$.

Irreducible G ($\boldsymbol{G}$) is clearly conducible.

If G ($\boldsymbol{G}$) is conducible, then R splits directly into a sum of linear subspaces on which G ($\boldsymbol{G}$) acts irreducibly.

Indeed, there is an S_1 sub R, $S_1 \neq \{0\}$, on which G acts irreducibly; then $R = S_1 + T_1$, a direct sum, with T_1 invariant sub R. If T_1 is not acted on irreducibly, some S_2 sub T_1 is irreducibly acted on, $T_1 = S_2 + T_2$, a direct sum, with T_2 invariant sub T_1, and so on.

35.4. Conducibility Theorem $R \in \text{Spa Lin}$, $\dim R < \infty$, $G \subset \text{Aut } R$, $\boldsymbol{G} \subset \text{End } R$, $G \in \text{Gru Lie Lin}$, $\boldsymbol{G} \in \text{Alg Lie Lin}$. Then G or $\boldsymbol{G}$ is conducible under any of the following conditions:

(1) G is compact.
(2) $\boldsymbol{G}$ is the infinitesimal algebra of compact G.
(3) G is complex semisimple.
(4) $\boldsymbol{G}$ is complex semisimple.
(5) G is real semisimple, R is complex.
(6) $\boldsymbol{G}$ is real semisimple, R is complex.
(7) G is real semisimple, R is real.
(8) $\boldsymbol{G}$ is real semisimple, R is real.

Remark It is the import of the conducibility theorem that the study of linear representations can be reduced to that of the irreducible ones.

An elementary converse of this theorem was proved in 19.15.

Proof (1) By 35.1, R may be supposed to be equipped with an invariant inner product; by 35.2, G is conducible.

(2) Immediate consequence of (1).

(4) If S is $\boldsymbol{G}$-invariant, it is $\boldsymbol{G}_{\text{un}}$-invariant. By (2), $R = S + T$, a direct sum, for some $\boldsymbol{G}_{\text{un}}$-invariant T sub R. Then T is also invariant under the complex extension $\boldsymbol{G}$ of $\boldsymbol{G}_{\text{un}}$.

(3) Is an immediate consequence of (4).

(6) $\boldsymbol{G} \cap \mathrm{i}\boldsymbol{G}$ is an ideal in $\boldsymbol{G} + \mathrm{i}\boldsymbol{G}$. From this it follows that $\boldsymbol{G}' = \boldsymbol{G} + \mathrm{i}\boldsymbol{G}$ is again semisimple. If S is $\boldsymbol{G}$-invariant, it is $\boldsymbol{G}'$-invariant. By (4) $R = S + T$, a direct sum, with some $\boldsymbol{G}'$-invariant T sub R; but then T is also invariant under $\boldsymbol{G}$.

(5) Immediate consequence of (6).

(8) $\boldsymbol{G}$ may be supposed to be extended to R_{Com}. To the complexification of R belongs involutory semilinear D, such that $Dx = x$ for $x \in R$. Then

$$\boldsymbol{a}Dx = D\boldsymbol{a}x \quad \text{for} \quad \boldsymbol{a} \in \boldsymbol{G},\ x \in R_{\text{Com}}.$$

With S sub R, S_{Com} is invariant sub R_{Com}. By (6) it has an invariant linear complement T'.

Now $T = (1 + D)((1 - D)^{-1}(\mathrm{i}S) \cap T')$ is an invariant linear complement of S in R. The invariance and reality of T are obvious. If $x \in T'$ and $(1 - D)x \in \mathrm{i}S$, then, if $(1 + D)x \in S$, $x = \frac{1}{2}(1 - D)x + \frac{1}{2}(1 + D)x \in S_{\text{Com}}$, whence $x = 0$ and $(1 + D)x = 0$; therefore $S \cap T = \{0\}$. If $x \in R$ and $x = s' + t'$, with $s' \in S_{\text{Com}}$, $t' \in T'$, then $(1 - D)t' = (1 - D)(-s') \in \mathrm{i}S$, so $(1 + D)t' \in T$, from which $x = \frac{1}{2}(1 + D)s' + \frac{1}{2}(1 + D)t' \in S + T$, as required.

(7) Immediate consequence of (8).

35.7–9. Compact Groups

35.7. Proposition If G generated by $\boldsymbol{G}$ is compact, then $\boldsymbol{G}$ is the direct sum of its center and of a semisimple Lie algebra.

Indeed, $\boldsymbol{G}_{\text{Com}}$, being conducible, admits such a splitting, according to 19.15, and the same splitting applies to $\boldsymbol{G}$.

35.8 A compact counterpart of Theorem 19.8:

Proposition Let F be a compact linear Lie group, normal in the linear Lie group G. Then F behaves locally as a direct factor of G and every $\tilde{g}$ $(g \in G)$ acts on F as an inner automorphism of F.

Proof The $\tilde{f}$ with $f \in F$ produce a compact linear Lie group acting on $\boldsymbol{G}$, which leaves $\boldsymbol{F}$ invariant; as a linear space $\boldsymbol{G}$ splits as a direct sum, $\boldsymbol{G} = \boldsymbol{F} + \boldsymbol{F}_1$, with $\boldsymbol{F}_1$ invariant under $\tilde{f}$ $(f \in F)$; hence $[\boldsymbol{F}, \boldsymbol{F}_1] \subset \boldsymbol{F}_1$. On the other hand, $\boldsymbol{F}$ is an ideal in $\boldsymbol{G}$; thus $[\boldsymbol{F}, \boldsymbol{F}_1] \subset \boldsymbol{F}$. Consequently, $[\boldsymbol{F}, \boldsymbol{F}_1] = \{\boldsymbol{0}\}$. Now $\exp \tilde{\boldsymbol{f}}_1$ with $\boldsymbol{f}_1 \in \boldsymbol{F}_1$ acts on $\boldsymbol{F}$ as the identity; therefore $\exp \tilde{\boldsymbol{f}} \cdot \exp \tilde{\boldsymbol{f}}_1 (\boldsymbol{f} \in \boldsymbol{F}, \boldsymbol{f}_1 \in \boldsymbol{F}_1)$ acts as an inner automorphsim, as does every $\tilde{g}$ with $g \in G$ near 1, and consequently any $g \in G$.

35.9 A torus group A in $G \in$ Gru Lie Lin Com SS is compact, and thus, by restriction of the adjoint representation, has a conducible representation in $\boldsymbol{G}$. In the terminology of Section 18, A, and consequently $\boldsymbol{A}$, can be said to be ad-pure. So by 19.20 $\boldsymbol{A}$ is contained in a trunk of $\boldsymbol{G}$.

Proposition A maximal torus group within a complex linear semisimple Lie group is a unitary trunk.

Indeed, it is contained in a trunk, the maximal torus of which is uniquely determined.

35.10. Historical Note It seems that E. Cartan assumed conducibility of semisimple linear Lie groups as obvious. Integration in compact groups, first used by A. Hurwitz, *Gött. Nachr.* **1897**, 71–90, and then by I. Schur, *Sitzber. Preuss. Akad.* **1924**, 189–208, 297–321, 346–355, was applied by F. Peter and H. Weyl to prove conducibility (*Math. Ann.* **97**, 737–755 (1927) = *Selecta* H. Weyl, 387–404). The elementary converse of the conducibility theorem (19.15) had already been proved by E. Cartan, *Ann. Ecole Norm.* (3) **26**, 99 (1909).

Conducibility is proved in Section 50 by algebraic methods.

36. ORTHOGONALITY RELATIONS

36.1–6. Irreducibility and Equivalence

36.1. Definition A linear representation of a group G (a Lie algebra $\boldsymbol{G}$) in $R \in$ Spa Lin, that is, a homomorphic mapping of G ($\boldsymbol{G}$) into Aut R (End R), is called *reducible*, *irreducible*, or *conducible*, according to whether its image has the said property.

Definition If f, g are linear representations of G in R, S, then f is called *enchained* to g (by means of k) if $k \neq 0$ is a linear mapping of R into S such that

$$kf(a) = g(a)k \qquad \text{for all} \quad a \in G.$$

They are called *equivalent* if k can be chosen as a one-to-one mapping of R onto S.

Remark Enchainment and equivalence mean the same as nontrivial homomorphism and isomorphism if applied to R and S considered as G-modules.

This equivalence notion is applied with Lie algebras as well. It is a class-forming notion.

36.2. Proposition (Schur's Lemma) Enchained irreducible linear representations of a group G are equivalent.

Proof Let f, g in R, S be enchained by $k \neq 0$. Let N be the kernel of k. Then by $kf(a) = g(a)k$

$$kf(a)N = g(a)kN = \{0\};$$

thus $f(a)N \subset N$. By irreducibility $N = R$ or $\{0\}$. The first possibility is excluded by $k \neq 0$. So $N = \{0\}$, that is, k is one-to-one.

Furthermore,

$$g(a)kR = kf(a)R \subset kR;$$

thus kR is invariant under $g(a)$. By irreducibility $kR = \{0\}$ or $= S$. The first possibility is excluded by $k \neq 0$. So $kR = S$, that is, k is onto.

36.3. Proposition $R \in$ Spa Lin Com, dim $R < \infty$, $c \in$ End R. If c commutes with every element of an irreducible subset G of End R, then c is a scalar multiplication.

Proof Let λ be an eigenvalue of c and let S be the set of $x \in R$ such that $cx = \lambda x$. Now S is sub R and invariant under G, since $cax = acx = \lambda ax$ for all $a \in G$, $x \in S$. Hence $S = R$ and $cx = \lambda x$ for all $x \in R$.

36.4. Proposition The mapping k providing an equivalence $kf(a) = g(a)k$ between two irreducible linear representations of the group G in finite-dimensional complex linear spaces is unique up to a scalar factor.

Proof If for all $a \in G$, $kf(a) = g(a)k$ and $k_1 f(a) = g(a)k_1$, then $k^{-1}k_1$ commutes with all $f(a)$ and by 36.3 is a scalar multiplication.

36.5. Proposition $R \in$ Spa Lin Inp, G sub Aut R, S sub R, S complete, S invariant under G, $k =$ orthogonal projection of R on S. Then $ak = ka$ for every $a \in G$.

Proof The orthoplement S' of S is also invariant (cf. 35.2).

$$akx + a(1-k)x = ax = kax + (1-k)ax \quad \text{for} \quad a \in G, x \in R.$$

In both splittings of ax the first summand belongs to S, the second to S'. Such a splitting is unique, which proves $ak = ka$.

36.6. Proposition $R \in$ Spa Lin Inp, G sub Aut R, S sub R, and T sub R, both G-invariant and irreducibly acted on by G, S complete. If the restrictions of G to S and T are inequivalent, then S and T are orthogonal.

Proof Let k be the orthogonal projection on S. By Proposition 36.5 $kax = akx$ for all $a \in G$, $x \in R$. Indicating the two restrictions by f and g, one gets $kg(a)x = f(a)kx$ for $x \in T$; thus, by 36.2, $kT = \{0\}$, which proves the assertion.

36.7–9. The Universal Representation and Its Components

36.7. Definition In the linear space Φ of complex continuous functions on the compact group G with the continuous invariant average $\mathscr{M}$ an *inner product* is defined by

$$(\varphi, \psi) = \mathscr{M} \Upsilon_a \varphi(a) \overline{\psi(a)}$$

($\overline{\psi(a)}$ being the complex conjugate of $\psi(a)$).

The representation $\mathscr{R}$ of G in Φ by right translation,

$$\mathscr{R}_c = \Upsilon_\varphi \Upsilon_a \varphi(ac),$$

is called the *universal* one.

By 34.3.4 the inner product is definite. Therefore Φ becomes a unitary linear space, which, however, need not be complete.

The $\mathscr{R}_c$ are unitary:

$$(\mathscr{R}_c \varphi, \mathscr{R}_c \psi) = \mathscr{M} \Upsilon_a \varphi(ac) \overline{\psi(ac)}$$
$$= \mathscr{M} \Upsilon_a \varphi(a) \overline{\psi(a)} = (\varphi, \psi).$$

36.8. Proposition Up to equivalence every continuous irreducible linear representation f of compact G in $R \in$ Spa Lin Com ($\dim R < \infty$) can also be isolated from $\mathscr{R}$ by restricting the latter to an invariant linear subspace of Φ.

Proof Choose a linear functional $u \neq 0$ on R and define $\Phi_{f,u}$ as the set of $\Upsilon_a uf(a)x$. Then $\Phi_{f,u}$ sub Φ. By

$$k = \Upsilon_x \Upsilon_a uf(a)x$$

R is mapped onto $\Phi_{f,u}$. Now k is linear, and $\neq 0$ because $u \neq 0$.

$$kx = \Upsilon_a uf(a)x,$$

$$\mathscr{R}_c kx = \Upsilon_a uf(ac)x = \Upsilon_a uf(a) f(c) x = kf(c)x;$$

thus

$$\mathscr{R}_c k = kf(c).$$

The kernel of k is invariant under $f(c)$ for all c, hence $= \{0\}$. Thus k provides an equivalence of f and Υ_c ($\mathscr{R}_c$ restricted to $\Phi_{f,u}$).

Definition For any continuous finite-dimensional linear representation f of G call $\Phi_{f,u}$ the set of $\Upsilon_a uf(a)x$; Υ_c ($\mathscr{R}_c$ restricted to $\Phi_{f,u}$) is called f_u. The linear space spanned by $\Phi_{f,u}$, if u ranges through all linear functionals on R, is called Φ_f; or, alternatively, Φ_f is the linear space spanned by the matrix coefficients of f on some basis of R.

For equivalent f, Φ_f is the same; Φ_f splits in correspondence with the inequivalent irreducible components of f.

36.9 In 36.8 it was shown that any finite-dimensional continuous irreducible linear representation f of compact G can be recovered within Φ, namely, as f_u acting on $\Phi_{f,u}$. Now it is shown:

Proposition Let f be a finite-dimensional continuous linear representation of compact G in R. Then any S sub Φ acted on by $\mathscr{R}$ equivalently to f is some $\Phi_{f,u}$ (on which $\mathscr{R}$ acts as f_u).

Proof Let k be the given equivalence; thus

$$\mathscr{R}_a k = kf(a) \quad \text{for all} \quad a \in G.$$

Put

$$u = \curlyvee_{x \in R}((kx)(1)).$$

Then

$$(kx)(a) = (\mathscr{R}_a kx)(1) = (kf(a)x)\,(1) = uf(a)\,x.$$

Thus

$$kx = \curlyvee_a uf(a)\,x,$$

$$kR = \Phi_{f,u}.$$

36.10–11. Orthonormality

36.10 By 36.9 the linear subspaces of Φ which are acted on by $\mathscr{R}$ equivalently to irreducible f are contained in Φ_f (see Definition 36.8). Thus as a consequence of 36.6:

Proposition If f and g are inequivalent, then Φ_f is orthogonal to Φ_g.

36.11. Proposition $R \in$ Spa Lin Com Inp, $\dim R = n$; an orthonormal basis of R is given; f is a continuous unitary irreducible representation of compact G in R. Then the matrix coefficients of f as elements of Φ are mutually orthogonal, each showing the norm $n^{-1/2}$.

Proof For given $u, v \in R$

$$(x, y)' = \mathscr{M} \curlyvee_a (f(a)\,x, u)\overline{(f(a)\,y, v)}$$

defines a sesquilinear form on R, which is invariant under $f(a)$ for all $a \in G$. Now $(x, y)' = (hx, y)$ for some $h \in \text{End } R$.

$$(hx, y) = (hf(a)\,x, f(a)\,y) = (f(a)^{-1}\,hf(a)\,x, y),$$

$$h = f(a)^{-1}\,hf(a).$$

By 36.3, h turns out to be a scalar multiplication, Therefore the ratio

$$(x, y)'/(x, y)$$

does not depend on x,y, though it may still depend on u,v. By a symmetric argument:

36.11.1 $$\mathcal{M}\Upsilon_a\,(f(a)\,x, u)\,\overline{(f(a)\,y, v)} = \gamma(x, y)\,(u, v),$$

where γ is a constant.

A coordinate function is a $\Upsilon_x(x,u)$, where u is a basis member. A matrix coefficient of f has the form $\Upsilon_x(f(a)\,x,u)$, where x,u are basis members. For different pairs $\ulcorner x,u \urcorner$, $\ulcorner y,v \urcorner$ of basis members 36.11.1 vanishes, which proves the orthogonality of different matrix coefficients as members of Φ. Summing up 36.11.1 over $x=y$, $u=v$ ranging over a basis, one gets, after the $\mathcal{M}\Upsilon_a$-sign, the sum of absolute squares of the matrix coefficients of a unitary matrix, which is n. The second member becomes γn^2, which proves $\gamma = n^{-1}$. Substituting this into 36.11.1 one confirms the assertion on the norm.

36.12–15. Totality

36.12. Proposition For compact G the Φ_f, with f running through a complete set of inequivalent continuous irreducible finite-dimensional linear representations of G, span a linear subspace Φ' of Φ which is dense in Φ, even in the uniform topology.

The proof (see 36.14) uses standard methods of the theory of integral equations, expounded in 36.13.

36.13 Let $R \in$ Spa Lin Com Inp, with inner product $(\ldots, \ldots)$ and norm $\|\ldots\|$ defined by

$$\|x\| = (x, x)^{1/2}.$$

For a linear mapping A of R into R,

$$\|A\| = \sup_{\|x\| \leq 1} \|Ax\|,$$

as in 2.2; A is *bounded* if $\|A\| < \infty$.

Let L be a linear mapping of R into itself such that L is hermitean, which means

$$(Lx, y) = (x, Ly) \quad \text{for} \quad x, y \in R,$$

and relatively compact, which means that L maps

$$\uparrow_x \|x\| \leqslant 1 \text{ onto a relatively compact set}$$

(i.e., with compact closure). Note that L is bounded.

36.13.1 $$\|L^2\| = \|L\|^2.$$

Proof Set $\alpha = \|L\|$; then

$$\|Lx\| \leqslant \alpha\|x\| \quad \text{for all} \quad x \in R.$$

Now for $\|x\| \leqslant 1$:

$$\|L^2 x\| \leqslant \alpha\|Lx\| \leqslant \alpha^2\|x\| \leqslant \alpha^2$$

and

$$\|Lx\|^2 = (Lx, Lx) = (L^2 x, x) \leqslant \|L^2 x\| \cdot \|x\| \leqslant \|L^2\| \cdot \|x\|^2 \leqslant \|L^2\|;$$

this proves the assertion.

36.13.2 There is a $z \in R$ with $\|z\| = 1$ such that

$$\|L\| = \|Lz\|.$$

Proof Set $\alpha = \|L\|$ once again. By 36.13.1 there is a sequence of $x_j \in R$ with $\|x_j\| = 1$ such that

$$\lim \|L^2 x_j\| = \alpha^2.$$

Because L is relatively compact, one may even assume

$$\lim Lx_j = \text{some } y \in R.$$

It may be supposed that $L \neq 0$; that is $\alpha \neq 0$, hence $y \neq 0$. Now put

$$z_j = \|Lx_j\|^{-1} Lx_j.$$

The sequence of z_j also converges, say to z; $\|z\| = 1$. Taking the limit in

$$\|L^2 x_j\| \leqslant \|L\| \cdot \|Lx_j\| \leqslant \|L^2\|,$$

one finds

$$\lim \|Lx_j\| = \|y\| = \alpha;$$

hence

$$\|Lz\| = \lim \|Lz_j\| = \lim \frac{\|L^2 x_j\|}{\|Lx_j\|} = \frac{\alpha^2}{\alpha} = \alpha.$$

36.13.3 For $\alpha = \|L\|$: α or $-\alpha$ is an eigenvalue of L.

Proof By 36.13.2 there is a $z \in R$ with $\|z\| = 1$ and $\|Lz\| = \alpha$. For real λ and arbitrary $x \in R$

$$(L(z + \lambda x), L(z + \lambda x)) - \alpha^2(z + \lambda x,\ z + \lambda x) \leqslant 0;$$

inspection of the linear term in λ with replacement of x by ix yields

$$((L^2 - \alpha^2)\, z, x) = 0 \qquad \text{for all} \quad x \in R;$$

hence $(L^2 - \alpha^2)z = 0$, that is, $(L - \alpha)(L + \alpha)z = 0$, which shows that z is an eigenvector of L belonging to α or $(L - \alpha)z$ is one belonging to $-\alpha$.

36.13.4 All eigenvalues of L are real. Eigenvectors of L belonging to different eigenvalues are mutually orthogonal.

This is well known.

36.13.5 For any $\gamma > 0$ the eigenvectors of L belonging to eigenvalues λ with $|\lambda| \geqslant \gamma$ span a finite-dimensional space R_γ.

Proof If this were not true, there would be an infinite orthonormal sequence of x_j with $Lx_j = \lambda_j x_j$, $|\lambda_j| \geqslant \gamma$. Since L is relatively compact, one may suppose that the sequence of Lx_j converges. But

$$\|Lx_j - Lx_k\| = \|\lambda_j x_j - \lambda_k x_k\| = (\lambda_j{}^2 + \lambda_k{}^2)^{1/2} \geqslant \gamma\sqrt{2}$$

for $j \neq k$, which is a contradiction.

36.13.6 By 36.13.5 any orthonormal set of eigenvectors belonging to non-vanishing eigenvalues of L is countable. Let $z_1, z_2, \ldots,$ be a maximal one. Then for $x \in R$

$$Lx = \sum_1^\infty (Lx, z_\nu)\, z_\nu.$$

Proof The restriction of L to the orthoplement $R_\gamma^\perp$ of R_γ is still hermitean and relatively compact. It follows from 36.13.3 that $\|Lu\| < \gamma\|u\|$ for $u \in R_\gamma^\perp$. Put $x_n = x - \sum_1^n (x, z_\nu) z_\nu$. Now, for almost all n, $x_n \in R_\gamma^\perp$ (which follows from 36.13.4–5), whence $\|Lx_n\| < \gamma\|x_n\| \leqslant \gamma\|x\|$. This is true for any γ and almost all n. Thus $\lim Lx_n = 0$. Now

$$Lx_n = Lx - \sum_1^n (x, z_\nu)\, Lz_\nu = Lx - \sum_1^n (x, Lz_\nu)\, z_\nu$$

$$= Lx - \sum_1^n (Lx, z_\nu)\, z_\nu,$$

which shows

$$Lx = \sum_1^\infty (Lx, z_\nu) z_\nu.$$

36.13.7. Lemma Let $|\cdots|$ be another norm on R, with $\|x\| \leqslant |x|$ for all $x \in R$, and assume that the image under L of the set of x with $\|x\| \leqslant 1$ is even relatively compact in the norm $|\cdots|$. Then, with $x \in R$ and $z_1, z_2, \ldots$, as in 36.13.6,

$$Lx = \sum_1^\infty (Lx, z_\nu) z_\nu \qquad \text{with respect to } |\cdots|.$$

This follows from:

36.13.8. Lemma If $|\cdots|$ is as in 36.13.7 and $\lim a_n = a$ in $\|\cdots\|$, and the sequence of a_n is relatively compact in $|\cdots|$, then $\lim a_n = a$ in $|\cdots|$.

Proof Every subsequence of the a_n has a convergent subsequence in $|\cdots|$ whose limit cannot be anything else but a. If the a_n did not converge to a (everything in the sense of $|\cdots|$), there would be a subsequence that would not have a as a limit point, hence a subsubsequence converging to a point different from a, contradictory to the first observation.

36.14. *Proof of 36.12* Lemma 36.13.7 is applied to the space Φ of continuous functions on compact G (instead of R), with

$$(\varphi, \psi) = \mathscr{M} \curlyvee_a \varphi(a) \overline{\psi(a)}$$

as an inner product and $|\varphi| = \max_a |\varphi(a)|$ as the $|\cdots|$-norm; Φ is $|\cdots|$-complete.

A continuous function ϑ on G is chosen with

$$\vartheta(a^{-1}) = \overline{\vartheta(a)} \qquad \text{for} \quad a \in G$$

and L_ϑ (instead of L) is defined by

$$L_\vartheta \varphi = \curlyvee_a \mathscr{M} \curlyvee_b \vartheta(ab^{-1}) \varphi(b) = \curlyvee_a (\varphi, \mathscr{R}_{a^{-1}} \vartheta).$$

Obviously L_ϑ is hermitean (see 34.3.6). Because of the uniform continuity of ϑ, there is for any given $\varepsilon > 0$ a 1-neighborhood U in G such that $|\mathscr{R}_c \vartheta - \vartheta| < \varepsilon$ for $c \in U$. Now for $\|\varphi\| \leqslant 1$

$$|(L_\vartheta \varphi)(a_1) - (L_\vartheta \varphi)(a_2)| = |(\varphi, \mathscr{R}_{a_1^{-1}} \vartheta - \mathscr{R}_{a_2^{-1}} \vartheta)| \leqslant \|\varphi\| \cdot |\mathscr{R}_{a_1^{-1}} \vartheta - \mathscr{R}_{a_2^{-1}} \vartheta|$$
$$\leqslant |\mathscr{R}_{a_2 a_1^{-1}} \vartheta - \vartheta| < \varepsilon$$

as soon as $a_2 \in U a_1$. This shows that the set of functions $L_\vartheta \varphi$ with $\|\varphi\| \leqslant 1$ is equicontinuous and $|\cdots|$-bounded, hence relatively $|\cdots|$-compact, since Φ is $|\cdots|$-complete. Therefore L_ϑ is relatively $|\cdots|$-compact.

$$(\mathscr{R}_{c^{-1}} L_\vartheta \mathscr{R}_c \varphi)(a) = \mathscr{M} \curlyvee_b \vartheta(ac^{-1} b^{-1}) \varphi(bc) = \mathscr{M} \curlyvee_b \vartheta(ab^{-1}) \varphi(b) = (L_\vartheta \varphi)(a),$$

hence

$$L_\vartheta \mathscr{R}_c = \mathscr{R}_c L_\vartheta.$$

Therefore,

$$\text{if} \quad L_\vartheta \varphi = \lambda\varphi, \qquad \text{then} \quad L_\vartheta \mathscr{R}_c \varphi = \lambda \mathscr{R}_c \varphi.$$

Thus the λ-eigenspace of L_ϑ is $\mathscr{R}_G$-invariant.

The restriction of $\mathscr{R}$ to the λ-eigenspace of L_ϑ is called $\mathscr{R}^\lambda$ ($\lambda \neq 0$). This is a continuous finite-dimensional unitary linear representation of G. By 36.9 the λ-eigenspace of L_ϑ ($\lambda \neq 0$) is some $\Phi_{\mathscr{R}^\lambda, u}$, thus contained in $\Phi_{\mathscr{R}^\lambda}$ and therefore in Φ', which was the linear space spanned by all Φ_f belonging to continuous finite-dimensional linear representations f of G. By the lemma $L_\vartheta \Phi$ is contained in the $|\cdots|$-closure of the linear space spanned by the λ-eigenspaces ($\lambda \neq 0$). Thus $L_\vartheta \Phi \subset \overline{\Phi'}$.

Now for every $\varphi \in \Phi$ there is a ϑ such that $|L_\vartheta \varphi - \varphi|$ is arbitrarily small: make $\vartheta(a) \geqslant 0$ for all $a \in G$, $\vartheta(a) = 0$ outside a small 1-neighborhood in G, and $\mathscr{M}\vartheta = 1$. Consequently, $\overline{\bigcup_\vartheta L_\vartheta \Phi} = \Phi$ and therefore $\overline{\Phi'} = \Phi$, all closures being taken in the $|\cdots|$-sense.

This proves Proposition 36.12.

36.15 The preceding results are summarized in a theorem:

Theorem For compact G, in the sense of the invariant average, the matrix coefficients of a complete set of inequivalent continuous irreducible finite-dimensional unitary representations, if divided by a factor $n^{-1/2}$ ($n =$ dimension of the representation), form an orthonormal system, which is total in that every continuous function on G can be uniformly approximated by finite linear combinations of the functions of the system.

37. THE CHARACTERS OF COMPACT GROUPS

37.1. Orthonormality

Definition The trace of a finite-dimensional linear representation of a group is called a *character* of G. It is the same for equivalent representations. A character is called *continuous*, *irreducible*, or *n-dimensional*, depending on whether a representation from which it can be derived has this property.

The continuous characters of compact G belong to Φ (see 36.7).

Definition The elements of Φ that are constant on every inner class of G are called *class functions*.

The continuous characters are special class functions.

Theorem The continuous irreducible characters of compact G are orthogonal if the respective representations are not equivalent, and all among them have unit norm. They form a total orthonormal system for the subspace of class functions in the sense that every class function can be uniformly approximated by finite linear combinations of these characters.

Proof The first assertion is an immediate consequence of the fact that a character is a sum of the diagonal matrix coefficients with respect to a basis.

Let φ be a class function. As an element of Φ, up to a given $\varepsilon > 0$, it equals a finite sum

$$\sum a_{jkf} \Upsilon_a(f(a)\, x_j{}^f, x_k{}^f),$$

where f means a continuous irreducible linear representation of G in some R_f with the basis $x_1{}^f, \ldots, x_{n_f}^f$. Now

$$\mathscr{M} \Upsilon_c f(c^{-1}ac),$$

which commutes with all $f(b)$ $(b \in G)$, is a scalar multiplication according to Proposition 36.3. The multiplier, found by tracing, is

$$n_f^{-1} \operatorname{tr} f(a).$$

Now, since φ is a class function,

$$\varphi(a) = \mathscr{M} \Upsilon_c \varphi(c^{-1}ac),$$

which up to ε can be replaced by

$$\mathscr{M} \Upsilon_c \sum \alpha_{jkf}(f(c^{-1}ac)\, x_j{}^f, x_k{}^f) = \sum \alpha_{jkf}\, n_f^{-1} \operatorname{tr} f(a)(x_j{}^f, x_k{}^f).$$

This proves the second assertion.

37.2–4. Reduction to the Trunk

37.2 G is now supposed to be a centerfree unitarily restricted semisimple linear Lie group. The notions and notations are those of Section 31; G is known to be compact and therefore 37.1 may be applied. The average $\mathscr{M}$ on G can be calculated by integrating with a suitably gauged infinitesimal measure $d\mu$.

The conjugacy theorem (31.5) states that a class function is determined by its behavior in the principal domain D. One may ask how the orthogonality properties of characters, as formulated in 37.1, can be expressed in terms of the restrictions of the characters to D or to H.

Theorem Every invariant infinitesimal measure $d\mu$ on G is related to an invariant infinitesimal measure dν on H such that for any continuous class function Θ

$$\int_G \Theta\, d\mu = \int_H \Theta(h) \prod_{\alpha \in W*} (1 - \exp \alpha(\boldsymbol{h}))\, d\nu(h),$$

$\boldsymbol{h}$ and h being related by $\exp \boldsymbol{h} = h$.

Proof When integrating a function Θ over G, the complement of F (see 31.9), which is nowhere dense, does not matter; F is wrapped in $\ulcorner G/H, D \urcorner$ by means of $\curlyvee_{\ulcorner q,\boldsymbol{h}\urcorner} qh$ (see 32.1). This wrapping transplants Θ to $\ulcorner G/H, D\urcorner$. Under the condition that the infinitesimal measure $d\mu$ on G is also transplanted from F to $\ulcorner G/H, D\urcorner$ as an infinitesimal measure $d\hat{\mu}$ the integration can be performed in $\ulcorner G/H, D\urcorner$ just as well; of course, the number of sheets s has to be taken into account. Note that if Θ is a class function its transplant $\hat{\Theta}$ to $\ulcorner G/H, D\urcorner$ in a point $\ulcorner q, h\urcorner$ depends only on h.

Another than the transplant measure $d\hat{\mu}$ is better adapted to integration in $\ulcorner G/H, D\urcorner$: Near H one can identify F with $\ulcorner G/H, D\urcorner$ by means of

37.2.1 $$gh \to \ulcorner q, h\urcorner \quad \text{with} \quad q = gH.$$

Then, heuristically, $\ulcorner G/H, D\urcorner$ touches G tangentially along D (identified with $\ulcorner H/H, D\urcorner$). Now by 37.2.1 $d\mu$ is transferred from G along D to $\ulcorner G/H, D\urcorner$ along $\ulcorner H/H, D\urcorner$. The new infinitesimal measure $d\mu^*$ is invariant under H applied to the second member within the $\ulcorner , \urcorner$-brackets. By left multiplication on G/H it is carried over all $\ulcorner G/H, D\urcorner$.

$d\mu^* = d\mu_1 \cdot d\mu_2$ is a Cartesian product measure in $\ulcorner G/H, D\urcorner$ with $d\mu_1$ as a G-invariant infinitesimal measure on G/H and $d\mu_2$ as an H-invariant one on H, at present restricted to D. Along $\ulcorner H/H, D\urcorner$ it coincides with that in F by the identification 37.2.1.

If Θ is a class function, then

$$\int_F \Theta\, d\mu = \frac{1}{s} \int_{\ulcorner G/H, D\urcorner} \hat{\Theta}\, d\hat{\mu} = \frac{1}{s} \int \hat{\Theta} \frac{d\hat{\mu}}{d\mu^*} d\mu^* = \frac{1}{s} \int \hat{\Theta} \frac{d\hat{\mu}}{d\mu^*} d\mu_1\, d\mu_2$$
$$= \frac{1}{s} \mu_1(G/H) \int_D \Theta \frac{d\hat{\mu}}{d\mu^*} d\mu_2,$$

which reduces the integration to one in D. How to calculate $d\hat{\mu}/d\mu^*$ at some point of $\ulcorner H/H, D\urcorner$ becomes clear from the diagram

$$\begin{array}{ccc} & \text{wrapping} & \\ \ulcorner q, h\urcorner & \longrightarrow & qh \\ q = gH \ \uparrow & & \| \ \ q = gH \\ gh & \longrightarrow & \tilde{g}h \\ & \varphi & \end{array}$$

The transition by the vertical arrow is that of 37.2.1 which preserves the infinitesimal measure. Therefore their behavior under wrapping is described by the mapping called φ in 31.6. This gives

$$\frac{d\hat{\mu}}{d\mu^*}(h) = \det \operatorname{grad}_h \varphi = \prod_{\alpha \in W^*} (1 - \exp \alpha(\boldsymbol{h})) \quad \text{if} \quad h = \exp \boldsymbol{h} \in D.$$

This shows

$$\int_F \Theta \, d\mu = \gamma \int_D \Theta(h) \prod_{\alpha \in W^*} (1 - \exp \alpha(\boldsymbol{h}))\, d\mu_2(h),$$

where γ does not depend on Θ. (Note that $\exp \alpha(\boldsymbol{h})$ depends on h rather than on $\boldsymbol{h}$.)

By 33.14.7 an inner automorphism of G leaving H invariant changes $\bar{D}$ in a fundamental domain to which it is equivalent under Int mod W^* while preserving the differential measure and the value of the integral. Summing up over all equivalent fundamental domains, one gets, essentially, the integral over H; hence

$$\int_G \Theta \, d\mu = \gamma' \int_H \Theta(h) \prod_{\alpha \in W^*} (1 - \exp \alpha(\boldsymbol{h}))\, d\mu_2(h),$$

where γ' can be made 1 by gauging $d\mu_2$ suitably.

Because of its H-invariance, $d\mu_2$ is an invariant infinitesimal measure on the l-dimensional torus H. In the sequel it is indicated by $d\nu$.

37.3. Definition Q is defined as a function on $\boldsymbol{H}$ (or rather on H), by

$$Q(\boldsymbol{h}) = \prod_{\alpha \in W^+} (1 - \exp \alpha(\boldsymbol{h})),$$

and for any continuous irreducible finite-dimensional linear representation f of G,

$$\theta_f(h) = Q(\boldsymbol{h}) \operatorname{tr} f(h) \quad \text{if } \boldsymbol{h} \in \boldsymbol{H}, \quad h = \exp \boldsymbol{h}.$$

Since $\alpha(\boldsymbol{h})$ is purely imaginary, one gets

$$\overline{Q(\boldsymbol{h})} = \prod_{\alpha \in W^-} (1 - \exp \alpha(\boldsymbol{h})).$$

From 37.1 it follows:

Theorem With a suitably gauged invariant infinitesimal measure $d\nu$ on H

$$\int \theta_f(h) \overline{\theta_g(h)} \, d\nu = \left\{ \begin{matrix} 0 \text{ for inequivalent} \\ 1 \text{ for equivalent} \end{matrix} \right\} f, g.$$

Therefore the irreducible characters multiplied by Q form an orthonormal system with respect to the ordinary measure on H (total with respect to class functions).

An algebraic proof for this result is given in Section 48.

37.4 The results of 37.3 remain valid for an arbitrary unitarily restricted semisimple G (not necessarily centerfree):

G is a wrapping of $\tilde{G}$ by means of a certain λ. The measures $d\mu$ and $d\tilde{\mu}$ in them are related to one another by invariance up to a constant factor under the wrapping λ as far as λ is one-to-one. A class function Θ on G defines a class function Θ on $\tilde{G}$ by means of

$$\breve{\Theta}(\tilde{a}) = \sum_{b \in \lambda^{-1}\tilde{a}} \Theta(b).$$

Then

$$\int_G \Theta(a)\, d\mu(a) = \text{const} \cdot \int_{\tilde{G}} \breve{\Theta}(\tilde{a})\, d\tilde{\mu}(\tilde{a})$$
$$= \text{const}' \cdot \int_{\tilde{H}} \breve{\Theta}(\tilde{h}) \prod (1 - \exp \alpha(\tilde{\boldsymbol{h}}))\, d\tilde{\nu}(\tilde{h}),$$

where $\tilde{h} = \exp \tilde{\boldsymbol{h}}$. Because of 32.7–8 and $\alpha(\boldsymbol{h}) = \alpha(\tilde{\boldsymbol{h}})$, this may be replaced by

$$\text{const}'' \cdot \int_H \Theta(h) \prod (1 - \exp \alpha(\boldsymbol{h}))\, d\nu(h),$$

which proves the assertion.

37.5.† The Natural Gauge The tangent space $\boldsymbol{G}$ of compact semisimple G is naturally gifted with a positive inner product by the negative of the Killing form. In turn, this inner product in $\boldsymbol{G}$ fixes a natural elementary volume, namely, by assigning the value 1 to an orthonormal basis. This leads to a natural invariant infinitesimal measure and to a measure on G, independent of the choice of the basis. One might wonder how large G_{un} measures with this natural yardstick.

37.5.1. Definition The *natural measure* μ_0 on compact semisimple G is determined by an invariant *natural infinitesimal measure* $d\mu_0$ that assigns to some $(-\psi_{\text{un}})$-orthonormal basis the elementary volume 1.

37.5.2. Problem To determine the total μ_0-measure-value of G.

It suffices to solve it for centerfree simple G.

In $\boldsymbol{H}$ an elementary volume ν', which assigns the value 1 to a $(-\psi|_{\boldsymbol{H}})$-orthonormal basis, is introduced. It determines an invariant infinitesimal measure $d\nu$ in H. With a slight deviation in terminology from Theorem 37.2 the invariant measure μ in G is determined such that for every class function Θ

$$\int_G \Theta\, d\mu = \int_D \Theta(h) \prod_{\alpha \in W*} (1 - \exp \alpha(\boldsymbol{h}))\, d\nu(h).$$

† The contents of 37.5 are not used in the sequel.

Anticipating a formula to be verified in 47.5.3, one gets

$$\mu(G) = k\,\nu(D) = k\nu'(\boldsymbol{D}),$$

where k is the order of the kaleidoscope group.

$\nu'(\boldsymbol{D})$ can easily be calculated. Let G be given in ordered second dressing, $\rho_1, \ldots, \rho_l$ the primitive rootforms, and $\sum q_i \rho_i$ the top rootform. As in 32.3, let $\boldsymbol{a}_1, \ldots, \boldsymbol{a}_l$ in $\boldsymbol{H}$ be determined by

$$\rho_i(a_j) = \begin{cases} 0 & \text{for } i \neq j, \\ \mathrm{i} & \text{for } i = j. \end{cases}$$

Then $\boldsymbol{D}$ is the l-simplex with vertices

$$\boldsymbol{0} \quad \text{and the} \quad 2\pi q_j^{-1} \boldsymbol{a}_j \; (j = 1, \ldots, l).$$

Its volume according to ν is

$$\frac{1}{l!}(2\pi)^l \,(\det{}^\ulcorner - \psi(\boldsymbol{a}_i, \boldsymbol{a}_j)^\urcorner{}_{i,j=1}^l)^{1/2} \prod_j q_j^{-1}$$

$$= \frac{1}{l!}(2\pi)^l \,(\det{}^\ulcorner(\rho_i, \rho_j)^\urcorner{}_{i,j=1}^l)^{-1/2} \prod_j q_j^{-1}.$$

This leads to the formula:

37.5.3 $$\mu(G) = \frac{k}{l!}(2\pi)^l \,(\det{}^\ulcorner(\rho_i, \rho_j)^\urcorner{}_{i,j=1}^l)^{-1/2} \prod_j q_j^{-1}.$$

It is clear how this formula has to be modified for nonsimple G.

$\mu_0(G)$ is computed by comparing μ_0 with μ. Put

37.5.4 $$\gamma = \frac{\mu_0(\cdots)}{\mu(\cdots)}.$$

$\boldsymbol{B}_\varepsilon$ means a ball around $\boldsymbol{0}$ in $\boldsymbol{G}$ with radius ε, according to the $(-\psi_{\mathrm{un}})$-metric, and $\boldsymbol{B}'_\varepsilon$ is its intersection with $\boldsymbol{H}$. The characteristic function of $\exp \boldsymbol{B}'_\varepsilon$ is a class function. For small ε

$$\mu(\exp \boldsymbol{B}_\varepsilon) = \int_{\boldsymbol{h} \in \boldsymbol{B}_\varepsilon'} \prod_{\alpha \in W^*} (1 - \exp \alpha(\boldsymbol{h}))\, d\nu'(\boldsymbol{h})$$

$$= \int_{\boldsymbol{h} \in \boldsymbol{B}_\varepsilon'} \prod_{\alpha \in W^*} \alpha(\boldsymbol{h})\, d\nu'(\boldsymbol{h}) + \cdots$$

$$= \varepsilon^r \int_{\boldsymbol{h} \in \boldsymbol{B}_1'} \prod_{\alpha \in W^*} \alpha(\boldsymbol{h})\, d\nu'(\boldsymbol{h}) + \cdots,$$

where the dots represent a term of order ε^{r+1}, and $r = \dim \boldsymbol{G}$.

On the other hand, a well-known formula assesses the volume of $\boldsymbol{B}_\varepsilon$ as

$$\frac{\varepsilon^r \pi^{(1/2)r}}{\Gamma(\frac{1}{2}r+1)};$$

hence

$$\mu_0(\exp \boldsymbol{B}_\varepsilon) = \frac{\varepsilon^r \pi^{(1/2)r}}{\Gamma(\frac{1}{2}r+1)} + \cdots .$$

This gives

37.5.5
$$\gamma = \frac{\pi^{(1/2)r}}{\Gamma(\frac{1}{2}r+1)\int_{\boldsymbol{B}_1'} \prod_{\alpha\in W^*} \alpha(\boldsymbol{h})\, dv'(\boldsymbol{h})}.$$

In order to be evaluated, the integral in the denominator is replaced by

37.5.6
$$I = \int_H e^{\psi(\boldsymbol{h},\boldsymbol{h})} \prod_{\alpha\in W^*} \alpha(\boldsymbol{h})\, dv'(\boldsymbol{h}).$$

Corresponding to the

$$r - l = 2m$$

elements α of W^*, independent real variables ξ_α are assumed and

$$A(\xi) = \int_H e^{\psi(\boldsymbol{h},\boldsymbol{h})} (\sum_\alpha \xi_\alpha \alpha(\boldsymbol{h}))^{2m}\, dv'(\boldsymbol{h})$$

is considered. The coefficient of $\prod_\alpha \xi_\alpha$ in $A(\xi)$, written as a polynomial, is just

$$(2m)!\,I.$$

To compute $A(\xi)$, orthonormal coordinates $u_1, \ldots, u_l$ are assumed in $\boldsymbol{H}$ such that u_1 is a fixed multiple of $\sum \xi_\alpha \alpha$; hence

$$u_1 = (\sum \xi_\alpha \alpha, \sum \xi_\alpha \alpha)^{-1/2}\,\mathrm{i} \sum \xi_\alpha \alpha.$$

Then

$$\begin{aligned}
A(\xi) &= (-1)^m (\sum \xi_\alpha \alpha, \sum \xi_\alpha \alpha)^m \int_H \mathrm{e}^{-\sum_j u_j(\boldsymbol{h})^2} u_1^{2m}\, du_1 \cdots du_l \\
&= (-1)^m (\sum \xi_\alpha \alpha, \sum \xi_\alpha \alpha)^m \cdot 2^l \cdot \int_0^\infty \mathrm{e}^{-u_1^2} u_1^{2m}\, du_1 \left(\int_0^\infty \mathrm{e}^{-u^2}\, du\right)^{l-1} \\
&= (-1)^m (\sum \xi_\alpha \alpha, \sum \xi_\alpha \alpha)^m \cdot 2^l \cdot \frac{1\cdot 3 \cdots (2m-1)}{2^{m+1}} \sqrt{\pi}\cdot(\tfrac{1}{2}\sqrt{\pi})^{l-1} \\
&= (-1)^m (\sum \xi_\alpha \alpha, \sum \xi_\alpha \alpha)^m \cdot 2^{-m} \cdot 1\cdot 3 \cdots (2m-1)\, \pi^{(1/2)l}.
\end{aligned}$$

The coefficient of $\prod_\alpha \xi_\alpha$ in $(-1)^m(\sum \xi_\alpha \alpha, \sum \xi_\alpha \alpha)^m$ is

$$\tau = (-1)^m \sum (\alpha_{i_1}, \alpha_{i_2})(\alpha_{i_3}, \alpha_{i_4}) \cdots (\alpha_{i_{2m-1}}, \alpha_{i_{2m}}),$$

where the sum runs over all permutations i of W^*. This gives

$$I = \frac{1}{(2m)!} 2^{-m} \cdot 1 \cdot 3 \cdots (2m-1)\, \pi^{(1/2)l}\, \tau$$

37.5.7 $$= \frac{1}{m!} 2^{-2m} \pi^{(1/2)l}\, \tau.$$

To come back to γ, put

$$F_\lambda = \int_{B\lambda'} \prod_\alpha \alpha(\boldsymbol{h})\, dv'(\boldsymbol{h}).$$

Then

$$F_\lambda = \lambda^r F_1$$

$$dF_\lambda = r\lambda^{r-1} F_1\, d\lambda.$$

Now by 37.5.6

$$I = \int_0^\infty e^{-\lambda^2}\, dF_\lambda = rF_1 \int_0^\infty e^{-\lambda^2} \lambda^{r-1}\, d\lambda$$

$$= \tfrac{1}{2} r F_1 \cdot \Gamma(\tfrac{1}{2} r) = F_1 \cdot \Gamma(\tfrac{1}{2} r + 1).$$

$$F_1 = \frac{I}{\Gamma(\frac{1}{2} r + 1)}$$

is now substituted into the denominator of 37.5.5 by using the value of I obtained in 37.5.7:

$$\gamma = \frac{\pi^{(1/2)r}}{I} = \frac{2^{2m}\, m!\, \pi^m}{\tau}.$$

Now by 37.5.3–4:

Theorem With the natural measure μ_0 for centerfree simple G

$$\mu_0(G) = \frac{k 2^r\, m!\, \pi^{l+m} (\det \ulcorner (\rho_i, \rho_j) \urcorner_{i,j=1}^{l})^{-1/2}}{l! \cdot \prod q_i \cdot \tau},$$

where $m = \frac{1}{2}(r - l)$, the q_i are the coefficients of the top rootform on a natural basis $\rho_1, \ldots, \rho_l$, and

$$\tau = (-1)^m \sum (\alpha_{i_1}, \alpha_{i_2})(\alpha_{i_3}, \alpha_{i_4}) \cdots (\alpha_{i_{2m-1}}, \alpha_{i_{2m}}),$$

with the sum running over all permutations i of W^*.

Nonsimple G requires an evident modification.

Unfortunately, the numerical value of τ does not seem to be readily accessible, except for the simple groups of rank $\leqslant 3$. In fact,

$$l = 1: \quad \tau = 1,$$

$$l = 2: \quad \tau = 2(m!)^2 \prod_{\alpha \in W+} (\alpha, \alpha);$$

hence

$$\mathsf{A}_1: \quad \tau = 1.$$

$$\mathsf{A}_2: \quad \tau = \frac{8}{3}.$$

$$\mathsf{B}_2: \quad \tau = \frac{32}{9}.$$

$$\mathsf{G}_2: \quad \tau = \frac{75}{8}.$$

Furthermore,

$$\mathsf{A}_3: \quad \frac{\tau}{m!} \prod_{\alpha \in W^+} (\alpha, \alpha) = 288.$$

$$\mathsf{B}_3: \quad = 6! \cdot 48.$$

$$\mathsf{C}_3: \quad = 6! \cdot 48.$$

37.6. Historical Note The Frobenius-I.Schur character theory for finite groups was extended to compact groups by F. Peter and H. Weyl, *Math. Ann.* **97** (1927) = *Selecta* H. Weyl, 387–404. The formula for the natural volume of G was derived by H. Freudenthal.

38. SOME GLOBAL PROPERTIES OF SEMISIMPLE LINEAR LIE GROUPS

$G \in$ Gru Lie Lin Com SS in third dressing, presented by linear mappings of $R \in$ Spa Lin Com (dim $R = n < \infty$); therefore $G \subset$ Aut R.

Since by 32.2.4 G_{un} is compact, R can be provided with a G_{un}-invariant inner product $(\ldots, \ldots)$.

For $a \in$ End R one defines a^* by $(ax, y) = (x, a^* y)$ as before.

38.1–4. The Hermitean-Unitary Split

38.1 The hermitean elements of End R are those $\boldsymbol{a}$ with $\boldsymbol{a}^* = \boldsymbol{a}$, the antihermitean those with $\boldsymbol{a}^* = -\boldsymbol{a}$; End R is the direct sum of the subspace $\boldsymbol{S}$ of the hermitean elements and the subspace $\boldsymbol{U}$ of the antihermitean elements, as follows from the involutory nature of $*$.

The eigenvalues of an hermitean element are real, those of an antihermitean purely imaginary; both kinds of elements appear in diagonal form on a suitable orthonormal basis of R. The hermitean elements of End R with positive (nonnegative) eigenvalues only are called positive definite (semidefinite); they are the $\boldsymbol{a} \in \boldsymbol{S}$ with $(\boldsymbol{a}x, x) > 0$ $((\boldsymbol{a}x, x) \geqslant 0)$ for $x \in R$, $x \neq 0$.

Let S be the set of all positive definite hermitean elements of Aut R, U the group of unitary elements of Aut R, that is, of those a for which $a^* = a^{-1}$; $\boldsymbol{U}$ is the infinitesimal algebra of U, and exp $\boldsymbol{S} \subset S$.

S is closed in Aut R, for if a is in the closure of S it is by continuity still positive semidefinite hermitean, but, since, $a \in$ Aut R, it has no vanishing eigenvalues and is even positive definite.

If the kernel of the trace on End R is interpreted as a member of $\mathbf{A}_{n-1}$ (see 16.2), its intersection with $\boldsymbol{U}$ coincides with the unitary restriction formed according to 24.6.

38.2. Theorem exp maps $\boldsymbol{S}$ homeomorphically onto S, with a nowhere degenerate gradient, and S is a closed analytic submanifold of Aut R.

This is a consequence of Theorem 18.1.4, and 38.1.

38.3. Theorem As an analytic manifold Aut R is the product of its closed submanifolds U and S by means of the multiplication in Aut R; explicitly, every $a \in$ Aut R can be uniquely written as $a = su$, with $s \in S$, $u \in U$ depending analytically on a.

Proof U is a closed submanifold because it is a compact Lie group; S is so by 38.2.

If $a \in$ Aut R and $a = s_1 u_1 = s_2 u_2$ with $s_i \in S$, $u_i \in U$ $(i = 1,2)$, then $aa^* = s_1 u_1 u_1^* s_1^* = s_1^2 = s_2^2$; since division by 2 is unique in $\boldsymbol{S}$, extraction of square roots is so in S; hence $s_1 = s_2$ and $u_1 = u_2$.

If $a \in \text{Aut } R$, then $aa^* \in S$; now take s as the square root of aa^* in S and $u = s^{-1}a$; then $a = su$ as required, with s, and u as well, depending analytically on a.

38.4. Theorem As an analytic manifold G is the product of its closed submanifolds G_{un} and $\exp \mathrm{i}\boldsymbol{G}_{\text{un}}$ by means of the multiplication in G; $\exp \mathrm{i}\boldsymbol{G}_{\text{un}} = G \cap S$, $G_{\text{un}} = G \cap U$, that is, $\exp \mathrm{i}\boldsymbol{G}_{\text{un}}$ consists of all positive definite hermitean elements of G, and G_{un} consists of all unitary elements of G.

Proof Because it is a compact Lie group, G_{un} is a closed submanifold, as is $\exp \mathrm{i}\boldsymbol{G}_{\text{un}}$ also because it is the image of $\mathrm{i}\boldsymbol{G}_{\text{un}} = \boldsymbol{G} \cap \boldsymbol{S}$ under exp. Now $G_{\text{un}} \cdot \exp \mathrm{i}\boldsymbol{G}_{\text{un}}$ is a closed submanifold of Aut R, hence also a closed submanifold of G, but with the same dimension as G; hence $G = G_{\text{un}} \cdot \exp \mathrm{i}\boldsymbol{G}_{\text{un}}$. It also follows from the uniqueness in 38.3 that $G \cap U = G_{\text{un}}$, $G \cap S = \exp \mathrm{i}\boldsymbol{G}_{\text{un}}$.

38.5. Fundamental Group, Center, Closedness

Theorem

(1) The fundamental groups of a complex semisimple linear Lie group G and its unitary restriction are isomorphic in a natural way.

(2) The center of a complex semisimple linear Lie group G is finite.

(3) The center of a real semisimple linear Lie Group G is finite.

(4) A real or complex semisimple linear Lie group acting in $R \in$ Spa Lin Rea or Com is closed in Aut R. (Anticipated in 30.1.)

Proof

(1) G is homeomorphic with the topological product of G_{un} and $\exp \mathrm{i}\boldsymbol{G}_{\text{un}}$ in a natural way (38.4), and the fundamental group of $\exp \mathrm{i}\boldsymbol{G}_{\text{un}}$ is trivial.

(2) The center may be interpreted as a factor group of the fundamental group of the adjoint $\tilde{G}$; by the first part of this theorem and Theorem 32.2.4 the fundamental group of $\tilde{G}$ is finite.

(3) The center of G is contained in that of G_{Com}.

(4) By Theorem 19.10 and Proposition 12.16 this follows from the finiteness of the center.

Remark Do not draw the conclusion that every real semisimple linear Lie group has a finite fundamental group. The universal wrapping need not be realizable as a *linear* Lie group. The class of connected groups locally isomorphic to semisimple linear Lie groups is larger than that of those isomorphic to semisimple linear Lie groups. However, there is a universal *linear* wrapping for any $G \in$ Gru Lie Lin SS (see 62.9).

38.6. Historical Note The hermitean-unitary split is due to E. Cartan. It has still to be viewed in a broader context (see Section 64).

39–50

THE ALGEBRAIC APPROACH TO LINEAR REPRESENTATIONS

39. THE ASSOCIATIVE ENVELOPE OF A LIE ALGEBRA

In the following general theorems on a Lie algebra $\boldsymbol{G}$, the finiteness of the basis $\boldsymbol{X}$ is not involved, only its existence. The scalars need not come from a field; a commutative ring with 1-element is sufficient.

The aim is to embed $\boldsymbol{G}$ into an associative algebra such that:

39.1 $$[\boldsymbol{a}, \boldsymbol{b}] = \boldsymbol{ab} - \boldsymbol{ba} \qquad \text{for} \quad \boldsymbol{a}, \boldsymbol{b} \in \boldsymbol{G},$$

and to ensure that no other relations but 39.1 are introduced.

39.2 The basis $\boldsymbol{X}$ is supposed to be ordered ($<$).

The free associative algebra with unit-element 1 generated by $\boldsymbol{X}$ is called $\mathscr{A}(\boldsymbol{X})$; $\boldsymbol{G}$ is identified in a natural way with a subset of $\mathscr{A}(\boldsymbol{X})$.

$\boldsymbol{C}$ is the subset of $\boldsymbol{xy} - \boldsymbol{yx} - [\boldsymbol{x}, \boldsymbol{y}]$ with $\boldsymbol{x}, \boldsymbol{y} \in \boldsymbol{X}$ (or $\boldsymbol{G}$).

$\mathscr{J}(\boldsymbol{C})$ is the ideal generated by $\boldsymbol{C}$ in $\mathscr{A}(\boldsymbol{X})$.

Definition $\mathscr{E}(\boldsymbol{G}) = \mathscr{A}(\boldsymbol{X}) \bmod \mathscr{J}(\boldsymbol{C})$ is called the *associative envelope* of $\boldsymbol{G}$. (The dependence of $\mathscr{E}(\boldsymbol{G})$ on $\boldsymbol{X}$ is inessential.)

Clearly this is an associative algebra in which 39.1 prevails. It is not evident whether what corresponds to $\boldsymbol{G}$ in $\mathscr{A}(\boldsymbol{X})$ is mapped one-to-one into $\mathscr{E}(\boldsymbol{G})$ by the reduction mod $\mathscr{J}(\boldsymbol{C})$. However, a still stronger proposition will be proved.

39.3 A product of elements of $\boldsymbol{X}$ (*monomial*) is called *orderly* if its factors appear in the correct order; these terms will also be used for the scalar multiples. An element of $\mathscr{A}(\boldsymbol{X})$ is called *orderly* if it is a sum of orderly monomials.

Up to first degree monomials, $\boldsymbol{yx}$ can be replaced by $\boldsymbol{xy}$ mod $\mathscr{J}(\boldsymbol{C})$. Consequently, up to lower degree terms every monomial can be replaced by an orderly monomial mod $\mathscr{J}(\boldsymbol{C})$. By induction on the degree one can replace any element of $\mathscr{A}(\boldsymbol{X})$ with an orderly one mod $\mathscr{J}(\boldsymbol{C})$. Therefore every class of $\mathscr{A}(\boldsymbol{X})$ mod $\mathscr{J}(\boldsymbol{C})$ contains an orderly representative. It will be proved:

Theorem The only orderly element in $\mathscr{J}(\boldsymbol{C})$ is $\boldsymbol{0}$. In other words, the subspace of orderly elements of $\mathscr{A}(\boldsymbol{X})$ is a linear complement of $\mathscr{J}(\boldsymbol{C})$.

Consequence As a subset of $\mathscr{A}(\boldsymbol{G})$, $\boldsymbol{G}$ is mapped one-to-one into $\mathscr{E}(\boldsymbol{G})$ by the reduction mod $\mathscr{J}(\boldsymbol{C})$.

39.4 Another property is the following.

Theorem Let φ be a mapping of $\boldsymbol{G}$ into any associative algebra A such that $\varphi[\boldsymbol{a},\boldsymbol{b}] = \varphi\boldsymbol{a}\cdot\varphi\boldsymbol{b} - \varphi\boldsymbol{b}\cdot\varphi\boldsymbol{a}$. Then φ can be uniquely extended to a homomorphism of $\mathscr{E}(\boldsymbol{G})$ into A. Furthermore, $\mathscr{E}(\boldsymbol{G})$ is characterized by this property.

39.5 A linear representation of $\mathscr{E}(\boldsymbol{G})$ will serve to prove Theorem 39.3.

Let X be a copy of $\boldsymbol{X}$. The element of X corresponding to one of $\boldsymbol{X}$ is written as its light face counterpart. If $\boldsymbol{x} < \boldsymbol{y}$, then $x < y$, by definition.

The free commutative associative algebra with unit-element 1 generated by X is denoted by $\mathscr{S}(X)$. The subset of elements of degree $\leqslant n$ is denoted by $\mathscr{S}_n(X)$. The set of monomials of degree n is denoted by $\mathscr{M}_n(X)$.

If $x \in X$ and $u \in \mathscr{M}_n(X)$, then $x \leqslant u$ means $x \leqslant$ every factor involved in u.

The next step is to define a multiplication

$$\boldsymbol{g}c \in \mathscr{S}(X) \qquad \text{for} \quad \boldsymbol{g} \in \boldsymbol{G}, \quad c \in \mathscr{S}(X),$$

in such a way that

39.5.1 $\curlyvee_c \boldsymbol{g}c$ is linear, if $\mathscr{S}(X)$ is considered as a linear space.

39.5.2 $(\alpha_1 \boldsymbol{g}_1 + \alpha_2 \boldsymbol{g}_2)c = \alpha_1 \boldsymbol{g}_1 c + \alpha_2 \boldsymbol{g}_2 c$ for scalars α_1, α_2.

It suffices to define this product for $\boldsymbol{g} \in \boldsymbol{X}$ and $c \in \bigcup_n \mathscr{M}_n(X)$ and to require that it be extended by the use of 39.5.1–2.

The definition proceeds by induction on the degree. The basic assumption is

$$\boldsymbol{x}1 = x \qquad \text{for} \quad \boldsymbol{x} \in \boldsymbol{X}.$$

Under the assumption that

$$\boldsymbol{g}u \text{ is defined for all } \boldsymbol{g} \in \boldsymbol{G},\ u \in \mathscr{S}_{n-1}(X),$$

$$\boldsymbol{x}u \text{ is defined for all } \boldsymbol{x} \in \boldsymbol{X},\ u \in \mathscr{M}_n(X):$$

39.5.3 $$\boldsymbol{x}u = xu \qquad \text{if} \quad x \leqslant u,$$

39.5.4 $$\boldsymbol{x}u = \boldsymbol{y}\boldsymbol{x}v + [\boldsymbol{x}, \boldsymbol{y}]v$$

$$\text{if not } x \leqslant u,\ u = yv, \text{ and } y \leqslant v.$$

Note that

39.5.5 $$\boldsymbol{x}w = xw \bmod \mathscr{S}_n(X) \qquad \text{if} \quad w \in \mathscr{S}_n(X).$$

It is shown by induction that

39.5.6 $\quad \boldsymbol{x}\boldsymbol{y}u - \boldsymbol{y}\boldsymbol{x}u = [\boldsymbol{x}, \boldsymbol{y}]u \quad$ for $\boldsymbol{x}, \boldsymbol{y} \in \boldsymbol{G}, \quad u \in \mathscr{S}(X)$.

The induction step consists in assuming that 39.5.6 is true for $u \in \mathscr{S}_{n-1}(X)$ and ascertaining it for $u \in \mathscr{M}_n(X)$ while restricting $\boldsymbol{x}, \boldsymbol{y}$ to X. One may add the assumption

39.5.7 $$y \leqslant x,$$

which means no restriction at all.

39.5.8 The induction step is allowed if, in addition, $y \leqslant u$. Indeed, then $y \leqslant xu$, hence

$$\boldsymbol{x}\boldsymbol{y}u = \boldsymbol{x}yu = \boldsymbol{y}\boldsymbol{x}u + [\boldsymbol{x}, \boldsymbol{y}]u,$$

where the first equality sign is justified by 39.5.3 applied to $\boldsymbol{y}u$ instead of $\boldsymbol{x}u$ and the second by 39.5.4, with u instead of v.

The induction step has still to be justified, if not $y \leqslant u$. Then one can split

39.5.9 $$u = zv, \qquad z \in X, \quad v \in \mathscr{M}_{n-1}(X),$$

39.5.10 $$z \leqslant v,$$

39.5.11 $$z < y,$$

39.5.12 $$z < x$$

(the last inequality because of 39.5.7, which will no longer be used explicitly so that the symmetry between x and y is now restored).

Now

$$\boldsymbol{y}u = \boldsymbol{y}zv = \boldsymbol{y}\boldsymbol{z}v = \boldsymbol{z}\boldsymbol{y}v + [\boldsymbol{y}, \boldsymbol{z}]v = \boldsymbol{z}(yv) + \boldsymbol{z}(\boldsymbol{y}v - yv) + [\boldsymbol{y}, \boldsymbol{z}]v,$$

where the first and second equality signs are due to 39.5.9–10, and the third to the induction assumption, the fourth being trivial algebra. Multiplying by $\boldsymbol{x}$, one gets for the three summands,

(1) $$\boldsymbol{x}\boldsymbol{z}(yv) = \boldsymbol{z}\boldsymbol{x}(yv) + [\boldsymbol{x}, \boldsymbol{z}](yv),$$

where 39.5.8 has been applied with $\boldsymbol{z}$ instead of $\boldsymbol{y}$ and yv instead of u, thanks to 39.5.10–11 which ensures that $z \leqslant yv$;

(2) $$\boldsymbol{x}\boldsymbol{z}(\boldsymbol{y}v - yv) = \boldsymbol{z}\boldsymbol{x}(\boldsymbol{y}v - yv) + [\boldsymbol{x}, \boldsymbol{z}](\boldsymbol{y}v - yv),$$

where the induction assumption could be applied, thanks to 39.5.5, which ensures $\boldsymbol{y}v - yv \in \mathscr{S}_{n-1}(X)$;

(3) $$\boldsymbol{x}[\boldsymbol{y}, \boldsymbol{z}]v = [\boldsymbol{y}, \boldsymbol{z}]\boldsymbol{x}v + [\boldsymbol{x}, [\boldsymbol{y}, \boldsymbol{z}]]v,$$

where the induction assumption applies because $v \in \mathscr{S}_{n-1}(X)$.

Together this means

$$\boldsymbol{x}\boldsymbol{y}u = z\boldsymbol{x}\boldsymbol{y}v + [\boldsymbol{x}, z]\boldsymbol{y}v + [\boldsymbol{y}, z]\,\boldsymbol{x}v + [\boldsymbol{x}, [\boldsymbol{y}, z]]\,v.$$

In $\boldsymbol{y}\boldsymbol{x}u$ the second and third summand together would be the same; thus by Jacobi associativity,

$$\begin{aligned} \boldsymbol{x}\boldsymbol{y}u - \boldsymbol{y}\boldsymbol{x}u &= z[\boldsymbol{x}, \boldsymbol{y}]\,v + [[\boldsymbol{x}, \boldsymbol{y}], z]\,v \\ &= [\boldsymbol{x}, \boldsymbol{y}]\,zv = [\boldsymbol{x}, \boldsymbol{y}]\,zv = [\boldsymbol{x}, \boldsymbol{y}]\,u, \end{aligned}$$

where again the induction assumption has been used as well as 39.5.10 and 39.5.3.

This proves 39.5.6.

39.6 In an obvious way the multiplication can be extended such that

$$\boldsymbol{a}c \in \mathscr{S}(X) \qquad \text{for} \quad \boldsymbol{a} \in \mathscr{A}(X), \qquad c \in \mathscr{S}(X)$$

and $\vartheta = \curlyvee_{\boldsymbol{a}} \curlyvee_c \boldsymbol{a}c$ is a homomorphism of $\mathscr{A}(\boldsymbol{X})$ into End $\mathscr{S}(\boldsymbol{X})$.

Now 39.5.6 can be reworded as

$$\boldsymbol{C}\mathscr{S}(X) = \{0\},$$

which implies

39.6.1 $$\mathscr{J}(\boldsymbol{C})\,\mathscr{S}(X) = \{0\}.$$

To prove Theorem 39.3 take an orderly $\boldsymbol{a}$ in $\mathscr{J}(\boldsymbol{C})$. Then, from 39.6.1

$$\boldsymbol{a} \cdot 1 = 0.$$

$\boldsymbol{a} \cdot 1$ arises from the orderly $\boldsymbol{a}$ by substituting for every $\boldsymbol{x} \in \boldsymbol{X}$ involved in $\boldsymbol{a}$ its counterpart $x \in X$. So $\boldsymbol{a} \cdot 1 = 0$ only if $\boldsymbol{a} = \boldsymbol{0}$, which proves Theorem 39.3.

39.7 Another conclusion is the following.

Proposition As defined in 39.6, ϑ represents $\mathscr{E}(\boldsymbol{G})$ faithfully in End $\mathscr{S}(X)$.

Proof 39.6.1 shows that the kernel of ϑ contains $\mathscr{J}(\boldsymbol{C})$. Conversely if $\vartheta\boldsymbol{a} = 0$, one can find an orderly $\boldsymbol{b}$ such that $\boldsymbol{a} = \boldsymbol{b} \bmod \mathscr{J}(\boldsymbol{C})$. Then $\vartheta\boldsymbol{b} = 0$, hence $\boldsymbol{b} = \boldsymbol{0}$, hence $\boldsymbol{a} \in \mathscr{J}(\boldsymbol{C})$.

39.8. Historical Note The first correct proof for the existence of an associative envelope of a Lie algebra was provided by E. Witt, *J. reine angew. Math.* **177**, 152–160 (1937). The present proof was given in "Séminaire Sophus Lie 1954–1955."

40. THE CASIMIR TOOL

$G \in$ Alg Lie Com SS, dim $G = r$.

$a_1, \ldots, a_r$ and $a^1, \ldots, a^r$ are correlate bases of G with respect to the Killing form; that is,

$$\operatorname{tr} \tilde{a}_i \tilde{a}^j = \begin{cases} 1 & \text{for } i = j, \\ 0 & \text{for } i \neq j. \end{cases}$$

40.1. Definition The element

$$z = \sum_i a^i a_i$$

of the associative envelope of G is called the *Casimir tool* of G.

The definition is justified by showing that z does not depend on the choice of the bases, provided they are correlate.

Assume b^i, b_i, defined by

$$b^i = \sum_p \gamma_p{}^i a^p, \qquad \sum_q \gamma_j{}^q b_q = a_j,$$

with det $\gamma \neq 0$; then, by passing to the adjoint elements, multiplying, and tracing,

$$\sum_q \gamma_j{}^q \operatorname{tr} \tilde{b}^i \tilde{b}_q = \sum_p \gamma_p{}^i \operatorname{tr} \tilde{a}^p \tilde{a}_j = \gamma_j{}^i,$$

hence,

$$\operatorname{tr} \tilde{b}^i \tilde{b}_q \qquad = \begin{cases} 1 & \text{for } i = q, \\ 0 & \text{for } i \neq q. \end{cases}$$

Consequently, $b_1, \ldots, b_r$ and $b^1, \ldots, b^r$ are also correlate bases, and clearly every pair of correlate bases can be obtained in this way. Moreover,

$$\sum_i b^i b_i = \sum_{p,i} \gamma_p{}^i a^p b_i = \sum_p a^p a_p.$$

In particular, $\sum a^i a_i = \sum a_i a^i$.

40.2 If $\tilde{c}$ is an element of the adjoint group $\tilde{G}$, then

$$\tilde{c}a_1, \ldots, \tilde{c}a_r \qquad \text{and} \qquad \tilde{c}a^1, \ldots, \tilde{c}a^r$$

again form a pair of correlate bases. Now with $c = \exp tc$ ($c \in G$):

$$\sum (\exp t\tilde{c})\, a_i \cdot (\exp t\tilde{c})\, a^i$$

is constant. Differentiating at $t = 0$, one gets

$$\sum ([c, a_i] \cdot a^i + a_i \cdot [c, a^i]) = 0,$$

hence

$$c \sum a_i a^i - \sum a_i a^i c = 0.$$

It turns out that the Casimir tool commutes with every element of G. Consequently:

Theorem The Casimir tool of G is in the center of the associative envelope of G.

A proof that avoids the use of the adjoint *group* is more involved:

$$\sum_j \operatorname{tr}(\tilde{a}^i \tilde{a}_j)\, a^j = a^i;$$

hence by linear combination, for any $x \in G$,

40.2.1 $$\sum_j \operatorname{tr}(\tilde{x}\tilde{a}_j)\, a^j = x;$$

in particular, for $x = [c, a^i]$,

$$\sum_j \operatorname{tr}(\widetilde{[c, a^i]}\, \tilde{a}_j) a^j = [c, a^i].$$

Multiplying by a_i and summing up, one gets

$$\sum_{j,i} \operatorname{tr}(\widetilde{[c, a^i]}\, \tilde{a}_j)\, a^j a_i = \sum_i [c, a^i]\, a_i$$

and likewise

$$\sum_{j,i} \operatorname{tr}(\tilde{a}^i\, \widetilde{[c, a_j]})\, a^j a_i = \sum a^j [c, a_j].$$

The two first members together are $\mathbf{0}$ because of the infinitesimal invariance of the Killing form under the adjoint Lie algebra. Thus,

$$\begin{aligned} \mathbf{0} &= \sum [c, a^i]\, a_i + \sum a^i [c, a_i] = \sum (ca^i a_i - a^i ca_i + a^i ca_i - a^i a_i c) \\ &= cz - zc. \end{aligned}$$

40.3 A remark on the use of correlate bases: From 40.2.1, one gets

$$\operatorname{tr}(\tilde{x}\tilde{y}) = \sum_i \operatorname{tr}(\tilde{x}\tilde{a}_i) \cdot \operatorname{tr}(\tilde{y}\tilde{a}_i).$$

If $h_1, \ldots, h_l$ and $h^1, \ldots, h^l$ form a pair of correlate bases of the trunk H and second dressing is assumed, then

$$h_1, \ldots, h_l, \quad e_\alpha \qquad (\alpha \in W^*),$$

and

$$h^1, \ldots, h^l, \quad e_{-\alpha} \qquad (\alpha \in W^*)$$

form such a pair for G. Then

$$\operatorname{tr} \tilde{h}\tilde{h}' = \sum_i \operatorname{tr}(\tilde{h}\tilde{h}_i) \operatorname{tr}(\tilde{h}'\tilde{h}^i);$$

hence if

$$\zeta h = \xi, \qquad \zeta h' = \xi'$$

(see 21.1.5), then

$$(\xi, \xi') = \sum \xi(h_i)\,\xi(h^i) \qquad \text{for any} \quad \xi, \xi' \in H^*.$$

40.4. Historical Note H. B. G. Casimir, *Proc. Kon. Ned. Akad. Wet.* **A34**, 844–846 (1931), introduced what here has been called the Casimir tool. It has proved to be an important counterpart of the Killing form. The full center of the envelope was investigated by Harish-Chandra, *Trans. Amer. Math. Soc.* **70**, 28–96 (1951). (See also 77.24.)

41. WEIGHTS AND INTEGRAL FORMS

It is the aim to investigate the finite-dimensional linear representations of complex semisimple $\boldsymbol{G}$ by algebraic methods. For the time being, however, the finite dimensionality of $R \in$ Spa Lin Com in which $\boldsymbol{G}$ is represented is not used unless it is explicitly mentioned.

If dim $R < \infty$, the linear Lie group infinitesimally generated by the representation of $\boldsymbol{G}$ may be used.

To simplify the notation an element of $\boldsymbol{G}$ and the linear mapping of R representing it are often indicated by the same letter.

The notations are as usual, in particular, $\boldsymbol{H}$ for an ordered trunk. $\boldsymbol{G}$ is assumed in ordered second dressing.

41.1. Weights Suppose a linear representation is given.

Definition If there is an $x \in R$, $x \neq 0$ such that

$$\boldsymbol{h}x = \lambda(\boldsymbol{h})\,x \qquad (\lambda \text{ linear on } \boldsymbol{H}),$$

$\lambda \in \boldsymbol{H}^*$ is called a *weight* of the representation and this particular x is said to belong to the weight λ, as a *weight vector*. The linear space of all x belonging to λ, 0 included, is called the *weight space*† of λ in the given representation. Its dimension is called the *multiplicity*† of the weight λ. The order in $\boldsymbol{H}^*_{\text{st}}$ applies to the weights in it.

The notion of weight is defined in the same way if $\boldsymbol{G}$ is not semisimple but the direct sum of a semisimple Lie algebra and an abelian one. The subsequent considerations can be modified rather trivially to cover this case, provided that the abelian part is conducibly represented.

$\boldsymbol{H}$ being abelian, there are weights as soon as dim $R < \infty$. (See 13.6.)

Clearly the weights of the adjoint representation $\curlyvee_c \tilde{c}$ are the rootforms.

41.1.1 If f is a linear representation of $\boldsymbol{G}$ and T is an automorphism of $\boldsymbol{G}$, then

$$g = \curlyvee_a f(T\boldsymbol{a})$$

† The terminology does not agree a priori with the usual one. It does, however, if $\boldsymbol{H}$ is pure, and in such cases the notions will, in the main, be applied.

is a new linear representation of G. Take $H' = T^{-1}H$ as a trunk; if x is a λ-weightvector of f, then x is a μ-weightvector of g, where

$$\mu = \Upsilon_{h' \in H'} \lambda(Th'),$$

since

$$g(h')\,x = f(Th')\,x = \lambda(Th')\,x = \mu(h')\,x.$$

41.1.2 Of course then the trunk may have been changed. It is important to know how, for a given linear representation (say identity), the system of weights depends on the choice of the trunk. It is shown that this dependence is not essential.

Suppose that $\dim R < \infty$. Any other trunk H' has the form $\tilde{c}H$, where c is in G, infinitesimally generated by fG. Now for $h' = \tilde{c}h \in H'$ and a λ-weightvector x

$$h'\,cx = chc^{-1}\,cx = chx = \lambda(h)\,cx = \lambda(\tilde{c}^{-1}\,h')\,cx,$$

which transfers the weight system (multiplicities included) from H to H' by means of the linear mapping

$$\Upsilon_{\xi}\,\Upsilon_{h' \in H'}\,\xi(\tilde{c}^{-1}\,h').$$

41.1.3 In analogy with 22.1.4 the use of G can be avoided.

Continue to assume that $\dim R < \infty$. With a continuous change of H weights are changing continuously; therefore some weak structure of the weight system will be unchanged. This weak structure includes multiplicities as well as the ladders introduced in the next sections. Again the weak structure suffices to fix the strong one.

The foregoing may be restated as follows.

41.1.4. Proposition For finite-dimensional representations the weight system does not depend essentially on the choice of the trunk.

41.2. Ladders If x belongs to the weight λ, then

$$he_{\alpha}\,x = [h, e_{\alpha}]\,x + e_{\alpha}\,hx = \alpha(h)\,e_{\alpha}\,x + \lambda(h)\,e_{\alpha}\,x,$$

which proves:

If x belongs to the weight λ then $e_{\alpha}x = 0$ or $e_{\alpha}x$ belongs to the weight $\lambda + \alpha$.

Definition A sequence $x_0, x_1, \ldots \in R$ of weight vectors is called an *α-ladder* if

$e_{-\alpha}x_0 = 0$,

$e_{\alpha}x_j$ is a scalar multiple of x_{j+1},

it stops at x_p iff $e_{\alpha}x_p = 0$.

If such a p exists, it is called the *ladder length*.

The weights to which the $x_0, x_1, \ldots$ belong are also said to form an α-*ladder*.

Proposition α-ladders of weights have an interval α.

41.3. Ladder Length Let x_0 belong to the weight λ, assume that

$$e_{-\alpha} x_0 = 0,$$

and define

$$x_j = e_\alpha{}^j x_0.$$

Then x_j belongs to the weight $\lambda + j\alpha$ or $x_j = 0$.

Inductively one finds scalars ρ_j with

41.3.1 $$e_{-\alpha} x_{j+1} = \rho_j x_j.$$

Putting $\rho_{-1} = 0$ and taking 41.3.1 for granted, one raises the subscript j by

$$\begin{aligned} e_{-\alpha} x_{j+2} &= e_{-\alpha} e_\alpha x_{j+1} \\ &= [e_{-\alpha}, e_\alpha] x_{j+1} + e_\alpha e_{-\alpha} x_{j+1} \\ &= -h_\alpha x_{j+1} + \rho_j e_\alpha x_j \\ &= -(\lambda + (j+1)\alpha)(h_\alpha) x_{j+1} + \rho_j x_{j+1}, \end{aligned}$$

which creates the recursive relation

$$\rho_{j+1} = \rho_j - (\lambda + (j+1)\alpha)(h_\alpha).$$

Adding up these equations $(j = -1, 0, \ldots, i-1)$, one finds

41.3.2 $$\begin{aligned} \rho_i &= -\sum_0^i (\lambda + j\alpha)(h_\alpha) \\ &= -(i+1)(\lambda + \tfrac{1}{2} i\alpha)(h_\alpha) \\ &= -(i+1)((\lambda, \alpha) + \tfrac{1}{2} i(\alpha, \alpha)), \end{aligned}$$

because of second dressing (see 21.1.8).

If the α-ladder $x_0, x_1, \ldots$ is finite, say of length p, then $\rho_p = 0$; thus,

41.3.3 $$p = -2\frac{(\lambda, \alpha)}{(\alpha, \alpha)}.$$

In this case,

41.3.4 $$\rho_j = \tfrac{1}{2}(j+1)(p-j)(\alpha, \alpha).$$

As in 21.1.8, one can state the following.

41.3.5. Proposition A finite α-ladder of weights starting at λ has length $-2((\lambda, \alpha)/(\alpha, \alpha))$. It is turned upside down into a $(-\alpha)$-ladder by S_α (see 20.10, 21.1.8). All finite α-ladders differing by real multiples of α have the same midpoint.

In particular, if λ is a weight, $\alpha \in W^+$, and j, k are maximal and minimal integers such that $\lambda + j\alpha$, $\lambda + k\alpha$ are weights, then $S_\alpha(\lambda + j\alpha) = \lambda + k\alpha$, and all $\lambda + p\alpha$ with $k \leqslant p \leqslant j$ are weights.

41.4–5. Integral Elements

41.4 The foregoing leads to a definition.

Definition $\xi \in \boldsymbol{H}^*$ is called *integral*, or $\xi \in \boldsymbol{H}^*_{\text{ing}}$,

$$\text{if } -2\frac{(\xi, \alpha)}{(\alpha, \alpha)} \text{ is an integer for every } \alpha \in W^*.$$

Obviously $W \subset \boldsymbol{H}^*_{\text{ing}} \subset \boldsymbol{H}^*_{\text{st}}$.

The following has been proved.

Proposition Weights in finite α-ladders ($\alpha \in W^*$) are integral elements of $\boldsymbol{H}^*_{\text{st}}$.

41.5. Proposition $\xi \in \boldsymbol{H}^*_{\text{ing}}$ iff $-2((\xi, \rho)/(\rho, \rho))$ are integers for all $\rho \in W^{++}$.

Proof "Only if" is obvious. The condition can be restated in this form: $S_\rho \xi - \xi$ is an integral multiple of $\rho \in W^{++}$. If it is fulfilled, then clearly $S\xi - \xi$ is a linear combination from W^{++} with integral coefficients for any $S \in \operatorname{Int} W^*$. In particular,

$$S_\alpha \xi - \xi = -2\frac{(\xi, \alpha)}{(\alpha, \alpha)}\alpha$$

is so for $\alpha = \sum p_j \rho_j \in W^+$. Thus all $-2((\xi, \alpha)/(\alpha, \alpha))p_j$ are integers, whereas by 25.4.1 the p_j have no common divisor. Therefore $-2((\xi, \alpha)/(\alpha, \alpha))$ is integral for every $\alpha \in W^+$, which is the assertion of the proposition.

41.6–7. The Weyl Tool

41.6. Proposition S_ρ ($\rho \in W^{++}$) interchanges $\pm\rho$ and is a permutation on $W^+ \setminus \{\rho\}$.

Proof If $\alpha \in W^+ \setminus \{\rho\}$, then on the basis W^{++} α has a positive coefficient for some $\sigma \in W^{++}$ with $\sigma \neq \rho$. So has

$$S_\rho \alpha = \alpha - 2\frac{(\rho, \alpha)}{(\rho, \rho)}\rho.$$

Hence all its nonzero coefficients are positive and $S_\rho \alpha \in W^+$.

41.7. Definition $\delta = \frac{1}{2}\sum_{\alpha \in W^+} \alpha$ is called the *Weyl tool.*

Proposition $2((\delta, \rho)/(\rho, \rho)) = 1$ for all $\rho \in W^{++}$; hence δ is dominant and $\delta \in \boldsymbol{H}^*_{\text{ing}}$.

Proof By applying Proposition 41.6 one gets

$$S_\rho 2\delta = 2\delta - 2\rho \qquad \text{for} \quad \rho \in W^{++},$$

thus,

$$2\frac{(\delta, \rho)}{(\rho, \rho)} = 1 \qquad \text{for} \quad \rho \in W^{++}.$$

42. SOURCE, TOP WEIGHT, AND LIMITATION OF A REPRESENTATION

The notations are as before.

42.1. Source

Definition If every $\boldsymbol{G}$-invariant subspace of R containing $x \in R$ coincides with R, x is called a *source* of the representation of $\boldsymbol{G}$.

If x is a source and $\boldsymbol{a}_1, \ldots, \boldsymbol{a}_r$ form a basis of $\boldsymbol{G}$, then R is linearly spanned by the

$$\boldsymbol{a}_{i_1}\boldsymbol{a}_{i_2}\cdots\boldsymbol{a}_{i_m}x.$$

Actually the

$$\boldsymbol{a}_1^{j_1}\boldsymbol{a}_2^{j_2}\cdots\boldsymbol{a}_r^{j_r}x$$

suffice, for every "wrong pair" $\boldsymbol{a}_d\boldsymbol{a}_c$ $(c < d)$ can be replaced by $\boldsymbol{a}_c\boldsymbol{a}_d + [\boldsymbol{a}_d, \boldsymbol{a}_c]$, where the second summand gives rise to shorter products. On a basis of $\boldsymbol{G}$ using second-dressing branches, the

42.1.1 $$\boldsymbol{e}_{-\alpha 1}^{i_1}\cdots\boldsymbol{e}_{-\alpha m}^{i_m}\boldsymbol{e}_{\alpha 1}^{j_1}\cdots\boldsymbol{e}_{\alpha m}^{j_m}\boldsymbol{h}_1^{k_1}\cdots\boldsymbol{h}_l^{k_l}x$$

span R, where $\alpha_1, \ldots, \alpha_m$ are the positive rootforms arranged in some linear order, preferably compatible with the partial order in $\boldsymbol{H}^*_{\text{st}}$.

If, moreover, x belongs to a weight λ, then in 42.1.1 the factors $\boldsymbol{h}$ may be canceled because of $\boldsymbol{h}_i x = \lambda(\boldsymbol{h}_i)x$. Then the element in 42.1.1 (if $\neq 0$) belongs to the weight

$$\lambda + \sum_q (j_q - i_q)\,\alpha_q,$$

and there are no other weights.

This shows:

Proposition If there is a source of weight λ, then, for every weight μ, the difference $\mu - \lambda$ is an integral linear combination from W^*. If there is a source of integral weight, all weights are integral.

42.2–3. Source of Top Weight

42.2. Definition Given a representation, a weight exceeding the others, if it exists, is called the *top weight.*

Suppose a maximal weight λ and a source x belonging to λ as its weight vector. Then $\boldsymbol{e}_\alpha x$ ($\alpha \in W^+$) vanishes, since otherwise it would belong to the weight $\lambda + \alpha > \lambda$. Then all terms 42.1.1 with some $j_\nu > 0$ can be left out of consideration. Therefore λ is even the top weight; R is already spanned by the

42.2.1 $$\boldsymbol{e}_{-\rho_1} \cdots \boldsymbol{e}_{-\rho_m} x,$$

where $\rho_1, \ldots, \rho_m$ stem from W^{++} in an arbitrary succession in which repetitions are allowed. This follows from the fact that every $\boldsymbol{e}_{-\alpha}$ ($\alpha \in W^+$) can be obtained from the $\boldsymbol{e}_{-\rho}$ ($\rho \in W^{++}$) as a scalar multiple of compound commutators.

The weight of 42.2.1 (if $\neq 0$) is $\lambda - \sum \rho_q$.

It follows:

42.2.2. Proposition Suppose there is a maximal weight λ and a source belonging to λ. Then

(1) λ has the multiplicity 1.
(2) Every weight μ has a finite multiplicity.
(3) λ is the top weight.

42.2.3 From 41.1.1 it is known what happens to weights under an automorphism T of $\boldsymbol{G}$. If T leaves $\boldsymbol{H}$ and W^{++} invariant, it preserves the partial order on $\boldsymbol{H}_{\mathrm{st}}^*$ and thus maps the top weight into the top weight. Hence:

Proposition If λ is the top weight of the linear representation f of $\boldsymbol{G}$ and T is an automorphism of $\boldsymbol{G}$ leaving $\boldsymbol{H}$ and W^{++} invariant, then

$$T^{-1}\lambda = \curlyvee_{h \in \boldsymbol{H}} \lambda(Th)$$

is the top weight of

$$\Upsilon_{a\in G} f(Ta).$$

42.3. Definition The representation with a top weight source vector x is *limited* if for every $\rho \in W^{++}$ almost all $e_{-\rho}^{j} x$ vanish.

Note that in case of limitation the $(-\rho)$-ladder ($\rho \in W^{++}$) starting at x has length p computed by 41.3.3.

Proposition If the representation is limited, then for any $y \in R$ almost all $e_{-\rho}^{j}\, y$ ($\rho \in W^{++}$) vanish. For every $\rho \in W^{++}$ every weight belongs to a ρ-ladder.

Proof One may suppose

$$y = e_{-\rho_1} \cdots e_{-\rho_m} x$$

($\rho_1, \ldots, \rho_m \in W^{++}$ as in 42.2.1) and then proceed by induction along m. The induction step is justified by the following statement:

$$\text{If} \quad e_{-\rho}^{n}\, y = 0, \qquad \text{then} \qquad e_{-\rho}^{n+3}\, e_{-\sigma}\, y = 0 \qquad \text{for} \quad \rho, \sigma \in W^{++}.$$

This statement is true, since

$$e_{-\rho}^{n+3}\, e_{-\sigma}\, y = e_{-\rho}^{n+2}\, e_{-\sigma} e_{-\rho}\, y + \kappa e_{-\rho}^{n+2}\, e_{-\rho-\sigma}\, y = \cdots$$
$$= e_{-\sigma}\, e_{-\rho}^{n+3}\, y + \kappa'\, e_{-\rho-\sigma}\, e_{-\rho}^{n+2}\, y + \kappa''\, e_{-2\rho-\sigma}\, e_{-\rho}^{n+1}\, y + \kappa'''\, e_{-3\rho-\sigma}\, e_{-\rho}^{n}\, y = 0$$

with scalars $\kappa, \ldots, \kappa', \kappa'', \kappa'''$; remember that $-\sigma - 4\rho$ cannot be a rootform.

It follows that for every weight μ and every $\rho \in W^{++}$ there is an integer $j \geqslant 0$ such that $\mu - j\rho$ starts a ρ-ladder. Let k be the maximal integer such that $\mu + k\rho$ is a weight. Then $S_\rho(\mu - j\rho) \leqslant \mu + k\rho$, hence $S_\rho(\mu + k\rho) \leqslant \mu - j\rho \leqslant \mu \leqslant \mu + k\rho$ which shows that μ belongs to the ρ-ladder starting at $S_\rho(\mu + k\rho)$.

42.4. An Inequality Under the assumptions of Propositions 42.2.2 and 42.3 any ρ-ladder of weights ($\rho \in W^{++}$) is bounded from above according to 42.2.2 and from below by 42.3. Therefore it is finite.

A still more efficient bound is exhibited in the following proposition.

Proposition Let the representation be limited with top weight λ and a source belonging to λ. Then

$$(\mu + \delta, \mu + \delta) < (\lambda + \delta, \lambda + \delta)$$

for each other weight μ (see 41.7).

Proof For some $\rho \in W^{++}$ let $\nu = \mu + j\rho$ be the weight with maximal integral j if the weight μ is given; 41.3.5 applied to ν instead of λ and $-\rho$ instead of α shows

$$j \leqslant 2\frac{(\nu, \rho)}{(\rho, \rho)}.$$

Using 41.7, one gets

$$\begin{aligned}(\nu+\delta,\nu+\delta)-(\mu+\delta,\mu+\delta) &= (\nu+\delta,\nu+\delta)-(\nu+\delta-j\rho,\nu+\delta-j\rho)\\ &= -j^2(\rho,\rho)+2j(\rho,\nu)+2j(\rho,\delta)\\ &\geqslant(-j^2+j^2+j)(\rho,\rho)=j(\rho,\rho).\end{aligned}$$

As long as $\mu\neq\lambda$, there is some $\rho\in W^{++}$ such that $j>0$; but then $j(\rho,\rho)>0$ and

$$(\nu+\delta,\nu+\delta)>(\mu+\delta,\mu+\delta)$$

for some higher weight ν. This inductive argument does not stop until $\mu=\lambda$. This proves the assertion.

42.5. Finite Dimensionality and Irreducibility If the representation is irreducible, every $x\in R$, $x\neq 0$ is a source. If, moreover, it is finite-dimensional, the number of weights is finite, one is top weight, and the representation is limited. The converse is also true:

Theorem Let the representation of $G\in$ Alg Lie Com SS in $R\in$ Spa Lin Com be limited with a top weight and a source belonging to it. It is then finite-dimensional and irreducible.

Proof The weights as points of a lattice can nowhere accumulate. By the inequality 42.4 they are bounded. Thus their number is finite. By 42.2.2 their multiplicities are finite. By 42.2.1, R is spanned by weight vectors. Thus $\dim R<\infty$.

Let S be sub R and invariant, $S\neq\{0\}$. One still has to show that $S=R$. Since $\dim S<\infty$, there is a $y\in S$ belonging to a weight μ, which is supposed to be maximal with respect to this property. Since $\boldsymbol{e}_\alpha S\subset S$,

$$\boldsymbol{e}_\alpha y=0 \qquad \text{for all} \quad \alpha\in W^+.$$

The given representation of $\boldsymbol{G}$ extends to the associative envelope, which is mapped into End R. The Casimir tool (40.3) is mapped into

$$z=\sum_{\alpha\in W^*}\boldsymbol{e}_\alpha\boldsymbol{e}_{-\alpha}+\sum_j\boldsymbol{h}^j\boldsymbol{h}_j.$$

Now

$$\begin{aligned}zy &= \sum_{\alpha\in W^+}(\boldsymbol{e}_\alpha\boldsymbol{e}_{-\alpha}+\boldsymbol{e}_{-\alpha}\boldsymbol{e}_\alpha)y+\sum_j\boldsymbol{h}^j\boldsymbol{h}_jy\\ &= \sum_{\alpha\in W^+}(2\boldsymbol{e}_{-\alpha}\boldsymbol{e}_\alpha+\boldsymbol{h}_\alpha)y+\sum\mu(\boldsymbol{h}^j)\mu(\boldsymbol{h}_j)y\\ &= \sum_{\alpha\in W^+}(\mu,\alpha)y+(\mu,\mu)y \qquad \text{(see 40.3)}\\ &= (\mu,2\delta)y+(\mu,\mu)y \qquad \text{(see 41.7)}\\ &= ((\mu+\delta,\mu+\delta)-(\delta,\delta))y.\end{aligned}$$

Let x be a source belonging to the top weight λ. Then there is a $\boldsymbol{u}$ in the envelope of $\boldsymbol{G}$ such that

$$y = \boldsymbol{u}x,$$

and by the same argument as above

$$zx = ((\lambda + \delta, \lambda + \delta) - (\delta, \delta))\, x.$$

Because of $\boldsymbol{zu} = \boldsymbol{uz}$ (see 40.2), $zy = \boldsymbol{zu}x = \boldsymbol{uz}x$, it follows

$$(\lambda + \delta, \lambda + \delta) = (\mu + \delta, \mu + \delta),$$

thus by 42.4

$$\mu = \lambda.$$

Because of Proposition 42.2.2(1) y is a scalar multiple of x; thus $S = R$, which proves the assertion.

43. FINITE-DIMENSIONAL IRREDUCIBLE REPRESENTATIONS

The notations are as before.

Results are summarized and a few related ones are added.

43.1. Theorem Let the linear representation in $R \in$ Spa Lin Com (dim $R < \infty$) of $\boldsymbol{G} \in$ Alg Lie Com SS be irreducible with the top weight $\hat{\lambda}$ in ordered second dressing. Then

43.1.1 R is spanned by weight vectors.

43.1.2 The weights belong to $\boldsymbol{H}^*_{\text{ing}}$.

43.1.3 The length of an α-ladder of weights starting at λ is $-2\dfrac{(\lambda, \alpha)}{(\alpha, \alpha)}$.

43.1.4 S_α turns the α-ladders upside down.

43.1.5 Int W^* maps weights into weights.

43.1.6 The top weight is dominant and has multiplicity 1.

43.1.7 Int W^*-equivalent weights have the same multiplicity.

43.1.8 The maximum of $(\lambda + \delta, \lambda + \delta)$ for weights λ is attained by the top weight $\hat{\lambda}$ only.

43.1.9 The image of the Casimir tool under the representation is the scalar multiplier $(\hat{\lambda}+\delta, \hat{\lambda}+\delta)-(\delta,\delta)$, where $\hat{\lambda}$ is the top weight.

43.1.10 The set of weights is characterized by the following statement: it contains the top weight and for any $\rho \in W^{++}$, if it contains μ, also contains all mod ρ congruent elements of $\boldsymbol{H}_{\text{st}}^{*}$ between μ and $S_\rho \mu$.

43.1.11 Within the closure of the dominant chamber the (dominant) weights μ are characterized by the following condition: $\hat{\lambda}-\mu$ is a sum of members of W^{++}; otherwise stated: $\mu \leqslant \hat{\lambda}$ in the minimal partial order.

43.1.12 $e_\alpha e_{-\alpha} x = \frac{1}{2}(j+1)(p-j)(\alpha,\alpha)x$ if x belongs to an α-ladder, in which it occupies the $(j+1)$th place and is followed up by $p-j$ elements.

Proof (1) See 42.2.1; (2) see 41.4; (3) see 41.3.3; (4) see 41.3.5; (5) consequence of 43.1.4; (6) see 42.2.2 and note that by 43.1.5 the Int W^*-equivalents of $\hat{\lambda}$ are weights, thus lower than or equal to $\hat{\lambda}$. (8) See 42.4. (9) By 40.2, the image of the Casimir tool commutes with all $\boldsymbol{G}$; by 36.3, applied to Lie algebras, it is a scalar multiplier; its actual value was computed in 42.5, when it was applied to the top weight vector. (10) Consequence of 41.3.5; (12) see 41.3.4; (7) and (11) are left to be proved.

As to (7), $S \in \text{Int } W^*$ is induced by an inner automorphism of $\boldsymbol{G}$ (see 33.1), say $\tilde{c}$, leaving $\boldsymbol{H}$ invariant. According to 41.1.2, c maps the weight space of λ into that of $\curlyvee_{\boldsymbol{h}} \lambda(\tilde{c}^{-1}\boldsymbol{h}) = S\lambda$. By reversing this argument one concludes that this mapping is onto. Therefore both eigenspaces have the same dimension.

Remark Any $u \in \text{Aut } R$ that normalizes $\boldsymbol{G}$ and $\boldsymbol{H}$ induces

$$\curlyvee_{x\in \boldsymbol{G}} uxu^{-1} \in \text{Aut } \boldsymbol{G}$$

and

$$\curlyvee_{\xi \in \boldsymbol{H}_{\text{st}}^*} \curlyvee_{\boldsymbol{h}\in\boldsymbol{H}} \xi(u\boldsymbol{h}u^{-1}) \in \text{Aut } W^*.$$

It is still true that this kind of automorphism preserves the multiplicity of weights.

As to (11), according to the proposition of 42.1, every weight fulfills the condition.

Suppose that ξ is dominant and that $\xi + \sum p_j \rho_j$ ($\rho_j \in W^{++}$, p_j integer $\geqslant 0$) is a weight. One must ascertain that ξ is also a weight.

It may be supposed that $\sum p_i \rho_i \neq 0$. Since

$$(\sum p_i \rho_i, \sum p_i \rho_i) > 0,$$

there is a j such that

$$p_j > 0, \qquad (\sum p_i \rho_i, \rho_j) > 0.$$

Hence

$$(\xi + \sum p_i \rho_i, \rho_j) = (\xi, \rho_j) + (\sum p_i \rho_i, \rho_j) > 0,$$

since ξ is dominant. Now by 43.1.10,

$$\xi + \sum p_i \rho_i - \rho_j$$

is a weight. Repeating the argument one can descend to ξ, which turns out to be a weight.

This completes the proof of 43.1.

43.2. An Alternative Approach

Theorem Under the conditions of Theorem 43.1 the weight system does not depend essentially on the choice of the trunk. An automorphism T of $\boldsymbol{G}$ which leaves the trunk invariant turns the top weight $\hat{\lambda}$ of f into the top weight of $\Upsilon_{\boldsymbol{a}} f(T^{-1}\boldsymbol{a})$ up to Int W^*-equivalence.

This follows from 41.1.4, 42.2.3, 33.4.3, and 33.5. If the appeal to the group G is to be avoided (see 41.1.3), one must rely on the weak structure of the weight system which has to include information on multiplicities and tell whether the difference between two weights is a rootform (see 41.2). These data determine the ladders and their lengths which, thanks to the ladder-length formula, locate the weights with respect to the rootforms and consequently fix the weight system within a linear space.

In the proof of 43.1.7 another appeal was made to G. This proof can also be modified to rest on the more elementary fact that S extends to an automorphism T of $\boldsymbol{G}$ (rather than to an *inner* automorphism). It is still true that the λ-weight space of the representation $\Upsilon_{\boldsymbol{a}} f(T^{-1}\boldsymbol{a})$ equals the $S\lambda$-weight space of the original f. In particular, by 43.1.5 both have the same set of weights and consequently the same top weight. In Section 44 finite-dimensional irreducible representations with the same top weight turn out to be equivalent by means of an equivalence that maps weight spaces belonging to the same weight onto each other. This being taken for granted, it turns out that the λ-weight space of the original representation is mapped onto that of the representation $\Upsilon_{\boldsymbol{a}} f(T^{-1}\boldsymbol{a})$, which in turn coincides with the $S\lambda$-weight space of the original one. So the λ-weight space and the $S\lambda$-weight space of the original representation have the same dimension, which proves the assertion.

43.3–6. The Value of the Casimir Tool

43.3 If $\boldsymbol{G} \in$ Alg Lie Com SSS, then the adjoint representation ad is irreducible. The weights are the rootforms; the top weight is the top rootform $\hat{\alpha}$.

The image ad z of the Casimir tool under the adjoint mapping ad, according to the notation of 40.1, is

$$\text{ad } z = \sum_i \tilde{a}^i \tilde{a}_i.$$

Because of the definition of the correlate bases, one gets

$$\text{tr ad } z = \dim G,$$

and because ad z is a scalar multiplier in G

$$\text{ad } z = 1.$$

With 43.1.9, this leads to the following.

Proposition The adjoint image of the Casimir tool is the identity. $(\hat{\alpha} + \delta, \hat{\alpha} + \delta) - (\delta, \delta) = 1$ for the top rootform $\hat{\alpha}$ if G is simple.

(If G is not simple, the proposition still holds for every simple component of G.)

43.4 $G \in$ Alg Lie Lin Com SS, $G \subset$ End R, $R \in$ Spa Lin Com, dim $R < \infty$.

tr(ab) as a (symmetric) function of $a, b \in G$ is an infinitesimal invariant of the adjoint Lie algebra $\tilde{G}$, since

$$\text{tr } ((\tilde{c}a)\, b + a(\tilde{c}b)) = \text{tr } (cab - acb + acb - abc) = 0.$$

If, moreover, G is simple, thus $\tilde{G}$ irreducible, it has to be a constant multiple of the Killing form:

43.4.1 $$\text{tr } (ab) = \kappa \text{ tr } (\tilde{a}\tilde{b}).$$

For later use it is important to know:

43.4.2. Proposition If G is simple, $\kappa > 0$. (Proof in 43.6.)

43.5 Let linear simple semisimple G be acting in R and let z_0 and $z_\sim$ be its Casimir tool considered as acting on R and G, respectively, in agreement with the extension of G to its associative envelope $\mathscr{E}(G)$. It then follows from 43.4.1 that

43.5.1 $$\text{tr } z_0 = \kappa \text{ tr } z_\sim.$$

Let $\hat{\lambda}$ be the top weight of irreducible simple semisimple G, and $\hat{\alpha}$ the top weight of the adjoint representation, that is, the top rootform. Then by 43.1.9

43.5.2 $$\text{tr } z_0 = \dim R \cdot ((\hat{\lambda} + \delta, \hat{\lambda} + \delta) - (\delta, \delta)),$$

43.5.3 $\operatorname{tr} z_{\sim} = \dim \boldsymbol{G} \cdot ((\hat{\alpha} + \delta, \hat{\alpha} + \delta) - (\delta, \delta)) = \dim \boldsymbol{G}$

because of 43.3.

From 43.5.2–3 and 43.5.1 the following obtains.

43.6. Proposition $\kappa = ((\dim R)/(\dim \boldsymbol{G}))((\hat{\lambda} + \delta, \hat{\lambda} + \delta) - (\delta, \delta))$ if simple semisimple $\boldsymbol{G}$ is irreducibly represented in R ($\dim R > 1$) with top weight $\hat{\lambda}$.

Since $(\hat{\lambda}, \delta) > 0$ and $(\hat{\lambda}, \hat{\lambda}) > 0$, $(\hat{\lambda} + \delta, \hat{\lambda} + \delta) - (\delta, \delta) > 0$. If this is applied to the irreducible components of the identical representation, one gets Proposition 43.4.2.

44. THE CONSTRUCTION OF ALL FINITE-DIMENSIONAL REPRESENTATIONS

The notations are as before.

44.1 Thanks to the conducibility theorem, to know all representations of $\boldsymbol{G} \in$ Alg Lie Lin Com SS in $R \in$ Spa Lin Com ($\dim R < \infty$), one can restrict oneself to the irreducible ones. These are exhausted by the following theorem.

Theorem Up to equivalence a finite-dimensional irreducible linear representation of semisimple $\boldsymbol{G}$ in ordered second dressing is characterized by its top weight. Possible top weights are just the dominant integral elements of $\boldsymbol{H}^*_{\mathrm{st}}$.

Remark This stresses again that different integral elements of the dominant chamber cannot be Int W^*-equivalent. The same was shown, however, in 33.8.1 without assuming integrality.

The first part of the theorem is proved in 44.6, the second in 44.2–5.

44.2 The second part is proved by an explicit construction of a finite-dimensional irreducible representation from a dominant $\lambda \in \boldsymbol{H}^*_{\mathrm{ing}}$ which has to play the role of top weight.

The vector x belonging to λ must be annihilated by

$$\text{all } \boldsymbol{e}_\alpha \ (\alpha \in W^+), \text{ all } \boldsymbol{h} - \lambda(\boldsymbol{h}) \ (\boldsymbol{h} \in \boldsymbol{H}), \text{ and all } \boldsymbol{e}_{-\rho}^{p_{-\rho}+1} \left(\rho \in W^{++}, p_{-\rho} = 2\frac{(\lambda, \rho)}{(\rho, \rho)}\right).$$

This suggests a construction of R as a linear image of the associative envelope $\mathscr{E}(\boldsymbol{G})$ of $\boldsymbol{G}$; the role of the 0 in R then has to be played by the left ideal $\boldsymbol{M}$ of $\mathscr{E}(\boldsymbol{G})$ generated by the elements mentioned above.

The construction proceeds in two steps. First one uses the left ideal $\boldsymbol{M}'$ of $\mathscr{E}(\boldsymbol{G})$ generated by

$$\boldsymbol{e}_\alpha \quad (\alpha \in W^+), \qquad \boldsymbol{h} - \lambda(\boldsymbol{h}) \quad (\boldsymbol{h} \in \boldsymbol{H}),$$

and defines

$$f' = \curlyvee_{a \in G} \curlyvee_{u+M',\, u \in \mathscr{E}(G)} (au + M').$$

Then for every $a \in G$, $f'(a)$ is a linear mapping of

$$R' = \mathscr{E}(G) \bmod M'$$

into itself and f' is a linear representation of G in R'.
The following conclusions seem to be obvious:

44.2.1 $x' = 1 + M'$ is a source of f',

44.2.2 x' belongs to the weight λ since all $h - \lambda(h) \in M'$,

44.2.3 λ is the top weight because x' is annihilated by all e_α $(\alpha \in W^+)$.

The conclusion that λ is a weight, however, may be drawn only if $x' \neq 0$. This rests on proving that $-1 \notin M'$, which is done in 44.3.

44.3 Assume

44.3.1
$$-1 = \sum_{\alpha \in W+} u_\alpha e_\alpha + \sum_j v_j(h_j - \lambda(h_j)),$$

where the h_j are running through a basis of H and the u_α, v_j are taken from $\mathscr{E}(G)$. This assumption has to be refuted.

The actual construction of $\mathscr{E}(G)$ in Section 39 has to be taken under consideration. One may assume that the ordered basis X of G consisted of all

$$e_{-\alpha}\ (\alpha \in W^+),\ \text{all } e_\alpha\ (\alpha \in W^+),\ \text{and all } h_j$$

in this arrangement. All terms in 44.3.1 are now assumed as belonging to $\mathscr{A}(X)$, and 44.3.1 itself is considered as a congruence mod $\mathscr{J}(C)$. Furthermore, u_α, v_j are assumed to be orderly.

Thanks to Theorem 39.3, the decision whether 44.3.1 is possible is easy when the right-hand member of 44.3.1 is orderly. In the present form, however it is not. It has still to be refashioned mod $\mathscr{J}(C)$. This can be done as follows:

u_α is a sum of orderly monomials u'. In every $u' e_\alpha$ the e_α is moved mod $\mathscr{J}(C)$ step by step to the left, first through a few h_i, then through a few e_β $(\beta \in W^+)$. The by-product of any step is a shorter monomial with at least one branch belonging to a positive rootform as a factor. Fortunately, e_α need not change places with any $e_{-\beta}$. In $v_j(h_j - \lambda(h_j))$ only slight rearrangements are required. Finally, the right-hand member of 44.3.1 will have been made orderly. With the original right-hand member it still shares the property that it will become 0 on substitution of 0 for all e_α $(\alpha \in W^+)$ and $\lambda(h_j)$ for all h_j. By the uniqueness of the orderly element in each left coset mod $\mathscr{J}(\boldsymbol{C})$ the new right-hand member has to be -1. This is a contradiction.

44.4 Though f' fulfills 44.2.1–3, it need not be irreducible; R' has still to be reduced mod an $\mathscr{E}(\boldsymbol{G})$-invariant subspace T. Abbreviating the notation by writing

$$\boldsymbol{a}' \text{ instead of } f'(\boldsymbol{a}) \text{ for any } \boldsymbol{a} \in \mathscr{E}(\boldsymbol{G}),$$

one defines T as the smallest $\mathscr{E}(\boldsymbol{G})$-invariant subspace of R' containing all

44.4.1 $$\boldsymbol{e}'^{p_{-\rho}+1}_{-\rho} x' \qquad \left(\rho \in W^{++}, p_{-\rho} = 2\frac{(\lambda, \rho)}{(\rho, \rho)}\right).$$

The representation f induced in $R = R'$ mod T is limited. Thanks to 44.2.1–3, it fulfills the supposition of Theorem 42.5. Therefore it is finite-dimensional and irreducible. Again, to be sure that it still has a vector of weight λ, one must show that $x' \notin T$.

T is spanned by the weight vectors

44.4.2 $$\boldsymbol{u}' \boldsymbol{e}'^{p_{-\rho}+1}_{-\rho} x',$$

where

$$\boldsymbol{u}' = \boldsymbol{e}'_{-\rho_1} \cdots \boldsymbol{e}'_{-\rho_a} \boldsymbol{e}'_{\sigma_1} \cdots \boldsymbol{e}'_{\sigma_b} \boldsymbol{h}'^{k_1}_1 \cdots \boldsymbol{h}'^{k_l}_l$$

may be assumed such that $\rho_1, \ldots, \rho_a, \sigma_1, \ldots, \sigma_b$ stem from W^{++} in an arbitrary succession with possible repetitions. Here the $\boldsymbol{h}'$ can be dismissed because they are acting like scalars. x' can belong to T only if there are vectors 44.4.2 of the same weight as x'. This can happen only if $b \geqslant 1$. It will be shown, however, that

44.4.3 $$\boldsymbol{e}'_\sigma \boldsymbol{e}'^{p_{-\rho}+1}_{-\rho} x' = 0,$$

which then makes $x' \in T$ impossible.

To ascertain 44.4.3, $\boldsymbol{e}'_\sigma$ is moved to the right. If $\sigma \neq \rho$, then $\sigma - \rho \notin W$, $[\boldsymbol{e}'_\sigma, \boldsymbol{e}'_{-\rho}] = \boldsymbol{0}$; therefore $\boldsymbol{e}'_\sigma$ passes readily through the $\boldsymbol{e}'_{-\rho}$ and finally annihilates x' which is a top weight vector. If $\sigma = \rho$, then

$$\boldsymbol{e}'_\rho \boldsymbol{e}'^{p_{-\rho}+1}_{-\rho} x' = 0$$

because of 41.3.1 and the choice of $p_{-\rho}$. (Note that this formula must be applied with $p_{-\rho}$ instead of i, and ρ instead of α, and that it does not depend on an assumption of finiteness of ladders.)

This completes the proof of the second part of Theorem 44.1.

44.5 Reconsidering the construction of the representation, one may state the following.

Proposition G is irreducibly represented by

$$\curlyvee_{a \in G} \curlyvee_{u+M, u \in \mathscr{E}(G)} (au + M),$$

with the top weight λ in the linear space $\mathscr{E}(G)$ mod M, where M is the left ideal generated by the

$$e_\alpha \quad (\alpha \in W^+), \qquad h - \lambda(h) \quad (h \in H), \qquad e_{-\rho}^{p_{-\rho}+1} \quad \left(\rho \in W^{++}, p_{-\rho} = 2\frac{(\lambda, \rho)}{(\rho, \rho)}\right).$$

44.6 To prove the first part of Theorem 44.1, one has to consider another irreducible representation f^* of G in a space R^* (dim $R^* < \infty$), with the same top weight λ and the λ-weight vector x^*. f^* extends to a homomorphism of $\mathscr{E}(G)$ into End R^*. It must be brought into equivalence with f represented in R with the λ-weight vector x.

$$f^*(e_\alpha)\, x^* = f^*(h - \lambda(h))\, x^* = 0 \qquad \text{for} \quad \alpha \in W^+, \quad h \in H$$

because x^* belongs to the top weight λ. Thus $f^*(M')x^* = \{0\}$, which implies that $f^*(M)x^*$ is spanned by

$$f^*(u_\rho)\, f^*(e_{-\rho}^{p_{-\rho}+1})\, x^* \qquad (\rho \in W^{++}),$$

which all vanish because f^* is finite-dimensional and the length of the $(-\rho)$-ladder starting at λ is just $p_{-\rho}$. Therefore,

$$f^*(M)x^* = \{0\}.$$

Now

$$\varphi(u + M) = f^*(u)\, x^*$$

defines a linear mapping φ of R into R^*.

$$\begin{aligned} \varphi f(a)(u + M) = \varphi(au + M) &= (f^*(au))\, x^* = f^*(a)\, f^*(u)\, x^* \\ &= f^*(a)\, \varphi(u + M); \end{aligned}$$

hence

$$\varphi f(a) = f^*(a)\, \varphi,$$

which shows f and f^* to be enchained by means of φ and therefore equivalent according to 36.2.

Finally, it is evident that equivalent representations actually have the same top weight on any ordered trunk.

This completes the proof of Theorem 44.1.

44.7. Proposition The set of all weights of all finite-dimensional linear representations of G is H^*_{ing}.

Indeed, these weights belong to H^*_{ing}; on the other hand, every element of H^*_{ing} is Int W^*-equivalent to a dominant one, which by 44.1 is a weight of a finite-dimensional linear representation. By 43.1.5 the same is true of the given element of $\boldsymbol{H}^*_{\text{ing}}$.

45. THE FUNDAMENTAL WEIGHTS

The notations are as before.

45.1. Definition The $\pi_j \in \boldsymbol{H}^*_{\text{st}}$ defined by

$$2\frac{(\pi_i, \rho_j)}{(\rho_j, \rho_j)} = \begin{cases} 1 & \text{for} \quad i = j, \\ 0 & \text{for} \quad i \neq j, \end{cases}$$

where $\rho_1, \ldots, \rho_l$ form the natural basis W^{++} of $\boldsymbol{H}^*_{\text{st}}$, are called the *fundamental weights*. The irreducible representations with these as top weights are also called *fundamental*. They are denoted correspondingly by f_j or simply by π_j.

The π_j are dominant and integral and therefore really are possible top weights.

Clearly, every possible top weight λ is in a unique way a sum of fundamental weights, namely,

45.1.1
$$\lambda = \sum 2\frac{(\lambda, \rho_j)}{(\rho_j, \rho_j)}\pi_j.$$

Note that $\sum \pi_j = \delta$.

45.2 Linear representations f, g of a group G in $R, S \in$ Spa Lin produce a new one, $f \otimes g$ in $R \otimes S$, by *Kronecker* (or *tensor*) *multiplication.* On bases $x_1, x_2, \ldots$ of $R, y_1, y_2, \ldots$ of S, $x_i \otimes y_j, i, j = 1, 2, \ldots$ of $R \otimes S$, one defines

$$((f \otimes g)(a))(x_i \otimes y_j) = (f(a)x_i) \otimes (g(a)y_j) \qquad \text{for} \quad a \in G.$$

For Lie algebras $\boldsymbol{G}$ this implies the following

Definition $((f \otimes g)(\boldsymbol{a}))(x_i \otimes y_j) = (f(\boldsymbol{a})x_i) \otimes y_j + x_i \otimes (g(\boldsymbol{a})y_j)$.

Kronecker or tensor products with more factors are analogously defined.

$f \otimes g$ is readily seen to be a linear representation of $\boldsymbol{G}$ in $R \otimes S$ if f, g are so in R, S.

45.3 For finite-dimensional f and g, if x_i, y_j belong to the weights λ_i, μ_j, then $x_i \otimes y_j$ belongs to $\lambda_i + \mu_j$, which consequently is a weight of $f \otimes g$. Note, however, that the irreducibility of f and g does not imply that of $f \otimes g$. Because of the conducibility, an element belonging to a top weight of $f \otimes g$ is still the source of an irreducible linear representation with this top weight. Therefore, if λ is a possible top weight, its presentation as a sum $\sum p_i \pi_i$ of fundamental weights shows that an irreducible representation with top weight λ can be recovered in a Kronecker product of p_i factors π_i $(i = 1, \ldots, l)$.

Theorem The finite-dimensional irreducible linear representations of $\boldsymbol{G} \in$ Alg Lie Com SS can be obtained from the fundamental ones by Kronecker multiplication (45.2) and isolating the linear subspace a source of which is a vector belonging to the top weight.

45.4 The weights, top weights, and fundamental weights of a direct sum $\boldsymbol{G} = \boldsymbol{G}_1 + \boldsymbol{G}_2$ split according to the splitting of the trunk $\boldsymbol{H} = \boldsymbol{H}_1 + \boldsymbol{H}_2$ into components that are weights, top weights, and fundamental weights of the components. Therefore their knowledge is reduced to that for simple semisimple Lie algebras.

45.5 A linear representation of a group G in a finite-dimensional linear space R admits a dual one in the dual space R^* of R:

$$f^* = \curlyvee_{a \in G} \curlyvee_{u \in R^*} \curlyvee_{x \in R}\, uf(a^{-1})\, x.$$

This leads to the following definition.

Definition The *dual* of a linear representation f of $\boldsymbol{G} \in$ Alg Lie in R is

$$f^* = \curlyvee_{\boldsymbol{a} \in \boldsymbol{G}} \curlyvee_{u \in R^*} \curlyvee_{x \in R} \left(-uf(\boldsymbol{a})\, x\right).$$

Proposition Dual representations of semisimple Lie algebras have opposite weight systems.

This is easily shown with the use of a basis of weight vectors.

In the particular case $\boldsymbol{G} \in \mathbf{A}_l$, up to equivalence effectuated by a basis choice,

$$f^* = f\eta,$$

where η is the outer automorphism of 24.6, $\eta = \curlyvee_{\boldsymbol{a}}(-\boldsymbol{a}')$.

45.6. Integral Forms, Dominant Elements, and Fundamental Weights and Representations for $\boldsymbol{G} \in \mathbf{A}_l, \mathbf{B}_l, \mathbf{C}_l, \mathbf{D}_l$, in the terminology and with the natural bases found in Section 16 (see also 25.7 and Table C).

$\mathbf{A}_l$: the ω_j are linear functions on $\boldsymbol{H}$ subject to $\sum \omega_i(\boldsymbol{h}) = 0$.
For $\xi \in \boldsymbol{H}^*$ the coefficients p_j in

$$\xi = \sum p_j \omega_j$$

are determined up to a common summand. It is more convenient to suppose that they are "reduced," that is, such that

$$\sum p_j = 0.$$

The inner product of

$$\xi = \sum p_j \omega_j, \qquad \eta = \sum q_j \omega_j$$

is defined by

$$(\xi, \eta) = \sum p_j q_j$$

as soon as one of the factors is presented in reduced form. The rootform denotations $\omega_i - \omega_j$ are that kind. Hence

$$(\omega_i - \omega_{i+1}, \omega_j - \omega_{j+1}) = \begin{cases} 2 & \text{for} \quad i = j \\ -1 & \text{for} \quad |i - j| = 1 \\ 0 & \text{for} \quad |i - j| > 1. \end{cases}$$

Up to a common factor (indicated in Table **C**) this is just what is required in second dressing.

Integral respectively dominant elements $\xi = \sum p_j \omega_j \in \boldsymbol{H}_{\mathrm{st}}^*$ have to make

$$2 \frac{(\sum p_i \omega_i, \omega_j - \omega_{j+1})}{(\omega_j - \omega_{j+1}, \omega_j - \omega_{j+1})}$$

integral respectively $\geqslant 0$ which means that

$$p_i = p_j \bmod 1, \qquad \text{respectively } p_j \geqslant p_{j+1} \quad (j = 1, \ldots, l).$$

The fundamental weights (now in an unreduced presentation) are

$$\begin{aligned} \pi_1 &= \omega_1 \\ \pi_2 &= \omega_1 + \omega_2 \\ &\vdots \\ \pi_l &= \omega_1 + \omega_2 + \cdots + \omega_l. \end{aligned}$$

In its usual representation (see Section 16) by the special linear group of $(l+1)$-space the ith basis vector belongs to ω_i. The top weight is just $\omega_1 = \pi_1$.

To construct the next fundamental representation, one takes two copies of $(l+1)$-space with bases $x_1, \ldots, x_{l+1}$ and $y_1, \ldots, y_{l+1}$, and acted on by $\boldsymbol{G} \in \mathbf{A}_l$. Their Kronecker product splits as a direct sum of two invariant subspaces, the symmetric part with basis elements $x_i \otimes y_j + x_j \otimes y_i$ $(i \leqslant j)$ and the skew part with $x_i \otimes y_j - x_j \otimes y_i$ $(i < j)$. For the symmetric part the weights are the $\omega_i + \omega_j$ $(i \leqslant j)$ with $2\omega_1$ as the top weight; for the skew part they are $\omega_i + \omega_j$ $(i < j)$ with $\omega_1 + \omega_2$ as the top weight. Now it easily follows from 42.2.5 that both are irreducible.

Thus π_2 is the representation induced by $\pi_1(\boldsymbol{G})$ in the linear space $R^{(2)}$ of skew 2-tensors of $(l+1)$-space R. It is closely connected with the manifold of straight lines in projective l-space (Plücker coordinates; see 25.8.4′).

Similarly, π_k can be defined in the space $R^{(k)}$ of skew k-tensors of $(l+1)$-space (connected with the $(k-1)$-planes in projective l-space).

$R^{(k)}$ and $R^{(l+1-k)}$ are in a natural way duals of each other. π_k is easily seen to be equivalent to $-\pi_{l+1-k}$. Therefore by 45.5, up to equivalence, the representations π_k and π_{l+1-k} are duals of each other. In other words, the automorphism $\curlyvee_a(-\boldsymbol{a}')$ interchanges π_k and π_{l+1-k}.

B$_l$: The l functions ω_j on $\boldsymbol{H}$ are given the inner product

$$(\omega_i, \omega_j) = \begin{cases} 1 & \text{for} \quad i=j, \\ 0 & \text{for} \quad i \neq j. \end{cases}$$

The elements of W^{++} in the enumeration of 25.7 are $\omega_l, \omega_1 - \omega_2, \ldots, \omega_{l-1} - \omega_l$, which again verify the conditions of second dressing up to a common factor (to be found in Table C).

Integral $\xi = \sum p_j \omega_j$ has to fulfill: $2p_l, p_j - p_{j+1}$ integral.

Dominance requires: $p_j \geqslant p_{j+1} \geqslant 0$.

Fundamental weights:

$$\begin{aligned} \pi_1 &= \tfrac{1}{2}(\omega_1 + \cdots + \omega_l) \\ \pi_2 &= \omega_1 \\ \pi_3 &= \omega_1 + \omega_2 \\ &\vdots \\ \pi_l &= \omega_1 + \omega_2 + \cdots + \omega_{l-1}. \end{aligned}$$

π_2 belongs to the usual presentation of $\boldsymbol{G}$ (see Section 16) by means of the special orthogonal group of $(2l+1)$-space. The various π_k $(k > 2)$ are constructed, as in the case of **A**$_l$, with an analogous geometric interpretation This point will be elaborated in 70.1–2.

The meaning of π_1 is given in Section 49.

Note that here the symmetric part of the tensor product of π_2 with itself is not irreducible. The invariant quadratic form produces a one-dimensional invariant linear subspace.

C$_l$: Inner product as for **B**$_l$.

$$W^{++}: \quad \omega_1 - \omega_2, \ldots, \omega_{l-1} - \omega_l, 2\omega_l.$$

Integral $\xi = \sum p_j \omega_j$: p_j integral.

Dominance: $p_j \geqslant p_{j+1} \geqslant 0$.

Fundamental weights:

$$\pi_1 = \omega_1$$
$$\pi_2 = \omega_1 + \omega_2$$
$$\vdots$$
$$\pi_l = \omega_1 + \omega_2 + \cdots + \omega_l.$$

Interpretation as for $\mathbf{A}_l$.

Note, however, that here the skew part of the tensor product of π_1 with itself is not irreducible. The invariant skew form produces a one-dimensional invariant linear subspace. In general, the linear space of skew k-tensors need not be irreducible.

$\mathbf{D}_l$: Inner product as for $\mathbf{B}_l$.

W^{++}: $\omega_{l-1} - \omega_l$, $\omega_{l-1} + \omega_{l+1}$, $\omega_1 - \omega_2$, $\omega_2 - \omega_3, \ldots, \omega_{l-2} - \omega_{l-1}$.

Integral $\xi = \sum p_j \omega_j$: $p_j - p_{j+1}, p_{l-1} + p_l$ integral, that is,

$$2p_i = p_i - p_j = 0 \bmod 1.$$

Dominance: $p_1 \geqslant p_2 \geqslant \cdots \geqslant p_{l-1} \geqslant |p_l|$.

Fundamental weights:

$$\pi_1 = \tfrac{1}{2}(\omega_1 + \omega_2 + \cdots + \omega_{l-1} - \omega_l)$$
$$\pi_2 = \tfrac{1}{2}(\omega_1 + \omega_2 + \cdots + \omega_{l-1} + \omega_l)$$
$$\pi_3 = \omega_1$$
$$\pi_4 = \omega_1 + \omega_2$$
$$\vdots$$
$$\pi_l = \omega_1 + \omega_2 + \cdots + \omega_{l-2}.$$

The interpretation of $\pi_3, \ldots, \pi_l$ causes no trouble; π_1, π_2 will be explained in Section 49.

45.7 The fundamental weights on a natural basis for all $G \in$ Alg Lie Com SSS are to be found in Table F.

45.8. Historical Note to Sections 41–45 The theory of irreducible linear representations of complex semisimple Lie algebras with notions like top weight goes back to E. Cartan, *Bull. Soc. Math. France* **41**, 53–96 (1913) = *Œuvres I*, **1**, 355–398, though his proofs for general theorems like those corresponding to 44.1 are not convincing. The present method was derived from Harish-Chandra's *Trans. Amer. Math. Soc.* **70**, 28–96 (1951). His approach has been simplified mainly by the use of the inequality 42.4 which has proved to be of primordial importance (H. Freudenthal, *Proc. Kon. Akad. Wet. Amsterdam* **A57**, 369–376 (1954) = *Indagationes Math.* **16**). It should be noticed however, that Harish-Chandra's method can also be used for an a priori construction of the complex semisimple Lie algebras themselves.

46. THE FUNDAMENTAL GROUP OF UNITARILY RESTRICTED SEMISIMPLE LIE GROUPS

$G \in$ Gru Lie Lin Com SS, in ordered second dressing; up to 46.4 centerfree. The problem dealt with in Section 32 is

46.1–4. Reenvisaged

46.1 In 32.2 the fundamental group Φ of G_{un} (and of G) was described by the set $\boldsymbol{Z} \subset \bar{\boldsymbol{D}} \subset \boldsymbol{H}_{\text{un}}$:

$$\boldsymbol{h} \in \boldsymbol{Z} \leftrightarrow \boldsymbol{h} \in \bar{\boldsymbol{D}} \wedge \alpha(\boldsymbol{h}) = 0 \quad \text{or} \quad 2\pi\mathrm{i} \quad \text{for every} \quad \alpha \in W^+.$$

The straight path from $\boldsymbol{0}$ to $\boldsymbol{h} \in \boldsymbol{Z}$ is mapped by exp into a closed path on $\boldsymbol{G}$, a representative of a member of Φ. The fundamental group operation could be performed as an addition on the elements of $\boldsymbol{Z}$; to stay in $\boldsymbol{Z}$ or rather to bring the sum back into $\boldsymbol{Z}$ one had to use the operations of the kaleidoscope group Int W^* which do not change the homotopy class of a path.

This is an unsatisfactory description, which will now be reshaped.

First, the set $\boldsymbol{Z}$ is extended to the corner lattice (33.14.3):

$$\boldsymbol{h} \in \boldsymbol{Z} \leftrightarrow \alpha(\boldsymbol{h}) = 0 \bmod 2\pi\mathrm{i} \qquad (\alpha \in W^*).$$

Again exp maps the straight paths (cf. 31.4 for terminology) from $\boldsymbol{0}$ to $\boldsymbol{h} \in \boldsymbol{Z}$ into closed paths on G. How to find the homotopy equivalences among them? Some of them are known by the fact that inner automorphisms do not change the homotopy class. This information will be sufficient.

Denote by ϑ the canonical homomorphism

$$\Upsilon_{\boldsymbol{h} \in \boldsymbol{Z}}[\Upsilon_{t,0 \leqslant t \leqslant 1} \exp t\boldsymbol{h}]$$

of the additive group $\boldsymbol{Z}$ onto Φ, and by $\boldsymbol{Y}$ its kernel. Now, as mentioned above, Int W^* exerts no influence on Φ, that is,

$$\vartheta S_\alpha \boldsymbol{h} = \vartheta \boldsymbol{h} \qquad \text{for} \quad \boldsymbol{h} \in \boldsymbol{Z}, \quad \alpha \in W^*.$$

Thus $2\pi\mathrm{i} \cdot 2\alpha(\boldsymbol{h})\boldsymbol{h}_\alpha/(\alpha,\alpha) \in \boldsymbol{Y}$, which for $\alpha \in W^{++}$ and suitable $\boldsymbol{h} \in \boldsymbol{Z}$ implies $2\pi\mathrm{i} \cdot 2\boldsymbol{h}_\alpha/(\alpha,\alpha) \in \boldsymbol{Y}$ for $\alpha \in W^{++}$, hence by Proposition 41.5 for all $\alpha \in W^*$. Therefore, if $S_{\alpha,m}$ is the reflection in the kernel of $\alpha - m \cdot 2\pi\mathrm{i}$ for $\alpha \in W^*$ and m an integer

$$\boldsymbol{h} - S_{\alpha,m}\boldsymbol{h} = (\alpha(\boldsymbol{h}) - m \cdot 2\pi\mathrm{i})\frac{2\boldsymbol{h}_\alpha}{(\alpha, \alpha)}$$

is in $\boldsymbol{Y}$ because it is an integral multiple of $2\boldsymbol{h}_\alpha/(\alpha, \alpha) \cdot 2\pi\mathrm{i}$, since $\alpha(\boldsymbol{h}) = 0 \bmod 2\pi\mathrm{i}$.

By 33.14.6, any $\boldsymbol{h} \in \boldsymbol{Z}$ can be mapped by a composition of these reflections into a corner of $\boldsymbol{D}$. On the set of corners of $\boldsymbol{D}$ ϑ is one-to-one. So, if $\boldsymbol{h} \in \boldsymbol{Y}$, it follows that $\boldsymbol{h}$ is an integral combination of the $2\boldsymbol{h}_\alpha/(\alpha, \alpha)\cdot 2\pi\mathrm{i}$ with $\alpha \in W^*$.

The result is the following.

Theorem For centerfree G_{un} let $\boldsymbol{Z}$ be the additive subgroup of $\boldsymbol{H}_{\mathrm{un}}$ consisting of the $\boldsymbol{h}$ with $\alpha(\boldsymbol{h}) = 0 \bmod 2\pi\mathrm{i}$ for all $\alpha \in W^*$, and let $\boldsymbol{Y}$ be its subgroup generated by the $2\pi\mathrm{i}(2\boldsymbol{h}_\alpha/(\alpha, \alpha))$. Then $\boldsymbol{Z} \bmod \boldsymbol{Y}$ is isomorphic to the fundamental group Φ of G_{un} by the following mapping: let $\boldsymbol{w}$ be a path from $\boldsymbol{0}$ to $\boldsymbol{h} \in \boldsymbol{Z}$; then $\exp \boldsymbol{w}$ represents the element of Φ that corresponds to $\boldsymbol{h} + \boldsymbol{Y}$.

46.2 The result can be reformulated by employing duality for abelian groups.

Definition A *character* mod $2\pi\mathrm{i}$ of a (discrete) additive abelian group A is a homomorphism into the addition group of imaginary numbers mod $2\pi\mathrm{i}$. The characters of A again form an abelian addition group denoted by A^*, the *dual* of A, which, if topologized by pointwise convergence, is compact.

If A is finite, A and A^* are isomorphic.

In the present case the dual of $\boldsymbol{Z} \bmod \boldsymbol{Y}$ is made up in a natural way by the characters mod $2\pi\mathrm{i}$ of $\boldsymbol{Z}$ that vanish on $\boldsymbol{Y}$.

Let $\xi_{\boldsymbol{Z}}$ be a character mod $2\pi\mathrm{i}$ of $\boldsymbol{Z}$. Let $\boldsymbol{Z}_0$ be an integral basis of $\boldsymbol{Z}$. $\xi_{\boldsymbol{Z}}(\boldsymbol{Z}_0)$ is a set of imaginary numbers mod $2\pi\mathrm{i}$. There is a $\xi \in \boldsymbol{H}_{\mathrm{st}}^*$ such that $\xi(\boldsymbol{z}) = \xi_{\boldsymbol{Z}}(\boldsymbol{z}) \bmod 2\pi\mathrm{i}$ in every point of $\boldsymbol{Z}_0$. Then $\xi(\boldsymbol{z}) = \xi_{\boldsymbol{Z}}(\boldsymbol{z}) \bmod 2\pi\mathrm{i}$ for any $\boldsymbol{z} \in \boldsymbol{Z}$. Such a ξ is said to extend $\xi_{\boldsymbol{Z}}$ to $\boldsymbol{H}_{\mathrm{un}}$. This extension is not unique.

Suppose now that $\xi_{\boldsymbol{Z}}$ vanishes on $\boldsymbol{Y}$. For ξ this means

$$2\pi\mathrm{i} \cdot 2\frac{\xi(\boldsymbol{h}_\alpha)}{(\alpha, \alpha)} = 0 \bmod 2\pi\mathrm{i} \qquad \text{for all} \quad \alpha \in W^*.$$

Since $\xi(\boldsymbol{h}_\alpha) = (\xi, \alpha)$, this is equivalent to $\xi \in \boldsymbol{H}_{\mathrm{ing}}^*$.

To relate this to the dual of $\boldsymbol{Z} \bmod \boldsymbol{Y}$ one has to identify the elements ξ of $\boldsymbol{H}_{\mathrm{ing}}^*$ that behave the same way mod $2\pi\mathrm{i}$ on $\boldsymbol{Z}$. ξ behaving as 0 on $\boldsymbol{Z}$ means that $\xi(\boldsymbol{z}) = 0 \bmod 2\pi\mathrm{i}$ whenever $\alpha(\boldsymbol{z}) = 0 \bmod 2\pi\mathrm{i}$ for all $\alpha \in W^*$. In other words, ξ is an integral linear combination from W^*.

This suggests the following.

46.3. Definition Put $\Lambda = \boldsymbol{H}_{\mathrm{ing}}^* =$ the addition group of the set of *all* possible weights of $\boldsymbol{G}$ and, if f is a finite-dimensional linear representation of $\boldsymbol{G}$, call Λ_f the (discrete abelian) subgroup of Λ generated by the weights of f. In particular, $\Lambda_\sim$ is the group generated by W^*.

The result proved now reads as follows.

Theorem The fundamental group Φ of centerfree G_{un} is the dual of $\Lambda \bmod \Lambda_{\sim}$ in the way that for any $\exp \boldsymbol{w} \in \varphi \in \Phi$, where $\boldsymbol{w}$ is a path on $\boldsymbol{H}_{\mathrm{un}}$ starting at $\mathbf{0}$, the character mod $2\pi\mathrm{i}$

$$\Upsilon_{\varphi}(\xi(\boldsymbol{w}(1)) \bmod 2\pi\mathrm{i})$$

of Φ has to be identified with the element $\xi + \Lambda_{\sim}$ of $\Lambda \bmod \Lambda_{\sim}$.

Remark Note that the identical action of Int W^* on Φ is reflected in the identical action of Int W^* on $\Lambda \bmod \Lambda_{\sim}$; the latter property is a direct consequence of the definitions of Λ, $\Lambda_{\sim}$, and Int W^*.

46.4 In computations of fundamental groups (or rather their duals) a convenient basis of Λ consists of the fundamental weights (see Table F).

Notation $\mathsf{Z}_p(\pi)$ means the p-cyclic group with the generator $\pi + \Lambda_{\sim}$.

An easy computation leads to the following list of homotopic relations (indicated by $\backsim$) and descriptions of the

Duals of the Fundamental Groups of Centerfree G_{un} of $G \in$

$\mathbf{A}_l$: $\pi_k \backsim k\pi_1, (l+1)\pi_1 \backsim 0$: $\mathsf{Z}_{l+1}(\pi_1)$.

$\mathbf{B}_l$: $2\pi_1 \backsim \pi_2 \backsim \cdots \backsim \pi_l \backsim 0$: $\mathsf{Z}_2(\pi_1)$.

$\mathbf{C}_l$: $2\pi_1 \backsim 0, \pi_k \backsim k\pi_1$ for $k < l$, $\pi_l \backsim \pi_1$: $\mathsf{Z}_2(\pi_1)$.

$\mathbf{D}_l$: $\pi_k \backsim 0$ for even $k > 2$, $\pi_k \backsim \pi_3$ for odd $k > 1$,
$2\pi_3 \backsim 0$, $2\pi_1 \backsim 2\pi_2$. Furthermore,
$2\pi_1 \backsim \pi_3$, $\pi_1 + \pi_2 \backsim 0$ for odd l: $\mathsf{Z}_4(\pi_1)$,
$2\pi_1 \backsim 2\pi_2 \backsim 0$, $\pi_3 \backsim \pi_1 + \pi_2$ for even l: $\mathsf{Z}_2(\pi_1) + \mathsf{Z}_2(\pi_2)$.

$\mathbf{E}_6$: $\pi_1 \backsim \pi_5, \pi_3 \backsim \pi_4 \backsim 2\pi_1, 3\pi_1 \backsim 0, \pi_2 \backsim \pi_6 \backsim 0$: $\mathsf{Z}_3(\pi_1)$.

$\mathbf{E}_7$: $\pi_2 \backsim \pi_3 \backsim \pi_6, 2\pi_2 \backsim \pi_1 \backsim \pi_4 \backsim \pi_5 \backsim \pi_7 \backsim 0$: $\mathsf{Z}_2(\pi_2)$.

$\mathbf{E}_8$: trivial.

$\mathbf{F}_4$: trivial.

$\mathbf{G}_2$: trivial.

46.5–6. Fundamental Group of a Representation

46.5 The assumption that G is centerfree is now dropped. The infinitesimal algebra $\boldsymbol{G}$ of G can be considered as the image of $\tilde{\boldsymbol{G}}$ under a linear representation f. Then G is the linear Lie group infinitesimally generated by the linear

Lie algebra $f\tilde{\boldsymbol{G}}$. If G_i $(i=1,2)$ are isomorphic, and their $\boldsymbol{G}_i$ are identified according to this isomorphism $(=\boldsymbol{G})$, then, in general, different f_i may be needed to generate the G_i from the linear Lie algebras $f_i\tilde{G}$. However, under these conditions:

46.5.1. Proposition The set Λ_f is the same for isomorphic G_{un}.
Indeed, it is characterized by

$$\lambda \in \Lambda_f \leftrightarrow \lambda(\boldsymbol{h}) = 0 \bmod 2\pi\mathrm{i} \qquad \text{for all } \boldsymbol{h} \text{ with } \exp f(\tilde{\boldsymbol{h}}) = 1,$$

since the weights of f generating Λ_f are just the eigenvalues on $\boldsymbol{H}$.

G_{un} wraps $\tilde{G}_{\text{un}}$ by means of the inverse of f. Those closed paths $\curlyvee_{t,\,0\leqslant t\leqslant 1} \exp t\tilde{\boldsymbol{h}}$ with $\boldsymbol{h}\in\boldsymbol{Z}$ that are wrapped by closed paths are characterized by $\exp f(\tilde{\boldsymbol{h}})=1$, hence by $\lambda(\boldsymbol{h})=0 \bmod 2\pi\mathrm{i}$ for all $\lambda\in\Lambda_f$. This leads to an extension of Theorem 46.1:

46.5.2. Theorem For G_{un} infinitesimally generated by $f(\tilde{\boldsymbol{G}}_{\text{un}})$ let $\boldsymbol{Z}_f$ be the additive subgroup of $\boldsymbol{H}_{\text{un}}$ consisting of the $\boldsymbol{h}$ with $\lambda(\boldsymbol{h})=0 \bmod 2\pi\mathrm{i}$ for all $\lambda\in\Lambda_f$. Then $\boldsymbol{Z}_f \bmod \boldsymbol{Y}$ is isomorphic with the fundamental group of G_{un} as in Theorem 46.1.

Translated by duality this becomes the following.

46.5.3. Theorem The fundamental group Φ of a unitarily restricted semisimple linear Lie group G_{un} is the dual of $\Lambda \bmod \Lambda_f$ if G is produced by $f\tilde{\boldsymbol{G}}$. The duality has essentially the same meaning as in Theorem 46.3; that is, with the provision that $\exp f\boldsymbol{w}$ replaces $\exp \boldsymbol{w}$ and that Λ_f replaces $\Lambda_\sim$. The center of G_{un} is isomorphic to the dual of $\Lambda_f \bmod \Lambda_\sim$.

The last statement is an immediate consequence of the foregoing.

46.6. Proposition If in the foregoing f is irreducible with the top weight $\hat{\lambda}$, then the center of the group infinitesimally generated by $f\tilde{\boldsymbol{G}}_{\text{un}}$ is p-cyclic, where p is the least positive integer such that $p\hat{\lambda}\in\Lambda_\sim$.

Indeed, then all weights of f are contained in $\hat{\lambda}+\Lambda_\sim$ (see 42.1).

46.7–9. Wrappings Realized

46.7 The universal wrapping of G_{un} has a center that is isomorphic with the fundamental group of $\tilde{G}_{\text{un}}$. Therefore it cannot be realized by an *irreducible* unitarily restricted semisimple Lie group unless the fundamental group of $\tilde{G}$ is cyclic.

Proposition The universal wrapping of G_{un} is realized in the cases

$\mathbf{A}_l$ by π_1, $\mathbf{B}_l$ by π_1, $\mathbf{C}_l$ by π_l, $\mathbf{D}_l$ (l odd) by π_1, $\mathbf{E}_6$ by π_1, $\mathbf{E}_7$ by π_2.

In the case $\mathbf{D}_l$ (l even) it can be done by combining π_1, π_2 into a reducible representation.

46.8. Theorem Any wrapping of the centerfree unitarily restricted semisimple G_{un} can be realized by a linear Lie group.

Proof The wrapping is characterized by its fundamental group as a subgroup of the fundamental group of G_{un}; its dual is isomorphic to Λ' mod $\Lambda_\sim$, where Λ' is a subgroup of Λ containing $\Lambda_\sim$. There is a (finite) set Λ'' of representatives of Λ' mod $\Lambda_\sim$, all of which are dominant (cf. Remark 46.3). $\Lambda' = \Lambda'' + \Lambda_\sim$. The representations with top weights in Λ'' can be combined to give a representation f, for which $\Lambda_f = \Lambda'$.

46.9 According to 38.5 the fundamental group of complex semisimple G is known by that of its unitary restriction.

46.10 Another Approach If rather than the fundamental group of G_{un} (generated by $f(\tilde{G}_{\text{un}})$), its center were the aim, one could proceed in a simpler way than that followed in the present exposition. This way can be sketched in a few words.

(1) The center of G_{un} is contained in the trunk H_{un}.

(2) Its elements $\exp \boldsymbol{h}$ are characterized by $\exp \tilde{\boldsymbol{h}} = 1$; in other words, by $\alpha(\boldsymbol{h}) = 0 \bmod 2\pi i$ for all $\alpha \in W^*$; that is by $\lambda(\boldsymbol{h}) = 0 \bmod 2\pi i$ for all $\lambda \in \Lambda_\sim$.

(3) $\exp \boldsymbol{h} = 1$ if and only if $\lambda(\boldsymbol{h}) = 0 \bmod 2\pi i$ for all $\lambda \in \Lambda_f$.

(4) From this it follows that the center is isomorphic to the dual of Λ_f mod $\Lambda_\sim$.

This method, however, sets no upper bound, as it were, for the fundamental group. To know that the fundamental group of G_{un} is finite, that the universal wrapping of G_{un} can be realized by a linear and even by a unitary Lie group, and so on, one must, to the present knowledge, apply more profound methods that is, homotopy theory, as has been done in this exposition, or homology theory.

47. WEYL'S CHARACTER AND DIMENSION FORMULA

47.1–6. Skew Functions and Characters

47.1 The double characterization up to equivalence of irreducible representations of $\boldsymbol{G}$ and G_{un} by their top weights and characters suggests the possibility of expressing the one by the other.

Until further notice G_{un} is supposed simply connected. Without this supposition one would not be sure whether a given linear representation f of $\boldsymbol{G}$ extends to G. By 46.8, this supposition is allowed. In any case $\boldsymbol{G}$ is taken in ordered second dressing.

47.2 A character of G_{un} is known by its behavior on H_{un}. One can work more comfortably in $\boldsymbol{H}^*_{\text{un}}$, defining χ_f by

47.2.1
$$\chi_f(\zeta \boldsymbol{h}) = \operatorname{tr} \exp f\boldsymbol{h}$$

(for the mapping ζ of $\boldsymbol{H}$ onto $\boldsymbol{H}^*$ cf. 21.1.5). For $\tau = \zeta\boldsymbol{h}$ the eigenvalues of $f\boldsymbol{h}$ are the weight values $\lambda(\boldsymbol{h}) = (\lambda, \tau)$, each of which has a multiplicity

47.2.2
$$m_\lambda = \dim R_\lambda,$$

where R_λ is the λ-weight space. The eigenvalues of $\exp f\boldsymbol{h}$ are the $\exp(\lambda, \tau)$; thus,

47.2.3
$$\chi_f(\tau) = \sum_\lambda m_\lambda \exp(\lambda, \tau).$$

For $S \in \operatorname{Int} W^*$

$$\chi_f(S\tau) = \sum_\lambda m_\lambda \exp(\lambda, S\tau) = \sum_\lambda m_\lambda \exp(S^{-1}\lambda, \tau) = \sum m_{S\lambda} \exp(\lambda, \tau);$$

thus by 43.1.7,

47.2.4
$$\chi_f(S\tau) = \chi_f(\tau).$$

47.3 In addition to these functions invariant under Int W^*, it is convenient to consider *skew* functions Θ, defined by

$$\Theta(S\tau) = \det S \cdot \Theta(\tau) \qquad \text{for all} \quad S \in \operatorname{Int} W^*;$$

in particular, *elementary* skew functions Θ_μ, defined for $\mu \in \boldsymbol{H}^*_{\text{st}}$:

47.3.1
$$\Theta_\mu(\tau) = \sum_{S \in \operatorname{Int} W^*} \det S \cdot \exp(S\mu, \tau).$$

Note that for $S \in \operatorname{Int} W^*$

$$\Theta_{S\mu}(\tau) = \det S \cdot \Theta_\mu(\tau).$$

Let μ be integral and dominant. If $(\mu, \rho) = 0$ for some $\rho \in W^{++}$, then

$$\Theta_\mu(\tau) = \Theta_{S_\rho \mu}(\tau) = -\Theta_\mu(\tau).$$

Thus

$$\Theta_\mu(\tau) = 0 \qquad \text{for all} \quad \tau \in \boldsymbol{H}^*_{\text{un}}$$

unless

$$2\frac{(\mu,\rho)}{(\rho,\rho)}\geqslant 1 \qquad \text{for all} \quad \rho\in W^{++}.$$

But then, using the Weyl tool δ,

$$2\frac{(\mu-\delta,\rho)}{(\rho,\rho)}\geqslant 0 \qquad \text{for all} \quad \rho\in W^{++}$$

and $\mu-\delta$ is still dominant. Thus:

Proposition The only nonvanishing elementary skew functions Θ_μ with integral dominant μ are the $\Theta_{\nu+\delta}$ with integral dominant ν.

47.4 Definition

$$Q(\tau)=\prod_{\alpha\in W+}(\exp\tfrac{1}{2}(\alpha,\tau)-\exp(-\tfrac{1}{2}(\alpha,\tau))).$$

This definition differs slightly though inessentially from that of 37.3.

According to 41.6, S_ρ ($\rho\in W^{++}$) permutes the elements of W^+ except ρ, which is interchanged with $-\rho$. Thus,

$$Q(S_\rho\tau)=-Q(\tau),$$

which means by Proposition 33.2.2 that Q is skew.

In working out the product one gets a sum of terms $\pm\exp(\xi,\tau)$. The highest ξ that occurs is $\sum_{\alpha\in W+}\frac{1}{2}\alpha=\delta$ (the Weyl tool); the others differ from δ by an integral combination of positive rootforms. Q is a linear combination of elementary skew Θ_μ with integral dominant μ. The highest μ that can occur is δ. Actually, it occurs with a unit coefficient. By 47.3 all Θ_μ with a lower μ vanish. Hence:

47.4.1. Proposition $\quad Q(\tau)=\Theta_\delta(\tau).$

47.5 Guided by 37.3, one is advised to replace χ_f by θ_f,

47.5.1 $$\theta_f(\tau)=\chi_f(\tau)\,Q(\tau).$$

The θ_f, as defined in 37.3, fulfill orthogonality relations in H. The new ones do not differ much, though there may be some doubt whether Q can still be transplanted to H for integration purposes; that is, whether $Q(\zeta\boldsymbol{h})$ depends on $h=\exp\boldsymbol{h}$ rather than on $\boldsymbol{h}$. This univalence requirement is fulfilled by $\Upsilon_h\exp(\alpha,\zeta\boldsymbol{h})$, though not by $\Upsilon_h\exp(\frac{1}{2}\alpha,\zeta\boldsymbol{h})$. Since G_{un} is simply connected, however, any linear representation of $\boldsymbol{G}$ will extend to G and therefore any possible weight λ will make $\Upsilon_h\exp(\lambda,\zeta\boldsymbol{h})$ univalent. This holds for δ as well since δ is integral and dominant and thus is a possible weight. It also holds for all $S\delta$ ($S\in\mathrm{Int}\ W^*$). Thanks to the sum expression for $Q=\Theta_\delta$ it holds for Q

and finally it holds for Θ_μ if μ is integral by the same arguments.

Clearly, the new θ_f fulfill the same orthogonality relations as the old. (See 37.1, 37.4.)

Integrating some $\Upsilon_\tau \exp(\mu, \tau)$ over H_{un} with the usual measure if μ is integral, one gets 0 unless $\mu = 0$, because, on the one hand, the integral should be invariant under the translation $\Upsilon_\tau(\tau + \tau_0)$ (τ_0 fixed $\in \boldsymbol{H}^*_{\mathrm{un}}$), and on the other the same translation causes a multiplication by $\exp(\mu, \tau_0)$.

Hence:

47.5.2. Proposition $\Theta_\lambda, \Theta_\mu$ are orthogonal as functions on H_{un} unless λ, μ are equivalent under Int W^*.

A property anticipated in 37.5 can now be verified:

47.5.3. Proposition If the measures μ on G_{un} and ν on H_{un} are related as in Theorem 37.2, and k is the order of the kaleidoscope group Int W^*, then

$$\mu(G_{\mathrm{un}}) = k\nu(H_{\mathrm{un}}).$$

Indeed, by 47.4.1,

$$\mu(G_{\mathrm{un}}) = \int_{H_{\mathrm{un}}} |\Theta_\delta|^2 \, d\nu,$$

where, after substitution according to 47.3.1, under the integral sign, the only summands contributing effectively are k times 1.

Note that the proposition remains valid if the assumption of G_{un} being simply connected is dropped.

47.6. Proposition $\theta_f = \Theta_{\hat{\lambda}+\delta}$ if $\hat{\lambda}$ is the top weight of f.

Proof As a product of symmetric χ_f and skew Q, the left-hand side is skew, thus a linear combination of elementary skew terms Θ_μ with integral dominant μ. If the product is performed, the highest μ that occurs is $\hat{\lambda} + \delta$. Because $m_{\hat{\lambda}} = 1$ (see 43.1.6), it occurs with a unit coefficient. The proposition asserts that no other dominant μ will occur. It is inductively verified by taking the proposition for granted for all linear representations g with a lower top weight $\hat{\mu}$; thus,

47.6.1 $$\theta_g = \Theta_{\hat{\mu}+\delta} \quad \text{for} \quad \hat{\mu} < \hat{\lambda}.$$

By 47.5 θ_f is orthogonal to θ_g, hence by 47.6.1 to all $\Theta_{\hat{\mu}+\delta}$ with $\hat{\mu} < \hat{\lambda}$, which would be impossible if such an expression occurred in θ_f. This proves the assertion.

47.7. Weyl's Character Formula On the trunk H of complex semisimple G the character of the irreducible linear representation of $\boldsymbol{G}$ with top weight $\hat{\lambda}$ is given by 47.2.1 and

$$\chi_{\hat{\lambda}}(\tau) = \frac{\sum_{S \in \mathrm{Int}\, W^*} \det S \cdot \exp(S(\hat{\lambda}+\delta), \tau)}{\sum_{S \in \mathrm{Int}\, W^*} \det S \cdot \exp(S\delta, \tau)}$$

Indeed, one obtains χ from 47.5.1, 47.6, and 47.4.1 as $\Theta_{\hat{\lambda}+\delta}/\Theta_\delta$, which by 47.3.1 is just the asserted quotient. Properly stated, this was proved only for $\tau \in \boldsymbol{H}^*_{\mathrm{un}}$. It extends, however, to $\boldsymbol{H}^*$ by analytic continuation. Wherever the denominator vanishes, the quotient is interpreted by continuity.

47.8. Weyl's Dimension Formula The dimension of the $R \in$ Spa Lin in which complex semisimple $\boldsymbol{G}$ is irreducibly represented with the top weight $\hat{\lambda}$ is

$$\dim R = \frac{\prod_{\alpha \in W+} (\hat{\lambda}+\delta, \alpha)}{\prod_{\alpha \in W+} (\delta, \alpha)}.$$

Proof The dimension equals the value of the character at $\tau = 0$, where all eigenvalues are 1. It is computed by continuity, taking $\tau = t\delta$ and letting t tend to zero:

In the numerator

$$\sum \det S \cdot \exp(S(\hat{\lambda}+\delta), t\delta) = \sum \det S \cdot \exp(S\delta, t(\hat{\lambda}+\delta)) = Q(t(\hat{\lambda}+\delta))$$

and because of 47.4.1,

$$= \prod_{\alpha \in W+} (\exp \tfrac{1}{2}t(\hat{\lambda}+\delta, \alpha) - \exp(-\tfrac{1}{2}t(\hat{\lambda}+\delta, \alpha)))$$

$$= \prod_{\alpha \in W+} (t(\hat{\lambda}+\delta, \alpha) + \cdots).$$

In the denominator, analogously

$$\prod_{\alpha \in W+} (t(\delta, \alpha) + \cdots).$$

The quotient takes the announced form if t tends to zero.

47.9. Historical Note The formulas are the most marvelous results of H. Weyl's papers in *Math. Z.* **24** (1926) = *Selecta* 352–359.

The dimension formula is quite comfortable. The character formula is less practicable.

An algebraic proof of these formulas is furnished in Section 48.

47.10. An Elaboration It is worthwhile to elaborate on the proof in 47.8. There dim R was computed as the first nonvanishing coefficient in the power series for $\chi_{\hat\lambda}(t\delta)$. If the next coefficient is taken into account, one gets

$$\chi_{\hat\lambda}(t\delta)=\frac{Q(t(\hat\lambda+\delta))}{Q(t\delta)}=\dim R\left(1+\tfrac{1}{24}\sum_{\alpha\in W+}((\alpha,\hat\lambda+\delta)^2-(\alpha,\delta)^2)\,t^2+\cdots\right)$$

47.10.1 $$=\dim R(1+\tfrac{1}{48}((\hat\lambda+\delta,\hat\lambda+\delta)-(\delta,\delta))\,t^2+\cdots),$$

where the formula in 21.1.9 has been used.

On the other hand,

$$\chi_{\hat\lambda}(t\delta)=\sum_{\lambda}\exp(\lambda,\delta t),$$

where the sum runs over the weights λ according to their multiplicity in the representation.

A comparison of the coefficients in 47.10.1 and in

$$\chi_{\hat\lambda}(t\delta)=\sum_{\lambda}(1+(\lambda,\delta)\,t+\tfrac{1}{2}(\lambda,\delta)^2t^2+\cdots)$$

leads to

47.10.2 $$\sum_{\lambda}(\lambda,\delta)^2=\tfrac{1}{24}\dim R((\hat\lambda+\delta,\hat\lambda+\delta)-(\delta,\delta)).$$

In particular, for the adjoint representation of simple G, that is, $\hat\lambda=\hat\alpha$, one gets

$$(\delta,\delta)=\sum_{\alpha\in W}(\alpha,\delta)^2=\tfrac{1}{24}\dim \boldsymbol{G}((\hat\alpha+\delta,\hat\alpha+\delta)-(\delta,\delta))=\tfrac{1}{24}\dim \boldsymbol{G},$$

where the first equality is again justified by 21.1.9, and the third by Proposition 43.3.

The result is the following.

47.11. Strange Formula $\dim \boldsymbol{G}=24(\delta,\delta)$ for $\boldsymbol{G}\in$ Alg Lie Com SSS. It would be interesting to have a direct proof of this relation. Possibly it is related to Gordon Brown's formula (21.5).

48. ALGEBRAIC PROOF OF WEYL'S FORMULAS

The proofs in Section 47 are based on integration. The present section gives an algebraic proof.

f is an irreducible linear representation of $\boldsymbol{G}\in$ Alg Lie Com SS, in R, with top weight $\hat\lambda$; $\dim R<\infty$.

48.1 For $\alpha \in W^*$ put

$$f(e_{-\alpha})f(e_\alpha) = P_1, \qquad f(e_\alpha)f(e_{-\alpha}) = P_2;$$

thus

$$P_2 - P_1 = f(h_\alpha).$$

Then, if R_λ is the λ-weight space and $\lambda + \alpha$ is again a weight,

$$P_1 R_\lambda \subset R_\lambda, \qquad f(e_\alpha) R_\lambda \subset R_{\lambda+\alpha}, \qquad f(e_{-\alpha}) R_{\lambda+\alpha} \subset R_\lambda.$$

There are positive integers a, b such that

$$P_1^{a+i} R_\lambda = P_1{}^a R_\lambda = T \qquad \text{for all} \quad i > 0,$$
$$P_2^{b+i} R_{\lambda+\alpha} = P_2{}^b R_{\lambda+\alpha} = U \qquad \text{for all} \quad i > 0.$$

Then

$$f(e_\alpha) T = U, \qquad f(e_{-\alpha}) U = T,$$

which shows that

$f(e_\alpha)$ maps T one-to-one onto U, and
$f(e_{-\alpha})$ maps U one-to-one onto T.

Since

$$f(e_\alpha) P_1 = P_2 f(e_\alpha)$$

one gets

$$\mathrm{tr}_T P_1 = \mathrm{tr}_U P_2.$$

A contribution to the trace of P_1 in R_λ is yielded by the subspace T only and, likewise, to that of P_2 in $R_{\lambda+\alpha}$ by U only. Thus,

$$\mathrm{tr}_{R_{\lambda+\alpha}} P_2 = \mathrm{tr}_U P_2 = \mathrm{tr}_T P_1 = \mathrm{tr}_{R_\lambda} P_1 = \mathrm{tr}_{R_\lambda} (P_2 - f(h_\alpha)).$$

Hence,

$$\mathrm{tr}_{R_\lambda} P_2 - \mathrm{tr}_{R_{\lambda+\alpha}} P_2 = m_\lambda(\lambda, \alpha),$$

where m_λ is the multiplicity of the weight λ in f. Substituting $\lambda + \alpha$, $\lambda + 2\alpha$, ..., instead of λ, and adding, one gets

$$\mathrm{tr}_{R_\lambda} f(e_\alpha) f(e_{-\alpha}) = \sum_{p=0}^{\infty} m_{\lambda+p\alpha}(\lambda + p\alpha, \alpha).$$

Actually, the series stops because almost all m_λ, belonging to λ that are not weights, vanish.

Summation over all $\alpha \in W^*$, and addition of

$$\mathrm{tr}_{R_\lambda} \sum f(h^i) f(h_i) = (\lambda, \lambda) m_\lambda,$$

where h^i, h_i form dual bases of H, delivers the trace in R_λ of the f-image of the

Casimir tool

$$\operatorname{tr}_{R_\lambda}\Big(\sum_{\alpha\in W^*} f(e_\alpha)f(e_{-\alpha})+\sum_j f(h^j)f(h_j)\Big)=c_{\hat\lambda}\,m_\lambda,$$

where

$$c_\mu=(\mu+\delta,\,\mu+\delta)-(\delta,\delta).$$

Thus,

48.2
$$\sum_{\alpha\in W^*}\sum_{p=0}^{\infty}(\lambda+p\alpha,\alpha)\,m_{\lambda+p\alpha}+(\lambda,\lambda)\,m_\lambda=c_{\hat\lambda}\,m_\lambda.$$

Here the inner sum may be taken instead from $p=1$ upward, since for $p=0$ the contributions from $\pm\alpha$ cancel.

Likewise $\sum_\mu(\mu,\alpha)m_\mu$ vanishes as soon as the sum runs over an entire α-ladder of weights μ or over an α-ladder cut off symmetrically, since then

$$\sum(\mu,\alpha)\,m_\mu=\sum(S_\alpha\mu,\alpha)\,m_{S_\alpha\mu}=\sum(S_\alpha\mu,\alpha)\,m_\mu=-\sum(\mu,\alpha)\,m_\mu.$$

It follows that the inner sum in 48.2 vanishes as soon as integral λ is no weight. In that case m_λ vanishes as well. So 48.2 is still correct, if integral λ is not a weight.

Combining in 48.2 the contributions from $\pm\alpha$ by using

$$\sum_{p=-\infty}^{\infty}(\lambda+p\alpha,\alpha)m_{\lambda+p\alpha}=0,$$

one gets

$$\sum_{\alpha\in W+}(\lambda,\alpha)\,m_\lambda+2\sum_{\alpha\in W+}\sum_{p=1}^{\infty}(\lambda+p\alpha,\alpha)\,m_{\lambda+p\alpha}+(\lambda,\lambda)\,m_\lambda=c_{\hat\lambda}\,m_\lambda.$$

The first and third summand together are

$$(\lambda,\lambda+2\delta)\,m_\lambda=((\lambda+\delta,\,\lambda+\delta)-(\delta,\delta))\,m_\lambda=c_\lambda\,m_\lambda;$$

thus

48.3
$$2\sum_{\alpha\in W+}\sum_{p=1}^{\infty}(\lambda+p\alpha,\alpha)\,m_{\lambda+p\alpha}=(c_{\hat\lambda}-c_\lambda)\,m_\lambda.$$

This formula allows the recursive computation of the multiplicities descending from $m_{\hat\lambda}=1$ and $m_\lambda=0$ for $\lambda>\hat\lambda$. The first member involves multiplicities of weights $>\lambda$ only and the coefficient $c_{\hat\lambda}-c_\lambda$ in the second member is well known not to vanish (see 43.1.8). The formula is more practical than Weyl's, which will be derived from it, or rather from 48.2.

48.4 The equation system 48.2 is now subjected to the Laplace transformation that consists in multiplication by $\exp(\lambda,\tau)$ and summation over all

$\lambda \in \Lambda_f$ or, rather, which amounts to the same, summation over all of $\boldsymbol{H}^*_{\text{ing}}$. This is how

$$\chi(\tau) = \sum m_\lambda \exp(\lambda, \tau)$$

makes its appearance.

If μ is substituted for $\lambda + p\alpha$, the first summand contributes

$$\begin{aligned}
&\sum_{\lambda} \sum_{\alpha \in W^*} \sum_{p=1}^{\infty} (\lambda + p\alpha, \alpha)\, m_{\lambda+p\alpha} \exp(\lambda, \tau)\\
&\quad = \sum_{\mu,\alpha,p} (\mu, \alpha)\, m_\mu \exp(\mu - p\alpha, \tau)\\
&\quad = \sum_{\mu,\alpha} (\mu, \alpha)\, m_\mu \exp(\mu, \tau) \cdot \sum_{p=1}^{\infty} \exp(-p(\alpha, \tau))\\
&\quad = \sum_{\mu,\alpha} (\mu, \alpha)\, m_\mu \exp(\mu, \tau) \cdot \frac{\exp(-(\alpha, \tau))}{1 - \exp(-(\alpha, \tau))}.
\end{aligned}$$

Now with ζ as in 21.1.5 and canonically identifying $\boldsymbol{H}$ with its double linear dual,

$$\begin{aligned}
\exp(\mu, \tau) \cdot \zeta^{-1} \mu &= \operatorname{grad}_\tau \curlyvee_\tau \exp(\mu, \tau),\\
\frac{\exp(-(\alpha, \tau))}{1 - \exp(-(\alpha, \tau))} \cdot \zeta^{-1} \alpha &= \operatorname{grad}_\tau \curlyvee_\tau \log(1 - \exp(-(\alpha, \tau))),\\
(\lambda, \lambda) \exp(\lambda, \tau) &= \Delta_\tau \curlyvee_\tau \exp(\lambda, \tau),
\end{aligned}$$

where the Laplace operator $\Delta = \operatorname{div}\operatorname{grad}$ is understood with respect to the inner product in $\boldsymbol{H}^*$.

The result is

48.5 $$(\operatorname{grad} \curlyvee_\tau \sum_{\alpha \in W^*} \log(1 - \exp(-\alpha, \tau)), \operatorname{grad} \chi) + \Delta\chi = c_{\hat\lambda}\, \chi,$$

which can be simplified by the use of Q (see 47.4, 47.4.1):

$$\begin{aligned}
Q(\tau) &= \prod_{\alpha \in W+} (\exp \tfrac{1}{2}(\alpha, \tau) - \exp(-\tfrac{1}{2}(\alpha, \tau)))\\
&= \sum_S \det S \cdot \exp(S\delta, \tau),\\
Q(\tau)^2 &= \pm \prod_{\alpha \in W^*} (1 - (\exp(-\alpha, \tau))).
\end{aligned}$$

Now 48.5 becomes

$$(2 \operatorname{grad} \log Q, \operatorname{grad} \chi) + \Delta\chi = c_{\hat\lambda}\, \chi.$$

Because of

$$\operatorname{grad} \log Q = (\operatorname{grad} Q)/Q,$$

this becomes

$$2(\text{grad } Q, \text{grad } \chi) + Q\Delta\chi = c_{\hat\lambda}\, Q\chi.$$

Putting $Q\chi = \theta$, as in 37.3 and 47.5.1, one arrives at

48.6 $$(\Delta\theta/\theta) - (\Delta Q/Q) = c_{\hat\lambda}.$$

The same presentation of Q (47.4.1) shows

$$\Delta Q = (\delta, \delta)\, Q.$$

Hence

48.7 $$\Delta\theta = (\hat\lambda + \delta, \hat\lambda + \delta)\,\theta.$$

θ is a linear combination of elementary skew

$$\Theta_\mu(\tau) = \sum_S \det S \cdot \exp(S\mu, \tau),$$

with integral dominant μ, all $\leqslant \hat\lambda + \delta$. For any among them

$$(\Delta\Theta_\mu)(\tau) = \sum_S \det S \cdot (S\mu, S\mu) \exp(S\mu, \tau)$$

$$= (\mu, \mu)\, \Theta_\mu(\tau).$$

The linear independence of the nonzero Θ_μ (a consequence of their orthogonality in H) implies that

$$(\mu, \mu) = (\hat\lambda + \delta, \hat\lambda + \delta)$$

as soon as Θ_μ occurs in the same expression for θ; dominant $\mu \leqslant \hat\lambda + \delta$ makes

$$\mu = \hat\lambda + \delta.$$

Since $\exp(\hat\lambda + \delta, \tau)$ occurs with a unit coefficient in both θ and $\Theta_{\hat\lambda + \delta}$, one gets

$$\theta = \Theta_{\hat\lambda + \delta},$$

which proves Weyl's formula.

Note that the use of series and differentiations in this proof was merely formal.

48.8. Historical Note The contents of this section are based on H. Freudenthal, *Proc. Kon. Akad. Wet. Amsterdam* **A57**, 369–376 (1954) = *Indagationes Math.* **16**. Examples of the practical use of formula 48.3 were given by H. Freudenthal, *Proc. Kon. Akad. Wet. Amsterdam* **A57**, 487–491 (1954); **A59**, 511–514 (1956).

49. CLIFFORD ALGEBRAS AND SPIN REPRESENTATIONS†

The fundamental representations of $\boldsymbol{G} \in \mathbf{B}_l$, $\mathbf{D}_l$ with half-integral weights (π_1, respectively, π_1 and π_2) are still waiting for realizations. They are called *spin* representations. Since the usual presentation of $\boldsymbol{G}$ (π_2, respectively π_3) has a center of order 2, the spin representations give 1-2-images of the special orthogonal groups. *Clifford algebras* are involved in their construction.

49.1–3. The Infinitesimal Approach

49.1 The special orthogonal group G of n-space is now taken with respect to an invariant unit form in matrix presentation. Its infinitesimal elements are the skew matrices. For distinct $a, b, \boldsymbol{d}_{a,b}$ means the n–n-matrix with 1 in the place $\ulcorner a, b \urcorner$, -1 in the place $\ulcorner b, a \urcorner$, and 0 elsewhere. The $\boldsymbol{d}_{a,b}$ $(a < b)$ form a basis of $\boldsymbol{G}$. Note that $\boldsymbol{d}_{a,b} = -\boldsymbol{d}_{b,a}$.

$$[\boldsymbol{d}_{a,b}, \boldsymbol{d}_{c,d}] = 0 \qquad \text{if} \quad a \neq c, d; \quad b \neq c, d,$$
$$[\boldsymbol{d}_{a,b}, \boldsymbol{d}_{b,c}] = \boldsymbol{d}_{a,c} \qquad \text{if} \quad a \neq b, \quad b \neq c, \quad c \neq a.$$

These relations determine the Lie algebra algebraically. Put

$$l = [n/2];$$

a' denotes the subscript $a + l$ if $0 < a \leqslant l$ and $a - l$ if $l < a \leqslant 2l$.

The ordered trunk $\boldsymbol{H}$ is the linear space spanned by $\boldsymbol{d}_{a,a'}$ $(0 < a \leqslant l)$ as a basis, partially ordered according to the order of the subscripts a. On this basis the $\boldsymbol{d}_{a,a'}$-coordinate of $\boldsymbol{h}$ is denoted by $\omega_a(\boldsymbol{h})$. The branches and rootforms are

$$\boldsymbol{d}_{a,b} - \boldsymbol{d}_{a',b'} \pm \mathrm{i}\boldsymbol{d}_{a,b'} \pm \mathrm{i}\boldsymbol{d}_{a',b} \quad \text{belonging to} \quad \pm\mathrm{i}(\omega_a + \omega_b),$$
$$\boldsymbol{d}_{a,b} + \boldsymbol{d}_{a',b'} - \mathrm{i}\boldsymbol{d}_{a,b'} + \mathrm{i}\boldsymbol{d}_{a',b} \quad \text{belonging to} \quad \mathrm{i}(\omega_a - \omega_b),$$

and for odd n, in addition,

$$\boldsymbol{d}_{a,n} \pm \mathrm{i}\boldsymbol{d}_{a',n} \quad \text{belonging to} \quad \pm\mathrm{i}\omega_a$$

$(a \neq b,\ a \leqslant l,\ b \leqslant l)$; the signs are understood to be correspondingly dependent.

49.2 The expression $\xi_1{}^2 + \cdots + \xi_n{}^2$ can be factorized into

$$(\xi_1 p_1 + \cdots + \xi_n p_n)^2$$

by the introduction of p_a fulfilling

49.2.1 $$p_a{}^2 = 1, \qquad p_a p_b + p_b p_a = 0 \quad \text{for} \quad a \neq b.$$

† The contents of Section 49 are not used in the sequel.

These p_a are considered to generate an associative algebra with 1-element, the *Clifford algebra* C_n, with the products

49.2.2 $$p_1^{\varepsilon_1} p_2^{\varepsilon_2} \cdots p_n^{\varepsilon_n} \qquad (\varepsilon_a = 0, 1)$$

constituting a basis of C_n.

The existence of C_n is proved by induction. Let C_n be an associative algebra with the basis 49.2.2 and subject to 49.2.1. Suppose dashing defined by

$$\bar{p}_a = -p_a,$$

which generates an involutory automorphism of C_n. The ordered pairs of elements of C_n are appointed as elements of C_{n+1}. Addition and scalar multiplication are defined as usual in direct sums of linear spaces; moreover,

$$\ulcorner u_1, u_2 \urcorner \cdot \ulcorner v_1, v_2 \urcorner = \ulcorner u_1 v_1 + u_2 \bar{v}_2, u_2 \bar{v}_1 + u_1 v_2 \urcorner,$$
$$\overline{\ulcorner u_1, u_2 \urcorner} = \ulcorner \bar{u}_1, -\bar{u}_2 \urcorner.$$

The usual laws, especially that of associativity, are easily verified. One can also verify that dashing is again an involutory automorphism. The identification of u with $\ulcorner u, 0 \urcorner$ embeds C_n in C_{n+1}.

$$\ulcorner u_1, u_2 \urcorner \cdot \ulcorner 0, 1 \urcorner = \ulcorner u_2, u_1 \urcorner,$$
$$\ulcorner 0, 1 \urcorner \cdot \ulcorner u_1, u_2 \urcorner = \ulcorner \bar{u}_2, \bar{u}_1 \urcorner,$$
$$\overline{\ulcorner 0, 1 \urcorner} = -\ulcorner 0, 1 \urcorner.$$

By putting $\ulcorner 0, 1 \urcorner = p_{n+1}$ and doubling the old basis by right multiplication by p_{n+1} the induction step is completed.

49.3 The second-degree elements of C_n form a Lie algebra $\boldsymbol{G}'$ if

$$[u, v] = uv - vu$$

is accepted as a definition. The linear mapping K determined by

49.3.1 $$K\boldsymbol{d}_{a,b} = \tfrac{1}{2} p_a p_b \qquad (0 < a < b \leqslant n)$$

is easily seen to be an isomorphism of $\boldsymbol{G}$ onto $\boldsymbol{G}'$. The left multiplications

49.3.2 $$L_q = \curlyvee_u qu \qquad (q \in \boldsymbol{G}')$$

cause a linear representation

$$L = \curlyvee_{q \in \boldsymbol{G}'} L_q$$

of $\boldsymbol{G}'$ in C_n. So LK is a linear representation of $\boldsymbol{G}$ in C_n.

For $q = Kd_{a,a'} = \frac{1}{2}p_a p_{a'}$ one gets $q^2 = -\frac{1}{4}$; hence,

$$L_q^{\,2} u = L_{q^2} u = -\tfrac{1}{4}u.$$

All eigenvalues of L_q are $\pm\frac{1}{2}$i. So possible weights of the representation LK with respect to the trunk $\boldsymbol{H}$ are

$$\tfrac{1}{2}\mathrm{i}(\pm\omega_1 \pm \cdots \pm \omega_l),$$

for which weight vectors, depending on the signs, are chosen:

49.3.3 $(\mathbf{D}_l)\quad u_1^\pm u_2^\pm \cdots u_l^\pm, \qquad (\mathbf{B}_l)\quad u_1^\pm u_2^\pm \cdots u_l^\pm u_0,$

with

$$u_j^+ = p_j + \mathrm{i}p_{j'}, \qquad u_j^- = 1 + \mathrm{i}p_j p_{j'}, \qquad u_0 = 1 + p_n.$$

It is easily seen that left multiplication by p_a $(a = 1, \ldots, n)$ permutes them up to factors ± 1, $\pm$i. So they span a $\boldsymbol{G}'$-invariant subspace R of C_n of dimension 2^l, in which $\boldsymbol{G}'$ is represented according to π_1 for $\boldsymbol{G} \in \mathbf{B}_l$ and according to a (reducible) combination of π_1 and π_2 for $\boldsymbol{G} \in \mathbf{D}_l$.

It is easy to describe the action of the basic $\frac{1}{2}L_{p_a p_b}$ on R in a more explicit way by matrices on an eigenvector basis. This may be omitted.

49.4–6. The Group Approach

49.4 By the above device the spin representations of the Lie *algebras* $\boldsymbol{G} \in \mathbf{B}_l$, $\mathbf{D}_l$ have been described. The result is not quite satisfactory. One would like to have the spin representations of the special orthogonal *groups* in an explicit form.

To unify the exposition it is convenient to denote the universal wrapping of the special orthogonal group of n-space by G. This is a group locally isomorphic with a linear Lie group, as in 6.4. In an obvious way $\boldsymbol{G}$ can be understood as its infinitesimal algebra. Again,

$$l = [\tfrac{1}{2}n] \qquad \text{and} \qquad \delta = n - 2l = 0, 1.$$

G is represented in n-space by a 2–1-homomorphism ϑ and in 2^l-space by a 1–1-homomorphism σ. In the case $\delta = 0$, σ is reducible and splits into π_1 and π_2.

To avoid half-integers the meaning of the ω_i is changed so that the non-vanishing rootforms are

$$\pm 2\omega_i \pm 2\omega_j \quad (i \neq j) \quad \text{for} \quad \delta = 0,$$
$$\pm 2\omega_i \pm 2\omega_j \quad (i \neq j), \quad \pm 2\omega_k \quad \text{for} \quad \delta = 1.$$

The weights, all with multiplicity 1, are for

$$\vartheta\colon\ \pm 2\omega_i \quad \text{for} \quad \delta = 0, \text{ supplemented by } 0 \text{ for } \delta = 1,$$
$$\sigma\colon\ \pm\omega_1 \pm \cdots \pm \omega_l.$$

If the eigenvalues of $\vartheta(x)$ are $\mathrm{e}^{\pm 2\omega_i}$, supplemented by 1 for $\delta = 1$, then the value of the character χ of σ for $x \in H$ is the sum over all sign distributions:

$$\Sigma \exp(\pm \omega_1 \pm \cdots \pm \omega_l) = \Sigma\, e^{\pm\omega_1} \cdots e^{\pm\omega_l} = \prod_j (e^{\omega_j} + e^{-\omega_j})$$

$$= e^{\Sigma\omega_j} \prod_j (1 + e^{-2\omega_j}) = e^{-\Sigma\omega_j} \prod_j (1 + e^{2\omega_j}),$$

defined up to a factor ± 1.

The square of this character value is

$$\prod_j (1 + e^{2\omega_j})(1 + e^{-2\omega_j}) = \prod_\lambda (1 + e^\lambda),$$

where λ ranges over all nonzero weights of ϑ, thus,

$$= \det(1 + \vartheta(x)) \qquad \text{for} \quad \delta = 0,$$
$$= \tfrac{1}{2} \det(1 + \vartheta(x)) \qquad \text{for} \quad \delta = 1.$$

Thus, first for $x \in H$ and then for general x,

49.4.1 $$\chi(x) = \pm(2^{-\delta} \det(1 + \vartheta(x)))^{1/2},$$

where the sign is to be settled by analytic continuation.

49.5 In the space of continuous functions on G a subspace K, spanned by the functions $\curlyvee_x\, \chi(xa)$ $(a \in G)$ or, equivalently, by the matrix coefficients of σ, is singled out. Its dimension is $(2^l)^2$ for $\delta = 1$ and $2(2^{l-1})^2$ for $\delta = 0$ (see 49.3). Thus,

$$\dim K = 2^{n-1}.$$

(An explicit basis of K is indicated in 49.6.)

49.6 As the next step the set of symbols $1, \ldots, n$, or rather that of all its subsets with an even number of elements, is considered. This set of subsets is called N. It has 2^{n-1} elements.

For any $\nu \in N$ let e_ν be one of the two elements of G with the property

$\vartheta(e_\nu)$ is the diagonal matrix $\ulcorner\lambda_1, \ldots, \lambda_n\urcorner$, with

$$\lambda_j = 1 \quad \text{for} \quad j \notin \nu, \quad \lambda_j = -1 \quad \text{for} \quad j \in \nu.$$

(A fixed orthonormal basis was chosen in n-space.)

If $\vartheta(x) = \vartheta(y)$ for $x \neq y$, it is convenient to write $y = -x$. Then $\sigma(-x) = -\sigma(x)$ since the quotient of $\sigma(x)$ and $\sigma(-x)$ is of the form $\exp \sigma(\boldsymbol{h}) \neq 1$ with $\boldsymbol{h} \in \boldsymbol{H}$, $2\omega_i(\boldsymbol{h}) = 0$ whence $(\pm\,\omega_1 \pm \cdots \pm \omega_l)(\boldsymbol{h})$ all equal $\pi i \bmod 2\pi i$.

$$e_\mu e_\nu = \pm e_\rho \qquad \text{where } \rho = (\mu \cup \nu) \setminus (\mu \cap \nu).$$

By 49.4.1

$$\chi(e_\nu) = 0 \qquad \text{if} \quad \nu \text{ is nonvoid,}$$
$$ = \pm 2^l \qquad \text{if} \quad \nu \text{ is void.}$$

The $\Upsilon_x \chi(xe_\nu)$ are linearly independent because of

$$\chi(e_\mu e_\nu) = 2^l \varepsilon_\mu \qquad \text{for} \quad \mu = \nu \quad (\varepsilon_\mu = \pm 1),$$
$$ = 0 \qquad \text{for} \quad \mu \neq \nu.$$

(See 49.4.1.) They form a basis of K. Hence for $a \in G$,

$$\chi(xa) = \sum_{\nu \in N} \gamma_\nu(a) \, \chi(xe_\nu),$$

where the coefficients $\gamma_\nu(a)$ can be found by putting $x = e_\mu$:

$$\gamma_\mu(a) = 2^{-l} \varepsilon_\mu \, \chi(e_\mu a).$$

This leads to the formula

$$\chi(xa) = 2^{-l} \sum_{\nu \in N} \varepsilon_\nu \, \chi(e_\nu a) \, \chi(xe_\nu),$$

which remains valid if $\Upsilon_x \chi(xa)$ is replaced by any linear combination

$$f(x) = \sum_a m_a \, \chi(xa)$$

of such functions; thus,

$$f(x) = 2^{-l} \sum_{\nu \in N} \varepsilon_\nu f(e_\nu) \, \chi(xe_\nu).$$

In particular, if f is any matrix coefficient of σ, and even for σ instead of f,

$$\sigma(x) = 2^{-l} \sum_{\nu \in N} \varepsilon_\nu \, \chi(xe_\nu) \, \sigma(e_\nu)$$

49.6.1
$$= 2^{-(1/2)n} \sum_{\nu \in N} \varepsilon_\nu (\det(1 + \vartheta(x) \vartheta(e_\nu)))^{1/2} \sigma(e_\nu),$$

where the square root involving the subscript ν has to be interpreted as a continuous function on G which takes the value $2^{(1/2)n} \varepsilon_\nu$ at $x = e_\nu$.

49.7. Reduction of Irrationalities Up to the precise knowledge of the $\sigma(e_\nu)$ this is an explicit spin representation of the orthogonal group. However, it depends on 2^{n-1} irrationalities while one square root is likely to do the job. This reduction is now performed.

It is easily seen that for n–n-matrices a, b the relations

$$b = (1 - a)(1 + a)^{-1} \qquad \text{and} \qquad a = (1 - b)(1 + b)^{-1}$$

imply each other (so long as they are meaningful) and that orthogonality of a implies skewness of b, and conversely.

A square root of the determinant of a skew $2k$-matrix b is a rational function of the matrix coefficients β_{ij}, the so-called pfaffian of b, written pf(b),

$$\mathrm{pf}(b) = \frac{1}{2^k k!} \Sigma\, \mathrm{sgn}\,(i_1 i_2 \cdots i_{2k})\, \beta_{i_1 i_2} \beta_{i_3 i_4} \cdots \beta_{i_{2k-1} i_{2k}},$$

where sgn means the permutation sign. (The proof is omitted.)

Suppose orthogonal a general enough to admit skew $b = (1-a)(1+a)^{-1}$. Then

49.7.1 $$\det(1 + a\vartheta(e_\nu)) = \det((1+b) + (1-b)\vartheta(e_\nu)) \det(1+b)^{-1}$$
$$= \det((1+\vartheta(e_\nu)) + b(1-\vartheta(e_\nu)) \det(1+b)^{-1}.$$

To make the computation easier, one considers the case $\nu = \{1, \ldots, m\}$ with even m. Then $1 + \vartheta(e_\nu)$ has 0 on the main diagonal places $1, 2, \ldots, m$, and 2 on the other diagonal places, whereas in $b(1-\vartheta(e_\nu))$ the first m columns of b are multiplied by 2 and the others are annihilated. Therefore the first factor in 49.7.1 is 2^n times the determinant of the matrix b_ν formed by the first m rows and columns of b.

49.7.2 $$\det(1 + a\vartheta(e_\nu)) = 2^n \det b_\nu \det(1+b)^{-1}.$$

To apply this to 49.6.1 one must substitute $\vartheta(x)$ for a. Instead of b one writes $\eta(x)$; that is,

49.7.3 $$\eta(x) = (1 - \vartheta(x))(1 + \vartheta(x))^{-1}.$$

$\eta(x)$ is skew. Its submatrix constituted by the rows and columns the numbers of which occur in ν, is called $\eta_\nu(x)$. Then 49.6.1 becomes

49.7.4 $$\sigma(x) = (\det(1 + \eta(x))^{-1})^{1/2} \cdot \sum_{\nu \in N} \varepsilon_\nu(\pm\, \mathrm{pf}(\eta_\nu(x))\, \sigma(e_\nu),$$

where pf(η_ν) means 1 for void ν.

The doubtful signs are settled by a suitable choice of the e_ν. For $i<j$ the curve $\curlyvee_\tau a_\tau$ on G is defined by $a_0 = 1$ and

$$\vartheta(a_\tau) = \begin{pmatrix} 1 & & & & \\ & \ddots & & & \\ & & \cos\tau \cdots \sin\tau & & \\ & & \vdots & & \\ & & -\sin\tau \cdots \cos\tau & & \\ & & & \ddots & \\ & & & & 1 \end{pmatrix},$$

where the cosines and sines are placed in the ith and jth rows and columns. Next there is defined

$$e_{\{i,j\}} = a_\pi;$$

furthermore, if $i_1 < i_2 < \cdots < i_m$,

$$e_{\{i_1, i_2, \ldots, i_m\}} = e_{\{i_1, i_2\}} e_{\{i_3, i_4\}} \cdots e_{\{i_{m-1}, i_m\}}.$$

A straightforward computation gives $-\tan \frac{1}{2}\tau$ for the i, jth matrix coefficient of $\eta(a_\tau)$ and $\cos \frac{1}{2}\tau$ as a value of $(\det(1 + \eta(a_\tau))^{-1})^{1/2}$. Furthermore,

49.7.5 $$\varepsilon_\nu = (-1)^{[\nu]}$$

if $[\nu]$ is half the number of elements of ν. With the substitution $x = e_\nu$ the right-hand member of 49.7.4 should become $\sigma(e_\nu)$. This requires plus signs in 49.7.4, which now reads

49.7.6 $$\sigma(x) = (\det(1 + \eta(x))^{-1})^{1/2} \sum_{\nu \in N} (-1)^{[\nu]} \operatorname{pf}(\eta_\nu(x))\, \sigma(e_\nu),$$

with a positive square root at $x = 1$.

To make this an explicit formula, one has to determine the matrices $\sigma(e_\nu)$. The representation of $\boldsymbol{G}$ induced by σ is equivalent with LK restricted to R, as defined in 49.3. By virtue of this equivalence one may and does assume

$$\sigma(\boldsymbol{x}) = L_{K\boldsymbol{x}} \qquad \text{for} \quad \boldsymbol{x} \in \boldsymbol{G}.$$

Putting

$$x = \exp \boldsymbol{x} = 1 + \tau \boldsymbol{x} + \cdots,$$

where $\boldsymbol{x}$ is an infinitesimal element of G such that

$$\vartheta(x) = \exp \vartheta(\boldsymbol{x}) = 1 + \tau \boldsymbol{d}_{i,j} + \cdots \qquad (i < j)$$

(see 49.1), one gets

$$\eta(x) = -\tfrac{1}{2}\tau \boldsymbol{d}_{i,j} + \cdots,$$

$$\operatorname{pf}(\eta_\nu(x)) = \begin{cases} -\frac{1}{2}\tau & \text{for} \quad \nu = \{i, j\}, \\ 0 & \text{for other nonvoid } \nu, \end{cases}$$

$$\det(1 + \eta(x))^{-1} = 1 + \tau^2(\cdots).$$

This shows

$$\sigma(\boldsymbol{d}_{i,j}) = \tfrac{1}{2}\sigma(e_\nu);$$

thus,

$$\sigma(e_\nu) = L_{p_i p_j} \qquad \text{for} \quad \nu = \{i, j\}, \quad i < j.$$

Putting

49.7.7 $p_\nu = p_{i_1} p_{i_2} \cdots p_{i_k}$ if $\nu = \{i_1, i_2, \ldots, i_k\}$, $i_1 < i_2 < \ldots < i_k$,

one finally gets

49.7.8 $$\sigma(x) = L_{f(x)}$$

with

$$f(x) = (\det(1 + \eta(x))^{-1})^{1/2} \cdot \sum_{\nu \in N} (-1)^{[\nu]} \operatorname{pf}(\eta_\nu(x)) p_\nu.$$

The results are summarized in the following theorem.

Theorem Let ϑ be the usual presentation of the special n-orthogonal group and σ its spin representation (π_1 in case $\mathbf{B}_l$; π_1, π_2 combined in case $\mathbf{D}_l$). With the use of the Clifford algebra C_n σ is infinitesimally given by the action of the Lie-algebra G' within C_n, which consists of the second degree elements, as left multipliers (49.3.1–2) in the space R described by 49.3.3.

In group terms σ is expressed in ϑ by 49.7.8. Here η is to be understood according to 49.7.3, $\nu \in N$ is a subset ν of $\{1, \ldots, n\}$ with an even number of elements, $[\nu]$ is half this number, $\operatorname{pf}(\eta_\nu(x))$ is the pfaffian of the submatrix formed by the rows and columns of $\eta(x)$ with numbers in ν, p_ν is defined by 49.7.7, and L_u ($u \in C_n$) is the action of u as a left multiplier on the space R (49.3.3).

49.8. The Other Fundamental Representations G can also be represented by

$$\tau = \curlyvee_x \curlyvee_{a \in R} f(x)\, a f(x)^{-1}.$$

The elements of R of degree k, together with 0, form a linear subspace, invariant under the $\tau(x)$. Under the action of τ they behave as the linear spaces of skew k-tensors; this leads to the other fundamental representations. (Without proof.)

49.9. Historical Note The spin representation of the special orthogonal group by means of the Clifford algebra was discovered by R. Lipschitz (Untersuchungen über die Summen von Quadraten, Bonn, 1886) and then forgotten. E. Cartan [*Bull. Soc. Math. France* **41**, 53–96 (1913) = *Œuvres I* **1**, 355–398] gave a construction of the spin representation of the Lie algebra. R. Brauer and H. Weyl [*Amer. J. Math.* **57**, 425–449 (1935) = *Selecta* H. Weyl 431–454] characterized the spin group, but did not give an explicit construction. H. Freudenthal, using characters [*Proc. Kon. Akad. Wet. Amsterdam* **A59**, 515–522 (1956) = *Indagationes Math.* **18** (1956)], rediscovered Lipschitz' results, though the reduction to one square root was not achieved until he became acquainted with Lipschitz' work.

See also *Ann. Math.* **69**, 247–251 (1959).

50. THE CONDUCIBILITY THEOREM (ALGEBRAICALLY PROVED) AND E. E. LEVI'S THEOREM†

The conducibility of a complex semisimple linear Lie algebra $\boldsymbol{G}$ was proved in 35.4 by integration in the unitary restricted group G_{un}. Starting with the linear Lie algebra $\boldsymbol{G}$, one can give a purely algebraic proof; the other forms of the conducibility theorem can be derived from this case.

The same method of proof applies to E. E. Levi's theorem. Though these proofs could be combined, the exposition is clearer if the shorter conducibility proof is given separately. (See 50.7 and 50.11.)

50.1. Conducibility Theorem A finite-dimensional linear representation of $\boldsymbol{G} \in$ Alg Lie Com SS is conducible.

50.2. E. E. Levi's Theorem Let $\boldsymbol{G} \in$ Alg Lie Com and let $\boldsymbol{A}$ be the radical of $\boldsymbol{G}$. Then there is $\boldsymbol{F}$ sub $\boldsymbol{G}$, $\boldsymbol{F} \in$ Alg Lie Com SS, such that $\boldsymbol{G} = \boldsymbol{F} + \boldsymbol{A}$, $\boldsymbol{F} \cap \boldsymbol{A} = \{\boldsymbol{0}\}$.

50.3.1 The Casimir tool of semisimple $\boldsymbol{G}$ is an important instrument in the proof. It was defined (40.1) as the element

$$z = \sum_j \boldsymbol{a}^j \boldsymbol{a}_j$$

of the associative envelope $\mathscr{E}(\boldsymbol{G})$ of semisimple $\boldsymbol{G}$, where the bases $\boldsymbol{a}_1, \ldots, \boldsymbol{a}_r$, $\boldsymbol{a}^1, \ldots, \boldsymbol{a}^r$ had to be correlated; that is,

$$\operatorname{tr}(\tilde{\boldsymbol{a}}^i \tilde{\boldsymbol{a}}_j) = \begin{cases} 1 & \text{for } i = j, \\ 0 & \text{for } i \neq j; \end{cases}$$

z did not depend on the choice of the basis. It belongs to the center of $\mathscr{E}(\boldsymbol{G})$.

For any representation f of $\boldsymbol{G}$ in R (extended to $\mathscr{E}(\boldsymbol{G})$) z^f now means the image of z under f. If f is irreducible with top weight $\hat{\lambda}$, then z^f behaves in R as the scalar multiplier (43.1.9)

$$(\hat{\lambda} + \delta, \hat{\lambda} + \delta) - (\delta, \delta),$$

which, by Proposition 43.6, is positive unless $\hat{\lambda} = 0$. Hence, as an element of End R, z^f is nondegenerate if f is irreducible and not the null representation.

50.3.2. Proposition For any linear representation f of $\boldsymbol{G} \in$ Alg Lie Com SS in R

$$\operatorname{tr} z^f \geqslant 0.$$

† The contents of Section 50 are not used in the sequel.

If

$$\operatorname{tr} z^f = 0,$$

then f is a null representation.

Proof On a suitable basis

$$f(\boldsymbol{a}) = \begin{pmatrix} g_1(\boldsymbol{a}) & & * \\ & \ddots & \\ 0 & & g_k(\boldsymbol{a}) \end{pmatrix},$$

with irreducible representations g_j of $\boldsymbol{G}$ in R_j. Thus,

$$\operatorname{tr} z^f = \sum \operatorname{tr} z^{g_j} \geqslant 0,$$

according to 50.3.1.

z^{g_j} is a scalar multiplier. If $\operatorname{tr} z^f = 0$, then $\operatorname{tr} z^{g_j} = 0$; hence $z^{g_j} = 0$ for all j. By 50.3.1 every g_j is an irreducible null representation; thus $\dim R_j = 1$. This makes $f(\boldsymbol{G})$, which is a homomorphic image of $\boldsymbol{G}$, solvable. Consequently $f(\boldsymbol{G}) = \{\boldsymbol{0}\}$.

50.3.3 Under the same supposition, with respect to the eigenvalues of z^f, R is split into z^f-invariant N, M sub R,

$$R = N + M,$$

such that z^f is nilpotent in N and nondegenerate in M.

Proposition f leaves M and N invariant, and acts as a null representation in N.

This follows from $z^f f(\boldsymbol{a}) = f(\boldsymbol{a}) z^f$ and from 50.3.2.

50.4 The Casimir tool is now generalized.

Let f, g be linear mappings of semisimple $\boldsymbol{G}$ into End R, where $R \in$ Spa Lin Com. Then, still,

50.4.1 $$z^{f,g} = \sum_j f(\boldsymbol{a}^j)\, g(\boldsymbol{a}_j)$$

does not depend on the choice of the correlate bases, as is readily seen by rewriting the proof of 40.1, and again

50.4.2 $$\sum_j \big(f([\boldsymbol{c}, \boldsymbol{a}^j])\, g(\boldsymbol{a}_j) + f(\boldsymbol{a}^j)\, g[\boldsymbol{c}, \boldsymbol{a}_j]\big) = 0 \quad \text{for} \quad \boldsymbol{c} \in \boldsymbol{G}.$$

As soon as f becomes a representation, one can of course substitute $[f(\boldsymbol{c}), f(\boldsymbol{a}_j)]$ for $f([\boldsymbol{c}, \boldsymbol{a}_j])$; likewise with g.

$$z^{g,f} = \sum_j g(\boldsymbol{a}^j) f(\boldsymbol{a}_j) = \sum g(\boldsymbol{a}_j) f(\boldsymbol{a}^j),$$

since the bases may be interchanged. Thus by defining $z^{[f,g]}$ as

50.4.3 $$z^{[f,g]} = z^{f,g} - z^{g,f} = \sum_j [f(\boldsymbol{a}^j), g(\boldsymbol{a}_j)],$$

one gets

50.4.4 $$\sum ([f([\boldsymbol{c}, \boldsymbol{a}^j]), g(\boldsymbol{a}_j)] + [f(\boldsymbol{a}^j), g([\boldsymbol{c}, \boldsymbol{a}_j])]) = 0 \quad \text{for} \quad \boldsymbol{c} \in \boldsymbol{G}.$$

Again, if f and g are representations, by applying the Jacobi associativity law to the first summand one gets

$$\sum ([[f(\boldsymbol{c}), g(\boldsymbol{a}_j)], f(\boldsymbol{a}^j)] + [f(\boldsymbol{c}), [f(\boldsymbol{a}^j), g(\boldsymbol{a}_j)]] + [f(\boldsymbol{a}^j), [g(\boldsymbol{c}), g(\boldsymbol{a}_j)]]) = 0;$$

thus,

50.4.5 $$[f(\boldsymbol{c}), z^{[f,g]}] = \sum_j [f(\boldsymbol{a}^j), [g(\boldsymbol{a}_j), g(\boldsymbol{c}) - f(\boldsymbol{c})]].$$

50.5 To prove Theorem 50.1, consider a linear representation f of semisimple $\boldsymbol{G}$ in R with an invariant L sub R.

There is an M sub R and a linear representation g of $\boldsymbol{G}$ in R such that

$$L + M = R, \qquad L \cap M = \{0\},$$

$$g(\boldsymbol{a})\, M \subset M, \quad g(\boldsymbol{a})\, x = f(\boldsymbol{a})\, x \qquad \text{for} \quad x \in L, \quad (f(\boldsymbol{a}) - g(\boldsymbol{a}))\, M \subset L.$$

(If f is a matrix representation on a basis that extends a basis of L, thus

$$f(\boldsymbol{a}) = \begin{pmatrix} f_L(\boldsymbol{a}) & * \\ 0 & f_M(\boldsymbol{a}) \end{pmatrix},$$

then g arises by "cleaning" f, that is, omitting the contribution $*$.)

The theorem actually states the equivalence of f and g. It suffices to prove it under the assumptions

$$f_L \text{ and } f_M \text{ irreducible.}$$

The easy induction that leads from this case to the general one may be omitted.

50.6 The set of linear mappings ϑ of R into R such that

$$\vartheta M \subset L, \qquad \vartheta L = \{0\}$$

is denoted by Θ. It is a linear Lie algebra. Because $\Theta^2 = \{0\}$, one gets $[\Theta, \Theta] = \{0\}$. Clearly

50.6.1 $$f(\boldsymbol{a}) - g(\boldsymbol{a}) \in \Theta \qquad \text{for} \quad \boldsymbol{a} \in \boldsymbol{G}.$$

The equivalence of f and g will be settled by some $1 - \kappa$, with $\kappa \in \Theta$ such that

$$(1 - \kappa) f(\boldsymbol{a})(1 + \kappa) = g(\boldsymbol{a}).$$

(Note that $(1 - \kappa)(1 + \kappa) = 1$.) This condition on κ can also be written

50.6.2 $$[f(\boldsymbol{a}), \kappa] = g(\boldsymbol{a}) - f(\boldsymbol{a}) \qquad \text{for all} \quad \boldsymbol{a} \in \boldsymbol{G}.$$

50.7 In Θ a new linear representation $\tilde{f}$ of $\boldsymbol{G}$ is defined by

$$\tilde{f}(\boldsymbol{a})\vartheta = [f(\boldsymbol{a}), \vartheta] \qquad (= [g(\boldsymbol{a}), \vartheta]).$$

Then, because of 50.6.1, one can write 50.4.5 as

50.7.1 $$\tilde{f}(\boldsymbol{c})\, z^{[f,g]} = \sum_j \tilde{f}(\boldsymbol{a}^j)\, \tilde{f}(\boldsymbol{a}_j)(g(\boldsymbol{c}) - f(\boldsymbol{c})) = z^{\tilde{f}}(g(\boldsymbol{c}) - f(\boldsymbol{c})).$$

In the new notation condition 50.6.2 reads

50.7.2 $$\tilde{f}(\boldsymbol{a})\, \kappa = g(\boldsymbol{a}) - f(\boldsymbol{a}).$$

With 50.7.1 the desired result in 50.7.2 is nearly attained, but one still has to remove $z^{\tilde{f}}$ from the last member of 50.7.1. This will be done by solving

50.7.3 $$z^{\tilde{f}}\, \kappa = z^{[f,g]}$$

with respect to $\kappa \in \Theta$. Note that according to 50.3.3

$$\Theta = \Phi + \Phi_1,$$

a direct sum, where

50.7.4 $$\tilde{f}(\boldsymbol{a})\, \Phi = \{0\}, \qquad z^{\tilde{f}} \Phi = \{0\},$$

50.7.5 $$\tilde{f}(\boldsymbol{a})\, \Phi_1 \subset \Phi_1, \qquad z^{\tilde{f}} \text{ nondegenerate on } \Phi_1.$$

Substituting $z^{[f,g]}$ from 50.7.3 into 50.7.1 and observing (50.3.1)

50.7.6 $$\tilde{f}(\boldsymbol{a})\, z^{\tilde{f}} = z^{\tilde{f}}\, \tilde{f}(\boldsymbol{a}),$$

one gets as an equivalent condition on κ

50.7.7 $$z^{\tilde{f}}\, \tilde{f}(\boldsymbol{a})\, \kappa = z^{\tilde{f}}(g(\boldsymbol{a}) - f(\boldsymbol{a}));$$

in other words

50.7.8 $$\tilde{f}(\boldsymbol{a})\,\kappa-(g(\boldsymbol{a})-f(\boldsymbol{a}))\in\Phi \qquad \text{for all} \quad \boldsymbol{a}\in\boldsymbol{G}.$$

According to 50.7.4,
$$f(\boldsymbol{a})\,\vartheta=\vartheta f(\boldsymbol{a}) \qquad \text{for} \quad \vartheta\in\Phi.$$

Because of their reducibility of f_L and f_M, this means that $\vartheta=0$ or ϑ causes an (essentially unique) equivalence of f_M and f_L, and dim $\Phi=1$.

In the first case $\Phi=\{0\}$, $z^{\tilde{f}}$ is nondegenerate and 50.7.3, and consequently 50.7.2, can be solved. In the second case 50.7.3 can still be solved mod Φ. Because of 50.7.4, this solution fulfills 50.7.7 exactly. This gives a κ such that
$$\tilde{f}(\boldsymbol{a})\,\kappa=g(\boldsymbol{a})-f(\boldsymbol{a})+u(\boldsymbol{a})\,\vartheta_0,$$
where $0\neq\vartheta_0\in\Phi$ and the scalar $u(\boldsymbol{a})$ depends linearly on $\boldsymbol{a}\in\boldsymbol{G}$.

Computing
$$\tilde{f}([\boldsymbol{a},\boldsymbol{b}])\,\kappa=\tilde{f}(\boldsymbol{a})\,\tilde{f}(\boldsymbol{b})\,\kappa-\tilde{f}(\boldsymbol{b})\,\tilde{f}(\boldsymbol{a})\,\kappa,$$
while taking 50.6.1 into account, one gets for the second member
$$\begin{aligned}&[f(\boldsymbol{a}),g(\boldsymbol{b})-f(\boldsymbol{b})]-[f(\boldsymbol{b}),g(\boldsymbol{a})-f(\boldsymbol{a})]\\ &=[g(\boldsymbol{a}),g(\boldsymbol{b})-f(\boldsymbol{b})]-[f(\boldsymbol{b}),g(\boldsymbol{a})-f(\boldsymbol{a})]\\ &=g([\boldsymbol{a},\boldsymbol{b}])-f([\boldsymbol{a},\boldsymbol{b}]),\end{aligned}$$
and for the first member,
$$g([\boldsymbol{a},\boldsymbol{b}])-f([\boldsymbol{a},\boldsymbol{b}])+u([\boldsymbol{a},\boldsymbol{b}])\,\vartheta_0.$$

This shows that u vanishes on the commutator algebra of $\boldsymbol{G}$, which because of the semisimplicity is $\boldsymbol{G}$ itself.

Therefore 50.7.2 is solvable, which verifies the assertion of 50.5 and therefore of Theorem 50.1.

50.8 To prove Theorem 50.2 one considers $\boldsymbol{G}\in$ Alg Lie Lin Com presented in $R\in$ Spa Lin Com with an invariant L sub R. Again there is an M sub R and a linear representation g of $\boldsymbol{G}$ in R such that

50.8.1 $$L+M=R, \qquad L\cap M=\{0\},$$

50.8.2 $$g(\boldsymbol{a})\,M\subset M, \qquad g(\boldsymbol{a})\,x=\boldsymbol{a}x \qquad \text{for} \quad x\in L,$$
$$(\boldsymbol{a}-g(\boldsymbol{a}))\,R\subset L \qquad \text{for} \quad \boldsymbol{a}\in\boldsymbol{G};$$

g is unique up to equivalence.

Proposition Under these conditions, suppose that $g(\boldsymbol{G})$ is semisimple and irreducible on both L and M. Then M and g can be modified such that $g(\boldsymbol{G})$ sub $\boldsymbol{G}$.

This will be proved in 50.9–10.

50.9 The set of linear mappings ϑ of R into R such that

$$\vartheta M \subset L, \qquad \vartheta L = \{0\}$$

is again denoted by Θ. Again

$$[\Theta, \Theta] = \{\mathbf{0}\},$$

and

$$\boldsymbol{a} - g(\boldsymbol{a}) \in \Theta \qquad \text{for all} \quad \boldsymbol{a} \in \boldsymbol{G}.$$

The kernel of g is denoted by $\boldsymbol{A}$.
If $\boldsymbol{a} \in \boldsymbol{A}$, then $g(\boldsymbol{a}) = \mathbf{0}$; thus $\boldsymbol{a} \in \Theta$. Hence $\boldsymbol{A} \subset \Theta$ and $\boldsymbol{A}$ abelian.

50.10 Take a linear subspace $\boldsymbol{E}$ of $\boldsymbol{G}$ such that

$$\boldsymbol{G} = \boldsymbol{E} + \boldsymbol{A}, \qquad \boldsymbol{E} \cap \boldsymbol{A} = \{\mathbf{0}\}.$$

In this splitting the $\boldsymbol{E}$-component of $\boldsymbol{a} \in \boldsymbol{G}$ is denoted by $e(\boldsymbol{a})$. Thus,

$$e(\boldsymbol{a}) = \boldsymbol{a} \bmod \boldsymbol{A}, \qquad e(\boldsymbol{a}) \in \boldsymbol{E}, \qquad \boldsymbol{a} - e(\boldsymbol{a}) \in \Theta.$$

Clearly e need not be a representation of $\boldsymbol{G}$, but

50.10.1 $$e([\boldsymbol{a}, \boldsymbol{b}]) = [e(\boldsymbol{a}), e(\boldsymbol{b})] + u(\boldsymbol{a}, \boldsymbol{b})$$

where

$$u(\boldsymbol{a}, \boldsymbol{b}) \in \boldsymbol{A}.$$

The desired modification of g will be obtained by replacing $g(\boldsymbol{a})$ by

$$g(\boldsymbol{a}) + [g(\boldsymbol{a}), \omega] \qquad \text{with a suitable } \omega \in \Theta.$$

This does not influence the second and third relations in 50.8.2. Since

$$\begin{aligned}
&[g(\boldsymbol{a}) + [g(\boldsymbol{a}), \omega], g(\boldsymbol{b}) + [g(\boldsymbol{b}), \omega]] \\
&\quad = [g(\boldsymbol{a}), g(\boldsymbol{b})] + [g(\boldsymbol{a}), [g(\boldsymbol{b}), \omega]] - [g(\boldsymbol{b}), [g(\boldsymbol{a}), \omega]] \\
&\quad = [g(\boldsymbol{a}), g(\boldsymbol{b})] + [[g(\boldsymbol{a}), g(\boldsymbol{b})], \omega],
\end{aligned}$$

the new $g(\boldsymbol{G})$ will again be a Lie algebra. The only thing one has to arrange is that

50.10.2 $$g(\boldsymbol{a}) + [g(\boldsymbol{a}), \omega] \in \boldsymbol{G}.$$

Then the new M is obtained as $(1 - \omega) M$, which is indeed invariant under the $g(\boldsymbol{a}) + [g(\boldsymbol{a}), \omega]$.

To solve 50.10.2 one applies 50.4.4, with g, e instead of f, g. Then

$$\sum_j ([[g(\boldsymbol{c}), g(\boldsymbol{a}^j)], e(\boldsymbol{a}_j)] + [g(\boldsymbol{a}^j), e([\boldsymbol{c}, \boldsymbol{a}_j])]) = \boldsymbol{0} \qquad \text{for} \quad \boldsymbol{c} \in \boldsymbol{G},$$

which by 50.10.1 becomes

$$\sum_j ([[g(\boldsymbol{c}), g(\boldsymbol{a}^j)], e(\boldsymbol{a}_j)] + [g(\boldsymbol{a}^j), [e(\boldsymbol{c}), e(\boldsymbol{a}_j)] + u(\boldsymbol{c}, \boldsymbol{a}_j)]) = \boldsymbol{0}.$$

The Jacobi associativity law applied to the first summand leads to

$$[g(\boldsymbol{c}), z^{[g,e]}] + \sum_j ([g(\boldsymbol{a}^j), [e(\boldsymbol{a}_j), g(\boldsymbol{c}) - e(\boldsymbol{c})]] + [g(\boldsymbol{a}^j), u(\boldsymbol{c}, \boldsymbol{a}_j)]) = \boldsymbol{0}.$$

Again

$$z^{\tilde{g}}\vartheta = \sum_j [g(\boldsymbol{a}^j), [g(\boldsymbol{a}_j), \vartheta]] = \sum_j [g(\boldsymbol{a}^j), [e(\boldsymbol{a}_j), \vartheta]]$$

defines a linear mapping $z^{\tilde{g}}$ of Θ into Θ. By the same argument as in 50.7.4–5 Θ splits directly into Φ, where $z^{\tilde{g}}$ is nilpotent, and into Φ_1 where $z^{\tilde{g}}$ is non-degenerate; both are $\tilde{g}(\boldsymbol{a})$-invariant. Similarly, $\tilde{g}(\boldsymbol{a})\,\Phi = \{\boldsymbol{0}\}$ and $\dim \Phi \leqslant 1$. Again

$$z^{\tilde{g}}\kappa = z^{[g,e]} \bmod \Phi$$

can be solved by $\kappa \in z^{\tilde{g}}\Theta$ and

$$z^{\tilde{g}}\kappa_j = u(\boldsymbol{c}, \boldsymbol{a}_j) \bmod \Phi$$

by $\kappa_j \in z^{\tilde{g}}\Theta \cap \boldsymbol{A}$ because $\boldsymbol{A}$ is $z^{\tilde{g}}$-invariant.

Since the $g(\boldsymbol{b})$ commute with the elements of Φ, this leads to

$$[g(\boldsymbol{c}), z^{\tilde{g}}\kappa] + z^{\tilde{g}}(g(\boldsymbol{c}) - e(\boldsymbol{c})) + \sum_j ([g(\boldsymbol{a}^j), z^{\tilde{g}}\kappa_j]) = \boldsymbol{0}$$

and, since $z^{\tilde{g}}$ commutes with $\tilde{g}(\boldsymbol{b})$, to

$$z^{\tilde{g}}([g(\boldsymbol{c}), \kappa] + g(\boldsymbol{c}) - e(\boldsymbol{c}) + \sum_j [g(\boldsymbol{a}^j), \kappa_j]) = \boldsymbol{0}.$$

Now

$$e(\boldsymbol{c}) - \sum_j [g(\boldsymbol{a}^j), \kappa_j] = e(\boldsymbol{c}) - \sum_j [e(\boldsymbol{a}^j), \kappa_j] \in \boldsymbol{G};$$

hence

$$g(\boldsymbol{c}) + [g(\boldsymbol{c}), \kappa] + v(g(\boldsymbol{c}))\vartheta_0 \in \boldsymbol{G}$$

for some linear function v and some fixed $\vartheta_0 \in \Phi$.

The commutator argument again shows that $v = 0$, which proves that

$$g(\boldsymbol{c}) + [g(\boldsymbol{c}), \kappa] \in \boldsymbol{G} \qquad \text{for all} \quad \boldsymbol{c} \in \boldsymbol{G}$$

and thus proves 50.10.2. This completes the proof of Proposition 50.8.

50.11 Proposition 50.8 is the basis of an induction by which Theorem 50.2 will be proved.

At any step in the sequel the existence of the Levi-splitting for lower dimensional Lie algebras will be taken for granted.

Let $\boldsymbol{G} \in$ Alg Lie Com and let $\boldsymbol{A}$ be the radical of $\boldsymbol{G}$.

Let $\boldsymbol{B}$ be an ideal of $\boldsymbol{G}$ within $\boldsymbol{A}$ and $\boldsymbol{B} \neq \{\boldsymbol{0}\}, \neq \boldsymbol{A}$. Then $\boldsymbol{G}$ mod $\boldsymbol{B}$ admits a Levi-splitting; thus

$$\boldsymbol{G} = \boldsymbol{F}_1 + \boldsymbol{A}, \qquad \text{where } \boldsymbol{F}_1 \cap \boldsymbol{A} = \boldsymbol{B} \subset \boldsymbol{F}_1, \text{ and } \boldsymbol{F}_1 \text{ mod } \boldsymbol{B} \text{ is semisimple.}$$

Again $\boldsymbol{F}_1$ admits a Levi-splitting.

$$\boldsymbol{F}_1 = \boldsymbol{F}_2 + \boldsymbol{B}, \qquad \text{where } \boldsymbol{F}_2 \cap \boldsymbol{B} = \{\boldsymbol{0}\} \text{ and } \boldsymbol{F}_2 \text{ is semisimple.}$$

Thus $\boldsymbol{G} = \boldsymbol{F}_2 + \boldsymbol{A}$ and a Levi-splitting of $\boldsymbol{G}$ is obtained.

As a consequence, it may now be supposed that the radical $\boldsymbol{A}$ of $\boldsymbol{G}$ does not contain an ideal of $\boldsymbol{G}$ different from $\boldsymbol{A}$ and $\{\boldsymbol{0}\}$. Thus $\boldsymbol{A}$ is abelian and $\tilde{\boldsymbol{G}}$ acts irreducibly on $\boldsymbol{A}$.

Now suppose that $\boldsymbol{G}$ mod $\boldsymbol{A}$ is not simple. Then there are proper ideals $\boldsymbol{G}_1, \boldsymbol{G}_2$ of $\boldsymbol{G}$, different from $\boldsymbol{A}$, such that

50.11.1 $$\boldsymbol{G} = \boldsymbol{G}_1 + \boldsymbol{G}_2, \qquad \boldsymbol{G}_1 \cap \boldsymbol{G}_2 = \boldsymbol{A}.$$

There are Levi-splittings

50.11.2 $$\boldsymbol{G}_i = \boldsymbol{F}_i + \boldsymbol{A} \quad \text{with semisimple } \boldsymbol{F}_i.$$

$\curlyvee_{f \in \boldsymbol{F}_1} \curlyvee_{x \in \boldsymbol{G}} \tilde{f}x$ leaves $\boldsymbol{G}_2$ and $\boldsymbol{A} \subset \boldsymbol{G}_2$ invariant, hence because of its conducibility, also a linear subspace $\boldsymbol{K}$ of $\boldsymbol{G}_2$ such that

50.11.3 $$\boldsymbol{G}_2 = \boldsymbol{K} + \boldsymbol{A}, \qquad \boldsymbol{K} \cap \boldsymbol{A} = \{\boldsymbol{0}\}.$$

Because of $[\boldsymbol{F}_1, \boldsymbol{F}_2] \subset \boldsymbol{A}$, one even gets

$$[\boldsymbol{F}_1, \boldsymbol{K}] = \{\boldsymbol{0}\}.$$

$\boldsymbol{K}$ generates a Lie algebra $\boldsymbol{K}'$, which still fulfills

50.11.4 $$[\boldsymbol{F}_1, \boldsymbol{K}'] = \{\boldsymbol{0}\}.$$

50.11.5 $$\boldsymbol{K} \subset \boldsymbol{K}' \subset \boldsymbol{G}_2 = \boldsymbol{K} + \boldsymbol{A},$$
$$\boldsymbol{K} \cap \boldsymbol{A} = \{\boldsymbol{0}\},$$

thus there is a linear subspace $\boldsymbol{A}'$ of $\boldsymbol{A}$ such that

50.11.6 $$\boldsymbol{K}' = \boldsymbol{K} + \boldsymbol{A}'.$$

Now

$$[A', A'] \subset A \cap K' \subset A'.$$

This shows that A' is the radical of K'. There is a Levi-splitting

50.11.7 $$K' = L + A' \quad \text{with semisimple } L.$$

Now, because of 50.11.1–7,

$$G = G_1 + G_2 = F_1 + G_2 = F_1 + K + A = F_1 + K' + A = F_1 + L + A$$

and, because of 50.11.4, 7, $F = F_1 + L$ semisimple and

$$G = F + A,$$

a Levi-splitting.

Therefore G mod A may be assumed to be simple. Consequently $\tilde{G}$ may be supposed irreducible on both A and G mod A. If G and $\tilde{G}$ are isomorphic, Proposition 50.8 can be applied to $\tilde{G}$ acting in G. The role of the "clean" representation is then played by the reduction mod A. Proposition 50.8 guarantees the existence of a subalgebra F isomorphic with G mod A. If, however, G has a nontrivial center, the center is in A and therefore equals A. Then $\tilde{G}$ is semisimple and the conducibility theorem applies to the effect that A possesses a $\tilde{G}$-invariant linear complement, which is even an ideal.

This proves Theorem 50.2.

50.12. Historical Note H. B. Casimir and B. L. van der Waerden [*Math. Ann.* **111**, 1–12 (1935)] proved the conducibility theorem with the use of the Casimir tool and weight theory. J. H. C. Whitehead [*Proc. Cambridge Phil. Soc.* **32**, 229–237 (1936); *Quart. J. Math.* **8**, 220–237 (1937)] gave a more elementary proof in which no appeal was made to weight theory, and by the same method he proved E. E. Levi's theorem. It seems that this was the first correct proof of this theorem. The present proofs, based on the same ideas as Whitehead's, were first published by H. Freudenthal [*J. Madras Univer.* **B27**, 225–236 (1957)]. They could be simplified by the use of cohomology language.

51–62

REALITY IN LIE GROUPS AND ALGEBRAS AND THEIR LINEAR REPRESENTATIONS

51. MAXIMALLY COMPACT DRESSING

Of any complex semisimple Lie algebra only two real types have been explicitly dealt with, the unitary and the standard ones. The goal is now a complete classification of real types, as given in Section 26 for the complex case. It is expressed as a classification of involutory semimorphisms. Its theory is developed in the present section.

51.1–3 contain general remarks.

From 51.4 onward $\boldsymbol{G}$ is supposed to be a complex semisimple Lie algebra with the involutory semimorphism C. Also, $\boldsymbol{G}$ is supposed to be linear, the infinitesimal algebra of a linear Lie group G; however, in assertions and proofs concerning $\boldsymbol{G}$ alone, this is only a matter of notational convenience.

51.1–3. Preliminaries

51.1. Proposition If Φ is an automorphism or semimorphism of $\boldsymbol{G} \in$ Alg Lie ($G \in$ Gru Lie Lin), then

$$\widetilde{\Phi \boldsymbol{a}} = \Phi \tilde{\boldsymbol{a}} \Phi^{-1} \qquad (\widetilde{\Phi a} = \Phi \tilde{a} \Phi^{-1}).$$

Remark The second statement can also be derived from the first, e.g. by using exp. This shows that the second statement also holds for local automorphisms and semimorphisms. Thus, even local automorphisms and semimorphisms normalize Int G.

Proof $\widetilde{\Phi \boldsymbol{a}} \boldsymbol{x} = [\Phi \boldsymbol{a}, \boldsymbol{x}] = \Phi[\boldsymbol{a}, \Phi^{-1} \boldsymbol{x}] = \Phi \tilde{\boldsymbol{a}} \Phi^{-1} \boldsymbol{x}$.

$\widetilde{\Phi a} \boldsymbol{x} = (\Phi a) \boldsymbol{x} (\Phi a)^{-1} = \Phi(a(\Phi^{-1} \boldsymbol{x}) a^{-1}) = \Phi \tilde{a} \Phi^{-1} \boldsymbol{x}$.

51.2 Any real Lie algebra can be obtained by real restriction from a complex one, namely, from its complex extension.

Two isomorphic real Lie algebras $\boldsymbol{G}_1, \boldsymbol{G}_2$ possess isomorphic complex extensions. Then the question is, when do two involutory semimorphisms C_1, C_2 of complex $\boldsymbol{G}$ lead to isomorphic real $\boldsymbol{G}_1, \boldsymbol{G}_2$? Such an isomorphism of $\boldsymbol{G}_1$ onto $\boldsymbol{G}_2$ extends to $\boldsymbol{G}$ as an automorphism A of $\boldsymbol{G}$ with the special feature that $\boldsymbol{x} = C_1 \boldsymbol{x}$ implies $A\boldsymbol{x} = C_2 A \boldsymbol{x}$, hence $AC_1 = C_2 A$, first on $\boldsymbol{G}_1$, then on $\boldsymbol{G}$.

This suggests the following definition.

Definition The involutory semimorphisms C_1, C_2 of $\boldsymbol{G} \in$ Alg Lie Com are called *isotypic* if there is an automorphism A of $\boldsymbol{G}$ such that

$$C_2 = AC_1 A^{-1},$$

and *inner isotypic* if A can be chosen as an inner automorphism.

Proposition Two involutory semimorphisms of $\boldsymbol{G} \in$ Alg Lie Com lead to isomorphic real restrictions iff they are isotypic.

"Only if" has been proved; the proof of "if" is the same argument reversed.

Classification of the real types of $\boldsymbol{G}$ up to isomorphism comes to the same thing as that of the semimorphisms of $\boldsymbol{G}$ up to isotypism.

51.3 If $\boldsymbol{G} \in$ Alg Lie Com SS has the semimorphic image $\boldsymbol{G}'$ by means of C, then $\boldsymbol{G}$ and $\boldsymbol{G}'$ are isomorphic, for example by means of CC_{un}, where C_{un} is some unitary semimorphism of $\boldsymbol{G}$.

The equivalence of the following conditions was proved in 1.12.

Definition $\boldsymbol{F} \in$ Alg Lie Rea SSS is described as a *twin* type if it derives from $\boldsymbol{G} \in$ Alg Lie Com SSS by waiving, or, equivalently, if its complex extension is not simple, or, equivalently, if it is the C-restriction of a direct sum $\boldsymbol{G} + C\boldsymbol{G}$, where $C\boldsymbol{G}$ is a copy of $\boldsymbol{G} \in$ Alg Lie Com SSS.

If $\boldsymbol{L} \in$ Alg Lie Com, the result of waiving in $\boldsymbol{L}$ is denoted by $\boldsymbol{L}_{**}$.

Proposition $\boldsymbol{F} \in$ Alg Lie Rea SS is a direct sum of twin-type algebras and algebras with a simple complex extension.

Proof $\boldsymbol{F}$ is the C-restriction of some $\boldsymbol{G} \in$ Alg Lie Com SS, which splits into simple direct summands $\boldsymbol{G}_j$. The splitting is C-invariant. Summands $\boldsymbol{G}_j \neq C\boldsymbol{G}_j$ account for a twin summand of $\boldsymbol{F}$, whereas $\boldsymbol{G}_j = C\boldsymbol{G}_j$ produces a summand with simple complex extension.

51.4. The Class of CC_{un}

Proposition Let C be an involutory semimorphism of $\boldsymbol{G} \in$ Alg Lie Com SS, and C_{un} a unitary one. Then $(CC_{\text{un}})^2 \in \text{Int}\, \boldsymbol{G}$.

Proof 33.9(6) and 33.3.1 grant the existence of an $A \in \text{Aut}\, \boldsymbol{G}$ such that $CC_{\text{un}} \in A \cdot \text{Int}\, \boldsymbol{G}$, and $AC_{\text{un}} = C_{\text{un}} A$. Thus, using Proposition 51.1,

$$C_{\text{un}} C = C_{\text{un}}(CC_{\text{un}})\, C_{\text{un}} \in C_{\text{un}} A \cdot \text{Int}\, \boldsymbol{G} \cdot C_{\text{un}} = C_{\text{un}} A C_{\text{un}}\, \text{Int}\, \boldsymbol{G} = A \cdot \text{Int}\, \boldsymbol{G},$$

$$1 = C_{\text{un}}\, C \cdot CC_{\text{un}} \in A^2 \cdot \text{Int}\, \boldsymbol{G},$$

hence, $A^2 \in \text{Int}\, \boldsymbol{G}$, which proves the assertion.

51.5.1–10. C-Third Dressing and the Hermitean-Unitary Split

In further investigations it proves convenient to have C commute with C_{un}.

51.5.1. Definition For an involutory semimorphism C with $C\boldsymbol{H} = \boldsymbol{H}$ a third dressing with respect to $\boldsymbol{H}$ is called a *C-third dressing* if the C_{un} belonging to the dressing fulfills

$$CC_{\mathrm{un}} = C_{\mathrm{un}} C.$$

The existence of such a dressing will be shown in 51.6. Meanwhile a few properties of a C-third dressing are derived. First a few definitions elaborating on the notions of Section 38.

51.5.2. Definition $\boldsymbol{u} \in \boldsymbol{G}_{\mathrm{un}} \leftrightarrow C_{\mathrm{un}}\boldsymbol{u} = \boldsymbol{u}$,

$$\boldsymbol{s} \in \boldsymbol{G}_{\mathrm{he}} \leftrightarrow C_{\mathrm{un}}\boldsymbol{s} = -\boldsymbol{s} \leftrightarrow \boldsymbol{s} \in \mathrm{i}\boldsymbol{G}_{\mathrm{un}}.$$

G_{un} infinitesimally generated by $\boldsymbol{G}_{\mathrm{un}}$, $\quad G_{\mathrm{he}} = \exp \boldsymbol{G}_{\mathrm{he}}$.

The elements of $\boldsymbol{G}_{\mathrm{he}}$ and G_{he} are called *hermitean*. For a C_{un}-invariant trunk $\boldsymbol{H}$ (cf. 33.13),

$$\boldsymbol{H}_{\mathrm{he}} = \boldsymbol{H}_{\mathrm{st}} = \boldsymbol{H} \cap \boldsymbol{G}_{\mathrm{he}},$$

$$H_{\mathrm{he}} = H_{\mathrm{st}} = H \cap G_{\mathrm{he}} \quad \text{infinitesimally generated by } \boldsymbol{H}_{\mathrm{he}}.$$

51.5.3. Proposition $[\boldsymbol{G}_{\mathrm{un}}, \boldsymbol{G}_{\mathrm{un}}] \subset \boldsymbol{G}_{\mathrm{un}}$, $[\boldsymbol{G}_{\mathrm{un}}, \boldsymbol{G}_{\mathrm{he}}] \subset \boldsymbol{G}_{\mathrm{he}}$, $[\boldsymbol{G}_{\mathrm{he}}, \boldsymbol{G}_{\mathrm{he}}] \subset \boldsymbol{G}_{\mathrm{un}}$.
An immediate consequence of the definition.

51.5.4 For an involutory semimorphism C and a C-invariant trunk $\boldsymbol{H}$:

Definition $\boldsymbol{G}_C = \uparrow_{\boldsymbol{a}\in\boldsymbol{G}}(C\boldsymbol{a} = \boldsymbol{a})$,

G_C infinitesimally generated by $\boldsymbol{G}_C$.

$\boldsymbol{H}_C = \uparrow_{\boldsymbol{a}\in\boldsymbol{H}}(C\boldsymbol{h} = \boldsymbol{h})$,

H_C infinitesimally generated by $\boldsymbol{H}_C$.

Note that C need not be extendible to an automorphism of (real) G, though it is if, for example, G is simply connected or centerfree. Even if C is extendible to G, then still G_C is only the 1-component of the group of C-invariant elements of G.

51.5.5. Proposition If $CC_{\mathrm{un}} = C_{\mathrm{un}} C$, then $C\boldsymbol{G}_{\mathrm{un}} = \boldsymbol{G}_{\mathrm{un}}$, $C\boldsymbol{G}_{\mathrm{he}} = \boldsymbol{G}_{\mathrm{he}}$.

51.5.6. Proposition If $CC_{\mathrm{un}} = C_{\mathrm{un}} C$, $C\boldsymbol{H} = C_{\mathrm{un}}\boldsymbol{H} = \boldsymbol{H}$, then $C\boldsymbol{H}_{\mathrm{un}} = \boldsymbol{H}_{\mathrm{un}}$, $C\boldsymbol{H}_{\mathrm{he}} = \boldsymbol{H}_{\mathrm{he}}$.

51.5.7. Definition If $CC_{\text{un}} = C_{\text{un}}C$, then set

$$\boldsymbol{G}_{C,\text{un}} = \boldsymbol{G}_C \cap \boldsymbol{G}_{\text{un}}, \qquad \boldsymbol{G}_{C,\text{he}} = \boldsymbol{G}_C \cap \boldsymbol{G}_{\text{he}},$$

$$G_{C,\text{un}} \text{ infinitesimally generated by } \boldsymbol{G}_{C,\text{un}}, \qquad G_{C,\text{he}} = \exp \boldsymbol{G}_{C,\text{he}}.$$

Furthermore, if $C\boldsymbol{H} = C_{\text{un}}\boldsymbol{H} = \boldsymbol{H}$, then set

$$\boldsymbol{H}_{C,\text{un}} = \boldsymbol{H}_C \cap \boldsymbol{H}_{\text{un}}, \qquad \boldsymbol{H}_{C,\text{he}} = \boldsymbol{H}_C \cap \boldsymbol{H}_{\text{he}},$$

$$H_{C,\text{un}} \text{ infinitesimally generated by } \boldsymbol{H}_{C,\text{un}},$$

$$H_{C,\text{he}} \text{ infinitesimally generated by } \boldsymbol{H}_{C,\text{he}}.$$

Finally, $\boldsymbol{H}_{C,\text{un},\text{Com}}$ and $\boldsymbol{H}_{C,\text{he},\text{Com}}$ will denote the complexifications of $\boldsymbol{H}_{C,\text{un}}$ and $\boldsymbol{H}_{C,\text{he}}$ in $\boldsymbol{H}$ respectively, and $\boldsymbol{H}^*_{C,\text{un}}$, $\boldsymbol{H}^*_{C,\text{un},\text{Com}}$, $\boldsymbol{H}^*_{C,\text{he}}$, $\boldsymbol{H}^*_{C,\text{he},\text{Com}}$, the ζ-images of $\boldsymbol{H}_{C,\text{un}}$, $\boldsymbol{H}_{C,\text{un},\text{Com}}$, $\boldsymbol{H}_{C,\text{he}}$, $\boldsymbol{H}_{C,\text{he},\text{Com}}$ in $\boldsymbol{H}^*$, respectively.

51.5.8. Proposition Suppose that $CC_{\text{un}} = C_{\text{un}}C$. Then

(1) $\boldsymbol{G} = \boldsymbol{G}_{\text{un}} + \boldsymbol{G}_{\text{he}}$ direct as linear spaces,

(2) $\boldsymbol{G}_C = \boldsymbol{G}_{C,\text{un}} + \boldsymbol{G}_{C,\text{he}}$ direct as linear spaces,

(3) $\boldsymbol{G}_{\text{un}} = \boldsymbol{G}_{C,\text{un}} + \text{i}\boldsymbol{G}_{C,\text{he}}$ direct as linear spaces,

(4) $\psi_C(\boldsymbol{G}_{C,\text{un}}, \boldsymbol{G}_{C,\text{he}}) = 0$.

Proof (1) was proved in Section 38. (2) The splitting $\boldsymbol{a} = \boldsymbol{s} + \boldsymbol{u}$ ($\boldsymbol{s} \in \boldsymbol{G}_{\text{he}}$, $\boldsymbol{u} \in \boldsymbol{G}_{\text{un}}$) is unique; $C\boldsymbol{s} \in \boldsymbol{G}_{\text{he}}$, $C\boldsymbol{u} \in \boldsymbol{G}_{\text{un}}$ (see 51.5.5), $C\boldsymbol{a} = C\boldsymbol{s} + C\boldsymbol{u}$, therefore, if $C\boldsymbol{a} = \boldsymbol{a}$, then $C\boldsymbol{s} = \boldsymbol{s}$, $C\boldsymbol{u} = \boldsymbol{u}$. (3) $\boldsymbol{a} \in \boldsymbol{G}_{\text{un}}$ is the sum of $\frac{1}{2}(1 + C)\boldsymbol{a} \in \boldsymbol{G}_{C,\text{un}}$ and $-\frac{1}{2}\text{i}(1 + C)\text{i}\boldsymbol{a} \in \text{i}\boldsymbol{G}_{C,\text{he}}$; (4) follows from 51.5.3.

Remark $C = C_{\text{un}}$ iff $\boldsymbol{G}_{C,\text{he}} = \{\boldsymbol{0}\}$.

51.5.9 As soon as the existence of C-third dressings has been ascertained, Proposition 51.5.8(1–2) may be stated as follows:

Theorem Up to isomorphism the real restrictions $\boldsymbol{G}_C$ of $\boldsymbol{G} \in$ Alg Lie Com SS arise from $\boldsymbol{G}_{\text{un}}$ by splitting $\boldsymbol{G}_{\text{un}}$ directly into subspaces $\boldsymbol{K}$, $\boldsymbol{L}$ such that

$$[\boldsymbol{K}, \boldsymbol{K}] \subset \boldsymbol{K}, \qquad [\boldsymbol{K}, \boldsymbol{L}] \subset \boldsymbol{L}, \qquad [\boldsymbol{L}, \boldsymbol{L}] \subset \boldsymbol{K},$$

and putting $\boldsymbol{G}_C = \boldsymbol{K} + \text{i}\boldsymbol{L}$.

Proof Given $\boldsymbol{G}_C$, split $\boldsymbol{G}_{\text{un}}$ into $\boldsymbol{K} = \boldsymbol{G}_{C,\text{un}}$, $\boldsymbol{L} = \text{i}\boldsymbol{G}_{C,\text{he}}$, and verify the above relations. Conversely, given the splitting with the above properties, one can easily show that $[\boldsymbol{K} + \text{i}\boldsymbol{L}, \boldsymbol{K} + \text{i}\boldsymbol{L}] \subset \boldsymbol{K} + \text{i}\boldsymbol{L}$, hence that $\boldsymbol{K} + \text{i}\boldsymbol{L}$ is a real restriction of $\boldsymbol{G}$.

51.5.10. Theorem As an analytic manifold, G_C is the product of its closed submanifolds $G_{C,\text{un}}$ and $G_{C,\text{he}}$ by means of the multiplication in G; $G_{C,\text{he}} = G_C \cap G_{\text{he}}$, and $G_{C,\text{un}} = G_C \cap G_{\text{un}}$.

The proof runs along the same lines as that of Theorem 38.4. Note that G_C is closed, as shown in 38.5(4).

51.5.11–12. The Maximal Compact Subgroup

51.5.11. Theorem $G_{C,\text{un}}$ is a maximal compact subgroup of G_C.

Proof The compactness is evident. According to Theorem 51.5.10, any subgroup of G_C larger than $G_{C,\text{un}}$ would contain an element $\neq 1$ of G_{he}, which cannot generate a relatively compact subgroup.

Remarks (1) In fact, every maximal compact subgroup of G_C can be obtained in this way; all are conjugate within G_C. This, however, is a rather profound fact, which will be proved in 65.4.

(2) If, instead of G_C, one considers a group $\hat{G}_C$ which is a wrapping of G_C, then the subgroup $\hat{G}_{C,\text{un}}$ corresponding to $G_{C,\text{un}}$ (generated by $\boldsymbol{G}_{C,\text{un}}$) may cease to be compact. In fact, if $\hat{G}_C$ is the universal wrapping of G_C, then $\hat{G}_{C,\text{un}}$ is some wrapping of $G_{C,\text{un}}$ (actually, it is the universal one; see 62.3); it may happen that $G_{C,\text{un}}$ is not semisimple but has an abelian direct factor; then $\hat{G}_{C,\text{un}}$ is not compact.

51.5.12. Theorem $G_{C,\text{un}}$ is its own normalizer in G_C.

Proof s_0 normalizing $G_{C,\text{un}}$ may be assumed in $G_{C,\text{he}}$, hence of the form $s_0 = \exp \boldsymbol{s}_0$ with some $\boldsymbol{s}_0 \in \boldsymbol{G}_{C,\text{he}}$. For $u \in G_{C,\text{un}}$: $s_0 u s_0^{-1} = u_1 \in G_{C,\text{un}}$. Thus $u^{-1} u_1 s_0 = u^{-1} s_0 u \in G_{C,\text{he}}$. Because of the uniqueness of the hermitean-unitary split, this shows $u^{-1} s_0 u = s_0$ for all $u \in G_{C,\text{un}}$; hence $[\boldsymbol{u}, \boldsymbol{s}_0] = \boldsymbol{0}$ for all $\boldsymbol{u} \in \boldsymbol{G}_{C,\text{un}}$. In

$$\psi(\tilde{\boldsymbol{s}}_0 \boldsymbol{u}, \boldsymbol{s}) + \psi(\boldsymbol{u}, \tilde{\boldsymbol{s}}_0 \boldsymbol{s}) = 0$$

the first summand vanishes for all $\boldsymbol{u} \in \boldsymbol{G}_{C,\text{un}}$ and all $\boldsymbol{s} \in \boldsymbol{G}_{C,\text{he}}$. Therefore $\tilde{\boldsymbol{s}}_0 \boldsymbol{s}$ belongs to the orthoplement $\boldsymbol{G}_{C,\text{he}}$ of $\boldsymbol{G}_{C,\text{un}}$. On the other hand, $\tilde{\boldsymbol{s}}_0 \boldsymbol{s} \in \boldsymbol{G}_{C,\text{un}}$. Hence $\tilde{\boldsymbol{s}}_0 \boldsymbol{s} = \boldsymbol{0}$ apart from $\tilde{\boldsymbol{s}}_0 \boldsymbol{u} = \boldsymbol{0}$, which shows that $\tilde{\boldsymbol{s}}_0 = \boldsymbol{0}$; hence $\boldsymbol{s}_0 = \boldsymbol{0}$, $s_0 = 1$.

51.6. *C*-Third Redressing

Definition If $CH = \boldsymbol{H}$, then define C^* by

$$(C^* \xi)(\boldsymbol{h}) = \overline{\xi(C\boldsymbol{h})} \qquad \text{for all} \quad \boldsymbol{h} \in \boldsymbol{H}, \quad \xi \in \boldsymbol{H}^*.$$

Clearly C^* is linear and belongs to Aut W^*.

If $\boldsymbol{H}$ is a C-invariant trunk and C_{un} is based on $\boldsymbol{H}$, then C and C_{un} commute if restricted to $\boldsymbol{H}$, since C permutes W^* and consequently leaves $\boldsymbol{H}_{\text{st}}$ and $\boldsymbol{H}_{\text{un}}$ invariant.

By a suitable choice more can be attained.

Theorem A given third dressing on a trunk $\boldsymbol{H} = C\boldsymbol{H}$ can be changed into a C-third dressing on the same trunk.

Proof A provisional C_{un} based on $\boldsymbol{H}$ has to be changed into $\tilde{g}C_{\text{un}}\tilde{g}^{-1}$ with some $g = \exp \boldsymbol{g}$, $\boldsymbol{g} \in \boldsymbol{H}_{\text{st}}$, such that

$$C\tilde{g}C_{\text{un}}\tilde{g}^{-1} = \tilde{g}C_{\text{un}}\tilde{g}^{-1}C,$$

equivalently,

51.6.1 $$(\tilde{g}^2 C_{\text{un}} C)^2 = 1.$$

With some scalars κ_α,

$$C\boldsymbol{e}_\alpha = \kappa_\alpha \boldsymbol{e}_{C^*\alpha}.$$

From $C^2 = 1$ it follows that

51.6.2 $$\bar{\kappa}_\alpha \kappa_{C^*\alpha} = 1;$$

from $[\boldsymbol{e}_\alpha, \boldsymbol{e}_{-\alpha}] = \boldsymbol{h}_\alpha$,

51.6.3 $$\kappa_\alpha \kappa_{-\alpha} = 1;$$

from $[\boldsymbol{e}_\alpha, \boldsymbol{e}_\beta] = N_{\alpha,\beta}\boldsymbol{e}_{\alpha+\beta}$ and $|N_{\alpha,\beta}| = |N_{C^*\alpha, C^*\beta}|$ (cf. 23.2),

51.6.4 $$\kappa_\alpha \bar{\kappa}_\alpha \cdot \kappa_\beta \bar{\kappa}_\beta = \kappa_{\alpha+\beta}\bar{\kappa}_{\alpha+\beta}.$$

This shows the existence of $\boldsymbol{h} \in \boldsymbol{H}_{\text{st}}$ with

$$\exp \alpha(\boldsymbol{h}) = \kappa_\alpha \bar{\kappa}_\alpha \qquad \text{for all} \quad \alpha \in W^*.$$

From 51.6.2 it follows that

51.6.5 $$\exp(\alpha + C^*\alpha)(\boldsymbol{h}) = 1;$$

thus, because of $\boldsymbol{h} \in \boldsymbol{H}_{\text{st}}$,

51.6.6 $$(\alpha + C^*\alpha)(\boldsymbol{h}) = 0.$$

To satisfy 51.6.1 its first member with $g = \exp \boldsymbol{g}$ is applied to $\boldsymbol{e}_\alpha$, which gives

$$\bar{\kappa}_{-C^*\alpha}\bar{\kappa}_\alpha \exp 2(\alpha - C^*\alpha)(\boldsymbol{g}) \cdot \boldsymbol{e}_\alpha = \kappa_\alpha \bar{\kappa}_\alpha \exp 2(\alpha - C^*\alpha)(\boldsymbol{g}) \cdot \boldsymbol{e}_\alpha$$

because of 51.6.2–3. To fulfill 51.6.1 one must solve $\boldsymbol{g}$ from

51.6.7 $$2(C^*\alpha - \alpha)(\boldsymbol{g}) = \alpha(\boldsymbol{h}).$$

For this one need only take $-\frac{1}{4}\boldsymbol{h}$ for $\boldsymbol{g}$, as follows immediately from 51.6.6.

51.7. Kinds of Trunks The conjugacy theorem for trunks is a particular feature of unitary and complex semisimple Lie algebras (thus also of the twin type). In all other cases different kinds of trunks have to be distinguished. A first orientation of the variety of possibilities is furnished by the following

Proposition Let the trunk $\boldsymbol{H}$ be C-invariant. Then up to conjugacy within G_C every C-invariant trunk $\boldsymbol{H}'$ is of the form $\tilde{u}\boldsymbol{H}$, where u belongs to the unitary restriction determined by a C-third dressing on $\boldsymbol{H}$.

Remark Of course, not every $\tilde{u}\boldsymbol{H}$ provides a C-invariant trunk.

Proof With C-third dressings on $\boldsymbol{H}$ and $\boldsymbol{H}'$, one obtains C_{un} and C'_{un}, both commuting with C. By 33.13 they are conjugate,

$$C'_{\text{un}} = \tilde{a}C_{\text{un}}\tilde{a}^{-1} = \tilde{a}(\widetilde{C_{\text{un}}a^{-1}})\,C_{\text{un}},$$

such that

$$\tilde{a}\boldsymbol{H} = \boldsymbol{H}'.$$

Now $\tilde{a}(\widetilde{C_{\text{un}}a^{-1}})$ also commutes with C. With the hermitean-unitary splitting

$$a = su, \qquad C_{\text{un}}s = s^{-1}, \qquad C_{\text{un}}u = u,$$

one finds $C\tilde{s}^2 = \tilde{s}^2C$. If $s = \exp \boldsymbol{s}$ for some (unique) $\boldsymbol{s} \in \boldsymbol{G}_{\text{he}}$, then, by the C-invariance of $\boldsymbol{G}_{\text{he}}$, $C\boldsymbol{s} = \boldsymbol{s}$ also, whence $s \in G_{C,\text{he}}$ by 51.5.10. Now $\tilde{s}^{-1}\boldsymbol{H}' = \tilde{u}\boldsymbol{H}$ is a C-invariant trunk of the kind wanted.

51.8. Maximally Compact Trunks H_C of a C-invariant trunk H splits directly into a torus group $H_{C,\text{un}}$ and a flat abelian group $H_{C,\text{he}}$, called, respectively, the *torus* part of H_C and the *flat*, *hermitean*, or *standard* part of H_C (and correspondingly for $\boldsymbol{H}_C$). (See 30.5.)

Note that the flat part would not be uniquely determined if H_C were considered as a real group, disregarding the complex structure of the H in which it is embedded; in the present case, however, it is uniquely determined.

Definition A C-invariant trunk $\boldsymbol{H}$ of $\boldsymbol{G}$ is called *maximally* (*minimally*) *compact* (with respect to C) if H_C contains a maximal torus of G_C (if no proper subset of the torus of H_C can be the torus of H'_C for another C-invariant trunk $\boldsymbol{H}'$).

Maximally compact trunks are studied here, minimally compact ones in Section 60.

The existence of maximally compact trunks is granted by the following

Proposition Every torus of G_C is in a maximally compact trunk.

Proof Take a maximal torus T in G_C. Then 35.9 embeds $\boldsymbol{T}$ into a trunk $\boldsymbol{H}$ of $\boldsymbol{G}$. Take $\boldsymbol{h}$ regular in $\boldsymbol{H}$. Then $C\boldsymbol{h}$ is also regular. Among the $\tau\boldsymbol{h} + \bar{\tau}C\boldsymbol{h}$ is a regular one, say, $\boldsymbol{h}'$. Now $\boldsymbol{h}'$ is C-invariant and determines a C-invariant trunk $\boldsymbol{H}'$; $\boldsymbol{h}$ commutes with every element of $\boldsymbol{T}$ and so does $C\boldsymbol{h}$, since $\boldsymbol{T}$ is C-invariant. Therefore $\boldsymbol{h}'$ commutes with every element of $\boldsymbol{T}$, and consequently $\boldsymbol{T} \subset \boldsymbol{H}' = C\boldsymbol{H}'$. Since T was taken as a maximal torus of G_C, $\boldsymbol{H}'$ is a maximally compact trunk.

51.9. Criteria on Maximally Compact Trunks

Theorem The following assertions on $\boldsymbol{G} \in$ Alg Lie Com SS in third dressing and the semimorphism C are equivalent:

(1) $\boldsymbol{H}$ is a maximally compact trunk (with respect to C).
(2) No $\alpha \in W^*$ vanishes identically on the torus part $\boldsymbol{H}_{C,\mathrm{un}}$ of $\boldsymbol{H}_C$.
(3) The torus part $\boldsymbol{H}_{C,\mathrm{un}}$ of $\boldsymbol{H}_C$ contains a regular element of $\boldsymbol{G}$.
(4) $CC_{\mathrm{un}}\alpha \neq -\alpha$ if $\alpha \in W^*$ and if C_{un} is defined by a C-third dressing on $\boldsymbol{H}$.
(5) CC_{un} (as in 4) leaves some chamber invariant.

Proof One may suppose that $CC_{\mathrm{un}} = C_{\mathrm{un}}C$ anyhow (51.6).

$\neg 2 \to \neg 4$ (with the same α): Suppose $\alpha(\boldsymbol{h}) = 0$ for $\boldsymbol{h} \in \boldsymbol{H}_C \cap \boldsymbol{H}_{\mathrm{un}}$. Then $\alpha(\boldsymbol{h} + CC_{\mathrm{un}}\boldsymbol{h}) = 0$ for all $\boldsymbol{h} \in \boldsymbol{H}_{\mathrm{un}}$ and, since α is linear, for all $\boldsymbol{h} \in \boldsymbol{H}$. Thus $((1 + CC_{\mathrm{un}})\alpha)(\boldsymbol{h}) = 0$ for all $\boldsymbol{h} \in \boldsymbol{H}$ which falsifies 4 with the same α.

$\neg 2 \to \neg 1$ (using $\neg 4$): Put $\boldsymbol{B} = \boldsymbol{H}_{C,\mathrm{un}}$. Suppose that $\alpha(\boldsymbol{B}) = \{0\}$ for some $\alpha \in W^*$. Then $[\boldsymbol{B}, \boldsymbol{e}_{\pm\alpha}] = \{\boldsymbol{0}\}$. From $\neg 4$ it follows that $C^*\alpha = -C^*_{\mathrm{un}}\alpha$, hence $C\boldsymbol{e}_\alpha = \nu_\alpha \boldsymbol{e}_\alpha$ with $|\nu_\alpha| = 1$. Putting $\nu_\alpha^{1/2}\boldsymbol{e}_\alpha = \boldsymbol{a}$, one gets $C\boldsymbol{a} = \boldsymbol{a}$. Putting $\boldsymbol{b} = \boldsymbol{a} + C_{\mathrm{un}}\boldsymbol{a}$, one gets $\boldsymbol{b} = C_{\mathrm{un}}\boldsymbol{b} = C\boldsymbol{b} \neq \boldsymbol{0}$, and $[\boldsymbol{B}, \boldsymbol{b}] = \{\boldsymbol{0}\}$. Now $\exp \tau\boldsymbol{b}$ (τ real) $\in G_{C,\mathrm{un}}$ and commutes with every element of $\boldsymbol{B}$. Therefore $\boldsymbol{B}$ and $\exp \tau\boldsymbol{b}$ (real τ) generate a torus, which proves the existence of a torus subgroup of G_C larger than B.

$2 \to 3$ is trivial.

$3 \to 1$: Let $\boldsymbol{h} \in \boldsymbol{H}_{C,\mathrm{un}}$ be regular and let $\boldsymbol{B} \subset \boldsymbol{G}_C, \supset \boldsymbol{H}_{C,\mathrm{un}}$, and B maximal compact abelian. Then $[\boldsymbol{h}, \boldsymbol{B}] = \{\boldsymbol{0}\}$, and, since $\boldsymbol{h}$ is regular, $\boldsymbol{B} \subset \boldsymbol{H}$. Since B is compact, $\boldsymbol{B} \subset \boldsymbol{H}_{\mathrm{un}} \cap \boldsymbol{G}_C = \boldsymbol{H}_{C,\mathrm{un}}$. Thus $H_{C,\mathrm{un}}$ is maximal compact abelian within G_C, which proves that $\boldsymbol{H}$ is a maximally compact trunk.

$4 \to 5$: $\boldsymbol{h}' = (1 + CC_{\mathrm{un}})\boldsymbol{h}$ for $\boldsymbol{h} \in \boldsymbol{H}_{\mathrm{st}}$ is CC_{un}-invariant; $\alpha(\boldsymbol{h}') = ((1 + CC_{\mathrm{un}})\alpha)(\boldsymbol{h})$. Therefore $\boldsymbol{h}$ can be chosen such that $\alpha(\boldsymbol{h}') = 0$ for no $\alpha \in W^*$. $\zeta\boldsymbol{h}'$ is in some chamber, which is also CC_{un}-invariant.

$5 \to 4$ is obvious. Then

$\neg 4 \to \neg 2$: Suppose that $CC_{\mathrm{un}}\alpha = -\alpha$ for some $\alpha \in W^*$. For $\boldsymbol{h} \in \boldsymbol{H}_{C,\mathrm{un}}$ one gets

$$\alpha(\boldsymbol{h}) = \alpha(CC_{\mathrm{un}}\boldsymbol{h}) = (CC_{\mathrm{un}}\alpha)(\boldsymbol{h}) = -\alpha(\boldsymbol{h});$$

therefore

$$\alpha(\boldsymbol{h}) = 0.$$

51.10. Conjugacy of Maximally Compact Trunks

Theorem Two maximally compact trunks of $\boldsymbol{G}$ (with respect to C) are conjugate by means of elements of G_C.

Proof C-third dressing with respect to the trunk $\boldsymbol{H}$ is supposed. 51.7 allows one to restrict the proof to the trunks $\boldsymbol{H}$ and $\boldsymbol{H}' = \tilde{u}\boldsymbol{H} = C\tilde{u}\boldsymbol{H}$, where $u \in G_{\text{un}}$. Let B be the torus part of H_C and B' that of H'_C. Then

$$\boldsymbol{B} \subset \boldsymbol{G}_{\text{un}} \cap \boldsymbol{G}_C = \boldsymbol{F};$$

$\tilde{u}^{-1}B'$ is compact and contained in H, hence in $H_{\text{un}} \subset G_{\text{un}}$; thus $\tilde{u}^{-1}\boldsymbol{B}' \subset \boldsymbol{G}_{\text{un}}$,

$$\boldsymbol{B}' \subset \boldsymbol{G}_{\text{un}}$$

as well as $\boldsymbol{B}' \subset \boldsymbol{G}_C$. Therefore $\boldsymbol{B}, \boldsymbol{B}'$ are both in $\boldsymbol{F}$. Now $\boldsymbol{F}$ is the infinitesimal algebra of the compact linear Lie group $F = G_{C,\text{un}}$, which according to 19.15 splits directly:

$$\boldsymbol{F} = \boldsymbol{F}_0 + \boldsymbol{F}_1$$

with abelian $\boldsymbol{F}_0$ and semisimple $\boldsymbol{F}_1$. Furthermore, $\boldsymbol{B}, \boldsymbol{B}'$, as maximal abelian subalgebras of $\boldsymbol{F}$, split directly:

$$\boldsymbol{B} = \boldsymbol{F}_0 + \boldsymbol{B}_1, \qquad \boldsymbol{B}' = \boldsymbol{F}_0 + \boldsymbol{B}'_1,$$

where

$$\boldsymbol{B}_1 = \boldsymbol{F}_1 \cap \boldsymbol{B}, \qquad \boldsymbol{B}'_1 = \boldsymbol{F}_1 \cap \boldsymbol{B}';$$

$\boldsymbol{B}_1$ and $\boldsymbol{B}'_1$ are necessarily trunks of $\boldsymbol{F}$. By virtue of the conjugacy theorem in F_1, there is an $a \in F \subset G_C$ such that $\boldsymbol{B}'_1 = \tilde{a}\boldsymbol{B}_1$ and consequently $\boldsymbol{B}' = \tilde{a}\boldsymbol{B}$. Now both $\tilde{a}\boldsymbol{H}$ and H' are trunks containing $\boldsymbol{B}'$, which possesses a regular element; hence $\tilde{a}\boldsymbol{H} = \boldsymbol{H}'$ as desired.

51.11. Maximally Compact Dressing

Definition A C-third dressing on $C\boldsymbol{H} = \boldsymbol{H}$ is called a *maximally compact dressing* if $\boldsymbol{H}$ is maximally compact. The term *ordered maximally compact dressing* is reserved for a choice of the partial order which makes a CC_{un}-invariant chamber of $\boldsymbol{H}^*_{\text{st}}$ dominant.

In 51.6 and 51.8–9 the possibility of ordered maximally compact dressing was proved.

Theorem Under ordered maximally compact dressing on $\boldsymbol{H}$

51.11.1 $$C = \tilde{h}AC_{\text{un}},$$

where A is the straight extension of an automorphism of W^{++} (see 33.3.1), $h \in H_{\text{un}}$,

$$AW^{++} = W^{++},$$

51.11.2 $$A^2 = 1,$$

51.11.3 $$AC_{\text{un}} = C_{\text{un}} A,$$

51.11.4 $$\widetilde{Ah} = \tilde{h}^{-1}.$$

Proof CC_{un} leaves W^{++} invariant and induces an automorphism A of W^{++} with $A^2 = 1$, according to 51.4. A extends according to 33.3.1 to $\boldsymbol{G}$, and to H; $CC_{\text{un}} A$ leaves $\boldsymbol{H}$ elementwise invariant and preserves $\boldsymbol{G}_{\text{un}}$. By 33.9(2) it is induced by some $h^{-1} \in H_{\text{un}}$. Finally $1 = C^2 = \tilde{h}AC_{\text{un}}\tilde{h}AC_{\text{un}} = \tilde{h}\widetilde{Ah}$.

51.12–15. Reductions toward Classification

51.12 With a view to isotypism the presentation of C according to Theorem 51.11 can still be simplified. This will be done in 51.12–14.

Proposition Up to inner isotypism of

$$C = \tilde{h}AC_{\text{un}},$$

as presented in 51.11, $h = \exp \boldsymbol{h}, \boldsymbol{h} \in \boldsymbol{H}_{\text{un}}$ may be supposed to fulfill

$$\rho(\boldsymbol{h}) = 0 \qquad \text{if} \quad \rho \neq A\rho,$$
$$\rho(\boldsymbol{h}) = 0, \pi\text{i} \qquad \text{if} \quad \rho = A\rho,$$

for $\rho \in W^{++}$; hence

$$Ah = h.$$

Proof In the given $C = \tilde{h}AC_{\text{un}}$, because of 51.11.4,

$$h = \exp \boldsymbol{h}, \qquad \boldsymbol{h} \in \boldsymbol{H}_{\text{un}},$$

51.12.1 $$\rho(\boldsymbol{h} + A\boldsymbol{h}) = 0 \bmod 2\pi\text{i} \qquad \text{for} \quad \rho \in W^{++}.$$

By means of

$$h_0 = \exp \boldsymbol{h}_0, \qquad \boldsymbol{h}_0 \in \boldsymbol{H}_{\text{un}},$$

C should be replaced by inner isotypic

$$C' = \tilde{h}_0 C\tilde{h}_0^{-1} = \tilde{h}_0 \widetilde{Ah_0^{-1}}\, C.$$

Putting

$$\exp \boldsymbol{h}' = h' = h\, h_0(Ah_0^{-1}),$$

one gets the new C' in the form

$$C' = \widetilde{h'} A C_{\mathrm{un}}.$$

As to $\boldsymbol{h}'$, one can take it as

$$\boldsymbol{h}' = \boldsymbol{h} + \boldsymbol{h}_0 - A\boldsymbol{h}_0;$$

$\boldsymbol{h}_0$ is chosen such that for each two elements of W^{++} interchanged by A,

$$\begin{aligned} \rho(\boldsymbol{h}_0) &= -\rho(\boldsymbol{h}) && \text{for one element } \rho \text{ among them} \\ \rho(\boldsymbol{h}_0) &= 0 && \text{for the other one.} \end{aligned}$$

Then with a view to 51.12.1

$$\begin{aligned} \rho(\boldsymbol{h}') &= 0 \bmod \pi\mathrm{i} && \text{for } A\rho = \rho, \\ \rho(\boldsymbol{h}') &= 0 \bmod 2\pi\mathrm{i} && \text{for } A\rho \neq \rho, \end{aligned}$$

Without changing h', one can modify $\boldsymbol{h}'$ such that

$$\begin{aligned} \rho(\boldsymbol{h}') &= 0 \quad \text{or} \quad \pi\mathrm{i} && \text{for } A\rho = \rho, \\ \rho(\boldsymbol{h}') &= 0 && \text{for } A\rho \neq \rho. \end{aligned}$$

This proves the assertion.

51.13 If $A = 1$, the reduction of

$$C = \tilde{h} C_{\mathrm{un}} = \widetilde{\exp \boldsymbol{h}}\, C_{\mathrm{un}}$$

can be continued by the use of some $S \in \operatorname{Int} W^*$, which extends to some $\tilde{u}$ with $u \in G_{\mathrm{un}}$; C is replaced by inner isotypic

$$C' = \tilde{u} C \tilde{u}^{-1} = \tilde{u}\tilde{h}\tilde{u}^{-1} C_{\mathrm{un}} = \widetilde{\exp S\boldsymbol{h}}\, C_{\mathrm{un}}.$$

For $\boldsymbol{h}$ this means that it may be submitted to the action of Int W^* as well as replaced by $\boldsymbol{h}'$ such that $\rho(\boldsymbol{h}) = \rho(\boldsymbol{h}') \bmod 2\pi\mathrm{i}$ for $\rho \in W^{++}$.

In the terminology of 33.14.4 this says the following.

Proposition In $C = \tilde{h} C_{\mathrm{un}}$ ($h = \exp \boldsymbol{h}$, $\boldsymbol{h} \in \boldsymbol{H}_{\mathrm{un}}$) up to inner isotypy of C one can change $\boldsymbol{h}$ into any Int mod W^*-equivalent. In $C = \tilde{h} A C_{\mathrm{un}}$ (see Proposition 51.12) the same change is allowed with respect to the subgraph of A-invariant elements of W^{++}.

51.14 Thus $\boldsymbol{h}$ may be assumed in the closure of the principal domain $\bar{\boldsymbol{D}}$ (or in that belonging to the A-invariant part of the graph). Whence:

Theorem After ordered maximally compact dressing of $G \in$ Alg Lie Com SS with respect to the involutory semimorphism C, up to inner isotypy by means of an element of G_{un}, C can be assumed to be such that

51.14.1 $$C = \tilde{h} A C_{\text{un}},$$

where A is the straight extension of an automorphism of W^{++},

51.14.2 $$AW^{++} = W^{++},$$

51.14.3 $$AC_{\text{un}} = C_{\text{un}} A,$$

51.14.4 $$A^2 = 1,$$

51.14.5 $$h = \exp 2\pi i \boldsymbol{h}, \qquad \boldsymbol{h} \in \boldsymbol{H}_{\text{he}},$$

51.14.6 $$\rho(\boldsymbol{h}) = 0 \qquad \text{for} \quad \rho \in W^{++}, \quad \rho \neq A\rho,$$

51.14.7 $$\rho(\boldsymbol{h}) = 0, \tfrac{1}{2} \qquad \text{for} \quad \rho \in W^{++}, \quad \rho = A\rho,$$

51.14.8 $$\alpha(\boldsymbol{h}) \leqslant 1 \qquad \text{for every } \alpha \in W^{+} \text{ which is a sum of } A\text{-invariant elements of } W^{++}.$$

51.15 Further simplifications are possible for simple $\boldsymbol{G}$.

$$A = 1$$

Proposition If, under the conditions of 51.14, $\boldsymbol{G}$ is simple, 51.14.8 can be replaced by

51.15.1 $$\hat{\alpha}(\boldsymbol{h}) \leqslant 1 \qquad \text{for the top rootform } \hat{\alpha}.$$

This is a consequence of 25.6.

Table E of top rootforms shows that to satisfy 51.15.1 $\rho(\boldsymbol{h}) = \frac{1}{2}$ is allowed for two primitive rootforms ρ at most and that such a pair of nonvanishing $\rho(\boldsymbol{h})$ is only possible for

$$\mathbf{A}_l, \quad \mathbf{D}_l\ (\rho_1, \rho_2, \rho_3), \quad \mathbf{E}_6\ (\rho_1, \rho_3).$$

However, even in these cases, the number of nonvanishing $\rho(\boldsymbol{h})$ will be reduced to 1 by the use of Proposition 51.13; then

51.15.2 $$\rho(\boldsymbol{h}) \neq 0 \qquad \text{for at most one} \quad \rho \in W^{++}.$$

$\mathbf{A}_l$: Suppose that $i < j$, $\rho_i(\boldsymbol{h}) = \rho_j(\boldsymbol{h}) = \frac{1}{2}$, $\rho_k(\boldsymbol{h}) = 0$ for $k \neq i, j$. Put $\alpha =$

$\rho_i + \rho_{i+1} + \cdots + \rho_{j-1}$. Thus $\alpha \in W^+$. Applying S_α, one gets

$$\begin{aligned}\rho_k(S_\alpha \boldsymbol{h}) &= (S_\alpha \rho_k)(\boldsymbol{h}) \\ &= (\rho_{i-1} + \alpha)(\boldsymbol{h}) = \tfrac{1}{2} && \text{for} \quad k = i-1 \\ &= (\rho_i - \alpha)(\boldsymbol{h}) = 0 && \text{for} \quad k = i \\ &= (\rho_{j-1} - \alpha)(\boldsymbol{h}) = -\tfrac{1}{2} && \text{for} \quad k = j-1 \neq i \\ &= (\alpha + \rho_j)(\boldsymbol{h}) = 1 && \text{for} \quad k = j \\ &= 0 \text{ otherwise.}\end{aligned}$$

The unit appearing for $k = j$ can be replaced by 0 without changing h. By applying S_α the pair of primitive roots for which $\boldsymbol{h}$ does not vanish moves to the left. Repeating this procedure one finally arrives at the announced result.

$\mathbf{D}_l$: Let $\rho(\boldsymbol{h})$, $\sigma(\boldsymbol{h}) \neq 0$ for some distinct $\rho, \sigma \in W^{++}$. Then both are endpoints of the graph, and at least one of them, say ρ, is the endpoint of a short branch. Let α be the sum of the elements of W^{++} different from ρ, and let τ be the third endpoint. Then $S_\alpha \rho = \rho + \alpha$, $S_\alpha \sigma = \sigma - \alpha$, $S_\alpha \tau = \tau - \alpha$. Thus

$$\rho(S_\alpha \boldsymbol{h}) = \sigma(S_\alpha \boldsymbol{h}) = 0 \bmod 1,$$

$$\tau(S_\alpha \boldsymbol{h}) = \tfrac{1}{2} \bmod 1,$$

the other primitive rootforms being 0 in $S_\alpha \boldsymbol{h}$. So application of S_α yields the required result.

$\mathbf{E}_6$: Here the only troublesome case is with $\rho_1(\boldsymbol{h}) = \rho_3(\boldsymbol{h}) = \frac{1}{2}$. Then one can for instance apply consecutively

$$S_{\rho_2+\rho_3+\rho_4+\rho_5+\rho_6}, \quad S_{\rho_2}, \quad S_{\rho_2+\rho_6}, \quad S_{\rho_5}, \quad S_{\rho_3}.$$

$$A \neq 1$$

In any event, the subgraph of A-invariant elements of W^{++} is of the kind $\mathbf{A}$. By 51.14.6–8, $\rho(\boldsymbol{h}) \neq 0$ only happens for a ρ of the subgraph and then at most twice. One can again attain 51.15.2 by the same procedure as in the case $A = 1$.

A as required in 51.14.2–4 is uniquely defined except for $\mathbf{D}_4$. Even in this case, up to outer automorphisms, it may be supposed to be the plus-automorphism of 33.11 (interchanging ρ_1, ρ_2 in $\mathbf{D}_4$). Then admissible $\boldsymbol{h}$, according to 51.14.5–7, 51.15.1–2, may be supposed to fulfill

$\mathbf{A}_l\,(l > 1)$: $\quad \rho_j(\boldsymbol{h}) = 0 \quad$ for all $\quad j \neq \frac{1}{2}(l+1)$,

$\qquad \rho_j(h) = 0, \frac{1}{2} \quad$ for $\quad j = \frac{1}{2}(l+1), \qquad$ if l is odd.

$\mathbf{D}_l$: $\quad \rho_1(\boldsymbol{h}) = \rho_2(\boldsymbol{h}) = 0$,

$\qquad \rho_j(\boldsymbol{h}) = 0, \frac{1}{2} \quad$ for $\quad j \neq 1, 2, \quad$ yet at most one $\frac{1}{2}$ only.

$\mathbf{E}_6$:
$$\rho_j(\boldsymbol{h}) = 0 \quad \text{for} \quad j \neq 2,$$
$$\rho_j(\boldsymbol{h}) = 0, \tfrac{1}{2} \quad \text{for} \quad j = 2.$$

(By use of the kaleidoscope group this comprises the case $\rho_j(\boldsymbol{h}) = 0$ for $j \neq 6$, $\rho_6(\boldsymbol{h}) = \frac{1}{2}$.)

51.16. The Twin Case The twin case is conveniently fitted into the same frame.

Let $\boldsymbol{F} \in$ Alg Lie Rea SSS of twin type; then its complex extension $\boldsymbol{F}_{\text{Com}}$ is the direct sum $\boldsymbol{G} + C\boldsymbol{G}$ with simple $\boldsymbol{G}$ and the involutory semimorphism C. If $\boldsymbol{H}$ is an ordered trunk of $\boldsymbol{G}$, then $C\boldsymbol{H}$, with transfer of the order, is one of $C\boldsymbol{G}$. The ordered third dressing of $\boldsymbol{G}$ is mapped into one of $C\boldsymbol{G}$ by C.

Definition In ordered third dressing of $\boldsymbol{G} + C\boldsymbol{G}$ the choice of the trunk is $\boldsymbol{H} + C\boldsymbol{H}$ and C^* is assumed to interchange $\boldsymbol{H}^*_{\text{st}}$ and $C\boldsymbol{H}^*_{\text{st}}$ in orderly fashion (hence to interchange the dominant chambers); if the partial order is extended to a total one, $\boldsymbol{H}^*_{\text{st}}$ is assumed to precede $C\boldsymbol{H}^*_{\text{st}}$. The third dressing is C-invariant. The plus-automorphism of $\boldsymbol{F}_{\text{Com}}$ is defined to interchange $\boldsymbol{G}$ and $C\boldsymbol{G}$ in an obvious way, that is by $P_{\text{tw}} = CC_{\text{un}}M$, where M is the minus-automorphism.

Then again
$$C = AC_{\text{un}} \qquad \text{with} \quad A = P_{\text{tw}}M;$$
$\boldsymbol{F}$ appears as the C-restriction of $\boldsymbol{G} + C\boldsymbol{G}$.

51.17. Classification Dressing

Definition $\boldsymbol{L} \in$ Alg Lie Com SSS in ordered third dressing. Let $\boldsymbol{G}$ be identical to $\boldsymbol{L}$ or to the direct sum of two copies of $\boldsymbol{L}$ (with the ordered third dressing defined as in 51.16). Let C_{un} be based on the trunk $\boldsymbol{H}$ of $\boldsymbol{G}$. Let A be 1 or the plus-automorphism P (in the case $\boldsymbol{G} \neq \boldsymbol{L}: P_{\text{tw}}M$). Let W^{++} be enumerated as in 25.7 and 26.23. Let $h = \exp 2\pi i\boldsymbol{h}$ with
$$\rho(\boldsymbol{h}) = 0 \qquad \text{for all} \quad \rho \in W^{++}(\boldsymbol{G})$$
or
$$\rho_j(\boldsymbol{h}) = \tfrac{1}{2}, \quad \rho(\boldsymbol{h}) = 0 \qquad \text{for} \quad \rho_j, \rho \in W^{++}(\boldsymbol{G}), \quad \rho \neq \rho_j,$$
where
$$A\rho_j = \rho_j$$
and ρ_j occurs with a coefficient $\leqslant 2$ in the top rootform of $\boldsymbol{L}$.†

† This condition could be omitted when defining the $\boldsymbol{L}_j$. It would not, however, lead to new classes.

If

$$C = \tilde{h} A C_{\mathrm{un}},$$

then the C-restriction of $\boldsymbol{G}$ is called of

inner type if $\boldsymbol{G} = \boldsymbol{L}$ and $A = 1$,

outer type if $\boldsymbol{G} = \boldsymbol{L}$ and $A \neq 1$,

twin type if $\boldsymbol{G} \neq \boldsymbol{L}$ (and $A \neq 1$).

Inner types are indicated by $\boldsymbol{L}_j$,

outer types are indicated by $\boldsymbol{L}_{j,*}$,

twin types are indicated by $\boldsymbol{L}_{**}$,

where j will be taken as 0 if $\rho(\boldsymbol{h}) = 0$ for all $\rho \in W^{++}$.

If $\boldsymbol{L} \in \mathbf{L}$, then the class of real Lie algebras isomorphic with $\boldsymbol{L}_j$, $\boldsymbol{L}_{j,*}$, $\boldsymbol{L}_{**}$ is denoted by $\mathbf{L}_j$, $\mathbf{L}_{j,*}$, $\mathbf{L}_{**}$.

The class of real linear Lie groups with an infinitesimal algebra in $\mathbf{L}_j$, $\mathbf{L}_{j,*}$, $\mathbf{L}_{**}$ is called L_j, $\mathsf{L}_{j,*}$, L_{**}.

The discussion led to the following theorem:

Theorem Every $\boldsymbol{G} \in$ Alg Lie Rea SSS belongs to at least one of the classes $\mathbf{L}_j$, $\mathbf{L}_{j,*}$, $\mathbf{L}_{**}$. It appears in ordered maximally compact dressing.

51.18–20. Isomorphisms

51.18 Different subscripts j with the same $\boldsymbol{L}$ may indicate isomorphic Lie algebras. The following is a method of finding such isomorphisms.

Suppose a graph W^{++} with simple bonds only. Then by 33.2.4 all elements of W^* are equivalent under Int W^*. Let the top rootform $\hat{\alpha}$ be a fundamental weight and let $\rho_i \in W^{++}$ be such that $(\hat{\alpha}, \rho_i) \neq 0$. Let ρ_j be some endpoint of the graph and ρ_k its neighbor. Then

$$\rho_k(\boldsymbol{h}) = \tfrac{1}{2}, \qquad \rho(\boldsymbol{h}) = 0 \bmod 1 \qquad \text{for} \quad \rho \in W^{++}, \quad \rho \neq \rho_k,$$

is solved by $(\rho_j, \rho_j)^{-1} \boldsymbol{h}_{\rho_j}$; this, under Int W^*, is equivalent to $\boldsymbol{h}' = (\hat{\alpha}, \hat{\alpha})^{-1} \boldsymbol{h}_{\hat{\alpha}}$. Since $\hat{\alpha}$ is a fundamental weight,

$$\rho_i(\boldsymbol{h}') = \tfrac{1}{2}, \qquad \rho(\boldsymbol{h}') = 0 \bmod 1 \qquad \text{for} \quad \rho \in W^{++}, \quad \rho \neq \rho_i;$$

hence

$$\mathbf{L}_i = \mathbf{L}_k.$$

51.19 Still a consequence of 51.5.11:

Theorem If $G \in$ Alg Lie Com SS and G_C is compact, then up to isotypy $C = C_{\mathrm{un}}$.

The compact ones in the classification of 51.17 are characterized by the lack of an asterisk and the subscript 0.

51.20 In the detailed classification that follows in Sections 52–53 the various real $G_C \in$ Alg Lie Rea SSS will be described by specifying their $\boldsymbol{G}_{C,\mathrm{un}}$, that is, the infinitesimal algebra of a maximal compact subgroup $G_{C,\mathrm{un}}$ of G_C. The structure of $\boldsymbol{G}_{C,\mathrm{un}}$ can be used as a criterion of nonisomorphy of the indicated types, though in almost all cases simpler criteria like the signature of the restricted Killing form are available.

$$\boldsymbol{G}_{C,\mathrm{un}} = +1\text{-eigenspace of } CC_{\mathrm{un}} \text{ in } \boldsymbol{G}_{\mathrm{un}},$$
$$\mathrm{i}\boldsymbol{G}_{C,\mathrm{he}} = -1\text{-eigenspace of } CC_{\mathrm{un}} \text{ in } \boldsymbol{G}_{\mathrm{un}},$$
$$\text{signature } \boldsymbol{G}_C = -\mathrm{tr}\, CC_{\mathrm{un}} = \dim \boldsymbol{G}_{C,\mathrm{he}} - \dim \boldsymbol{G}_{C,\mathrm{un}} = \dim \boldsymbol{G}_C - 2\dim \boldsymbol{G}_{C,\mathrm{un}}.$$

51.21. The Description of the Graph of $\boldsymbol{G}_{C,\mathrm{un}}$ $\boldsymbol{G}_{C,\mathrm{un}}$ always will be either semisimple or the direct sum of a semisimple algebra and a 1-dimensional abelian algebra, mutually orthogonal under ψ_G. The intersection of $\boldsymbol{H}$ with the semisimple part of $\boldsymbol{G}_{C,\mathrm{un,Com}}$ (interpreted within $\boldsymbol{G}$) is a trunk, and the dual of this trunk is interpreted within $\boldsymbol{H}^*_{C,\mathrm{un,Com}} \subset \boldsymbol{H}^*$ by means of ζ. In particular, the rootforms of the semisimple part of $\boldsymbol{G}_{C,\mathrm{un,Com}}$, the *rootforms of* $\boldsymbol{G}_{C,\mathrm{un}}$ for short, are now elements of $\boldsymbol{H}^*_{C,\mathrm{un,Com}}$ and even of $\mathrm{i}\boldsymbol{H}^*_{C,\mathrm{un}}$.

The restriction of ψ_G to $\boldsymbol{G}_{C,\mathrm{un,Com}}$ is invariant under the adjoint of $G_{C,\mathrm{un}}$, and therefore if $\boldsymbol{G}_{C,\mathrm{un,Com}}$ is simple semisimple (and consequently $\tilde{G}_{C,\mathrm{un,Com}}$ is irreducible) $\psi_G|\boldsymbol{G}_{C,\mathrm{un,Com}}$ equals $\psi_{\boldsymbol{G}_{C,\mathrm{un,Com}}}$ up to a constant factor $\neq 0$. In general, the same is still true on every simple semisimple direct summand of $\boldsymbol{G}_{C,\mathrm{un,Com}}$, whereas the summands themselves are orthogonal to each other according to both quadratic forms.

This property, if restricted to the trunk and transferred to the dual trunk by means of ζ, leads to the following

Proposition The inner product in the graph of $\boldsymbol{G}_{C,\mathrm{un}}$ is, up to factors constant in every component, the restriction of the inner product in $\boldsymbol{H}^*$.

51.22. Further Notations and Conventions $\boldsymbol{G}_{C,\mathrm{un}}$ will often split into two or even more summands. If they belong to the compact types of $\mathbf{L}$, $\mathbf{M}$, ..., the isomorphism class of the sum is indicated by $\mathbf{L} + \mathbf{M} + \cdots$. To account for one-dimensional summands, one makes the convention:

$$\mathbf{D}_1 = \text{the class of 1-dimensional complex Lie algebras.}$$

This convention supplements the known equalities (see 25.8 and Table G):

$$\mathbf{A}_1 = \mathbf{B}_1 = \mathbf{C}_1, \qquad \mathbf{B}_2 = \mathbf{C}_2, \qquad \mathbf{D}_2 = \mathbf{A}_1 + \mathbf{A}_1, \qquad \mathbf{D}_3 = \mathbf{A}_3.$$

Any $\mathbf{A}_0$, $\mathbf{B}_0$, $\mathbf{C}_0$, $\mathbf{D}_0$, if it occurs, means

$$\mathbf{O} = \text{the class of the null-algebras.}$$

$\tilde{G}_{C,\mathrm{un}}$ causes a linear representation ϑ in $G_{C,\mathrm{he}}$. In Sections 62–63 it will be shown that ϑ determines the global structure of $G_{C,\mathrm{un}}$ and consequently the fundamental group of G_C. For this later use ϑ is indicated here by the top weight(s) of its canonical complexification. In this context a notation like $\pi_k(\mathbf{L}) + \pi_m(\mathbf{M})$ or $\pi_{k,m}(\mathbf{L} + \mathbf{M})$ means that the first summand is represented according to π_k and the second according to π_m; then π_k and π_m are the restrictions of the top weight of ϑ to the trunks of $\mathbf{L}$ and $\mathbf{M}$, respectively. It so happens that ϑ is reducible iff $G_{C,\mathrm{un}}$ is not semisimple, in which case $G_{C,\mathrm{un}}$ contains just one summand of the class $\mathbf{D}_1$. Such a summand is always represented with two opposite weights, which fact will not explicitly be mentioned in the subscripts of π.

A few more conventions:

$$\begin{aligned}
\pi_3(\mathbf{D}_2) &= \pi_{1,1}(\mathbf{A}_1 + \mathbf{A}_1) = \pi_1(\mathbf{A}_1) + \pi_1(\mathbf{A}_1),\\
2\pi_3(\mathbf{D}_2) &= 2\pi_1(\mathbf{A}_1) + 2\pi_1(\mathbf{A}_1),\\
\pi_3(\mathbf{D}_3) &= \pi_2(\mathbf{A}_3),\\
2\pi_3(\mathbf{D}_3) &= 2\pi_2(\mathbf{A}_3),\\
\pi_2(\mathbf{B}_1) &= 2\pi_1(\mathbf{A}_1),\\
2\pi_2(\mathbf{B}_1) &= 4\pi_1(\mathbf{A}_1).
\end{aligned}$$

51.23. Historical Note E. Cartan's method of real classification [*Ann. Ecole Norm.* (3) **31**, 263–355 (1914) = *Œuvres I* **1**, 339–491] was rather casual. F. Gantmakher [*Mat. Sbornik* **5** (47), 217–249 (1938)] built a theory of real classification on H. Weyl's approach to semisimple Lie groups and Cartan's further developments. His theory has here been refined and greatly simplified by the use of primitive roots and the notion of maximally compact dressing. The most elementary proof of 51.6 has been found by H. de Vries. The actual classification will now require a minimum of casual distinctions and computations. The notation 51.17, which shows great systematic advantages, was proposed and used long since by H. Freudenthal.

52. CLASSIFICATION OF INNER TYPES

52.1 $G \in$ Alg Lie Com SSS in ordered maximally compact dressing, G_C of inner type.

If $G_C \in \mathbf{L}_j$ $(j \neq 0)$, then

$$G_{C,\mathrm{un}} = \text{real linear span of } H_{\mathrm{un}} \text{ and the } \tau_\alpha e_\alpha - \bar{\tau}_\alpha e_{-\alpha}, \text{ where } \rho_j \text{ occurs in } \alpha$$

with an even coefficient, and

$$G_{C,\mathrm{he}} = \text{real linear span of the } \mathrm{i}(\tau_\alpha e_\alpha - \bar\tau_\alpha e_{-\alpha}), \text{ where } \rho_j \text{ occurs in } \alpha$$

with an odd coefficient.

The compact types $\mathbf{L}_0$ are omitted.

52.2 $\mathbf{A}_{l,j}$ ($l \geqslant 1$): The outer automorphism P (for $l > 1$) shows that $\mathbf{A}_{l,j}$ and $\mathbf{A}_{l,l+1-j}$ are identical. The same, however, can be established by an inner isotypism, which can be constructed by the method used in 51.15.2.

The graph of $G_{C,\mathrm{un}}$ is

$$\rho_1 — \rho_2 — \cdots — \rho_{j-1}, \qquad \rho_{j+1} — \rho_{j+2} — \cdots — \rho_l.$$

$G_{C,\mathrm{un}}$ belongs to $\mathbf{A}_{j-1} + \mathbf{A}_{l-j} + \mathbf{D}_1$.

Signature: $1 - (l + 1 - 2j)^2$.

Top weights of (reducible) ϑ: $\hat\alpha$ and $-\rho_j$; that is

$$\pi_{1,l-j}(\mathbf{A}_{j-1} + \mathbf{A}_{l-j} + \mathbf{D}_1) \quad \text{and} \quad \pi_{j-1,1}(\mathbf{A}_{j-1} + \mathbf{A}_{l-j} + \mathbf{D}_1).$$

52.3 $\mathbf{D}_{l,j}$ ($l \geqslant 4$); $j \neq 0, 1, 2$: A procedure like that of 51.15.2 shows that $\mathbf{D}_{l,j}$ and $\mathbf{D}_{l,l+4-j}$ coincide. Therefore j will be restricted: $3 \leqslant j \leqslant \frac{1}{2}(l+4)$.

The graph of $G_{C,\mathrm{un}}$ is

$$\rho_3 — \rho_4 — \cdots — \rho_{j-2} \begin{cases} \diagup \rho_{j-1} \\ \diagdown \rho_{j-1} + 2\rho_j + \cdots + 2\rho_l + \rho_1 + \rho_2 \end{cases}$$

$$\rho_{j+1} — \rho_{j+2} — \cdots — \rho_l \begin{cases} \diagup \rho_1 \\ \diagdown \rho_2 \end{cases}$$

For $j = 3$ the first component of the graph is nonexistent; for $j = 4$ it reduces to the last two dots; for $j = 5$ it reduces to the last three dots.

$G_{C,\mathrm{un}}$ belongs to $\mathbf{D}_{j-2} + \mathbf{D}_{l-j+2}$ (for $j = 3, 4, 5$ because of the conventions made in 51.22).

Signature: $l - 2(l + 4 - 2j)^2$.

Top weight of ϑ arising from $\rho_3 + \cdots + \rho_j + 2\rho_{j+1} + \cdots + 2\rho_l + \rho_1 + \rho_2$ is

$$\pi_{3,3}(\mathbf{D}_{j-2} + \mathbf{D}_{l-j+2}).$$

For $j = 3$, however, ϑ becomes reducible with top weight

$$\pi_3(\mathbf{D}_1 + \mathbf{D}_{l-1}) \quad \text{twice}$$

arising from $\hat\alpha$ and $-\rho_3$.

For $j = 4, 5$, π_3 must be interpreted according to the conventions 51.22.

For $j = 1, 2$, the types coincide by means of P. The isotypy can be established by an inner automorphism for odd l.

$\mathbf{D}_{l,1}$: The graph of $G_{C,\mathrm{un}}$ is

$$\rho_3 - \rho_4 - \cdots - \rho_l - \rho_2.$$

$G_{C,\mathrm{un}}$ belongs to $\mathbf{A}_{l-1} + \mathbf{D}_1$.
Signature: $-l$.
Top weights of ϑ: $\rho_3 + 2\rho_4 + \cdots + 2\rho_l + \rho_1 + \rho_2, -\rho_1$; that is

$$\pi_2(\mathbf{A}_{l-1} + \mathbf{D}_1), \qquad \pi_{l-2}(\mathbf{A}_{l-1} + \mathbf{D}_1).$$

Note that for $l=4$ the types $\mathbf{D}_{l,1}$ $\mathbf{D}_{l,2}$, $\mathbf{D}_{l,3}$ coincide by outer automorphisms.

52.4 $\mathbf{E}_{6,j}$: Because of the coefficient 3 of ρ_6 in $\hat{\alpha}$, $j=6$ may be dropped. According to 51.18, $j=4,5$ lead to the same type as $j=2$, and, thanks to the plus-automorphism, $j=1,3$ are the same, though this can also be established by an inner automorphism, using the method of 51.15.2. In addition to the compact type, $j=1,2$ are left.

$\mathbf{E}_{6,1}$: The graph of $G_{C,\mathrm{un}}$ is

$$\rho_3 - \rho_5 - \rho_6 \begin{smallmatrix} \diagup \rho_2 \\ \diagdown \rho_4 \end{smallmatrix} .$$

$G_{C,\mathrm{un}}$ belongs to $\mathbf{D}_5 + \mathbf{D}_1$.
Signature: -14.
Top weights of ϑ: $\hat{\alpha}$ and $-\rho_1$; that is,

$$\pi_1(\mathbf{D}_5 + \mathbf{D}_1), \qquad \pi_2(\mathbf{D}_5 + \mathbf{D}_1).$$

$\mathbf{E}_{6,2}$: The graph of $G_{C,\mathrm{un}}$ is

$$\rho_3 - \rho_5 - \rho_6 - \rho_4 - \rho_1, \quad \hat{\alpha}.$$

$G_{C,\mathrm{un}}$ belongs to $\mathbf{A}_5 + \mathbf{A}_1$.
Signature: 2.
Top weight of ϑ: $\hat{\alpha} - \rho_2$; that is,

$$\pi_{3,1}(\mathbf{A}_5 + \mathbf{A}_1).$$

52.5 $\mathbf{E}_{7,j}$: Because of the coefficients >2 of ρ_j in $\hat{\alpha}$, $j=5,6,7$ may be dropped. By 51.18, $j=4$ gives the same as $j=1$. In addition to $j=0$, $j=1,2,3$ are left.

$\mathbf{E}_{7,1}$: The graph of $G_{C,\mathrm{un}}$ is

$$\rho_2 - \rho_4 - \rho_6 - \rho_7 \begin{smallmatrix} \diagup \rho_5 \\ \diagdown \rho_3 \end{smallmatrix}, \quad \hat{\alpha}.$$

$G_{C,\text{un}}$ belongs to $\mathbf{D}_6 + \mathbf{A}_1$.
Signature: –5.
Top weight of ϑ: $\hat{\alpha} - \rho_1$; that is,

$$\pi_{1,1}(\mathbf{D}_6 + \mathbf{A}_1).$$

$\mathbf{E}_{7,2}$: The graph of $G_{C,\text{un}}$ is

$$\begin{array}{ccccccccc} & & & & \rho_3 & & & & \\ & & & & | & & & & \\ \rho_4 & — & \rho_6 & — & \rho_7 & — & \rho_5 & — & \rho_1. \end{array}$$

$G_{C,\text{un}}$ belongs to $\mathbf{E}_6 + \mathbf{D}_1$.
Signature: –25.
Top weights of ϑ: $\hat{\alpha}$, and $-\rho_2$; that is,

$$\pi_1(\mathbf{E}_6 + \mathbf{D}_1), \qquad \pi_3(\mathbf{E}_6 + \mathbf{D}_1).$$

$\mathbf{E}_{7,3}$: The graph of $G_{C,\text{un}}$ is

$$\rho_1 — \rho_5 — \rho_7 — \rho_6 — \rho_4 — \rho_2 — (\rho_4 + 2\rho_6 + 3\rho_7 + 2\rho_5 + \rho_1 + 2\rho_3).$$

$G_{C,\text{un}}$ belongs to $\mathbf{A}_7$.
Signature: 7.
Top weight of ϑ: $\rho_2 + 2\rho_4 + 3\rho_6 + 3\rho_7 + \rho_3 + 2\rho_5 + \rho_1$; that is,

$$\pi_4(\mathbf{A}_7).$$

52.6 $\mathbf{E}_{8,j}$: After an inspection of the coefficients in the top rootform, $j = 1, 2$ in addition to $j = 0$ are left.

$\mathbf{E}_{8,1}$: The graph of $G_{C,\text{un}}$ is

$$\begin{array}{ccccccccccc} & & & & & & \rho_4 & & & & \\ & & & & & & | & & & & \\ \rho_3 & — & \rho_5 & — & \rho_7 & — & \rho_8 & — & \rho_6 & — & \rho_2, \quad \hat{\alpha}. \end{array}$$

$G_{C,\text{un}}$ belongs to $\mathbf{E}_7 + \mathbf{A}_1$.
Signature: –24.
Top weight of ϑ: $\hat{\alpha} - \rho$; that is,

$$\pi_{2,1}(\mathbf{E}_7 + \mathbf{A}_1).$$

$\mathbf{E}_{8,2}$: The graph of $G_{C,\text{un}}$ is

$$(\rho_3 + 2\rho_5 + 3\rho_7 + 4\rho_8 + 3\rho_6 + 2\rho_2 + 2\rho_4) — \rho_1 — \rho_3 — \rho_5 — \rho_7 — \rho_8 \begin{array}{l} \diagup \rho_6 \\ \diagdown \rho_4 \end{array}$$

$G_{C,\mathrm{un}}$ belongs to $\mathbf{D}_8$.
Signature: 8.
Top weight of ϑ: $\rho_1 + 2\rho_3 + 3\rho_5 + 4\rho_7 + 5\rho_8 + 3\rho_4 + 3\rho_6 + \rho_2$; that is,

$$\pi_1(\mathbf{D}_8).$$

52.7 $\mathbf{B}_{l,j}$ $(l \geqslant 3)$: For $j \neq 0, 1$, the graph of $G_{C,\mathrm{un}}$ is

$$\rho_2 - \rho_3 - \cdots - \rho_{j-2} \begin{cases} \rho_{j-1} \\ \rho_{j-1} + 2\rho_j + \cdots + 2\rho_l + 2\rho_1 \end{cases}$$

$$\rho_{j+1} - \cdots - \rho_l \Rightarrow \rho_1.$$

For $j = 2$ the first component is nonexistent; for $j = 3$ it reduces to the last two dots; for $j = l$ the second component consists of the dot ρ_1.

$G_{C,\mathrm{un}}$ belongs to $\mathbf{D}_{j-1} + \mathbf{B}_{l-j+1}$ with the usual conventions.
Signature: $l - 2(l + 3 - 2j)(l + 2 - 2j)$.
Top weight of ϑ: $\rho_2 + \cdots + \rho_j + 2\rho_{j+1} + \cdots + 2\rho_l + 2\rho_1$; that is,

$$\pi_{3,2}(\mathbf{D}_{j-1} + \mathbf{B}_{l-j+1})$$

with the usual conventions, in particular, for $j = l$, to interpret $\pi_2(\mathbf{B}_1)$ as $2\pi_1(\mathbf{B}_1)$.

For $j = 2$, however, ϑ becomes reducible with top weights $\hat{\alpha}$ and $-\rho_2$; that is

$$\pi_2(\mathbf{D}_1 + \mathbf{B}_{l-1}) \quad \text{twice.}$$

$\mathbf{B}_{l,1}$: The graph of $G_{C,\mathrm{un}}$ is

$$\rho_2 - \rho_3 - \cdots - \rho_{l-1} \begin{cases} \rho_l + 2\rho_1 \\ \rho_l \end{cases}$$

$G_{C,\mathrm{un}}$ belongs to $\mathbf{D}_l$.
Signature: $l(3 - 2l)$.
Top weight of ϑ: $\rho_2 + \rho_3 + \cdots + \rho_l$; that is,

$$\pi_3(\mathbf{D}_l).$$

Remark $\mathbf{B}_{l,1}$ can also be interpreted by admitting $j = l + 1$ in $\mathbf{B}_{l,j}$ and putting $\mathbf{B}_0 = \mathbf{O}$.

52.8 $\mathbf{C}_{l,j}$ $(l \geqslant 2)$: For $j \neq 0, l$, the graph of $G_{C,\mathrm{un}}$ is

$$\rho_1 - \cdots - \rho_{j-1} \Leftarrow 2\rho_j + 2\rho_{j+1} + \cdots + 2\rho_{l-1} + \rho_l$$

$$\rho_{j+1} - \cdots - \rho_{l-1} \Leftarrow \rho_l.$$

Again by the method of 51.15.2 one proves

$$\mathbf{C}_{l,j} = \mathbf{C}_{l,l-j} \quad \text{for} \quad j = 1, 2, \ldots, l-1.$$

$G_{C,\text{un}}$ belongs to $\mathbf{C}_j + \mathbf{C}_{l-j}$.
Signature: $-l - 2(l-2j)^2$.
Top weight of ϑ: $\rho_1 + \cdots + \rho_j + 2\rho_{j+1} + \cdots + 2\rho_{l-1} + \rho_l$; that is,

$$\pi_{1,1}(\mathbf{C}_j + \mathbf{C}_{l-j}).$$

$\mathbf{C}_{l,l}$: The graph of $G_{C,\text{un}}$ is

$$\rho_1 \text{—} \rho_2 \text{—} \cdots \text{—} \rho_{l-1}.$$

$G_{C,\text{un}}$ belongs to $\mathbf{A}_{l-1} + \mathbf{D}_1$.
Signature: l.
Top weights of ϑ: $\hat{\alpha}$, and $-\rho_l$; that is,

$$2\pi_1(\mathbf{A}_{l-1} + \mathbf{D}_1), \qquad 2\pi_{l-1}(\mathbf{A}_{l-1} + \mathbf{D}_1).$$

52.9 $\mathbf{F}_{4,j}$: After an inspection of the coefficients in the top rootform $j = 0, 1, 2$ are left.

$\mathbf{F}_{4,1}$: The graph of $G_{C,\text{un}}$ is

$$(2\rho_1 + 2\rho_3 + \rho_4) \text{—} \rho_2 \text{—} \rho_4 \Rightarrow \rho_3.$$

$G_{C,\text{un}}$ belongs to $\mathbf{B}_4$.
Signature: -20.
Top weight of ϑ: $\rho_1 + \rho_2 + 3\rho_3 + 2\rho_4$.

$$\pi_1(\mathbf{B}_4).$$

$\mathbf{F}_{4,2}$: The graph of $G_{C,\text{un}}$ is

$$\rho_1 \text{—} \rho_3 \Leftarrow \rho_4, \quad \hat{\alpha}.$$

$G_{C,\text{un}}$ belongs to $\mathbf{C}_3 + \mathbf{A}_1$.
Signature: 4.
Top weight of ϑ: $\hat{\alpha} - \rho_2$; that is,

$$\pi_{3,1}(\mathbf{C}_3 + \mathbf{A}_1).$$

52.10 $\mathbf{G}_{2,j}$: $j = 1$ is excluded.

$\mathbf{G}_{2,2}$: The graph of $G_{C,\text{un}}$ is

$$\rho_1, \; 2\rho_2 + 3\rho_1.$$

$G_{C,\text{un}}$ belongs to $\mathbf{A}_1 + \mathbf{A}_1$.
Signature: 2.
Top weight of ϑ: $\rho_2 + 3\rho_1$; that is

$$3\pi_1(\mathbf{A}_1) + \pi_1(\mathbf{A}_1).$$

53. CLASSIFICATION OF OUTER TYPES

53.1 Part of the general remarks of 52.1 apply here as well. For the outer types the reduced form of C was $\tilde{h}PC_{\text{un}}$. If $\boldsymbol{h} \neq \mathbf{0}$, then $\boldsymbol{G}_C \in \mathbf{L}_{j,*}$ is really spanned by

$$\boldsymbol{h}' \in \boldsymbol{H}_{\text{un}} \quad \text{with} \quad P\boldsymbol{h}' = \boldsymbol{h}',$$
$$\boldsymbol{h}' \in \boldsymbol{H}_{\text{he}} \quad \text{with} \quad P\boldsymbol{h}' = -\boldsymbol{h}',$$

$$\boldsymbol{e}_\alpha - P\boldsymbol{e}_{-\alpha},\ \mathrm{i}(\boldsymbol{e}_\alpha + P\boldsymbol{e}_{-\alpha}), \quad \text{where } \rho_j \text{ occurs evenly in } \alpha,$$
$$\boldsymbol{e}_\alpha + P\boldsymbol{e}_{-\alpha},\ \mathrm{i}(\boldsymbol{e}_\alpha - P\boldsymbol{e}_{-\alpha}), \quad \text{where } \rho_j \text{ occurs oddly in } \alpha;$$

if $\boldsymbol{h} = \mathbf{0}$, the case of an oddly occurring ρ_j is always considered void.

Note that $P\boldsymbol{e}_\alpha = \pm \boldsymbol{e}_{P\alpha}$ always.

The infinitesimal algebra $\boldsymbol{G}_{C,\text{un}}$ of the maximal compact subgroup is spanned by

$$\boldsymbol{h}' \in \boldsymbol{H}_{\text{un}} \quad \text{with} \quad P\boldsymbol{h}' = \boldsymbol{h}',$$

$$\left.\begin{array}{l}(\boldsymbol{e}_\alpha - \boldsymbol{e}_{-\alpha}) + (P\boldsymbol{e}_\alpha - P\boldsymbol{e}_{-\alpha}) \\ \mathrm{i}(\boldsymbol{e}_\alpha + \boldsymbol{e}_{-\alpha}) + \mathrm{i}(P\boldsymbol{e}_\alpha + P\boldsymbol{e}_{-\alpha})\end{array}\right\} \quad \text{where } \rho_j \text{ occurs evenly in } \alpha,$$

$$\left.\begin{array}{l}(\boldsymbol{e}_\alpha - \boldsymbol{e}_{-\alpha}) - (P\boldsymbol{e}_\alpha - P\boldsymbol{e}_{-\alpha}) \\ \mathrm{i}(\boldsymbol{e}_\alpha + \boldsymbol{e}_{-\alpha}) - \mathrm{i}(P\boldsymbol{e}_\alpha + P\boldsymbol{e}_{-\alpha})\end{array}\right\} \quad \text{where } \rho_j \text{ occurs oddly in } \alpha.$$

The complex extension of $\boldsymbol{G}_{C,\text{un}}$ is spanned by

$$\boldsymbol{h}' \in \boldsymbol{H}_{\text{un}} \quad \text{with} \quad P\boldsymbol{h}' = \boldsymbol{h}',$$
$$\boldsymbol{e}_\alpha + P\boldsymbol{e}_\alpha, \quad \text{where } \rho_j \text{ occurs evenly in } \alpha,$$
$$\boldsymbol{e}_\alpha - P\boldsymbol{e}_\alpha, \quad \text{where } \rho_j \text{ occurs oddly in } \alpha.$$

The complex extension of $\boldsymbol{G}_{C,\text{he}}$ is spanned by

$$\boldsymbol{h}' \in \boldsymbol{H}_{\text{he}} \quad \text{with} \quad P\boldsymbol{h}' = -\boldsymbol{h}',$$
$$\boldsymbol{e}_\alpha - P\boldsymbol{e}_\alpha, \quad \text{where } \rho_j \text{ occurs oddly in } \alpha,$$
$$\boldsymbol{e}_\alpha + P\boldsymbol{e}_\alpha, \quad \text{where } \rho_j \text{ occurs evenly in } \alpha.$$

It appears that the rootforms of $\boldsymbol{G}_{C,\text{un}}$ are the restrictions to its trunk of the rootforms of G; these restrictions coincide with those of

$$\tfrac{1}{2}(\alpha + P\alpha) \quad \text{with} \quad \alpha \in W^*$$

under the condition that for admitting $\alpha = P\alpha$ it is required that

$$\text{either} \quad Pe_\alpha = e_\alpha \quad \text{and } \rho_j \text{ evenly in } \alpha,$$
$$\text{or} \quad Pe_\alpha = -e_\alpha \quad \text{and } \rho_j \text{ oddly in } \alpha.$$

The rootforms of $G_{C,\mathrm{un}}$ are restrictions of rootforms of G symmetrized with respect to P and, by the conventions of 51.21, presented as these symmetrized rootforms themselves. Proposition 51.21 allows one to compute the essentials of the inner product in the graph of $G_{C,\mathrm{un}}$ from the inner product of H^*. Nevertheless, the same result will also be obtained in every particular case by an explicit construction of ladders of branches.

To facilitate the computations the branches of the rootforms $\alpha \neq P\alpha$ of G are supposed to be normed such that

$$Pe_\alpha = e_{P\alpha}.$$

It will be noted later that this norming is possible for $\alpha = P\alpha$ as well, except in the case of $\mathbf{A}_{2m}$, where necessarily $Pe_\alpha = -e_\alpha$ for $\alpha = P\alpha$.

53.2–3 $\mathbf{A}_{l,0,*}$: Here $P\rho_k = \rho_{l+1-k}$, $\quad h = 0$.

53.2 *l odd* $= 2m - 1$: The rootforms of $G_{C,\mathrm{un}}$,

$$\rho_m = \tfrac{1}{2}(\rho_m + P\rho_m),$$
$$\rho_m + \tfrac{1}{2}(\rho_{m-1} + \rho_{m+1}) = \tfrac{1}{2}((\rho_{m-1} + \rho_m) + P(\rho_{m-1} + \rho_m)),$$
$$\rho_m + (\rho_{m-1} + \rho_{m+1}) = \tfrac{1}{2}((\rho_{m-1} + \rho_m + \rho_{m+1}) + P(\rho_{m-1} + \rho_m + \rho_{m+1})),$$

form a 2-ladder, with the branches

$$e_{\rho_m}, \qquad e_{\rho_{m-1}+\rho_m} + e_{\rho_{m-1}} + e_{\rho_m}, \qquad 2e_{\rho_{m-1}+\rho_m+\rho_{m+1}}$$

(norming disregarded).

Note that in $G \in \mathbf{A}_{2m-1}$ the branches can be normed such that $Pe_\alpha = e_{P\alpha}$. For those of rootforms $\alpha \neq P\alpha$ this is assumed; for those of the rootforms $\alpha = \rho_i + \cdots + \rho_{2m-i}$ if follows from

$$[e_{\rho_i}, [e_{\rho_{i+1}+\cdots+\rho_{2m-i-1}}, e_{\rho_{2m-i}}]] = [e_{\rho_{2m-i}}, [e_{\rho_{i+1}+\cdots+\rho_{2m-i-1}}, e_{\rho_i}]].$$

The graph of $G_{C,\mathrm{un}}$ is

$$\tfrac{1}{2}(\rho_1 + \rho_l) - \tfrac{1}{2}(\rho_2 + \rho_{l-1}) - \cdots - \tfrac{1}{2}(\rho_{m-1} + \rho_{m+1}) \Leftarrow \rho_m.$$

$G_{C,\mathrm{un}}$ belongs to $\mathbf{C}_m$.
Signature: $-(l + 2)$.

The top weight of ϑ results from symmetrizing the highest non-P-invariant rootform; thus

$$\tfrac{1}{2}((\rho_1 + \cdots + \rho_{l-1}) + (\rho_2 + \cdots + \rho_l)) = \hat{\alpha} - \tfrac{1}{2}(\rho_1 + \rho_l).$$

The representation is given by

$$\pi_2(\mathbf{C}_m).$$

53.3 *l even* $= 2m$: The rootforms of $G_{C,\mathrm{un}}$,

$$\tfrac{1}{2}(\rho_{m-1} + \rho_{m+2}), \tfrac{1}{2}(\rho_{m-1} + \rho_{m+2}) + \tfrac{1}{2}(\rho_m + \rho_{m+1}), \tfrac{1}{2}(\rho_{m-1} + \rho_{m+2}) + (\rho_m + \rho_{m+1}),$$

form a 2-ladder with the branches

$$e_{\rho_{m-1}} + e_{\rho_{m+2}}, \qquad e_{\rho_{m-1}+\rho_m} + e_{\rho_{m+2}+\rho_{m+1}}, \qquad e_{\rho_{m-1}+\rho_m+\rho_{m+1}} + e_{\rho_{m+2}+\rho_{m+1}+\rho_m}.$$

For $G \in \mathbf{A}_{2m}$ one gets $Pe_\alpha = -e_{P\alpha}$ if $\alpha = P\alpha$. This follows for $\alpha = \rho_i + \cdots + \rho_{2m+1-i}$ from

$$[e_{\rho_i + \cdots + \rho_m}, e_{\rho_{m+1} + \cdots + \rho_{2m+1-i}}] = -[e_{\rho_{m+1} + \cdots + \rho_{2m+1-i}}, e_{\rho_i + \cdots + \rho_m}].$$

The graph of $G_{C,\mathrm{un}}$ is

$$\tfrac{1}{2}(\rho_1 + \rho_l) — \tfrac{1}{2}(\rho_2 + \rho_{l-1}) — \cdots — \tfrac{1}{2}(\rho_{m-1} + \rho_{m+2}) \Rightarrow \tfrac{1}{2}(\rho_m + \rho_{m+1}).$$

$G_{C,\mathrm{un}}$ belongs to $\mathbf{B}_m$.
Signature: l.
Top weight of ϑ: $\rho_1 + \cdots + \rho_l$; that is,

$$2\pi_2(\mathbf{B}_m),$$

which for $m = 1$ must be interpreted as $4\pi_2(\mathbf{A}_1)$.

53.4 $\mathbf{A}_{l,m,*}$, $l = 2m - 1 \geqslant 3$: Though ρ_m and $\rho_{m-1} + \rho_m + \rho_{m+1}$ do not yield rootforms of $G_{C,\mathrm{un}}$, $\tfrac{1}{2}((\rho_{m-1} + \rho_m) + (\rho_{m+1} + \rho_m))$ does. Its inner product with $\tfrac{1}{2}(\rho_{m-1} + \rho_m)$ vanishes, though not that with $\tfrac{1}{2}(\rho_{m-2} + \rho_{m+2})$.
The graph of $G_{C,\mathrm{un}}$ is

$$\tfrac{1}{2}(\rho_1 + \rho_l) — \tfrac{1}{2}(\rho_2 + \rho_{l-1}) — \cdots — \tfrac{1}{2}(\rho_{m-2} + \rho_{m+2}) \begin{cases} \diagup\ \tfrac{1}{2}(\rho_{m-1} + \rho_{m+1}) \\ \diagdown\ \tfrac{1}{2}(\rho_{m-1} + \rho_{m+1}) + \rho_m \end{cases}$$

$G_{C,\mathrm{un}}$ belongs to $\mathbf{D}_m$.
For $m = 2, 3$, the graph reduces to the last two or three dots, respectively. It is interpreted as usual.
Signature: l.
Top weight of ϑ: $\rho_1 + \cdots + \rho_l$, with the eigenvector $e_{\rho_1 + \cdots + \rho_l}$; that is,

$$2\pi_3(\mathbf{D}_m),$$

which for $m=2$ must be interpreted as $2\pi_1(\mathbf{A}_1)+2\pi_1(\mathbf{A}_1)$ and for $m=3$ as $2\pi_2(\mathbf{A}_3)$.

53.5–6 $\mathbf{D}_{l,j,*}$ $(l\geqslant 4)$: Here $P\rho_1=\rho_2$, $P\rho_i=\rho_i$ $(i>2)$.

53.5 $\mathbf{D}_{l,0,*}$ $(l\geqslant 4)$: One observes a ladder of length 2,

$$\rho_l,\qquad \rho_l+\tfrac{1}{2}(\rho_1+\rho_2),\qquad \rho_l+(\rho_1+\rho_2),$$

belonging to e_{ρ_l}, $e_{\rho_1+\rho_l}+e_{\rho_2+\rho_l}$, $2e_{\rho_1+\rho_2+\rho_l}$. The branches can again be normed with $Pe_\alpha=e_{P\alpha}$.

The graph of $G_{C,\mathrm{un}}$ is

$$\rho_3—\rho_4—\cdots—\rho_l\Rightarrow\tfrac{1}{2}(\rho_1+\rho_2).$$

$G_{C,\mathrm{un}}$ belongs to $\mathbf{B}_{l-1}$.
Signature: $l-2(1-l)^2$.
Top weight of ϑ:

$$\tfrac{1}{2}((\rho_1+\rho_3+\cdots+\rho_l)+(\rho_2+\rho_3+\cdots+\rho_l))=\tfrac{1}{2}(\rho_1+\rho_2)+\rho_3+\cdots+\rho_l;$$

that is,

$$\pi_2(\mathbf{B}_{l-1}).$$

It can also be interpreted by admitting $j=l+1$ in the next one and putting $\mathbf{B}_0=\mathbf{O}$.

53.6 $\mathbf{D}_{l,j,*}$ $(l\geqslant 4)$, $j>2$, isomorphic with $\mathbf{D}_{l,l-j+3,*}$: The restriction of ρ_j is not a rootform of $G_{C,\mathrm{un}}$ but that of

$$\rho_j+\rho_{j+1}+\cdots+\rho_l+\tfrac{1}{2}(\rho_1+\rho_2)$$

is available as a primitive rootform.

The graph of $G_{C,\mathrm{un}}$ is

$$\rho_3—\rho_4—\cdots—\rho_{j-1}\Rightarrow\rho_j+\rho_{j+1}+\cdots+\rho_l+\tfrac{1}{2}(\rho_1+\rho_2),$$
$$\rho_{j+1}—\rho_{j+2}—\cdots—\rho_l\Rightarrow\tfrac{1}{2}(\rho_1+\rho_2).$$

$G_{C,\mathrm{un}}$ belongs to $\mathbf{B}_{j-2}+\mathbf{B}_{l-j+1}$, with the usual conventions on degeneracy (see 51.22).

Signature: $l-2(l+3-2j)^2$.

Top weight of ϑ is the highest P-invariant rootform containing ρ_j oddly: $\rho_3+\cdots+\rho_j+2\rho_{j+1}+\cdots+2\rho_l+\rho_1+\rho_2$; that is

$$\pi_{2,2}(\mathbf{B}_{j-2}+\mathbf{B}_{l-j+1}),$$

with the usual conventions (51.22).

53.7–8 $\mathbf{E}_{6,j,*}$: Here P maps $\rho_1\leftrightarrow\rho_3$, $\rho_4\leftrightarrow\rho_5$, $\rho_2\leftrightarrow\rho_2$, $\rho_6\rightarrow\rho_6$. The branches can be normed with $Pe_\alpha=e_{P\alpha}$.

53.7 $\mathbf{E}_{6,0,*}$: The graph of $G_{C,\mathrm{un}}$ is

$$\rho_2 — \rho_6 \Rightarrow \tfrac{1}{2}(\rho_4+\rho_5) — \tfrac{1}{2}(\rho_1+\rho_3)$$

where the double bond is explained by the ladder

$$\rho_6 — \rho_6 + \tfrac{1}{2}(\rho_4+\rho_5) — \rho_6+\rho_4+\rho_5.$$

$G_{C,\mathrm{un}}$ belongs to $\mathbf{F}_4$.
Signature: –26.
Top weight of ϑ: $\rho_2 + 2\rho_6 + \tfrac{3}{2}(\rho_4+\rho_5) + \rho_1 + \rho_3$; that is,

$$\pi_1(\mathbf{F}_4).$$

53.8 $\mathbf{E}_{6,2,*}$: ρ_2 is not a rootform of $G_{C,\mathrm{un}}$. Instead

$$\tfrac{1}{2}((\rho_2+\rho_4+\rho_6)+(\rho_2+\rho_5+\rho_6)) = \tfrac{1}{2}(\rho_4+\rho_5)+(\rho_2+\rho_6)$$

is available. The graph of $G_{C,\mathrm{un}}$ is

$$\rho_6 \Rightarrow \tfrac{1}{2}(\rho_4+\rho_5) — \tfrac{1}{2}(\rho_1+\rho_3) — \tfrac{1}{2}(\rho_4+\rho_5)+\rho_6+\rho_2.$$

$G_{C,\mathrm{un}}$ belongs to $\mathbf{C}_4$.
Signature: 6.
Top weight of ϑ: $\hat{\alpha} - \rho_2$; that is,

$$\pi_4(\mathbf{C}_4).$$

54. FURTHER REMARKS ON REAL CLASSIFICATION

54.1. Examples of the various nontwin real types of $\mathbf{A}_l$, $\mathbf{B}_l$, $\mathbf{C}_l$, $\mathbf{D}_l$.

A group belonging to such an algebra is presented as the 1-component G_0 of the group G of volume-preserving automorphisms of a linear space R over

(1) some skew field (Rea, Com, or Qio),
(2) of some dimension,

in some cases endowed with a nondegenerate sesquilinear (bilinear if the field is Rea) form Q which can be

(3) symmetric or skew,

and which is of some

(4) signature.

In the case in which R is over Qio, "volume preserving" means "volume preserving for R regarded over Rea".

		(1)	(2)	(3)	(4)
(1)	$\mathbf{A}_{l,j}$ (not $l=j=1$)	Com	$l+1$	sym	$l+1-2j$
(2)	$\mathbf{A}_{1,1}$	Rea	2	—	—
(3)	$\mathbf{A}_{l,m,*}$ $(l=2m-1>1)$	Rea	$l+1$	—	—
(4)	$\mathbf{A}_{l,0,*}$ $(l=2m)$	Rea	$l+1$	—	—
(5)	$\mathbf{A}_{l,0,*}$ $(l=2m-1>1)$	Qio	m	—	—
(6)	$\mathbf{B}_{l,j}$ $(l>1, j\geqslant 2)$	Rea	$2l+1$	sym	$2l-4j+5$
(7)	$\mathbf{B}_{l,0}$	Rea	$2l+1$	sym	$2l+1$
(8)	$\mathbf{B}_{l,1}$	Rea	$2l+1$	sym	$2l-1$
(9)	$\mathbf{C}_{l,j}$ $(j\neq l)$	Qio	l	sym	$l-2j$
(10)	$\mathbf{C}_{l,l}$	Rea	$2l$	skew	—
(11)	$\mathbf{D}_{l,j}$ $(j\neq 0,1,2)$	Rea	$2l$	sym	$2l-4j+8$
(12)	$\mathbf{D}_{l,0}$	Rea	$2l$	sym	$2l$
(13)	$\mathbf{D}_{l,1}$	Qio	l	skew	—
(14)	$\mathbf{D}_{l,j,*}$ $(j>2)$	Rea	$2l$	sym	$2l-4j+6$
(15)	$\mathbf{D}_{l,0,*}$	Rea	$2l$	sym	$2l-2$

Those cases among these descriptions that are not evident will be verified in 59.7.

Actually, the automorphism groups G are connected, except for the sixth, eighth, eleventh, fourteenth, and fifteenth cases, that is, if the first column bears the indication Rea, the third bears the indication sym, and the fourth column differs from the second.

This can be shown by an induction step from a subgroup F of G to G. To define F one must distinguish the

(a) second, third, fourth, and fifth cases,
(b) first, seventh, ninth, twelfth, and thirteenth cases,
(c) tenth case;

F is defined by its leaving invariant

(a) an $x_0 \in R$ with $x_0 \neq 0$,
(b) an $x_0 \in R$ with $Q(x_0, x_0) \neq 0$,
(c) some $x_0, y_0 \in R$ with $Q(x_0, y_0) \neq 0$.

The connectedness of F is the induction assumption, except for case (a), where it is easily derived from the assumed connectedness of a lower rank group of the table. To show the connectedness of G, one must prove that the set of

(a) $x \in R$ with $x \neq 0$,
(b) $x \in R$ with $Q(x,x) = Q(x_0, x_0)$,
(c) $\ulcorner x, y \urcorner \in \ulcorner R, R \urcorner$ with $Q(x,y) = Q(x_0, y_0)$

is connected and that G acts transitively on it. This transitivity is easily verified for (a) and (c). For (b) it suffices to verify the transitivity on nondegenerate, two-dimensional linear subspaces. This is easily done in the first case; it is slightly more difficult in the ninth, and somewhat tedious in the thirteenth. The connectedness of the orbits under consideration poses no problems.

A more comfortable proof of the whole statement rests on the fact to be proved in 65.4 that the maximal compact subgroups of a semisimple linear Lie group are conjugate. From this fact it follows that the normalizer J' of a maximal connected compact subgroup J in G intersects every component of G. An inspection shows that J' coincides with J, except in the sixth, eighth, eleventh, fourteenth and fifteenth cases. Now J is connected, and then so are J' and G.

In the excluded cases R splits into linear subspaces R_+ and R_- on which Q is positive and negative definite, respectively, and J leaves both invariant; G has two components. Indeed $J' \setminus J$ consists of the elements of G with negative determinant on R_+ as well as on R_-.

54.2. Maximal Signatures, Standard and Near Standard In every complex class the *minimal* signature of the real Killing form is attained by the unitary type and by no other. According to Sections 52–53, the *maximal* signatures in the simple classes, separately for inner and outer types, are attained by:

			signatures		
nst	$\mathbf{A}_{l,j}$		$\begin{matrix}0\\1\end{matrix}\Big\}$	for $j=\begin{cases}\frac{1}{2}l\\ \frac{1}{2}(l+1)\end{cases}$	
st	$\mathbf{A}_{l,j,*}$		l	for $j=\begin{cases}0\\ \frac{1}{2}(l+1)\end{cases}$	if l is $\begin{cases}\text{even}\\ \text{odd}\end{cases}$
st	$\mathbf{B}_l$		l	for $j=\frac{1}{2}(l+2)$	or $\frac{1}{2}(l+3)$
st	$\mathbf{C}_l$		l	for $j=l$	
nst	$\mathbf{D}_{l,j}$	l odd	$l-2$	for $j=\frac{1}{2}(l+3)$	
st		l even	l	for $j=\frac{1}{2}(l+4)$	
st	$\mathbf{D}_{l,j,*}$	l odd	l	for $j=\frac{1}{2}(l+3)$	
nst		l even	$l-2$	for $j=\frac{1}{2}(l+4)$	
nst	$\mathbf{E}_{6,2}$		2		
st	$\mathbf{E}_{6,2,*}$		6		
st	$\mathbf{E}_{7,3}$		7		
st	$\mathbf{E}_{8,2}$		8		
st	$\mathbf{F}_{4,2}$		4		
st	$\mathbf{G}_{2,2}$		2		

The standard types, characterized by the signature l, duly appear in this list although in a strange disguise. As to the others, it is striking that their signature always equals the number of primitive rootforms that are invariant under P. To cover them one might try the following

Definition For $\boldsymbol{G} \in$ Alg Lie Com SSS in ordered third dressing on $\boldsymbol{H}$, the *near standard* semimorphism C_{nst} is defined by

$$C_{\mathrm{nst}} = C_{\mathrm{st}} P = C_{\mathrm{un}} PM,$$

where P is the plus-automorphism according to $\boldsymbol{H}$. *Near standard restrictions* are defined correspondingly.

Proposition The signature of the near standard restriction equals the number of P-invariant elements of W^{++}.

Indeed, only the trunk contributes effectively here to the signature and with just this amount.

Note that all near standard types are inner except for $\mathbf{D}_l$, l even.

54.3. Central and Near Central It remains unsatisfactory that in the classification according to the pattern of 51.17 standard and near standard types appear in an utterly chaotic distribution. This can be corrected as follows.

54.3.1. Definition For $\boldsymbol{G} \in$ Alg Lie Com SSS in ordered third dressing let $\boldsymbol{h}$ be such that $\rho(\boldsymbol{h}) = \pi i$ for all $\rho \in W^{++}$ and $h = \exp \boldsymbol{h}$. The *central* and the *near central semimorphisms* are defined by

$$C_{\mathrm{cl}} = \tilde{h} C_{\mathrm{un}}, \qquad C_{\mathrm{ncl}} = \tilde{h} P C_{\mathrm{un}},$$

where P is the plus-automorphism. The *central* and *near central restrictions* are defined correspondingly.

54.3.2. Definition The *altitude* $a(\alpha)$ of $\alpha \in W^+$ is defined as the sum of its coefficients on the basis W^{++}. (See Tables C and D of altitudes.)

54.3.3 With h as defined in 54.3.1,

$$\tilde{h} e_\rho = -e_\rho \qquad \text{for} \quad \rho \in W^{++};$$

thus,

$$\tilde{h} e_{\pm\alpha} = (-1)^{a(\alpha)} e_{\pm\alpha} \qquad \text{for} \quad \alpha \in W^+.$$

To get the signature of $\boldsymbol{G}_{\mathrm{cl}}$ one must compute $-\mathrm{tr}(C_{\mathrm{cl}} C_{\mathrm{un}}) = -\mathrm{tr}\, \tilde{h}$.

The list of altitudes in most cases shows an equal number of rootforms at altitudes $2b$, $2b+1$; for the altitude 1 there are l of them. In these cases the branches contribute $-2l$ to tr $\tilde{h}$, whereas the contribution of the trunk is l; together they contribute $-l$, which indicates the standard type.

The exceptions are $\mathbf{A}_l$, $\mathbf{D}_l$ (l odd), $\mathbf{E}_6$; these are just the cases in which the minus-automorphism M is outer. From the list of altitudes it becomes clear that the loss of contributions from the branches just equals the loss of signature in the step from the standard to the near standard type.

So much for the central types. The near central semimorphisms arise from the central ones by a factor P, which in classification terminology means the adding of an asterisk. According to the list of 54.2 this process just changes standard into near standard types and vice versa.

54.4–5. Coincidences

54.4. Proposition For $\boldsymbol{G} \in$ Alg Lie Com SSS, if M is inner, the standard type coincides with the central, and the near standard with the near central. If M is outer, it is the opposite; the standard type coincides with the near central, the near standard with the central.

It is quite unsatisfactory that one has to rely on verifications to prove Propositions 54.2 and 54.4.

54.5 $C_{\mathrm{st}}, C_{\mathrm{nst}}$, on the one hand, and $C_{\mathrm{cl}}, C_{\mathrm{ncl}}$ on the other are isotypically identical. They differ in that they presuppose different dressings on the underlying trunk. The trunk is clearly maximally compact for C_{cl} and C_{ncl}; in Section 60 it will appear to be minimally compact for $C_{\mathrm{st}}, C_{\mathrm{nst}}$.

55. CONTRAVALENCE AND VIRTUAL REALITY OF LINEAR REPRESENTATIONS

55.1 Let $\boldsymbol{G} \in$ Alg Lie Com and its involutory semimorphism C be fixed. Then set

Φ: the class of linear representations of $\boldsymbol{G}$ in R,

$\Phi(C)$: the class of linear representations of $\boldsymbol{G}_C$ in R.

where R ranges over Spa Lin Com and Spa Lin Rea, respectively (dim $R < \infty$ everywhere).

The subscript irr denotes the subclass of irreducible representations.

55.2. Contravalence With $f \in \Phi$ acting on R and Q mapping R onto S semilinearly, $\tilde{Q}$ is defined by

$$(\tilde{Q}f)(\boldsymbol{a}) = Qf(C\boldsymbol{a})\,Q^{-1}.$$

Definition $\tilde{Q}f$ is *contravalent* to f with respect to C, or C-*contravalent*. If f is contravalent to itself, it is called *self-contravalent*.

It is evident that $\tilde{Q}f$ is again in Φ.

The relation of contravalence clearly preserves equivalence classes.

55.3. Extension and Restriction For $g \in \Phi(C)$ acting on the real restriction R_D of $R \in$ Spa Lin Com by means of the involutory semilinear mapping D, put

$$\mathfrak{e}_D g = \text{complex extension of } g \text{ from } \boldsymbol{G}_C \text{ to } \boldsymbol{G} \text{ and from } R_D \text{ to } R.$$

55.3.1 Complex extensions preserve equivalence.

If $f = \mathfrak{e}_D g$, then

55.3.2 $$Df(C\boldsymbol{a})\, Dx = f(\boldsymbol{a})\, x \qquad \text{for} \quad \boldsymbol{a} \in \boldsymbol{G}_C \quad \text{and} \quad x \in R_D.$$

Since both members are linear in $\boldsymbol{a}$ as well as in x, the relation subsists for all $\boldsymbol{a} \in \boldsymbol{G}$, $x \in R$. Hence

55.3.3 $$f = \mathfrak{e}_D g \rightarrow f \text{ self-contravalent.}$$

(It will be seen that the converse is not true even for semisimple $\boldsymbol{G}$.)

If $f \in \Phi$ then 55.3.2 is necessary and sufficient for the possibility of restricting f as a representation to $\boldsymbol{G}_C$ and $\boldsymbol{R}_D$. If this is fulfilled, then put

$$\mathfrak{r}_D f = C\text{-}D\text{-restriction of } f.$$

Clearly,

55.3.4 $$\mathfrak{r}_D \text{ respects irreducibility,}$$

55.3.5 $$\mathfrak{e}_D \mathfrak{r}_D f = f,$$

55.3.6 $$\mathfrak{r}_D \mathfrak{e}_D f = f \qquad \text{for} \quad f \in \Phi(C).$$

55.4. Virtual Reality

55.4.1. Definition $f \in \Phi$ is *virtually real* (with respect to C) if there is an involutory semilinear D such that $\mathfrak{r}_D f \in \Phi(C)$ or, equivalently, such that 55.3.2 is true.

55.4.2 The property of virtual reality is preserved under equivalence and contravalence.

55.4.3. Proposition If $f \in \Phi_{\text{irr}}$ is virtually real, then, up to equivalence, $\mathfrak{r}_D f$ does not depend on D.

Proof Since f is irreducible, $D_1 f(C\boldsymbol{a}) D_1 = f(\boldsymbol{a}) = D_2 f(C\boldsymbol{a}) D_2$ implies that $D_2 D_1$ is a scalar multiplier γ; hence $D_2 = \gamma D_1$. Now

$$1 = D_2{}^2 = \gamma D_1 \gamma D_1 = \gamma\bar{\gamma} D_1{}^2 = \gamma\bar{\gamma}.$$

Take α such that $\alpha^2 = \gamma$. Then $\alpha\bar{\alpha} = 1$, $\alpha = \bar{\alpha}\gamma$. For $x \in R_{D_1}$,

$$\alpha x = \alpha D_1 x = \bar{\alpha}\gamma D_1 x = \bar{\alpha} D_2 x = D_2 \alpha x,$$

which shows that $\Upsilon_x \alpha x$ maps R_{D_1} onto R_{D_2} linearly. Since this mapping commutes with all $f(\boldsymbol{a})$, it constitutes an equivalence of $\mathfrak{r}_{D_1} f$ and $\mathfrak{r}_{D_2} f$.

55.4.4 Direct consequences of this proposition are the following.

Proposition If for $f_i \in \Phi(C)$ $(i = 1, 2)$, the $\mathfrak{e}_{D_i} f_i$ are irreducible and equivalent, then the f_i are equivalent.

Proposition If, for $f_i = \mathfrak{r}_D g_i$, the g_i are irreducible and equivalent, then the f_i are equivalent by means of a D-real linear mapping.

55.5–8. Waiving and Twinning

55.5.1 For $f \in \Phi$ define

$\mathfrak{w} f \in \Phi(C)$ as the result of restricting $\boldsymbol{G}$ to $\boldsymbol{G}_C$ and waiving in R,

$\mathfrak{t}_D f \in \Phi$ as the result of twinning of R,

where D is the semilinear mapping belonging to the particular twinning which arises as in Proposition 1.9, so that R is the D-restriction of the twinning result.

In the last case one has $\mathfrak{t}_D f(\boldsymbol{a})\,\omega_{\pm} = \omega_{\pm}\, f(\boldsymbol{a})$ if ω_+ and ω_- belong to the twinning, first for $\boldsymbol{a} \in \boldsymbol{G}_C$, then for general $\boldsymbol{a} \in \boldsymbol{G}$. Twinning respects equivalence.

55.5.2 $\mathfrak{t}_D f = \mathfrak{e}_D \mathfrak{w} f$. (See 1.9.)

55.5.3. Proposition For $f_1, f_2 \in \Phi_{\text{irr}}$, $\mathfrak{w} f_1, \mathfrak{w} f_2$ are equivalent iff f_1, f_2 are equivalent or contravalent.

Proof "If" is obvious, since by waiving semilinear mappings become linear. "Only if": from the equivalence of $\mathfrak{w} f_1, \mathfrak{w} f_2$, that of $\mathfrak{t}_D f_1 = \mathfrak{e}_D \mathfrak{w} f_1$, $\mathfrak{t}_D f_2 = \mathfrak{e}_D \mathfrak{w} f_2$ follows by 55.5.2. Now, by the definition of twinning and because of the irreducibility of f_i it appears that $\mathfrak{t}_D f_i$ breaks into two parts, one equivalent to f_i, the other contravalent to f_i. This proves the proposition.

55.6. Proposition If $f \in \Phi_{\text{irr}}$, then $\mathfrak{w} f \notin \Phi_{\text{irr}}(C)$ iff $f = \mathfrak{e}_D\, g$ for some g and D.

Proof "If": Put $f = \mathfrak{e}_D\, g$ with $g \in \Phi(C)$ acting on $S \in$ Spa Lin Rea. Then $\mathfrak{w} f = \mathfrak{w} \mathfrak{e}_D\, g$ acts on $S + \mathrm{i}S$, which splits into invariant S and $\mathrm{i}S$. "Only if":

Let f act on R. Then $\mathfrak{w}f$ acts on S arising from R by waiving. If $\mathfrak{w}f$ is reducible, there is a true T sub S, invariant under $\mathfrak{w}f$. Now $\mathrm{i}T$ is of the same kind, and so are $T \cap \mathrm{i}T$ and $T + \mathrm{i}T$, which, however, are even sub R and f-invariant. Since $f \in \Phi_{\mathrm{irr}}$, one gets $T \cap \mathrm{i}T = \{0\}$, $T + \mathrm{i}T = R$, which means that R is a complex extension of T and f is a complex extension of its restriction to T and $\boldsymbol{G}_C$. This proves the assertion.

A counterpart of this proposition is the following.

55.7. Proposition If $g \in \Phi_{\mathrm{irr}}(C)$, then $\mathfrak{e}_D\, g \notin \Phi_{\mathrm{irr}}$ for any D iff $g \in \mathfrak{w}\Phi$.

Proof "If" is evident because $\mathfrak{e}_D\, g = \mathfrak{e}_D\, \mathfrak{w}f = \mathfrak{t}_D f$ splits. "Only if": let S true sub R be invariant under $f = \mathfrak{e}_D\, g$. Then DS is invariant under $Df(C\boldsymbol{a})\,D$ which equals $f(\boldsymbol{a})$ by 55.3.2. Now $S \cap DS$ and $S + DS$ are also invariant; they are complex extensions of $(S \cap DS)_D$ and $(S + DS)_D$. The latter are $g(\boldsymbol{a})$-invariant, and since $g \in \Phi_{\mathrm{irr}}(C)$ they equal $\{0\}$ and R_D. Therefore $S \cap DS = \{0\}$, $S + DS = R$, and $R_D = (1 + D)S$. Now, by 55.3.2, if f_+ is the restriction of f to S, then $1 + D$ restricted to S provides an equivalence between $\mathfrak{w}f_+$ and g. This proves the assertion.

55.8 Summarizing, one has the following:

Theorem Real restriction gives a one-to-one correspondence between the equivalence classes of virtually real elements of Φ_{irr} and the equivalence classes of those elements of $\Phi_{\mathrm{irr}}(C)$ whose complex extensions are still irreducible. Waiving provides a one-to-one correspondence between the classes of equi- and contravalence of not virtually real elements of Φ_{irr} and the equivalence classes of those elements of $\Phi_{\mathrm{irr}}(C)$ whose complex extensions are reducible.

56. CONTRAVALENCE OF WEIGHTS

$\boldsymbol{G} \in$ Alg Lie Com SS in ordered third dressing on a trunk $\boldsymbol{H}$, f an irreducible linear representation in $R \in$ Spa Lin Com (dim $R < \infty$), and C an involutory semimorphism of $\boldsymbol{G}$ with $C\boldsymbol{H} = \boldsymbol{H}$.

56.1. Definition $(C^*\xi)(\boldsymbol{h}) = \overline{\xi(C\boldsymbol{h})}$ for all $\xi \in \boldsymbol{H}^*$ and $\boldsymbol{h} \in \boldsymbol{H}$ defines C^*. (Repetition of 51.6.)

Proposition (1) C^* is linear. (2) $C^*_{\mathrm{st}} = 1$. (3) $C^*_{\mathrm{nst}} = P$. (4) $C^*_{\mathrm{un}} = M$. (5) $C^* \in \mathrm{Aut}\, W^*$. (6) If $\boldsymbol{G}_C$ is simple and under maximally compact dressing, then $C^* = 1$ for inner types, $C^* = P$ for outer types, $C^* = P_{\mathrm{tw}}$ for twin types.

Proof (1), (2), (3), and (4) are trivial, (5) $C^* C^*_{\mathrm{st}} \in \operatorname{Aut} W^*$; (6) follows from Definitions 51.16–17.

56.2. Definition Elements of $\boldsymbol{H}^*_{\mathrm{st}}$ are called *contravalent* (with respect to C) if they are equivalent under $C^* \cdot \operatorname{Int} W^*$.

The terms *C-contravalent* and *C-self-contravalent* in $\boldsymbol{H}^*_{\mathrm{st}}$ are self-explanatory.

56.2.1. Proposition Irreducible representations of $\boldsymbol{G}$ are contravalent iff their top weights are contravalent.

Proof Let Q be semilinear, thus $\tilde{Q}f$ contravalent to f (see 55.2). Let x be a λ-weight vector of irreducible f; thus,

$$f(\boldsymbol{h})\,x = \lambda(\boldsymbol{h})\,x \qquad \text{for} \quad \boldsymbol{h} \in \boldsymbol{H},$$

$$Qf(C\boldsymbol{h})\,Q^{-1} \cdot Qx = Q\lambda(C\boldsymbol{h})\,x = \overline{\lambda(C\boldsymbol{h})}\,Qx = (C^*\lambda)(\boldsymbol{h})\,Qx;$$

hence $C^*\lambda$ is a weight of $\tilde{Q}f$. Therefore C^* maps the weights of f into those of $\tilde{Q}f$ which therefore is equivalent to $\curlyvee_{\boldsymbol{a} \in \boldsymbol{G}} f(CC_{\mathrm{st}}\boldsymbol{a})$. By Theorem 43.2 C^* maps the top weight of f onto that of $\tilde{Q}f$ up to $\operatorname{Int} W^*$-equivalence.

The converse reasoning is now obvious.

56.2.2 An immediate consequence is the following:

Proposition An irreducible linear representation is self-contravalent iff its top weight is self-contravalent.

56.3 To check contravalence for weights one can restrict oneself to simple $\boldsymbol{G}_C$. Furthermore, it is convenient to assume $\boldsymbol{G}_C$ in maximally compact dressing. Then for

$$\begin{aligned} &\text{inner types:} && C = \tilde{h}C_{\mathrm{un}}, && C^* = M,\\ &\text{outer types:} && C = \tilde{h}PC_{\mathrm{un}}, && C^* = MP,\\ &\text{twin types:} && C = MP_{\mathrm{tw}}\,C_{\mathrm{un}}, && C^* = P_{\mathrm{tw}}. \end{aligned}$$

According to 33.12, if $M \notin \operatorname{Int} \cdot W^*$, then $M \in P \cdot \operatorname{Int} W^*$. Hence, according to the definition of 56.2, the following applies:

Proposition Dominant λ is self-contravalent if $\boldsymbol{G}_C$ and M are both inner or both outer. Dominant λ and $P\lambda$ are contravalent if for $\boldsymbol{G}_C$ and M one is inner and the other outer. For the twin type λ and $P_{\mathrm{tw}}\lambda$ are contravalent.

More explicity, one gets a basis for the self-contravalent dominant weights as follows:

Inner Type The fundamental weights except for

$\mathbf{A}_l$ $(l > 1)$: $\pi_k + \pi_{l+1-k}$ for $k \leqslant \frac{1}{2}l$, π_m for $l = 2m-1$,

$\mathbf{D}_l$ (l odd): $\pi_1 + \pi_2$, π_k $(k \neq 1, 2)$,

$\mathbf{E}_6$: $\pi_1 + \pi_3, \pi_2, \pi_4 + \pi_5, \pi_6$.

Outer Type The fundamental weights except for

$\mathbf{D}_l$ (l even): $\pi_1 + \pi_2$, π_k $(k \neq 1, 2)$.

Twin Type $\pi_k^{(1)} + \pi_k^{(2)}$; (1), (2) refer to the two summands.

57. SELF-CONTRAVALENCE

Self-contravalence is not sufficient for virtual reality.
Suppose that $\boldsymbol{G}_C \in$ Alg Lie Rea SS, $\boldsymbol{G}$ in ordered third dressing.

57.1–7. Toward a Criterion on Virtual Reality

57.1. Definition An irreducible linear representation f of $\boldsymbol{G}$ is called *areal* if it is not self-contravalent. It is called *antireal* if it is self-contravalent but not virtually real.

57.2 Suppose $\boldsymbol{G} \in$ Alg Lie Com SS in ordered C-third dressing on the trunk $\boldsymbol{H}$ and f an irreducible linear representation of $\boldsymbol{G}$ in R with the top weight λ. Suppose that λ is self-contravalent, hence equivalent to $C^*\lambda$. Let x, y be (essentially unique) vectors of weight λ and $C^*\lambda$; if $\lambda = C^*\lambda$, take $x = y$. Then, because of the irreducibility of f, there is an element

57.2.1 $$\boldsymbol{u} = \boldsymbol{e}_{-\rho_k} \cdots \boldsymbol{e}_{-\rho_1} \qquad (\rho_\nu \in W^{++};\ W^{++} \text{ unnumbered})$$

of the associative envelope of $\boldsymbol{G}$ such that

57.2.2 $$f(\boldsymbol{u})\,x \neq 0 \quad \text{is a multiple of } y;$$

thus in any case,

57.2.3 $$\lambda - C^*\lambda = \sum_1^k \rho_\nu.$$

Again,

57.2.4 $f(Cu)y$ is a multiple of x;

hence

57.2.5 $$f(Cu\cdot u)\,x = \kappa x.$$

Later on it will be seen that κ is always real $\neq 0$, though this fact could easily be proved now.

57.2.6 $\varepsilon =$ sign of κ if κ is real.

57.3. Theorem Under the assumption in 57.2 f is virtually real if and only if $\varepsilon = 1$. There is a semilinear D on R with

$$Df(Ca)\,D^{-1} = f(a) \qquad (a \in G)$$

and

$$D^2 = \varepsilon.$$

Proof Suppose that for some semilinear D with $D^2 = \varepsilon = \pm 1$

57.3.1 $$D\,f(Ca)\,D^{-1} = f(a).$$

With x of the top weight λ, Dx is of the weight $C^*\lambda$; therefore, with the notations of 57.2,

57.3.2 $$f(u)\,x = \gamma Dx \qquad \text{with} \quad \gamma \neq 0.$$

Applying D and using 57.3.1, one gets

$$f(Cu\cdot u)\,x = f(Cu)\,f(u)\,x = f(Cu)\,\gamma Dx$$
$$= \gamma Df(u)\,x = \gamma D\gamma Dx = \gamma\bar{\gamma}D^2x = \varepsilon\gamma\bar{\gamma}x;$$

thus,

$$\operatorname{sgn}\kappa = \varepsilon.$$

In particular, if f is virtually real, and correspondingly D is chosen such that $D^2 = 1$, then $\kappa > 0$ (which in turn implies $D^2 = 1$ for the chosen D).

Conversely, still supposing κ real, assume a provisional involutory semilinear D_0 on R such that

57.3.3 $$D_0 x = y, \qquad D_0 y = x.$$

It exists, since x, y, if linearly dependent, have been assumed equal. Remember that

57.3.4 $$f(\boldsymbol{u})\,x=\gamma y \quad \text{for some} \quad \gamma\neq 0.$$

Now
$$g=\curlyvee_{\boldsymbol{a}}\, D_0\, f(C\boldsymbol{a})\, D_0$$
is again a linear representation of $\boldsymbol{G}$, which in the partial order transformed by C^* has the top weight $C^*\lambda$ equivalent to λ. Therefore f and g are equivalent, and there is a linear mapping T of R onto itself with
$$T\,g(\boldsymbol{a})\,T^{-1}=f(\boldsymbol{a}) \qquad \text{for all} \quad \boldsymbol{a}\in\boldsymbol{G}.$$
Since x is also a weight vector of g, one may even suppose that T^{-1} maps x into a given multiple of x, say

57.3.5 $$Tx=\frac{\sqrt{|\kappa|}}{|\gamma|}\,x.$$

Substituting the definition of g, one gets

57.3.6 $$TD_0 f(C\boldsymbol{a})\,D_0 T^{-1}=f(\boldsymbol{a}),$$

and, substituting $C\boldsymbol{a}$ instead of $\boldsymbol{a}$,
$$TD_0 f(\boldsymbol{a})\,D_0 T^{-1}=f(C\boldsymbol{a}).$$
Combining these equations and putting

57.3.7 $$D=TD_0,$$

one notes that
$$D^2 \text{ commutes with all } f(\boldsymbol{a}).$$
Thus,

57.3.8 $$D^2=TD_0\,TD_0 \qquad \text{is a scalar multiplier.}$$

When applying 57.3.6 to $TD_0\gamma y$ and replacing $\boldsymbol{a}$ by $\boldsymbol{u}$, one gets
$$TD_0 f(C\boldsymbol{u})\,\gamma y=f(\boldsymbol{u})\,TD_0\,\gamma y.$$
Replacing γy in the first member according to 57.3.4 and 57.2.5, one gets
$$\kappa TD_0 x,$$
whereas in the second member, by 57.3.3, 57.3.5, and 57.3.4,
$$\bar{\gamma}\frac{\sqrt{|\kappa|}}{|\gamma|}\,f(\boldsymbol{u})\,x=\sqrt{|\kappa|}\,|\gamma|\,y.$$

Hence

$$\varepsilon\sqrt{|\kappa|}\, TD_0 x = |\gamma|\, y,$$

$$\varepsilon(\sqrt{|\kappa|}\, TD_0)^2 x = \sqrt{|\kappa|}\, TD_0\, |\gamma|\, y = \sqrt{|\kappa|}\, |\gamma|\, Tx = |\kappa|\, x$$

by 57.3.3, 57.3.5; hence by 57.3.7

$$D^2 x = \varepsilon x$$

and, thanks to 57.3.8,

$$D^2 = \varepsilon;$$

57.3.6 gives

$$Df(C\boldsymbol{a})\, D^{-1} = f(\boldsymbol{a}).$$

If $\varepsilon = 1$, this shows that f is virtually real. It also proves the other assertion of the theorem.

57.3.9. *Remark* It is easily seen from the irreducibility of f that D as asserted in the theorem is determined up to an arbitrary constant with absolute value 1.

From the theorem and the first part of its proof it follows also that the reality of κ and its sign are independent of the particular C-third dressing.

57.4. Theorem Every irreducible linear representation f of a standard type $\boldsymbol{G}_C$ and the self-contravalent irreducible representations of near standard or twin $\boldsymbol{G}_C$ are virtually real.

Proof By 56.1, if $C = C_{\text{st}}$,

$$C^*\lambda = \lambda;$$

but this is still true of near standard and twin C if f is self-contravalent because then by 56.2.2 and 56.1 $C^*\lambda$ is equivalent to λ and still dominant; thus $C^*\lambda = \lambda$.

To show that the irreducible representation with top weight λ is virtually real, one considers its construction (44.5) with a view to reality. The semimorphism C extends from $\boldsymbol{G}$ to the associative envelope $\mathscr{E}(\boldsymbol{G})$. But now the left-hand ideal annihilating the vector of top weight (denoted by $-1 + \boldsymbol{M}$ in 44.5) is C-invariant because of the following:

(1) C^* maps W^+ onto W^+, and C interchanges the $\boldsymbol{e}_\alpha$ ($\alpha \in W^+$) up to real factors (± 1).

(2) C maps $\boldsymbol{h} - \lambda(\boldsymbol{h})$ into $C\boldsymbol{h} - \overline{\lambda(\boldsymbol{h})} = C\boldsymbol{h} - (C^*\lambda)(C\boldsymbol{h}) = C\boldsymbol{h} - \lambda(C\boldsymbol{h})$.

(3) C interchanges the expressions $\boldsymbol{e}_{-\rho}^{p-\rho+1}$ up to signs.

Therefore C extends to $\mathscr{E}(\boldsymbol{G})$ mod $\boldsymbol{M}$ as a semilinear involution which is compatible with C. This proves the theorem.

57.5 Since the self-contravalence of an irreducible linear representation is preserved under isotypism and is not influenced by the choice of the trunk, one can apply the foregoing result to linear representations of any central or near central restriction, according to Proposition 54.4.

Observe now that in ordered maximally compact dressing

$$C_{\mathrm{cl}}\, \boldsymbol{e}_\rho = \boldsymbol{e}_{-\rho}, \qquad C_{\mathrm{ncl}}\, \boldsymbol{e}_\rho = \boldsymbol{e}_{-P\rho} \qquad \text{for} \quad \rho \in W^{++},$$

and substitute these data into 57.2.1 and 57.2.5 for $C = C_{\mathrm{cl}}$ and $C = C_{\mathrm{ncl}}$:

$$f(\boldsymbol{e}_{\rho k} \cdots \boldsymbol{e}_{\rho 1}\, \boldsymbol{e}_{-\rho k} \cdots \boldsymbol{e}_{-\rho 1})x = \kappa x$$

and

$$f(\boldsymbol{e}_{P\rho k} \cdots \boldsymbol{e}_{P\rho 1}\, \boldsymbol{e}_{-\rho k} \cdots \boldsymbol{e}_{-\rho 1})x = \kappa' x$$

with positive κ and κ' because of the virtual reality of self-contravalent f.

One can now forget about central and near central restrictions and state the following:

Proposition If $\boldsymbol{G} \in$ Alg Lie Com SS in ordered maximally compact dressing with respect to some C, if f is a self-contravalent irreducible linear representation of $\boldsymbol{G}$, x a vector of top weight λ, y a vector of weight $C^*\lambda$, and $f(\boldsymbol{e}_{-\rho k} \cdots \boldsymbol{e}_{-\rho 1})x$ is a multiple $\neq 0$ of y $(\rho_\nu \in W^{++})$,

then for inner $\boldsymbol{G}_C$

57.5.1
$$f(\boldsymbol{e}_{\rho k} \cdots \boldsymbol{e}_{\rho 1}\, \boldsymbol{e}_{-\rho k} \cdots \boldsymbol{e}_{-\rho 1})x$$

and for outer $\boldsymbol{G}_C$

57.5.2
$$f(\boldsymbol{e}_{P\rho k} \cdots \boldsymbol{e}_{P\rho 1}\, \boldsymbol{e}_{-\rho k} \cdots \boldsymbol{e}_{-\rho 1})x$$

are positive multiples of x.

Though proved only for simple $\boldsymbol{G}$, the proposition applies in general. Twin factors do not contribute, and all simple factors behave independently, since their branches commute and every branch acts only on the component of the trunk to which it belongs. In any real simple factor where it occurs P is to be interpreted as the plus-automorphism.

57.6 To compute ε for any self-contravalent irreducible linear representation f with top weight λ one must compare 57.5.1–2 with

57.6.1
$$f(C\boldsymbol{e}_{-\rho k} \cdots C\boldsymbol{e}_{-\rho 1}\, \boldsymbol{e}_{-\rho k} \cdots \boldsymbol{e}_{-\rho 1})x = \kappa x.$$

Now in ordered maximally compact dressing (see 51.11; by Remark 57.3.9 it does not matter which one)

$$C = \tilde{h} A C_{\mathrm{un}},$$

with the conditions 51.11.2–4. Since

$$\lambda - C^*\lambda = \lambda + A\lambda,$$

$A\rho_\nu$ appears in $\lambda - C^*\lambda$ as often as ρ_ν. If $\rho \neq A\rho$,

$$Ce_{-\rho} = -(\exp(A\rho)(\boldsymbol{h}))\, e_{A\rho},$$

and

$$Ce_{-A\rho} = -(\exp \rho(\boldsymbol{h}))\, e_\rho$$

together do not contribute to κ in 57.6.1 if compared with 57.5.2, since $h \cdot Ah = 1$ (51.11.4). If $\rho = A\rho$, the contribution compared with that in 57.5.1–2 is

$$-\exp \rho(\boldsymbol{h}) = \pm 1.$$

Since 57.5.1–2 were positive multiples of x, κ is always real and its sign is determined by these contributions. Whence:

Theorem Let $G \in$ Alg Lie Com SS be given in ordered maximally compact dressing with respect to

$$C = \tilde{h} A C_{\text{un}},$$

where

$$h = \exp 2\pi i \boldsymbol{h}, \qquad \boldsymbol{h} \in \boldsymbol{H}_{\text{st}},$$

$$\rho(\boldsymbol{h}) = 0, \tfrac{1}{2} \qquad \text{for} \quad A\rho = \rho \in W^{++},$$

$$AW^{++} = W^{++},$$

$$A^2 = 1,$$

$$AC_{\text{un}} = C_{\text{un}} A.$$

Let λ be the top weight of self-contravalent f,

$$C^*\lambda - \lambda = \sum q_\nu \rho_\nu \qquad (\rho_\nu \in W^{++}),$$

with integral q_ν. Put

$$\left.\begin{array}{ll} \varepsilon_\nu = -1 & \text{for} \quad \rho_\nu(\boldsymbol{h}) = 0 \\ \varepsilon_\nu = 1 & \text{for} \quad \rho_\nu(\boldsymbol{h}) = \tfrac{1}{2} \end{array}\right\} \quad \text{if} \quad \rho_\nu = A\rho_\nu.$$

Then the ε in Theorem 57.3 is computed as

$$\varepsilon = \prod \varepsilon_\nu^{q_\nu}.$$

f is virtually real if $\varepsilon = 1$ and antireal if $\varepsilon = -1$.

Remark Actually, one may drop all twin factors and, using the classification of 51.17 for every simple summand $\mathbf{L}_j$ or $\mathbf{L}_{j,*}$, put $\varepsilon_\nu = -1$ except for $\varepsilon_j = 1$.

57.7 It is unfortunate that by the identification of standard and near standard with central and near central types the proof of 57.6 finally rests on the verification in 54.3. Another approach would be to show that up to a positive factor $\boldsymbol{e}_{-\rho_k} \cdots \boldsymbol{e}_{-\rho_1} x$ does not depend on the choice of $\rho_1, \ldots, \rho_k \in W^{++}$ as long as $x, \boldsymbol{e}_{-\rho_1} x, \ldots, \boldsymbol{e}_{-\rho_k} \cdots \boldsymbol{e}_{-\rho_1} x$ is a descent by complete ladders. This has been shown by H. de Vries (unpublished). D.-N. Verma in his Yale thesis of 1966 (Theorem 4.1, and Remark 4.3) even proved that under the same condition $\boldsymbol{e}_{-\rho_k} \cdots \boldsymbol{e}_{-\rho_1}$ is uniquely determined within the associative envelope.

57.8. Antireality and Quaternion Space

Theorem An antireal linear representation of real semisimple $\boldsymbol{G}_C$ in complex R can be interpreted as a representation by quaternion linear mappings of a quaternion linear space of half the dimension of R.

Proof In the antireal case the expressions

$$\alpha + \beta D$$

(α, β complex, D the semilinear mapping of Theorem 57.3 with $D^2 = -1$) may be considered as left-hand operators on R. They form a skew field in which

$$D\alpha = \bar{\alpha} D.$$

A conjugation can be defined in this field,

$$\overline{\alpha + \beta D} = \bar{a} - \beta D$$

such that

$$\overline{uv} = \bar{v}\bar{u}.$$

Thus the skew field is that of quaternions (Qio). R can be interpreted as a linear space Q over Qio. Its dimension is half that of R.

The $f(\boldsymbol{a})$ with $\boldsymbol{a} \in \boldsymbol{G}_C$ are endomorphisms of Q:

$$f(\boldsymbol{a})(\alpha + \beta D)x = \alpha\, f(\boldsymbol{a})x + \beta\, f(\boldsymbol{a})\, Dx = \alpha\, f(\boldsymbol{a})x + \beta D f(\boldsymbol{a})x = (\alpha + \beta D) f(\boldsymbol{a})x.$$

57.9. Historical Note E. Cartan classified the real representations of semisimple Lie algebras [*J. Math. Pures Appl.* **10**, (6) 149–186 (1914) = *Oeuvres* I **1**, 493–530], mainly by verifications. The explicit formula for ε, and the relation between $\varepsilon = -1$ and quaternionic representations, was found by H. Freudenthal.

58. COMPUTING ε FOR SIMPLE LIE ALGEBRAS

A basis of self-contravalent dominant integral elements of $\boldsymbol{H}^*$ was given in 56.3. All possible self-contravalent top weights can be combined from them with nonnegative integral coefficients. In such combinations ε behaves multiplicatively. Therefore it suffices to compute ε for the members of that list. The list of fundamental weights of Table F is used also.

A$_{l,j}$: $\pi_k + \pi_{l+1-k}$ $(k \leqslant \frac{1}{2}l)$ expressed in the primitive rootforms has the coefficients

$$1, 2, \ldots, k, \ldots, k, \ldots, k, \ldots, 2, 1.$$

$C^*(\pi_k + \pi_{l+1-k}) = -\pi_k - \pi_{l+1-k}$; thus in

$$\pi_k + \pi_{l+1-k} - C^*(\pi_k + \pi_{l+1-k})$$

all coefficients are even:

$$\varepsilon = +1.$$

For l odd, $l = 2m - 1$, π_m has the coefficients

$$\frac{1}{2}, \frac{2}{2}, \ldots, \frac{m}{2}, \ldots, \frac{2}{2}, \frac{1}{2};$$

$C^*\pi_m = -\pi_m$; thus

$$\varepsilon = (-1)^{j+m}.$$

A$_{l,j,*}$: For l odd, $l = 2m - 1$: $C^*\pi_k = -\pi_{l+1-k}$. $\pi_k - C^*\pi_k$ has the coefficents

$$1, 2, \ldots, k, \ldots, k, \ldots, k, \ldots, 2, 1.$$

Therefore

$$\text{for } j = 0: \quad \varepsilon = (-1)^k,$$

$$\text{for } j = m: \quad \varepsilon = +1,$$

$$\text{for } l \text{ even}, j = 0: \quad \varepsilon = +1.$$

B$_{l,j}$: $C^*\pi_k = -\pi_k$,

$$\pi_k - C^*\pi_k = 2\pi_k = 0 \bmod 2 \qquad \text{for} \quad k \neq 1,$$

$$= l\rho_1 + \rho_2 + 2\rho_3 + \cdots + (l-1)\rho_l \qquad \text{for} \quad k = 1;$$

$$\text{for } k \neq 1: \quad \varepsilon = +1,$$

$$\text{for } k = 1: \quad \varepsilon = (-1)^{\binom{l+1}{2}} \qquad \text{if} \quad j = 0,$$

$$\varepsilon = (-1)^{\binom{l}{2}} \qquad \text{if} \quad j = 1,$$

$$\varepsilon = (-1)^{\binom{l+1}{2}+j-1} \qquad \text{if} \quad j > 1.$$

A unified formula is possible if the signature σ $(= 2l - 4j + 5$ for $j > 0$, $= 2l + 1$ for $j = 0)$ of the quadratic form is used by which real π_2 was presented (see 54.1 and 59.7; do not confuse it with that of the Killing form). An easy computation shows

$$\text{for } k=1: \quad \varepsilon=+1 \quad \text{if} \quad \sigma=\pm 1 \bmod 8,$$
$$\varepsilon=-1 \quad \text{if} \quad \sigma=\pm 3 \bmod 8.$$

$\mathbf{C}_{l,j}$:

$$C^* \pi_k = -\pi_k,$$
$$\pi_k - C^* \pi_k = k\rho_l \bmod 2.$$
$$\varepsilon=(-1)^k \quad \text{for} \quad j \neq l,$$
$$\varepsilon=+1 \quad \text{for} \quad j=l.$$

$\mathbf{D}_{l,j}$: For $k \neq 1, 2$,

$$C^* \pi_k = -\pi_k,$$
$$\pi_k - C^* \pi_k = (k-2)(\rho_1+\rho_2) \bmod 2.$$

Thus

$$\text{for } j \neq 1,2: \quad \varepsilon=+1,$$
$$\text{for } j=1: \quad \varepsilon=(-1)^k.$$

For the other basic self-contravalent top weights one must distinguish between "l odd" and "l even."

For l even:

$$C^* \pi_k = -\pi_k \qquad (k=1,2),$$
$$\pi_1 - C^* \pi_1 = \tfrac{1}{2}l\rho_1 + \tfrac{1}{2}(l-2)\rho_2 + \rho_3 + 2\rho_4 + \cdots + (l-2)\rho_l,$$
$$\pi_2 - C^* \pi_2 = \tfrac{1}{2}(l-2)\rho_1 + \tfrac{1}{2}l\rho_2 + \rho_3 + 2\rho_4 + \cdots + (l-2)\rho_l,$$

Thus

$$\text{for } j \neq 1,2: \quad \varepsilon=(-1)^{\binom{l}{2}+j} \quad \text{if} \quad k=1,2;$$
$$\text{for } j=1: \quad \varepsilon=+1 \quad \text{if} \quad k=1,$$
$$\varepsilon=-1 \quad \text{if} \quad k=2.$$

For l odd: only

$$C^*(\pi_1+\pi_2) = -\pi_1 - \pi_2$$

is left, for which

$$(\pi_1+\pi_2) - C^*(\pi_1+\pi_2) = 0 \bmod 2.$$

Thus

$$\varepsilon=+1 \quad \text{if} \quad k=1,2.$$

In the case of even l, using the signature $\sigma = 2l - 4j + 8$ as in $\mathbf{B}_{l,j}$, one gets: if $k = 1,2$ and $j \neq 1,2$,

$$\varepsilon = +1 \qquad \text{if} \quad \sigma = 0 \bmod 8,$$

$$\varepsilon = -1 \qquad \text{if} \quad \sigma = 4 \bmod 8.$$

Remark The result $\varepsilon = +1$, if $k = 1$, $\varepsilon = -1$, if $k = 2$, for $j = 1$ and l even is unexpected.† π_1 and π_2 are reduced to each other by an outer automorphism of the complex Lie algebra. Clearly, this symmetry is destroyed by urging $j = 1$.

$\mathbf{D}_{l,j,*}$ $(j \neq 1,2)$: For $k \neq 1,2$

$$C^* \pi_k = -\pi_k,$$

$$\pi_k - C^* \pi_k = (k-2)(\rho_1 + \rho_2) \bmod 2.$$

Thus for all cases

$$\varepsilon = +1.$$

For the other basic element one must distinguish between "l even" and "l odd."

For l even

$$C^*(\pi_1 + \pi_2) = -\pi_2 - \pi_1,$$

$$\pi_1 + \pi_2 - C^*(\pi_1 + \pi_2) = \rho_1 + \rho_2 \bmod 2.$$

Thus, for all cases,

$$\varepsilon = +1.$$

For l odd

$$C^* \pi_1 = -\pi_2,$$

$$\pi_1 - C^* \pi_1 = \tfrac{1}{2}(l-1)(\rho_1 + \rho_2) + \rho_3 + 2\rho_4 + \cdots + (l-2)\rho_l.$$

Thus for $k = 1$ ($k = 2$ is the same case),

$$\varepsilon = (-1)^{\binom{l}{2} + j}.$$

Using again the signature $\sigma = 2l - 4j + 6$ $(j > 2)$, one can write this as

$$\text{for } k = 1: \quad \varepsilon = +1 \qquad \text{if} \quad \sigma = 0 \bmod 8,$$

$$\varepsilon = -1 \qquad \text{if} \quad \sigma = 4 \bmod 8.$$

$\mathbf{E}_{6,j}$ $(j = 0,1,2)$: All coefficients in $(\pi_1 + \pi_3) - C^*(\pi_1 + \pi_3)$, $\pi_2 - C^* \pi_2$, $(\pi_4 + \pi_5) - C^*(\pi_4 + \pi_5)$, $\pi_6 - C^* \pi_6$ are even. Thus

$$\varepsilon = +1.$$

† It differs from Cartan's.

$\mathbf{E}_{6,j,*}$ $(j=0,2)$: In every $\pi_k - C^*\pi_k$ the coefficient of ρ_2 and the sum of all coefficients is even:

$$\varepsilon = +1.$$

$\mathbf{E}_{7,j}$ $(j=0,1,2,3)$: For $\pi_1, \pi_4, \pi_5, \pi_7$: $\varepsilon = +1$

for π_2, π_3, π_6: $\varepsilon = +1$ if $j = 2, 3$,

$\varepsilon = -1$ if $j = 0, 1$.

$\mathbf{E}_8$: $\varepsilon = +1.$

$\mathbf{F}_4$: $\varepsilon = +1.$

$\mathbf{G}_2$: $\varepsilon = +1.$

59. INVARIANT BILINEAR AND SESQUILINEAR FORMS

59.1. Unitary Representations In 35.1 it was shown that every finite-dimensional linear representation f of a compact group is essentially unitary. For the infinitesimal algebra G_{un} of a compact semisimple group this means the existence of a definite hermitean inner product $\langle \ldots, \ldots \rangle$ in R such that

$$\langle f(\boldsymbol{a})\,x, y\rangle + \langle x, f(\boldsymbol{a})\,y\rangle = 0 \qquad \text{for} \quad \boldsymbol{a} \in \boldsymbol{G}_{\text{un}}.$$

Expressed in $\boldsymbol{G}$ this reads

59.1.1 $$\langle f(\boldsymbol{a})\,x, y\rangle + \langle x, f(C_{\text{un}}\,\boldsymbol{a})\,y\rangle = 0 \qquad \text{for} \quad \boldsymbol{a} \in \boldsymbol{G}.$$

With $\boldsymbol{h}$ in the trunk instead of $\boldsymbol{a}$ and vectors x_λ, x_μ belonging to the weights λ, μ, this becomes

$$\lambda(\boldsymbol{h})\langle x_\lambda, x_\mu\rangle + (C^*_{\text{un}}\,\mu)(\boldsymbol{h})\langle x_\lambda, x_\mu\rangle = 0,$$

and because of $C^*_{\text{un}} = -1$,

59.1.2 $$\langle x_\lambda, x_\mu\rangle = 0 \qquad \text{for} \quad \lambda \neq \mu.$$

Putting $\boldsymbol{a} = \boldsymbol{e}_\alpha$, one gets from 59.1.1

$$\langle f(\boldsymbol{e}_\alpha)\,x, y\rangle = \langle x, f(\boldsymbol{e}_{-\alpha})\,y\rangle.$$

Consider products of branches and put $\boldsymbol{u}^* = \boldsymbol{e}_{\mp\alpha}$ if $\boldsymbol{u} = \boldsymbol{e}_{\pm\alpha}$ and $(\boldsymbol{uv})^* = \boldsymbol{v}^*\boldsymbol{u}^*$. Then

$$\langle f(\boldsymbol{u})\,x, y\rangle = \langle x, f(\boldsymbol{u}^*)\,y\rangle.$$

In particular,

59.1.3 $$\langle f(\boldsymbol{u})x_\lambda, f(\boldsymbol{u})x_\lambda\rangle = \langle f(\boldsymbol{u}^*\boldsymbol{u})x_\lambda, x_\lambda\rangle.$$

Thus, if the weight λ has multiplicity 1, then $f(\boldsymbol{u}^*\boldsymbol{u})x_\lambda$ is a nonnegative multiple of x_λ.

The existence of invariant $\langle \ldots, \ldots\rangle$ was proved by integration, but an algebraic construction is still lacking. For irreducible f one should proceed by postulating 59.1.2, taking x_λ for the top weight λ arbitrarily, and x_μ of lower weights μ, which can be put into the form $f(\boldsymbol{u})x_\lambda$, by postulating 59.1.3. A crucial point is to prove that $f(\boldsymbol{u}^*\boldsymbol{u})x_\lambda$ is a nonnegative multiple of x_λ. It is rather easy to show that the coefficient is real. The difficulty to ascertain its positiveness algebraically seems still greater than the analogous problem in 57.5.1–2.

59.2–8 $\boldsymbol{G} \in$ Alg Lie Com SS in C-third dressing and f an irreducible representation of $\boldsymbol{G}$ in R. If f is not areal with respect to C, C_{un}, then semi-linear D, D_{un}, and $\varepsilon, \varepsilon_{\mathrm{un}} = \pm 1$ are determined according to Theorem 57.3 by

$$Df(C\boldsymbol{a})\,D^{-1} = f(\boldsymbol{a}), \qquad D^2 = \varepsilon,$$

$$D_{\mathrm{un}}f(C_{\mathrm{un}}\boldsymbol{a})\,D_{\mathrm{un}}^{-1} = f(\boldsymbol{a}), \qquad D_{\mathrm{un}}^2 = \varepsilon_{\mathrm{un}}.$$

Invariant (i.e., infinitesimally invariant) bilinear and sesquilinear forms will be investigated. Note that they are nondegenerate as soon as they are nontrivial (nonzero) since their radicals are invariant.

$\langle \ldots, \ldots\rangle$ always means a $f(\boldsymbol{G}_{\mathrm{un}})$-invariant positive definite inner product on R.

59.2. Uniqueness of Invariants Invariant bilinear or sesquilinear† forms, if they exist, are unique up to a scalar factor. Indeed, if, for instance, $(\ldots, \ldots)$ is bilinear and nondegenerate, then some other $(\ldots, \ldots)'$ can be expressed in terms of $(\ldots, \ldots)$ by $(x, y)' = (Kx, y)$ with some linear mapping K; if they are both invariant,

$$(f(\boldsymbol{a})x, y) + (x, f(\boldsymbol{a})y) = 0 \qquad \text{for all} \quad \boldsymbol{a} \in \boldsymbol{G},$$

$$(Kf(\boldsymbol{a})x, y) + (Kx, f(\boldsymbol{a})y) = 0 \qquad \text{for all} \quad \boldsymbol{a} \in \boldsymbol{G},$$

then, by substituting Kx instead of x in the first line, one gets

$$(Kf(\boldsymbol{a})x, y) = (f(\boldsymbol{a})Kx, y) \qquad \text{for all} \quad \boldsymbol{a} \in \boldsymbol{G},$$

which shows that

$$Kf(\boldsymbol{a}) = f(\boldsymbol{a})K \qquad \text{for all} \quad \boldsymbol{a} \in \boldsymbol{G};$$

hence, because of the irreducibility of f, K is a scalar multiplier.

† Linear in the first and semilinear in the second variable.

Any invariant bilinear form can be split into an invariant symmetric and an invariant skew part:

$$(x, y) = \tfrac{1}{2}((x, y) + (y, x)) + \tfrac{1}{2}((x, y) - (y, x)).$$

Therefore it is either symmetric or skew.

For sesquilinear forms analogous remarks are valid. Skew sesquilinear forms become symmetric by multiplication with i.

An immediate consequence is the following:

Proposition If $\langle \ldots, \ldots \rangle$ is the $f(\boldsymbol{G}_{\mathrm{un}})$-invariant (positive definite) inner product and f is not areal with respect to C, then

$$\langle Dy, Dx \rangle = \langle x, y \rangle;$$

hence,

$$\langle x, Dy \rangle = \varepsilon \langle y, Dx \rangle.$$

Proof The new inner product $\langle \ldots, \ldots \rangle'$ defined by

$$\langle x, y \rangle' = \langle Dy, Dx \rangle$$

is still $f(\boldsymbol{G}_{\mathrm{un}})$ invariant, since

$$\begin{aligned} \langle f(\boldsymbol{a})x, y\rangle' + \langle x, f(C_{\mathrm{un}}\boldsymbol{a})y\rangle' &= \langle Dy, Df(\boldsymbol{a})x\rangle + \langle Df(C_{\mathrm{un}}\boldsymbol{a})y, Dx\rangle \\ &= \langle Dy, f(C\boldsymbol{a})\, Dx\rangle + \langle f(C_{\mathrm{un}}\, C\boldsymbol{a})\, Dy, Dx\rangle = 0. \end{aligned}$$

Because of the irreducibility of f (see 59.2), for some γ,

$$\langle Dy, Dx \rangle = \gamma \langle x, y \rangle.$$

Substituting Dx, Dy instead of x, y and taking the positive definiteness of $\langle \ldots, \ldots \rangle$ into account, one indeed gets

$$\langle Dy, Dx \rangle = \langle x, y \rangle.$$

59.3. *G*-Invariant Forms

Theorem $\boldsymbol{G}$ possesses a nondegenerate bilinear symmetric (skew) invariant under f iff f is virtually real (antireal) with respect to C_{un}. The invariant can be taken as $\curlyvee_{\ulcorner x,y \urcorner} \langle x, D_{\mathrm{un}} y \rangle$ where $\langle \ldots, \ldots \rangle$ is the $f(\boldsymbol{G}_{\mathrm{un}})$-invariant inner product.

Proof The invariance formula

$$(f(\boldsymbol{a})x, y) + (x, f(\boldsymbol{a})y) = 0$$

applied to weight vectors x_λ, x_μ and $\boldsymbol{h} \in \boldsymbol{H}$ yields

$$(f(\boldsymbol{h})\, x_\lambda, x_\mu) + (x_\lambda,\ f(\boldsymbol{h})\, x_\mu) = 0,$$

$$(\lambda(\boldsymbol{h}) + \mu(\boldsymbol{h}))\,(x_\lambda, x_\mu) = 0;$$

thus,

$$(x_\lambda, x_\mu) = 0 \qquad \text{unless} \quad \lambda = -\mu,$$

in other words,

$$(x_\lambda, x_\mu) = 0 \qquad \text{unless} \quad \mu = C^*_{\text{un}}\,\lambda.$$

In order for $(\ldots, \ldots)$ to be nondegenerate, $C^*_{\text{un}}\lambda$ must be a weight of f if λ is so, and have the same multiplicity. Therefore C^*_{un} maps weights into weights while preserving multiplicities. Thus $\curlyvee_{\boldsymbol{a}}\overline{f(C_{\text{un}}\boldsymbol{a})}$ and f are equivalent and f must be C_{un}-self-contravalent; that is, it cannot be C_{un}-areal.

Conversely, let f be not areal with respect to C_{un}. Then

$$(x, y) = \langle x, D_{\text{un}}\, y\rangle$$

defines a bilinear form on R which is $f(\boldsymbol{G})$-invariant, since

$$(f(\boldsymbol{a})\, x, y) + (x,\ f(\boldsymbol{a})\, y) = \langle f(\boldsymbol{a})\, x,\ D_{\text{un}}\, y\rangle + \langle x,\ D_{\text{un}}\, f(\boldsymbol{a})\, y\rangle$$

$$= \langle f(\boldsymbol{a})\, x,\ D_{\text{un}}\, y\rangle + \langle x,\ f(C_{\text{un}}\boldsymbol{a})\, D_{\text{un}}\, y\rangle = 0.$$

It is evident that $(\ldots, \ldots)$ is nontrivial; it may be symmetric or skew.

Now, according to 59.2,

$$\langle x,\ D_{\text{un}}\, y\rangle = \varepsilon_{\text{un}}\langle y,\ D_{\text{un}}\, x\rangle,$$

which proves the last assertion, and the one about symmetry.

59.4. G_C-Invariant Forms

Theorem G_C possesses a nondegenerate sesquilinear form invariant under f iff its top weight λ is equivalent to $CC_{\text{un}}\lambda$. For simple $\boldsymbol{G}$ this means that f has to be areal with respect to both C and C_{un} or with respect to neither C nor C_{un}.

Proof Again using the $f(\boldsymbol{G}_{\text{un}})$-invariant inner product $\langle \ldots, \ldots\rangle$, one can write any nondegenerate sesquilinear form as

$$\curlyvee_{\ulcorner \boldsymbol{x},\boldsymbol{y} \urcorner}\langle Kx,\ y\rangle$$

with nondegenerate K.

Its $\boldsymbol{G}_C$-invariance means

$$\langle Kf(\boldsymbol{a})\, x, y\rangle + \langle Kx,\ f(C\boldsymbol{a})\, y\rangle = 0.$$

Replacing $\boldsymbol{a}$ by $CC_{\mathrm{un}}\boldsymbol{a}$ and x by $K^{-1}x$, one gets

$$\langle Kf(CC_{\mathrm{un}}\boldsymbol{a})\,K^{-1}x, y\rangle + \langle x, f(C_{\mathrm{un}}\boldsymbol{a})\,y\rangle = 0.$$

Moreover,

$$\langle f(\boldsymbol{a})\,x, y\rangle + \langle x, f(C_{\mathrm{un}}\boldsymbol{a})\,y\rangle = 0,$$

which shows that

59.4.1 $$Kf(CC_{\mathrm{un}}\boldsymbol{a})\,K^{-1} = f(\boldsymbol{a}),$$

hence that f and $\curlyvee_{\boldsymbol{a}} f(CC_{\mathrm{un}}\boldsymbol{a})$ are equivalent and by 44.1 that λ and $CC_{\mathrm{un}}\lambda$ are equivalent. All arguments can be turned the other way round.

For simple $\boldsymbol{G}$ the equivalence of the other conditions follows by inspection (56.3).

Note that a bilinear form invariant under $f(\boldsymbol{G}_C)$ is also invariant under $f(\boldsymbol{G})$; therefore Theorem 59.3 applies then.

59.5. G_C-Invariants in Real and Quaternion Space If f is areal with respect to neither C nor C_{un}, then more information is available via the semilinear D, D_{un}.

Theorem If $\langle \ldots, \ldots \rangle$ is the $f(\boldsymbol{G}_{\mathrm{un}})$-invariant inner product, then

59.5.1 $$\curlyvee_{\ulcorner x,y \urcorner}\langle x, D_{\mathrm{un}}\,Dy\rangle$$

is an $f(\boldsymbol{G}_C)$-invariant sesquilinear form, which can be made hermitean by a suitable norming of D; it is hermitean iff $(D_{\mathrm{un}}D)^2 = 1$.

If $\varepsilon = 1$, its restriction to R_D coincides with that of the bilinear form of 59.3; it is real and symmetric if $\varepsilon_{\mathrm{un}} = 1$; it is imaginary and skew if $\varepsilon_{\mathrm{un}} = -1$.

If $\varepsilon = -1$, then considering R as the quaternion linear space Q (see 57.8), one gets an $f(\boldsymbol{G}_C)$-invariant quaternion sesquilinear form $(\ldots, \ldots)$,

59.5.2 $$(x, y) = \beta\langle x, DD_{\mathrm{un}}\,y\rangle + \beta D\langle D_{\mathrm{un}}\,x, y\rangle$$

with $\bar{\beta} = -\varepsilon_{\mathrm{un}}\beta$ (e.g., $\beta = 1$ for $\varepsilon_{\mathrm{un}} = -1$, $\beta = \mathrm{i}$ for $\varepsilon_{\mathrm{un}} = 1$). If $\varepsilon_{\mathrm{un}} = -1$, it is hermitean, if $\varepsilon_{\mathrm{un}} = 1$, it is skew hermitean.

Proof The $f(\boldsymbol{G}_C)$-invariance of 59.5.1 follows from

$$f(CC_{\mathrm{un}}\boldsymbol{a}) = D^{-1}\,D_{\mathrm{un}}^{-1} f(\boldsymbol{a})\,D_{\mathrm{un}}\,D.$$

Furthermore, because of $(CC_{\mathrm{un}})^2 = 1$ and the irreducibility of f,

$$(D_{\mathrm{un}}\,D)^2 = \text{scalar } \gamma,$$

hence

$$(DD_{\text{un}})^2 = D_{\text{un}}^{-1}(D_{\text{un}}\,D)^2\,D_{\text{un}} = \bar{\gamma},$$

and by multiplying both equations

$$\gamma\bar{\gamma} = 1.$$

By Remark 57.3.9 one may use βD instead of D, with $\beta^2 = \gamma^{-1}$. This allows one to suppose

$$(D_{\text{un}}\,D)^2 = 1.$$

Thus, because of 59.2,

$$\langle x, D_{\text{un}}\,Dy\rangle = \varepsilon_{\text{un}}\langle Dy, D_{\text{un}}\,x\rangle = \varepsilon_{\text{un}}\,\varepsilon\langle DD_{\text{un}}\,x, y\rangle = \langle D_{\text{un}}\,Dx, y\rangle,$$

which calculation proves the equivalence of the hermitean symmetry of 59.5.1 with the equality $(D_{\text{un}}\,D)^2 = 1$.

The remark about the case $\varepsilon = 1$ is obvious from 59.2.

Suppose that $\varepsilon = -1$. The invariance of 59.5.2 follows from that of the summands. $(\ldots, \ldots)$ is sesquilinear: For complex α

$$(\alpha x, y) = \alpha(x, y), \qquad (x, \alpha y) = (x, y)\,\bar{\alpha}.$$

Further

$$\begin{aligned}(Dx, y) &= \beta\langle Dx, DD_{\text{un}}\,y\rangle + \beta D\langle D_{\text{un}}\,Dx, y\rangle \\ &= \beta\langle D_{\text{un}}\,y, x\rangle - \beta\varepsilon_{\text{un}}\,D\langle DD_{\text{un}}\,x, y\rangle,\end{aligned}$$

and

$$D(x, y) = \bar{\beta}D\langle x, DD_{\text{un}}\,y\rangle - \bar{\beta}\langle D_{\text{un}}\,x, y\rangle,$$

which by the assumption $\bar{\beta} = -\varepsilon_{\text{un}}\,\beta$ leads to

$$D(x, y) = (Dx, y).$$

This proves the linearity of $(\ldots, \ldots)$ in the first variable.

Moreover,

$$\begin{aligned}(y, x) &= \beta\langle y, DD_{\text{un}}\,x\rangle + \beta D\langle D_{\text{un}}y, x\rangle, \\ \overline{(y, x)} &= \bar{\beta}\langle x, DD_{\text{un}}\,y\rangle - \beta\varepsilon_{\text{un}}\,D\langle D_{\text{un}}\,x, y\rangle \\ &= -\varepsilon_{\text{un}}(x, y).\end{aligned}$$

This reveals the symmetry character of $(\ldots, \ldots)$ as dependent on ε_{un}, and finally it completes the proof that $(\ldots, \ldots)$ is sesquilinear.

59.5.3. *Remark* With the normings of Theorems 57.3 and 59.5 D and D_{un} determine each other up to a sign.

59.6. Toward Computation To compute the invariants in particular cases, maximally compact dressing is assumed:

$$CC_{\text{un}} = C_{\text{un}}C = \tilde{h}A.$$

The invariants are expressed in terms of the inner product $\langle \ldots, \ldots \rangle$ by

$$\curlyvee_{\ulcorner x,y \urcorner} \langle Kx, y \rangle,$$

which should be calculated for weight vectors x, y. According to 59.4.1, if x_μ belongs to the weight μ, then Kx_μ does to the weight $A\mu$. By 59.1.2 $\langle Kx_\mu, x_\nu \rangle$ vanishes unless $A\mu = \nu$. Therefore one can restrict the computation to $\langle Kx_\mu, x'_{A\mu} \rangle$. (The prime on $x'_{A\mu}$ accounts for the circumstance that by chance $A\mu$ may equal μ, though there might be several independent μ-weight vectors.)

Starting from the top weight λ, one has

$$\mu = \lambda - \sum p_\nu \rho_\nu$$

and a linear combination $\boldsymbol{u}$ of products of $\boldsymbol{e}_{-\rho}$ ($\rho \in W^{++}$) such that

$$x_\mu = f(\boldsymbol{u}) x_\lambda.$$

Applying 59.4.1 and taking

$$CC_{\text{un}} \boldsymbol{e}_{-\rho_\nu} = \tilde{h}A\boldsymbol{e}_{-\rho_\nu} = -\varepsilon_\nu \boldsymbol{e}_{-A\rho_\nu}$$

into account (see 57.6), one gets

$$-\varepsilon_\nu Kf(\boldsymbol{e}_{-A\rho_\nu}) K^{-1} = f(\boldsymbol{e}_{-\rho_\nu});$$

therefore

$$\prod (-\varepsilon_\nu)^{p_\nu} Kf(A\boldsymbol{u}) K^{-1} = f(\boldsymbol{u}).$$

If $A\lambda = \lambda$, then, after having replaced K by a suitable multiple (real if the sesquilinear form was already hermitean),

$$\begin{aligned} Kx_\lambda &= x_\lambda, \\ x_\mu &= f(\boldsymbol{u}) x_\lambda \\ &= \prod (-\varepsilon_\nu)^{p_\nu} Kf(A\boldsymbol{u}) x_\lambda \\ &= \prod (-\varepsilon_\nu)^{p_\nu} Kx_{A\mu} \end{aligned}$$

for a suitable choice of $x_{A\mu}$, which, however, coincides with x_μ if $A = 1$. Therefore

$$Kx_\mu = \prod (-\varepsilon_\nu)^{p_\nu} x_\mu \qquad \text{for} \quad A = 1.$$

This then completely determines the nondegenerate hermitean form

$$\curlyvee_{\ulcorner x,y \urcorner} \langle Kx, y \rangle.$$

If f is areal with respect to neither C nor $C_{\rm un}$ and D, $D_{\rm un}$ are normalized as in Remark 59.5.3, then in the case $A\lambda = \lambda$

$$K = \pm DD_{\rm un},$$

and, if necessary by replacing D by $-D$, even

$$K = DD_{\rm un}.$$

59.7. Examples For the lowest dimensional linear representations of $G \in$ Alg Lie Com SSS one gets the following results by which the assertions of 54.1 come true.

$\pi_1(\mathbf{A}_{l,j})$: In the notation of Section 16, $\omega_1, \ldots, \omega_{l+1}$ are the weights, with orthonormal weight vectors $x_1, \ldots, x_{l+1}$. $Kx_\nu = x_\nu$ for $\nu \leqslant j$, $Kx_\nu = -x_\nu$ for $\nu > j$. The invariant hermitean form has the signature $2j-(l+1)$. By comparing the dimensions, one verifies that the group consists of *all* linear mappings with unit determinants that leave this form invariant.

$\pi_1(\mathbf{A}_{2m,0,*})$, $\pi_1(\mathbf{A}_{2m-1,m,*})$: By 59.3 no invariant form exists. Comparison of dimensions shows that the group consists of all real linear mappings of R_D with unit determinants.

$\pi_1(\mathbf{A}_{2m-1,0,*})$: Since $\varepsilon = -1$, the representation takes place in quaternion m-space. All its automorphisms form a $4m^2$-dimensional group; those with unit determinants produce the correct dimension. (The determinant is defined as a real number after waiving the quaternion structure.)

$\pi_2(\mathbf{B}_{l,j})$: $\varepsilon_{\rm un} = \varepsilon = 1$. Weights $\pm\omega_\nu$, 0 with vectors $x_{\pm\nu}, x_0$.† Because of Proposition 59.2, one may suppose that $D_{\rm un}x_\nu = x_{-\nu}$, since $D_{\rm un}$ permutes the eigenvectors as $C_{\rm un}^*$ permutes the weights. Then, in the normalization of 59.6, $D = KD_{\rm un}$.

$$\text{For } j>1: \quad Kx_{\pm\nu} = x_{\pm\nu} \quad \text{if } 1 \leqslant \nu < j,$$
$$Kx_{\pm\nu} = -x_{\pm\nu} \quad \text{if } j \leqslant \nu \leqslant l,$$
$$Kx_0 = -x_0.$$

R_D is spanned by $\mathrm{i}x_0$, $\tau x_\nu + \bar\tau x_{-\nu}$ $(1 \leqslant \nu < j)$, $\tau x_\nu - \bar\tau x_{-\nu}$ $(j \leqslant \nu \leqslant l)$, which make $\langle Kx, x\rangle < 0, > 0, < 0$. The invariant quadratic form has the signature $-1 + (2j-2) - 2(l-j+1) = 4j-2l-5$.

$$\text{For } j=1: \quad Kx_{\pm\nu} = x_{\pm\nu} \quad \text{if } 1 \leqslant \nu \leqslant l,$$
$$Kx_0 = -x_0.$$

R_D is spanned by $\mathrm{i}x_0, \tau x_\nu + \bar\tau x_{-\nu}$ $(1 \leqslant \nu \leqslant l)$. Signature $2l-1$.

† Here, and in the remainder of this section, the signs in the subscripts are used dependently.

Comparing dimensions, one verifies that the groups are the 1-components of the full invariance groups of these forms.

$\pi_1(\mathbf{C}_{l,j}), j<l$: $\varepsilon_{\text{un}} = \varepsilon = -1$. Weights $\pm\omega_\nu$, with vectors $x_{\pm\nu}$. One may suppose that $D_{\text{un}} x_\nu = x_{-\nu}$, $D_{\text{un}} x_{-\nu} = -x_\nu$.

$$Kx_{\pm\nu} = x_{\pm\nu} \qquad \text{for} \quad 1 \leqslant \nu \leqslant j,$$

$$Kx_{\pm\nu} = -x_{\pm\nu} \qquad \text{for} \quad j < \nu \leqslant l.$$

The x_ν ($\nu > 0$) form an orthogonal basis over the quaternions. The invariant quaternion hermitean form has the signature $j-(l-j)$. Comparing dimensions, one verifies that it is the full invariance group.

$\pi_1(\mathbf{C}_{l,l})$: $\varepsilon_{\text{un}} = -1$, $\varepsilon = 1$. By 59.3 an invariant real skew form on R_D. The full real symplectic group.

$\pi_3(\mathbf{D}_{l,j}), j \neq 1,2$: $\varepsilon_{\text{un}} = \varepsilon = 1$. Weights $\pm\omega_\nu$ with vectors $x_{\pm\nu}$. One may suppose that $D_{\text{un}} x_\nu = x_{-\nu}$.

$$Kx_{\pm\nu} = x_{\pm\nu} \qquad \text{for} \quad 1 \leqslant \nu \leqslant j-2,$$

$$Kx_{\pm\nu} = -x_{\pm\nu} \qquad \text{for} \quad j-1 \leqslant \nu \leqslant l.$$

Computations as in $\pi_2(\mathbf{B}_{l,j})$ lead to a quadratic form with signature

$$2(j-2) - 2(l-j+2) = -2l + 4j - 8.$$

$\pi_3(\mathbf{D}_{l,1})$: $\varepsilon_{\text{un}} = 1$, $\varepsilon = -1$. An invariant skew hermitean quaternion form. Comparing dimensions shows that the form characterizes the group.

With $x_{\pm\nu}$ and D_{un} as before, the form as indicated in Theorem 59.5 becomes $(x_\nu, x_\nu) = \mathrm{i}$ for $\nu < 1$, $(x_1, x_1) = -\mathrm{i}$. As a matter of fact, all nondegenerate skew-hermitean forms on quaternion n-space are equivalent under automorphisms of quaternion n-space. This is an elementary fact,† but it can also be derived from the equivalence of the linear Lie groups leaving such forms invariant.

$\pi_3(\mathbf{D}_{l,j,*})$: $\varepsilon_{\text{un}} = \varepsilon = 1$. A basis as in $\mathbf{D}_{l,j}$ shows

if $j \geqslant 3$:

$$Kx_{\pm\nu} = x_{\pm\nu} \qquad \text{for} \quad 1 \leqslant \nu \leqslant j-2,$$

$$Kx_{\pm\nu} = -x_{\pm\nu} \qquad \text{for} \quad j-1 \leqslant \nu < l,$$

$$Kx_{\pm l} = -x_{\mp l};$$

if $j = 0$:

$$Kx_{\pm\nu} = x_{\pm\nu} \qquad \text{for} \quad 1 \leqslant \nu \leqslant l-1,$$

$$Kx_{\pm l} = x_{\mp l}.$$

R_D is spanned by $\tau x_\nu + \bar{\tau} x_{-\nu}$ ($1 \leqslant \nu \leqslant j-2$), $\tau x_\nu - \bar{\tau} x_{-\nu}$ ($j-1 \leqslant \nu < l$), $\mathrm{i}(x_l + x_{-l})$ for $j \geqslant 3$; by $\tau x_\nu + \bar{\tau} x_{-\nu}$ ($1 \leqslant \nu < l$), $x_l + x_{-l}$, $x_l - x_{-l}$ for $j = 0$.

† J. Dieudonné, *Trans. Amer. Math. Soc.* **72**, 383 (1952).

The signature of the quadratic form is

for $j \geqslant 3$: $\quad (2(j-2)+1)-(2(l-j+2)-1)=4j-2l-6;$

for $j=0$: $\quad 2l-2.$

Again, the quadratic form characterizes the group.

$\pi_1(\mathbf{E}_{6,1})$: dim $R=27$. Areal both with respect to C_{un} and C. There are, respectively, 1, 16, 10 weights of the form $\pi_1-0\cdot\rho_1-\cdots$, $\pi_1-1\cdot\rho_1-\cdots$, $\pi_1-2\rho_1-\cdots$. Signature of the invariant hermitean form $11-16=-5$.

$\pi_1(\mathbf{E}_{6,2})$: dim $R=27$. Areal both with respect to C_{un} and C. There are, respectively, 6, 15, 6 weights of the form $\pi_1-0\cdot\rho_2-\cdots$, $\pi_1-1\cdot\rho_2-\cdots$, $\pi_1-2\cdot\rho_2-\cdots$. Signature of the invariant hermitean form $12-15=-3$.

$\pi_1(\mathbf{E}_{6,0,*})$, $\pi_1(\mathbf{E}_{6,2,*})$: By 59.3 no invariant bilinear form.

$\pi_2(\mathbf{E}_{7,0})$, $\pi_2(\mathbf{E}_{7,1})$: dim $R=56$. $\varepsilon_{\text{un}}=\varepsilon=-1$. There are quaternion hermitean forms. The opposite of a weight is a weight; all are simple. As a quaternion orthogonal basis one may choose vectors of weights in which ρ_2 has a positive coefficient. For

$\pi_2(\mathbf{E}_{7,0})$ the signature equals the quaternion dimension 28. For

$\pi_2(\mathbf{E}_{7,1})$ there are 11, 16, 1 weights of the form $\pi_2-0\cdot\rho_1-\cdots$, $\pi_2-1\cdot\rho_1,\cdots$, $\pi_2-2\rho_1-\cdots$ in which ρ_1 has a positive coefficient. The signature of the form is -4.

$\pi_2(\mathbf{E}_{7,2})$, $\pi_2(\mathbf{E}_{7,3})$: dim $R=56$. $\varepsilon_{\text{un}}=-1$, $\varepsilon=1$. Skew real bilinear forms.

$\pi_1(\mathbf{E}_{8,j})$: $\varepsilon_{\text{un}}=\varepsilon=1$. The invariant quadratic form is the Killing form, since the representation is adjoint; for signatures, see 52.6.

$\pi_1(\mathbf{F}_{4,1})$, $\pi_1(\mathbf{F}_{4,2})$: dim $R=26$. $\varepsilon_{\text{un}}=\varepsilon=1$. The invariant quadratic form has the signature $1-8+8-8+1=-6$, $5-14+7=-2$. (The weight 0 has the multiplicity 2.)

$\pi_1(\mathbf{G}_{2,2})$: dim $R=7$. $\varepsilon_{\text{un}}=\varepsilon=1$. The invariant quadratic form has the signature $2-3+2=1$.

59.8. Real Invariants in the Areal Case If f is not virtually real with respect to C, one may still ask for invariants under $\mathfrak{w}f(G_C)$. However, this opens no new views.

$\mathfrak{w}f$ is obtained from f by waiving the complex structure of R. This procedure transforms a bilinear or sesquilinear $f(G_C)$-invariant form into a bilinear one, invariant under $\mathfrak{w}f(G_C)$; by separating the real and imaginary parts, one obtains real invariant forms.

Conversely, if $(\ldots, \ldots)$ is a real bilinear invariant of $\mathfrak{w}f(\boldsymbol{G}_C)$, then $\curlyvee_{\ulcorner x,y \urcorner}(\mathrm{i}x, y)$, $\curlyvee_{\ulcorner x,y \urcorner}(x, \mathrm{i}y)$, $\curlyvee_{\ulcorner x,y \urcorner}(\mathrm{i}x, \mathrm{i}y)$ are also invariant, and so is

$$\curlyvee_{\ulcorner x,y \urcorner}((x, y) \pm (\mathrm{i}x, \mathrm{i}y) - \mathrm{i}(\mathrm{i}x, y) \pm \mathrm{i}(x, \mathrm{i}y)).$$

It is bilinear for the lower signs and sesquilinear for the upper. It is impossible for both to vanish unless $(\ldots, \ldots)$ does.

Theorem All bilinear invariants of $\mathfrak{w}f(\boldsymbol{G}_C)$ in the not virtually real case can be obtained from bilinear and sesquilinear invariants of $f(\boldsymbol{G}_C)$ by waiving.

In the antireal case, however, they exist only if f is not areal with respect to C_{un}, and then all real bilinear invariants are assembled in the quaternion sesquilinear form 59.5.2.

59.9. Historical Note Though many particular results were obtained by E. Cartan, the general methods and theorems of this section are new.

60. MINIMALLY COMPACT DRESSING

$\boldsymbol{G} \in$ Alg Lie Com SS in ordered C-third dressing on $\boldsymbol{H}$; thus $C\boldsymbol{H} = \boldsymbol{H} = C_{\mathrm{un}}\boldsymbol{H}$. For notational convenience $\boldsymbol{G}$ is assumed to be the infinitesimal algebra of a linear Lie group G. Sometimes C-third dressing occurs on a trunk $\boldsymbol{H}'$; then C'_{un} plays the role of C_{un}, and he is replaced by he′.

60.1–8. he-Notions

60.1. Definition A maximal abelian subset of $\boldsymbol{G}_{C,\mathrm{he}}$ is called a he-*trunk*.

The notion depends on the choice of C_{un}.

Since the elements of $\boldsymbol{G}_{C,\mathrm{he}} = \mathrm{i}\boldsymbol{G}_{C,\mathrm{un}}$ are ad-pure, any he-trunk is ad-pure, hence contained in a trunk.

Proposition Let $\boldsymbol{A}$ be a he-trunk.

(1) The centralizer in $\boldsymbol{G}_C$ of $\boldsymbol{A}$ is contained in $\boldsymbol{A} + \boldsymbol{G}_{C,\mathrm{un}}$.

(2) Any maximal abelian subset $\boldsymbol{D}$ between $\boldsymbol{A}$ and $\boldsymbol{G}_C$ is a trunk of $\boldsymbol{G}_C$.

(3) Any abelian subspace between $\boldsymbol{A}$ and $\boldsymbol{G}_C$ has the form $\boldsymbol{A} + \boldsymbol{B}$ with $\boldsymbol{B} \subset \boldsymbol{G}_{C,\mathrm{un}}$.

(4) If there is a he-trunk in $\boldsymbol{H}$, it is $\boldsymbol{H}_{C,\mathrm{he}}$.

(5) Every C-invariant trunk containing $\boldsymbol{A}$ is C_{un}-invariant.

(6) Two C-invariant trunks containing $\boldsymbol{A}$ are conjugate by means of some $u \in G_{C,\mathrm{un}}$ centralizing $\boldsymbol{A}$.

Proof

(1) Splitting $\boldsymbol{a} \in \boldsymbol{G}_C$ in $\boldsymbol{a} = \boldsymbol{s} + \boldsymbol{u}$ with $\boldsymbol{s} \in \boldsymbol{G}_{C,\mathrm{he}}$, $\boldsymbol{u} \in \boldsymbol{G}_{C,\mathrm{un}}$ (see 51.5.8–9), one gets

$$[\boldsymbol{s}, \boldsymbol{A}] \subset \boldsymbol{G}_{C,\mathrm{un}}, \qquad [\boldsymbol{u}, \boldsymbol{A}] \subset \boldsymbol{G}_{C,\mathrm{he}},$$

and if $[\boldsymbol{a}, \boldsymbol{A}] = \{\boldsymbol{0}\}$

$$[\boldsymbol{s} + \boldsymbol{u}, \boldsymbol{A}] = \{\boldsymbol{0}\};$$

hence,

$$[\boldsymbol{s}, \boldsymbol{A}] = [\boldsymbol{u}, \boldsymbol{A}] = \{\boldsymbol{0}\}.$$

The maximality of $\boldsymbol{A}$ causes $\boldsymbol{s} \in \boldsymbol{A}$, which proves (1).

(2) Because of (1), $\boldsymbol{D} = \boldsymbol{A} + \boldsymbol{B}$ with some $\boldsymbol{B} \subset \boldsymbol{G}_{C,\mathrm{un}}$; $\boldsymbol{A}$ and $\boldsymbol{B}$ are ad-pure, and so are $\boldsymbol{D}$ and its complex extension $\boldsymbol{D}_{\mathrm{Com}}$ in $\boldsymbol{G}$; $\boldsymbol{D}_{\mathrm{Com}}$ is C-invariant. If $\boldsymbol{x}$ centralizes $\boldsymbol{D}_{\mathrm{Com}}$, then $C\boldsymbol{x}$, $\frac{1}{2}(\boldsymbol{x} + C\boldsymbol{x})$, and $(1/2\mathrm{i})(\boldsymbol{x} - C\boldsymbol{x})$ do likewise. The latter are C-invariant, and because of the maximality of $\boldsymbol{D}$ they belong to $\boldsymbol{D}$. Thus $\boldsymbol{x} \in \boldsymbol{D}_{\mathrm{Com}}$, which proves ad-pure $\boldsymbol{D}_{\mathrm{Com}}$ to be a trunk of $\boldsymbol{G}$ and $\boldsymbol{D}$ to be a trunk of $\boldsymbol{G}_C$.

(3) Follows from (1).

(4) Follows from (1), if $\boldsymbol{A}$ is assumed in $\boldsymbol{H}$.

(5) Follows from (3).

(6) According to (1), the centralizer of $\boldsymbol{A}$ in $\boldsymbol{G}_C$ takes the form $\boldsymbol{A} + \boldsymbol{Z}$ with $\boldsymbol{Z} \subset \boldsymbol{G}_{C,\mathrm{un}}$. $\boldsymbol{Z}$ generates a compact group, namely, the 1-component of the centralizer of A in $G_{C,\mathrm{un}}$. Therefore by 35.7, $\boldsymbol{Z} = \boldsymbol{Z}_0 + \boldsymbol{Z}_1$ directly, where $\boldsymbol{Z}_0$ is central and $\boldsymbol{Z}_1$ is semisimple. $\boldsymbol{Z}_1$ generates compact Z_1.

Let $\boldsymbol{H}_i$ $(i = 1, 2)$ be two C-invariant trunks of $\boldsymbol{G}$ around $\boldsymbol{A}$. Since they centralize $\boldsymbol{A}$, their C-restrictions $\boldsymbol{H}_{i,C}$ are in $\boldsymbol{A} + \boldsymbol{Z}$; hence they are centralized by $\boldsymbol{Z}_0$ which is in the center of $\boldsymbol{A} + \boldsymbol{Z}$. Being trunks they must contain $\boldsymbol{Z}_0$. Therefore

$$\boldsymbol{H}_{i,C} = \boldsymbol{A} + \boldsymbol{Z}_0 + \boldsymbol{H}_{i,C} \cap \boldsymbol{Z}_1.$$

The $(\boldsymbol{H}_i \cap \boldsymbol{Z}_1)_{\mathrm{Com}}$ are still ad-pure with respect to semisimple $\boldsymbol{Z}_{1,\mathrm{Com}}$. Clearly, they are maximal in this respect and consequently are trunks of $\boldsymbol{Z}_{1,\mathrm{Com}}$ as are the $\boldsymbol{H}_i \cap \boldsymbol{Z}_1$ of $\boldsymbol{Z}_1$. Since $\boldsymbol{Z}_1$ generates a compact semisimple group Z_1, according to the conjugacy theorem they are conjugate by means of some $u \in Z_1$. So are the $\boldsymbol{H}_{i,C}$ and finally the $\boldsymbol{H}_i$.

60.2. Definition An abelian subset $\boldsymbol{A}$ of $\boldsymbol{G}_C$ is called i-*compact* if exp i$\boldsymbol{A}$ is relatively compact.

Clearly, a he-trunk is i-compact, and because of 60.1 it is even maximally so. The converse is also valid:

Proposition $\boldsymbol{A}$ is maximal i-compact if and only if $\boldsymbol{A}$ is a he′-trunk for a suitable unitary semimorphism C'_{un}—in fact, for any C-third dressing semimorphism on any C-invariant trunk containing $\boldsymbol{A}$.

Proof By 35.9 compact exp i$\boldsymbol{A}$, hence i$\boldsymbol{A}$, is contained in a trunk. Thus $\boldsymbol{A}$ is centralized by some regular $\boldsymbol{x} \in \boldsymbol{G}$ and also by $C\boldsymbol{x}$ and $\tau\boldsymbol{x} + \bar{\tau}C\boldsymbol{x}$, which is C-invariant and, for suitable τ, regular. $\boldsymbol{A}$ is contained in its trunk, which again is C-invariant.

Let $\boldsymbol{H}'$ be any C-invariant trunk around $\boldsymbol{A}$. With respect to this $\boldsymbol{H}'$ a C-third-dressing C'_{un} is chosen. It serves to define $\boldsymbol{G}_{\text{he}'}$. Since $\boldsymbol{A} \subset \boldsymbol{G}_{\text{he}'}$, there is a he′-trunk $\boldsymbol{B} \supset \boldsymbol{A}$. Now $\boldsymbol{B}$ is i-compact, and $\boldsymbol{A}$ is maximally so. Thus $\boldsymbol{A} = \boldsymbol{B}$ and $\boldsymbol{A}$ is itself a he′-trunk.

60.6. Definition $\boldsymbol{a} \in \boldsymbol{G}_{C,\text{he}}$ is called he-*regular* if rank $\tilde{\boldsymbol{x}}$ for $\boldsymbol{x} \in \boldsymbol{G}_{C,\text{he}}$ takes its maximum at $\boldsymbol{a}$, equivalently, if rank $\tilde{\boldsymbol{x}}$ is constant in some neighborhood of $\boldsymbol{a}$ within $\boldsymbol{G}_{C,\text{he}}$.

Proposition Every element of $\boldsymbol{G}_{C,\text{he}}$ is in some he-trunk. A he-regular element of $\boldsymbol{G}_{C,\text{he}}$ is in one he-trunk only.

Proof The first assertion is obvious. Let $\boldsymbol{h}$ be he-regular and $\boldsymbol{A}$ its centralizer within $\boldsymbol{G}_{C,\text{he}}$. Then $\tilde{\boldsymbol{h}}\boldsymbol{A} = \{\boldsymbol{0}\}$ and $\tilde{\boldsymbol{a}}\boldsymbol{A} \subset \boldsymbol{A}$ for $\boldsymbol{a} \in \boldsymbol{A}$. Now he-regularity of $\boldsymbol{h}$ prevents $\tilde{\boldsymbol{a}}|_{\boldsymbol{A}}$ for $\boldsymbol{a}$ in $\boldsymbol{A}$ near $\boldsymbol{h}$ from having nonvanishing eigenvalues. On the other hand, because of $\boldsymbol{A} \subset \boldsymbol{G}_{C,\text{he}}$, any $\boldsymbol{a} \in \boldsymbol{A}$ is ad-pure. Hence $\tilde{\boldsymbol{a}}\boldsymbol{A} = \{\boldsymbol{0}\}$ for $\boldsymbol{a} \in \boldsymbol{A}$. This shows that $\boldsymbol{A}$ is a he-trunk, and the only one containing $\boldsymbol{h}$.

Remark If $\boldsymbol{A}$ is a he-trunk and rank $\tilde{\boldsymbol{x}}$ ($\boldsymbol{x} \in \boldsymbol{A}$) takes its maximum at $\boldsymbol{a}$, then the centralizer $\boldsymbol{B}$ of $\boldsymbol{a}$ in $\boldsymbol{G}_{C,\text{he}}$ coincides with $\boldsymbol{A}$.

Indeed, $\boldsymbol{A} \subset \boldsymbol{B}$, and by the previous argument, $\boldsymbol{B}$ centralizes a neighborhood of $\boldsymbol{a}$ in $\boldsymbol{A}$, whence $\boldsymbol{A}$ itself, which however was chosen maximal abelian in $\boldsymbol{G}_{C,\text{he}}$.

In 60.12 even the regularity of such an $\boldsymbol{a}$ will be proved.

60.7. Definition $\alpha \in W^*$ is called a he-*nil-rootform* if $\alpha(\boldsymbol{H}_{C,\text{he}}) = \{0\}$.

Proposition $\alpha \in W^*$ is a he-nil-rootform iff $\alpha = CC_{\text{un}}\alpha$.

Proof If α is a he-nil-rootform, then for all $\boldsymbol{h} \in \boldsymbol{H}_{\text{he}}$

$$((1 - CC_{\text{un}})\alpha)(\boldsymbol{h}) = \alpha((1 - CC_{\text{un}})\boldsymbol{h}) = \alpha((1 + C)\boldsymbol{h}) = 0,$$

and conversely. Since $(1 - CC_{\text{un}})\alpha$ is linear, vanishing on $\boldsymbol{H}_{\text{he}}$ and on $\boldsymbol{H}$ imply each other.

60.8. Proposition If $\boldsymbol{h} \in \boldsymbol{H}_{C,\mathrm{he}}$ is he-regular, then $\alpha(\boldsymbol{h}) \neq 0$ for every $\alpha \in W^*$ that is not a he-nil-rootform.

Indeed, if $\boldsymbol{h}$ is regular, then rank $\tilde{\boldsymbol{x}}$ is also constant in a neighborhood of $\boldsymbol{h}$ within $\boldsymbol{H}_{C,\mathrm{he}}$.

The converse is true if $\boldsymbol{H}_{C,\mathrm{he}}$ is a he-trunk. It will be verified in the course of the proof of 60.10. Meanwhile, $\boldsymbol{h} \in \boldsymbol{H}_{C,\mathrm{he}}$ is called he-*semiregular* if $\alpha(\boldsymbol{h}) \neq 0$ for all non-he-nil-rootforms α.

60.9. Criterion on Trunks Containing a he-Trunk If α is a he-nil-rootform, then $CC_{\mathrm{un}}\boldsymbol{e}_\alpha = \pm\boldsymbol{e}_\alpha$, since $(CC_{\mathrm{un}})^2 = 1$.

Proposition H $(= CH = C_{\mathrm{un}}H)$ contains a he-trunk iff $CC_{\mathrm{un}}\boldsymbol{e}_\alpha = \boldsymbol{e}_\alpha$ for every he-nil-rootform α.

Proof $\boldsymbol{H}$ containing a he-trunk means that $\boldsymbol{H}_{C,\mathrm{he}}$ is maximal abelian in $\boldsymbol{G}_{C,\mathrm{he}}$, thus that $\boldsymbol{a} \in \boldsymbol{G}_{C,\mathrm{he}}$ and $[\boldsymbol{a}, \boldsymbol{H}_{C,\mathrm{he}}] = \{\boldsymbol{0}\}$ implies $\boldsymbol{a} \in \boldsymbol{H}_{C,\mathrm{he}}$. Any $\boldsymbol{a} \in \boldsymbol{G}_{C,\mathrm{he}}$ is mod $\boldsymbol{H}_{C,\mathrm{he}}$ the sum of expressions

60.9.1 $$(1 - CC_{\mathrm{un}})(\tau_\alpha \boldsymbol{e}_\alpha + \bar{\tau}_\alpha \boldsymbol{e}_{-\alpha})$$

with $\tau_\alpha \neq 0$. For $\boldsymbol{h} \in \boldsymbol{H}_{C,\mathrm{he}}$, $[\boldsymbol{h}, \boldsymbol{a}]$ becomes a sum of expressions

60.9.2 $$\alpha(\boldsymbol{h})(1 + CC_{\mathrm{un}})(\tau_\alpha \boldsymbol{e}_\alpha - \bar{\tau}_\alpha \boldsymbol{e}_{-\alpha}).$$

Thus $\boldsymbol{H}_{C,\mathrm{he}}$ is a he-trunk iff the vanishing of 60.9.2 implies that of 60.9.1. This implication can be broken into the conjunction of two implications:

$$\alpha \text{ a he-nil-rootform} \rightarrow (1 - CC_{\mathrm{un}})(\tau_\alpha \boldsymbol{e}_\alpha + \bar{\tau}_\alpha \boldsymbol{e}_{-\alpha}) = \boldsymbol{0},$$

and

$$[\alpha \text{ non-he-nil-rootform} \wedge (1 + CC_{\mathrm{un}})(\tau_\alpha \boldsymbol{e}_\alpha - \bar{\tau}_\alpha \boldsymbol{e}_{-\alpha}) = \boldsymbol{0}] \rightarrow (1 - CC_{\mathrm{un}})(\tau_\alpha \boldsymbol{e}_\alpha + \bar{\tau}_\alpha \boldsymbol{e}_{-\alpha}) = \boldsymbol{0}.$$

Now the second implication is valid anyhow, since if the antecedens were true, then by linear combination $(1 + CC_{\mathrm{un}})\tau_\alpha \boldsymbol{e}_\alpha = \boldsymbol{0}$, hence $CC_{\mathrm{un}}\alpha = \alpha$ which by 60.7 contradicts the first part of the antecedens.

Therefore $\boldsymbol{H}$ being a he-trunk is equivalent to the validity of the first implication for all $\tau_\alpha \neq 0$, which is just the condition to be proved.

60.10. $G_{C,\mathrm{un}}$-Conjugacy of Trunks Containing a he-Trunk Clearly the property that $\boldsymbol{H}$ contains a he-trunk is $\tilde{G}_{C,\mathrm{un}}$-invariant. The converse is also true:

Proposition If $\boldsymbol{H}$ contains a he-trunk, then every C-invariant trunk containing a he-trunk is a $G_{C,\mathrm{un}}$-conjugate of $\boldsymbol{H}$.

Proof By 60.1.4 $\boldsymbol{H}_{C,\text{he}}$ can be assumed to be a he-trunk. By 60.1.6 the C-invariant trunks around $\boldsymbol{H}_{C,\text{he}}$ are $G_{C,\text{un}}$-conjugate. Therefore it suffices to prove that $\tilde{u}\boldsymbol{H}_{C,\text{he}}$ runs through all he-trunks if u runs through $G_{C,\text{un}}$.

If for a non-he-nil-rootform α one applies $\tilde{a}$ with

$$a = \exp(1 + CC_{\text{un}})(\tau_\alpha \boldsymbol{e}_\alpha - \bar{\tau}_\alpha \boldsymbol{e}_{-\alpha}) \in G_{C,\text{un}}$$

to $\boldsymbol{h} \in \boldsymbol{H}_{C,\text{he}}$, then one obtains

$$\tilde{a}\boldsymbol{h} = \boldsymbol{h} - \alpha(\boldsymbol{h})(1 - CC_{\text{un}})(\tau_\alpha \boldsymbol{e}_\alpha + \bar{\tau}_\alpha \boldsymbol{e}_{-\alpha}) + \cdots.$$

Suppose that $\boldsymbol{h}_0 \in \boldsymbol{H}_{C,\text{he}}$ is he-semiregular. Then $\alpha(\boldsymbol{h}_0) \neq 0$ and according to 60.9.1 the

$$\alpha(\boldsymbol{h}_0)(1 - CC_{\text{un}})(\tau_\alpha \boldsymbol{e}_\alpha + \bar{\tau}_\alpha \boldsymbol{e}_{-\alpha})$$

span $\boldsymbol{G}_{C,\text{he}}$ mod $\boldsymbol{H}_{C,\text{he}}$. This means that the $\tilde{a}\boldsymbol{h}$ cover an $\boldsymbol{h}_0$-neighborhood in $\boldsymbol{G}_{C,\text{he}}$ if $\boldsymbol{h}$ runs through an $\boldsymbol{h}_0$-neighborhood in $\boldsymbol{H}_{C,\text{he}}$ and a runs through a 1-neighborhood in $G_{C,\text{un}}$. Hence rank $\tilde{\boldsymbol{x}}$ (which is a $G_{C,\text{un}}$-invariant) is constant in a neighborhood of $\boldsymbol{h}_0$ within $\boldsymbol{G}_{C,\text{he}}$, which shows that $\boldsymbol{h}_0$ is he-regular and confirms the announced converse of Proposition 60.8.

$$\boldsymbol{Y} = \cup_{a \in G_{C,\text{un}}} \tilde{a}\boldsymbol{H}_{C,\text{he}}$$

is closed in $\boldsymbol{G}_{C,\text{he}}$ because of the compactness of $G_{C,\text{un}}$. Every he-regular point of $\boldsymbol{H}_{C,\text{he}}$, and therefore any $G_{C,\text{un}}$-conjugate of such a point, was proved to be an interior point of $\boldsymbol{Y}$ with respect to $\boldsymbol{G}_{C,\text{he}}$. Therefore the boundary points of $\boldsymbol{Y}$ are images of such $\boldsymbol{h} \in \boldsymbol{H}_{C,\text{he}}$ in which at least one non-he-nil-rootform vanishes. An argument as in 31.9 shows that the boundary of $\boldsymbol{Y}$ has codimension $\geqslant 3$. So it does not decompose $\boldsymbol{G}_{C,\text{he}}$, and $\boldsymbol{Y}$ coincides with $\boldsymbol{G}_{C,\text{he}}$.

This proves that every element of $\boldsymbol{G}_{C,\text{he}}$ is a $G_{C,\text{un}}$-conjugate of an element of $\boldsymbol{H}_{C,\text{he}}$. Now let $\boldsymbol{A}$ be an arbitrary he-trunk and $\boldsymbol{b} \in \boldsymbol{A}$ such that rank $\tilde{\boldsymbol{x}}$ for $\boldsymbol{x} \in \boldsymbol{A}$ will reach its maximum at $\boldsymbol{b}$. For some $u \in G_{C,\text{un}}$ it happens that $\tilde{u}^{-1}\boldsymbol{b} \in \boldsymbol{H}_{C,\text{he}}$. Now $\tilde{u}^{-1}\boldsymbol{A}$ is again a he-trunk and, according to Remark 60.6, the centralizer of $\tilde{u}^{-1}\boldsymbol{b}$ in $\boldsymbol{H}_{C,\text{he}}$. Hence $\boldsymbol{H}_{C,\text{he}} \subset \tilde{u}^{-1}\boldsymbol{A}$, thus $\boldsymbol{H}_{C,\text{he}} = \tilde{u}^{-1}\boldsymbol{A}$, thus $\boldsymbol{A} = \tilde{u}\boldsymbol{H}_{C,\text{he}}$.

60.13. G_C-Conjugacy of Trunks Containing a Maximal i-Compact Subset Clearly, the property of $\boldsymbol{H}$ containing a maximal i-compact subset is $\tilde{G}_C$-invariant. The converse is also true:

Proposition $\tilde{G}_C$ acts transitively on the set of C-invariant trunks of $\boldsymbol{G}_C$ containing a maximal i-compact subset.

Proof Let $\boldsymbol{H}, \boldsymbol{H}'$ be such trunks. C_{un} is chosen as a C-third dressing unitary semimorphism with respect to $\boldsymbol{H}$. Then by 60.2 $\boldsymbol{H}$ contains a he-trunk. By 51.7 there is a G_C-conjugate $\boldsymbol{H}''$ of $\boldsymbol{H}'$ such that $\tilde{\boldsymbol{u}}\boldsymbol{H} = \boldsymbol{H}''$ for some $u \in G_{\text{un}}$. $\boldsymbol{H}''$ is still C-, and C_{un}-invariant and contains a maximal i-compact subset. By Proposition 33.13 C_{un} counts as a C-third dressing unitary semimorphism for $\boldsymbol{H}''$; hence by 60.2 $\boldsymbol{H}''$ also contains a he-trunk. Therefore 60.10 can be applied to the effect that $\boldsymbol{H}, \boldsymbol{H}''$ are $G_{C,\mathrm{un}}$-conjugate. This proves that $\boldsymbol{H}, \boldsymbol{H}'$ are G_C-conjugate.

60.14. Real Rank

Definition The dimension of a maximal i-compact subset of $\boldsymbol{G}_C$ is called the *real rank* l_{re}, or l', of $\boldsymbol{G}_C$.

By 60.1 and 60.13 it does not depend on the choice of the set.

Evidently:

Proposition The real rank of $\boldsymbol{G}_{\mathrm{un}}$ is 0, that of $\boldsymbol{G}_{\mathrm{st}}$ equals the rank l of $\boldsymbol{G}$.

60.15. A Procedure For a trunk $\boldsymbol{H} = C\boldsymbol{H} = C_{\mathrm{un}}\boldsymbol{H}$ ($CC_{\mathrm{un}} = C_{\mathrm{un}}C$) that does not contain a maximal i-compact subset of $\boldsymbol{G}_C$ the condition of Proposition 60.9 is not fulfilled. Therefore for some he-nil-rootform α

$$CC_{\mathrm{un}}\boldsymbol{e}_\alpha = -\boldsymbol{e}_\alpha,$$

hence,

$$CC_{\mathrm{un}}\boldsymbol{e}_{-\alpha} = -\boldsymbol{e}_{-\alpha}, \qquad \text{because of} \qquad CC_{\mathrm{un}}\boldsymbol{h}_\alpha = \boldsymbol{h}_\alpha.$$

On the evidence of such an α there is a

Procedure of changing $\boldsymbol{H}$ into a trunk $\boldsymbol{H}' = C\boldsymbol{H}' = C_{\mathrm{un}}\boldsymbol{H}'$ such that $\boldsymbol{H} \cap \boldsymbol{H}'$ is the kernel of α (which contains $\boldsymbol{H}_{C,\mathrm{he}}$) and $\mathrm{i}\boldsymbol{h}_\alpha \in \boldsymbol{H}_{C,\mathrm{un}}$ is replaced by some $\boldsymbol{h}' \in \boldsymbol{G}_{C,\mathrm{he}}$.

By this step the dimension of the i-compact part $\boldsymbol{H}_{C,\mathrm{he}}$ of $\boldsymbol{H}_C$ is raised and that of the torus part is lowered by one.

$$U_\alpha = \exp \tau(\tilde{\boldsymbol{e}}_\alpha + \tilde{\boldsymbol{e}}_{-\alpha}), \qquad \tau = \tfrac{1}{2}\pi(2(\alpha,\alpha))^{-1/2}\mathrm{i},$$

leaves the kernel of α invariant. According to 33.1,

$$U_\alpha{}^2 = S_\alpha,$$

where

$$S_\alpha\alpha = -\alpha, \qquad S_\alpha\boldsymbol{h}_\alpha = -\boldsymbol{h}_\alpha, \qquad S_\alpha\boldsymbol{e}_\alpha = \boldsymbol{e}_{-\alpha}, \qquad S_\alpha\boldsymbol{e}_{-\alpha} = \boldsymbol{e}_\alpha.$$

Moreover,

$$C_{\mathrm{un}}U_\alpha C_{\mathrm{un}}^{-1} = U_\alpha,$$

since $C_{\mathrm{un}}\boldsymbol{e}_\alpha = -\boldsymbol{e}_{-\alpha}$ and τ is imaginary;

$$CU_\alpha C^{-1} = U_\alpha^{-1} = U_\alpha S_\alpha^{-1},$$

since $C\boldsymbol{e}_\alpha = \boldsymbol{e}_{-\alpha}$; thus

$$CU_\alpha\boldsymbol{h}_\alpha = U_\alpha S_\alpha^{-1}C\boldsymbol{h}_\alpha = U_\alpha\boldsymbol{h}_\alpha,$$

since $C\boldsymbol{h}_\alpha = \boldsymbol{h}_{-\alpha}$. On the other hand,

$$C_{\mathrm{un}}U_\alpha\boldsymbol{h}_\alpha = -U_\alpha\boldsymbol{h}_\alpha.$$

Therefore

$$U_\alpha \boldsymbol{h}_\alpha \in \boldsymbol{G}_{C,\mathrm{he}}$$

Moreover, since U_α leaves the kernel of α invariant, $\boldsymbol{H}' = U_\alpha \boldsymbol{H}$ is a new trunk with the required properties.

60.16–17. Minimally Compact Trunks

60.16 The time has come to recall the definition of minimally compact trunk (51.8). The procedure in 60.15 shows that if a C-invariant trunk does not contain a maximal i-compact subset of $\boldsymbol{G}_C$, its torus part can be diminished so it was not minimally compact. If it does contain such a subset, the dimension of its torus is $l - l_{\mathrm{re}}$, which is a lower bound for any torus in G_C, thus the trunk is minimally compact.

60.17. Some of the preceding results are summarized.

Proposition The trunks containing a maximal i-compact trunk are just the minimally compact trunks.

Conjugacy Theorem of Minimally Compact Trunks The C-minimally compact trunks are G_C-conjugate.

Definition A C-third dressing on minimally compact $\boldsymbol{H} = C\boldsymbol{H}$ is called a *minimally compact dressing.*

60.18. Real Ordered Dressing A special ordered dressing is adapted to the study of nonmaximally compact trunks.

Definition An ordered dressing is called *real* (with respect to C) if

60.18.1 $$\alpha \in W^+ \wedge C^*\alpha < 0 \to C^*\alpha = -\alpha.$$

Remember that C^* acts as $+1$ on $\boldsymbol{H}^*_{C,\mathrm{he}}$ and as -1 on $\mathrm{i}\boldsymbol{H}^*_{C,\mathrm{un}}$. It is not required that C and C_{un} commute, though their restrictions to the trunk $\boldsymbol{H} = C\boldsymbol{H} = C_{\mathrm{un}}\boldsymbol{H}$ necessarily do.

The existence of a real order is seen as follows. Take $\boldsymbol{h}_0 \in \boldsymbol{H}_{\mathrm{st}}$ such that $\alpha(\boldsymbol{h}_0) \neq 0$ for all $\alpha \in W^*$, and for every $\alpha \in W^* \setminus \mathrm{i}\boldsymbol{H}^*_{C,\mathrm{un}}$

$$|\alpha_1(\boldsymbol{h}_0)| > |\alpha_2(\boldsymbol{h}_0)|$$

if $\alpha = \alpha_1 + \alpha_2$, $\alpha_1 \in \boldsymbol{H}^*_{C,\mathrm{he}}$, $\alpha_2 \in \mathrm{i}\boldsymbol{H}^*_{C,\mathrm{un}}$; now take the minimal partial order contained in the partial order as constructed in Proposition 25.2.2.

Proposition In a real order CC_{un} acts on (suitably numbered) W^{++} as follows:

$$CC_{\text{un}}\rho_j = \rho_j \qquad \text{for } j = 1, \ldots, k,$$

$$CC_{\text{un}}\rho_j = -\rho_j \bmod \rho_1, \ldots, \rho_k \qquad \text{for } j = k+1, \ldots, m,$$

$$CC_{\text{un}}\rho_j = -\rho_{l+m+1-j} \bmod \rho_1, \ldots, \rho_k \qquad \text{for } j = m+1, \ldots, l;$$

or, eliminating C_{un},

$$C^*\rho_j = -\rho_j \qquad \text{for } j = 1, \ldots, k,$$

$$C^*\rho_j = \rho_j \bmod \rho_1, \ldots, \rho_k \qquad \text{for } j = k+1, \ldots, m,$$

$$C^*\rho_j = \rho_{l+m+1-j} \bmod \rho_1, \ldots, \rho_k \qquad \text{for } j = m+1, \ldots, l.$$

Proof CC_{un} behaves as -1 on $\boldsymbol{H}^*_{C,\text{he}}$ and as $+1$ on $\mathrm{i}\boldsymbol{H}^*_{C,\text{un}}$.

On the given order let $\rho_1, \ldots, \rho_k$ be the primitive rootforms invariant under CC_{un} and $\rho_{k+1}, \ldots, \rho_l$ the others; $CC_{\text{un}}\rho_j < 0$ by 60.18.1 for $j > k$. Let N be the linear mapping CC_{un} reduced mod $\rho_1, \ldots, \rho_k$, Then $N^2 = 1$ and all matrix coefficients of N on the basis $\rho_{k+1}, \ldots, \rho_l$ are nonpositive integers. This can only happen if in every row and column of $-N$ there is not more than one nonvanishing coefficient, which has to be 1. Consequently, $-N$ is a permutation matrix and the matrix of CC_{un} on the basis W^{++} can be put into the form

60.18.2 $$\begin{pmatrix} 1 & * & * \\ 0 & -1 & 0 \\ 0 & 0 & -V \end{pmatrix} \quad \text{with} \quad V = \begin{pmatrix} 0 & & & & 1 \\ & & & 1 & \\ & & \cdot^{\cdot^{\cdot}} & & \\ & 1 & & & \\ 1 & & & & 0 \end{pmatrix}.$$

This proves the assertion.

60.19. How Far Is C Determined by Its Behavior on $\boldsymbol{H}$

Theorem If $\boldsymbol{H} = C\boldsymbol{H}$, then C is determined up to inner isotypy by its behavior on $\boldsymbol{H}$ and on the branches (in third dressing with respect to $\boldsymbol{H}$) $\boldsymbol{e}_\alpha$ with $C^*\alpha = -\alpha$.

Remark For maximally compact trunks the proposition carries no new information. (See 51.12.) For minimally compact trunks it states that C is completely determined by its behavior on the trunk alone.

Proof C, C' are taken to coincide on $\boldsymbol{H}$ and on the branches $\boldsymbol{e}_\alpha$ with $C^*\alpha = -\alpha$; C_{un} has been taken with respect to $\boldsymbol{H}$ and with $CC_{\text{un}} = C_{\text{un}}C$. If used, G is supposed to be centerfree. The first step is to replace C' by inner isotypic C'' such that $C''C_{\text{un}} = C_{\text{un}}C''$ is also valid.

Since C, C' are the same on H, there is an $\boldsymbol{h} \in \boldsymbol{H}$, $h = \exp \boldsymbol{h}$ such that

60.19.1 $$C' = \tilde{h}C,$$

and because of $C'^2 = 1$, $\tilde{h}\widetilde{Ch} = 1$; hence

60.19.2 $$\alpha(\boldsymbol{h} + C\boldsymbol{h}) = 0 \bmod 2\pi i \qquad \text{for} \quad \alpha \in W^*.$$

One tries

$$C'' = \tilde{h}_0 C' \tilde{h}_0^{-1} \qquad \text{with} \quad h_0 = \exp \boldsymbol{h}_0, \qquad \boldsymbol{h}_0 \in \boldsymbol{H}.$$

To have

$$C'' C_{\mathrm{un}} = C_{\mathrm{un}} C''$$

means

$$\tilde{h}_0 \tilde{h} C \tilde{h}_0^{-1} C_{\mathrm{un}} = C_{\mathrm{un}} \tilde{h}_0 \tilde{h} C \tilde{h}_0^{-1}$$

or, equivalently,

$$C_{\mathrm{un}}(h_0 h (C h_0^{-1})) = h_0 h (C h_0^{-1}),$$

in other words,

$$\alpha(\boldsymbol{h}_0 - C\boldsymbol{h}_0 + \boldsymbol{h}) \qquad \text{imaginary for all } \alpha \in W^*.$$

This can be satisfied by putting $\boldsymbol{h}_0 = -\frac{1}{2}\boldsymbol{h}$. Indeed, then

$$\alpha(\boldsymbol{h}_0 - C\boldsymbol{h}_0 + \boldsymbol{h}) = \tfrac{1}{2}\alpha(\boldsymbol{h} + C\boldsymbol{h})$$

which by 60.19.2 is even $= 0 \bmod \pi i$.

Henceforth it is supposed that

$$CC_{\mathrm{un}} = C_{\mathrm{un}} C, \qquad C' C_{\mathrm{un}} = C_{\mathrm{un}} C',$$

thus,

$$\tilde{h} C_{\mathrm{un}} = C_{\mathrm{un}} \tilde{h}, \qquad C_{\mathrm{un}} h = h, \qquad \boldsymbol{h} \in \boldsymbol{H}_{\mathrm{un}}.$$

So 60.19.2 can be written as

60.19.2′ $$\alpha(\boldsymbol{h} + CC_{\mathrm{un}} \boldsymbol{h}) = 0 \bmod 2\pi i \qquad \text{for} \qquad \alpha \in W^*.$$

Now the identical behavior of C, C' on $\boldsymbol{e}_\alpha$ with $\alpha = CC_{\mathrm{un}}\alpha$ is used. This means that $\tilde{h}\boldsymbol{e}_\alpha = \boldsymbol{e}_\alpha$ for such α; thus

$$\alpha(\boldsymbol{h}) = 0 \bmod 2\pi i \qquad \text{for} \quad \alpha = CC_{\mathrm{un}}\alpha.$$

On a real order (60.18) this amounts to

$$\rho_j(\boldsymbol{h}) = 0 \bmod 2\pi i \qquad \text{for} \quad j = 1, \ldots, k.$$

Without impairing the relation $h = \exp \boldsymbol{h}$, one may even change $\boldsymbol{h}$ such that

60.19.3 $$\rho_j(\boldsymbol{h}) = 0 \qquad \text{for} \quad j = 1, \ldots, k.$$

In H_{st} a basis $p_1, \ldots, p_l$ is taken, correlated with that of $\rho_1, \ldots, \rho_l$:

$$\rho_i(p_j) = \begin{cases} 0 & \text{for } i \neq j, \\ 1 & \text{for } i = j. \end{cases}$$

On that basis the action of CC_{un} is described by the transpose of the matrix 60.18.2. Then, with imaginary coefficients c_j,

$$h = \sum_{j=k+1}^{m} c_j p_j + \sum_{m+1}^{l} c_j p_j.$$

Further,

60.19.4 $$CC_{un} p_j = -p_j \quad \text{for } j = k+1, \ldots, m,$$
$$CC_{un} p_j = -p_{l+m+1-j} \quad \text{for } j = m+1, \ldots, l,$$

and using 60.19.2′

60.19.5 $$c_j = c_{l+m+1-j} \bmod 2\pi\mathrm{i} \qquad \text{for } j = m+1, \ldots, l.$$

To prove that C' and C are isotypic, a $g \in H_{un}$ such that $\tilde{g}CC_{un}\tilde{g}^{-1} = \tilde{h}CC_{un}$ with $g = \exp g$ is required. This means that g has to fulfill

60.19.6 $$\alpha(g - CC_{un} g) = \alpha(h) \bmod 2\pi\mathrm{i} \qquad \text{for } \alpha \in W^*.$$

$$g = \tfrac{1}{2} \sum_{j=k+1}^{m} c_j p_j + \sum_{j=m+1}^{\frac{1}{2}(l-m)} c_j p_j$$

satisfies this, since (60.19.4)

$$-CC_{un} g = \tfrac{1}{2} \sum_{j=k+1}^{m} c_j p_j + \sum_{j=m+1}^{\frac{1}{2}(l-m)} c_j p_{l+m+1-j}$$

substituted into 60.19.6, if 60.19.5 is taken into account, verifies 60.19.6.

60.21. A Procedure The contents of the present section is a procedure for changing an arbitrary trunk H in C-third dressing into a minimally compact trunk.

C_{un} is defined on $H, H = CH = C_{un}H$, $CC_{un} = C_{un}C$.

Let B be the subset of W^* defined by

$$\alpha \in B \leftrightarrow CC_{un} e_\alpha = -e_\alpha.$$

Then for $\alpha \in B$, also $CC_{un}\alpha = \alpha$, $CC_{un} e_{-\alpha} = -e_{-\alpha}$.

Let B' be a maximal subset of B such that

60.21.1 $$\alpha, \beta \in B' \wedge \alpha \neq \beta \rightarrow [e_\alpha, e_{\pm\beta}] = 0.$$

When using the U_α and S_α from 60.15, one notes that the U_α with $\alpha \in B'$ commute with each other because of 60.21.1. One defines

$$U = \prod_{\alpha \in B'} U_\alpha, \qquad S = \prod_\alpha S_\alpha.$$

Then from 60.15

$$C_{\text{un}}\, U C_{\text{un}}^{-1} = U, \qquad CUC^{-1} = U^{-1} = US^{-1}.$$

For the actual computation it is more convenient to change the semimorphism up to isotypy than to change the trunk. Thus

60.21.2 $$C' = U^{-1} C U = S^{-1} C$$

is an isotypic semimorphism with still $C'\boldsymbol{H} = \boldsymbol{H}$ and $C' C_{\text{un}} = C_{\text{un}} C'$.

Since $S\alpha = -\alpha$, $S\boldsymbol{e}_\alpha = \boldsymbol{e}_{-\alpha}$ for $\alpha \in B'$, one gets

$$C' C_{\text{un}}\, \alpha = -\alpha, \qquad C' C_{\text{un}}\, \boldsymbol{e}_\alpha = -\boldsymbol{e}_{-\alpha}.$$

Under some additional assumptions $\boldsymbol{H}$ will come out as a minimally compact trunk with respect to C' (as will $U\boldsymbol{H}$ with respect to C).

To prove this one must consider any

$$\gamma \in W^*, \qquad \gamma = C' C_{\text{un}}\, \gamma$$

and ascertain that

60.21.3 $$C' C_{\text{un}}\, \boldsymbol{e}_\gamma = \boldsymbol{e}_\gamma,$$

which will show the minimal compactness of $\boldsymbol{H}$, thanks to 60.9.

By 60.21.2

$$CC_{\text{un}}\, \gamma = SC' C_{\text{un}}\, \gamma = S\gamma = \gamma - 2 \sum_{\alpha \in B'} \frac{(\gamma, \alpha)}{(\alpha, \alpha)} \alpha,$$

thus,

$$\gamma - CC_{\text{un}}\, \gamma = 2 \sum_{\alpha \in B'} \frac{(\gamma, \alpha)}{(\alpha, \alpha)} \alpha.$$

CC_{un} maps the first member into its opposite while leaving the second invariant; hence

60.21.4 $$CC_{\text{un}}\, \gamma = \gamma, \qquad 2 \sum_{\alpha \in B'} \frac{(\gamma, \alpha)}{(\alpha, \alpha)} \alpha = 0.$$

Since the members of B' are mutually orthogonal and consequently linearly independent, it follows from the last equation that

$$(\gamma, B') = \{0\}.$$

If W possesses no ladder of length 2 except those passing through 0, one may continue with the conclusion that

60.21.5 $$\alpha \in B' \to [e_\alpha, e_{\pm\gamma}] = 0,$$

hence

60.21.6 $$Se_\gamma = e_\gamma.$$

60.21.4–5, together with the maximality of B', show that

$$CC_{\text{un}}\, e_\gamma = e_\gamma$$

from which by 60.21.2 and 60.21.6

$$C'C_{\text{un}}\, e_\gamma = S^{-1}\, CC_{\text{un}}\, e_\gamma = S^{-1}\, e_\gamma = e_\gamma.$$

If, however, W does possess nontrivial ladders of length 2, it can happen that

$$[e_\alpha, e_{\pm\gamma}] \neq 0 \qquad \text{though} \quad (\gamma, \alpha) = 0,$$

namely, if α is the midpoint of its γ-ladder. Nevertheless, the former conclusion holds good as long as

60.21.7 for $\gamma \in W^*$, $(\gamma, B') = \{0\}$, the midpoint of no γ-ladder belongs to B'.

60.22–23. Toward Computing Minimally Compact Trunks

60.22 What matters according to 60.19, is to know the behavior of C' as obtained in 60.21 on H. H^*_{st} splits under $C'C_{\text{un}}$ into $H^*_{\text{st},+}$ and $H^*_{\text{st},-}$, which belong to the eigenvalues +1 and −1 of $C'C_{\text{un}}$. (Also $H^*_{\text{st},+} = \text{i}H^*_{C',\text{un}}$, $H^*_{\text{st},-} = H^*_{C',\text{he}}$.) In the subspace spanned by B', $C'C_{\text{un}}$ behaves as $-CC_{\text{un}}$, in its orthoplement as CC_{un}. If maximally compact C-dressing was the point of departure, then on H the splitting of H_{st} under CC_{un} is into the +1-eigenspace $(1 + CC_{\text{un}})H_{\text{st}}$ and the −1-eigenspace $(1 - CC_{\text{un}})H_{\text{st}}$ (for inner types = 0); B belongs to $(1 + CC_{\text{un}})H^*_{\text{st}}$, as does B', whence:

Proposition If H is a maximally compact trunk with respect to C, and isotypic C' has arisen by the method in 60.21 such that H is minimally compact with respect to C', then, under C-third dressing and with the notation of 60.21, the (−1)-eigenspace of $C'C_{\text{un}}$ on H^*_{st} is spanned by B' and $(1 - CC_{\text{un}})H^*_{\text{st}}$, which are linearly independent. Its dimension is the real rank of G_C.

60.23 The procedure of 60.21 will actually be performed on all types of $G \in$ Alg Lie Rea SSS, starting from the classification dressing of Sections

52–53. Since, according to 60.19, it is enough to know $C'C_{\text{un}}$ in H^*_{st}, a basis of the (−1)-eigenspace of $C'C_{\text{un}}$ is indicated. Twin and compact types may be disregarded.

Basis of the (−1)-Eigenspace of CC_{un} in H^* under Minimally Compact Dressing

(See a somewhat different form in Section 75.)

A$_{l,j}$, $j \leqslant \frac{1}{2}(l+1)$: $\rho_j, \rho_{j-1}+\rho_j+\rho_{j+1}, \ldots, \rho_1+\cdots+\rho_j+\cdots+\rho_{2j-1}$.
Or, otherwise: $\omega_j-\omega_{j+1}, \omega_{j-1}-\omega_{j+1}, \ldots, \omega_1-\omega_{2j}$.
Real rank: j.

B$_{l,j}$, $1<j\leqslant\frac{1}{2}l+1$: $\rho_j, \rho_{j-1}+\rho_j+\rho_{j+1}, \ldots, \rho_2+\cdots+\rho_j+\cdots+\rho_{2j-2}$, $\rho_j+2\rho_{j+1}+\cdots+2\rho_l+2\rho_1, \rho_{j-1}+\rho_j+\rho_{j+1}+2\rho_{j+2}+\cdots+2\rho_1, \ldots,$

$$\rho_2+\cdots+\rho_{2j-2}+\begin{cases} 2\rho_{2j-1} & \text{for } l\neq 2j-2, \\ 2\rho_1 & \text{for } l=2j-2. \end{cases}$$

Or, otherwise: $\omega_{j-1}\pm\omega_j, \omega_{j-2}\pm\omega_{j+1}, \ldots, \omega_1\pm\omega_{2j-2}$.
Note that no intermediate rootforms show up.
Real rank: $2(j-1)$.

B$_{l,j}$, $j>\frac{1}{2}l+1$: $\rho_j, \rho_{j-1}+\rho_j+\rho_{j+1}, \ldots, \rho_{2j-l}+\cdots+\rho_j+\cdots+\rho_l, \rho_{2j-l-1}+\cdots+\rho_l+\rho_1, \rho_j+2\rho_{j+1}+\cdots+2\rho_l+2\rho_1, \ldots, \rho_{2j-l}+\cdots+\rho_l+2\rho_1$.
Or, otherwise: $\omega_{j-1}\pm\omega_j, \omega_{j-2}\pm\omega_{j+1}, \ldots, \omega_{2j-l-1}\pm\omega_l, \omega_{2j-l-2}$. There is one intermediate rootform, $\rho_{2j-l+1}+\cdots+\rho_1$, namely, in the γ-ladders with $\gamma=\pm(\rho_k+\cdots+\rho_l+\rho_1)(k>2j-l+1)$; however, this γ is orthogonal neither to $\rho_k+\cdots+\rho_{2j-k}+2\rho_{2j-k+1}+\cdots+2\rho_1$ for $k\leqslant j$ nor to $\rho_{2j-l}+\cdots+\rho_l+2\rho_1$ for $k>j$.
Real rank: $2l-2j+3$.

B$_{l,1}$: ρ_1 or, otherwise, ω_l.
Real rank: 1.

C$_{l,j}$, $j\leqslant\frac{1}{2}l$: $\rho_j, \rho_{j-1}+\rho_j+\rho_{j+1}, \ldots, \rho_1+\cdots+\rho_j+\cdots+\rho_{2j-1}$ $(2j-1<l-1)$, respectively, $2\rho_1+\cdots+2\rho_{2j-1}+\rho_l$ $(2j-1=l-1)$.
Or, otherwise: $\omega_j-\omega_{j+1}, \ldots, \omega_1-\omega_{2j}$.
No intermediate rootforms show up.
Real rank: j.

C$_{l,l}$: $\rho_l, 2\rho_{l-1}+\rho_l, 2\rho_{l-2}+2\rho_{l-1}+\rho_l, \ldots, 2\rho_1+\cdots+2\rho_{l-1}+\rho_l$.
Or, otherwise: $2\omega_1, \ldots, 2\omega_l$.
No intermediate rootforms show up.
Real rank: l.

D$_{l,j}$, $3\leqslant j\leqslant\frac{1}{2}l+2$: $\rho_j, \rho_{j-1}+\rho_j+\rho_{j+1}, \ldots, \rho_3+\cdots+\rho_{2j-3}, \rho_j+2\rho_{j+1}+\cdots+2\rho_l+\rho_1+\rho_2, \ldots, \rho_3+\cdots+\rho_{2j-3}+2\rho_{2j-2}+\cdots+2\rho_l+\rho_1+\rho_2$.
Or, otherwise: $\omega_{j-2}\pm\omega_{j-1}, \omega_{j-3}\pm\omega_j, \ldots, \omega_1\pm\omega_{2j-4}$.
Real rank: $2j-4$.

D$_{l,1}$: $\rho_1, \rho_1+\rho_2+2\rho_l+\rho_{l-1}, \rho_1+\rho_2+2\rho_l+2\rho_{l-2}+\rho_{l-3}, \ldots,$

$$\rho_1+\rho_2+2\rho_l+\cdots+2\rho_4+\rho_3 \quad \text{for} \quad l \text{ even},$$

$$\rho_1+\rho_2+2\rho_l+\cdots+2\rho_5+\rho_4 \quad \text{for} \quad l \text{ odd}.$$

Or, otherwise: $\omega_{l-1}-\omega_l, \omega_{l-3}+\omega_{l-2}, \ldots.$
Real rank: $[\frac{1}{2}l]$.

The notation of rootforms in the exceptional types indicates the coefficient of a primitive rootform at its place in the graph.

E$_{6,1}$:

$$\overset{0}{00001}, \ \overset{1}{01221}.$$

Real rank: 2.

E$_{6,2}$:

$$\overset{1}{00000}, \ \overset{1}{01210}, \ \overset{1}{11211}, \ \overset{1}{12221}.$$

Real rank: 4.

E$_{7,1}$:

$$\overset{0}{000001}, \ \overset{1}{001221}, \ \overset{1}{122221}, \ \overset{2}{123421}.$$

Real rank: 4.

E$_{7,2}$:

$$\overset{0}{100000}, \ \overset{1}{122210}, \ \overset{2}{123432}.$$

Real rank: 3.

E$_{7,3}$:

$$\overset{1}{000000}, \ \overset{1}{001210}, \ \overset{1}{011211}, \ \overset{1}{112211},$$

$$\overset{1}{111221}, \ \overset{1}{122210}, \ \overset{1}{012221}.$$

Real rank: 7.

E$_{8,1}$:

$$\overset{0}{1000000}, \ \overset{1}{1222210}, \ \overset{2}{1223432},$$

$$\overset{3}{1245642}.$$

Real rank: 4.

E$_{8,2}$:

$$\overset{0}{0000001}, \ \overset{1}{0001221}, \ \overset{1}{0122221},$$

$$\overset{1}{1122321}, \ \overset{2}{1123321}, \ \overset{1}{1223321},$$

$$\overset{2}{1222321}, \ \overset{2}{0123421}$$

Real rank: 8.

$\mathbf{F}_{4,1}$: $00 \Rightarrow 01.$

No intermediate one.
Real rank: 1.

$\mathbf{F}_{4,2}$: $10 \Rightarrow 00,\quad 12 \Rightarrow 20,\quad 12 \Rightarrow 22,\quad 12 \Rightarrow 42.$

No intermediate one.
Real rank: 4.

$\mathbf{G}_{2,2}$: $1 \Rightarrow 0,\quad 1 \Rightarrow 2.$

Real rank: 2.

$\mathbf{A}_{l,0,*}$, l odd: $\rho_i - \rho_{l+1-i}$ $(i=1, 2, \ldots, \frac{1}{2}(l-1))$.
Or, otherwise: $\omega_i + \omega_{l+2-i}$ $(i = 1, 2, \ldots, \frac{1}{2}(l-1))$.
Real rank: $\frac{1}{2}(l-1)$.

$\mathbf{A}_{l,0,*}$, $l = 2m$: $\rho_i - \rho_{2m+1-i}$ $(i = 1, 2, \ldots, m)$, $\rho_m + \rho_{m+1}$, $\rho_{m-1} + \rho_m + \rho_{m+1} + \rho_{m+2}, \ldots, \rho_1 + \cdots + \rho_{2m}$.
Or, otherwise: $\omega_i + \omega_{2m+2-i}$ $(i = 1, 2, \ldots, m)$, $\omega_m - \omega_{m+2}$, $\omega_{m-1} - \omega_{m+3}, \ldots, \omega_1 - \omega_l$.
Real rank: l.

$\mathbf{A}_{2m-1,m,*}$: $\rho_i - \rho_{2m-i}$ $(i=1, 2, \ldots, m-1)$, ρ_m, $\rho_{m-1} + \rho_m + \rho_{m+1}, \ldots, \rho_1 + \cdots + \rho_l$.
Or, otherwise: $\omega_i - \omega_{2m+1-i}$ $(i = 1, 2, \ldots, m-1)$, $\omega_m - \omega_{m+1}$, $\omega_{m-1} - \omega_{m+2}, \ldots, \omega_1 - \omega_l$.
Real rank: $2m-1$.

$\mathbf{D}_{l,0,*}$: $\rho_1 - \rho_2$.
Or, otherwise: ω_l.
Real rank: 1.

$\mathbf{D}_{l,j,*}$, $3 \leqslant j \leqslant \frac{1}{2}l + 2$: ρ_j, $\rho_{j-1} + \rho_j + \rho_{j+1}, \ldots, \rho_3 + \cdots + \rho_{2j-3}$, $\rho_j + 2\rho_{j+1} + \cdots + 2\rho_l + \rho_1 + \rho_2, \ldots, \rho_3 + \cdots + \rho_{2j-3} + 2\rho_{2j-2} + \cdots + 2\rho_l + \rho_1 + \rho_2$, $\rho_1 - \rho_2$.
Or, otherwise: $\omega_{j-2} \pm \omega_{j-1}$, $\omega_{j-3} \pm \omega_j, \ldots, \omega_1 \pm \omega_{2j-4}$, ω_1.
Real rank: $2j-3$.

$\mathbf{E}_{6,0,*}$: $\rho_1 - \rho_3$, $\rho_4 - \rho_5$.
Real rank: 2.

$\mathbf{E}_{6,2,*}$: $\overset{1}{00000}$, $\overset{1}{01210}$, $\overset{1}{11211}$, $\overset{1}{12221}$, $\rho_1 - \rho_3$, $\rho_4 - \rho_5$.

Real rank: 6.

60.24. Historical Note Minimally compact trunks for the different real types were found by E. Cartan [*Ann. Ecole Norm.* **44**, 345–467 (1927) = *Œuvres* I **2**, 867–989]. He also stated their conjugacy. The criterion of 60.9 seems to have been formulated first by H. Freudenthal, though it was prepared by investigations to be dealt with in the next section. The theorem in 60.19 was proved by H. de Vries. The procedure of constructing minimally compact trunks (60.21) is possibly the same as that by which E. Cartan obtained his minimally compact trunks.

61. REAL SEMISIMPLE LINEAR LIE GROUPS AS PRODUCTS OF MAXIMAL COMPACT AND SOLVABLE GROUPS

61.1. Theorem $G \in$ Gru Lie Lin Com SS; C is an involutory semimorphism, C_{un} is a unitary one, and $CC_{\text{un}} = C_{\text{un}}C$. Then there is a closed solvable Lie subgroup X of G_C such that every $g \in G_C$ splits uniquely as $g = ux$ with $u \in G_{C,\text{un}}$, $x \in X$.

61.2 The splitting is first performed on the infinitesimal algebras.

The trunk $\boldsymbol{H}$ of $\boldsymbol{G}$ is chosen minimally compact, $\boldsymbol{H} = C\boldsymbol{H} = C_{\text{un}}\boldsymbol{H}$, in real order; this means that if $\alpha \in W, \alpha > 0$, $CC_{\text{un}}\alpha \neq \alpha$, then $CC_{\text{un}}\alpha < 0$.

Let $\boldsymbol{E}^+, \boldsymbol{E}^-$ be the linear spaces spanned by the $\boldsymbol{e}_\alpha$ with $\alpha \neq CC_{\text{un}}\alpha$, and $\alpha > 0$, respectively, $\alpha < 0$; in other words by the $\boldsymbol{e}_\alpha$ with $\alpha > 0$ and $CC_{\text{un}}\alpha < 0$, respectively, with $\alpha < 0$ and $CC_{\text{un}}\alpha > 0$. Then

$$CC_{\text{un}}\boldsymbol{E}^+ = \boldsymbol{E}^-.$$

Put

$$\boldsymbol{E}_C^+ = (1 + C)\boldsymbol{E}^+, \qquad \boldsymbol{E}_C^- = (1 + C)\boldsymbol{E}^-.$$

Then $C\boldsymbol{E}_C^+ = \boldsymbol{E}_C^+$, $C\boldsymbol{E}_C^- = \boldsymbol{E}_C^-$; hence

61.2.1 $$C_{\text{un}}\boldsymbol{E}_C^+ = \boldsymbol{E}_C^-.$$

By means of $CC_{\text{un}}(1 + C_{\text{un}})(1 + C) = (1 + C_{\text{un}})(1 + C)$ one shows the elementwise invariance of $(1 + C_{\text{un}})\boldsymbol{E}_C^+$ under CC_{un}, hence under C and C_{un}. Therefore

$$(1 + C_{\text{un}})\boldsymbol{E}_C^+ \subset \boldsymbol{G}_{C,\text{un}},$$

and by 61.2.1

61.2.2 $$\boldsymbol{E}_C^- \subset (1 + C_{\text{un}})\boldsymbol{E}_C^+ + \boldsymbol{E}_C^+ \subset \boldsymbol{G}_{C,\text{un}} + \boldsymbol{E}_C^+.$$

Furthermore,

$$\boldsymbol{G}_{C,\text{he}} = (1 - C_{\text{un}})(1 + C)(\boldsymbol{E}^+ + \boldsymbol{E}^- + \boldsymbol{H})$$

because the $\boldsymbol{e}_\alpha$ with $\alpha = CC_{\text{un}}\alpha$ vanish under application of $(1 - C_{\text{un}})(1 + C)$.

$$\boldsymbol{G}_{C,\text{he}} = (1 - C_{\text{un}})(\boldsymbol{E}_C^+ + \boldsymbol{E}_C^- + \boldsymbol{H}_C)$$

by 61.2.1

$$\subset \boldsymbol{E}_C^+ + \boldsymbol{E}_C^- + \boldsymbol{H}_{C,\text{he}},$$

by 61.2.2

$$\subset \boldsymbol{G}_{C,\mathrm{un}} + \boldsymbol{E}_C^+ + \boldsymbol{H}_{C,\mathrm{he}}.$$

Now put

$$\boldsymbol{X} = \boldsymbol{E}_C^+ + \boldsymbol{H}_{C,\mathrm{he}}.$$

Then $\boldsymbol{X}$ is a solvable Lie algebra sub $\boldsymbol{G}_C$, and

$$\boldsymbol{G}_C = \boldsymbol{G}_{C,\mathrm{un}} + \boldsymbol{G}_{C,\mathrm{he}} \subset \boldsymbol{G}_{C,\mathrm{un}} + \boldsymbol{X} \subset \boldsymbol{G}_C,$$

hence,

$$\boldsymbol{G}_C = \boldsymbol{G}_{C,\mathrm{un}} + \boldsymbol{X}.$$

No element $\neq \boldsymbol{0}$ of $\boldsymbol{X}$ is CC_{un}-invariant; hence,

$$\boldsymbol{G}_{C,\mathrm{un}} \cap \boldsymbol{X} = \{\boldsymbol{0}\},$$

which proves the splitting for algebras.

61.3 The argument is extended to the groups by means of a general proposition:

Proposition Suppose that $G \in$ Gru Top Con, A compact sub G, B connected sub G, U_A, U_B 1-neighborhoods in A, respectively, B such that 1 is an interior point of $U_A U_B$. Then $AB = G$ and G/B is compact.

Proof The compactness of A guarantees the existence of a 1-neighborhood V_B in B such that

$$a^{-1} V_B a \subset U_A U_B \qquad \text{for all} \quad a \in A.$$

Then

$$V_B A \subset A U_A U_B \subset AB, \qquad V_B V_B A \subset V_B AB \subset AB,$$

and so on. The connected group B is generated by V_B; hence

$$BA \subset AB.$$

Now

$$A(AB) = AB, \qquad B(AB) = (BA)B \subset AB,$$

$$(AB)(AB) \subset AB, \qquad (AB)^{-1} = BA \subset AB.$$

Therefore AB is an open subgroup of the connected group G, hence AB equals G.

Moreover, G/B is compact as a continuous image of compact A.

61.4 By 61.2 Proposition 61.3 applies to $G = G_C$, $A = G_{C,\mathrm{un}}$, B generated by $\boldsymbol{X}$, which is solvable. The splitting is unique, since $ux = 1$ ($u \in G_{C,\mathrm{un}}$, $x \in X$)

implies that on a suitable basis x is triangular as well as unitary, thus diagonal, whereas its eigenvalues are the exponentials of those of an element of $\boldsymbol{H}_{C,\text{he}}$, thus positive, whence $x = 1$.

It follows from 18.1.5 that exp is in fact a homeomorphism of $\boldsymbol{X}$ onto X and that X is closed in G_C. (See 4.13.)

61.5. Historical Note The preceding theorem is not found in the places to which it is usually ascribed. It probably originated in a paper by K. Iwasawa, *Ann. Math.* **50**, 507–558 (1949) (Lemma 3.11).

62. THE FUNDAMENTAL GROUPS OF THE REAL TYPES

62.1 Before being used in the computation of the fundamental groups of real semisimple groups, the terminology on the operations with fundamental groups of compact groups has to be slightly extended.

Consider a $\boldsymbol{G} \in$ Alg Lie Com (dim $\boldsymbol{G} < \infty$),

$$\boldsymbol{G} = \boldsymbol{G}^{(1)} + \boldsymbol{G}^{(2)}, \qquad \text{a direct sum,}$$

where $\boldsymbol{G}^{(1)}$ is semisimple and $\boldsymbol{G}^{(2)}$ is the center of $\boldsymbol{G}$. In $\boldsymbol{G}^{(2)}$ real subspaces $\boldsymbol{G}^{(2)}_{\text{st}}$ and $\boldsymbol{G}^{(2)}_{\text{un}} = \mathrm{i}\boldsymbol{G}^{(2)}_{\text{st}}$ are marked such that after waiving in $\boldsymbol{G}^{(2)}$

$$\boldsymbol{G}^{(2)} = \boldsymbol{G}^{(2)}_{\text{st}} + \boldsymbol{G}^{(2)}_{\text{un}}, \qquad \text{a direct sum.}$$

Furthermore, it is agreed that

$$\boldsymbol{H}^{(2)} = \boldsymbol{G}^{(2)}, \qquad \boldsymbol{H}^{(2)}_{\text{st}} = \boldsymbol{G}^{(2)}_{\text{st}}, \qquad \boldsymbol{H}^{(2)}_{\text{un}} = \boldsymbol{G}^{(2)}_{\text{un}}.$$

If $\boldsymbol{H}^{(1)}$ is a trunk of $\boldsymbol{G}^{(1)}$, then $\boldsymbol{H} = \boldsymbol{H}^{(1)} + \boldsymbol{H}^{(2)}$ is a trunk of $\boldsymbol{G}$. For a unitary semimorphism C_{un} of $\boldsymbol{G}^{(1)}$, one defines

$$\boldsymbol{G}_{\text{un}} = \boldsymbol{G}^{(1)}_{\text{un}} + \boldsymbol{G}^{(2)}_{\text{un}}, \qquad \boldsymbol{H}_{\text{un}} = \boldsymbol{H}^{(1)}_{\text{un}} + \boldsymbol{H}^{(2)}_{\text{un}}, \qquad \boldsymbol{H}_{\text{st}} = \boldsymbol{H}^{(1)}_{\text{st}} + \boldsymbol{H}^{(2)}_{\text{st}}.$$

As noted in 41.1, the notion of weight with respect to the trunk $\boldsymbol{H}$ makes good sense for a linear representation f of $\boldsymbol{G}$ as long as $\boldsymbol{G}^{(2)}$ is conducibly represented by f.

Only such linear representations f of $\boldsymbol{G}$ are admitted such that the group generated by $f(\boldsymbol{G}_{\text{un}})$ is compact. Then the group generated by $f(\boldsymbol{G}^{(2)}_{\text{un}})$ is the 1-component of the center of that generated by $f(\boldsymbol{G}_{\text{un}})$, thus compact; hence $\boldsymbol{G}^{(2)}$ is surely conducibly represented. The restriction $\lambda^{(2)}$ of a weight λ of f to $\boldsymbol{H}^{(2)}$ is even a linear representation of $\boldsymbol{G}^{(2)}$; exp $\lambda^{(2)}$ maps the addition group of $\boldsymbol{H}^{(2)}_{\text{un}}$ homeomorphically with a compact image. So $\lambda^{(2)}$ is imaginary-valued on $\boldsymbol{H}^{(2)}_{\text{un}}$ and real-valued on $\boldsymbol{H}^{(2)}_{\text{st}}$. Any real-valued linear function on $\boldsymbol{H}^{(2)}_{\text{st}}$ can be obtained this way by starting with a suitable f.

In 46.3 $\Lambda = \boldsymbol{H}^*_{\text{ing}}$ was defined as the addition group of integral elements of

$\boldsymbol{H}^*_{\text{st}}$, that is, of possible weights of linear representations of a semisimple complex Lie algebra. It is now called $\Lambda(\boldsymbol{G}^{(1)})$.

The foregoing leads to the following definition:

Definition $\Lambda(\boldsymbol{G}^{(2)})$ is the addition group of linear functions of $\boldsymbol{H}^{(2)}$ that are real-valued on $\boldsymbol{H}^{(2)}_{\text{st}}$. Furthermore

$$\Lambda(\boldsymbol{G}) = \Lambda(\boldsymbol{G}^{(1)}) + \Lambda(\boldsymbol{G}^{(2)}).$$

(More correctly, the $\boldsymbol{G}^{(j)}$-restriction of an element of $\Lambda(\boldsymbol{G})$ is in $\Lambda(\boldsymbol{G}^{(j)})$.) Again $\Lambda_f(\boldsymbol{G})$ means the addition group generated by the weights of f.

The fundamental group of the group generated by $f(\boldsymbol{G}_{\text{un}})$ need no longer be finite, though it is still finitely generated and thus a direct sum of cyclic groups. The dual (46.2) of an infinite cyclic group is isomorphic to the addition group of imaginary numbers mod $2\pi\mathrm{i}$. Its isomorphism type is denoted by Z_0. The dual of the fundamental group is a direct sum of groups Z_m $(m = 0, 1, 2, \ldots)$.

One can easily verify an extension of Theorem 46.5.3:

Theorem The dual of the fundamental group of the group generated by $f(\boldsymbol{G}_{\text{un}})$ is isomorphic with $\Lambda(\boldsymbol{G})$ mod $\Lambda_f(\boldsymbol{G})$.

The duality takes the same sense as in Theorems 46.3 and 46.5.3.

62.2 $G_C \in$ Alg Lie Rea SS; $\boldsymbol{G}$ is supposed to be the adjoint of a Lie algebra isomorphic with $\boldsymbol{G}$, thus certainly G_C is centerfree.

Problem Compute the fundamental group of G_C.

62.3. Proposition The fundamental group of G_C is the same as that of $G_{C,\text{un}}$.

Proof The proof follows from 51.5.10 and the fact that $G_{C,\text{he}}$ is homeomorphic with the vector space $\boldsymbol{G}_{C,\text{he}}$.

62.4 $G_{C,\text{un}}$ need not be semisimple; according to the classification, it might have a nondiscrete center. For this reason the terminology for the computation of the fundamental group has been extended in 62.1.

The notions of 62.1 are now applied to

$$\boldsymbol{G}_{C,\text{un},\text{Com}} = \boldsymbol{G}_{C,\text{un}} + \mathrm{i}\boldsymbol{G}_{C,\text{un}} \qquad \text{instead of } \boldsymbol{G}.$$

$G_{C,\text{un}}$ is faithfully represented as a subgroup of the adjoint of $\boldsymbol{G}_C$ because G_C is centerfree. Therefore the role of f will be played by

$$\curlyvee_{a \in G_{C,\text{un}}} \curlyvee_{\boldsymbol{x} \in \boldsymbol{G}} \tilde{a}\boldsymbol{x}.$$

62.5 To use weights, G is assumed in ordered maximally compact dressing with respect to C and the trunk $\boldsymbol{H}$. As in 51.14,

$$C = \tilde{h} A C_{\text{un}}.$$

In addition to C one considers

$$C_0 = A C_{\text{un}}.$$

Clearly

$$\boldsymbol{G}_{C_0,\text{un},\text{Com}} = \boldsymbol{G}_A,$$

which means the subalgebra of A-invariant elements.

As a trunk of $\boldsymbol{G}_{C,\text{un},\text{Com}}$ and $\boldsymbol{G}_{C_0,\text{un},\text{Com}}$ one uses $(1 + A)\boldsymbol{H}$. Now, according to the definition of f, the weights of f are the rootforms of $\boldsymbol{G}$ on $\boldsymbol{H}$ restricted to $(1 + A)\boldsymbol{H}$. As in 51.21, one rather interprets $\boldsymbol{H}^*_{C,\text{un},\text{Com}}$ and $\boldsymbol{H}^*_{C_0,\text{un},\text{Com}}$ in $\boldsymbol{H}^*$. Then one arrives at the following:

Proposition The dual of the fundamental group of $G_{C,\text{un}}$ (or G_C) in the sense of Theorem 62.1 is isomorphic to

$$\Lambda(\boldsymbol{G}_{C,\text{un},\text{Com}}) \bmod \Lambda_\sim(\boldsymbol{G}_{C_0,\text{un},\text{Com}}),$$

that is,

$$\Lambda(\boldsymbol{G}_{C,\text{un},\text{Com}}) \bmod (1 + A)\,\Lambda_\sim(\boldsymbol{G}).$$

Here, of course, one again uses the fact that restriction to $(1 + A)\boldsymbol{H}$ is translated in symmetrization with respect to A.

It suffices to compute the fundamental group for simple G_C.

For the compact case it is known, in the twin case it is the same as in the complex case, thus as in the compact case; these cases are now disregarded.

In 62.6–7 the fundamental group will be computed for the inner types and in 62.8 for the outer types, according to the classification in Sections 52–53. The results are expressed in terms of the fundamental weights of $\boldsymbol{G}_A$.

62.6 $G \in \mathbf{L}_j$, inner type; hence $A = 1$.

The fundamental group is isomorphic to

$$\Lambda(\boldsymbol{G}_{C,\text{un},\text{Com}}) \bmod \Lambda_\sim(\boldsymbol{G}).$$

First the rootforms of $\boldsymbol{G}_{C,\text{un},\text{Com}}$ are expressed in terms of those of $\boldsymbol{G}$. Two cases must be distinguished with respect to the subscript j (compare Section 52):

62.6.1 ρ_j appears in no positive rootform of $\boldsymbol{G}_{C,\text{un},\text{Com}}$ with an even coefficient.

62.6.2 ρ_j appears with an even coefficient in the rootform $\sum c_\nu \rho_\nu$ of $\boldsymbol{G}_{C,\text{un},\text{Com}}$, which is the lowest positive one with this property.

In the case 62.6.1 $G_{C,\mathrm{un,Com}}$ has a one-dimensional direct summand; ρ_j simply drops out as a rootform. In both cases a natural basis of $W^*(G_{C,\mathrm{un,Com}})$ is furnished by

$$\rho_i' = \rho_i \quad \text{for} \quad i \neq j, \qquad \rho_j' = \sum c_\nu \rho_\nu \qquad \text{if existent,}$$

that is, in the case 62.6.1 there is no ρ_j'.

In the case 62.6.1 a basis of $\Lambda(G_{C,\mathrm{un,Com}})$ is thus furnished by

$$\pi_i' = \pi_i,$$

where integral coefficients are admitted at π_i with $i \neq j$ and real coefficients at π_j.

In the case 62.6.2 an integral basis of $\Lambda(G_{C,\mathrm{un,Com}})$ is available. One can use the fundamental weights π_i' of $G_{C,\mathrm{un,Com}}$ which have to satisfy (cf. 51.21)

$$2\frac{(\pi_i', \rho_k')}{(\rho_k', \rho_k')} = \begin{cases} 0 & \text{for} \quad i \neq k, \\ 1 & \text{for} \quad i = k. \end{cases}$$

The π' can be expressed in the π by

$$\pi_i' = \pi_i - \frac{c_i}{c_j}\frac{(\rho_i, \rho_i)}{(\rho_j, \rho_j)}\pi_j \qquad \text{for} \quad i \neq j,$$

$$\pi_j' = \frac{1}{c_j}\frac{(\rho_j', \rho_j')}{(\rho_j, \rho_j)}\pi_j.$$

In Table F the π are given in terms of the ρ. To find generators of the fundamental group one must compute the π' mod the ρ. This is done for the different types in 62.7.

Notation The $\backsim$ sign is used for congruence mod $\rho_1, \ldots, \rho_l$.

Notation $\mathsf{Z}_m(a)$ for $m = 1, 2, 3, \ldots$ indicates the type of the m-cyclic group with the generator a mod $\Lambda_\sim(G_A)$; $\mathsf{Z}_0(a)$ indicates the addition group of τa with real τ mod 1; here a, but no nonintegral multiple of a, is congruent to 0.

62.7. The Duals of the Fundamental Groups of Noncompact Centerfree† Simple Groups of Inner Type

$\mathsf{A}_{l,j}$: No ρ_j'. $\pi_i' = \pi_i$ $(i \neq j)$ with integral coefficients, $\pi_j' = \pi_j$ with real coefficients. Since $\pi_k \backsim k\pi_1$, one can take π_1 and π_j as generators. For $1 < j < l+1$ put $d =$ greatest common divisor of $l+1$ and j,

$$d = vj + w(l+1).$$

Then

$$d\pi_1 = vj\pi_1 + w(l+1)\pi_1 \backsim v\pi_j.$$

† Though being centerfree is implied by simplicity, it is explicitly mentioned because Lie theory suggests a wider notion of simplicity, namely local simplicity.

Put

$$\vartheta = \pi_1 - \frac{v}{d}\pi_j.$$

Then

$$d\vartheta \backsim 0.$$

To use ϑ, π_j as a basis one must show that no smaller integral multiple of ϑ can be congruent with a real multiple of π_j in, other words, that

62.7.1
$$x\pi_1 \backsim y\pi_j$$

can be solved with integral x only by multiples of d.

Comparing the coefficients of $\rho_1, \rho_j, \rho_{j+1}$ in 62.7.1, one gets congruences mod $l+1$:

$$xl = y(l+1-j), \qquad x(l-j+1) = y(l-j+1)\,j, \qquad x(l-j) = y(l-j)j.$$

The last two give $x = yj \bmod l+1$; if substituted in the first, this gives $y(l+1)\,j = y(l+1) \bmod l+1$, and since yj $(=x \bmod l+1)$ is integral, $y(l+1) = 0 \bmod l+1$, hence y integral. Therefore mod $l+1$, x is an integral multiple of j, thus d is a divisor of x. The result is

$$\mathsf{Z}_d(\vartheta) + \mathsf{Z}_0\left(\frac{l+1}{d}\pi_j\right).$$

For $j = 1$ this holds as well.

$\mathsf{B}_{l,j}, j \neq 1, 2$: $\rho_j' = \rho_{j-1} + 2\rho_j + \cdots + 2\rho_l + 2\rho_1, \quad (\rho_j', \rho_j') = (\rho_j, \rho_j) = 2(\rho_1, \rho_1),$

$$\pi_i' = \pi_i \backsim 0 \qquad \text{for} \quad 1 < i < j-1,$$

$$\pi_{j-1}' = \pi_{j-1} - \tfrac{1}{2}\pi_j \backsim \tfrac{1}{2}\pi_j \not\backsim 0,$$

$$\pi_j' = \tfrac{1}{2}\pi_j,$$

$$\pi_i' = \pi_i - \pi_j \backsim 0 \qquad \text{for} \quad i > j,$$

$$\pi_1' = \pi_1 - \tfrac{1}{2}\pi_j \not\backsim 0.$$

$$\mathsf{Z}_2(\pi_1) + \mathsf{Z}_2(\tfrac{1}{2}\pi_j).$$

$\mathsf{B}_{l,1}$: $\rho_1' = 2\rho_1 + \rho_l, \qquad (\rho_1', \rho_1') = 2(\rho_1, \rho_1).$

$$\pi_i' = \pi_i \backsim 0 \qquad \text{for} \quad i \neq 1, l,$$

$$\pi_l' = \pi_l - \pi_1 \backsim \pi_1,$$

$$\pi_1' = \pi_1.$$

$$\mathsf{Z}_2(\pi_1).$$

$\mathsf{B}_{l,2}$: No ρ_2'.

Comparing the coefficients of ρ_2 and ρ_3 (for $l=2$ those of ρ_1 and ρ_2) in

$$\pi_1 = \tfrac{1}{2}(l\rho_1 + \rho_2 + 2\rho_3 + \cdots + (l-1)\rho_l)$$

and

$$\pi_2 = \rho_1 + \rho_2 + \cdots + \rho_l,$$

one verifies that π_1 is congruent with no real multiple of π_2.

$$\mathsf{Z}_2(\pi_1) + \mathsf{Z}(\pi_2).$$

$\mathsf{C}_{l,j}, j<l$: $\rho_j' = 2\rho_j + \cdots + 2\rho_{l-1} + \rho_l$, $(\rho_j', \rho_j') = 2(\rho_j, \rho_j) = (\rho_l, \rho_l)$.

$$\pi_i' = \pi_i \qquad \text{for} \quad i \leqslant j,$$

$$\pi_i' = \pi_i - \pi_j \qquad \text{for} \quad j < i \leqslant l.$$

The same as for $\mathsf{C}_{l,0}$.

$$\mathsf{Z}_2(\pi_1).$$

$\mathsf{C}_{l,l}$: No ρ_l'.

Comparing

$$\pi_l = \rho_1 + 2\rho_2 + \cdots + (l-1)\rho_{l-1} + \tfrac{1}{2}l\rho_l,$$

and

$$\pi_1 = \rho_1 + \rho_2 + \cdots + \rho_{l-1} + \tfrac{1}{2}\rho_l,$$

one notes that a multiple of π_l cannot be congruent with π_1 unless l is odd.

$$\mathsf{Z}_0(2\pi_l) \quad \text{for odd } l, \qquad \mathsf{Z}_2(\pi_1) + \mathsf{Z}_0(\pi_1) \quad \text{for even } l.$$

$\mathsf{D}_{l,j}, j>3$: $\rho_j' = \rho_{j-1} + 2\rho_j + \cdots + 2\rho_l + \rho_1 + \rho_2$.

$$\pi_{1,2}' = \pi_{1,2} - \tfrac{1}{2}\pi_j,$$

$$\pi_i' = \pi_i \qquad \text{for} \quad 3 \leqslant i < j-1,$$

$$\pi_{j-1}' = \pi_{j-1} - \tfrac{1}{2}\pi_j,$$

$$\pi_j' = \tfrac{1}{2}\pi_j,$$

$$\pi_i' = \pi_i - \pi_j \qquad \text{for} \quad i > j.$$

$\pi_1, \pi_2, \frac{1}{2}\pi_j$ may serve as generators; π_j belongs to the group generated by π_1, π_2 but $\frac{1}{2}\pi_j$ does not. Indeed, if $\frac{1}{2}\pi_j \backsim u\pi_1 + v\pi_2$ were true for some integral u, v, then the coefficients of ρ_1, ρ_2 would yield $u = v \bmod 2$, whereas the coefficient of ρ_3 would require $u+v = 1 \bmod 2$. The order of $\frac{1}{2}\pi_j$ is 2 for even j, 4 for odd j.

l even: $\mathsf{Z}_2(\pi_1) + \mathsf{Z}_2(\pi_2) + \mathsf{Z}_2(\frac{1}{2}\pi_j)$ for even j,

$\mathsf{Z}_2(\pi_4) + \mathsf{Z}_4(\frac{1}{2}\pi_j)$ for odd j,

l odd: $\mathsf{Z}_4(\pi_1) + \mathsf{Z}_2(\frac{1}{2}\pi_j)$ for even j,

$\mathsf{Z}_4(\pi_1) + \mathsf{Z}_2(\pi_1 - \frac{1}{2}\pi_j)$ for odd j.

Note that $\pi_2 \backsim -\pi_1$ for odd l and $\pi_2 \backsim \pi_1 + \pi_j$ for even l and odd j.

$\mathsf{D}_{l,3}$: No ρ_3'.

$$\pi_3 = \tfrac{1}{2}(\rho_1 + \rho_2) + \rho_3 + \rho_4 + \cdots + \rho_l.$$

For even l: $\pi_1 + \pi_2 \backsim \pi_3$; for odd l: $2\pi_1 \backsim \pi_3$. In either case π_1 is congruent with no real multiple of π_3.

l even: $\mathsf{Z}_2(\pi_1) + \mathsf{Z}_0(2\pi_3)$,

l odd: $\mathsf{Z}_2(\pi_1 - \frac{1}{2}\pi_3) + \mathsf{Z}_0(2\pi_3)$.

Note that $\pi_2 \backsim -\pi_1$ for odd l.

$\mathsf{D}_{l,1}$: No ρ_1'.

For even l: π_2 is congruent with no real multiple of π_1 as is seen by comparing the coefficients.

l even: $\mathsf{Z}_2(\pi_2) + \mathsf{Z}_0(2\pi_1)$,

l odd: $\mathsf{Z}_0(4\pi_1)$.

$\mathsf{E}_{6,1}$: No ρ_1'.

$\mathsf{Z}_0(3\pi_1)$.

Note that $\pi_3 \backsim -\pi_1$.

$\mathsf{E}_{6,2}$: $\rho_2' = \rho_1 + 2\rho_2 + \rho_3 + 2\rho_4 + 2\rho_5 + 3\rho_6$.

$\pi_1' = \pi_1 - \frac{1}{2}\pi_2$,

$\pi_2' = \frac{1}{2}\pi_2$,

$\pi_3' = \pi_3 - \frac{1}{2}\pi_2 \backsim 2\pi_1 - \frac{1}{2}\pi_2$,

$\pi_4' = \pi_4 - \pi_2 \backsim 2\pi_1$,

$\pi_5' = \pi_5 - \pi_2 \backsim \pi_1$,

$\pi_6' = \pi_6 - \frac{3}{2}\pi_2 \backsim \frac{1}{2}\pi_2$.

Generators π_1, $\frac{1}{2}\pi_2$ of orders 3, 2.

$$\mathsf{Z}_6(\pi_1 + \tfrac{1}{2}\pi_2).$$

Note that $\pi_3 \backsim -\pi_1$.

$\mathsf{E}_{7,1}$: $\rho_1' = 2\rho_1 + \rho_2 + 2\rho_3 + 2\rho_4 + 3\rho_5 + 3\rho_6 + 4\rho_7$.

$$\pi_1' = \tfrac{1}{2}\pi_1,$$

$$\pi_2' = \pi_2 - \tfrac{1}{2}\pi_1 \not\backsim 0,$$

$$\pi_3' = \pi_3 - \pi_1 \backsim \pi_2,$$

$$\pi_4' = \pi_4 - \pi_1 \backsim 0,$$

$$\pi_5' = \pi_5 - \tfrac{3}{2}\pi_1 \backsim \tfrac{1}{2}\pi_1,$$

$$\pi_6' = \pi_6 - \tfrac{3}{2}\pi_1 \backsim \tfrac{1}{2}\pi_1 + \pi_2,$$

$$\pi_7' = \pi_7 - 2\pi_1 \backsim 0.$$

$$\mathsf{Z}_2(\tfrac{1}{2}\pi_1) + \mathsf{Z}_2(\pi_2).$$

$\mathsf{E}_{7,2}$: No ρ_2'.

$$\mathsf{Z}_0(2\pi_2).$$

$\mathsf{E}_{7,3}$: $\rho_3' = \rho_1 + 2\rho_3 + \rho_4 + 2\rho_5 + 2\rho_6 + 3\rho_7$.

$$\pi_1' = \pi_1 - \tfrac{1}{2}\pi_3 \backsim -\tfrac{1}{2}\pi_3,$$

$$\pi_2' = \pi_2 \backsim \pi_3,$$

$$\pi_3' = \tfrac{1}{2}\pi_3,$$

$$\pi_4' = \pi_4 - \tfrac{1}{2}\pi_3 \backsim -\tfrac{1}{2}\pi_3,$$

$$\pi_5' = \pi_5 - \pi_3 \backsim -\pi_3,$$

$$\pi_6' = \pi_6 - \pi_3 \backsim 0,$$

$$\pi_7' = \pi_7 - \tfrac{3}{2}\pi_3 \backsim -\tfrac{3}{2}\pi_3.$$

$$\mathsf{Z}_4(\tfrac{1}{2}\pi_3).$$

$\mathsf{E}_{8,1}$: $\rho_1' = 2\rho_1 + 2\rho_2 + 3\rho_3 + 3\rho_4 + 4\rho_5 + 4\rho_6 + 5\rho_7 + 6\rho_8$.

$$\pi_1' = \tfrac{1}{2}\pi_1 \not\backsim 0.$$

No multiples other than $\frac{1}{2}\pi_1$, whereas $\pi_i \backsim 0$ for all i.

$$\mathsf{Z}_2(\tfrac{1}{2}\pi_1).$$

$\mathsf{E}_{8,2}$: $\rho_2' = 2\rho_2 + \rho_3 + 2\rho_4 + 2\rho_5 + 3\rho_6 + 3\rho_7 + 4\rho_8.$

$\pi_2' = \frac{1}{2}\pi_2 \not\sim 0.$

$\mathsf{Z}_2(\frac{1}{2}\pi_2).$

$\mathsf{F}_{4,1}$: $\rho_1' = 2\rho_1 + 2\rho_3 + \rho_4, \qquad (\rho_1', \rho_1') = 2(\rho_1, \rho_1).$

$\pi_1' = \pi_1,$

$\pi_2' = \pi_2,$

$\pi_3' = \pi_3 - \pi_1,$

$\pi_4' = \pi_4 - \pi_1.$

Trivial.

$\mathsf{F}_{4,2}$: $\rho_2' = 2\rho_1 + 2\rho_2 + 4\rho_3 + 3\rho_4, \qquad (\rho_2', \rho_2') = (\rho_2, \rho_2).$

$\pi_1' = \pi_1 - \frac{1}{2}\pi_2,$

$\pi_2' = \frac{1}{2}\pi_2 \not\sim 0,$

$\pi_3' = \pi_3 - \pi_2,$

$\pi_4' = \pi_4 - \frac{3}{2}\pi_2.$

$\mathsf{Z}_2(\frac{1}{2}\pi_2).$

$\mathsf{G}_{2,2}$: $\rho_2' = 3\rho_1 + 2\rho_2, \qquad (\rho_2', \rho_2') = (\rho_2, \rho_2).$

$\pi_1' = \pi_1 - \frac{1}{2}\pi_2,$

$\pi_2' = \frac{1}{2}\pi_2 \not\sim 0.$

$\mathsf{Z}_2(\frac{1}{2}\pi_2).$

62.8. The Duals of the Fundamental Groups of Centerfree† Simple Groups of Outer Type It is a matter of convenience to write the symmetrized rootforms as

$$\rho_i' = \tfrac{1}{2}(\rho_i + P\rho_i).$$

The primitive rootforms of $G_{C,\mathrm{un},\mathrm{Com}}$ are indicated by ρ_j''. The fundamental weights π' corresponding to the ρ' are those of $G_{C0,\mathrm{un},\mathrm{Com}}$. They happen to coincide with the symmetrized π_i except in $\mathsf{A}_{2m,0,*}$, where

$$\tfrac{1}{2}(\pi_m + P\pi_m) = 2\pi_m';$$

this is precisely the case in which not all symmetrized rootforms are rootforms of $G_{C0,\mathrm{un},\mathrm{Com}}$. (See 53.1.)

† Cf. footnote in 62.7.

For $j \neq 0$ one needs the fundamental weights π'' corresponding to the ρ'', which are derived from π' by the method used in 62.6 to derive π' from π. Now $\backsim$ denotes congruent mod the ρ'.

$\mathsf{A}_{2m-1,0,*}$: $\rho_i' = \frac{1}{2}(\rho_i + \rho_{2m-i})$. The fundamental group is the same as in C_m.

$\mathsf{Z}_2(\pi_1')$.

$\mathsf{A}_{2m,0,*}$: $\rho_i' = \frac{1}{2}(\rho_i + \rho_{2m+1-i})$. As in B_m.

$\mathsf{Z}_2(\pi_m')$.

$\mathsf{A}_{2m-1,m,*}$: $\rho_i'' = \rho_i' \quad (i = 1, \ldots, m-1), \qquad \rho_m'' = \rho_{m-1}' + \rho_m'$.

$$\pi_i'' = \pi_i' \quad (i < m-1),$$

$$\pi_{m-1}'' = \pi_{m-1}' - \tfrac{1}{2}\pi_m',$$

$$\pi_m'' = \tfrac{1}{2}\pi_m'.$$

Now $\frac{1}{2}\pi_m' = \frac{1}{2}(\rho' + 2\rho_2' + \cdots + (m-1)\rho_{m-1}' + \frac{1}{2}m\rho_m')$ comes up, whereas in C_m one could do it with π_1' alone; $\frac{1}{2}\pi_m' \not\backsim \pi_1'$.

For even m: $\mathsf{Z}_2(\pi_1') + \mathsf{Z}_2(\frac{1}{2}\pi_m')$.

For odd m: $\mathsf{Z}_4(\frac{1}{2}\pi_m')$.

$\mathsf{D}_{l,0,*}$: $\rho_i' = \rho_i$ for $i \neq 1, 2, \qquad \rho_1' = \frac{1}{2}(\rho_1 + \rho_2)$. As in $\mathsf{B}_{l-1,0}$.

$\mathsf{Z}_2(\pi_1')$.

$\mathsf{D}_{l,j,*}, j \neq 0$: $\rho_i'' = \rho_i'$ for $i \neq j, \qquad \rho_j'' = \rho_j' + \rho_{j+1}' + \cdots + \rho_l' + \rho_1'$.

$$\pi_1'' = \pi_1' - \tfrac{1}{2}\pi_j',$$

$$\pi_i'' = \pi_i' \quad \text{for} \quad 2 < i < j,$$

$$\pi_j'' = \tfrac{1}{2}\pi_j',$$

$$\pi_i'' = \pi_i' - \pi_j' \qquad \text{for} \quad i > j.$$

In addition to π_1' one gets $\frac{1}{2}\pi_j'$ as a generator. Comparing the coefficients of ρ_1' and ρ_l' in

$$\pi_1' = \tfrac{1}{2}((l-1)\,\rho_1' + \rho_3' + 2\rho_4' + \cdots + (l-2)\,\rho_l'),$$

$$\tfrac{1}{2}\pi_j' = \tfrac{1}{2}((j-2)\,\rho_1' + \rho_3' + 2\rho_4' + \cdots + (j-2)(\rho_j' + \cdots + \rho_l')),$$

one verifies $\pi_1' \not\backsim \frac{1}{2}\pi_j'$.

$\mathsf{Z}_2(\pi_1') + \mathsf{Z}_2(\frac{1}{2}\pi_j')$.

$\mathsf{E}_{6,0,*}$: $\rho_1' = \frac{1}{2}(\rho_1 + \rho_3)$, $\rho_2' = \rho_2$, $\rho_4' = \frac{1}{2}(\rho_4 + \rho_5)$, $\rho_6' = \rho_6$. As in $\mathsf{F}_{4,0}$.

Trivial.

$\mathsf{E}_{6,2,*}$: $\rho_1'' = \rho_1'$, $\rho_2'' = \rho_4' + \rho_6' + \rho_2'$, $\rho_4'' = \rho_4'$, $\rho_6'' = \rho_6'$; $(\rho_2'', \rho_2'') = \frac{1}{2}(\rho_2', \rho_2')$.

$\pi_1'' = \pi_1'$,

$\pi_2'' = \frac{1}{2}\pi_2'$,

$\pi_4'' = \pi_4' - \frac{1}{2}\pi_2'$,

$\pi_6'' = \pi_6' - \pi_2'$.

Generator $\frac{1}{2}\pi_2' = \frac{1}{2}(2\rho_1' + 2\rho_2' + 4\rho_4' + 3\rho_6') \not\sim 0$.

$\mathsf{Z}_2(\frac{1}{2}\pi_2')$.

62.9. The Duals of the Fundamental Groups of the Universal Linear Wrappings In the compact case any wrapping (being compact again) can be realized as a linear group (see 46.8). This is true of the twin type as well, but in many other real types such a linear realization need not exist. The linear wrappings of centerfree G_C are real restrictions of the linear wrappings of G and are the 1-components of the originals of G_C under the projection mappings. It follows that the 1-component of the original of G_C in the universal wrapping of G is the *universal linear wrapping* of G_C.

The splitting of G_C into connected $G_{C,\mathrm{un}}$ and simply connected $G_{C,\mathrm{he}}$ is lifted to such a splitting of any wrapping of G_C. Hence the fundamental group of the universal linear wrapping of G_C is the same as that of the induced wrapping of $G_{C,\mathrm{un}}$. The addition group generated by the weights of the complexification of this representation of $\boldsymbol{G}_{C,\mathrm{un}}$ is that generated by the fundamental weights of $\boldsymbol{G}$, symmetrized in the outer case.

Hence by 62.1:

Theorem The dual of the fundamental group of the universal linear wrapping of G_C is $\Lambda(\boldsymbol{G}_{C,\mathrm{un,Com}})$ mod the group generated by the fundamental weights of $\boldsymbol{G}$, symmetrized in the outer case.

The particular cases are:

G_C compact or twin: Trivial.

$\mathsf{A}_{l,j}$: $\mathsf{Z}_0\left(\frac{1}{j}\pi_j\right)$.

$\mathsf{B}_{l,j}$ $(j \neq 1,2)$: $\mathsf{Z}_2(\frac{1}{2}\pi_j)$; $\mathsf{B}_{l,1}$: 0; $\mathsf{B}_{l,2}$: $\mathsf{Z}_0(\pi_2)$.

$\mathsf{C}_{l,j}$ $(j < l)$: 0; $\mathsf{C}_{l,l}$: $\mathsf{Z}_0(\pi_l)$.

$D_{l,j}$ $(j>3)$: $Z_2(\frac{1}{2}\pi_j)$; $D_{l,1}$: $Z_0(\pi_1)$; $D_{l,3}$: $Z_0(\pi_3)$.

$E_{6,1}$: $Z_0(\pi_1)$; $E_{6,2}$: $Z_2(\frac{1}{2}\pi_2)$.

$E_{7,1}$: $Z_2(\frac{1}{2}\pi_1)$; $E_{7,2}$: $Z_0(\pi_2)$; $E_{7,3}$: $Z_2(\frac{1}{2}\pi_3)$.

$E_{8,1}$: $Z_2(\frac{1}{2}\pi_1)$; $E_{8,2}$: $Z_2(\frac{1}{2}\pi_2)$.

$F_{4,1}$: 0; $F_{4,2}$: $Z_2(\frac{1}{2}\pi_2)$.

$G_{2,2}$: $Z_2(\frac{1}{2}\pi_2)$.

$A_{2m-1,0,*}$: 0; $A_{2m,0,*}$: $Z_2(\pi'_m)$; $A_{2m-1,m,*}$: $Z_2(\frac{1}{2}\pi'_m)$.

$D_{l,0,*}$: 0; $D_{l,j,*}$ $(j\geqslant 3)$: $Z_2(\frac{1}{2}\pi'_j)$.

$E_{6,0,*}$: 0; $E_{6,2,*}$: $Z_2(\frac{1}{2}\pi'_2)$.

62.10. Historical Note E. Cartan found the fundamental groups of centerfree semisimple Lie groups by rather casual methods [*Ann. Ecole Norm.* **44**, 345–467 (1927) = *Œuvres* I **2**, 867–990]. Current folklore says that E. Cartan dealt with the compact case only, though the authors who claim to have solved the noncompact case first and others who are supporting this claim do not fail to quote the paper in which Cartan published his results. Since there is some danger that modern research will eclipse Cartan's, it is useful to add the warning that those modern results are partly mistaken, even on primordial points, whereas Cartan's are completely correct.

63–67

SYMMETRIC SPACES

63. HOMOGENEOUS SPACES AND RIEMANNIAN MANIFOLDS—A SKETCH

63.1–3. Homogeneous Spaces

63.1.1. Definition The pair $\ulcorner G,J \urcorner$, in which G is a topological group and J a closed subgroup of G, determines the *homogeneous space*

$$R = G/J$$

that is, the left coset space of J in G, which is acted on by G by left multiplication in a transitive manner.

For any group G acting on a space R the *stability group* of $p \in R$ consists of the elements of G leaving p invariant.

63.1.2 For the just-defined homogeneous space the stability group of $x_0 = J$ is J itself; generally that of a point $g_1 x_0$ ($g_1 \in G$) is $g_1 J g_1^{-1}$.

63.1.3 How does J act on R? By left multiplication by $j \in J$, xJ is mapped into

$$jxJ = jxj^{-1}J$$

so that J acts on R as a subgroup of the group of inner automorphisms of G.

63.1.4 It goes without saying how the homogeneous space G/J is to be understood as a *direct product* of homogeneous spaces G_i/J_i if G, respectively, J, is the direct product of G_i, respectively, J_i.

63.1.5 The representation of G in $R = G/J$ is faithful iff J contains no normal subgroup $\neq \{1\}$ of G. Generally this will be assumed in the sequel.

63.1.6 G_1 sub G acts transitively on G/J iff $G_1 J = G$; in other words, if every left coset of J intersects G_1 or, equivalently, if every right coset of G_1 intersects J.

Then $G_1/G_1 \cap J$ is one-to-one continuously mapped onto G/J by assigning aJ to $a(G_1 \cap J)$ for all $a \in G_1$. This mapping becomes homeomorphic as soon as G and G_1 are locally compact, second countability Hausdorff spaces such that 4.8.4 applies.

63.1.7 A homogeneous space G/J is called *reduced* if there is no G_1 sub G acting transitively on G/J except G itself.

63.1.8 G may have several components. Its 1-component will usually be denoted by G_0. In the examples to be considered G_0 is isolated, that is, open, in G. Then $G_0/G_0 \cap J$ is open in $G/G_0 \cap J$, and if $G_0/G_0 \cap J$ is mapped into G/J by mapping $a\,(G_0 \cap J)$ $(a \in G_0)$ into aJ, then the image is open and connected, hence equals G_0/J. Applying 63.1.6 and remembering that the cosets of G_0 in G are the components of G, one gets the following:

$R = G/J$ is connected iff every component of G has a nonvoid intersection with J or, in other words, iff every left coset of J has a nonvoid intersection with G_0.

63.1.9 A homomorphism of G onto G' which takes J into a closed subgroup J' of G' and is locally topological on G extends to the homogeneous spaces G/J and G'/J' as a locally topological mapping.

On the other hand, leaving G unchanged, but replacing J by a larger, closed subgroup J' in which J is open, induces a locally topological mapping of G/J onto G'/J'.

These remarks may be summarized by stating that the local structure of R depends on the local structures of G and J only.

63.2 In the sequel attention must be paid to groups locally isomorphic to linear Lie groups. Their components are C^{an}-manifolds and their 1-components are C^{an}-groups (see 6.4).

Let G_1 be such a group and χ the given local isomorphism from the linear Lie group G to G_1. If no confusion is possible, in all local investigations near 1 G and G_1 will simply be identified. Among others, the infinitesimal algebra $\boldsymbol{G}$ of G will also be called infinitesimal algebra of G_1. Any $a \in G$ induces an automorphism in $\boldsymbol{G}$, to be denoted by $\tilde{a}$, since the inner automorphism induced by a near 1 is analytic by Theorem 11.4.

63.3.1 Let G be a group locally isomorphic to a linear Lie group, J a closed subgroup, $\boldsymbol{G}$, $\boldsymbol{J}$ the corresponding Lie algebras, and $\boldsymbol{N}$ a linear subspace of $\boldsymbol{G}$ such that

$$\boldsymbol{G} = \boldsymbol{J} + \boldsymbol{N}, \qquad \text{a direct sum.}$$

If $\boldsymbol{U}$ is a small $\boldsymbol{0}$-neighborhood in $\boldsymbol{N}$, then $\exp \boldsymbol{U}$ intersects xJ for x near 1 in exactly one point. The mapping φ_a, which assigns to xJ for x near a in G the only member of $a^{-1}xJ \cap \exp \boldsymbol{U}$, is an analytic mapping of an a-neighborhood in $R = G/J$ onto a 1-neighborhood in $\exp \boldsymbol{U}$. In the sequel R is supposed to be connected. Then with the φ_a as local presentations of R (see 5.6), R becomes an analytic manifold on which G acts as an analytic (nonlinear) Lie group.

Near $x_0 = J$, respectively 1, R can be identified with exp $\boldsymbol{U}$ by φ_1 or, for short, φ.

63.3.2 The behavior of J at x_0 and, more particularly, in the tangent space at x_0, is worth studying. Of course, J will act in the tangent space as a linear group.

The inner automorphisms $\tilde{a}$ of G as acting on $\boldsymbol{G}$ form a linear group acting on $\boldsymbol{G}$. Take $\boldsymbol{n} \in \boldsymbol{U}$. Then $\boldsymbol{n}$ is the tangent vector for $\tau = 0$ of the curve $\curlyvee_\tau$ exp $\tau\boldsymbol{n}$ in exp $\boldsymbol{U}$. Now $\tilde{j}$ $(j \in J)$ maps exp $\tau\boldsymbol{n}$ for small τ into

$$\tilde{j} \exp \tau\boldsymbol{n} = \exp \tau\tilde{j}\boldsymbol{n} = n_1(\tau)\, j_1(\tau),$$

where $n_1(\tau) \in \exp \boldsymbol{U}$, $j_1(\tau) \in J$, n_1 and j_1 being analytic functions. Differentiation at $\tau = 0$ shows

$$\tilde{j}\boldsymbol{n} = \boldsymbol{n}_1 + \boldsymbol{j}_1,$$

where

$$\boldsymbol{n}_1 = \left(\frac{d}{d\tau} n_1(\tau)\right)_{\tau=0}, \qquad \boldsymbol{j}_1 = \left(\frac{d}{d\tau} j_1(\tau)\right)_{\tau=0}.$$

Relating exp $\boldsymbol{U}$ to an x_0-neighborhood in R by φ^{-1}, one may consider $n_1(\tau)$ as the $\tilde{j}$-image of exp $\tau\boldsymbol{n}$ in R, and $\boldsymbol{n}_1$ as the $\tilde{j}$-image of $\boldsymbol{n}$ in the tangent space. It has been shown that

$$\boldsymbol{n}_1 = \tilde{j}\boldsymbol{n} \bmod \boldsymbol{J}.$$

Therefore the action of the stability group J in the tangent space of R at x_0 is described by that of the representation of J as a subgroup of Int $\boldsymbol{G}$, induced in $\boldsymbol{G}$ mod $\boldsymbol{J}$.

Note, however, that this description of J need not be exhaustive. Nontrivial $\tilde{j}$ $(j \in J)$ may be trivial on the tangent space. An example: the projective group on the straight line—the translations, that is, the projectivities with a double fixpoint at infinity, induce the identity mapping in the tangent space at infinity.

In such cases the behavior of J can be fully described with tangent spaces of higher differential order.

63.3.3 Suppose now that $\boldsymbol{N}$ in 63.3.1 can be chosen to be invariant under the $\tilde{j}(j \in J)$. This is possible when J is compact or semisimple and connected; then the representation of J in $\boldsymbol{G}$ as a subgroup of Int $\boldsymbol{G}$ is conducible, and $\boldsymbol{J}$, being invariant under $\tilde{j}$ $(j \in J)$, has a linear complement that is also invariant.

In this case the behavior of j in R is fully described by that of $\tilde{j}$ in $\boldsymbol{N}$ because $\tilde{j}$, considered as acting on R, is determined by its action on any nonvoid open set of R (which, with its inverse, is analytic). The representation of J in $\boldsymbol{N}$ by $\curlyvee_j \tilde{j}$ is faithful because it is so on R. Identifying R locally with $\boldsymbol{N}$, one may say that J behaves as a linear group near x_0.

63.3.4 In terms of fiber spaces, exp U, as introduced in 63.3.2, is a local cross section near 1 of the fibering of G by the J-cosets, as is $U_a = a \exp U$ near a for every $a \in G$. These cross sections can be used to relate the fundamental groups $\Phi(J)$, $\Phi(G)$, and $\Phi(R)$.

Theorem Let G be connected and locally isomorphic to a linear Lie group, let J be connected closed sub G, let j be the embedding of J in G, and $k = \curlyvee_a aJ$. Then the sequence of (additively written) fundamental groups

$$\Phi(J) \overset{j}{\to} \Phi(G) \overset{k}{\to} \Phi(R) \to \{0\}$$

is exact.

Proof Let U_a be as before. Then $k|_{U_a}$ is homeomorphic and its inverse lifts a neighborhood of ka onto U_a. It can first be used for piecewise and then for total lifting of any given path $w \in \mathscr{W}_{ka}(R)$ into a path $w' \in \mathscr{W}_a(G)$. Then $kw' = w$.

Let $\mathscr{W}_{k1}(R)$ and $\mathscr{W}_1(G)$ be topologized in an obvious way; k (more precisely left multiplication by k) maps $\mathscr{W}_1(G)$ continuously onto $\mathscr{W}_{k1}(R)$. For any $w \in \mathscr{W}_1(G)$ let V_w be the set of $w' \in \mathscr{W}_1(G)$ with $w'(\tau) \in U_{w(\tau)}$ for all τ. Then $k|_{V_w}$ is homeomorphic, and its inverse lifts a neighborhood of kw onto V_w. Again any path in $\mathscr{W}_{k1}(R)$ starting at kw can be lifted into a path in $\mathscr{W}_1(G)$ starting at w.

To return to the statements of the theorem, it is evident that for the fundamental groups kj is the null-homomorphism. One must still prove first that k is onto and second, that the kernel of k is contained in $\Phi(J)$.

Let a closed path $w \in \mathscr{W}_1{}^1(R)$ be given. It is lifted into a path $w' \in \mathscr{W}_1(G)$, which necessarily finishes in J. Since J is connected, w' can be lengthened by a path within J to get a closed path $w'' \in \mathscr{W}_1{}^1(G)$ such that kw'' is homotopic with the given w. This proves the first part.

Now let $w_0' \in \mathscr{W}_1{}^1(G)$ be given such that kw_0' is homotopically trivial. This means the existence of a path $\curlyvee_\sigma w_\sigma$ on $\mathscr{W}_{k1}^{k1}(R)$ such that $w_0 = kw_0'$ and $w_1(\tau) = k1$ for all τ. This path is lifted into a path $\curlyvee_\sigma w_\sigma'$ on $\mathscr{W}_1(G)$. Then $w_1'(\tau)$, $w_\sigma'(1) \in J$ for all τ, σ. By 28.11 w_0' is homotopic with $w_1' \circ \curlyvee_\sigma w_\sigma'(1)$, which lies in J. This proves the second part.

63.4–6. Geodesics

63.4. Definition A *differential* metric on a real C^2-manifold R assigns to the tangent space of R at any point p of R an inner product, depending twice continuously differentiably on p.

The inner product is supposed to possess the usual properties, positive definiteness included.

A C^2-manifold with a differential metric is called a *Riemannian* space.

By integration the notion of vector length in the tangent spaces extends to a notion of curve length for C^1-curves, invariant under weakly monotonic parameter change. After such a change any C^1-curve may be supposed to have a vanishing tangent vector at its beginning and end. Two such curves, the second starting where the first ends, can be put together to form a C^1-curve, with additivity of the curve length.

The *distance* $\delta(p, q)$ of two points p, q of R is defined as the lower bound of the lengths of C^1-curves joining p and q. Obviously it is nonnegative symmetric, and from the foregoing remarks it follows that it fulfills the triangle inequality. It will soon become clear that even δ fulfills the positiveness requirement of a metric and that the topology induced in R by the metric δ coincides with the original topology of R as a manifold.

Definition A *geodesic* φ is a C^1-mapping of an interval I of real numbers into R with the following property: for any $\tau \in I$ there is an $\varepsilon > 0$ such that $\tau' \in I$ and $|\tau - \tau'| < \varepsilon$ imply $\delta(\varphi(\tau), \varphi(\tau')) = |\tau - \tau'|$.

Geodesics arising from a given one by a monotonic parameter change or by extending or restricting the interval of definition are often considered *essentially equal.*

The classical way of finding geodesics is to look for shortest curves. Indeed, compared with other C^1-curves, any partial curve of a shortest curve is still a shortest curve between its endpoints, and, as will be seen, any shortest curve arises from a geodesic by a suitable reparametrization. On the other hand, it is evident that a sufficiently small arc of geodesic around a given parameter value is a shortest curve.

The variational approach to shortest curves will be sketched briefly.

The differential metric is transferred from an open neighborhood R_0 of p_0 in R to a 0-neighborhood E_0 in real cartesian n-space E by a C^2-homeomorphism f with nondegenerate gradient and $fp_0 = 0$. The discussion takes place in E_0. At a point x of E_0 the inner product of two tangent vectors

$$dx = \ulcorner dx_1, \ldots, dx_n \urcorner, \qquad dy = \ulcorner dy_1, \ldots, dy_n \urcorner$$

is given by

$$\langle dx, dy \rangle_x = \sum_{ij} g_{ij}(x)\, dx_i\, dy_j,$$

where $\ulcorner g_{ij}(x) \urcorner_{i,j=1}^{n}$ is a positive definite symmetric matrix, depending twice continuously differentiably on x. The *length* of a C^1-curve φ in E_0 from 0 to γ is given by

63.4.1 $$L_\gamma(\varphi) = \int_0^\gamma \left(\sum_{ij} g_{ij}(\varphi(\tau))\, \varphi_i'(\tau)\, \varphi_j'(\tau) \right)^{1/2} d\tau.$$

(Generally φ' now denotes the derivative of φ.)

The curve length is invariant under weakly monotonic C^1-changes of the parameter of φ.

To compare curve lengths, a family of C^2-curves φ^σ is studied; it is defined by a C^2-mapping Φ of a rectangle $\uparrow_{\ulcorner \tau, \sigma \urcorner} (0 \leqslant \tau \leqslant \alpha \wedge |\sigma| \leqslant \beta)$ of the cartesian 2-space into E_0 such that

$$\Phi(0,0) = 0,$$

63.4.2 $$\langle \varphi'(\tau), \varphi'(\tau) \rangle_{\varphi(\tau)} = 1 \quad \text{for} \quad 0 \leqslant \tau \leqslant \alpha,$$

where it is understood that

$$\varphi^\sigma = \curlyvee_\tau \Phi(\tau, \sigma),$$
$$\varphi = \varphi^0.$$

Furthermore ϑ is defined by

63.4.3 $$\vartheta(\tau) = \left(\frac{\partial \Phi(\tau, \sigma)}{\partial \sigma} \right)_{\sigma = 0},$$

and the coordinates of the introduced functions are indicated by subscripts in the usual way.

An easy calculation that involves a partial integration leads to the formula

63.4.4 $$\left(\frac{d}{d\sigma} \curlyvee_\sigma L_t(\varphi^\sigma) \right)_{\sigma=0} = \langle \varphi'(t), \vartheta(t) \rangle_{\varphi(t)} + \int_0^t \sum_k \left(\frac{1}{2} \sum_{ij} g_{ij,k}\, \varphi_i' \varphi_j' - \frac{d}{d\tau} \sum_i g_{ik}\, \varphi_i' \right) \vartheta_k \, d\tau,$$

where $g_{ij,k}$ is the partial derivative of g_{ij} in the kth coordinate and where, under the integration sign, the arguments τ, respectively, $\varphi(\tau)$, have to be read in $\varphi_i', \varphi_j', \vartheta_k$, respectively, g_{ik}, $g_{ij,k}$.

The coefficient of ϑ_k under the integration sign can also be written as

63.4.5 $$D_k(\varphi) = -\sum_i g_{ik}\, \varphi_i'' + \tfrac{1}{2} \sum_{ij} (g_{ij,k} - g_{jk,i} - g_{ki,j})\, \varphi_i' \varphi_j',$$

where φ_i'' is the second derivative of φ_i.

To find a necessary condition on $\curlyvee_{0 \leqslant \tau \leqslant t} \varphi(\tau)$ being a shortest curve, a family of curves with the same endpoint is chosen; that is,

$$\Phi(t, \sigma) \text{ independent of } \sigma \text{ for some fixed } t.$$

Then $\vartheta(t) = 0$, which causes the first summand in 63.4.4 to vanish.

For the length of $\Upsilon_{0\leqslant\tau\leqslant t}\varphi(\tau)$ to be minimal, one must have

$$\left(\frac{d}{d\sigma}\Upsilon_\sigma L_t(\varphi^\sigma)\right)_{\sigma=0} = 0.$$

By suitable choices of that family ϑ_k can be prescribed with such a degree of freedom that, as a necessary condition for φ to be a shortest curve, one gets

63.4.6 $$D_k(\varphi) = 0 \qquad \text{for all} \quad k.$$

This is now considered as a second-order system of differential equations to be solved with respect to φ under the initial condition

$$\varphi(0) = 0, \qquad \varphi'(0) = a,$$

where a is a given vector. Its (unique) solution is φ_a. Clearly

$$\varphi_{\beta a}(\tau) = \varphi_a(\beta\tau)$$

for real β as far as the expressions make sense; the φ_a will turn out to be shortest curves.

One can easily verify that

$$\frac{d}{d\tau}\sum g_{ij}\varphi'_{a,i}\varphi'_{a,j} = 0$$

because of the differential equations 63.4.6 (see also 63.4.5); hence

$$\langle\varphi'_a(\tau), \varphi'_a(\tau)\rangle_{\varphi_a(\tau)} = \langle a, a\rangle_0.$$

Therefore, if $\langle a,a\rangle_0 = 1$, then

63.4.7 $$L_t(\varphi_a) = t.$$

If E_0 has been chosen small enough, it will be smoothly covered by the solutions φ_a of 63.4.6 in the following sense. Near 0

$$\sigma = \Upsilon_a \varphi_a(1)$$

is C^2 with $\operatorname{grad}_0 \sigma = 1$, hence C^2-homeomorphic near 0. Since, for $a \neq 0$,

$$\Upsilon_a \ulcorner |a|, |a|^{-1} a \urcorner$$

is analytically invertible, it follows that for E_0 small enough and $x \in E_0 \setminus \{0\}$ there is one positive number $\delta(x)$ and one vector $c(x)$ with $\langle c(x), c(x)\rangle_0 = 1$ such that

63.4.8 $$\varphi_{c(x)}(\delta(x)) = x$$

and $\ulcorner \delta, c \urcorner$ is a C^2-homeomorphic mapping with a nondegenerate gradient.

In the sequel E_0 is assumed to fulfill this requirement.

Note that $\uparrow_x (\delta(x) = \rho)$ may then be considered a C^2-manifold (for $\rho > 0$).
The previously introduced family of curves is now specialized to consist of curves φ_a:

63.4.9 $$\Phi(\tau, \sigma) = \varphi_{a(\sigma)}(\tau) \qquad \text{for} \quad 0 \leqslant \tau \leqslant t,$$

where $\langle a(\sigma), a(\sigma)\rangle_0 = 1$ for all σ ($|\sigma| \leqslant$ some β) and $a(\sigma)$ is a C^2-function of σ. Then

63.4.10 $$L_t(\varphi_{a(\sigma)}) = t.$$

The derivative with respect to σ vanishes, and in 63.4.4 the second summand on the right side vanishes as well, since φ_a fulfills 63.4.6 if substituted for φ. This shows that

63.4.11 $$\langle \varphi'_{a(0)}(t), \vartheta(t)\rangle_{\varphi_{a(0)}(t)} = 0,$$

where

$$\vartheta(t) = \left(\frac{d}{d\sigma} \curlyvee_\sigma \varphi_{a(\sigma)}(t)\right)_{\sigma=0}$$

This means that every curve φ_a with $\langle a, a\rangle_0 = 1$ meets the surface $\uparrow_x (\delta(x) = t)$ at $\varphi_a(t)$ orthogonally in the sense of the inner product $\langle \ldots, \ldots\rangle$.

The time has come to compare an arbitrary C^1-curve η in E_0, starting at 0, with the curves φ_a. Such a curve η may be assumed in the form

$$\eta(\tau) = \varphi_{a(\tau)}(\varepsilon(\tau)) \qquad \text{for} \quad \tau > 0,$$

where the $a(\tau)$ are vectors with $\langle a(\tau), a(\tau)\rangle_0 = 1$, $\varepsilon(\tau) \geqslant 0$, and $\ulcorner a(\tau), \varepsilon(\tau)\urcorner$ is a C^1-function of τ. Since shortest curves are wanted, one may even suppose that

$$\varepsilon(\tau) > 0 \qquad \text{for} \quad \tau > 0.$$

Now

$$\left(\frac{d\eta}{d\tau}\right)_{\tau=t} = \left(\frac{d}{d\tau} \curlyvee_\tau \varphi_{a(\tau)}(\varepsilon(t))\right)_{\tau=t} + \left(\frac{d\varphi_{a(t)}(\varepsilon(\tau))}{d\tau}\right)_{\tau=t}$$

According to 63.4.11, the two summands are orthogonal to each other in the sense of the inner product $\langle \ldots, \ldots\rangle$ at $\eta(t)$. Hence

$$\langle \eta'(t), \eta'(t)\rangle_{\eta(t)} \geqslant \left(\frac{d\varepsilon(\tau)}{d\tau}\right)^2_{\tau=t},$$

with the equality sign only if

$$a'(t) = 0.$$

Integrating this inequality, one gets

$$L_t(\eta) \geqslant \int_0^t |\varepsilon'(\tau)|\, d\tau \geqslant \varepsilon(t),$$

with equality signs only if η is such that $a(\tau)$ is constant and ε is weakly monotonic, that is, if η has arisen from some φ_a by a weakly monotonic parameter change.

This shows that for C^1-curves η with $\eta(0)=0$, $\eta(t)=\varphi_a(t)$, where $\langle a,a\rangle_0 = 1$:

63.4.12 $$\inf_\eta L_t(\eta) = t = L_t(\varphi_a).$$

The C^1-curves used in the definition of distance on R were allowed to leave the neighborhood R_0 of p_0. It is easily seen that this does not lower the infimum. Then by 63.4.12 it follows that the f-originals of the φ_a are geodesics on R. From the remark on the equality signs it follows that any shortest C^1-curve in E_0 starting at 0 coincides with some reparametrized φ_a.

The notation φ_a, or, more completely, $\varphi_{p,a}$, is now used on R to indicate a geodesic starting at p, with the tangent vector a of unit length. The result is summarized in the following:

63.4.13. Proposition Geodesics are C^2-curves. Given a point p of R and a vector a of unit length in the tangent space of R at p, there is an essentially unique geodesic $\varphi_{p,a}$ with $\varphi_{p,a}(0)=p$, $\varphi'_{p,a}(0)=a$. There is an $\varepsilon_p > 0$ such that there is a unique geodesic starting from p and finishing at x of length $\delta(p,x)$ as long as $\delta(p,x) < \varepsilon_p$. On a compact set of p such an ε_p may be chosen as a constant. Then $\varphi_{p,a}(\tau)$ depends on the data p, a, and τ in a C^2-fashion.

From this it is clear that the topology of R as a manifold coincides with that induced by the metric.

63.4.14. Proposition The mapping

$$\sigma = \curlyvee_a \varphi_{p,a}(1)$$

of a sufficiently small 0-neighborhood of the tangent space at p into R is a C^2-homeomorphism whose gradient at 0 is the identity.

This mapping is closely akin to the exponential mapping of infinitesimal Lie algebras into their groups. Its inverse is called the *geodesic mapping* (at p). It can be used to identify near p the Riemannian space with its tangent space at p in a canonical way.

63.4.15 If, for a moment, σ is used to identify R near p with its tangent space, the geodesics through p (=0) are rectilinear. The C^2-data of the differential equation for geodesics lead to a C^2-family of solutions. Let the geodesic of length $|c|$ starting at a with a tangent vector $c/|c|$ have its endpoint at $\vartheta(a,c)$; then ϑ is C^2, $\vartheta(0,c)=c$, $\vartheta(a,0)=a$; hence

$$\vartheta(a,c)=a+c+\cdots,$$

where the dots mean something of an order higher than $|a|+|c|$. Putting $a'=\vartheta(a,c)$ and solving with respect to c, one gets

$$c=a'-a+\cdots,$$

where the dots mean something of an order higher than $|a|+|a'|$. Since $|c|=\delta(a,a')$, one gets

$$\lim\frac{\delta(a,a')}{|a-a'|}=1 \qquad \text{if} \quad \lim a=\lim a'=0.$$

Therefore up to higher order terms the Riemannian metric in R and the metric induced by the inner product in the tangent space at p are identified by σ.

63.5.1 If a metric space $\ulcorner R,\delta\urcorner$ is known to have arisen from an unknown differential metric, as defined in the beginning, the C^2-structure of R and its differential metric are (uniquely) recovered as follows:

For $p\in R$ choose $\gamma>0$ such that unique geodesic joining prevails for pairs of points in the closed γ-ball U around p. In U the midpoint z of a pair x, y (i.e., $\delta(x,z)=\delta(y,z)=\frac{1}{2}\,\delta(x,y)$) is uniquely determined by δ. Given $q\in R$ with $\delta(p,q)=\gamma$, define a continuous mapping ${}^q\varphi$ of $\uparrow_\tau$ $(0\leqslant\tau\leqslant\gamma)$ into R by the requirements ${}^q\varphi(0)=p$, ${}^q\varphi(\gamma)=q$; ${}^q\varphi(\frac{1}{2}(\tau_1+\tau_2))=$ midpoint of ${}^q\varphi(\tau_1)$ and ${}^q\varphi(\tau_2)$ (its existence is clear). The $\curlyvee_\tau {}^q\varphi(\alpha\tau)$ (as far as defined), with $q\in R$, $\delta(p,q)=\gamma$, $\alpha\geqslant 0$, form a set Φ_p. The meaning of Φ_p becomes clear if one maps $a\in\Phi_p$ into its tangent vector at $\tau=0$, denoted by κa, according to the C^2-structure from which $\ulcorner R,\delta\urcorner$ has been derived. The existence of the metric δ' in Φ_p, defined by

$$\delta'(a,b)=\lim_{\tau=0}\tau^{-1}\,\delta(a(\tau),b(\tau)),$$

then becomes clear, as does its identification by κ with the metric in the tangent space at p, from which $\ulcorner R,\delta\urcorner$ has arisen (see 63.4.15). In a linear space with a metric derived from an inner product the linear structure is determined by the metric and the origin, as is the inner product. In this way Φ_p is uniquely provided with a structure of linear space with inner product, which by κ is identified with that in the tangent space at p of $\ulcorner R,\delta\urcorner$. Finally the C^2-structure of R is recovered by $\curlyvee_{\varphi\in\Phi_p}\varphi(1)$ (as far as defined) as a local presentation of R near p; the differential metric at p is recovered as the metric of Φ_p.

The foregoing leads to a proposition and a remark:

Proposition The differential metric of a Riemannian space is uniquely determined by its metric.

Remark In the definition of geodesic "C^1-mapping" can be weakened to "continuous mapping."

63.5.2 The *direct product of Riemannian spaces* $R^{(i)}$ $(i = 1,2)$ is easily defined as the direct product of the underlying C^2-manifolds, where the tangent space at $\ulcorner p^{(1)}, p^{(2)} \urcorner$ and the inner product in it are the direct sum of those at $p^{(i)} \in R^{(i)}$ $(i = 1,2)$.

On the other hand, a *metric product* $\ulcorner R, \delta \urcorner$ of the resulting metric spaces $\ulcorner R^{(i)}, \delta^{(i)} \urcorner$ $(i = 1,2)$ is formed by putting for $p^{(i)}, q^{(i)} \in R^{(i)}$

$$\delta(\ulcorner p^{(1)}, p^{(2)} \urcorner, \ulcorner q^{(1)}, q^{(2)} \urcorner) = (\delta^{(1)}(p^{(1)}, q^{(1)})^2 + \delta^{(2)}(p^{(2)}, q^{(2)})^2)^{1/2}.$$

As a matter of fact, $\ulcorner R, \delta \urcorner$ is just the metric space resulting from the direct product of the $R^{(i)}$.

Indeed, this easily follows from the differential equation for shortest lines in R. It splits in those with respect to the $R^{(i)}$ such that if $\varphi^{(i)}$ is a solution for $R^{(i)}$ $(i = 1,2)$, then $\curlyvee_t \ulcorner \varphi^{(1)}(t), \varphi^{(2)}(t) \urcorner$ is one for R.

63.6 An important tool in global research on Riemannian spaces is the postulate of

Geodesic Latitude Any geodesic can be extended to one defined on the whole set of reals.

This property will now be assumed.

Proposition Under geodesic latitude, any pair p, q of points of R can be joined by a geodesic of length $\delta(p, q)$, and any bounded closed subset of R is compact.

Proof Let R_p be the set of $x \in R$ such that there is a geodesic of length $\delta(p, x)$ from p to x.

The first step is to show the following:

63.6.1 R_p is closed and every bounded closed subset of R_p is compact or, equivalently,

63.6.2 a bounded sequence $x_1, x_2, \ldots$ from R_p accumulates somewhere in R_p.

Such a sequence may be supposed to give the $\gamma_i = \delta(p, x_i)$ a limit γ. There is a geodesic φ_i such that $\varphi_i(0) = p$, $\varphi_i(\gamma_i) = x_i$. Now the sequence of $((d/d\tau)\,\varphi_i(\tau))_0$ may also be supposed to converge. The limit is the tangent vector at 0 of a geodesic φ with $\varphi(0) = p$. By geodesic latitude the geodesic φ may be extended for all $\tau \geqslant 0$. Proposition 63.4.13 implies that $\lim x_i = \lim \varphi_i(\gamma_i) = \varphi(\gamma) = x$, say. Further, $\delta(p,x) = \lim\ \delta(p,x_i) = \lim\ \gamma_i = \gamma$. This proves the assertion $\lim x_i = x \in R_p$.

The next step is to show that

63.6.3 $$R_p = R.$$

Let S_α be the set of x with $\delta(p,x) \leqslant \alpha$ and let γ be maximal such that $S_\gamma \subset R_p$. If $R_p \neq R$, then $\gamma < \infty$. S_γ is a closed bounded subset of R_p and thus compact. According to Proposition 63.4.13, let $\varepsilon > 0$ be chosen such that for $z \in S_\gamma$ and $\delta(z,x) \leqslant \varepsilon$ there is a geodesic of length $\delta(z,x)$ from z to x.

If $R_p \neq R$, then there is an $x \notin R_p$ with $\delta(p,x) < \gamma + \frac{1}{2}\varepsilon$. Let φ be a curve of length $< \gamma + \varepsilon$ that joins p to x. It leaves S_γ at some point y. Its length from p to y is $\geqslant \gamma$; therefore, from y to x it is $< \varepsilon$. Let $z \in S_\gamma$ be closest to x. Still $\delta(x,z) < \varepsilon$. The defining property of ε guarantees a geodesic φ'' of length $\delta(x,z)$ from z to x; it follows that $\delta(p,z) = \gamma$. The definition of R_p gives a geodesic φ' of length $\delta(p,z)$ from p to z. When put together they produce a curve of length $\gamma + \delta(z,x)$ joining p to x. A shorter connection would leave S_γ at a point closer to x than z was. Therefore the length of the constructed curve is just $\delta(p,x)$. It is a geodesic of length $\delta(p,x)$ that contradicts the assumption $x \notin R_p$.

This proves 63.6.3 and, together with 63.6.1, the proposition.

63.7–9. Isometries

63.7 Let R, R' be Riemannian spaces and f an isometry of R into R', which according to 63.5.1, is C^2. For $p \in R$, $p' = fp$, let σ_p, $\sigma_{p'}$ be the local mappings σ (see 63.4.14) of the tangent spaces at p, p' into R, R', respectively. Then the mapping of tangent spaces $\text{grad}_p f$, induced by f, is isometric according to 63.5.1. Furthermore,

$$f\sigma_p = \sigma_{p'}\,\text{grad}_p\, f.$$

Moreover, near p the isometry of R into R' is determined by the induced mapping of the tangent space at p.

Let f be an autometry of R, leaving invariant p and the vectors of a basis of the tangent space at p. Then f is the identity over all R.

Indeed, $\text{grad}_p f$ is the identity on the tangent space at p; hence f is so in a neighborhood of p. Let U be the maximal *open* subset of R, where f is the identity. Then f is the identity on $\bar{U}$. Let $q \in \bar{U}$. Then $\text{grad}_q f$ is the identity on an open subset of the tangent space at q, hence over all this tangent space. Therefore f is so in a neighborhood of q. So $q \in U$, $\bar{U} \subset U$, hence $U = R$.

Let f be an autometry of R leaving invariant the points p,q between which the shortest geodesic is essentially unique. Then f leaves invariant every point of this geodesic as well as its tangent vector at p.

From this the proposition follows easily:

Proposition Let I be the set of isometries of the Riemannian spaces R into R'. There is a finite subset N of R such that

any element of I is determined by its behavior on N,

if R, R' enjoy geodesic latitude, the convergence on N of a sequence from I implies its uniform convergence on every compact subset of R.

Definition Aut R is the *group of autometries* of R topologized by the topology of uniform convergence on every compact subset of R or, equivalently, if R is a Riemannian space enjoying geodesic latitude, by the topology of convergence on a suitably chosen finite set N.

A C^2-structure of Aut R, if existent, is understood to be induced by the C^2-structure of R in the same way as the topology of Aut R is by that of R.

63.8.1. Proposition Geodesic latitude supposed, the group of autometries of R leaving p invariant is compact, as is the group induced in the tangent space at p; Aut R is locally compact and fulfills second countability.

This follows easily from the local compactness and second countability of R and the compactness of distance spheres of R if, in the terminology of Proposition 63.7, Aut R is interpreted as a closed subset of R^N.

63.8.2 If, moreover, Aut R is transitive and J is its stability group at p, then 4.8.4 can be applied. Then:

Proposition If R enjoys geodesic latitude and Aut R is transitive, then Aut R/J as a homogeneous space can be identified with R by identifying gJ with gp ($g \in$ Aut R).

63.9 If R enjoys geodesic latitude, then Aut R is locally C^2-isomorphic with a linear Lie group, the C^2-structure of Aut R being according to Definition 63.7.

This fact will not be proved. When it is needed, it will be postulated.

63.10. Historical Note Homogeneous spaces go back to H. von Helmholtz, F. Klein, and S. Lie. Proposition 63.6 was proved by H. Hopf and W. Rinow [*Comment. Helvet.* **3**, 209–225 (1931)]. The present proof is somewhat simpler. The local Lie character of Aut R was proved by S. B. Myer and N. Steenrod [*Ann. Math.* **40**, 400–416 (1939)].

64. SYMMETRIC SPACES

64.1.1. Definition A *reflection* s_p in p in a Riemannian space R is an autometric mapping by which the geodesics through p are inverted (φ goes into $\Upsilon_\tau \varphi(-\tau)$ if φ is a geodesic with $\varphi(0)=p$.

Int R is the topological group of even products of reflections s_p ($p \in R$), considered as a subgroup of Aut R.

Note that possibly Int $R=\{1\}$.

Proposition For any $g \in$ Aut R, $gs_p g^{-1}$ is a reflection in gp. Int R is normal in Aut R.

64.1.2 Suppose that R enjoys a reflection s_p in each of its points p. Then a geodesic in R can be extended again and again by reflecting it in one of its points near a supposed endpoint. Therefore geodesic latitude is guaranteed. p, q have a midpoint m on a joining geodesic of length $\delta(p, q)$. Now $s_m s_p$ maps p into q. So Int R is transitive. It is connected since $s_{p_1} s_{p_2} \cdots s_{p_{2k}}$ moves to the identity if all p_i move to some fixed p. In the C^2-structure of Aut R, as meant by Definition 63.7, Int R is even C^2-connected.

In a small closed α-ball U in R around p take for every q the uniquely determined midpoint m of the geodesic of length $\delta(p, q)$ from p to q and define $t(q)=s_m s_p$. Then t maps U C^2-homeomorphically. Let J be the stability group of Int R at p. Then $t(U)$ is a local cross section of the set of J-cosets in Int R. Locally Int R and the topological product of U and J are homeomorphic. So local compactness may be transferred from J to Int R.

In any case, by 63.9 (if taken for granted) and 11.7, Int R, which is C^2-connected, becomes in its natural topology locally isomorphic with a linear Lie group. As soon as Int R is known to be locally compact in the topology inherited from Aut R, it follows from Propositions 4.8.7 and 4.13 that the natural topology of Int R is that induced by Aut R and that Int R is closed in Aut R. In 64.8 it will be shown that J is compact; hence Int R will be locally compact. Meanwhile, Int R, provided with its natural topology, will be denoted by $\mathrm{Int}^0 R$ instead.

The foregoing suggests the following definition.

Definition A *symmetric space* (Spa Sym) is a Riemannian space R with reflections s_p in all points $p \in R$ and such that Int R is the continuous image by means of the identity mapping of a connected group $\mathrm{Int}^0 R$ which is locally isomorphic with a linear Lie group.

It is the aim of the present section to classify symmetric spaces, at least locally. With a view to this task, it is useful to note that:

the direct product of symmetric spaces R_i is again a symmetric space R and then $\mathrm{Int}^0 R$ may be considered as the direct product of the $\mathrm{Int}^0 R_i$.

The following has been proved:

Proposition A symmetric space R possesses geodesic latitude. Any pair of points p, q in R can be joined by a geodesic of length $\delta(p, q)$. For any p, s_p is unique. Any closed bounded set in R is compact. The stability group J of $\mathrm{Int}^0 R$ at p is bounded (as acting in R as well as in the tangent space at p). $\mathrm{Int}^0 R/J$ can be identified with R by identifying gJ with gp after the choice of a point $p \in R$.

64.1.3 Wrappings of Riemannian spaces can obviously be performed by means of local isometries. The geodesics are wrapped by geodesics, and in universal wrappings autometries and reflections are wrapped by autometries and reflections, respectively. Universal wrappings of symmetric spaces are again symmetric spaces.

64.2 Let $R \in$ Spa Sym. Put, for short, $\mathrm{Int}^0 R = F$.

Let $\boldsymbol{F}, \boldsymbol{J}$ be the infinitesimal algebras of F, J (see the conventions in 63.2).

$\tilde{s}_p$ induces an automorphism T of F and $\boldsymbol{F}$.

$$j s_p j^{-1} = s_{jp} = s_p \qquad \text{for} \quad j \in J.$$

So $T = \tilde{s}_p$ leaves J and $\boldsymbol{J}$ elementwise invariant.

The closure $\bar{J}$ of J, taken in Int R, is compact; any linear representation of $\bar{J}$ is conducible. The adjoint action of J on $\boldsymbol{F}$ extends to $\bar{J}$; it is also conducible, with $\boldsymbol{J}$ as an invariant subspace. Therefore there is a linear complement $\boldsymbol{N}$ such that

$$\boldsymbol{F} = \boldsymbol{J} + \boldsymbol{N}, \qquad \boldsymbol{J} \cap \boldsymbol{N} = \{\boldsymbol{0}\}, \qquad [\boldsymbol{J}, \boldsymbol{N}] \subset \boldsymbol{N}.$$

By identifying fp with fJ ($f \in F$), R is known to be identified with F/J and the tangent space at p with $\boldsymbol{N}$ (see 63.3). So T behaves as the identity on $\boldsymbol{J}$ and as the scalar multiplier -1 on $\boldsymbol{N}$. Furthermore, the adjoint action of J on $\boldsymbol{N}$ is again bounded.

$\exp \boldsymbol{N}$ generates a group F', which will be shown to coincide with F. Any $f \in F$ near 1 is in $(\exp \boldsymbol{N})J$. Because of the invariance of $\exp \boldsymbol{N}$ under $\tilde{j}$ ($j \in J$), one gets

$$(\exp \boldsymbol{N})J \cdot (\exp \boldsymbol{N})J \subset (\exp \boldsymbol{N})(\exp \boldsymbol{N})J.$$

Continuing in this way, one establishes

$$F \subset F'J.$$

Thus any $f \in F$ can be written as $f'j$ with $f' \in F', j \in J$. Now $Tf^{-1} = j^{-1}Tf'^{-1}$ where $Tf'^{-1} \in F'$ because of $TF' \subset F'$. Therefore $f(Tf^{-1}) = f'j \cdot j^{-1}Tf'^{-1} \in F'$.

F is generated by the $f s_p f^{-1} \cdot f_1 s_p f_1^{-1} = f(\tilde{s}_p f^{-1}) \cdot (\tilde{s}_p f_1) f_1^{-1} = f(Tf^{-1}) \cdot (Tf_1 \cdot f_1^{-1}) \in F'$ (for f, $f_1 \in F$). So $F \subset F' \subset F$, which proves the assertion.

The foregoing is summarized in the following theorem.

Theorem Up to isomorphism $R \in$ Spa Sym can be obtained from a group G by means of an involutory† automorphism T as a homogeneous space G/J, where G, J, T fulfill the following conditions:

64.2.1 G is connected and locally isomorphic with a linear Lie group, with the infinitesimal algebra $\boldsymbol{G}$.

64.2.2 J is closed sub G, with the infinitesimal algebra $\boldsymbol{J}$. It contains no normal subgroup of G except $\{1\}$.

64.2.3 T leaves J and $\boldsymbol{J}$ elementwise invariant.

64.2.4 $\boldsymbol{G} = \boldsymbol{J} + \boldsymbol{N}$, where $T\boldsymbol{j} = \boldsymbol{j}$ for $\boldsymbol{j} \in \boldsymbol{J}$ and $T\boldsymbol{n} = -\boldsymbol{n}$ for $\boldsymbol{n} \in \boldsymbol{N}$.

64.2.5 The adjoint action of J on $\boldsymbol{N}$ is bounded.

64.2.6 G is generated by $\exp \boldsymbol{N}$.

64.2.7
$$G = \mathrm{Int}^0 R.$$

One should note, as the reader may already have done, that a situation as in 64.2.2–6 is obtained by starting from $\boldsymbol{G}$, C, C_{un}, as in the classification dressings in 51.17 with $C \neq C_{\mathrm{un}}$, and taking CC_{un} for T, $G_{C,\mathrm{un}}$ for J, G_C or G_{un} for G, with, for instance, $\boldsymbol{G}$, as in 51.17, either simple or the direct sum of two simple summands interchanged by T, and G_{un} centerfree.

64.3 Conversely, it will be shown how symmetric spaces can be constructed from these data.

64.3.1. Proposition Under the conditions in 64.2.1–2, if $\boldsymbol{G} = \boldsymbol{J} + \boldsymbol{N}$, a direct sum as linear spaces, $[\boldsymbol{J}, \boldsymbol{N}] \subset \boldsymbol{N}$, and 64.2.5 is fulfilled, then a G-invariant differential metric can be imposed on $R = G/J$.

Proof By 63.3.3 the tangent space of R at $p = J$ can be identified with $\boldsymbol{N}$ on which $j \in J$ acts as $\tilde{j}$.

Let $E \in$ Spa Lin, L sub Aut E, L bounded. Then the closure $\bar{L}$ of L in End E is compact. There is a γ such that $|\det a| \leqslant \gamma$ for all $a \in L$. Then $|\det a| \geqslant \gamma^{-1}$ as well, thus $\bar{L}$ sub Aut E. Therefore the closure of L is a compact linear group. This is applied to $\tilde{J}|_{\boldsymbol{N}}$, $\boldsymbol{N}$ instead of L, E.

From an arbitrarily assumed inner product $(\ldots, \ldots)$ in $\boldsymbol{N}$ a $\tilde{J}$-invariant product is obtained by averaging $\Upsilon_k \Upsilon \ulcorner_{\boldsymbol{n}_1, \boldsymbol{n}_2} \urcorner (k\boldsymbol{n}_1, k\boldsymbol{n}_2)$, with k running in the (compact) closure of $\tilde{J}|_{\boldsymbol{N}}$. (See also 35.1.) By left multiplication it is carried to

† As a useful convention, the mapping of a one-point set onto itself is considered involutory.

the other tangent spaces of R. This transfer is unambiguous, since if $gp = g_1 p$, then $g_1 = gj$ with a $j \in J$ leaving the inner product invariant. So R becomes Riemannian with $G \subset \text{Aut } R$.

Remark Under the conditions 64.2.1–5 a G-invariant differential metric can be imposed on R. Indeed, if $\boldsymbol{j} \in \boldsymbol{J}$, $\boldsymbol{n} \in \boldsymbol{N}$, then $T[\boldsymbol{j},\boldsymbol{n}] = [T\boldsymbol{j}, T\boldsymbol{n}] = -[\boldsymbol{j},\boldsymbol{n}]$; so $[\boldsymbol{J},\boldsymbol{N}] \subset \boldsymbol{N}$. Therefore the proposition applies.

64.3.2. Theorem Under the conditions in 64.2.1–5 any G-invariant differential metric turns $R = G/J$ into a symmetric space. The reflection s_p in $p = J$ is determined by

$$s_p(aJ) = T(aJ) = (Ta)\, J.$$

Furthermore,

$$s_p s_{gp} = (Tg)\, g^{-1} \text{ as acting in } G/J,$$

$$\text{Int } R \subset G \subset \text{Aut } R,$$

with G considered as acting on G/J.

Locally R can be identified with $\exp \boldsymbol{N}$. The geodesics through $1 = \exp \boldsymbol{0}$ (corresponding to p) are then the $\curlyvee_\tau \exp \tau\boldsymbol{n}$ ($\boldsymbol{n}$ of unit length in $\boldsymbol{N}$).

Proof R is supposed Riemannian with the G-invariant metric δ; J being T-invariant, T induces an involutory mapping s_p of R onto itself:

$$s_p(gJ) = T(gJ) = (Tg)\, J \qquad \text{for} \quad g \in G.$$

Since $T\boldsymbol{n} = -\boldsymbol{n}$ for $\boldsymbol{n} \in \boldsymbol{N}$, the tangent vectors at p are reversed by s_p. This reversal, however, does not change their inner products. s_p transforms δ into another metric δ':

$$\delta'(g_1 J, g_2 J) = \delta((Tg_1)\, J, (Tg_2)\, J).$$

Now from the fact that $\delta(gg_1 J, gg_2 J)$ does not depend on g it follows that

$$\delta'(gg_1 J, gg_2 J) = \delta((Tg)(Tg_1)\, J, (Tg)(Tg_2)\, J)$$

does not depend on g. The differential metrics belonging to δ, δ' are G-invariant and coincide at p, hence are equal. Therefore s_p is an autometry of $\ulcorner R, \delta \urcorner$.

$$s_{gp} = g s_p\, g^{-1} \qquad (g \in G)$$

also preserves the metric and the point $gp = gJ$, and reverses the tangent vectors in gp, whence is the reflection in gp.

The equality

$$s_p s_{gp} = (Tg)\, g^{-1}$$

is easily verified. It implies $s_p s_{gp} \in G$ and, more generally,

$$\text{Int } R \subset G.$$

Furthermore, by the same argument as in 64.1.2, Int R as a C^2-connected subgroup of G is the continuous image of $\mathrm{Int}^0 R$, locally isomorphic to a linear Lie group, which is the last condition to be fulfilled in order to make R a symmetric space.

If s_{gp} with

$$g = \exp \tau_0 \boldsymbol{n}, \qquad \tau_0 \text{ real}, \quad \boldsymbol{n} \in N, \quad |\boldsymbol{n}| = 1,$$

is applied to $(\exp \tau\boldsymbol{n})\, J$, one gets

$$\begin{aligned} s_{gp}((\exp \tau\boldsymbol{n})\, J) &= (\exp \tau_0 \boldsymbol{n})\, s_p((\exp(\tau - \tau_0)\,\boldsymbol{n})\, J) \\ &= \exp \tau_0 \boldsymbol{n}(T \exp(\tau - \tau_0)\,\boldsymbol{n})\, J \\ &= (\exp(2\tau_0 - \tau)\,\boldsymbol{n})\, J. \end{aligned}$$

Therefore, if $g = \exp \tau_0 \boldsymbol{n}$, then s_{gp} behaves on the set of the $(\exp \tau\boldsymbol{n})J$ as the reflection of the parameter τ in τ_0.

For any $g \in G$, gJ is an isolated fixpoint of s_{gp}, since s_{gp} reverses the tangent vectors at gJ. Choose $\gamma > 0$ such that at a distance $< \gamma$ there is no other fixed point of s_{gp} and such that any two points q, q' with $\delta(q, q') < \gamma$ are joined by an essentially unique geodesic of length $\delta(q, q')$.

Let

$$\vartheta_{\tau_1,\tau_2} = \Upsilon_{\tau_1 \leqslant \tau \leqslant \tau_2} (\exp \tau\boldsymbol{n})\, J$$

have a diameter $< \frac{1}{2}\gamma$ and let φ_{τ_1,τ_2} be the (unique) shortest geodesic with the same endpoints,

$$p_i = \vartheta_{\tau_1,\tau_2}(\tau_i) = \varphi_{\tau_1,\tau_2}(\beta\tau_i),$$

where β chosen such that

$$\delta(p_1, p_2) = \beta(\tau_2 - \tau_1).$$

Since the reflection s_{p_0} with

$$p_0 = \vartheta_{\tau_1,\tau_2}(\tfrac{1}{2}(\tau_1 + \tau_2))$$

interchanges p_1, p_2, it reverses the geodesic φ_{τ_1,τ_2} and it preserves its midpoint

$$p_0' = \varphi_{\tau_1,\tau_2}(\tfrac{1}{2}\beta(\tau_1 + \tau_2)).$$

According to the choice of γ, if $p_0 \neq p_0'$, then $\delta(p_0, p_0') \geqslant \gamma$. However, $\delta(p_0, p_0') \leqslant \delta(p_0, p_1) + \delta(p_1, p_0') \leqslant 2\delta(p_2, p_1) < \gamma$, whence it follows that $p_0 = p_0'$. Hence

$$\vartheta_{\tau_1,\tau_2}(\tfrac{1}{2}(\tau_1 + \tau_2)) = \varphi_{\tau_1,\tau_2}(\tfrac{1}{2}\beta(\tau_1 + \tau_2)).$$

This result can be used anew with $\frac{1}{2}(\tau_1 + \tau_2)$ instead of τ_1 or instead of τ_2. Repeated dichotomies and a continuity argument lead to the conclusion

$$\vartheta_{\tau_1,\tau_2}(\tau) = \varphi_{\tau_1,\tau_2}(\beta\tau) \qquad \text{if} \quad \tau_1 \leqslant \tau \leqslant \tau_2.$$

Since the tangent vector of $\vartheta_{\tau_1,\tau_2}$ as well as of φ_{τ_1,τ_2} has unit length, it follows that $\beta = 1$. This shows that $\Upsilon_\tau (\exp \tau\boldsymbol{n})\, J$ is a geodesic.

64.3.3. *Remarks*

(1) As a symmetric space, R is not uniquely determined by the data of the theorem. Its metric can be changed at least by a constant factor.

(2) On the other hand symmetric spaces R which are essentially the same can often be obtained from essentially different pairs $\ulcorner G, J \urcorner$. Putting $G' =$ 1-component of Aut R and $J' =$ stability group of p in G', one gets the same R from $\ulcorner G', J' \urcorner$ and from any pair $\ulcorner G'', J'' \urcorner$, where G'' is a closed connected group between G and G' and $J'' = J' \cap G''$.

However, if for example G has no nontrivial proper T-invariant, connected normal subgroup, then Int R which is normal in Aut R must coincide with G.

(3) Wrapping G or replacing J by a closed open subgroup of J induces a (locally isometric) wrapping of the symmetric space G/J constructed above. (See 63.1.9.)

(4) Since $\mathrm{Int}^0 R$ is transitive and T-invariant, its infinitesimal algebra contains $\boldsymbol{N}$; so $\mathrm{Int}^0 R$ is generated by exp $\boldsymbol{N}$, as has been shown in 64.2. Hence the conditions in 64.2.6 and 64.2.7, in the presence of the others, imply each other.

64.4 The preceding analysis suggests studying the following problem:

Problem To classify the real linear Lie algebras $\boldsymbol{G}$ with an involutory automorphism T such that:

the subset of T-invariant elements is a subalgebra $\boldsymbol{J}$ with a conducible representation in $\boldsymbol{G}$ as a subalgebra of $\tilde{\boldsymbol{G}}$,

$\boldsymbol{J}$ contains no nonzero ideal of $\boldsymbol{G}$, and

the set of $\boldsymbol{n} = -T\boldsymbol{n}$ generates $\boldsymbol{G}$.

Note that the boundedness of J has been weakened to the conducibility of $\mathrm{ad}_{\boldsymbol{G}}\boldsymbol{J}$.

This problem is dealt with in 64.5–6.

64.5 The set of $\boldsymbol{x} = -T\boldsymbol{x}$ is denoted by $\boldsymbol{N}$.

$$\boldsymbol{G} = \boldsymbol{J} + \boldsymbol{N}, \qquad [\boldsymbol{J}, \boldsymbol{J}] \subset \boldsymbol{J}, \qquad [\boldsymbol{J}, \boldsymbol{N}] \subset \boldsymbol{N}, \qquad [\boldsymbol{N}, \boldsymbol{N}] \subset \boldsymbol{J}.$$

Note that the last two requirements in 64.4 imply that $\boldsymbol{J}$ is faithfully represented in $\boldsymbol{N}$ as $\mathrm{ad}_{\boldsymbol{G}}\boldsymbol{J}|_{\boldsymbol{N}}$.

Let $\boldsymbol{A}$ be a maximal abelian T-invariant ideal and suppose that $\boldsymbol{A} \neq \{\boldsymbol{0}\}$. Because of $\boldsymbol{a} + T\boldsymbol{a} \in \boldsymbol{A}$ for $\boldsymbol{a} \in \boldsymbol{A}$,

$$\boldsymbol{A} = \boldsymbol{J}_1 + \boldsymbol{N}_1 \quad \text{with} \quad \boldsymbol{J}_1 \subset \boldsymbol{J}, \quad \boldsymbol{N}_1 \subset \boldsymbol{N}.$$

Since $\boldsymbol{A}$, $\boldsymbol{J}_1$, and $\boldsymbol{N}_1$ are invariant under $\tilde{\boldsymbol{j}}$ ($\boldsymbol{j} \in \boldsymbol{J}$), there are invariant linear complements $\boldsymbol{J}_2$, $\boldsymbol{N}_2$:

$$\boldsymbol{J} = \boldsymbol{J}_1 + \boldsymbol{J}_2, \qquad \boldsymbol{N} = \boldsymbol{N}_1 + \boldsymbol{N}_2, \qquad \boldsymbol{J}_1 \cap \boldsymbol{J}_2 = \boldsymbol{N}_1 \cap \boldsymbol{N}_2 = \{\boldsymbol{0}\},$$
$$[\boldsymbol{J}, \boldsymbol{J}_2] \subset \boldsymbol{J}_2, \qquad [\boldsymbol{J}, \boldsymbol{N}_2] \subset \boldsymbol{N}_2.$$

Since $J_1 = J \cap A$ is an ideal of J, one even gets $[J_1, J_2] \subset J_1$; hence

$$[J_1, J_2] = \{0\}.$$

Further,

$$\begin{aligned}[J_1, N_2 + A] &\subset [A, N_2 + A] \cap ([J_1, N_2] + [J_1, A]) \\ &\subset (A + [A, A]) \cap (N_2 + [A, A]) \\ &= A \cap N_2 = \{0\}.\end{aligned}$$

Thus J_1 is an ideal of G contained in J. Hence

$$J_1 = \{0\}, \qquad J_2 = J, \qquad N_1 = A.$$

Since

$$[J, [N, N]] \subset [[J, N], N] + [N, [J, N]],$$

$[N, N]$ spans an ideal J' of J. Therefore $J' + N$ is a subalgebra of G which has to coincide with G, since N is supposed to generate G. Consequently, $[N, N]$ spans J. This shows that $J \neq \{0\}$ unless G is abelian.

Put

$$G_1 = J + N_2.$$

Then G_1 is a T-invariant subalgebra. Since

$$[A, N_2] \subset A \cap [N, N] \subset A \cap J = \{0\},$$

and $[A, J]$ has the same span as

$$[A, [N, N]] = [A, [N_2, N_2]] \subset [[A, N_2], N_2] + [N_2, [A, N_2]] = \{0\},$$

one gets

$$[A, G_1] = \{0\};$$

thus

$$G = G_1 + A, \qquad \text{a direct sum of algebras.}$$

G_1 is semisimple, since otherwise the last but one member of the commutator sequence of its radical could be added to A in spite of its maximality.

Being semisimple, G_1 may possess a proper simple direct summand G_1'. Then $G_1' + TG_1'$ equals G_1 or is a direct summand of G_1. This procedure can be continued.

Definition A solution $\ulcorner G, T \urcorner$ with $G \neq \{0\}$ of Problem 64.4 is called *simple* if G has no nontrivial proper T-invariant ideal.

The following has been proved:

Theorem Any solution of Problem 64.4 splits directly into simple solutions, some semisimple and some abelian. For an abelian solution $J = \{0\}$.

64.6 The investigation now turns to the semisimple simple solutions.

Theorem Let $\ulcorner G,T \urcorner$ be semisimple simple and let J, N be as before. There are then three possibilities:

(1) G,T have arisen from complex semisimple G with an involutory automorphism by waiving.

(2) Under the representation of J in G as a subalgebra of $\tilde{G}$ the subspace N is irreducible over Com and J is semisimple.

(3) Instead, N_{Com} splits into two nonequivalent irreducible linear subspaces, both of which are abelian subalgebras; the group infinitesimally generated by $\mathrm{ad}_G J|_N$ contains the 1-component of its centralizer within the group of all volume-preserving linear mappings of N, and if N is irreducible over the reals, this centralizer itself; and J is the direct sum of a semisimple and a one-dimensional Lie algebra.

Proof Complexify G (with the conjugation C_0), extend T to G_{Com} as an automorphism such that $C_0 T = TC_0$, and suppose that

$$N_{\mathrm{Com}} = N_1 + N_2, \qquad N_1 \cap N_2 = \{0\}, \qquad [J, N_i] \subset N_i.$$

If $n_i \in N_i$, $n_i' \in N_i$, then by Jacobi-associativity

$$[[n_1, n_1'], n_2] + [[n_1', n_2], n_1] + [[n_2, n_1], n_1'] = 0,$$

where the first summand is in N_2 and the others are in N_1, which shows

$$[[N_1, N_1], N_2] = \{0\}$$

and likewise

$$[[N_2, N_2], N_1] = \{0\}.$$

Let J_1 be the maximal subalgebra of J_{Com} with

$$[J_1, N_2] = \{0\}.$$

Then by the foregoing

$$[N_1, N_1] \subset J_1.$$

Jacobi-associativity shows that J_1 is an ideal in J_{Com}. Let N_1' be the linear space spanned by $[J_1, N_1]$. Then $J_1 + N_1'$ is a T-invariant ideal of G_{Com}. The same is true of its complex conjugate $C_0 J_1 + C_0 N_1'$. Their sum and intersection, if C_0-restricted, must be G or $\{0\}$. If the C_0-restriction of the intersection is G, then $J_1 + N_1' = G_{\mathrm{Com}}$ and $N_2 = \{0\}$. If it is $\{0\}$ and $J_1 + N_1' \neq \{0\}$, then the C_0-restriction of the sum is G, and G may be supposed to be obtained from $J_1 + N_1'$ by waiving, which is the first kind of solution indicated in the assertion.

Therefore, disregarding the first and second kinds, one may suppose that $N_2 \neq \{0\}$ and $J_1 + N_1' = \{0\}$, hence $J_1 = \{0\}$, $[N_1, N_1] = \{0\}$.

This shows the following:

64.6.1 If $N_1 \neq \{0\}$, $N_2 \neq \{0\}$, then $[N_i, N_i] = \{0\}$, and for each i the only element of J_{Com} commuting with all elements of N_i is $\mathbf{0}$.

Suppose N_1, N_2 as before; $\operatorname{ad}_{G_{\text{Com}}} N_1$ is nilpotent: it maps N_1 into $\{\mathbf{0}\}$, its square maps J_{Com} into $\{\mathbf{0}\}$, and its third power maps N_2 into $\{\mathbf{0}\}$; of course, N_2 is also ad-nilpotent in G_{Com}.

ψ is nondegenerate on N_{Com}, since $\psi(J, N_{\text{Com}}) = \{0\}$. However, $\psi(N_i, N_i) = \{0\}$, since N_i is ad-nilpotent. Thus

64.6.2 $$\dim N_i = \tfrac{1}{2} \dim N_{\text{Com}}.$$

Since every J_{Com}-invariant linear subspace of N_{Com} has an invariant linear complement, the following applies:

64.6.3 The N_i are irreducibly acted on by J_{Com}.

It will now be shown that these actions cannot be equivalent. Equivalence would mean the existence of linear mappings ϑ_i $(i = 1, 2)$, respectively, of N_1 onto N_2 and of N_2 onto N_1 such that

64.6.4 $$j\vartheta_1 n_1 = \vartheta_1 j n_1 \qquad \text{for all} \quad j \in J_{\text{Com}}, \qquad n_1 \in N_1,$$

64.6.4a $$j\vartheta_2 n_2 = \vartheta_2 j n_2 \qquad \text{for all} \quad j \in J_{\text{Com}}, \qquad n_2 \in N_2.$$

By 55.4.4, if the N_i are real (i.e., C_0-invariant), ϑ_1 and ϑ_2 may be taken to be real; if the N_i are nonreal, they may be taken as each other's conjugate and so may ϑ_1 and ϑ_2; hence
$$\vartheta_2 = C_0 \vartheta_1 C_0.$$
Then the linear subspace of the $n_1 + \vartheta_1 n_1$ $(n_1 \in N_1)$ is still invariant under j $(j \in J_{\text{Com}})$ because of 64.6.4. So it is again abelian; hence
$$[n_1 + \vartheta_1 n_1, n_1' + \vartheta_1 n_1'] = \mathbf{0} \qquad \text{for} \quad n_1, n_1' \in N_1,$$

64.6.5 $$[\vartheta_1 n_1, n_1'] + [n_1, \vartheta_1 n_1'] = \mathbf{0}.$$

Likewise

64.6.5a $$[\vartheta_2 n_2, n_2'] + [n_2, \vartheta_2 n_2'] = \mathbf{0} \qquad \text{for} \quad n_2, n_2' \in N_2.$$

Now define the linear mapping ϑ of G_{Com} into itself as $\mathbf{0}$ on J_{Com} and coinciding with ϑ_i on N_i. This ϑ appears to be an infinitesimal automorphism of G_{Com} because of 64.6.4–4a, rewritten as
$$\vartheta[j, n] = [j, \vartheta n] + [\vartheta j, n],$$

and because of 64.6.5–5a. (Note that the other commutator relations are trivial.) Because of the reality requirements, ϑ may even be considered as an infinitesimal automorphism of $\boldsymbol{G}$. Now because $\boldsymbol{G}$ is semisimple, ϑ is inner and $\vartheta = \tilde{\boldsymbol{u}}$ for some $\boldsymbol{u} \in \boldsymbol{G}$, but, since $\vartheta T = T\vartheta$, $\boldsymbol{u}$ belongs to $\boldsymbol{J}$. This is contradictory because $\tilde{\boldsymbol{u}}$ ($\boldsymbol{u} \in \boldsymbol{J}$) preserves $\boldsymbol{N}_i$, whereas ϑ does not. Therefore the representations of $\boldsymbol{J}_{\mathrm{Com}}$ on $\boldsymbol{N}_1$ and $\boldsymbol{N}_2$ cannot be equivalent.

Finally the centralizer, as mentioned in the statement, consists of the restrictions σ_α to $\boldsymbol{N}$ of linear τ_α defined on $\boldsymbol{N}_{\mathrm{Com}}$ by

$$\tau_\alpha \boldsymbol{n}_i = \alpha_i \boldsymbol{n}_i \qquad \text{for} \quad \boldsymbol{n}_i \in \boldsymbol{N}_i$$

for $\alpha = \ulcorner \alpha_1, \alpha_2 \urcorner$ with $(\alpha_1 \alpha_2)^{\dim N_1} = 1$, and

$$\alpha_1, \alpha_2 \text{ real} \qquad \text{for real } \boldsymbol{N}_1, \boldsymbol{N}_2,$$

$$\bar{\alpha}_1 = \alpha_2 \qquad \text{for complex conjugate } \boldsymbol{N}_1, \boldsymbol{N}_2.$$

σ_α extends to an automorphism of $\boldsymbol{G}$ with $\sigma_\alpha \boldsymbol{j} = \boldsymbol{j}$ for $\boldsymbol{j} \in \boldsymbol{J}$ as soon as $\alpha_1 \alpha_2 = 1$. In the case of conjugate $\boldsymbol{N}_i$ this is fulfilled by all α with τ_α in the centralizer, which is connected; for real $\boldsymbol{N}_i$ it is still true for α with τ_α in the 1-component of the centralizer. Therefore the 1-component of the centralizer, as acting on $\boldsymbol{G}$, is within Int $\boldsymbol{G}$ and, since $\sigma_\alpha T = T\sigma_\alpha$, even within the group infinitesimally generated by $\mathrm{ad}_G \boldsymbol{J}$. However, by restriction to $\boldsymbol{N}$ this group is homomorphically mapped onto the group infinitesimally generated by $\mathrm{ad}_G \boldsymbol{J}|_N$, and by this homomorphism σ_α is mapped into $\sigma_\alpha|_N$.

For the structure of $\boldsymbol{J}$ in the second part of the statement, that is, if $\boldsymbol{J}$ acts complex irreducibly on $\boldsymbol{N}$, then up to a direct summand of scalar multiplications, spanned by some $\boldsymbol{z}$, $\boldsymbol{J}$ is semisimple. However, because of $\tilde{\boldsymbol{z}}\boldsymbol{j} = \boldsymbol{0}$ for $\boldsymbol{j} \in \boldsymbol{J}$, $\tilde{\boldsymbol{z}}\boldsymbol{n} = \alpha \boldsymbol{n}$ for $\boldsymbol{n} \in \boldsymbol{N}$ and some $\alpha \in$ Rea, one gets on the one hand $\tilde{\boldsymbol{z}}[\boldsymbol{n}, \boldsymbol{n}'] = 2\alpha[\boldsymbol{n}, \boldsymbol{n}']$ for $\boldsymbol{n}, \boldsymbol{n}' \in \boldsymbol{N}$, and on the other $[\boldsymbol{n}, \boldsymbol{n}'] \in \boldsymbol{J}$; thus $\tilde{\boldsymbol{z}}[\boldsymbol{n}, \boldsymbol{n}'] = \boldsymbol{0}$, whereas $[\boldsymbol{n}, \boldsymbol{n}'] \neq \boldsymbol{0}$ for some choice of $\boldsymbol{n}, \boldsymbol{n}'$; hence $\alpha = 0$. Then $\boldsymbol{z}$ would be a center element of $\boldsymbol{G}$ belonging to $\boldsymbol{J}$, which is not allowed. Therefore $\boldsymbol{J}$ is semisimple.

In the third case of the statement it was proved that the center of $\boldsymbol{J}$ is at least one-dimensional, and it follows from 64.6.1 that it is at most one-dimensional.

This completes the proof of the theorem.

64.7 In 64.2 the point of departure was a symmetric space R. From this datum a group $\mathrm{Int}^0 R$ of autometries with an involutory automorphism T was derived. In 64.3 the procedure was reversed: Starting from a group G (say $\mathrm{Int}^0 R$) with an involutory automorphism T (with certain properties), a symmetric space was constructed. To know all symmetric spaces it is useful to classify all Lie algebras $\boldsymbol{G}$ with such an involutory automorphism. A more general problem has been tackled in 64.4. As a first step, 64.5 made the restriction to simple semisimple solutions advisable. These solutions have been thoroughly analyzed in 64.6.

To take up the thread where it was left after 64.3, one has to turn back to groups instead of Lie algebras and, in particular, urge that J_0, infinitesimally generated by $\boldsymbol{J}$, has a bounded adjoint action on $\boldsymbol{N}$.

Theorem 64.5 suggests the following:

64.7.1. Definition Let $R \in \text{Spa Sym}$, $G = \text{Int}^0 R$, J be the stability group of $p \in R$ in G, and let T be the automorphism of G determined by s_p. Then R is called *abelian*, *semisimple*, or *simple*,† depending on whether such an attribute applies to $\ulcorner \boldsymbol{G}, T \urcorner$.

Proposition A symmetric space R is locally the product of simple symmetric spaces R_i.

Proof It may be supposed that R is simply connected (see 64.1.3). $\boldsymbol{G} = \boldsymbol{J} + \boldsymbol{N}$ as in 64.2. $\boldsymbol{G}$ splits directly into $\boldsymbol{G}_i$ $(i = 1, \dots, m)$ such that the $\ulcorner \boldsymbol{G}_i, T|_{\boldsymbol{G}_i} \urcorner$ are simple (see 64.5) and $\boldsymbol{J}$, $\boldsymbol{N}$ split correspondingly into $\boldsymbol{J}_i$, $\boldsymbol{N}_i$. The $\boldsymbol{G}_i$, $\boldsymbol{J}_i$ may be considered as generating G_i, J_i, which are locally isomorphic with linear Lie groups, J_i being closed in G_i. Homogeneous spaces R_i are defined as G_i/J_i; their product is denoted by R^*; R_i is considered as a subspace of R^* in a natural way. A mapping λ of R^* is defined by

$$\lambda \ulcorner g_1 J_1, \dots, g_m J_m \urcorner = g_1 \cdots g_m J \qquad (g_i \in G_i).$$

R^* wraps R by means of λ; since R is simply connected, λ is homeomorphic; it is now used to identify R^* with R as homogeneous spaces.

$\boldsymbol{N}$ considered as a tangent space of the Riemannian space $R = G/J$ is endowed with an inner product $(\dots, \dots)$. The splitting may be refashioned so that the tangent spaces $\boldsymbol{N}_i$ of *abelian* R_i at J_i are orthogonal to each other. Then the tangent spaces $\boldsymbol{N}_i$ of *all* R_i at J_i are orthogonal to one another. Indeed, let R_i be nonabelian, thus simple semisimple; then one obtains for $k \neq i$: $(\boldsymbol{N}_k, \boldsymbol{N}_i) \subset (\boldsymbol{N}_k, [\boldsymbol{J}_i, \boldsymbol{N}_i]) = ([\boldsymbol{J}_i, \boldsymbol{N}_k], \boldsymbol{N}_i) = \{0\}$ because of infinitesimal invariance and of $[\boldsymbol{J}_i, \boldsymbol{N}_k] = \{\boldsymbol{0}\}$.

Therefore at J the tangent space of R is the direct sum of those of the R_i, even with due regard to the inner product. This property is transferred by the action of G to any point of R. Thus the Riemannian space R is the direct product Riemannian subspaces R_i.

Geodesics in R_i are also geodesic in R (see 63.5.2). Therefore, if s_p is the

† It would be more appropriate to call these spaces locally simple and to reserve the term "simple" for those that do not split globally.

reflection of R in $p \in R_i$, then $s_p|_{R_i}$ is the reflection of R_i in p. R_i possesses a reflection in each of its points.

The even products of the s_p with $p \in R_i$ form a closed subgroup (even a direct factor) $(\mathrm{Int}^0 R)_i$ of $\mathrm{Int}^0 R$, which leaves R_k $(k \neq i)$ pointwise invariant. By restriction to R_i it is identified with $\mathrm{Int}^0 R_i$ which in this way is locally isomorphic to a linear Lie group. This proves the R_i to be (simple) symmetric spaces, the product of which is isometric to R.

Remark The proof shows that in a splitting of a symmetric space as a Riemannian space, the factors are again symmetric. A simple symmetric space is also "simple" as a Riemannian space.

64.8 Since simple abelian symmetric spaces are of a trivial nature, the preceding justifies restricting to simple semisimple symmetric spaces $R = G/J$ $(G = \mathrm{Int}^0 R)$, thus with simple semisimple $\ulcorner \boldsymbol{G}, \boldsymbol{T} \urcorner$. They will also be studied globally; therefore J and its 1-component J_0 must be distinguished.

The fact that the adjoint action of J_0 on N is bounded allows one to exclude the first possibility of Theorem 64.6, since a group generated by twin type $\boldsymbol{J}(\neq \{\boldsymbol{0}\})$ cannot fulfill this condition. From the third possibility reducibility over the reals can be canceled, for in that case, if J_0 is considered as acting in N, the real multiplications in the N_i belonging to the 1-component of the centralizer of J_0, thus to J_0 itself, would form an unbounded subgroup of J_0.

It is easily seen that a noncompact semisimple group has no faithful bounded linear representation. Therefore in the second and third cases the semisimple factor of J_0 acts on N as a compact group; moreover, in the third case the central factor has the same property. So J_0 itself is compact. J normalizes J_0 and thus in the third case coincides with J_0; in the second case, if J' is the centralizer of J_0 in J, then J/J' is finite because the number of automorphism classes of semisimple J_0 is finite; and J', being bounded, consists, up to J_0, of the scalar multipliers ± 1 at most. Therefore J/J_0 is finite, and J is again compact.

This shows that the distinction made in 64.1.2 between Int R and $\mathrm{Int}^0 R$ may be dropped. Int R is closed in Aut R. (This is true for general symmetric spaces as well.)

Therefore it may be supposed that:

J is compact, and J_0 as represented on N by $\tilde{j}$ $(j \in J_0)$ is real irreducible.

Note then that J has the same property.

By Theorem 64.3.1 N can be given a J-invariant real positive definite inner product $(\ldots, \ldots)$, but now it is unique up to a constant factor, even if indefinite ones were allowed. This is evident if the representation of J in N is complex irreducible, but it extends even to the third case of Theorem 64.6. Any other J-invariant inner product could be written $\curlyvee_{\boldsymbol{n},\boldsymbol{n}'}(\boldsymbol{Kn}, \boldsymbol{n}')$ with $K \in \mathrm{End}\, N$, symmetric with respect to $(\ldots, \ldots)$, and commuting with all $\tilde{j}$ $(j \in J)$; after subtracting some scalar multiplier on N, K may even be supposed to have zero trace. K, however, belongs to the centralizer of $\boldsymbol{J}$ as stated in Theorem 64.6. Thus K is an element of $\mathrm{ad}_G \boldsymbol{J}|_N$. Now

$$(K\boldsymbol{n}, \boldsymbol{n}') + (\boldsymbol{n}, K\boldsymbol{n}') = 0,$$

since any $\tilde{\boldsymbol{j}}$ ($\boldsymbol{j} \in \boldsymbol{J}$) leaves the inner product infinitesimally invariant. From the symmetry of K it follows that $K = 0$, which proves the assertion.

Such an inner product on $\boldsymbol{N}$ is closely connected to the Killing form on $\boldsymbol{G}$: $\boldsymbol{J}$ and $\boldsymbol{N}$ are mutually orthogonal in the sense of the Killing form ψ of $\boldsymbol{G}$ because

$$\tilde{\boldsymbol{j}}\tilde{\boldsymbol{n}}\boldsymbol{j}' \in \boldsymbol{N}, \qquad \tilde{\boldsymbol{j}}\tilde{\boldsymbol{n}}\boldsymbol{n}' \in \boldsymbol{J} \qquad \text{for} \quad \boldsymbol{j}, \boldsymbol{j}' \in \boldsymbol{J}, \qquad \boldsymbol{n}, \boldsymbol{n}' \in \boldsymbol{N};$$

ψ splits into its restrictions ψ_J, ψ_N to $\boldsymbol{J}, \boldsymbol{N}$.

Since $\boldsymbol{G}$ is semisimple, ψ is nondegenerate, as are ψ_J and ψ_N. The latter is an invariant under $\boldsymbol{J}$ as represented in $\boldsymbol{N}$ and as such it is a multiple of the given inner product on $\boldsymbol{N}$:

$$\psi_N(\boldsymbol{n}, \boldsymbol{n}') = \gamma(\boldsymbol{n}, \boldsymbol{n}'), \qquad \gamma \neq 0.$$

On the other hand,

$$\psi_J(\boldsymbol{j}, \boldsymbol{j}) \leqslant 0 \qquad \text{for} \quad \boldsymbol{j} \in \boldsymbol{J},$$

since J_0 is compact and therefore all eigenvalues of $\tilde{\boldsymbol{j}}$ ($\boldsymbol{j} \in \boldsymbol{J}$) are imaginary.

Now two cases are possible with the sign of γ:

Elliptic: ψ_N is negative definite.

Hyperbolic: ψ_N is positive definite.

Again let C_0 be the semimorphism that defines $\boldsymbol{G}$ within $\boldsymbol{G}_{\mathrm{Com}}$. In the elliptic case ψ is negative definite so $\tilde{G}$, being closed (see 38.5), is compact; then by 32.2.4 G is also compact and C_0 is some unitary semimorphism. In the hyperbolic case, with T extended to $\boldsymbol{G}_{\mathrm{Com}}$ as an automorphism,

$$C_1 = C_0 T = T C_0$$

is again an involutory semimorphism. The real algebra defined by C_1 is $\boldsymbol{G}_1 = \boldsymbol{J} + \mathrm{i}\boldsymbol{N}$, on which the Killing form of $\boldsymbol{G}_{\mathrm{Com}}$ breaks into ψ_J and $\psi_{\mathrm{i}N}$, both negative definite. Therefore in the hyperbolic case C_1 may be taken to be C_{un}. By momentarily writing $\boldsymbol{G}$ instead of $\boldsymbol{G}_{\mathrm{Com}}$ and putting

$$C_0 = C_{\mathrm{un}}, \qquad C = C_0 T = T C_0 \qquad \text{in the elliptic case,}$$

$$C_1 = C_{\mathrm{un}}, \qquad C = C_1 T = T C_1 \qquad \text{in the hyperbolic case,}$$

it appears that

$$\boldsymbol{J} = \boldsymbol{G}_{C,\mathrm{un}} \qquad \text{in either case,}$$

$$\boldsymbol{N} = \mathrm{i}\boldsymbol{G}_{C,\mathrm{he}} \qquad \text{in the elliptic case,}$$

$$\boldsymbol{N} = \boldsymbol{G}_{C,\mathrm{he}} \qquad \text{in the hyperbolic case.}$$

Note that $C \neq C_{\mathrm{un}}$ since $\boldsymbol{N} \neq \{\boldsymbol{0}\}$.

The requirement that $\ulcorner \boldsymbol{G}_{\text{un}}, T \urcorner$, or $\ulcorner \boldsymbol{G}_C, T \urcorner$, be simple is equivalent to the requirement that $\ulcorner \boldsymbol{G}, T \urcorner$ be simple (which means $\boldsymbol{G}$ without a nontrivial proper T-invariant ideal):

In any case, C_{un} leaves every direct summand of $\boldsymbol{G}$ invariant. If $\boldsymbol{G}_1$ is a T-invariant direct summand of $\boldsymbol{G}$, then $\boldsymbol{G}_{1,\text{un}}$ is a T-invariant direct summand of $\boldsymbol{G}_{\text{un}}$; moreover, $\boldsymbol{G}_1$ is C-invariant as well, and $\boldsymbol{G}_{1,C}$ is a direct summand of $\boldsymbol{G}_C$. Thus a T-splitting of $\boldsymbol{G}$ induces T-splittings of $\boldsymbol{G}_{\text{un}}$ and $\boldsymbol{G}_C$. Therefore simplicity of $\ulcorner \boldsymbol{G}_{\text{un}}, T \urcorner$ or $\ulcorner \boldsymbol{G}_C, T \urcorner$ implies simplicity of $\ulcorner \boldsymbol{G}, T \urcorner$. The converse is obvious.

64.9 The foregoing completely characterizes the infinitesimal structure of a simple semisimple space R, that is, $\boldsymbol{G}$ (infinitesimal algebra of Int R), $\boldsymbol{J}$, $\boldsymbol{N}$, and T acting on $\boldsymbol{G}$. Its possible global structures are now analyzed.

The Hyperbolic Case G may be supposed to generate a centerfree linear Lie group G_1 (e.g., take $\tilde{\boldsymbol{G}}$ instead of G and $G_1 = \text{Int } \boldsymbol{G}$). Then G_1 is the homomorphic image of (connected) G by means of a local isomorphism χ. According to 51.5.11, $\boldsymbol{J}$ generates in G_1 a maximal compact subgroup J_1; because of 51.5.10, any wrapping of G_1 can already be performed, as it were, within J_1; thus the χ-original of J_1 is connected and contains the center of G. Therefore J_0 is the χ-original of J_1, whereas it should not contain any nontrivial center elements of G. Hence χ is a global isomorphism. The admission of groups that are only *locally* isomorphic with linear Lie groups has not been an essential extension.

Thus G is centerfree and may be supposed linear; J has to be compact and contain J_0, generated by $\boldsymbol{J}$. Since J_0 is maximal compact, it turns out that $J = J_0$.

Therefore in the hyperbolic case G is centerfree and J is connected.

Note that by 51.5.12 J is even its own normalizer in G.

The Elliptic Case G may be considered as a wrapping of a compact semisimple linear Lie group, which by 32.2.4 is again compact and by 46.8 may be assumed to be linear. So the admission of groups that are only *locally* isomorphic with linear Lie groups again proves to be inessential.

Therefore G is supposed to be a compact semisimple linear Lie group. J may exceed J_0. Its elements are T-invariants. The subset of T-invariants is a closed subgroup of G and its 1-component clearly coincides with J_0. Now J is not allowed to contain a nontrivial normal subgroup of G; since $\ulcorner G, T \urcorner$ is simple, this amounts to saying that J should not contain nontrivial central elements of G. This is certainly required for J_0. Then the possible J's are the subgroups between J_0 and the subgroup of all T-invariants, and intersecting the center of G trivially.

If G is centerfree, the set of T-invariants coincides with the normalizer of J_0

in G: first, it is evident that every T-invariant normalizes J_0. Second, if $\tilde{a}$ leaves $\boldsymbol{J}$ invariant, it leaves its orthoplement $\boldsymbol{N}$ invariant; thus $\tilde{a}T\tilde{a}^{-1}$ determines the same $\boldsymbol{J}$ and $\boldsymbol{N}$ as T did; consequently, $\tilde{a}T\tilde{a}^{-1} = T$, $\widetilde{Ta} = \tilde{a}$, and, since G is centerfree, $Ta = a$.

The Abelian Case has still to be mentioned in this context. It is clear, however, that the admission of groups only locally isomorphic to linear Lie groups does not cause an essential extension.

64.10. This analysis leads to the following:

Definition If A is an abelian real linear Lie group, then A endowed with an A-invariant Riemannian metric belongs to the class of *abelian symmetric spaces*, $\mathrm{Sy}(A)$.

For $\boldsymbol{G} \in$ Alg Lie Lin Com SS, $\boldsymbol{G} \neq \{\boldsymbol{0}\}$, infinitesimally generating G, with different but commuting semimorphisms C, C_{un} (unitary), and $T = CC_{\mathrm{un}}$, suppose the following:

64.10.1 $\boldsymbol{G}_{C,\mathrm{un},\mathrm{Com}}$ contains no proper ideal of $\boldsymbol{G}$ except $\{\boldsymbol{0}\}$.

64.10.2 T extends to an automorphism of G.

64.10.3 $G_{C,\mathrm{un}}$ contains no center element $\neq 1$ of G.

Then with a group

64.10.4 $G^*_{C,\mathrm{un}}$ between $G_{C,\mathrm{un}}$ and its normalizer in G_{un}, consisting of T-invariant elements and containing no center element $\neq 1$ of G_{un},

$$G_{\mathrm{un}}/G^*_{C,\mathrm{un}}, \qquad \text{respectively,} \qquad G_C/G_{C,\mathrm{un}},$$

endowed with a G_{un}-invariant, respectively, G_C-invariant, Riemannian metric are called

elliptic, respectively, *hyperbolic*,

(*symmetric*) *spaces*. These collections of spaces are indicated by

$$\mathrm{Sye}(G_C, C_{\mathrm{un}}) \qquad \text{respectively,} \qquad \mathrm{Syh}(G_C, C_{\mathrm{un}}).$$

$$\mathrm{Sy}(G_C, C_{\mathrm{un}}) = \mathrm{Sye}(G_C, C_{\mathrm{un}}) \cup \mathrm{Syh}(G_C, C_{\mathrm{un}}).$$

Their elements are often supposed to be provided with the metric induced by the Killing form, as will be clear from the context. The reflection in the point $p = G^*_{C,\mathrm{un}}$, respectively, $G_{C,\mathrm{un}}$, is also denoted by T $(= CC_{\mathrm{un}})$.

The indication C_{un} will be often omitted, since the structure of the space does not depend on the choice of $C_{\rm un}$. Neither does it depend on the choice of C in its isotypic class.

The attributes *twin*, *inner*, *outer*, and so on, are attached to these symmetric spaces according to the properties of the underlying G_C.

Remarks

(1) Thanks to 64.10.1, 64.10.3, 64.10.4, $G_{\rm un}$ and G_C, respectively, act faithfully on the defined spaces; 64.10.1 states that C, $C_{\rm un}$ do not coincide on any ideal $\neq \{\mathbf{0}\}$ of $\boldsymbol{G}$; 64.10.3 is equivalent to G_C being centerfree.

(2) The extendibility of T needs to be required for G_C only in the hyperbolic case and for $G_{\rm un}$ only in the elliptic case; for the latter this makes no difference; for the hyperbolic case it might *a priori* but in fact it does not, since if T is extendible to G_C it can be made extendible to G by factoring out a central subgroup of G intersecting G_C trivially. This needs to be verified only in the troublesome cases of outer type D_l with l even.

Things proved can be summarized as follows:

Theorem Symmetric spaces are locally isometric with products of abelian, elliptic, and hyperbolic spaces. Abelian, elliptic, and hyperbolic spaces are locally isometric with products of simple spaces of the same kind. Simple spaces are isometric with simple abelian, elliptic, or hyperbolic spaces. Elliptic spaces are compact; hyperbolic spaces are not. Up to a negative, respectively, positive, factor the differential metric at $p = J$ of an elliptic, respectively, hyperbolic, simple space is the restriction of the Killing form.

Hyperbolic spaces are globally determined by their local structure.

For abelian, elliptic, and hyperbolic spaces R as before, Int R equals $A, G_{\rm un}$, and G_C respectively.

In a simple elliptic or hyperbolic space the 1-component J_0 ($=G_{C,\rm un}$) of the stability group J ($=G^*_{C,\rm un}$, respectively, $G_{C,\rm un}$) at p acts irreducibly and faithfully in the tangent space at p which can be identified with $\mathrm{i}\boldsymbol{G}_{C,\rm he}$, respectively, $\boldsymbol{G}_{C,\rm he}$. If in this representation J_0 stays irreducible over Com, J_0 is semisimple; if it becomes reducible, there are two irreducible components, which are non-equivalent, and J_0 is locally the direct product of a semisimple and a one-dimensional linear Lie group and contains its centralizer within the group of all volume-preserving linear mappings in the tangent space.

The last-mentioned facts could have been read in the classification of simple semisimple real Lie algebras (Sections 52–53). As a matter of fact, the representation ϑ becomes reducible if and only if a summand of type $\mathbf{D}_1$ appears in the algebra of the maximal compact subgroup (which corresponds to J_0), and this happens with nonequivalent components.

64.11 The case of simple $\ulcorner G_{\text{Com}}, T \urcorner$ with nonsimple G_{Com} merits a special analysis.

The Elliptic Case G is unitary and $G = G_1 + G_2$, a direct sum, where G_1, G_2 must be isomorphic by T. Locally G is the direct product of the locally simple G_1, G_2.

J_0 is the set of $g \cdot Tg$, with $g \in G_1$. Now assume that G_1 and G_2 intersect trivially, for example, G adjoint or simply connected. Every coset $g_1 g_2 J_0$ $(g_i \in G_i)$ intersects G_1 in one point $g_1 Tg_2^{-1}$. This cross section G_1 of cosets can be used as a model of G/J_0 if $g_1 g_2 J_0$ is identified with $g_1 Tg_2^{-1}$. On this model $a \cdot Tb$ $(a, b \in G_1)$ acts as

$$\curlyvee_{x \in G_1} axb^{-1};$$

G_1 itself appears as an elliptic symmetric space with a metric induced by the Killing form.

Note that here, as a homogeneous space, G/J_0 is not reduced in the sense of 63.1.7.

The Hyperbolic Case It may be supposed that G_C, which is of the twin type, arose from some complex G' by waiving. Therefore the hyperbolic space can be obtained as G'/G'_{un}, where G' is to be taken as a real group.

64.12. Historical Note The symmetric spaces are a beautiful discovery of E. Cartan. The greater part of the results in this section and the next ones are his, though the present methods widely differ from his. Cartan's path to symmetric spaces was all but straightforward. He scrutinized a statement he found in the literature, which said that Riemannian spaces in which the curvature tensor is preserved under parallel transport have a constant curvature tensor, and proved it to be wrong. He then analyzed that class of spaces by sophisticated techniques of differential geometry [*Bull. Soc. Math. France* **54**, 214–264 (1926); **55**, 114–134 (1927) = *Œuvres* I **2**, 587–660] and found that each such space bore a structure of homogeneous space. Actually, they are the symmetric spaces introduced in the present report; but this was an a posteriori discovery of Cartan. Later [*Ann. Ecole Norm.* **44**, 345–367 (1927) = *Œuvres* I **2**, 867–990] Cartan approached symmetric spaces from this point of view, though on several issues he relied on the results or presumed results of his former approach. Despite the fragmentary character and the many gaps in the general theory, all particular results are surprisingly correct.

E. Cartan devoted many more papers to symmetric spaces. M. Berger [*Ann. Ecole Norm.* **74**, 85–177 (1957)] recently dropped the assumption of definiteness of the Riemannian metric. Though this more general case has been taken into account in the preparation of Theorem 64.6, Berger's classification has not been reported, since it is extremely involved.

Modern tale says that E. Cartan knew only *compact* symmetric spaces. This statement probably owes its origin to a misreading of a remark by Berger.

S. Helgason wrote a monograph on symmetric spaces (*Differential Geometry and Symmetric Spaces*, Academic Press, New York, 1962).

65. MINIMAL AND MAXIMAL SYMMETRIC SPACES

65.1 By 64.10 a space in Syh(G_C) is determined globally by its local structure.

In contrast, members of Sye(G_C) depend globally on the choice of J. The smallest J is $G_{C,\mathrm{un}}$; the corresponding symmetric space is the only one with a connected stability group and it wraps all others of the same class. If G_{un} is centerfree, the largest J is the normalizer of $G_{C,\mathrm{un}}$ in G_{un}. Note that to get G faithfully represented in G/J one must bar nontrivial center elements of G from J.

Definition A space in Syh(G_C), Sye(G_C) is *maximal* (Syma) or *minimal* (Symi) depending on whether its stability group is minimal or maximal.

The elements of Syh(G_C) are both maximal and minimal.

65.2 Syh(G_C); $\quad G_{C,\mathrm{un}} = \boldsymbol{J}, \quad G_{C,\mathrm{he}} = \boldsymbol{N}, \quad \exp \boldsymbol{N} = N.$

As a model of an element of Syh(G_C) one can use $G_{C,\mathrm{he}}$ and even $\boldsymbol{N} = G_{C,\mathrm{he}}$ because of 51.5.10 and the one-to-one character of exp on $\boldsymbol{N}$. There the geodesics through $\boldsymbol{0}$ appear as straight lines (see 64.3.2). So in the case of Syh(G_C) geodesic connection is unique.

Splitting $g \in G_C$ into nj ($n \in N = \exp \boldsymbol{N}, j \in J$) can be performed by taking the square root in N of

$$g(Tg^{-1}) = nj(n^{-1}j)^{-1} = n^2.$$

For a moment call $\eta(g)$ the action of g on N as a model of G_C/J. To study η one must find $n_1 \in N$ that satisfies

$$gnJ = n_1 J;$$

in other words, one must split

$$gn = n_1 j \qquad (\text{some } j \in J).$$

With the aforementioned procedure,

$$n_1{}^2 = gn^2\, Tg^{-1},$$

thus

65.2.1
$$(\eta(g)\,n)^2 = gn^2\, Tg^{-1}.$$

This suggests another use of the model N of G_C/J. The new action is the transform ϑ of the action η by means of the square mapping Q,

$$Qn = n^2 \qquad \text{for} \quad n \in N;$$

and then ϑ is defined by

$$\vartheta(g) = Q\eta(g)\,Q^{-1}.$$

Therefore by 65.2.1

$$Q(\eta(g)\,n) = g(Qn)(Tg^{-1});$$

hence

$$\vartheta(g)n = gn(Tg^{-1}).$$

In particular,

$$\vartheta(j)\,n = jnj^{-1} \qquad \text{for} \quad j \in J,$$

$$\vartheta(n')\,n = n'\,nn' \qquad \text{for} \quad n' \in N.$$

The reflection in 1 again carries n into n^{-1}. Applying $\vartheta(n')$, one notes that:

the reflection in n' carries n into $n'\,n^{-1}\,n'$.

65.3 Sye(G_C); $\boldsymbol{G}_{C,\mathrm{un}} = \boldsymbol{J}$, J_0 generated by $\boldsymbol{J}, \boldsymbol{N} = \mathrm{i}\boldsymbol{G}_{C,\mathbf{he}}$, $N = \exp \boldsymbol{N}$.

By 32.10 the one-dimensional subgroups of G_{un} cover G_{un}, whence the geodesics $\curlyvee_\tau(\exp \tau\boldsymbol{n})\,J_0$ ($\boldsymbol{n} \in \boldsymbol{D}$) cover G_{un}/J_0 because of 64.3 and the possibility of geodesic connection. Splitting $g \in G_{\mathrm{un}}$ as $g = nj$, with $n \in N$, $j \in J_0$, is still possible, though no longer unique. The set of $g(Tg^{-1}) = njj^{-1}n$ is still contained in N, and since every element of N has a square root in N the set coincides with N.

One can still define

$$\vartheta(g)\,n = gn(Tg^{-1}).$$

Writing $n \in N$ as $f(Tf^{-1})$ with $f \in G_{\mathrm{un}}$, one gets

$$\vartheta(g)\,n = gf(T(gf)^{-1}),$$

which is again in N. This shows that $\vartheta(g)$ maps N onto N and makes ϑ a transitive representation of G_{un} in N. The stability group J_ϑ of ϑ at 1 consists of all $g \in G_{\mathrm{un}}$ with $g = Tg$. Therefore it is as large as it can be as soon as G_{un} is centerfree.

The results of 65.2–3 are summarized:

Theorem A minimal model in the case of Syh(G_C), respectively, Sye(G_C), with centerfree G_{un} is furnished by $N = \exp \boldsymbol{N}$ with $\boldsymbol{N} = \boldsymbol{G}_{C,\mathbf{he}}$, respectively, $\mathrm{i}\boldsymbol{G}_{C,\mathbf{he}}$, acted on by G_C, respectively, G_{un}, by means of ϑ with $\vartheta(g)n = gn(Tg^{-1})$. In the hyperbolic case the model is also maximal; those symmetric spaces are determined by their local shape.

65.4. Maximal Compact Subgroups The time has come to prove a previously announced theorem (51.5.11):

Theorem In real linear semisimple G_C all maximal compact subgroups are conjugate.

The theorem is a consequence of the following proposition:

Proposition In a symmetric space R in which geodesic joining is unique, the intersection of two balls with equal radii and different centers is contained in a ball of smaller radius.

Proof The uniqueness of geodesic joining in R implies that $\delta(a,x)+\delta(b,x)>\delta(a,b)$ unless x lies on the geodesic between a and b. Let m be the midpoint of a,b. The reflection s_m in m shows

$$\begin{aligned}2\delta(m,x) &= \delta(x,s_m x)\leqslant\delta(a,x)+\delta(a,s_m x)\\ &= \delta(a,x)+\delta(s_m b,s_m x)=\delta(a,x)+\delta(b,x).\end{aligned}$$

Supposing that $\delta(a,x)\leqslant\gamma$, $\delta(b,x)\leqslant\gamma$, one gets $\delta(m,x)<\gamma$ unless a is between x and $s_m x$ and $\delta(a,x)=\delta(b,x)=\gamma$; but then $\delta(a,s_m x)=\delta(b,x)=\gamma=\delta(a,x)$, which makes a the midpoint of x, $s_m x$; hence $a=m=b$.

Therefore $\delta(m, x)<\gamma$ on the compact set of x with $\delta(a, x)\leqslant\gamma$, $\delta(b, x)\leqslant\gamma$. This shows the existence of $\gamma'<\gamma$ with $\delta(m, x)\leqslant\gamma'$ on that set. The intersection of the γ-balls around a,b is contained in the γ'-ball around m.

Proof of the Theorem Take C_{un} commuting with C, form $G_{C,\text{un}}$, and the intersection Y of its G_C-conjugates, which is maximal normal sub G_C within $G_{C,\text{un}}$. Factorization with respect to Y transfers G_C into $G'_{C'}$, $G_{C,\text{un}}$ into $G'_{C',\text{un}'}$. Now $G'_{C',\text{un}'}$ contains no nontrivial normal subgroup of $G'_{C'}$. Note that $G'_{C'}$ is also centerfree.

$R=G'_{C'}/G'_{C',\text{un}'}$ is a symmetric space with uniqueness of geodesic joining. Let K be a compact subgroup of G_C, and K' its image in $G'_{C'}$. In R the set $P=K'G'_{C',\text{un}'}/G'_{C',\text{un}'}$ is K'-invariant and compact, thus bounded. According to the proposition, the ball with minimal radius containing P is unique and still K'-invariant, as is its center $m=g'G'_{C',\text{un}'}$ (for some $g'\in G'_{C'}$); $K'g'G'_{C',\text{un}'}=g'G'_{C',\text{un}'}$, translated in terms of G_C, becomes $KgG_{C,\text{un}}\subset gG_{C,\text{un}}$ with some $g\in G_C$. In other words, $g^{-1}Kg\subset G_{C,\text{un}}$. If K is maximal, this means that it is conjugate to $G_{C,\text{un}}$ by means of g.

Remark If one passes to nonlinear wrappings of G_C, the maximal compact subgroups may undergo essential modification (see 51.5.11, second Remark; 62.9). The theorem, however, can be shown to remain valid.

65.5 An analogous statement in the elliptic case would not be true, though in most subcases it is.

The statement would mean that isotypic C, C' (commuting with C_{un}) are inner isotypic. This is true of all simple inner and outer types except $\mathbf{D}_l$ (l even). In this case, from the viewpoint of inner isotypism $\mathbf{D}_{l,1}$ and $\mathbf{D}_{l,2}$ must be distinguished. For $l=4$ the variety is still greater; $\mathbf{D}_{4,1}$, $\mathbf{D}_{4,2}$, $\mathbf{D}_{4,3}$ must be distinguished. Furthermore, there are three inner different $\mathbf{D}_{4,0,*}$ and three inner different $\mathbf{D}_{4,1,*}$, $\mathbf{D}_{4,2,*}$, $\mathbf{D}_{4,3,*}$.

For twin types things can be still more involved.

These examples provide isometric elliptic symmetric spaces, the stability groups of which are not conjugate in G_{un}.

65.6. Historical Note The proof of 65.4 is a simplified version of E. Cartan's [*J. Math. pures et appl.* (9) **8**, 1–33 (1929), particularly p. 19 = *Œuvres* I **2**, 1029].

66. AUTOMETRISMS OF SYMMETRIC SPACES, AUTOMORPHISMS OF REAL SEMISIMPLE LIE GROUPS

66.1 The group of autometrisms of abelian symmetric spaces depends widely on the global structure of the space and of the (not unique) choice of the metric. For nonabelian spaces, however, one has the following:

Theorem In a simple space R of Sye(G_C) or Syh(G_C) the 1-component of Aut R is G_{un} and G_C, respectively.

Remark This statement is true for all symmetric spaces with no abelian factor.

Proof Int R, which is G_{un} or G_C, is closed normal in Aut R. The stability group $\hat{J}$ of Aut R at p normalizes the stability group J of Int R at p and its 1-component J_0. As represented in the tangent space at p, $\hat{J}$ preserves the metric and consequently the absolute value of the volume. Therefore, according to the argument used in 64.8 to prove the compactness of J, it can be seen that $\hat{J}/J_0$, hence $\hat{J}/J$, is finite. Since Aut $R=\hat{J}$ Int R, it follows that Aut R/Int R is finite. Hence Int R, being closed in Aut R, is also open.

66.2 In a simple semisimple symmetric space G/J every automorphism of G that leaves J invariant gives rise to an autometrism, since it preserves the Killing form on which the metric rests.

Even inner automorphisms of G may effect autometrisms that do not belong to the 1-component. An example is $\tilde{k}$ if k belongs to the normalizer of J. The autometrism

$$\Upsilon_{gJ}\, k^{-1}(\tilde{k}g)J = \Upsilon_{gJ}\, gJk^{-1}$$

in the same component as $\tilde{k}$ has the noteworthy property that it commutes with every element of G. An easy calculation shows that it coincides with an element of G as acting on R if and only if kJ contains a central element of G; thus, if for example G is centerfree and $k \notin J$, then the autometrism induced by $\tilde{k}$ will not belong to the 1-component of the autometrism group.

The next task is the determination of the full group of autometrisms.

66.3 Let $R \in \mathrm{Sy}(G_C)$ be simple, $F = \mathrm{Aut}\, R$, $F_0 = \mathrm{Int}\, R$, J be the stability group of F at p, J_0 the 1-component of J, and $\boldsymbol{F}, \boldsymbol{J}$ the infinitesimal algebras of F and J_0. Thus $F_0 = G_C$ or $G_{C\mathrm{un}}$, and $\boldsymbol{F} = \boldsymbol{G}_C$ or $\boldsymbol{G}_{C\mathrm{un}}$, under a natural identification.

Let $\mathrm{Aut}(\boldsymbol{F}, \boldsymbol{J})$ be the group of automorphisms of $\boldsymbol{F}$ leaving $\boldsymbol{J}$ invariant and $\mathrm{Aut}(\boldsymbol{F}, \boldsymbol{J}; J_0)$ its subgroup consisting of the $\tilde{j}$ with $j \in J_0$.

Proposition Under the foregoing assumptions, if $R \in \mathrm{Syma}(G_C)$, then F/F_0 is isomorphically related to a subgroup of $\mathrm{Aut}(\boldsymbol{F}, \boldsymbol{J})/\mathrm{Aut}(\boldsymbol{F}, \boldsymbol{J}; J_0)$ by assigning to $f \in F$ some $\tilde{j}$ with $j \in J \cap fF_0$; if F_0 is centerfree, the assignment is "onto."

Proof Since R is maximal, its stability group within F_0 is connected; thus $J \cap F_0 = J_0$.

Since R is connected, J intersects the component fF_0 of F (see 63.1.8). Therefore there is some $j \in J \cap fF_0$. A different choice $j_1 \in J \cap fF_0$ means that $j^{-1} j_1 \in J \cap F_0 = J_0$; thus $\tilde{j}_1 \in \tilde{j}\, \mathrm{Aut}(\boldsymbol{F}, \boldsymbol{J}; J_0)$ and the assignment is unique. Clearly the assignment is a homomorphism.

It is one-to-one, since if $j \in J \cap fF_0$ has the property $\tilde{j} = \tilde{j}_0$ for some $j_0 \in J_0$, then $\tilde{j}\boldsymbol{f} = \tilde{j}_0 \boldsymbol{f}$ for $\boldsymbol{f} \in \boldsymbol{F}$, hence $\tilde{j}f = \tilde{j}_0 f$ for $f \in F_0$; thus $z = j_0^{-1} j$ centralizes F_0 and consequently leaves invariant all fJ ($f \in F_0$), which are all points of R. Therefore $z = 1$ and $j \in J_0 \subset F_0$.

If F_0 is centerfree, any $\sigma \in \mathrm{Aut}(\boldsymbol{F}, \boldsymbol{J})$ extends to an automorphism of F_0, leaving J_0 invariant and acting autometrically on R. Therefore the assignment is "onto."

A consequence of the foregoing proposition and of 65.4 and 51.5.11–12 is the following:

Theorem The group of automorphism classes of nonunitary $\boldsymbol{G}_C$ ($\in$ Alg Lie Lin Rea SSS) and G_C (centerfree), that is, $\mathrm{Aut}\, \boldsymbol{G}_C/\mathrm{Int}\, \boldsymbol{G}_C$, or $\mathrm{Aut}\, G_C/\mathrm{Int}\, G_C$, is in a natural way isomorphic to the group of autometrism classes of $R \in \mathrm{Syma}\,(G_C)$, that is $\mathrm{Aut}\, R/\mathrm{Int}\, R$ with $R = G_C/G_{C\mathrm{un}}$.

66.4 In addition to the notations in 66.3 the following will be used:

$\boldsymbol{F} = \boldsymbol{J} + \boldsymbol{N}$ as usual.

$\vartheta =$ the representation $\curlyvee_j \tilde{j}$ of J in $\boldsymbol{N}$.

$\boldsymbol{J} = \boldsymbol{J}' + \boldsymbol{A}$, with semisimple $\boldsymbol{J}'$, where $\boldsymbol{A}$ is one- or zero-dimensional, according to whether or not ϑ is reducible over Com.

J_0', A are the corresponding linear Lie groups.

M the minus-automorphism under some ordered maximal compact dressing on some trunk $\boldsymbol{H}$.

$\boldsymbol{H}_{C,\mathrm{un}}$, as usual, the intersection of the aforesaid trunk $\boldsymbol{H}$ with $\boldsymbol{J}$, which is a trunk of $\boldsymbol{J}$ and contains $\boldsymbol{A}$.

Σ the group of linear mappings of $\boldsymbol{H}_{C,\mathrm{un}}$ into itself, leaving $\boldsymbol{A}$ elementwise invariant, and of which the induced mappings in $\mathrm{i}\boldsymbol{H}^*_{C,\mathrm{un}}$ leave invariant

$W^{++}(J')$,
the top weight(s) of ϑ, and
the inner product on $\mathrm{i}\boldsymbol{H}_{C,\mathrm{un}}$

as induced by $\boldsymbol{J}_{\mathrm{Com}}$ (or by $\boldsymbol{G}$, which for Σ will make no difference).

Proposition A representative system of $\mathrm{Aut}(\boldsymbol{F}, \boldsymbol{J})/\mathrm{Aut}(\boldsymbol{F}, \boldsymbol{J}; J_0)$ is furnished by the following construction:

Take one automorphic extension of $\boldsymbol{F}$ for every $\sigma \in \Sigma$ (its existence will be proved). Add the products with $M|_{\boldsymbol{F}}$ if ϑ is complex reducible and those with $T|_{\boldsymbol{F}}$ if R is outer or twin type.

Proof $\omega \in \mathrm{Aut}(\boldsymbol{F}, \boldsymbol{J})$ will be gradually modified within $\omega\,\mathrm{Aut}(\boldsymbol{F}, \boldsymbol{J}; J_0)$ and possibly multiplied by $M|_{\boldsymbol{F}}$ to push its $\boldsymbol{H}_{C,\mathrm{un}}$-restriction into Σ.

$\omega\boldsymbol{H}_{C,\mathrm{un}}$ is another trunk of $\boldsymbol{J}$. By means of some $\tilde{j}$ ($j \in J_0$) it is brought back to $\boldsymbol{H}_{C,\mathrm{un}}$. This allows one to suppose that $\omega\boldsymbol{H}_{C,\mathrm{un}} = \boldsymbol{H}_{C,\mathrm{un}}$ and likewise that the dominant chamber of $\boldsymbol{J}'$, that is, $W^{++}(\boldsymbol{J}')$, is invariant under ω.

On $\boldsymbol{A}$ the action of ω is 1 or -1. By multiplication by $M|_{\boldsymbol{F}}$, if needed, it can be made 1. The action of ω in $\boldsymbol{N}$ transforms ϑ into equivalent $\omega\vartheta\omega^{-1}$. Thus ω effects a permutation of the weights of ϑ. Because of the invariance of the dominant chamber and of $\boldsymbol{A}$ elementwise, this permutation leaves the top weight(s) invariant. (This is also true if there are two, for then they take opposite values on $\boldsymbol{A}$, as can be seen by calculating the 0-trace of an element $\tilde{\boldsymbol{a}}$, with $\boldsymbol{a} \in \boldsymbol{A}$, as acting on $\boldsymbol{G}$.) The new ω has its $\boldsymbol{H}_{C,\mathrm{un}}$-restriction in Σ.

This procedure is unambiguous: if the $\boldsymbol{H}_{C,\mathrm{un}}$-restrictions of ω_1, ω_2 are in Σ and $\omega_2 \in \omega_1\,\mathrm{Aut}(\boldsymbol{F}, \boldsymbol{J}; J_0)$, then $\omega_1^{-1}\omega_2 = \tilde{j}_0$ with $j_0 \in J_0$ has its $\boldsymbol{H}_{C,\mathrm{un}}$-restriction in Σ. Therefore $\tilde{j}_0$, acting trivially on the dominant chamber of $\boldsymbol{J}'$ and on $\boldsymbol{A}$, acts trivially on $\boldsymbol{H}_{C,\mathrm{un}}$. Therefore the $\boldsymbol{H}_{C,\mathrm{un}}$-restrictions of ω_1, ω_2 coincide. If ϑ is complex reducible, one should note that the minus-automorphism M is not induced by any element of J_0.

Clearly the procedure is homomorphic. Up to $\mathrm{Aut}(\boldsymbol{F}, \boldsymbol{J}; J_0)$ its kernel consists of 1 and T at most: Let the $\boldsymbol{H}_{C,\mathrm{un}}$-restriction of ω be trivial; up to

$\operatorname{Aut}(\boldsymbol{F}, \boldsymbol{J}; J_0)$ it may be assumed trivial on $\boldsymbol{J}'$ (see 33.9), thus on $\boldsymbol{J}$; then ω acting in $\boldsymbol{N}$ centralizes $\vartheta(J_0)$. If ϑ is complex reducible, it belongs to $\operatorname{Aut}(\boldsymbol{F}, \boldsymbol{J}; J_0)$ (see 64.10 or the third case of Theorem 64.6); if ϑ is complex irreducible, ω behaves as ± 1 on $\boldsymbol{N}$, in other words, as 1 or T on $\boldsymbol{F}$. For inner types $T = \tilde{h}$ (some $h \in H_{C,\mathrm{un}} \subset J_0$) and therefore can be disregarded.

The last thing to be done is to extend $\sigma \in \Sigma$ to $\boldsymbol{F}$ as an element of $\operatorname{Aut}(\boldsymbol{F}, \boldsymbol{J})$.

First of all σ extends as an automorphism to $\boldsymbol{J}'$ and $\boldsymbol{J}$. By $\vartheta'(\boldsymbol{j}) = \vartheta(\sigma\boldsymbol{j})$ a new linear representation ϑ' of $\boldsymbol{J}$ in $\boldsymbol{N}$ arises. It shares its top weight(s) (invariant under σ) with ϑ. Therefore there is a (real) linear mapping of $\boldsymbol{N}$ onto itself, again called σ, such that $\vartheta'(j) = \sigma\vartheta(j)\sigma^{-1}$. Since $\vartheta(\boldsymbol{j})$ equals $\tilde{\boldsymbol{j}}$ on $\boldsymbol{N}$, this means that $\widetilde{\sigma\boldsymbol{j}}\boldsymbol{n} = \sigma\tilde{\boldsymbol{j}}\sigma^{-1}\boldsymbol{n}$; in other words

66.4.1 $$[\sigma\boldsymbol{j}, \sigma\boldsymbol{n}] = \sigma[\boldsymbol{j}, \boldsymbol{n}] \qquad \text{for} \quad \boldsymbol{j} \in \boldsymbol{J}, \quad \boldsymbol{n} \in \boldsymbol{N}.$$

The $\vartheta(\boldsymbol{J})$-invariant metric on $\boldsymbol{N}$ is changed by σ into a $\vartheta'(\boldsymbol{J})$-invariant metric, which is again $\vartheta(\boldsymbol{J})$-invariant. The uniqueness-argument shows that the metrics are equal up to a positive constant factor. Renorming of σ makes them exactly equal. Then σ preserves the inner product on $\boldsymbol{N}$. On $\boldsymbol{J}$, where σ is automorphic, it did so before. Extended linearly to $\boldsymbol{F}$, it preserves the Killing form on $\boldsymbol{F} = \boldsymbol{J} + \boldsymbol{N}$:

66.4.2 $$\psi(\sigma\boldsymbol{f}_1, \sigma\boldsymbol{f}_2) = \psi(\boldsymbol{f}_1, \boldsymbol{f}_2).$$

Now 66.4.1 shows that

$$\sigma[\boldsymbol{j}, \boldsymbol{f}] = [\sigma\boldsymbol{j}, \sigma\boldsymbol{f}] \qquad \text{for} \quad \boldsymbol{j} \in \boldsymbol{J}, \quad \boldsymbol{f} \in \boldsymbol{F}.$$

Further,

$$\begin{aligned}\psi(\boldsymbol{j}, [\sigma\boldsymbol{n}_1, \sigma\boldsymbol{n}_2]) &= \psi([\boldsymbol{j}, \sigma\boldsymbol{n}_1], \sigma\boldsymbol{n}_2) = \psi(\sigma[\sigma^{-1}\boldsymbol{j}, \boldsymbol{n}_1], \sigma\boldsymbol{n}_2) \\ &= \psi([\sigma^{-1}\boldsymbol{j}, \boldsymbol{n}_1], \boldsymbol{n}_2) = \psi(\sigma^{-1}\boldsymbol{j}, [\boldsymbol{n}_1, \boldsymbol{n}_2]) \\ &= \psi(\boldsymbol{j}, \sigma[\boldsymbol{n}_1, \boldsymbol{n}_2]).\end{aligned}$$

Thus $\sigma[\boldsymbol{n}_1, \boldsymbol{n}_2] - [\sigma\boldsymbol{n}_1, \sigma\boldsymbol{n}_2]$, which belongs to $\boldsymbol{J}$, is orthogonal to all of $\boldsymbol{J}$. Thanks to the nondegeneracy of ψ on $\boldsymbol{J}$, it vanishes. This proves that σ extends the given one automorphically.

66.5 The foregoing proposition allows one to compute $\operatorname{Aut} R/\operatorname{Int} R$ for $R \in \operatorname{Syma}(G_C)$ of centerfree simple G_C. Spaces other than Syma spaces are covered by the following:

Proposition Let $R, R' \in \operatorname{Sye}(G_C)$ with simple† centerfree G arise from G_{un}/J_0, G_{un}/J_1, respectively, where J_0 is connected and $J_1 \supset J_0$. Then

† Cf. footnote in 62.7.

Aut $R'/\text{Int } R'$ arises from the subgroup consisting of those elements of Aut $R/\text{Int } R$ that contain an element leaving J_1 (as identified with a subgroup of Aut R) invariant (by means of conjugation), by reduction modulo the subgroup of those that contain a $\tilde{j}$ (considered as an element of Aut R) with $j \in J_1$. Of course, if $R' \in \text{Syemi}(G_C)$, that is, if J_1 is the normalizer of J_0 in G_{un}, the first-mentioned subgroup is the whole of Aut $R/\text{Int } R$.

66.6 To find the system Σ in any particular case one uses the weights of the representations ϑ from the classification list of Sections 52–53. Note that the presence of an A restricts Σ enormously; nontrivial elements can then exist only in $\mathsf{A}_{2m+1,m}$ and $\mathsf{D}_{l,3}$.

The following list includes the autometrism classes of Syema and Syhma for (noncompact) inner and outer G_C, hence the automorphism classes of G_C as well. The autometrism classes of twin G_C simply build up from outer automorphisms and T.

Though the theorem in 66.3 grants the extendibility of elements of Σ, one particular extension has been specified in each case.

The symbols $\beta, \beta', \ldots$ and $\gamma, \gamma', \ldots$ will indicate inner and outer automorphisms of G, respectively.

The groups Aut $R/\text{Int } R$, if abelian, are written additively.

66.7. The Autometrism Classes, Aut $R/\text{Int } R$, for Syma(G_C), G Centerfree, Simple,† Inner Type. The Automorphism Classes of G_C

$\mathsf{A}_{l,j}$: $\quad \boldsymbol{J} \in \mathbf{A}_{j-1} + \mathbf{A}_{l-j} + \mathbf{D}_1.$

For $l \neq 2j-1$ the automorphisms of the graph of $\boldsymbol{J}$ do not extend to $\boldsymbol{F}$. For $l = 2j-1$ one gets the symmetry of the graph of $\mathbf{A}_l$, called γ. Thus

$$l \neq 2j-1: \quad \mathsf{Z}_2(M),$$
$$l = 2j-1: \quad \mathsf{Z}_2(M) + \mathsf{Z}_2(\gamma) \quad \text{with} \quad \gamma + M \text{ inner.}$$

For $l = 1$ the summand $\mathsf{Z}_2(\gamma)$ does not occur.

$\mathsf{B}_{l,j}, j \geqslant 3$: $\quad \boldsymbol{J} \in \mathbf{D}_{j-1} + \mathbf{B}_{l-j+1}.$

$\mathbf{D}_{j-1}$ admits $\rho_{j-1} \leftrightarrow \rho_{j-1} + 2\rho_j + \cdots + 2\rho_l + 2\rho_1$, induced by an element of the kaleidoscope group of F_{Com}, namely $S_{\rho_j + \cdots + \rho_l + \rho_1}$, hence inner. For $j = 5$ the other symmetries of $\mathbf{D}_4$ cannot be extended without violating the invariance of the top weight of ϑ. Thus

$$\mathsf{Z}_2(\beta).$$

† Cf. footnote in 62.7.

$\mathsf{B}_{l,1}$: $\quad J \in \mathbf{D}_l$.

The mapping $\rho_l \leftrightarrow \rho_l + 2\rho_1$, induced by S_{ρ_1}. Here, also, this covers the case $l = 4$.

$$\mathsf{Z}_2(\beta).$$

$\mathsf{B}_{l,2}$: $\quad J \in \mathbf{D}_1 + \mathbf{B}_{l-1}$.

$$\mathsf{Z}_2(M).$$

$\mathsf{C}_{l,l}$: $\quad J \in \mathbf{A}_{l-1} + \mathbf{D}_1$.

The symmetry of $\mathbf{A}_{l-1}$ does not extend.

$$\mathsf{Z}_2(M).$$

$\mathsf{C}_{l,j}, j \neq l \neq 2j$: $\quad J \in \mathbf{C}_j + \mathbf{C}_{l-j}$.

Rigid graph.

Trivial.

$\mathsf{C}_{l,j}, l = 2j$.

The graph of J admits the interchange of the summands, induced by $S_{\rho_1 + \cdots + \rho_j} S_{\rho_2 + \cdots + \rho_{j+1}} \cdots S_{\rho_j + \cdots + \rho_{l-1}}$. Thus

$$\mathsf{Z}_2(\beta).$$

$\mathsf{D}_{l,1}, l > 4$: $\quad J \in \mathbf{A}_{l-1} + \mathbf{D}_1$.

The symmetry of the graph of $\mathbf{A}_{l-1}$ does not extend.

$$\mathsf{Z}_2(M).\dagger$$

$\mathsf{D}_{4,1}$. See $\mathsf{D}_{l,3}$ for $l = 4$.

$\mathsf{D}_{l,3}$: $\quad J \in \mathbf{D}_1 + \mathbf{D}_{l-1}$.

The graph symmetry is admitted.

$\mathsf{Z}_2(M) + \mathsf{Z}_2(\gamma)$ with inner $\gamma + M$ for odd l.

Note that for even l, M itself is inner.

$\mathsf{D}_{4,4}$: $\quad J \in \mathbf{A}_1 + \mathbf{A}_1 + \mathbf{A}_1 + \mathbf{A}_1$, the summands belonging to $\rho_1, \rho_2, \rho_3, \rho_3 + 2\rho_4 + \rho_1 + \rho_2$. These four rootforms are orthogonal to one another. Half their sum is a rootform $\rho_1 + \rho_2 + \rho_3 + \rho_4$ (the top weight of ϑ). S_{ρ_1}, S_{ρ_2}, S_{ρ_3},

† This result deviates from Cartan's.

$S_{\rho_3+2\rho_4+\rho_1+\rho_2}$, and $S_{\rho_1+\rho_2+\rho_3+\rho_4}$ produce all rootforms from them. Therefore the full permutation group of $\rho_1, \rho_2, \rho_3, \rho_3+2\rho_4+\rho_1+\rho_2$ is admitted.

The symmetric group of four permutands; the inner automorphisms produce the four-group.

$\mathsf{D}_{l,j}$, $l>4, j\geqslant 4$: $\quad J\in \mathbf{D}_{j-2}+\mathbf{D}_{l-j+2}$.

The symmetries of both summands extend. γ: $\rho_1 \leftrightarrow \rho_2$ (symmetry of $\mathbf{D}_l$) and $\gamma S_{\rho_j+\cdots+\rho_l+\rho_1} S_{\rho_j+\cdots+\rho_l+\rho_2}$. No more for $l\neq 2(j-2)$, even if $j=6$ or $l-2$. For $l=2(j-2)$ the aforesaid group increases by β':

$$S_{\rho_3+\cdots+\rho_j}\cdots S_{\rho_{j-2}+\cdots+\rho_{l-1}} S_{\rho_j+\cdots+\rho_l+\rho_1} S_{\rho_{j-1}+\cdots+\rho_l}$$

to interchange both summands. Thus

$l\neq 2(j-2)$: $\quad \mathsf{Z}_2(\gamma)+\mathsf{Z}_2(\gamma+\beta)$;

$l=2(j-2)$: $\quad$ extension of the foregoing by means of β' which interchanges the summands. Inner part: $\mathsf{Z}_2(\beta)+\mathsf{Z}_2(\beta')$.

$\mathsf{E}_{6,1}$: $\quad J\in\mathbf{D}_1+\mathbf{D}_5$.

The symmetry of $\mathbf{D}_5$ does not extend.

$\mathsf{Z}_2(M)$.

$\mathsf{E}_{6,2}$: $\quad J\in\mathbf{A}_1+\mathbf{A}_5$.

The symmetry γ of $\mathbf{E}_6$.

$\mathsf{Z}_2(\gamma)$.

$\mathsf{E}_{7,1}$: $\quad J\in\mathbf{A}_1+\mathbf{D}_6$.

The symmetry of $\mathbf{D}_6$ does not extend (confront it with $\hat{\alpha}$).

Trivial.

$\mathsf{E}_{7,2}$: $\quad J\in\mathbf{D}_1+\mathbf{E}_6$.

If the first summand is fixed, then ρ_4 is fixed, and so on.

$\mathsf{Z}_2(M)$.

Note that M is inner.

$\mathsf{E}_{7,3}$: $J \in \mathbf{A}_7$.

The symmetry of $\mathbf{A}_7$ extends, since the system of rootforms contains the configuration

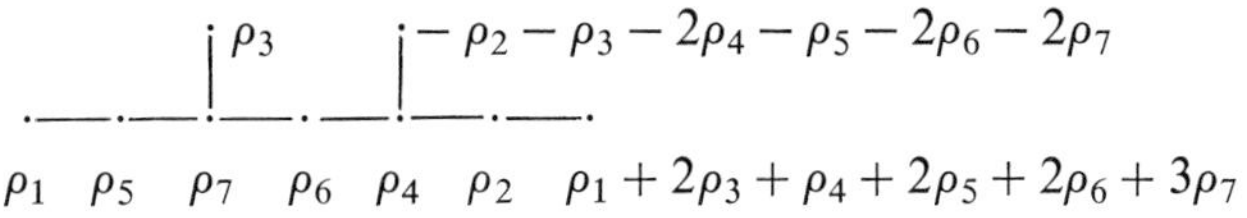

the symmetry of which produces an automorphism, necessarily inner in $\mathbf{E}_7$.

$\mathsf{Z}_2(\beta)$.

$\mathsf{E}_{8,1}$: $J \in \mathbf{E}_7 + \mathbf{A}_1$.

Rigid graph.

Trivial.

$\mathsf{E}_{8,2}$: $J \in \mathbf{D}_8$.

The symmetry $\rho_4 \leftrightarrow \rho_6$ does not extend.

Trivial.

$\mathsf{F}_{4,j}$: $J \in \mathbf{B}_4$ or $\mathbf{C}_3 + \mathbf{A}_1$.

A rigid graph in all cases.

Trivial.

$\mathsf{G}_{2,2}$: $J \in \mathbf{A}_1 + \mathbf{A}_1$.

The permutation $\rho_1 \leftrightarrow 3\rho_1 + 2\rho_2$ does not extend.

Trivial.

66.8. The Autometrism Classes, Aut R/Int R, for Syma(G_C), G Centerfree, Simple,† Outer Type. The Automorphism Classes of G_C

$\mathsf{A}_{l,0,*}$: J does not admit outer automorphisms.

$\mathsf{Z}_2(T)$.

† Cf. footnote in 62.7.

$\mathsf{A}_{2m-1,m,*}$: $\quad J \in \mathbf{D}_m$.

Here $\mathbf{D}_m$ admits of a symmetry. If extendible, it must be inner up to T.

$$T = \tilde{h}P, \qquad P\rho_i = \rho_{l+1-i}, \qquad Pe_\rho = e_{P\rho}, \qquad h = \exp \boldsymbol{h},$$

$$\rho_k(\boldsymbol{h}) = 0 \qquad (k \neq m), \qquad \rho_m(\boldsymbol{h}) = \pi\mathrm{i}.$$

One tries

$$S = \exp \tau(\tilde{e}_{\rho_m} + \tilde{e}_{-\rho_m}), \qquad \tau = \pi\mathrm{i}/\sqrt{2(\rho_m, \rho_m)}.$$

Then

$$S\boldsymbol{e}_{\rho_m} = \boldsymbol{e}_{-\rho_m}, \qquad S\boldsymbol{e}_{-\rho_m} = \boldsymbol{e}_{\rho_m}, \qquad S\boldsymbol{h}_{\rho_m} = \boldsymbol{h}_{\rho_m},$$

$$SP = PS.$$

$$\rho_m(S\boldsymbol{h}) = (S\rho_m)(\boldsymbol{h}) = -\pi\mathrm{i},$$

$$\rho_{m-1}(S\boldsymbol{h}) = (S\rho_{m-1})(\boldsymbol{h}) = (\rho_{m-1} + \rho_m)(\boldsymbol{h}) = \pi\mathrm{i} = \rho_{m+1}(S\boldsymbol{h}),$$

$$\rho_i(S\boldsymbol{h}) = 0 \qquad (i \neq m-1, m, m+1).$$

However, S does not commute with T as it should. It has to be changed to satisfy this condition. Put

$$\boldsymbol{h}_0 = \boldsymbol{h} - S\boldsymbol{h}, \qquad h_0 = \exp \boldsymbol{h}_0.$$

Then

$$\rho_m(\boldsymbol{h}_0) = 2\pi\mathrm{i}, \qquad \rho_{m-1}(\boldsymbol{h}_0) = \rho_{m+1}(\boldsymbol{h}_0) = -\pi\mathrm{i}, \qquad \text{otherwise} = 0;$$

$$STS^{-1} = S\tilde{h}S^{-1}P = \widetilde{Sh}P = \widetilde{Sh}\tilde{h}^{-1}T = \tilde{h}_0^{-1}T,$$

$$\begin{aligned} TS &= T \exp \tau(\tilde{e}_{\rho_m} + \tilde{e}_{-\rho_m}) \\ &= \exp \tau(T(\boldsymbol{e}_{\rho_m} + \boldsymbol{e}_{-\rho_m}))^{\sim} T \\ &= \exp(-\tau(\tilde{e}_{\rho_m} + \tilde{e}_{-\rho_m}))\, T; \end{aligned}$$

thus

$$STS = T, \qquad S^2 = STS^{-1}\, STS = \tilde{h}_0^{-1}.$$

Now S is going to be replaced by some

$$S' = \tilde{h}_1 S$$

which commutes with T. This means that h_1 has to fulfill

$$\tilde{h}_1 \tilde{h}_0^{-1} \widetilde{Th_1^{-1}} = 1$$

or, with $h_1 = \exp \boldsymbol{h}_1$,

$$\boldsymbol{h}_1 - T\boldsymbol{h}_1 = \boldsymbol{h}_0 \bmod 2\pi\mathrm{i} \qquad \text{for the rootforms.}$$

From this h_1 can be solved with

$$\rho_m(h_1)=0, \qquad \rho_{m-1}(h_1)=-\tfrac{1}{2}\pi i, \qquad \rho_{m+1}(h_1)=\tfrac{1}{2}\pi i, \qquad \text{otherwise } 0.$$

Now S' commuting with T leaves J invariant and produces the automorphism wanted. Thus

$$Z_2(T)+Z_2(\beta).$$

$D_{l,j,*}$, $l \neq 2j-3$.

No automorphism of the graph of J.

$$Z_2(T).$$

$D_{l,j,*}$, $l=2j-3$: $\quad J \in \mathbf{B}_{j-2}+\mathbf{B}_{j-2}$.

The graph admits the interchange of the summands. Put

$$S=S_{\rho_3+\cdots+\rho_j}\cdots S_{\rho_{j-1}+\cdots+\rho_{l-1}}S_{\rho_j+\cdots+\rho_l}.$$

The rootforms are permuted in the correct way by S. Moreover, $SP=PS$, but S does not commute with $T=\tilde{h}P$. The correcting factor is found as in $A_{2m-1,m,*}$:

$$P\rho_1=\rho_2, \qquad P\rho_2=\rho_1, \qquad P\rho_k=\rho_k \quad (k\neq 1,2), \qquad Pe_\rho=e_{P\rho},$$

$$\rho_j(h)=\pi i, \qquad \rho_k(h)=0 \quad (k\neq j),$$

$$\rho_j(Sh)=-\pi i, \qquad \rho_1(Sh)=\rho_2(Sh)=\pi i, \qquad \text{otherwise } 0,$$

and so on:

$$TS=S^{-1}T,$$

and so on.

$$Z_2(T)+Z_2(\beta).$$

$E_{6,0,*}$ and $E_{6,2,*}$.

No graph automorphism.

$$Z_2(T).$$

67. FUNDAMENTAL GROUPS OF SYMMETRIC SPACES

67.1 Hyperbolic symmetric spaces are topologically euclidean, with a trivial fundamental group. For elliptic symmetric spaces of the twin type the fundamental group is that of the unitary type. The case $R \in \mathrm{Syema}(G_C)$ is settled by Theorem 63.3.4. Indeed, $R=G_{\mathrm{un}}/G_{C,\mathrm{un}}$, where $G_{C,\mathrm{un}}$ is the maximal *connected* subgroup of G_{un} consisting of T-invariants. If j, as in 63.3.4, means the embedding of $G_{C,un}$ into G_{un}, then the $\alpha \in j\Phi(G_{C,un})$ are characterized by containing a T-invariant path. Now for centerfree G_{un} the system of straight paths defined by $\boldsymbol{Z}$ in 32.2.4 intersects every element α of $\Phi(G_{C,un})$ at most once, and this system is T-invariant. Therefore for centerfree G_{un}, hence, in general, every $\alpha = T\alpha$ contains a path $w = Tw$. Whence:

Proposition For $R = G_{un}/G_{C,un}$, $\Phi(R)$ is isomorphic to $\Phi(G_{un})$ mod kernel $(1-T)$. Its dual $\Phi^*(R)$ is isomorphic to $(1-T)\,\Phi^*(G_{un})$.

67.2. Dual of the Fundamental Group of $R \in \mathrm{Syema}(G_C)$, G Simple, Centerfree

For all inner types: Trivial.

$\mathsf{A}_{l,*}$: Elements $\pi_k - T\pi_k \backsim (2k-l+1)\,\pi_1$.

l odd: $\mathsf{Z}_{\frac{1}{2}(l+1)}(\pi_2)$,

l even: $\mathsf{Z}_{l+1}(\pi_1)$.

$\mathsf{D}_{l,*}$: Elements $\pi_1 + \pi_2$ and π_k $(k > 2)$.

l odd: $\mathsf{Z}_2(2\pi_1) = \mathsf{Z}_2(\pi_3)$,

l even: $\mathsf{Z}_2(\pi_1 + \pi_2) = \mathsf{Z}_2(\pi_3)$.

$\mathsf{E}_{6,*}$: $\mathsf{Z}_3(\pi_1)$.

67.3. Proposition Let G be simple centerfree, $R \in \mathrm{Syemi}(G_C)$, $F_0 = G_{un}$, $J_0 = G_{C,un}$, and J the normalizer of J_0 in F_0. Then $\Phi(R)/\Phi(F_0/J_0)$ is isomorphic with J/J_0.

This is evident since F_0/J_0 is a wrapping of $R = F_0/J$.

J/J_0 is found in 66.7–8; the normalizer classes produce the isometrisms indicated by β, β', and M (if it is inner).

If J/J_0 or $\Phi(F_0/J_0)$ is trivial, the proposition gives full information on $\Phi(R)$. Otherwise some additional arguments are needed.

67.4. Fundamental Group of $R \in \mathrm{Syemi}(G_C)$, G Simple, Centerfree

$\mathsf{A}_{l,j}$,	$l \neq 2j-1$:	Trivial.
	$l = 2j-1$:	$\mathsf{Z}_2(\gamma + M)$.
$\mathsf{B}_{l,j}$,	$j \geqslant 3$:	$\mathsf{Z}_2(\beta)$.
$\mathsf{B}_{l,1}$:		$\mathsf{Z}_2(\beta)$.
$\mathsf{B}_{l,2}$:		$\mathsf{Z}_2(M)$.
$\mathsf{C}_{l,l}$:		$\mathsf{Z}_2(M)$.

$\mathsf{C}_{l,j}$, $j \neq l \neq 2j$:	Trivial.
$\mathsf{C}_{l,j}$, $l = 2j$:	$\mathsf{Z}_2(\beta)$.
$\mathsf{D}_{l,1}$, $l > 4$, l even:	$\mathsf{Z}_2(M)$.
l odd:	Trivial.†
$\mathsf{D}_{l,3}$, l even:	$\mathsf{Z}_2(M)$.
l odd:	$\mathsf{Z}_2(\gamma + M)$.
$\mathsf{D}_{4,4}$:	$\mathsf{Z}_2(\beta) + \mathsf{Z}_2(\beta')$.
$\mathsf{D}_{l,j}$, $l > 4$, $j \geqslant 4$, $l \neq 2(j-2)$:	$\mathsf{Z}_2(\beta)$.
$l = 2(j-2)$:	$\mathsf{Z}_2(\beta) + \mathsf{Z}_2(\beta')$.
$\mathsf{E}_{6,1}$, $\mathsf{E}_{6,2}$:	Trivial.
$\mathsf{E}_{7,1}$:	Trivial.
$\mathsf{E}_{7,2}$:	$\mathsf{Z}_2(M)$.
$\mathsf{E}_{7,3}$:	$\mathsf{Z}_2(\beta)$.
$\mathsf{E}_{8,j}$, $\mathsf{F}_{4,j}$, $\mathsf{G}_{2,2}$:	Trivial.
$\mathsf{A}_{l,0,*}$ $\mathsf{D}_{l,j,*}$ $(l \neq 2j-3)$, $\mathsf{E}_{6,j,*}$:	Syemi = Syema.
$\mathsf{A}_{2m-1,m,*}$:	$\mathsf{Z}_{2m}(\beta)$.
$\mathsf{D}_{l,j,*}$ $(l = 2j-3)$:	$\mathsf{Z}_4(\beta)$.

Proof for $\mathsf{A}_{2m-1,m,*}$: The notations of 66.8 are used. The fundamental group can be considered as an extension of $\mathsf{Z}_m(\pi_2)$ by $\mathsf{Z}_2(\beta)$. A path from 1 to $\tilde{h}_1 S$ in the normalizer of J_0 is found as the adjoint image of a path

$$\Upsilon_t \exp t\boldsymbol{h}_1 \exp t\tau(\boldsymbol{e}_{\rho_m} + \boldsymbol{e}_{-\rho_m}) \qquad (0 \leqslant t \leqslant 1)$$

in the universal wrapping of $F_0 = \text{Int } R$. The square of the path is

$$\Upsilon_t \exp t\boldsymbol{h}_1 \exp t\tau(\boldsymbol{e}_{\rho_m} + \boldsymbol{e}_{-\rho_m}) \qquad (0 \leqslant t \leqslant 2).$$

The path

$$\Upsilon_t \exp \tfrac{1}{2}t\boldsymbol{h}_0 \exp t\tau(\boldsymbol{e}_{\rho_m} + \boldsymbol{e}_{-\rho_m}) \qquad (0 \leqslant t \leqslant 2)$$

has its adjoint within J_0. Therefore in F_0/J_0 it is trivial. Multiplication of the last but one by the inverse of the last gives

$$\Upsilon_t \exp t(\boldsymbol{h}_1 - \tfrac{1}{2}\boldsymbol{h}_0) \qquad (0 \leqslant t \leqslant 2).$$

Now

$$\rho_m(2\boldsymbol{h}_1 - \boldsymbol{h}_0) = -2\pi\mathrm{i}, \qquad \rho_{m-1}(2\boldsymbol{h}_1 - \boldsymbol{h}_0) = 0, \qquad \rho_{m+1}(2\boldsymbol{h}_1 - \boldsymbol{h}_0) = 2\pi\mathrm{i},$$

and $= 0$ otherwise, which shows

$$\pi_2(2\boldsymbol{h}_1 - \boldsymbol{h}_0) = -\frac{2}{l+1}\,2\pi\mathrm{i} = -\frac{1}{m}\,2\pi\mathrm{i}.$$

π_2 is a generator of order m of the dual fundamental group of F_0/J_0. Thus,

$$\Upsilon_t \exp t(\boldsymbol{h}_1 - \tfrac{1}{2}\boldsymbol{h}_0) \qquad (0 \leqslant t \leqslant 2)$$

† This result deviates from Cartan's.

turns out to be an element of order m;

$$\curlyvee_t \exp t\boldsymbol{h}_1 \exp t\tau(\boldsymbol{e}_{\rho m} + \boldsymbol{e}_{-\rho m}) \qquad (0 \leqslant t \leqslant 1)$$

is of order $2m$ in the fundamental group of F_0/J.

For $\mathsf{D}_{l,j,*}$ $(l = 2j - 3)$ the proof is much the same.

67.5 In the inner case all wrappings of $R \in \mathrm{Syemi}(G_C)$ (G simple, centerfree) are realized by elements of $\mathrm{Sye}(G_C)$. An element of $\mathrm{Syema}(G_C)$ is simply connected. So wrapping $F_0 = G_{\mathrm{un}}$ does not affect R, since the arising center dives into the stability group.

In the outer types $R \in \mathrm{Syema}(G_C)$ is not simply connected (67.2). Therefore wrappings of G may cause true wrappings of R. Let $\hat{G}$ be the universal wrapping of G and $\hat{G}_{\mathrm{un}} = \hat{F}_0$, $\hat{G}_C$, $\hat{G}_{C,\mathrm{un}} = J_0$ the induced wrappings of G_{un}, G_C, $G_{C,\mathrm{un}}$, respectively, within $\hat{G}$. The new symmetric space $\hat{R} = \hat{F}_0/J_0$ will wrap R in any case; however, J_0 may have a nontrivial intersection with the center of $\hat{G}_{\mathrm{un}}$. This intersection Z can be found by comparing the results of 62.8 and 62.9. The 1-component of Aut $\hat{R}$ is isomorphic to $\hat{F}_0/Z$.

Proposition $\hat{R}$ is simply connected.

Proof It suffices to show that the index of Z in the center of $\hat{F}_0$ equals the order of the fundamental group of R. This is shown in the list in 67.6, obtained from 46.4, 67.2, 62.8, and 62.9.

67.6 A_l: center of $\hat{F}_0$: $\mathsf{Z}_{l+1}(\pi_1)$.
$\Phi(R)$: $\mathsf{Z}_{\frac{1}{2}(l+1)}(2\pi_1)$ for odd l, $\mathsf{Z}_{l+1}(\pi_1)$ for even l.
Z: $\mathsf{Z}_2(\pi_1')$ for $A_{l,0,*}$, odd l, 0 for even l.
$\mathsf{Z}_2(\pi_m')$ for $A_{2m-1,m,*}$, odd m, $\mathsf{Z}_2(\pi_1')$, even m.

D_l: center of $\hat{F}_0$: $\mathsf{Z}_2(\pi_1) + \mathsf{Z}_2(\pi_2)$ for even l, $\mathsf{Z}_4(\pi_1)$ for odd l.
(ΦR): $\mathsf{Z}_2(\pi_3)$.
Z: $\mathsf{Z}_2(\pi_1')$.

E_6: center of $\hat{F}_0$: $\mathsf{Z}_3(\pi_1)$.
$\Phi(R)$: $\mathsf{Z}_3(\pi_1)$.
Z: 0.

Remark The validity of the proposition is also an easy consequence of 64.1.3 and the considerations in 64.9.

67.7 Aut R/Int R can sometimes be smaller than that of the maximal space. One must check the action of Aut R/Int R on the fundamental group of $R \in$ Syema, in other words, on J/J_0 as far as the inner types are concerned. In the outer case there is still the a priori condition that T be an autometrism. It turns out that only for $\mathsf{D}_{2(j-2),j}$ and the outer types of D_4 can it happen that Aut R/Int R is smaller than for the maximal type.

68–75

TITS GEOMETRIES

68. A LIST OF FUNDAMENTAL THEOREMS

The aim of this section is to list a series of closely related theorems, a few known to the reader, one to be proved here, and the greater part in the next section.

68.1–14 $G \in$ Alg Lie Com, and if needed $\in$ Alg Lie Lin Com; then G is generated by $\boldsymbol{G}$.

Notation If $\boldsymbol{X}$ sub $\boldsymbol{G}$, then Int$(\boldsymbol{G}, \boldsymbol{X})$ is the subgroup of inner automorphisms of $\boldsymbol{G}$ leaving $\boldsymbol{X}$ invariant and $\tilde{X}$ is the group generated by the exp $\tilde{\boldsymbol{x}}$ with $\boldsymbol{x} \in \boldsymbol{X}$ as acting on $\boldsymbol{G}$.

68.1. Trunks

A regular element of $\boldsymbol{G}$ was defined as one in which rank $\tilde{\boldsymbol{x}}$ $(\boldsymbol{x} \in \boldsymbol{G})$ attains its maximum. The trunk $\boldsymbol{H}$ of a regular element $\boldsymbol{h}$ was the set of $\boldsymbol{x}$ belonging to the 0-root of $\boldsymbol{h}$, that is, $\tilde{\boldsymbol{h}}^p \boldsymbol{x} = \boldsymbol{0}$ for large p. The following is well known from 17.8 and 33.9:

68.1.1. Theorem All trunks of $\boldsymbol{G}$ are Int $\boldsymbol{G}$-equivalent.

68.1.2 If $\boldsymbol{G}$ is semisimple and $\boldsymbol{H}$ is some trunk of $\boldsymbol{G}$, then $\tilde{H}$ is the subgroup of Int $\boldsymbol{G}$ leaving $\boldsymbol{H}$ elementwise invariant and Int$(\boldsymbol{G},\boldsymbol{H})/\tilde{H}$ is isomorphic with Int $W^*(\boldsymbol{G},\boldsymbol{H})$.

68.2–3. Maximal Solvable Subalgebras

68.2 The *maximal solvable subalgebras* of $\boldsymbol{G}$ are of particular importance. They are also called *Borel algebras* (after A. Borel).

Theorems

68.2.1 A maximal solvable $\boldsymbol{B}$ sub $\boldsymbol{G}$ contains a trunk of $\boldsymbol{G}$.

68.2.2 The maximal solvable subalgebras of $\boldsymbol{G}$ are Int $\boldsymbol{G}$-equivalent.

68.2.3 If $\boldsymbol{B}$ is maximal solvable sub $\boldsymbol{G}$, then $\mathrm{Int}(\boldsymbol{G}, \boldsymbol{B}) = \tilde{\boldsymbol{B}}$.

68.2.4 For semisimple $\boldsymbol{G}$ an element of $\mathrm{Int}(\boldsymbol{G}, \boldsymbol{B})$ leaving $\boldsymbol{B}$ elementwise invariant is the identity.

68.2.5 The groups infinitesimally generated by maximal solvable subalgebras of $\boldsymbol{G}$ are closed and characterized by being maximal solvable Lie or maximal solvable connected. They are Int $\boldsymbol{G}$-equivalent and their own normalizers.

68.3 If $\boldsymbol{G} \in$ Alg Lie Com SS and $\boldsymbol{H}$ is an ordered trunk of $\boldsymbol{G}$, then clearly $\boldsymbol{H}$, together with the branches $\boldsymbol{e}_\alpha$ $(\alpha > 0)$, spans a maximal solvable subalgebra. The next theorem asserts that this construction exhausts all of them.

Theorem If $\boldsymbol{G} \in$ Alg Lie Com SS, then any maximal solvable subalgebra $\boldsymbol{B}$ of $\boldsymbol{G}$ is spanned by an arbitrary trunk $\boldsymbol{H}$ of $\boldsymbol{G}$ within $\boldsymbol{B}$ and the branches $\boldsymbol{e}_\alpha$ with $\alpha > 0$ under a suitable order on $\boldsymbol{H}^*_{\mathrm{st}}$. The maximal solvable subalgebras of $\boldsymbol{G}$ around a trunk $\boldsymbol{H}$ are $\mathrm{Int}(\boldsymbol{G}, \boldsymbol{H})$-equivalent and in a one-to-one relation with the chambers on $\boldsymbol{H}$.

68.4–6. Nonsemisimple Maximal Proper Subalgebras

68.4. Theorem $\boldsymbol{G} \in$ Alg Lie Com SS.

Any maximal proper subalgebra of $\boldsymbol{G}$, which is *not* semisimple, contains a trunk of $\boldsymbol{G}$.

The case of $\mathbf{B}_{l-1}$ in $\mathbf{D}_l$ shows that a semisimple $\boldsymbol{G}$ can have semisimple maximal proper subalgebras with no regular element.

68.5. Definition Let $\boldsymbol{G} \in$ Alg Lie Com SS be dressed on an ordered trunk $\boldsymbol{H}$. For $\rho \in W^{++}$ the set of $\alpha \in W^+$ with a vanishing ρ-coordinate on the basis W^{++} is denoted by $W^+(\rho)$. The linear space spanned by $\boldsymbol{H}$, all $\boldsymbol{e}_\alpha$ with $\alpha > 0$, and all $\boldsymbol{e}_{-\alpha}$ with $\alpha \in W^+(\rho)$ is denoted by $\boldsymbol{G}(\rho, \boldsymbol{H})$ or $\boldsymbol{G}(\rho)$, for short.

68.6. Theorem $\boldsymbol{G} \in$ Alg Lie Com SS.

68.6.1 $\boldsymbol{G}(\rho)$, as defined in 68.5, is a maximal proper subalgebra of $\boldsymbol{G}$ and nonsemisimple.

68.6.2 Any nonsemisimple maximal proper subalgebra $\boldsymbol{M}$ of $\boldsymbol{G}$ on any suitably ordered trunk $\boldsymbol{H}$ of $\boldsymbol{G}$ within $\boldsymbol{M}$ gets the form $\boldsymbol{G}(\rho, \boldsymbol{H})$ for some $\rho \in W^{++}(\boldsymbol{G}, \boldsymbol{H})$.

68.7. Parabolic Subalgebras

68.7.1. Definition The proper subalgebras of $\boldsymbol{G}$ containing a maximal solvable one and the groups generated by them are called *parabolic*.

Note that a parabolic subalgebra of $\boldsymbol{G}$ must contain rad $\boldsymbol{G}$.

68.7.2. Theorem If $\boldsymbol{M}$ is parabolic sub $\boldsymbol{G}$, then Int $(\boldsymbol{G},\boldsymbol{M}) = \tilde{\boldsymbol{M}}$.

Parabolic subgroups are closed and their own normalizers.

68.7.3. Theorem Parabolic $\boldsymbol{M}$ sub $\boldsymbol{G}$ is the intersection of (a finite number of) maximal parabolic subalgebras of $\boldsymbol{G}$ around the same trunk, and likewise for parabolic subgroups of G.

68.7.4. Theorem For semisimple $\boldsymbol{G}$ the notions of maximal parabolic and of nonsemisimple maximal proper subalgebra coincide.

68.7.5. Theorem For any ordered trunk $\boldsymbol{H}$ every maximal parabolic subalgebra of semisimple $\boldsymbol{G}$ is Int $\boldsymbol{G}$-equivalent with some $\boldsymbol{G}(\rho)$.

For any ordered trunk $\boldsymbol{H}$, $G(\rho,\boldsymbol{H})$ and $G(\sigma,\boldsymbol{H})$ are Int $\boldsymbol{G}$-equivalent only if $\rho = \sigma$.

68.8. Nilpotents, and Semisimple Subalgebras of Rank 1

68.8.1. Theorem To any ad-nilpotent $\boldsymbol{e} \in \boldsymbol{G} \in$ Alg Lie Com SS an ad-pure $\boldsymbol{h} \in \boldsymbol{G}$ can be found such that $\tilde{\boldsymbol{h}}\boldsymbol{e} = \boldsymbol{e}$.

68.8.3. Theorem Any ad-nilpotent $\boldsymbol{e} \in \boldsymbol{G} \in$ Alg Lie Com SS is contained in a semisimple subalgebra of $\boldsymbol{G}$ of rank 1.

68.9. Bruhat's Lemma The intersection of two maximal solvable subalgebras of $\boldsymbol{G} \in$ Alg Lie Com SS contains a trunk of $\boldsymbol{G}$.

68.10–11. Some Homogeneous Spaces

68.10 Int $\boldsymbol{G}$ acts transitively on the set of maximal solvable subalgebras of $\boldsymbol{G}$. There is even double transitivity in a weak sense:

Theorem Let $\boldsymbol{G} \in$ Alg Lie Com SS. Then the (ordered) pairs of maximal solvable subalgebras of $\boldsymbol{G}$ which have no more than just a trunk in common are Int $\boldsymbol{G}$-equivalent and form an open everywhere dense subset in the manifold of all (ordered) pairs of maximal solvable subalgebras of $\boldsymbol{G}$.

68.11. Theorem Let $G \in$ Gru Lie Lin Com, A a maximal solvable Lie sub-group. Then the manifold G/A is compact.

68.12–14. A Proof

68.12 Only the theorems of 68.2 are proved this section. The proof rests on the rather elementary fact (to be proved in 69.25 and 69.37) that:

the maximal solvable subalgebras of $\boldsymbol{G}$ with a regular element are equivalent under Int $\boldsymbol{G}$ and form a compact manifold,

and on a proposition that for the sake of convenience is formulated in projective terms.

A group acting on the linear space R can also be interpreted as acting on the projective space $R_\#$ derived from R. Lie's theorem (13.9) then means that a solvable Lie group possesses a fixed point.

Proposition Suppose that $G \in$ Gru Lie Lin Com, solvable, acting on $R \in$ Spa Lin Com, interpreted as acting on $R_\#$. Then any minimal closed G-invariant subset of $R_\#$ consists of one point.

Proof by induction on dim $R_\#$. The truth for dim $R_\# = 1$ is a matter of inspecting the solvable linear Lie groups acting on two-dimensional space. From a triangular form of G it is seen that either every point of R_* is a fixed point or that only one point of R_* is left fixed and all others form one orbit, from which the validity of the proposition is obvious. Therefore suppose that dim $R_\# > 1$ and let $M \subset R_\#$ be such a minimal closed invariant subset. Its projective span is again invariant and may therefore be supposed to coincide with $R_\#$. As acting on $R_\#$, solvable G possesses a fixed point p. If $p \in M$, then because of its minimality M coincides with $\{p\}$, which agrees with the assertion. If $p \notin M$, then in $R'_\# = R_\#$ mod p (i.e., the projective space of straight lines through p) M reappears as a closed subset M'. It is again minimal invariant under the solvable group induced by G in $R'_\#$. By induction M' may be supposed to consist of one point only. This means that M lies on a straight line through p, and finally that dim $R_\# = 1$, which is just the induction basis.

68.13. *Proof* of 68.2.1. Let $\mathscr{B}$ be the set of maximal solvable subalgebras of $\boldsymbol{G}$ with a regular element and let $\boldsymbol{A}$ be any solvable subalgebra of $\boldsymbol{G}$. The $\tilde{\boldsymbol{a}}$ ($\boldsymbol{a} \in \boldsymbol{A}$) generate a solvable linear Lie group A' acting on the linear space $\boldsymbol{G}$ and consequently on $\mathscr{B}$. Now $\mathscr{B}$ and the action of A' on $\mathscr{B}$ can be interpreted in a linear space R (and in the related projective space $R_\#$) as follows:

Let dim $\boldsymbol{B} = k$ for $\boldsymbol{B} \in \mathscr{B}$ and take R as the linear space of skew k-tensors on $\boldsymbol{G}$. (Using a basis of $\boldsymbol{G}$, the k-dimensional linear subspaces $\boldsymbol{L}$ of $\boldsymbol{G}$ are described by their Plücker coordinates in R; take a basis of $\boldsymbol{L}$ and form the k-determinants from the coordinates of the basis elements.) Now A' induces a solvable linear Lie group A'' acting on R and consequently on $R_{\#}$. The image of $\mathscr{B}$ in $R_{\#}$ is again closed and A''-invariant. By 68.12 it contains some element of $\mathscr{B}$ fixed under A''. This means the existence of a solvable subalgebra $\boldsymbol{B}$ with a regular element such that $\tilde{a}\boldsymbol{B} = \boldsymbol{B}$ for $\tilde{a} \in A'$, hence $\tilde{\boldsymbol{a}}\boldsymbol{B} \subset \boldsymbol{B}$ for $\boldsymbol{a} \in \boldsymbol{A}$. Now the linear span of $\boldsymbol{B}$ and any $\boldsymbol{a} \in \boldsymbol{A}$ is again solvable; therefore $\boldsymbol{a} \in \boldsymbol{B}$ for any $\boldsymbol{a} \in \boldsymbol{A}$, hence $\boldsymbol{A} \subset \boldsymbol{B}$. If, moreover, $\boldsymbol{A}$ is maximal, then $\boldsymbol{A} = \boldsymbol{B}$ which proves that every maximal solvable subalgebra has a regular element. The remainder of the theorem is an easy consequence verified in a later context.

68.14 The facts proved in 68.12–13 are not used in the discussion of the theorems stated in 68.1–11. The fact (68.2.1) that a maximal solvable subalgebra of $\boldsymbol{G}$ contains a regular element is related to Lie algebras rather than to groups. For this reason it will be proved algebraically in Section 69, together with the analogous assertion on maximal nonsemisimple subalgebras of semisimple Lie algebras (68.4). From this the conjugacy assertions will be derived by using the conjugacy of trunks.

68.15. Historical Note The statements on the existence of regular elements in maximal solvable and nonsemisimple maximal subalgebras and some others, such as 68.8.1 and 68.8.3, are being credited to V. V. Morozov on account of his unpublished Kazan thesis of 1943, which seems to have been lost. Without doubt it is a great merit to have proposed these theorems and to have initiated this new chapter of the theory of Lie algebras. On the other hand, it is a fact that Morozov's published work on these points contains nothing that by any standard whatsoever could be called a mathematical proof [*Dokl. Akad. Nauk. SSSR* **36**, 83–86 (1942)].

F. I. Karpelevič [*Dokl. Akad. Nauk SSSR* **76**, 775–778 (1951)] is sometimes quoted as having simplified Morozov's proofs, though rather Karpelevič used Morozov's full results to derive statements that in Morozov's strategy must have appeared as lemmas from which his final results were derived.

It is distressing that until now no serious proof for a series of primordial theorems, though often quoted and used, has been available in the literature. Exceptions are Morozov's rather weak statements 68.8.1 and 68.8.3, which were first proved by N. Jacobson [*Proc. Amer. Math. Soc.* **2**, 105–133 (1951)]. The proof of 68.2 in 68.12–13 has been fashioned after one for algebraic groups, thanks to an oral indication by J. Tits; 68.10–11 likewise go back to J. Tits [*Mem. Acad. Bruxelles* in 8°, **29**, No. 3, 94 (1955)]. Bruhat's lemma (68.9) seems to have been diffused by oral tradition. Its usual formulation and proofs have concealed the fact that it is almost trivial, at least for linear Lie groups and algebras.

For an axiomatic and more detailed description of the situation as in 68.7 see J. Tits [*Compt. Rend., Paris* **254**, 2910–2912 (1963)].

The theorems announced in the present section are proved in the next, together with other statements. The proofs, except those mentioned before, are due to H. Freudenthal, though simplified by H. de Vries.

69. PROOFS OF THE STATEMENTS OF SECTION 68

$\boldsymbol{G} \in$ Alg Lie Com.

69.1. Proposition If $\boldsymbol{G} \in$ Alg Lie Lin Com SS, then $\curlyvee_{a,b}\operatorname{tr}(\boldsymbol{ab})$ is a linear combination of the Killing forms of the simple summands of $\boldsymbol{G}$, with positive coefficients.

Proof According to 43.4.1, this is true of simple $\boldsymbol{G}$, even if reducible. Assume $\boldsymbol{G} = \boldsymbol{G}_1 + \boldsymbol{G}_2$ (direct sum) and the proposition true for every nonzero linear representation of $\boldsymbol{G}_1$ and $\boldsymbol{G}_2$. It is sufficient to prove the proposition for irreducible $\boldsymbol{G}$. From 45.3 it is easily seen that up to equivalence any irreducible representation of $\boldsymbol{G}$, as well as the identical one, originates as follows: let $\boldsymbol{G}_i$ act on $R_i \in$ Spa Lin Com, $i = 1, 2$, and let $\boldsymbol{G}$ act on $R = R_1 \otimes R_2$ in such a way that for $\boldsymbol{a}_i \in \boldsymbol{G}_i$, $x_i \in R_i$

$$(\boldsymbol{a}_1 + \boldsymbol{a}_2)(x_1 \otimes x_2) = (\boldsymbol{a}_1 x_1) \otimes x_2 + x_1 \otimes (\boldsymbol{a}_2 x_2).$$

$c_1 \in \operatorname{End} R_1$ induces $c \in \operatorname{End} R$, where

$$\operatorname{tr} c = (\dim R_2) \operatorname{tr} c_1.$$

$\boldsymbol{a}_1, \boldsymbol{b}_1 \in \boldsymbol{G}_1$ induce $\boldsymbol{a}, \boldsymbol{b} \in \boldsymbol{G}$ acting on R,

$$\operatorname{tr}_R \boldsymbol{ab} = (\dim R_2) \operatorname{tr}_{R_1} \boldsymbol{a}_1 \boldsymbol{b}_1.$$

$\boldsymbol{a}_1 \in \boldsymbol{G}_1$, $\boldsymbol{b}_2 \in \boldsymbol{G}_2$ induce $\boldsymbol{a}, \boldsymbol{b} \in \boldsymbol{G}$ acting on R,

$$\operatorname{tr}_R \boldsymbol{ab} = \operatorname{tr} \boldsymbol{a}_1 \cdot \operatorname{tr} \boldsymbol{b}_2 = 0.$$

Hence

$$\operatorname{tr}(\boldsymbol{a}_1 + \boldsymbol{a}_2)(\boldsymbol{b}_1 + \boldsymbol{b}_2) = \dim R_2 \operatorname{tr} \boldsymbol{a}_1 \boldsymbol{b}_1 + \dim R_1 \operatorname{tr} \boldsymbol{a}_2 \boldsymbol{b}_2.$$

This proves the assertion.

69.2. Generalization of the Second Criterion on Solvability (17.17)

Proposition For $\boldsymbol{G} \in$ Alg Lie Com Lin the following conditions are equivalent: (i) $\boldsymbol{G}$ is solvable, (ii) $\operatorname{tr} \boldsymbol{ab} = 0$ for $\boldsymbol{a} \in \boldsymbol{G}$, $\boldsymbol{b} \in C(\boldsymbol{G})$, (iii) $\operatorname{tr} \boldsymbol{ab} = 0$ for $\boldsymbol{a}, \boldsymbol{b} \in C(\boldsymbol{G})$.

Proof (i) $\to$ (ii) and (ii) $\to$ (iii) are clear. Now suppose that $\boldsymbol{G}$ is not solvable. $\boldsymbol{G}$ acts on R which can be written directly as $R_1 + \cdots + R_p$ such that for every i

$R_1 + \cdots + R_i$ is $\boldsymbol{G}$-invariant and

$R_1 + \cdots + R_{i+1} \bmod R_1 + \cdots + R_i$ is irreducibly acted on by $\boldsymbol{G}$.

Since $\boldsymbol{G}$ is not solvable, dim $R_i > 1$ at least once. Let t_i be the projection onto R_i, thus $\sum_i t_i x = x$. If $\boldsymbol{a}' \in \operatorname{End} R$ for $\boldsymbol{a} \in \boldsymbol{G}$ is defined by

$$\boldsymbol{a}' x = t_i \boldsymbol{a} x \qquad \text{for} \quad x \in R_i \qquad \text{and all} \quad i,$$

then $\curlyvee_a \boldsymbol{a}'$ maps $\boldsymbol{G}$ homomorphically onto some $\boldsymbol{G}'$ and $C(\boldsymbol{G})$ onto $C(\boldsymbol{G}')$. Since $\boldsymbol{G}'$ is irreducible on every R_i and dim $R_i > 1$ at least once, it appears that $C(\boldsymbol{G}')$ is simisimple and $\neq \{\mathbf{0}\}$. Thus tr $\boldsymbol{a}'\boldsymbol{b}'$ does not vanish identically on $C(\boldsymbol{G}')$ according to 69.1. The same is true of tr $\boldsymbol{ab}$, which equals tr $\boldsymbol{a}'\boldsymbol{b}'$. This proves the assertion.

69.3. Proposition If $\boldsymbol{G} \in$ Alg Lie Com Lin and $\boldsymbol{N}$ is the subalgebra of nilpotent elements of rad $\boldsymbol{G}$, then $\boldsymbol{N}$ is an ideal of $\boldsymbol{G}$, and rad($\boldsymbol{G}$ mod $\boldsymbol{N}$) = (rad $\boldsymbol{G}$) mod $\boldsymbol{N}$ is the center of $\boldsymbol{G}$ mod $\boldsymbol{N}$.

Proof From a triangular form of rad $\boldsymbol{G}$ it is clear that $\boldsymbol{N}$ is an ideal of rad $\boldsymbol{G}$, containing the commutator algebra of rad $\boldsymbol{G}$. Let $\boldsymbol{g} \in \boldsymbol{G}$. Then $\boldsymbol{g}$ and rad $\boldsymbol{G}$ span a solvable subalgebra whose commutator algebra consists of nilpotent elements and is contained in rad $\boldsymbol{G}$. Therefore $\tilde{\boldsymbol{g}}$ rad $\boldsymbol{G} \subset \boldsymbol{N}$, for all $\boldsymbol{g} \in \boldsymbol{G}$, from which the proposition follows.

69.4. Proposition If $\boldsymbol{G} \in$ Alg Lie Com Lin and $\boldsymbol{R}$ is the subspace consisting of all elements $\boldsymbol{r}$ such that tr $\boldsymbol{ar} = 0$ for all $\boldsymbol{a} \in \boldsymbol{G}$, then (i) $\boldsymbol{R} \subset$ rad $\boldsymbol{G}$, (ii) $\boldsymbol{R}$ contains the nilpotent elements within rad $\boldsymbol{G}$, (iii) $\boldsymbol{R}$ is an ideal of $\boldsymbol{G}$, (iv) (rad $\boldsymbol{G}$) mod $\boldsymbol{R}$ is the center of $\boldsymbol{G}$ mod $\boldsymbol{R}$.

Proof $\boldsymbol{R}$ is an ideal since $\operatorname{tr}(\boldsymbol{a}[\boldsymbol{b}, \boldsymbol{r}]) = \operatorname{tr}([\boldsymbol{a}, \boldsymbol{b}]\boldsymbol{r}) = 0$ for $\boldsymbol{a}, \boldsymbol{b} \in \boldsymbol{G}$, $\boldsymbol{r} \in \boldsymbol{R}$. The solvability of $\boldsymbol{R}$ follows from 69.2; hence $\boldsymbol{R} \subset$ rad $\boldsymbol{G}$. If $\boldsymbol{a} \in \boldsymbol{G}$, than $\boldsymbol{a}$ and rad $\boldsymbol{G}$ span a solvable subalgebra, from a triangular form of which it follows that tr $\boldsymbol{an} = 0$ if $\boldsymbol{n}$ is a nilpotent element of rad $\boldsymbol{G}$. Hence $\boldsymbol{R}$ contains the ideal $\boldsymbol{N}$ of nilpotent elements within rad $\boldsymbol{G}$. From 69.3 it follows that (rad $\boldsymbol{G}$) mod $\boldsymbol{R}$ is central in $\boldsymbol{G}$ mod $\boldsymbol{R}$; therefore (rad $\boldsymbol{G}$) mod $\boldsymbol{R}$ = rad($\boldsymbol{G}$ mod $\boldsymbol{R}$) is the center of $\boldsymbol{G}$ mod $\boldsymbol{R}$.

69.5. Proposition For $\boldsymbol{A}$ sub $\boldsymbol{G}$, the following conditions are equivalent: (i) $\boldsymbol{A}$ is solvable, (ii) $\psi(\boldsymbol{a}, \boldsymbol{b}) = 0$ for $\boldsymbol{a} \in \boldsymbol{A}$, $\boldsymbol{b} \in C(\boldsymbol{A})$, (iii) $\psi(\boldsymbol{a}, \boldsymbol{b}) = 0$ for $\boldsymbol{a}, \boldsymbol{b} \in C(\boldsymbol{A})$.

Proof Apply 69.2 to the image of $\boldsymbol{A}$ under $\curlyvee_{\boldsymbol{a} \in \boldsymbol{A}} \curlyvee_{\boldsymbol{g} \in \boldsymbol{G}} \tilde{\boldsymbol{a}}\boldsymbol{g}$, that is, to $\operatorname{ad}_G \boldsymbol{A}$; note that the kernel of this representation is $\boldsymbol{A} \cap \boldsymbol{Z}$, where $\boldsymbol{Z}$ is the center of $\boldsymbol{G}$ and $\boldsymbol{A} \cap \boldsymbol{Z} \subset$ rad $\boldsymbol{A}$.

69.6. Notation If $\boldsymbol{M}$ sub $\boldsymbol{G}$ and ψ is the Killing form of $\boldsymbol{G}$, then

$$\boldsymbol{M}^{\perp} = \text{the orthoplement of } \boldsymbol{M} \text{ with respect to } \psi \text{ and}$$
$$\boldsymbol{M}^{\square} = \boldsymbol{M}^{\perp} \cap \boldsymbol{M}$$

Proposition If $\boldsymbol{M}$ sub $\boldsymbol{G}$, then (i) $\boldsymbol{M}^{\square} \subset \operatorname{rad} \boldsymbol{M}$, (ii) $\boldsymbol{M}^{\square}$ contains the ad-nilpotent elements within rad $\boldsymbol{M}$, (iii) $\boldsymbol{M}^{\square}$ is an ideal of $\boldsymbol{M}$, and (iv) (rad $\boldsymbol{M}$) mod $\boldsymbol{M}^{\square}$ is the center of $\boldsymbol{M}$ mod $\boldsymbol{M}^{\square}$.

Proof Apply 69.4 to the image of $\boldsymbol{M}$ under the representation $\curlyvee_{m\in M} \curlyvee_{g \in G} \tilde{\boldsymbol{m}}\boldsymbol{g}$; note that its kernel lies within $\boldsymbol{M}^{\square}$.

69.7. Proposition If $\boldsymbol{M}$ sub $\boldsymbol{G} \in$ Alg Lie Com and $\operatorname{ad}_G \boldsymbol{M}$ admits cleaving, then $\operatorname{ad}_G \boldsymbol{M}^{\square}$ also admits cleaving.

Proof Since $\boldsymbol{M}^{\square}$ is an ideal of $\boldsymbol{M}$, $\tilde{\boldsymbol{x}}\boldsymbol{M} \subset \boldsymbol{M}^{\square}$ for $\boldsymbol{x} \in \boldsymbol{M}^{\square}$. By the last assertion of 18.1.1 the cleaving components of $\tilde{\boldsymbol{x}}$ also map $\boldsymbol{M}$ into $\boldsymbol{M}^{\square}$; let them be pure $\tilde{\boldsymbol{a}}$ and nilpotent $\tilde{\boldsymbol{e}}$ (some $\boldsymbol{a}, \boldsymbol{e} \in \boldsymbol{M}$). This shows that $\boldsymbol{e} + \boldsymbol{M}^{\square}$ is in the center of $\boldsymbol{M}$ mod $\boldsymbol{M}^{\square}$; hence by 69.6 (iv) in (rad $\boldsymbol{M}$) mod $\boldsymbol{M}^{\square}$, thus $\boldsymbol{e} \in \boldsymbol{M}^{\square}$ by 69.6 (ii), which proves the assertion.

69.11. Proposition Suppose $\boldsymbol{G} \in$ Alg Lie Com Lin, $\boldsymbol{G}$ solvable, and let $\boldsymbol{G}$ admit cleaving. Let $\boldsymbol{N}$ be the ideal of nilpotent elements of $\boldsymbol{G}$. Then, if $\boldsymbol{A}$ is a maximal pure subspace of $\boldsymbol{G}$, $\boldsymbol{G} = \boldsymbol{A} + \boldsymbol{N}$, a direct sum, of subspaces.

Proof By 19.20 the idealizer of $\boldsymbol{A}$ is contained in $\boldsymbol{A} + \boldsymbol{N}$. Therefore, if $\boldsymbol{G} \neq \boldsymbol{A} + \boldsymbol{N}$, then by the fact that the elements of $\boldsymbol{A}$ are ad-pure there would be a $\boldsymbol{g} \in \boldsymbol{G}$, $\boldsymbol{g} \notin \boldsymbol{A} + \boldsymbol{N}$, and $\boldsymbol{a} \in \boldsymbol{A}$ such that $\tilde{\boldsymbol{a}}\boldsymbol{g}$ is a nonzero multiple of $\boldsymbol{g}$; this contradicts the fact that $\boldsymbol{N}$ contains the commutator algebra of $\boldsymbol{G}$.

69.14. Proposition If $\boldsymbol{G} \in$ Alg Lie Com SS, $\boldsymbol{H}$ a trunk of $\boldsymbol{G}$, and $\boldsymbol{A} \subset \boldsymbol{H}$, then the centralizer of $\boldsymbol{A}$ is the direct sum of a subalgebra of $\boldsymbol{H}$ and a semisimple one of $\boldsymbol{G}$.

This follows from 20.15.

69.15. Proposition Let $\boldsymbol{G} \in$ Alg Lie Com SS, $\boldsymbol{M}$ sub $\boldsymbol{G}$ its own idealizer, and $\boldsymbol{A}$ a maximal ad-pure linear subspace of $\boldsymbol{M}$. Then ψ is nondegenerate on $\boldsymbol{A}$.

Proof According to 19.22, $\boldsymbol{A}$ lies in a trunk $\boldsymbol{H}$ of $\boldsymbol{G}$. For $\alpha \in W$ the restriction to $\boldsymbol{A}$ of α is denoted by α'. The class of $\xi \in W$ with $\xi' = \alpha'$ is denoted by $[\alpha]$.

$\boldsymbol{G}$ splits with respect to $\boldsymbol{h} \in \boldsymbol{H}$ into eigenspaces $\boldsymbol{G}_{\alpha}$ $(\alpha \in W)$.

$\boldsymbol{G}$ splits with respect to $\boldsymbol{a} \in \boldsymbol{A}$ into eigenspaces $\boldsymbol{G}_{\alpha'}$ $(\alpha \in W)$.
Put

$$\boldsymbol{M} \cap \boldsymbol{G}_{\alpha'} = \boldsymbol{M}_{\alpha'}.$$

$$\boldsymbol{G}_{\alpha'} = \sum_{\gamma \in [\alpha]} \boldsymbol{G}_\gamma,$$

$$\boldsymbol{M} = \sum_{\alpha'} \boldsymbol{M}_{\alpha'},$$

all sums being direct.

Let $\boldsymbol{B}$ be the set of $\boldsymbol{h} \in \boldsymbol{H}$ such that $\alpha(\boldsymbol{h}) = \beta(\boldsymbol{h})$ for all α, β with $\alpha' = \beta'$. Thus $\boldsymbol{A} \subset \boldsymbol{B}$. It will be shown that $\boldsymbol{A} = \boldsymbol{B}$.

Every $\boldsymbol{x} \in \boldsymbol{G}_{\alpha'}$ has the form

$$\boldsymbol{x} = \sum_{\gamma \in [\alpha]} \boldsymbol{x}_\gamma \qquad \text{with} \quad \boldsymbol{x}_\gamma \in \boldsymbol{G}_\gamma.$$

For $\boldsymbol{h} \in \boldsymbol{B}$

$$\tilde{\boldsymbol{h}}\boldsymbol{x} = \sum_{\gamma \in [\alpha]} \gamma(\boldsymbol{h})\, \boldsymbol{x}_\gamma = \alpha(\boldsymbol{h}) \sum \boldsymbol{x}_\gamma = \alpha(\boldsymbol{h})\, \boldsymbol{x}.$$

Thus

$$\tilde{\boldsymbol{B}}\boldsymbol{M}_{\alpha'} \subset \boldsymbol{M}_{\alpha'}, \qquad \tilde{\boldsymbol{B}}\boldsymbol{M} \subset \boldsymbol{M},$$

and since $\boldsymbol{M}$ is its own idealizer, $\boldsymbol{B} \subset \boldsymbol{M}$. Hence $\boldsymbol{B} \subset \boldsymbol{M} \cap \boldsymbol{H} = \boldsymbol{A}$, and thus $\boldsymbol{A} = \boldsymbol{B}$.

Now $\boldsymbol{A}$ can be singled out of $\boldsymbol{H}$ as the set of $\boldsymbol{h}$ fulfilling $\alpha(\boldsymbol{h}) = \beta(\boldsymbol{h})$ for certain pairs $\alpha, \beta \in W$. Thus $\boldsymbol{A}$ is spanned by rational linear combinations of nodes and ψ is nondegenerate on $\boldsymbol{A}$ by 21.2.

69.16. Proposition If $\boldsymbol{G} \in$ Alg Lie Com SS and $\boldsymbol{M}$ sub $\boldsymbol{G}$ is its own idealizer, then $\boldsymbol{M}^{\square}$ consists of the ad-nilpotents within rad $\boldsymbol{M}$.

Remark This is a stronger version of 69.6 (ii) in this special situation.

Proof Since $\boldsymbol{M}$ is its own idealizer, it follows from 18.1.1 that the cleaving components of elements of $\mathrm{ad}_{\boldsymbol{G}}\boldsymbol{M}$ are again in $\mathrm{ad}_{\boldsymbol{G}}\boldsymbol{M}$; therefore cleaving is possible in $\mathrm{ad}_{\boldsymbol{G}}\boldsymbol{M}$. By 69.7 cleaving is possible in $\mathrm{ad}_{\boldsymbol{G}}\boldsymbol{M}^{\square}$. Hence by 69.11 $\boldsymbol{M}^{\square} = \boldsymbol{A}_1 + \boldsymbol{N}$ is a direct sum of subspaces, in which $\boldsymbol{A}_1$ is ad-pure and $\boldsymbol{N}$ consists of the ad-nilpotents in $\boldsymbol{M}^{\square}$. Let $\boldsymbol{A}$ be a maximal ad-pure subspace contained in $\boldsymbol{M}$ and containing $\boldsymbol{A}_1$. By 69.15 ψ is nondegenerate on $\boldsymbol{A}$. But $\psi(\boldsymbol{A}, \boldsymbol{A}_1) \subset \psi(\boldsymbol{M}, \boldsymbol{M}^{\square}) = \{0\}$, whence $\boldsymbol{A}_1 = \{0\}$. This proves the assertion.

69.17. Proposition Suppose that $\boldsymbol{N}$ sub $\boldsymbol{F}$ sub $\boldsymbol{G} \in$ Alg Lie Com, $\boldsymbol{N}$ is ad-nilpotent in $\boldsymbol{G}$, $\boldsymbol{F}$ is not ad-nilpotent in $\boldsymbol{G}$, and ad-cleaving with respect to $\boldsymbol{G}$ is possible in $\boldsymbol{F}$. Then some ad-pure $\boldsymbol{x} \neq \boldsymbol{0}$ from $\boldsymbol{F}$ fulfills $\psi(\boldsymbol{x}, \boldsymbol{N}) = \{0\}$.

Proof N may be supposed to be maximal ad-nilpotent contained in F. When looking for an eigenvector of the representation induced by $\tilde{N}$ in F mod N, one finds an $x \in F \setminus N$ with $\tilde{N}x \subset N$. Because of the maximality of N, such an x is not ad-nilpotent and after cleaving it may even be taken ad-pure. It clearly fulfills $\psi(x, N) = \{0\}$.

69.18. Proposition Suppose that $G \in$ Alg Lie Com SS, M sub G is its own idealizer, $M^{\perp} \subset M$, and A is a maximal ad-pure subset of M. Then A is a trunk of G.

Proof The notation of the proof of 69.15 is used, in particular a trunk H of G with $A \subset H \subset G_0'$. Then by 19.20 applied to $\mathrm{ad}_G M$

69.18.1 $\qquad M_{0'} = A + N, \qquad$ a direct sum, with ad-nilpotent N.

By 69.14

69.18.2 $\quad G_{0'} = A_1 + G', \quad$ a direct sum, with $A \subset A_1 \subset H$ and semisimple G'.

One must now show

$$A_1 = A, \qquad G' = \{0\}.$$

(Then indeed $A = H$.)

Suppose $G' \neq \{0\}$. Since (69.18.1), $N \subset M_{0'} \subset G_{0'}$, and N is ad-nilpotent, $N \subset G'$ (see 69.18.2). By 69.17 there is an ad-pure $x \neq 0$, $x \in G'$, such that

$$\psi(x, N) = \{0\}.$$

x may even be supposed to be in H, although H may have to be modified, without impairing A_1.

$$\psi(A, N) = \{0\}$$

because of 69.18.1. Thus

$$\psi(x + A, N) = \{0\}.$$

Since ψ is nondegenerate on A (see 69.15), x may be replaced mod A by x' such that moreover

$$\psi(x', A) = \{0\}.$$

Since $x' \in x + A$,

$$\psi(x', N) = \{0\}.$$

Thus

$$\psi(x', M_{0'}) = \{0\}$$

for some $x' \in G_{0'} \setminus M_{0'}$ thus for some $x' \notin M$.

Now $\psi(G_{0'}, G_{\alpha'}) = \{0\}$ for $\alpha' \neq 0'$, and $M_{\alpha'} \subset G_{\alpha'}$; thus

$$\psi(x', M_{\alpha'}) = \{0\} \qquad \text{for} \quad \alpha' \neq 0',$$

$$\psi(x', M) = \{0\},$$

but $x' \in M^{\perp}$ contradicts $x' \notin M$ because of the supposition that $M^{\perp} \subset M$. This proves

$$G' = \{0\}.$$

Now suppose that A is a proper subset of A_1. Then, since ψ is nondegenerate on A (see 69.15),

$$\psi(x', A) = \{0\} \qquad \text{for some} \quad x' \in A_1 \setminus A.$$

By the same reasoning this leads to a contradiction, which proves the statement.

69.19. Proposition If $G \in$ Alg Lie Com SS and M is maximal solvable, then $M^{\perp} \subset M$.

Proof Suppose that it is not so. Then the $\tilde{x}$ ($x \in M$) have a simultaneous eigenvector in $M^{\perp}$ mod $M^{\square}$. Thus for some $c \in M^{\perp} \setminus M$ and some λ

$$(\tilde{x} - \lambda(x))\, c \in M^{\square} \qquad \text{for all} \quad x \in M.$$

$$\psi(c, (\tilde{x} - \lambda(x))\, c) \in \psi(M^{\perp}, M^{\square}) = \{0\}.$$

$$\psi(c, \tilde{x}c) = -\psi(c, \tilde{c}x) = \psi(\tilde{c}c, x) = 0.$$

Thus

$$\lambda(x)\, \psi(c, c) = 0.$$

$\lambda = 0$ would mean $\tilde{x}c \in M$ for all $x \in M$, thus $\tilde{c}M \subset M$, which contradicts the maximality of M. Therefore

$$\psi(c, c) = 0.$$

Let K be the algebra spanned by M and c, L that spanned by $M^{\square}$ and c. Then L is ideal in K, and K mod L is solvable. So L must not be solvable. However,

$$\psi(M^{\square}, M^{\square}) = \psi(M^{\square}, c) = \{0\} \qquad \text{and} \qquad \psi(c, c) = 0,$$

which makes L solvable. The assertion is proved.

69.20. Proposition If $G \in$ Alg Lie $\overline{\text{C}}$om SS, M a maximal proper subalgebra of G, and M nonsemisimple, then $M^{\perp} \subset M$.

Proof M is its own idealizer and $M^{\perp}$ is invariant under $\tilde{M}$, therefore, in particular, under $\widetilde{M^{\square}}$.

Suppose that $M^{\square} \neq \{0\}$. By 69.16 $M^{\square}$ is ad-nilpotent. If the proposition were not true, then for some $p \geqslant 0$

$$\widetilde{M^{\square}}^{p} M^{\perp} \not\subset M, \qquad \widetilde{M^{\square}}^{p+1} M^{\perp} \subset M.$$

On the other hand,

$$\widetilde{M^{\square}} M^{\perp} \subset \tilde{M} M^{\perp} \subset M^{\perp}$$

and by induction

$$\widetilde{M^{\square}}^{p+1} M^{\perp} \subset M^{\perp}.$$

Thus

$$\widetilde{M^{\square}}^{p+1} M^{\perp} \subset M^{\square},$$

$$\widetilde{M^{\square}}(\widetilde{M^{\square}}^{p} M^{\perp}) \subset M^{\square},$$

hence $\widetilde{M^{\square}}^{p} M^{\perp}$ in the idealizer of $M^{\square}$. Now the idealizer of $M^{\square}$ is nonsemisimple and proper sub G, since $M^{\square}$ was ad-nilpotent and supposed to be $\neq \{0\}$. Because of its maximality, M coincides with the idealizer of $M^{\square}$ and therefore $\widetilde{M^{\square}}^{p} M^{\perp} \subset M$, which contradicts the definition of p.

To complete the proof that $M^{\perp} \subset M$, one must exclude

69.20.1 $$M^{\square} = \{0\}.$$

Here the semisimplicity of G must be used.

If 69.20.1 were true, then by 69.6 (ii, iv) rad M would be the center of M and no ad-nilpotent $\neq \mathbf{0}$ would be in rad M. Since M is maximal, it is its own idealizer; hence ad-cleaving subsists in M and in its center (see 18.1.1), that is, in rad M. Therefore rad M is ad-pure. Under rad M, in the adjoint action, G splits into eigenspaces G_α with $M = G_0$. Since rad $M \neq \{0\}$, one can choose $\alpha \neq 0$ such that G_α exists and $G_{2\alpha}$ does not. Then $G_0 + G_\alpha$ is larger sub G than M, but it does not yet exhaust G, since rad$(G_0 + G_\alpha) =$ (rad M) $+ G_\alpha$ so that $G_0 + G_\alpha$ is not semisimple. This contradicts the maximality of M and disproves 69.20.1.

69.21.1. Proposition A maximal solvable subalgebra of $G \in$ Alg Lie Com contains a trunk of G.

69.21.2. Proposition A maximal proper subalgebra of $G \in$ Alg Lie Com SS which is not semisimple contains a trunk of G.

69.21.3. *Proofs* Proposition 69.21.2 follows from 69.18 and 69.20. Likewise 69.21.1 follows from 69.18–19 with respect to $G' = G$ mod rad G and from 17.12.

69.21.4. *Remark* Propositions 69.21.1–2 contain Theorems 68.2.1 and 68.4.

69.23. Definition If $\boldsymbol{G} \in$ Alg Lie Com SS, $\boldsymbol{H}$ a trunk of $\boldsymbol{G}$, $\boldsymbol{M}$ sub $\boldsymbol{G}$ spanned by a subset of $\boldsymbol{H}$ and a set of branches belonging to $\boldsymbol{H}$, then $\alpha \in W^*$ is called *free* (with respect to $\boldsymbol{M}$) if

$$\boldsymbol{e}_\alpha \in \boldsymbol{M} \qquad \text{and} \qquad \boldsymbol{e}_{-\alpha} \notin \boldsymbol{M}.$$

Proposition Under a suitable order on $\boldsymbol{H}_{st}^*$ all free rootforms are positive.

Proof Instead it will be shown that a suitable element of the kaleidoscope group maps all free rootforms into positive rootforms. For a proof by induction on the number of positive free rootforms and along the order in $\boldsymbol{H}_{st}^*$ it is sufficient to show that by means of the kaleidoscope group every maximal negative free rootform can be raised without changing the signs of the positive free rootforms.

First remember that for $\rho \in W^{++}$ all rootforms except $\pm\rho$ preserve their signs under S_ρ. Let $-\alpha$ be a maximal negative free rootform. There is a $\rho \in W^{++}$ such that $S_\rho(-\alpha) > -\alpha$. If ρ is not free, then S_ρ also maps the positive free rootforms into positive rootforms. So ρ may be assumed to be free; but then, with $\boldsymbol{e}_{-\alpha}, \boldsymbol{e}_\rho \in \boldsymbol{M}$ also $\boldsymbol{e}_{\rho-\alpha} \in \boldsymbol{M}$ (note that of necessity $\alpha \neq \rho$). This contradicts the maximality of $-\alpha$, since if $\rho - \alpha$ were not free, then with $\boldsymbol{e}_{\alpha-\rho}$ and $\boldsymbol{e}_\rho$ also $\boldsymbol{e}_\alpha$ would be in $\boldsymbol{M}$, in contradiction to the fact that $-\alpha$ is free.

69.24.1. Proposition Any maximal solvable subalgebra $\boldsymbol{M}$ of $\boldsymbol{G} \in$ Alg Lie Com SS is spanned by an arbitrary trunk $\boldsymbol{H} \subset \boldsymbol{M}$ and the branches $\boldsymbol{e}_\alpha$, with $\alpha > 0$ under a suitable order of $\boldsymbol{H}_{st}^*$.

Proof By 69.21.1 $\boldsymbol{M}$ contains a trunk, say $\boldsymbol{H}$. By 20.15 it fulfills the conditions of 69.23. Since $\boldsymbol{e}_\alpha$, $\boldsymbol{e}_{-\alpha}$ generate a semisimple subalgebra, it is not allowed that both of them belong to $\boldsymbol{M}$. Therefore, if $\boldsymbol{e}_\alpha \in \boldsymbol{M}$, then α is free. By 69.23 an order exists such that $\alpha > 0$ for each $\boldsymbol{e}_\alpha \in \boldsymbol{M}$. The subalgebra spanned by $\boldsymbol{H}$ and all $\boldsymbol{e}_\alpha$ with $\alpha > 0$ is still solvable. Therefore it coincides with $\boldsymbol{M}$, which proves the assertion.

69.24.2. Proposition Among the algebras $\boldsymbol{M}$ sub $\boldsymbol{G} \in$ Alg Lie Com SS around $\boldsymbol{H}$ the maximal solvable ones are characterized by the following property: for every $\alpha \in W^*$ exactly one of the branches $\boldsymbol{e}_\alpha, \boldsymbol{e}_{-\alpha}$ belongs to $\boldsymbol{M}$.

This is a consequence of 69.24.1 or proved in the same way.

69.25 The maximal solvable subalgebras around $\boldsymbol{H}$ are thus one-to-one related to the chambers in $\boldsymbol{H}_{st}^*$. By 33.4.3 and 33.9(4) they are equivalent to one another under $\operatorname{Int}(\boldsymbol{G}, \boldsymbol{H})$. Further, since two trunks are equivalent under

Int G, one gets the Int G-equivalence of maximal solvable subalgebras and, as in 69.21.3, the following more general proposition.

Proposition All maximal solvable subalgebras of $G \in$ Alg Lie Com are equivalent under Int G.

Remark This is Theorem 68.2.2.

69.26 Again suppose first that G is semisimple. An element $\tilde{a}$ of Int G leaving maximal solvable M invariant changes a trunk H within M into a trunk. The same is achieved by some $\tilde{b} \in \tilde{M}$. Then $\tilde{b}^{-1}\tilde{a} \in$ Int G leaves M and H invariant, thus the chamber in H_{st}^* corresponding to M, thus every element of H. Hence $\tilde{b}^{-1}\tilde{a} \in \tilde{H}$, $\tilde{a} \in \tilde{M}$.

If, moreover, $\tilde{a}$ leaves M elementwise invariant, then $\tilde{a} = \exp \tilde{h}$ for some $h \in H$, and finally it is the identity.

If the method in 69.21.3 is used again,† the following is obtained:

Proposition If $G \in$ Alg Lie Com, then any element of Int G leaving the maximal solvable M invariant belongs to $\tilde{M}$. Moreover, for semisimple G, if it leaves M elementwise invariant, it is the identity on G.

Theorems 68.2.–4 are completely proved by 69.21.1–2 and 69.24–26; 68.2.5 is an immediate consequence (see 13.3).

69.27. Proposition If $G \in$ Alg Lie Com SS, then $G(\rho)$, as defined in 68.5, is a maximal proper subalgebra and nonsemisimple.

Proof The orthoplement of $G(\rho)$ is spanned by the e_α such that ρ appears in α with a positive coefficient. It is an ad-nilpotent ideal of $G(\rho)$; therefore $G(\rho)$ is not semisimple. To show that it is a maximal proper subalgebra, consider the algebra G' generated by $G(\rho)$ and one $e_{-\alpha}$, where ρ appears in α with a positive coefficient, and prove that $G' = G$. For $\alpha = \rho$ this is obvious. For $\alpha > \rho$ there is a $\beta \in W^+$ such that $\alpha - \beta \in W^*$ and $\alpha - \beta \geqslant \rho$. Then $\tilde{e}_\beta e_{-\alpha}$, whence also $e_{\beta-\alpha}$, in G', and by an obvious induction $G' = G$. (One notes that by 20.15 any subalgebra containing $G(\rho)$ is spanned by H and branches.)

69.28.1. Proposition If $G \in$ Alg Lie Com SS, M is nonsemisimple maximal proper sub G, H is a trunk of G contained in M, and the order on H_{st}^* is such that every free α ($e_\alpha \in M$) is positive, then M is some $G(\rho)$ and thus maximal parabolic.

In particular, every maximal parabolic subalgebra of G around H is Int (G,H)-equivalent with some $G(\rho)$.

† Observe that the kernel of the homomorphism from Int G to Int (G mod rad G) may be disconnected. See 69.29.3.

Proof According to 20.15, $\boldsymbol{M}$ is spanned by $\boldsymbol{H}$ and a set of branches. If $\alpha \in W^*$ and $\boldsymbol{e}_{-\alpha} \notin \boldsymbol{M}$, then $\boldsymbol{e}_\alpha \in \boldsymbol{M}^\perp \subset \boldsymbol{M}$ by 69.20; therefore the set V of $\alpha \in W^*$ with $\boldsymbol{e}_\alpha \in \boldsymbol{M}$ has the property $\alpha \in V$ or $-\alpha \in V$ for $\alpha \in W^*$. By the fact that all free rootforms are positive one even has $W^+ \subset V$. Because $\boldsymbol{M} \neq \boldsymbol{G}$, there is a $\rho \in W^{++}$ such that $\boldsymbol{e}_{-\rho} \notin \boldsymbol{M}$, that is, ρ is free. Suppose there were a nonfree positive $\alpha \geqslant \rho$; assume α minimal. As remarked in the preceding proof, there is a $\beta > 0$ such that $\alpha - \beta \in W^*$ and $\alpha - \beta \geqslant \rho$. Then $\tilde{\boldsymbol{e}}_\beta \boldsymbol{e}_{-\alpha}$, hence also $\boldsymbol{e}_{\beta-\alpha}$, in $\boldsymbol{M}$, so $\alpha - \beta$ is still nonfree with $\alpha - \beta \geqslant \rho$; this contradicts the minimality of α. It follows that $\boldsymbol{M} \subset \boldsymbol{G}(\rho)$; hence $\boldsymbol{M} = \boldsymbol{G}(\rho)$.

69.28.2 If in the foregoing $\boldsymbol{M}$ is just a parabolic subalgebra, then by Proposition 69.24 one can still assume that $W^+ \subset V$, where V is as above. The rest of the proof shows that $\boldsymbol{M}$ is the intersection of the $\boldsymbol{G}(\rho)$ with ρ free and primitive. Hence:

Proposition Every parabolic subalgebra is an intersection of maximal parabolic subalgebras around one and the same trunk.

This remains true for arbitrary $\boldsymbol{G} \in$ Alg Lie Com by the principle applied in 69.21.3.†

69.28.3. Proposition Among the algebras $\boldsymbol{M}$ proper sub $\boldsymbol{G} \in$ Alg Lie Com SS around a trunk $\boldsymbol{H}$ the parabolic ones are characterized by the following property: for every $\alpha \in W^*$, $\boldsymbol{e}_\alpha \in \boldsymbol{M}$ or $\boldsymbol{e}_{-\alpha} \in \boldsymbol{M}$.

This is a consequence of 69.24.2.

69.29.1. Proposition If $\boldsymbol{G} \in$ Alg Lie Com SS and $\boldsymbol{H}$ is an ordered trunk of $\boldsymbol{G}$, then any nonsemisimple maximal proper subalgebra $\boldsymbol{M}$ of $\boldsymbol{G}$ is Int $\boldsymbol{G}$-equivalent to some $\boldsymbol{G}(\rho)$. Every element of Int $\boldsymbol{G}$ that leaves $\boldsymbol{M}$ invariant belongs to $\tilde{\boldsymbol{M}}$; an element of Int $\boldsymbol{G}$ that leaves $\boldsymbol{M}$ elementwise invariant is the identity. No $\boldsymbol{G}(\rho)$, $\boldsymbol{G}(\sigma)$ with $\rho \neq \sigma$ are Int $\boldsymbol{G}$-equivalent.

Proof By 69.21.2, $\boldsymbol{M}$ contains a trunk $\boldsymbol{H}'$ of $\boldsymbol{G}$. Under the action of Int $\boldsymbol{G}$ one may assume that $\boldsymbol{H}' = \boldsymbol{H}$. By 69.23 under a suitable order on $\boldsymbol{H}^*_{\mathrm{st}}$ all free rootforms (with respect to $\boldsymbol{M}$) are positive. By some $\tilde{s} \in$ Int $\boldsymbol{G}$ this order on $\boldsymbol{H}^*_{\mathrm{st}}$ is transformed into the given one on $\boldsymbol{H}^*_{\mathrm{st}}$. By the same change $\boldsymbol{M}$ may be supposed to fulfill the condition in 69.28.1 on the free rootforms. Therefore by 69.28.1 it is some $\boldsymbol{C}(\rho)$.

The next assertion is proved the same way as that of 69.26 or derived from it.

As to the last assertion, suppose that $\tilde{a}\boldsymbol{G}(\rho) = \boldsymbol{G}(\sigma)$ for some $\tilde{a} \in$ Int $\boldsymbol{G}$. Let $\boldsymbol{B}$ be the maximal solvable subalgebra spanned by $\boldsymbol{H}$ and the $\boldsymbol{e}_\alpha$ with

† See footnote, p. 408.

$\alpha > 0$. $\boldsymbol{B} \subset \boldsymbol{G}(\rho)$, $\boldsymbol{B} \subset \boldsymbol{G}(\sigma)$, $\tilde{a}\boldsymbol{B} \subset \boldsymbol{G}(\sigma)$. Now $\tilde{a}\boldsymbol{B} = \tilde{b}\boldsymbol{B}$ with some $\tilde{b} \in \widetilde{G(\sigma)}$. Therefore $\tilde{a}$, if replaced with $\tilde{b}^{-1}\tilde{a}$, may be supposed to preserve $\boldsymbol{B}$. Then $\tilde{a} \in \tilde{B} \subset \widetilde{G(\rho)}$, hence $\boldsymbol{G}(\sigma) = \tilde{a}\boldsymbol{G}(\rho) = \boldsymbol{G}(\rho)$.

69.29.2 If $\boldsymbol{M}$ is parabolic sub $\boldsymbol{G} \in$ Alg Lie Com, then every element of Int $\boldsymbol{G}$ leaving $\boldsymbol{M}$ invariant belongs to $\tilde{\boldsymbol{M}}$.

Proof For semisimple $\boldsymbol{G}$ this is proved in the same way as the analogous statement in 69.29.1 for maximal $\boldsymbol{M}$. By the principle used in 69.21.3 it is extended to arbitrary $\boldsymbol{G}$.†

69.29.3 If M is a parabolic subgroup of $G \in$ Gru Lie Lin Com SS and a is in the normalizer of M, then $\tilde{a}\boldsymbol{M} \subset \boldsymbol{M}$; thus $\tilde{a} \in \tilde{\boldsymbol{M}}$ by 69.29.2 and $a \in M$, since the center of G is in any trunk, thus in M. Therefore M is its own normalizer. Since any Lie subgroup of G is normal in its closure, it follows that M is closed. If $\boldsymbol{M}$ is presented as the intersection of maximal parabolic $\boldsymbol{M}_i$, generating M_i, then any $a \in \bigcap_i M_i$ normalizes all M_i, hence M; thus it belongs to M.

In the general case the statement is reduced to that about $M/\text{rad } G$ in $G/\text{rad } G$, which is essentially in Gru Lie Lin Com SS.

69.29.4 The following have been proved:

68.2.1 in 69.21.3.
68.2.2 in 69.25.
68.2.3 in 69.26.
68.2.4 in 69.26.
68.2.5 in 69.26 and 69.29.3.
68.4 in 69.21.3.
68.6.1 in 69.27.
68.6.2 in 69.28.1.
68.7.2 in 69.29.2–3.
68.7.3 in 69.28.2 and 69.29.3.
68.7.4 in 69.27 and 69.28.1.
68.7.5 in 69.29.1.

69.30. Bruhat's Lemma The intersection of two maximal solvable subalgebras of $\boldsymbol{G} \in$ Alg Lie Com SS contains a trunk of $\boldsymbol{G}$.

Proof Let $\boldsymbol{M}_1, \boldsymbol{M}_2$ be maximal solvable. Since $\boldsymbol{M}_1$ and $\boldsymbol{M}_2$ are their own idealizers, ad-cleaving with respect to $\boldsymbol{G}$ is possible in both $\boldsymbol{M}_1$ and $\boldsymbol{M}_2$, and by

† See footnote, p. 408.

its uniqueness also in $M_1 \cap M_2$. By 69.11

$$M_1 \cap M_2 = A + E$$

with A maximal ad-pure in $M_1 \cap M_2$, and E the subalgebra of ad-nilpotents in $M_1 \cap M_2$. Now $\psi(E, M_i) = \{0\}$; thus $\psi(E, M_1 + M_2) = \{0\}$, hence

$$\dim(M_1 + M_2) \leqslant \dim G - \dim E.$$

Further

$$\dim(M_1 \cap M_2) = \dim A + \dim E,$$

$$\dim(M_1 + M_2) + \dim(M_1 \cap M_2) = \dim M_1 + \dim M_2 = \dim G + \operatorname{rank} G,$$

which follows from 69.24.1. Hence

$$\dim G + \operatorname{rank} G \leqslant \dim G + \dim A.$$

Therefore

$$\dim A \geqslant \operatorname{rank} G$$

which proves A to be a trunk of G.

69.31 Bruhat's lemma is usually formulated as follows:

Proposition If $G \in$ Alg Lie Lin Com SS, M is maximal solvable sub G, H is a trunk of G in M, and S is the normalizer of H in G, then

$$G = MSM.$$

Proof One may assume that G is centerfree. Suppose $g \in G$. Then by 69.30 $M \cap \tilde{g}M$ contains a trunk of G, which by 68.1.1 can be written as $\tilde{m}H$ with $m \in M$. Thus $\tilde{m}^{-1}\,\tilde{g}M \supset H$. Now both M and $\tilde{m}^{-1}\,\tilde{g}M$ are maximal solvable subalgebras around H. By 68.3 there is some $s \in S$ with $\tilde{m}^{-1}\,\tilde{g}M = \tilde{s}M$ Therefore $\tilde{s}^{-1}\tilde{m}^{-1}\,\tilde{g} = \tilde{m}_1$ for some $m_1 \in M$, $\tilde{g} = \tilde{m}\tilde{s}\tilde{m}_1$, which proves the assertion.

69.32. Proposition If $G \in$ Alg Lie Com SS, then any ad-nilpotent of G is contained in some semisimple subalgebra of G of rank 1.

This is the content of Theorem 68.8.3. In the subalgebra F of rank 1 any ad-pure $h \neq 0$ spans a trunk. The representation of F by adjoint in the linear space G is conducible. Every irreducible component is spanned by weight vectors (43.1.1), on the basis of which $\tilde{h}$ is diagonalized. Therefore h is ad-pure. This shows that 68.8.1 follows from 68.8.3 and from the special case of rank 1 which is obvious from 69.24.1.

Proof of the Proposition. Let $e \neq 0$ be the ad-nilpotent. One may assume that G is the smallest semisimple subalgebra of G containing e.

Let N be the centralizer of e. Then ad-cleaving is possible in N. If N has a non-ad-nilpotent element, it has an ad-pure element $h \neq 0$. By 69.14 its centralizer would contain a smaller semisimple algebra containing e.

Thus $\boldsymbol{N}$ is ad-nilpotent. Since $\psi(\tilde{e}\boldsymbol{G}, \boldsymbol{N}) = -\psi(\boldsymbol{G}, \tilde{e}\boldsymbol{N}) = \{0\}$ and $\dim \boldsymbol{N}^{\perp} = \operatorname{codim} \boldsymbol{N} = \dim \tilde{e}\boldsymbol{G}$,

69.32.1 $$\tilde{e}\boldsymbol{G} = \boldsymbol{N}^{\perp}.$$

Further $\boldsymbol{e} \in \boldsymbol{N}^{\perp}$. Thus there is some $\boldsymbol{h} \in \boldsymbol{G}$ with $\tilde{e}(-\boldsymbol{h}) = \boldsymbol{e}$,

69.32.2 $$\tilde{h}\boldsymbol{e} = \boldsymbol{e}.$$

After ad-cleaving $\boldsymbol{h}$ may be taken ad-pure. From 69.32.2 it follows that

$$\tilde{h}\boldsymbol{N} \subset \boldsymbol{N}.$$

Therefore $\boldsymbol{h}, \boldsymbol{N}$ span a solvable algebra, $\psi(\boldsymbol{h}, \boldsymbol{N}) = \{0\}$, $\boldsymbol{h} \in \boldsymbol{N}^{\perp}$, and by 69.32.1

$$\tilde{e}\boldsymbol{f} = \boldsymbol{h} \qquad \text{for some} \quad \boldsymbol{f} \in \boldsymbol{G}.$$

Now $\boldsymbol{f}$ will be replaced by some $\boldsymbol{f}'$ such that still

$$\tilde{e}\boldsymbol{f}' = \boldsymbol{h},$$

and moreover

$$\tilde{h}\boldsymbol{f}' = -\boldsymbol{f}'.$$

Putting $\boldsymbol{f} - \boldsymbol{f}' = \boldsymbol{u} \in \boldsymbol{N}$, one must solve

$$(\tilde{h} + 1)\,\boldsymbol{u} = (\tilde{h} + 1)\,\boldsymbol{f}.$$

About the second member $\boldsymbol{g} = (\tilde{h} + 1)\,\boldsymbol{f}$, one knows that

$$\tilde{e}\boldsymbol{g} = \tilde{e}(\tilde{h} + 1)\,\boldsymbol{f} = (\tilde{h} + 1)\,\tilde{e}\boldsymbol{f} - \tilde{e}\boldsymbol{f} = \boldsymbol{0}.$$

Thus to find the wanted $\boldsymbol{f}'$, one must solve

$$(\tilde{h} + 1)\,\boldsymbol{u} = \boldsymbol{g} \in \boldsymbol{N}$$

with respect to $\boldsymbol{u} \in \boldsymbol{N}$. This can be done as soon as there is no $\boldsymbol{v} \neq \boldsymbol{0}$, $\boldsymbol{v} \in \boldsymbol{N}$ with

69.32.3 $$(\tilde{h} + 1)\,\boldsymbol{v} = \boldsymbol{0}.$$

Suppose there were such a $\boldsymbol{v}$. One easily proves by induction that

$$[\tilde{h}, \tilde{e}^{p}] = p\tilde{e}^{p},$$

$$[\tilde{e}^{p}, \tilde{f}] = p\tilde{h}\tilde{e}^{p-1} - \binom{p}{2}\tilde{e}^{p-1}.$$

Now

69.32.4 $$\tilde{e}^{p}\tilde{f}^{p}\boldsymbol{v} = t_p\,\boldsymbol{v}$$

with scalars t_p as can be shown inductively:

$$\tilde{e}\tilde{f}\,v = \tilde{f}\tilde{e}v + \tilde{h}v = -v,$$

$$\tilde{e}^{p+1}\tilde{f}^{p+1}v = \tilde{f}\tilde{e}^{p+1}\tilde{f}^{p}v + \left((p+1)\tilde{h}\tilde{e}^{p} - \binom{p+1}{2}\tilde{e}^{p}\right)\tilde{f}^{p}v$$

$$= \tilde{f}\tilde{e}\,t_p v + (p+1)\tilde{h}t_p v - \binom{p+1}{2}t_p v.$$

The first summand vanishes because of $v \in N$; thus $\tilde{e}v = 0$, and by 69.32.3 the others are together

$$-\binom{p+2}{2}t_p v,$$

which proves that recursively

$$t_1 = -1, \qquad t_{p+1} = -\binom{p+2}{2}t_p;$$

thus $t_p \neq 0$ for $p \geqslant 1$. Because of the nilpotency of $\tilde{e}$, this contradicts 69.32.4 and proves the assertion.

69.33. Proposition Let $G \in$ Alg Lie Com SS and H a trunk of G. Then for every maximal solvable B around H there is *one* maximal solvable B' around H such that $B \cap B'$ equals H.

Proof If H_{st}^* is suitably ordered, B is spanned by H and the e_α with $\alpha > 0$. Then B' meeting B exactly in H must be spanned by H and the e_α with $\alpha < 0$. This indeed leads to a maximal solvable subalgebra.

69.34. Proposition Let $G \in$ Alg Lie Com SS, $\mathscr{B}$ the manifold of all maximal solvable subalgebras of G, $B^+ \in \mathscr{B}$, and $\mathscr{B}_0$ the subset of $\mathscr{B}$, consisting of those B that intersect B^+ in more than just a trunk. Then $\mathscr{B}_0$ is nowhere dense and closed in $\mathscr{B}$.

Proof Let H be a trunk within B^+, and $B^- \in \mathscr{B}$ meeting B^+ exactly in H. Let E be the set of ad-nilpotents in B^-. In the direct sum splitting $G = B^+ + E$ let p be the projection onto E. For $\tilde{a} \in \operatorname{Int} G$ let $\varphi(\tilde{a})$ be the determinant of the restriction of $p\tilde{a}$ to E. Then φ is analytic and $\varphi(1) = 1$, and therefore the set in which φ vanishes is nowhere dense in Int G. Nonvanishing $\varphi(\tilde{a})$ means that $p\tilde{a}E = E$, hence $B^+ + \tilde{a}B^- = G$ and consequently $\dim(B^+ \cap \tilde{a}B^-) = \operatorname{rank} G$, thus $\tilde{a}B^- \notin \mathscr{B}_0$.

Any $B_0 \in \mathscr{B}$ has the form $\tilde{a}_0 B^-$ with suitable $\tilde{a}_0 \in \operatorname{Int} G$. Near $\tilde{a}_0$ there is some $\tilde{a} \in \text{Int } G$ such that $\varphi(\tilde{a}) \neq 0$; hence $\tilde{a}B^- \notin \mathscr{B}_0$. Now $B = \tilde{a}B^-$ is near $B_0 = \tilde{a}_0 B^-$, which shows that $\mathscr{B} \setminus \mathscr{B}_0$ is dense in $\mathscr{B}$.

On the other hand, it is obvious that $\mathscr{B} \setminus \mathscr{B}_0$ is open in $\mathscr{B}$.

This proves the assertion.

69.35. Proposition Let $G \in$ Alg Lie Com SS, $\mathscr{B}^2$ the manifold of ordered pairs of maximal solvable subalgebras of G, and $\mathscr{B}_0{}^2$ the subset of those that intersect one another in more than a trunk. Then $\mathscr{B}_0{}^2$ is nowhere dense and closed in $\mathscr{B}^2$ and Int G acts transitively on $\mathscr{B}^2 \setminus \mathscr{B}_0{}^2$.

Remark This is Theorem 68.10.

Proof It is again obvious that $\mathscr{B}^2 \setminus \mathscr{B}_0{}^2$ is open in $\mathscr{B}^2$. It is dense because by 69.34, for every fixed $B_2 \in \mathscr{B}$, the set $\ulcorner \mathscr{B} \setminus \mathscr{B}_0, \{B_2\} \urcorner$ is dense in $\ulcorner \mathscr{B}, \{B_2\} \urcorner$. This proves the first statement. If two elements $\ulcorner B_1, B_2 \urcorner$ and $\ulcorner B_1', B_2' \urcorner$ of $\mathscr{B}_0{}^2$ are given, then by transitivity under Int G one may suppose that $B_1 = B_1'$. By 68.1.1 applied in $B_1 = B_1'$ the trunks $B_1 \cap B_2$, $B_1' \cap B_2'$ may be supposed identical. But then by 69.33, $B_2 = B_2'$ as well.

69.37. Proposition If B is a maximal solvable subalgebra of $G \in$ Alg Lie Lin Com SS, then G/B is compact.

Proof B is closed by 13.3. Let G be in ordered third dressing on some trunk $H \subset B$ such that B is spanned by H and the e_α with $\alpha > 0$. Let D be the unitary restriction of G on the given dressing. Then G is the sum of B and D (as a real vector space), and one derives the assertion from Proposition 61.3.

Remark Of course the proposition remains valid if $G \in$ Alg Lie Lin Com only.

70. INTRODUCTION OF INCIDENCE GEOMETRIES OF SEMISIMPLE LIE GROUPS

70.1 $G \in \mathsf{A}_l$ that was presented in linear $(l+1)$-space R with an ordered basis, also admits of a projective interpretation. l-projective space $R_\#$ is usually defined as the set of linear subspaces of R, provided with the relationship of symmetrized inclusion. In this terminology a linear i-subspace S of R determines a projective $(i-1)$-subspace $S_\#$ of $R_\#$. As acting in $R_\#$, G is called the projective group of $R_\#$. It acts separately in the manifold of the linear i-subspaces of R (projective $(i-1)$-subspaces of $R_\#$); however, for $i = 0$ and

$i = l + 1$ this action is trivial, for then these manifolds consist of one point only. For this reason in the sequel the smallest and largest elements of $R_\#$ will be disregarded.

Let R_i be the subspace of R spanned by the first i basis vectors ($1 \leqslant i \leqslant l$). The trunk $\boldsymbol{H}$ of $\boldsymbol{G}$ is chosen as consisting of the diagonal matrices with coefficients $\omega_1, \ldots, \omega_{l+1}$ ($\sum \omega_i = 0$).

The *stability algebra* (infinitesimal algebra of the stability group) of R_i is spanned by $\boldsymbol{H}$ and the $\boldsymbol{e}_{\omega_p - \omega_q}$, with $p \leqslant i$ or $q > i$. Therefore just the $\boldsymbol{e}_{\omega_p - \omega_q}$ with $q \leqslant i < p$ are lacking, in other words, the $\boldsymbol{e}_\alpha$ with $\alpha = \sum m_j \rho_j$ and $m_i < 0$. This identifies the stability algebra of R_i (or $R_{i\#}$) as $\boldsymbol{G}(\rho_i)$. The identification extends to the belonging groups. Note that the stability group of R_i cannot be larger that $G(\rho_i)$, since $\widetilde{G(\rho_i)}$ is not in a larger proper subgroup of Int $\boldsymbol{G}$ and the center of G is in H, thus in $G(\rho_i)$. Note, further, that from the projective point of view the center of G is eliminated, since it leaves all elements of $R_\#$ fixed.

G is transitive over the manifold Γ_i of linear i-spaces sub R (projective $(i-1)$-spaces sub $R_\#$). Γ_i is a homogeneous space acted on by G. Its stability groups are the conjugates of $G(\rho_i)$. Disregarding its origin in R, one can consider Γ_i as the manifold of conjugates of $G(\rho_i)$ or of $\boldsymbol{G}(\rho_i)$, on which G acts by means of conjugation.

By their realization as subspaces of R, the elements of Γ_i and Γ_j are related in some way that admits of an interpretation in group theoretical terms.

First consider the triangular matrices of $\boldsymbol{G}$ (zeros below the diagonal), which form a maximal solvable subalgebra $\boldsymbol{B}$ of $\boldsymbol{G}$. The R_i are all nontrivial linear subspaces of R invariant under $\boldsymbol{B}$, and $\boldsymbol{B}$ can be characterized by its property of leaving each R_i invariant. Two nontrivial linear subspaces of R one of which contains the other, are called *incident*, and any system of mutually incident elements is called a *flag*. The system $R_1, R_2, \ldots, R_l$ is a maximal flag. G acts transitively on the manifold of maximal flags. The stability group of the maximal flag $\{R_1, \ldots, R_l\}$ is just B, which is maximal solvable, and since $\tilde{G}$ again acts transitively on the manifold of maximal solvable Lie subgroups of G one can identify the manifold of maximal flags with that of the maximal solvable Lie subgroups, G/B.

A pair of linear subspaces of R can be extended to a maximal flag if and only if they are incident. In group theory terms the criterion of incidence states that elements of Γ_i, Γ_j are incident if and only if their intersection contains a maximal solvable Lie subgroup of G, in other words, if and only if it is a parabolic subgroup of G.

70.2 $G \in \mathsf{D}_l$ can be discussed in an analogous way. Take $\boldsymbol{G}$ as presented in Section 16. Then take R_{i+2} spanned by the first i-basis vectors ($i = 1, 2, \ldots, l-2$), R_2 by the first l-basis vectors, and R_1 by the first $l-1$ and the $2l$th. (In the projective interpretation all of these spaces are lying on the invariant quadric

$\sum \xi_i \xi_{l+i} = 0$.) They are *totally isotropic*. Γ_i ($i \geqslant 3$) is now the homogeneous space of $(i-2)$-dimensional totally isotropic subspaces (i.e., lying on the quadric), and Γ_1 and Γ_2 are the two manifolds of l-dimensional totally isotropic subspaces. The $(l-1)$-dimensional spaces do not appear in this image as primordial elements; each is contained in exactly one of each of the sorts Γ_1 and Γ_2 and is their intersection.

To establish that the Γ_i are indeed orbits under G one must use *Witt's theorem*† which says that any two isometric subspaces of R can be mapped onto each other by an orthogonal transformation of the whole of R.

For $l \geqslant i \geqslant 3$, Γ_i consists of all totally isotropic subspaces of the same dimension $i-2$ and each of them is conjugate with R_{i+2} under G, that is, by a *special* orthogonal transformation, because the stability group of R_{i+2} in the full orthogonal group contains orthogonal transformations with determinant -1. For Γ_1 and Γ_2 one should note that R_1 is conjugate with R_2 by the interchange of the lth and $2l$th basis vectors, which has determinant -1, and that the stability group of R_1 in the full orthogonal group consists of volume-preserving transformations only.

The stability group of R_i is again $G(\rho_i)$, which leads to the same group theory interpretation of Γ_i as in A_l. All other things also go the same way as in A_l as soon as one takes the liberty of interpreting the system $R_1, R_2, \ldots, R_l$ as a flag. This agrees with the naïve notion of incidence of two elements except for the pair R_1, R_2. Now none of two l-dimensional totally isotropic subspaces of different kind can contain the other. The best they can do is to intersect in an $(l-1)$-dimensional subspace, and this is just what happens to R_1, R_2. Generally, incidence of elements of Γ_1 and Γ_2 has to be understood as intersecting $(l-1)$-dimensionally. After this interpretation, incidence in group theory terms again means having a parabolic intersection.

$G \in \mathsf{B}_l$ and C_l can be dealt with in an analogous way.

In both cases the sorts are constituted of totally isotropic subspaces of the same dimension, and incidence is the symmetrized inclusion relation, as in the case of A_l.

70.3 For any $\boldsymbol{G} \in$ Alg Lie Com SS by definition $\boldsymbol{G}(\rho_i)$ was spanned by ordered $\boldsymbol{H}$ and the branches $\boldsymbol{e}_\alpha$ with $\alpha = \sum p_\nu \rho_\nu$ such that $p_i \geqslant 0$. In terms of the fundamental weights, this condition on α can be re-expressed as

70.3.1 $$(\pi_i, \alpha) \geqslant 0.$$

Now consider the irreducible linear representation of $\boldsymbol{G}$ in some space R^i, with the fundamental weight π_i as top weight and the π_i-weightvector x. Then $\boldsymbol{G}(\rho_i)$ is just the subalgebra of $\boldsymbol{g} \in \boldsymbol{G}$ leaving x invariant up to a scalar factor;

† See, for instance, O. T. O'Meara, *Introduction to Quadratic Forms*, Springer, Berlin, 1963, pp. 97–99, or the more general proof in N. Bourbaki, *Algèbre*, Chapter 9, §4, No. 3, Th. 1.

in other words, leaving x fixed if it is considered as a point $x_\#$ of projective $R^i_\#$. This means that Γ_i in the earlier examples can also be interpreted as the manifold $Gx_\#$ in $R^i_\#$.

For A_l the representation π_i is that in the space R^i of skew i-tensors on R. The manifold corresponding to Γ_i in R^i is that of i-vectors, that is, skew products of i vectors, which on the other hand just describe the i-dimensional subspaces of R. The case of D_l is again somewhat different; the representations π_1, π_2 act on the spinor spaces (see Section 49).

70.4 The foregoing exploration leads to a general definition:

Definition For $\boldsymbol{G} \in$ Alg Lie Lin Com SS,

Γ, the set of maximal parabolic subgroups of G (infinitesimally generated by the maximal parabolic sub-algebras of $\boldsymbol{G}$), endowed with the incidence relation

$\ll a, b \in \Gamma$ incident iff $a \cap b$ is parabolic$\gg$,

is called the *incidence geometry* of G.

Γ is considered to be acted on by G by conjugation.

Its transitivity classes are the *sorts* of the incidence geometry.

70.5.1. Definition Let $\boldsymbol{H}$ be an ordered trunk of the above $\boldsymbol{G}$.

$\Gamma^0(\boldsymbol{H})$, or Γ^0 for short, is the restriction of Γ to the subset of $a \in \Gamma$ such that $H \subset a$.

$\Gamma(\boldsymbol{H}, \rho)$, or $\Gamma(\rho)$ for short, for $\rho \in W^{++}(\boldsymbol{G}, \boldsymbol{H})$, is the transitivity class of Γ containing $G(\rho)$.

Its intersection with Γ^0 is denoted by $\Gamma^0(\boldsymbol{H}, \rho)$ or $\Gamma^0(\rho)$.

70.5.2. Proposition Int $\boldsymbol{G}$-equivalent $a, b \in \Gamma^0(\rho)$ are Int$(\boldsymbol{G}, \boldsymbol{H})$-equivalent.

Proof $\tilde{u}a = b$ for some $u \in G$. Both H and $H' = \tilde{u}H$ are trunks of b. The conjugacy of trunks provides a $u_0 \in b$ with $\tilde{u}_0 H' = H$. Then $\tilde{u}_0\tilde{u} \in \mathrm{Int}(\boldsymbol{G}, \boldsymbol{H})$ and $\tilde{u}_0\tilde{u}a = \tilde{u}_0 b = b$.

Remark The proposition follows also from 69.28.1 and 69.29.1.

70.5.3. Proposition $\Gamma = \bigcup_{\rho \in W^{++}} \Gamma(\rho)$, where $\Gamma(\rho) \neq \Gamma_\sigma$ for $\rho \neq \sigma$. On Γ^0 the action of Int $\boldsymbol{G}$ is like $\mathrm{Int}(\boldsymbol{G}, \boldsymbol{H})/\tilde{H}$, isomorphic with Int W^*. Its transitivity classes in Γ^0 are the $\Gamma^0(\rho)$.

This is only a reinterpretation of known facts.

Information on incidence properties in Γ can already be obtained to a high degree in Γ^0, which is finite. This explains the importance of Γ^0 in the study of Γ. As an example:

70.5.4. Proposition If $a, b \in \Gamma(\rho)$ are incident, they are equal.

Proof By the action of Int $\boldsymbol{G}$ it may be assumed that $a \cap b$ contains the maximal solvable subgroup generated by $\boldsymbol{H}$ and the $\boldsymbol{e}_\alpha$ with $\alpha > 0$. Then $a = G(\rho)$, $b = G(\rho)$; hence $a = b$.

70.6 Any $a \in \Gamma^0$ equals $SG(\rho)$ for some $\rho \in W^{++}$ and $S \in \mathrm{Int}(\boldsymbol{G}, \boldsymbol{H})$. As usual, S will also be considered as an element of Int W^*.

Henceforth write π_ρ instead of π_i if $\rho = \rho_i$. According to 70.3.1,

$$\boldsymbol{G}(\rho) \text{ is spanned by } \boldsymbol{H} \text{ and the } \boldsymbol{e}_\alpha \text{ with } (\pi_\rho, \alpha) \geqslant 0.$$

Therefore,

$$S\boldsymbol{G}(\rho) \text{ is spanned by } \boldsymbol{H} \text{ and the } \boldsymbol{e}_{S\alpha} \text{ with } (\pi_\rho, \alpha) \geqslant 0,$$

in other words,

$$\text{by } \boldsymbol{H} \text{ and the } \boldsymbol{e}_\alpha \text{ with } (S\pi_\rho, \alpha) \geqslant 0.$$

This correspondence suggests the following:

70.6.1. Definition $\Pi(\rho) = (\mathrm{Int}\ W^*)\pi_\rho$ for $\rho \in W^{++}$,

$$\Pi = \cup_\rho \Pi(\rho).$$

$$w(SG(\rho)) = S\pi_\rho \qquad \text{if} \quad S \in \mathrm{Int}(\boldsymbol{G}, \boldsymbol{H});$$

so w maps $\Gamma^0(\rho)$ one-to-one onto $\Pi(\rho)$.

$\lambda, \mu \in \Pi$ are called *incident* if

$$(\lambda, \alpha)(\mu, \alpha) \geqslant 0 \qquad \text{for all} \quad \alpha \in W^*.$$

Obviously Π consists of all integral elements that are equivalent to fundamental weights. Clearly:

70.6.2. Proposition If $a \in \Gamma^0$, then the infinitesimal algebra of a is spanned by $\boldsymbol{H}$ and the $\boldsymbol{e}_\alpha$ with

$$(wa, \alpha) \geqslant 0.$$

The last part of the definition above is justified by the following:

70.6.3. Proposition $a, b \in \Gamma^0$ are incident if and only if wa, wb are so.

Proof $\boldsymbol{M}$ containing a maximal solvable subalgebra around $\boldsymbol{H}$ means that for any $\alpha \in W^*$ either $\boldsymbol{e}_\gamma$ or $\boldsymbol{e}_{-\gamma} \in \boldsymbol{M}$. Therefore, $a \cap b$ to be parabolic means that

$$\text{either } (wa, \gamma) \geqslant 0 \wedge (wb, \gamma) \geqslant 0 \qquad \text{or} \qquad (wa, \gamma) \leqslant 0 \wedge (wb, \gamma) \leqslant 0.$$

In other words, $(wa,\gamma)(wb,\gamma) \geqslant 0$, which proves the assertion.
Evidently:

70.6.4. Proposition By w the action of Int$(\boldsymbol{G},\boldsymbol{H})$ in Γ^0 is translated into that of Int W^* in Π.

70.7. Proposition If $F \subset \Gamma$ consists of mutually incident elements, then $\bigcap_{a \in F} a$ is parabolic.

Proof By Proposition 70.5.4 F is finite. The proof is inductive on the number of elements of F. Take the statement for granted for $F' = F \setminus \{c\}$ (some $c \in F$). There are maximal solvable subgroups B, B' with $B \subset \bigcap_{a \in F'} a$, and $B' \subset c$. Bruhat's lemma provides a trunk $H' \subset B \cap B'$; thus $H' \subset \bigcap_{a \in F} a$.

So one may suppose $F \subset \Gamma^0$. The mutual incidence in F then means

$$(\lambda, \alpha)(\mu, \alpha) \geqslant 0 \qquad \text{for all} \quad \alpha \in W^* \qquad \text{and} \qquad \lambda, \mu \in wF;$$

thus, if $\alpha \in W^*$ is given, either $(\lambda, \alpha) \geqslant 0$ for all $\lambda \in wF$ or $(\lambda, \alpha) \leqslant 0$ for all of them. Consequently, for any α, either $\boldsymbol{e}_\alpha$ or $\boldsymbol{e}_{-\alpha}$ is an infinitesimal element of all $a \in F$, which shows by 69.28.3 the existence of a maximal solvable Lie subgroup in their intersection.

70.8. Definition The intersections of closed halfspaces bounded by $\alpha^\perp$ ($\alpha \in W^*$) are called *parts* (of $\boldsymbol{H}^*_{\text{st}}$). If $V \subset W^*$ such that $V \cup (-V) = W^*$, then the intersection of the halfspaces $\uparrow_\xi(\xi, \alpha) \geqslant 0$ with $\alpha \in V$ is called a *cell*. An *edge* is a one-dimensional cell.

Clearly every closed chamber is a cell, and any cell is the intersection of closed chambers. Parts are convex. An i-dimensional part is unambiguously built up from i-dimensional cells, which are minimal i-dimensional parts.

By the definition of fundamental weight, the edges contained in the closed dominant chamber are the images of $\Upsilon_{\tau \geqslant 0}(\tau\pi_\rho)$ ($\rho \in W^{++}$). Thanks to the action of Int W^*, it follows that the edges are the sets of weakly positive multiples of elements of Π.

Proposition For $\lambda, \mu \in \Pi$ the following statements are equivalent: λ, μ are incident; λ, μ are in a common closed chamber; λ, μ are in a common cell.

70.9. Definition For $a, b \in \Gamma$ the *covariant* $\Gamma(a,b)$ of a, b denotes the set of all $c \in \Gamma$ that are G-fixed when a and b are G-fixed.

The stability groups of a,b,c are just their adjoint images (see 68.7.2). a,b are simultaneously invariant under precisely those $\tilde{x}$ for which $x \in a \cap b$; the invariance of c under the same $\tilde{x}$ means that $c \supset a \cap b$. So:

Proposition $\Gamma(a,b)$ is the set of $c \supset a \cap b$, $c \in \Gamma$.
Clearly, if a, $b \in \Gamma^0$, then $\Gamma(a,b) \subset \Gamma^0$.

70.10. Definition The smallest part containing λ, μ is denoted by $P(\lambda,\mu)$. If $\lambda, \mu \in \Pi$, then $\Pi(\lambda,\mu)$ means $P(\lambda,\mu) \cap \Pi$.

Proposition $\Pi(wa, wb) = w\Gamma(a,b)$ if $a, b \in \Gamma^0$.

Proof Translated by w, $c \supset a \cap b$ states that

$$\wedge_{\gamma \in W*}\{[(wa,\gamma) \geqslant 0 \wedge (wb,\gamma) \geqslant 0] \rightarrow (wc,\gamma) \geqslant 0\}.$$

In other words, wc is found in every part that contains wa and wb.

70.11. Proposition If $\boldsymbol{G} \in$ Alg Lie Com SSS and $\xi_1, \xi_2 \in \boldsymbol{H}^*_{\mathrm{st}} \setminus \{\boldsymbol{0}\}$, then there is an $\alpha \in W^*$ with $(\xi_i, \alpha) \neq 0$ for $i = 1,2$.

Proof The set of $\alpha \in W^*$ with $(\xi_i, \alpha) = 0$ is called W_i $(= -W_i)$. Suppose the statement is wrong. Then

$$W_1 \cup W_2 = W^*.$$

$W_i \neq W^*$ because the inner product is nondegenerate on $\boldsymbol{H}^*$. Take

$$\alpha_1 \in W_1 \setminus W_2, \qquad \alpha_2 \in W_2.$$

If

$$[\boldsymbol{e}_{\alpha 1}, \boldsymbol{e}_{\alpha 2}] \neq \boldsymbol{0},$$

then

$$\alpha_1 + \alpha_2 \in W;$$

thus either

$$\alpha_1 + \alpha_2 = 0 \qquad \text{(hence } \alpha_1 \in W_2\text{, which is impossible)}$$

or

$$\alpha_1 + \alpha_2 \in W_2 \qquad \text{(hence } \alpha_1 \in W_2\text{, which is impossible).}$$

Thus

$$\alpha_1 + \alpha_2 \in W_1 \setminus W_2.$$

For $V \subset W^*$ the linear span of the $\boldsymbol{e}_\alpha$ with $\alpha \in V$ is denoted by $\vartheta(V)$. Then it has been proved that

$$[\vartheta(W_1 \setminus W_2), \vartheta(W_2)] \subset \vartheta(W_1 \setminus W_2).$$

The space $\vartheta(W_1 \setminus W_2)$ is idealized by $\boldsymbol{H} + \vartheta(W_2)$, and so is the Lie algebra $\boldsymbol{D}$ generated by $\vartheta(W_1 \setminus W_2)$. Since $\boldsymbol{D} \subset \boldsymbol{H} + \vartheta(W_1) \neq \boldsymbol{G}$, it is a nontrivial proper ideal of $\boldsymbol{G}$, which contradicts the simplicity of $\boldsymbol{G}$.

70.12. Proposition If $\lambda, \mu \in \Pi$ are incident, then $(\lambda, \mu) \geqslant 0$. In the case of simple G this inequality is strengthened to $(\lambda, \mu) > 0$.

Proof According to 21.1.9,

$$(\lambda, \mu) = \sum_{\alpha \in W*} (\lambda, \alpha)(\mu, \alpha),$$

where all summands are $\geqslant 0$ if λ, μ are incident. $(\lambda, \mu) = 0$ is possible only if all summands vanish, but according to 70.11 this is forbidden by simplicity.

70.13. Definition For $x \in \Gamma$ the set of elements incident with x is called $J(x)$.

Theorem Suppose that G is simple. If $J(a) \cap J(b) \neq \bigcirc$, then there is a

$$c \in J(a) \cap J(b) \qquad \text{with} \quad J(a) \cap J(b) \subset J(c).$$

Proof By Bruhat's lemma, $a \cap b$ contains a trunk. Thus a, b may be supposed in Γ^0.

70.13.1 $$c \in J(a) \cap J(b) \cap \Gamma^0,$$

fulfilling

70.13.2 $$J(a) \cap J(b) \cap \Gamma^0 \subset J(c),$$

also fulfills

70.13.3 $$J(a) \cap J(b) \subset J(c).$$

Indeed, if $d \in J(a) \cap J(b)$, then both $a \cap c$ and $b \cap d$ are parabolic and therefore $a \cap b \cap c \cap d$ contains a trunk H'. Now $H = \tilde{x}H'$ by means of some $x \in a \cap b \cap c$; thus

$$\tilde{x}a = a, \qquad \tilde{x}b = b, \qquad \tilde{x}c = c, \qquad \tilde{x}d = d' \in \Gamma^0,$$

and again

$$d' \in J(a) \cap J(b);$$

hence by 70.13.2 $d' \in J(c)$, thus

$$d \in J(c),$$

which proves 70.13.3.

At the same time the following has been proved:

70.13.4 If $a,b \in \Gamma^0$, $J(a) \cap J(b) \neq \bigcirc$, then $J(a) \cap J(b) \cap \Gamma^0 \neq \bigcirc$.

A c that fulfills 70.13.1–2 will now be constructed. Put $\lambda = wa$, $\mu = wb$. Then

$$w(J(a) \cap J(b) \cap \Gamma_0)$$

is the set N of elements ν of Π such that

$$(\lambda, \alpha)(\nu, \alpha) \geqslant 0 \wedge (\mu, \alpha)(\nu, \alpha) \geqslant 0 \qquad \text{for all} \quad \alpha \in W^* \tag{N}$$

Note that for $\nu \in N$,

$$(\lambda, \alpha)(\mu, \alpha) < 0 \rightarrow (\nu, \alpha) = 0.$$

Let F be the subgroup of Int W^* generated by the reflections

$$S_\alpha \quad \text{with} \quad (\lambda, \alpha) = (\mu, \alpha) = 0.$$

Then λ, μ are invariant under F, as is N.

For $\nu \in N$ put

$$\nu' = \sum_{S \in F} S\nu.$$

Then $S\nu' = \nu'$ for $S \in F$, particularly for S_α with $(\lambda, \alpha) = (\mu, \alpha) = 0$; thus

$$(\lambda, \alpha) = (\mu, \alpha) = 0 \rightarrow (\nu', \alpha) = 0 \qquad \text{for} \quad \alpha \in W^*.$$

Further

$$(\lambda, \alpha) > 0 \vee (\mu, \alpha) > 0 \rightarrow (\nu', \alpha) \geqslant 0,$$

for under this condition $(\nu, \alpha) \geqslant 0$ for all $\nu \in N$ and N is invariant under F. Finally

$$(\lambda, \alpha)(\mu, \alpha) < 0 \rightarrow (\nu', \alpha) = 0,$$

since this is true with all $\nu \in N$ instead of ν'.

According to 70.12, $(\lambda, \nu) > 0$, $(\mu, \nu) > 0$, and, because of the F-invariance of λ, μ, also $(\lambda, \nu') > 0$, $(\mu, \nu') > 0$.

Thus $\nu' \neq 0$.

Now define D as the set of $\xi \in \boldsymbol{H}^*_{\mathrm{st}}$ such that for all $\alpha \in W^*$

$$(\lambda, \alpha) = (\mu, \alpha) = 0 \rightarrow (\xi, \alpha) = 0,$$

$$(\lambda, \alpha) \geqslant 0 \wedge (\mu, \alpha) \geqslant 0 \rightarrow (\xi, \alpha) \geqslant 0, \tag{D}$$

and

$$(\lambda, \alpha)(\mu, \alpha) < 0 \rightarrow (\xi, \alpha) = 0.$$

Then D has been proved to contain an element $\nu' \neq 0$. D is a positive-dimensional cell. It contains an edge and thus some

$$\kappa \in D \cap \Pi \subset N.$$

To use $w^{-1}\kappa$ as c, one must verify the conditions on κ corresponding to 70.13.1–2; that is,

$$\kappa \text{ incident with } \lambda, \mu \text{ and with every } \nu \in N.$$

The first two assertions are evident, since $\kappa \in N$. The third means

$$(\kappa, \alpha)(\nu, \alpha) \geqslant 0 \qquad \text{for all} \quad \alpha \in W^*, \qquad \nu \in N,$$

which needs verifying only for $(\kappa, \alpha) > 0$. Now in this case, by the definition of D, $(\lambda, \alpha) > 0$ or $(\mu, \alpha) > 0$; hence, according to the definition of N, $(\nu, \alpha) \geqslant 0$ and therefore $(\kappa,\alpha)(\nu, \alpha) \geqslant 0$. By this result the existence of c is granted.

70.14 Every maximal solvable Lie subgroup of $G(\rho)$ contains the radical rad $G(\rho)$ of $G(\rho)$, which is generated by rad $\boldsymbol{G}(\rho)$. The radical of $\boldsymbol{G}(\rho)$ is spanned by some $\boldsymbol{h} \in \boldsymbol{H}$ with $\boldsymbol{h} \neq \boldsymbol{0}$ and $\sigma(\boldsymbol{h}) = 0$ for all $\sigma \in W^{++} \setminus \{\rho\}$ and by all $\boldsymbol{e}_\alpha$ that involve ρ with a positive coefficient. rad $\boldsymbol{G}(\rho)$ can be used to decide whether some $b \in \Gamma^0$ is incident with $G(\rho)$. More specifically:

70.14.1. Proposition $b \in \Gamma$ is incident with $a \in \Gamma$ iff b contains rad a.

The necessity of this condition is evident. Its sufficiency need be proved only for $H \subset a \cap b$ and $a = G(\rho)$. It is then an immediate consequence of the following:

70.14.2. Proposition If $b \in \Gamma^0$ contains rad $G(\rho)$, then b is equivalent to some $G(\sigma)$ by means of an $\tilde{x} \in \operatorname{Int}(\boldsymbol{G}, \boldsymbol{H})$ with $x \in G(\rho)$.

Note that $G(\rho)$, $G(\sigma)$ are always incident.

Proof By 20.15 the $\boldsymbol{e}_\alpha$ and $\boldsymbol{h}_\alpha$ in which α does not involve ρ span a semisimple subalgebra $\boldsymbol{G}_1$, with the span of the $\boldsymbol{h}_\alpha$ (=kernel of π_ρ) as a trunk $\boldsymbol{H}_1$. Obviously $\boldsymbol{G}_1 \subset \boldsymbol{G}(\rho)$. If $\boldsymbol{G}_1 \subset \boldsymbol{b}$, then obviously $\boldsymbol{b} = \boldsymbol{G}(\rho)$. If $\boldsymbol{G}_1 \not\subset \boldsymbol{b}$, then $\boldsymbol{b} \cap \boldsymbol{G}_1$ is a parabolic subalgebra of $\boldsymbol{G}_1$; under an element of $\operatorname{Int}(\boldsymbol{G}_1, \boldsymbol{H}_1)$ every free rootform (see 69.23) of $\boldsymbol{b} \cap \boldsymbol{G}_1$ may be assumed positive. However, $\operatorname{Int}(\boldsymbol{G}_1, \boldsymbol{H}_1)$ is naturally included in $\operatorname{Int}(\boldsymbol{G}, \boldsymbol{H})$ and its elements leave rad $\boldsymbol{G}(\rho)$ invariant. Therefore the assumption entails $\boldsymbol{b} = \boldsymbol{G}(\sigma)$ for some $\sigma \in W^{++}$, $\sigma \neq \rho$.

70.14.3 Another immediate consequence of 70.14.2 is stated in the following:

Proposition If $b \in \Gamma^0$ is incident with $G(\rho)$, then b is equivalent to some $G(\sigma)$ by means of an element of $\operatorname{Int}(\boldsymbol{G}, \boldsymbol{H})$ that does not change $G(\rho)$.

This proposition allows one to assume incident a, b in the more convenient form $G(\rho)$, $G(\sigma)$.

70.14.4 By the same method the foregoing can be strengthened to obtain the following:

Proposition If $a = G(\rho)$, $b \in \Gamma^0(\sigma)$, $c \in \Gamma^0(\tau)$, ρ between σ and τ in W^{++} and a incident with both b and c, then by an element of a leaving H invariant b and c can be carried over into $G(\sigma)$ and $G(\tau)$.

It follows from the fact that rootforms that do not involve ρ cannot involve both σ and τ.

70.15. Definition A *chain* of length p in Γ is a sequence of $p+1$ elements of Γ in which every element is incident with its successor. A chain is called *irreducible* if all its elements are different.

Theorem If $a, b \in \Gamma$ and a pair of different $\rho, \sigma \in W^{++}$ are given, then a chain $c_0, c_1, \ldots, c_k, c_{k+1}$ can be found with $c_0 = a$, $c_{k+1} = b$, $c_j \in \Gamma(\rho) \cup \Gamma(\sigma)$ for $j = 1, \ldots, k$.

Proof It may be assumed that a, b are in Γ^0. Then in Π a sequence $\lambda_0, \lambda_1, \ldots, \lambda_k, \lambda_{k+1}$ must be found such that $\lambda_0 = wa$, $\lambda_{k+1} = wb$, and λ_j is incident with λ_{j+1}. In any case there is a sequence of closed chambers $C_0, \ldots, C_{k+1}$ such that $\dim(C_j \cap C_{j+1}) = l - 1$, $wa \in C_0$, and $wb \in C_{k+1}$. Now, since $C_j \cap C_{j+1}$ contains one element of each sort but one of Π (see 70.6.3 and 70.8), $C_j \cap C_{j+1} \cap (\Pi(\rho) \cup \Pi(\sigma)) \neq \bigcirc$, and the only thing one has to do is to choose λ_{j+1} in this set.

70.16. Definition $\Gamma \bmod a = J(a) \setminus \{a\}$ for $a \in \Gamma$, with the notions of Γ and J as defined in 70.4 and 70.13. $\Gamma \bmod a$ is endowed with the incidence structure that it bears as a subset of Γ.

Theorem If $a \in \Gamma(\rho)$, then $\Gamma \bmod a$ is isomorphic to the incidence geometry of $G(\rho)/\text{rad}\ G(\rho)$, the graph of which arises from that of G by deleting ρ and its bonds with other elements.

More precisely, if, for the sake of convenience, $a = G(\rho)$ is assumed: Let φ be the canonical mapping of $G(\rho)$ onto $G(\rho)/\text{rad}\ G(\rho)$. Then $\vartheta = \curlyvee_{b \in \Gamma \bmod a} \varphi(b \cap G(\rho))$ maps $\Gamma \bmod a$ isomorphically onto the incidence geometry Δ of $\varphi(G(\rho))$.

Proof Since $\varphi(G(\rho))$ is semisimple, Δ exists. By 70.14.1 $\Gamma \bmod a$ is the set of maximal parabolic subgroups of G around rad $G(\rho)$. The elements of $\Gamma \bmod a$ contain maximal solvable Lie subgroups $G(\rho)$ (necessarily containing rad $G(\rho)$). Since φ maps the maximal solvable Lie subgroups of $G(\rho)$ onto those of $G/\text{rad}\ G(\rho)$, ϑ preserves the parabolicity of the elements of $\Gamma \bmod a$; clearly it maps $\Gamma \bmod a$ onto Δ (to show that ϑ is onto, put an element of Δ in its canonical form). The mapping ϑ preserves incidence, for φ maps maximal solvable subgroups onto maximal solvable subgroups. Similarly, it is evident that the incidence of $\vartheta b, \vartheta c$ implies that of b, c. Finally, let $\vartheta b = \vartheta c$. Then by the foregoing a, b, c are mutually incident, so by 70.7 $a \cap b \cap c$ is parabolic and may be assumed to contain $\boldsymbol{H}$ and all $\boldsymbol{e}_\alpha$ with $\alpha \in W^+$. This, however, means that a, b, c are some $G(\rho)$, $G(\sigma)$, $G(\tau)$. But it is then evident that $\vartheta b = \vartheta c$ implies $b = c$, which completes the proof that ϑ is isomorphic. The remainder of the statement is evident.

70.17 If G splits directly into G_1, G_2, then the maximal solvable Lie subgroups of G split correspondingly into maximal solvable Lie subgroups of G_1 and G_2, and a maximal parabolic subgroup of G contains G_1 or G_2. Those containing G_i form a subset Γ_j of Γ $(i \neq j; i = 1, 2; j = 1, 2)$. Clearly every element of Γ_1 is incident with every element of Γ_2. Moreover, Γ_i, endowed with the incidence structure induced by Γ, is isomorphic to the incidence geometry of G_i.

This suggests a definition of direct sum of incidence geometries which will be substantiated later. Meanwhile Γ is called *simple* if G is simple.

70.18 As an immediate consequence of 70.16–17, one gets the following:

Theorem If, in the graph of G, ρ lies between σ and τ, then every element of $\Gamma(\sigma) \cap J(G(\rho))$ is incident with every element of $\Gamma(\tau) \cap J(G(\rho))$.

70.19 The following is a refinement of the statement of 70.13.

Theorem Let Γ be simple, let $a, b \in \Gamma$ be nonincident, and

$$J(a) \cap J(b) \cap \Gamma(\rho) \neq \bigcirc.$$

Then there is $d \in J(a) \cap J(b)$ such that

70.19.1
$$J(d) \cap \Gamma(\rho) = J(a) \cap J(b) \cap \Gamma(\rho).$$

Remark To illustrate this statement take $\boldsymbol{G} \in \mathbf{A}_l$. Then Γ may be identified with projective l-space and a, b with elements of it. For any ρ one can take for d either the intersection or the span of a, b (if it exists in Γ, i.e., has linear dimension $\neq 0$, $\neq l+1$).

Proof Suppose that $a \in \Gamma(\sigma)$, $b \in \Gamma(\tau)$. Since a, b are nonincident, and because of 70.18, ρ does not separate σ and τ in the graph of G. According to 70.13, there is a $c \in J(a) \cap J(b)$ with

70.19.2
$$J(a) \cap J(b) \subset J(c).$$

Suppose that $c \in \Gamma(\kappa)$. Again κ does not separate σ, τ. Moreover, $\kappa \neq \sigma$, $\kappa \neq \tau$.

If $\kappa = \rho$ or κ separates ρ and σ (and thus ρ and τ), then by 70.18 every element of $J(c) \cap \Gamma(\rho)$ is incident with a and b. Therefore

70.19.3 $$J(c) \cap \Gamma(\rho) \subset J(a) \cap J(b).$$

By combining 70.19.2–3 one can satisfy 70.19.1 by putting $d = c$.

If not, $W^{++} \setminus \{\kappa\}$ has a component containing ρ, σ, τ. Using the terminology of Theorem 70.16 with κ instead of ρ, one considers Γ mod c which by ϑ is mapped onto Δ. Now corresponding to the breach κ in $W^{++} \setminus \{\kappa\}$, Δ breaks into Δ_1 and Δ_2, where Δ_1 belongs to the component containing ρ, σ, τ; therefore ϑ maps $\Gamma(\rho) \cap J(c), a, b$ into Δ_1; furthermore, Δ_1, Δ_2 are elementwise incident. Now by induction the theorem may be taken for granted with respect to Δ_1. This means the existence of $d' \in \Delta_1$ with

$$d' \in J(\vartheta(a)) \cap J(\vartheta(b)) \quad \text{and} \quad J(d') \cap \Delta_1(\rho) = J(\vartheta(a)) \cap J(\vartheta(b)) \cap \Delta_1(\rho).$$

The contribution of Δ_2 being trivial because of the elementwise incidence of Δ_1, Δ_2, one may replace Δ_1 by Δ in this equation. Finally, by applying ϑ^{-1} one gets a d which fulfills 70.19.1 (again using 70.19.2).

70.20. The Special Case of rank 2 G is supposed to be of rank 2. The primitive rootforms on the ordered trunk $\boldsymbol{H}$ are ρ, σ.

$$(S_\rho S_\sigma)^m = 1,$$

where for

70.20.1 $$\begin{cases} G \in \mathbf{A}_1 + \mathbf{A}_1, & \mathbf{A}_2, & \mathbf{B}_2, & \mathbf{G}_2, \\ m = \quad 2, & 3, & 4, & 6. \end{cases}$$

The number of chambers is $2m$. According to adjacency, they are put into a cyclic order that also applies to the elements of Π as vectors in the plane. In this cyclic order elements of $\Pi(\rho)$ and $\Pi(\sigma)$ alternate with one another. Neighbors are incident.

If $\lambda, \mu, \nu \in \Pi$ and $\lambda + \mu \neq 0$, then ν is called *between* λ and μ if $\nu = s\lambda + t\mu$ for suitable positive s, t.

By w^{-1} the cyclic order and the betweenness are transferred to Γ^0.

In an irreducible chain within Γ^0 the members follow each other according to the cyclic order (or its inverse); if the length of the chain is $< m$, then its intermediate members are between the extremities.

70.20.2. Proposition If c is between a and b in Γ^0, then $a \cap b \subset c$.

Proof Let $\boldsymbol{e}_\alpha \in \boldsymbol{a} \cap \boldsymbol{b}$. Then $(wa, \alpha) \geqslant 0$, $(wb, \alpha) \geqslant 0$. Thus, if c between a and b, $(wc, \alpha) \geqslant 0$, thus $\boldsymbol{e}_\alpha \in \boldsymbol{c}$.

70.20.3. Proposition If the extremities of an irreducible chain of length $< m$ are in Γ^0, then the entire chain is in Γ^0.

Proof Let $a_0, \ldots, a_p$ constitute an irreducible chain, $a_0, a_p \in \Gamma^0$, $p < m$. The proof proceeds by induction on p. Both a_0 and $a_{p-1} \cap a_p$ contain a maximal solvable Lie subgroup of G. Therefore by Bruhat's lemma there is a trunk $H' \subset a_0 \cap a_{p-1} \cap a_p$. Both H and H' are in $a_0 \cap a_p$. Thus $\tilde{x}H' = H$ by means of some $x \in a_0 \cap a_p$. Since $\tilde{x}a_{p-1} \in \Gamma^0$, the inductive argument can be applied to the chain of $\tilde{x}a_i$ $(i = 0, \ldots, p-1)$ to the effect that $\tilde{x}a_i \in \Gamma^0$ for $i = 0, \ldots, p-1$. Since $x \in a_p$, this extends to $\tilde{x}a_i \in \Gamma^0$ for $i = 0, \ldots, p$. The supposition $p < m$ guarantees that $\tilde{x}a_i$ is between $\tilde{x}a_0 = a_0$ and $\tilde{x}a_p = a_p$ for $0 < i < p$; thus by 70.20.2, $x \in a_0 \cap a_p \subset \tilde{x}a_i$, hence $x \in a_i$, $a_i = \tilde{x}a_i \in \Gamma^0$, which proves the assertion.

70.20.4. Proposition The intersection of an irreducible chain of length $\leqslant m$ contains a trunk of G.

Proof Let $a_0, a_1, \ldots, a_p$ be the chain. Then there is a trunk H' in $a_0 \cap a_{p-1} \cap a_p$. Now $p - 1 < m$; thus by applying 70.20.3 with H' instead of H one gets $H' \subset a_i$ for $0 < i < p-1$ as well.

70.20.5. Theorem If G is of rank 2, then any pair of elements of Γ can be joined by a chain of length $\leqslant m$ (see 70.20.1). If, moreover, there is a chain of length $< m$ to join distinct $a, b \in \Gamma$, then there is exactly one irreducible chain of length $\leqslant m$ to join them.

Proof The first assertion follows from the fact that any pair $a, b \in \Gamma$ may be supposed within Γ^0. Let a, b be joined by an irreducible chain C of length $\leqslant m$. Then by 70.20.4 the entire chain C may be supposed within Γ^0.

Let a, b (now $\in \Gamma^0$) be joined once again by a chain C' of length $< m$. Then by thinning out, C' may be assumed irreducible, hence by 70.20.3 contained in Γ^0. Then either C and C' are equal or $C \cup C' = \Gamma^0$. The alternative, however, leads to a contradiction, for the lengths of C and C' are $\leqslant m$ and $< m$, whereas Γ^0 has $2m$ elements. This proves the theorem.

71. AN AXIOMATIC APPROACH TO INCIDENCE GEOMETRIES OF SEMISIMPLE LIE GROUPS

71.1. Definitions

71.1.1 An *incidence geometry* consists of a set and a reflexive symmetric binary relation called *incidence*.

71.1.2 An incidence geometry Γ is called the *direct sum* of the incidence geometries $\Gamma_1, \ldots, \Gamma_p$ if

as a set Γ is the disjoint union of $\Gamma_1, \ldots, \Gamma_p$,
the incidence relation on Γ_i is the restriction of that on Γ,
Γ_i, Γ_j are elementwise incident for $i \neq j$.

In this situation the Γ_i are called *direct summands* of Γ.

71.1.3 If Γ is an incidence geometry and a is an element of Γ, then Γ mod a is the incidence geometry consisting of the set of elements incident with a, except a itself, and of the restriction of the incidence relation on Γ.

71.1.4 Any *graph* to be mentioned is supposed to consist of a nonnegative finite number of *dots* and a finite number of mutual *bonds* which may be multiple and directed. A splitting of a graph into disjoint unconnected subgraphs is called *direct*. A graph gets *reduced* with respect to one of its dots by omitting that dot and its bonds with other dots.

71.1.5 An *incidence geometry on a graph* consists of an incidence geometry Γ, a graph K, and a mapping of the set of dots of K onto a set of subsets of Γ such that

the images of the dots are pairwise disjoint,
the union of the images of the dots is Γ,
incident elements of the image of a dot coincide.

The notion of isomorphism of incidence geometries on graphs is understood in the obvious way.

The number of dots is called the *rank* of the geometry.

71.1.6 An incidence geometry Γ on a graph is called the *direct sum* of the incidence geometries on graphs $\Gamma_1, \ldots, \Gamma_p$ if, as an incidence geometry, Γ splits directly into the incidence geometries $\Gamma_1, \ldots, \Gamma_p$ and this splitting is induced by one of the underlying graph into subgraphs belonging canonically to the Γ_i.

In this situation the Γ_i are called *direct summands* of Γ.

If Γ has no nontrivial proper direct summands, it is called *simple*.

71.1.7 If Γ is an incidence geometry on a graph and a is an element of Γ, then Γ mod a is interpreted in a canonical way as an incidence geometry on the reduction of the graph of Γ with respect to the dot to which a belongs. More precisely, Γ mod a is, by restriction of the incidence relation and intersection of the images of the dots, an incidence geometry on the reduction of the graph of Γ with respect to the dot to whose image a belongs.

71.2. Definition A system Σ of incidence geometries on graphs is called a *Tits geometry* if it fulfills the following conditions:

71.2.0 In every element of Σ the image of each dot is nonvoid.

71.2.1 For every $\Gamma \in \Sigma$ any direct splitting of the underlying graph induces one of Γ itself.

71.2.2 Every direct summand of $\Gamma \in \Sigma$ belongs to Σ.

71.2.3 If $\Gamma_1, \Gamma_2 \in \Sigma$ are disjoint, then there is a $\Gamma \in \Sigma$, which is the direct sum of Γ_1, Γ_2.

71.2.4 If $\Gamma \in \Sigma$ and a is an element of Γ, then $\Gamma \bmod a \in \Sigma$.

71.2.5 For any $\Gamma \in \Sigma$, if a, b are elements of Γ, and if $\Gamma(\rho), \Gamma(\sigma)$ are the images of different dots ρ, σ of Γ, then there is a number k and a sequence $c_0, \ldots, c_k$ of elements of Γ such that $a = c_0$, $c_k = b$, c_{i-1} incident with c_i ($i = 1, \ldots, k$), and $c_i \in \Gamma(\rho) \cup \Gamma(\sigma)$ for $i = 1, \ldots, k-1$.

71.2.6 For any simple $\Gamma \in \Sigma$, if $J(x)$ means the set of elements of Γ incident with the element x of Γ, and if a, b are nonincident elements and $\Gamma(\rho)$ is the image of a dot of Γ, then

$$\text{if} \quad J(a) \cap J(b) \cap \Gamma(\rho) \neq \bigcirc,$$

$$\text{then} \quad J(c) \cap \Gamma(\rho) = J(a) \cap J(b) \cap \Gamma(\rho)$$

for some

$$c \in J(a) \cap J(b).$$

71.2.7 $\Gamma \in \Sigma$ and Γ' isomorphic to Γ implies $\Gamma' \in \Sigma$.

71.3 An incidence geometry of a complex semisimple Lie group can in an obvious way be interpreted as an incidence geometry on a graph. Then some major results of Section 70 can be summarized in the following theorem:

Theorem The system of geometries isomorphic to the incidence geometries of complex semisimple Lie groups is a Tits geometry.

In particular, the validity of 71.2.1–3 is granted by 70.17, the validity of 71.2.4, 71.2.5, 71.2.6 by 70.16, 70.15, 70.19.

71.4 A Tits geometry is to a high degree determined by its members of rank 2 If these members are prescribed, then a great many properties of any member of the system can be derived from its graph. This will be illustrated in 71.6

In particular the Tits geometry of Theorem 71.3 is essentially obtained if only graphs of semisimple groups are admitted and if the former correspondence between graphs of Lie groups and incidence geometries for the case of those of rank 2 only is postulated. However, this will not be proved here.

71.5 The property of incidence geometries of Lie groups of rank 2 stated in Theorem 70.20.5 is generalized by the following definition.

Definition of generalized polygons: A *generalized m-gon* Γ is an incidence geometry on a graph of rank 2 such that

any pair of elements of Γ can be joined by a chain of length $\leqslant m$,

if two elements of Γ can be joined by a chain of length $<m$, then there is exactly one irreducible chain of length $\leqslant m$ to join them.

(The notions of chain and irreducible chain are understood as in 70.15.)

The most convenient kind of graph for a generalized m-gon is a pair of dots with a $(m-2)$fold bond. Then, however, to keep in line with the results of 70.2 one must indicate G_2 not by a threefold but rather by a fourfold bond.

71.6 In the remainder of this section incidence geometries to be analyzed are supposed to have been taken from a fixed Tits geometry with the special property that

all graphs involved are graphs of semisimple groups,

the geometries of rank 2 are generalized polygons (2-gons, 3-gons, 4-gons, and 6-gons for the graph of $\mathsf{A}_1 + \mathsf{A}_1$, A_2, B_2, and G_2).

A few examples will be discussed. In a given geometry Γ between given elements a shortest chain is constructed, starting with some chain granted by 71.2.5 and shortening it by the use of the other postulates: If in a chain

$$\cdots bac \cdots$$

b,a,c belong to $\Gamma(\sigma)$, $\Gamma(\rho)$, $\Gamma(\tau)$, respectively, then in Γ mod a, which by induction may be supposed to be better known than Γ, there is a chain from b to c that can be inserted instead of bac. If σ, τ are separated by ρ in the graph of Γ, then by 71.2.1–4 there is incidence between b and c, so that a may be simply omitted. By such operations one may succeed in shortening the original chain.

The dots of the graph will be numbered $1, \ldots, l$ in the usual way if l is the rank of Γ. The elements of the ith sort will be indicated by i, i', i'', and the like. However, to avoid distinguishing marks the same sign i will be used even for different elements of the sort i occurring in the same chain when no confusion is likely to occur.

Examples

71.6.1 A_2. Between any pair of elements there is a chain of length $\leqslant 3$. Therefore if $1, 1'$ are given: $121'$, which is unique. In the same way if $2, 2'$ are given, $212'$. Interpreting the dots 1,2 respectively as the sets of points or lines, the incidence axioms of the projective plane are fulfilled. Γ is a plane projective geometry.

71.6.2 A_l. The elements of sort 1, 2, 3, ... are called points, lines, planes, ... By induction on l it will be shown that two points can be joined by a line. In any case, there is a chain

$$121'2'12 \cdots 1.$$

One considers $\Gamma' = \Gamma \bmod 1'$ with the graph of A_{l-1}. In Γ' the roles of points, lines, ... are played by elements of sort 2, 3, ... Therefore the neighbors $2, 2'$ of $1'$ can be joined by $232'$. Substitution changes the given chain into

$$1232'12 \cdots 1,$$

in which the $2, 2'$ between 1 and 3 may be omitted by 71.2.4 and 71.2.1. The resulting chain is

$$1312 \cdots 1.$$

In $\Gamma \bmod 3$ one considers the "lower" direct summand, which is a projective plane, in which points can be joined by a line. This allows one to replace 3 with 2. The new chain

$$1212 \cdots 1$$

is two links shorter than the original. This reduction can be repeated until

$$121,$$

which shows the existence of a line joining two given points.

Its uniqueness for *distinct* points is shown as follows: Let

$$121'2'1$$

be a (closed) chain. By 71.2.6 applied to $1, 1'$ instead of a, b, there is an i incident with $1, 2, 1', 2'$. In $\Gamma \bmod i$ this argument can be repeated until one arrives at a geometry of rank 2 in which such a chain is excluded by assumption. This proves the uniqueness of joining points in Γ.

Another property is that a line and a plane, if incident with two different points, are incident with each other. Indeed, if line 2 and plane 3 are not incident, by 71.2.6 there is an i incident with 2, 3, and the two points. Again, arguing by $\Gamma \bmod i$, one arrives at a $2'$ or $3'$, incident with the given 2 and 3. Then $2 = 2'$ or $3 = 3'$, both of which are contradictory.

Three different lines intersecting in three different points are in a plane: one is given the closed chain

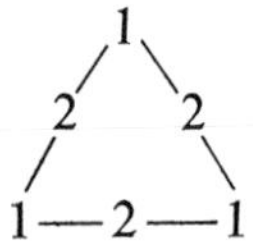

where the stroke is used to denote incidence. As before, one may replace some 1 by 3,

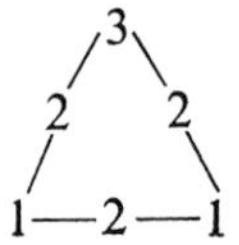

and thus omit the two upper 2's,

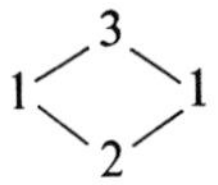

From the property already proved, it follows that 2, 3 are also incident, which shows that 3 is incident with all given 2's.

Continuing this procedure, one can prove that Γ fulfills all incidence axioms of projective space.

71.6.3 $B_2(C_2)$. Given nonincident 1, 2, there is a chain of length $\leqslant 4$ joining them; therefore 1212, which is even unique. Given that 1, 1 may by chance be incident or possess a unique chain 121 (joinable by a line). In any case, there is a chain 12121 between them.

This is the geometry on a 3-quadric in projective 4-space or, equivalently, the symplectic geometry of projective 3-space.

71.6.4 $B_3(C_3)$. In the symplectic interpretation 1, 2, 3 are the points, lines, and planes:

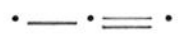

1 2 3

(1) For any 1, 2 there is a chain

1212,

which is unique if there is no chain 132.

(2) A chain 132 is unique for nonincident 1, 2.

(3) For any 1, 3 there is a chain

1323,

which is unique for nonincident 1, 3.

(4) For any 2, 3 there is a chain

$$2313,$$

which is unique if there is no chain 213.

(5) A chain 213 can be completed to

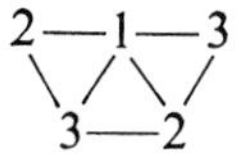

within the geometry reduced with respect to 1. The chain 213 is unique if 2, 3 are nonincident and so is the completion.

(6) A chain 121 is unique if 1, 1 are different.

(7) A chain 2312 can be completed to

$$
\begin{array}{ccc}
 & 3{-}1 & \\
\diagup & \diagdown\diagup & \diagdown \\
2 & 2 & 2 \\
\diagdown & \diagup\diagdown & \diagup \\
 & 1{-}3 &
\end{array}
$$

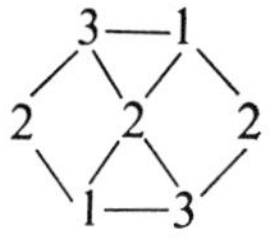

If there is no chain 212, it is unique and so is the completion.

(8) A chain 212 can be completed to

$$
\begin{array}{ccc}
2 & {-}1{-} & 2 \\
\diagdown\diagup & | & \diagdown\diagup \\
3 & {-}2{-} & 3
\end{array}
$$

It is unique if there is no chain 232; its completion is not.

(9) A chain 232 is unique if 2, 2 are different.

(10) A chain 313 can be completed to

$$
\begin{array}{ccc}
3 & {-}1{-} & 3 \\
\diagdown\diagup & | & \diagdown\diagup \\
2 & {-}3{-} & 2
\end{array}
$$

It is unique if there is no chain 323; its completion is not.

(11) A chain 323 is unique if 3, 3 are different.

(12) For any 1, 1 there are chains 12121 which are never unique; likewise for 2, 2 and 3, 3.

The facts from (5) onward, and (2), are easily proved. The existence of chains (1), (3), and (4) will be proved by an explicit construction; in this procedure elements with respect to which mod-reduction took place are underlined.

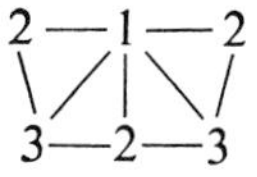

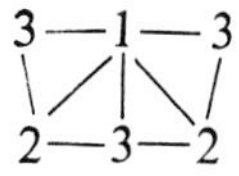

(3) One starts with a chain 132323 ··· 23 of unknown length:

1323232 ··· 3
1321232 ··· 3
13132 ··· 3
12132 ··· 3
123232 ··· 3
13232 ··· 3

by which the chain has become two links shorter.

This shows the existence of 1323 for given 1, 3.

(1) One starts with 13232 ··· 2 which by (3) can be shortened to 13232; hence,

13232
13212
1312
1212

This shows the existence of 1212.

(4)

2313131 ··· 3
2312131 ··· 3
23232131 ··· 3
2323131 ··· 3
2123131 ··· 3
213131 ··· 3
212131 ··· 3
2123231 ··· 3
213231 ··· 3
2323231 ··· 3
2321231 ··· 3
23131 ··· 3

which shows the existence of 2313.

As an example of a uniqueness proof, that for 1323 is given:

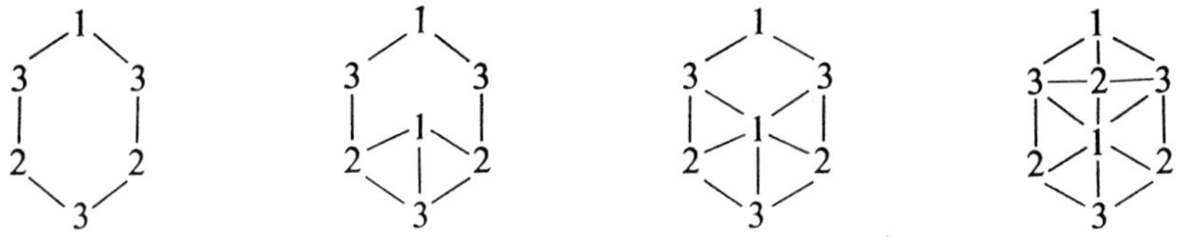

(In the last step 71.2.6 is used.) Reduction mod the lower 1 shows two chains 2323 in a B_2-geometry, which is forbidden.

71.6.5 F_4: •—•=•—•
$a \quad b \quad c \quad d$

Given a, d, there is a chain *adad*. In the proof the properties of B_3 are involved if reducing mod a or mod d.

One may start with

$$adcdcd \cdots d$$

and suppose that at least two pairs *cd* are present (if there is only one, it may be doubled).

$$a\underline{d}cdcd \cdots d$$
$$acb\underline{c}dcd \cdots d$$
$$acb\underline{d}cd \cdots d$$
$$acbca\underline{c}d \cdots d$$
$$ac\underline{b}cad \cdots d$$
$$a\underline{c}d\underline{c}ad \cdots d$$
$$adad \cdots d$$

If there are still pairs *cd* present, one continues as follows:

$$ada\underline{d}cd \cdots d$$
$$adacb\underline{c}d \cdots d$$
$$ad\underline{a}cbd \cdots d$$
$$adcd\underline{c}bd \cdots d$$
$$adcd\underline{b}d \cdots d$$
$$adcdcd \cdots d$$

which by the first procedure and by induction leads to *adad*.

71.7 Although interesting in itself, this haphazard search for shortest chains and uniqueness proofs is not satisfactory. A more algorithmic method would be desirable, though in the general case its existence might be doubted. If, however, one restricts oneself to incidence geometries of semisimple groups, group theory methods are available to solve these kinds of problems. They will be developed in the next sections.

72. COVARIANTS OF PAIRS OF ELEMENTS IN INCIDENCE GEOMETRIES OF SEMISIMPLE GROUPS

G is supposed to be semisimple complex. Other notations are taken from Section 70.

72.1 $\Gamma(a,b)$, as defined in 70.9, is the covariant of $a,b \in \Gamma$. By choosing the trunk H within $a \cap b$, $\Gamma(a,b)$ has been related to $\Pi(wa,wb)=P(wa,wb) \cap \Pi$ by 70.10. $P(\lambda,\mu)$ is the smallest part of $\boldsymbol{H}_{\mathrm{st}}^*$ containing λ and μ.

Since two trunks of $a \cap b$ are equivalent under inner automorphisms of G leaving a and b invariant, the metric properties of $\Pi(wa,wb)$ are covariant properties of a and b.

$\Pi(\lambda,\mu)$ will be discussed for any $\lambda,\mu \in \Pi$.

72.2 For $\alpha \in W^*$ the set of $\xi \in \boldsymbol{H}_{\mathrm{st}}^*$ with $(\xi,\alpha)=0$ is the hyperplane $\alpha^\perp$. The line-interval $[\lambda,\mu]$ is contained in the intersection N of all hyperplanes $\alpha^\perp$ passing through λ and μ.

Definition dim $N-1$ is called the *rank of the pair* $\lambda,\mu \in \Pi$.

Proposition If the cell C contains several points of $[\lambda,\mu]$, then dim $C \geqslant$ dim $N=$ rank $\ulcorner\lambda,\mu\urcorner+1$.

Indeed, such a cell contains a subinterval of $[\lambda,\mu]$; its linear span contains λ and μ, is the intersection of some hyperplanes $\alpha^\perp$ containing λ and μ, and therefore contains N.

72.3 Let $\xi_1, \ldots, \xi_{p-1} \in [\lambda,\mu]$ be the consecutive intersection points distinct from λ,μ of $[\lambda,\mu]$ with cells of dimension $\leqslant$ rank $\ulcorner\lambda,\mu\urcorner$, counted from λ to μ. In addition, put $\xi_0=\lambda$, $\xi_p=\mu$. Let C_i be the smallest cell containing ξ_i and put

$$D_i = C_i \cap \Pi \qquad (i=0,1,\ldots,p).$$

Note that

$$D_0=\{\lambda\}, \qquad D_p=\{\mu\}.$$

Every part containing λ,μ contains $[\lambda,\mu]$, thus ξ_i, and therefore the smallest cell in which ξ_i lies. Hence:

Proposition $D_i \subset \Pi(\lambda,\mu)$ for $i=0,1,\ldots,p$.

Note that some D_i may be void. Then $\xi_i = 0$ and $[\lambda, \mu]$ contains the origin; thus $-\mu$ is a positive multiple of λ. For some $S \in \operatorname{Int} W^*$, $S\lambda$ is a fundamental weight π. Now $S(-\mu)$ is also dominant, hence a fundamental weight, hence $S(-\mu) = S\lambda$. Thus $\mu = -\lambda$. Moreover, rank $\ulcorner \lambda, \mu \urcorner = 0$, $p = 2$, $D_1 = \bigcirc$.

72.4 The elements of $\{\xi_i\} \cup D_i$ are not separated by a hyperplane $\alpha^\perp$ ($\alpha \in W^*$). The same is true of the elements ξ_{i-1} and ξ_i and of the elements of $\{\xi_{i-1}\} \cup D_{i-1}$.

Proposition The elements of $D_{i-1} \cup D_i$ are mutually incident.

72.5. Proposition For $0 \leqslant i < j < k \leqslant p: D_i \cap D_k \subset D_j$.

Proof Let $\nu \in D_i \cap D_k$. Thus for all $\alpha \in W^*$

$$(\nu, \alpha)(\xi_i, \alpha) \geqslant 0, \qquad (\nu, \alpha)(\xi_k, \alpha) \geqslant 0.$$

If $(\nu, \alpha) \neq 0$, then (ξ_i, α), (ξ_k, α) have the same sign in the weak sense, thus (ξ_j, α) between them still has the same sign. Hence

$$(\nu, \alpha)(\xi_j, \alpha) \geqslant 0 \qquad \text{for all} \quad \alpha \in W^*,$$

which proves the assertion.

72.6. Notation $E_i = w^{-1} D_i$. $E = \ulcorner E_0, \ldots, E_p \urcorner$.
Note that if rank $\ulcorner \lambda, \mu \urcorner = 0$ then

$$E = \ulcorner \{w^{-1}\lambda\}, \bigcirc, \{w^{-1}\mu\} \urcorner.$$

Clearly the elements of $E_{i-1} \cup E_i$ are mutually incident.

$$E_0 = \{a\}, \qquad E_p = \{b\}.$$

Definition A sequence $\ulcorner E_0, \ldots, E_p \urcorner$ of finite subsets of Γ is called a *chain* if the elements of $E_{i-1} \cup E_i$ are mutually incident. Two chains $\ulcorner E_0, \ldots, E_p \urcorner$, $\ulcorner E_0^*, \ldots, E_q^* \urcorner$ are called *isomorphic* by means of φ if φ maps $\bigcup E_i$ one-to-one onto $\bigcup E_i^*$, such that E_i is mapped onto E_i^*, and for any ρ, if $x \in \Gamma(\rho)$, then $\varphi x \in \Gamma(\rho)$.

Clearly, according to 72.4, the E defined before is a chain, which up to Int G-equivalence does not depend on the choice of the trunk in $a \cap b$.

72.7. Theorem The pairs $\ulcorner a, b \urcorner$ and $\ulcorner a^*, b^* \urcorner$ are equivalent under Int G if and only if E determined by $\ulcorner a, b \urcorner$ and E^* determined by $\ulcorner a^*, b^* \urcorner$ (both with respect to some trunks) are isomorphic.

Proof "Only if" being obvious, one supposes that E, E^* are isomorphic; hence $p = q$. Since a, a^* belong to the same sort, they are equivalent under Int G; thus they may be supposed equal. Both $a \cap b$ and $a \cap b^*$ contain trunks of G, which are conjugate in a. Therefore, without changing $a = a^*$, one may arrange to have a common trunk H of G within $a \cap b$ and $a \cap b^*$. This trunk is used in the sequel. E, E^* may be supposed to be constructed on $\boldsymbol{H}$.

$$E_0 = \{a\} = \{a^*\} = E_0^*.$$

Since the elements of $E_0 \cup E_1$ as well as those of $E_0^* \cup E_1^* = E_0 \cup E_1^*$ are mutually incident, there are maximal solvable Lie subgroups B, B^* of G in $\bigcap_{c \in E_0 \cup E_1} c$ and $\bigcap_{c^* \in E_0 \cup E_1^*} c^*$. Both B and B^* are in a. Without changing a and H, by conjugation in a one may again arrange things so that $H \subset B = B^*$. Thus the elements of $E_0 \cup E_1 \cup E_1^*$ are mutually incident. Since φ relates elements of the same sort to one another, and $\varphi E_1 = E_1^*$, it follows that

$$E_1 = E_1^*.$$

After these preliminary transformations it will appear that

72.7.1 $$E_i = E_i^*$$

for all i; hence

$$b = b^*,$$

which is the assertion to be proved.

Instead of 72.7.1, one may prove

72.7.2 $$D_i = D_i^*$$

where $D_i = wE_i$, $D_i^* = wE_i^*$. Now suppose that this is true for all $i < j$ with some $j > 1$. Then the line intervals $[wa, wb]$ and $[wa, wb^*]$ meet the cell $C_{j-1} = C_{j-1}^*$ belonging to $D_{j-1} = D_{j-1}^*$ in interior points ξ_{j-1} and ξ_{j-1}^*. The points of $[\xi_{j-1}, \xi_j] \cup [\xi_{j-1}^*, \xi_j^*]$ are not separated by a hyperplane $\alpha^\perp$ because such a hyperplane would have to contain one of the points ξ_{j-1}, ξ_{j-1}^*, hence both, hence either it contains ξ_0, which contradicts its separation property, or it is pierced by both line intervals. Thus this set is contained in some closed chamber that consequently contains D_j as well as D_j^*. Since any closed chamber contains exactly one w-image of every sort, it follows that they are equal, which proves 72.7.2 for $i = j$.

72.8 The preceding theory is a practical tool for classifying the pairs of elements of Γ up to Int $\boldsymbol{G}$. This is shown by a rather involved example in Section 73.

73. THE CLASSES OF PAIRS OF ELEMENTS IN AN F_4-GEOMETRY

$G \in \mathsf{F}_4$. Ordered second dressing supposed on $\boldsymbol{H}$. Instead of a natural basis, an orthogonal one $\omega_1, \omega_2, \omega_3, \omega_4$ is chosen in $\boldsymbol{H}^*_{\text{st}}$ to make things look more symmetric, that is, such that

$$W^*: \quad \pm\omega_i \ (i=1,2,3,4), \qquad \pm\omega_i \pm \omega_j \ (i \neq j;\ 1,2,3,4),$$

$$\tfrac{1}{2}(\pm\omega_1 \pm \omega_2 \pm \omega_3 \pm \omega_4).$$

$$W^{++}: \qquad \rho_1 = \tfrac{1}{2}(\omega_1 - \omega_2 - \omega_3 - \omega_4),$$

$$\rho_2 = \omega_2 - \omega_3,$$

$$\rho_3 = \omega_4,$$

$$\rho_4 = \omega_3 - \omega_4.$$

Fundamental weights:

$$\pi_1 = \omega_1,$$

$$\pi_2 = \omega_1 + \omega_2,$$

$$\pi_3 = \tfrac{1}{2}(3\omega_1 + \omega_2 + \omega_3 + \omega_4),$$

$$\pi_4 = 2\omega_1 + \omega_2 + \omega_3.$$

On the basis $\ulcorner \omega_1, \omega_2, \omega_3, \omega_4 \urcorner$ the elements of Π are

$\Pi(\rho_1)$: $\ulcorner 1,0,0,0 \urcorner, \ldots$; $\tfrac{1}{2}\ulcorner 1,1,1,1 \urcorner, \ldots$; 24 elements.

$\Pi(\rho_2)$: $\ulcorner 1,1,0,0 \urcorner, \ldots$; 24 elements.

$\Pi(\rho_3)$: $\tfrac{1}{2}\ulcorner 3,1,1,1 \urcorner, \ldots$; $\ulcorner 1,1,1,0 \urcorner, \ldots$; 96 elements.

$\Pi(\rho_4)$: $\ulcorner 2,1,1,0 \urcorner, \ldots$; 96 elements.

The dots indicate that all permutations of the coordinates and sign changes in the coordinates have to be applied.

Π describes the geometry of the so-called 24-cell, a regular solid of 4-space. $\Pi(\rho_2)$, $\Pi(\rho_4)$, $\Pi(\rho_3)$, $\Pi(\rho_1)$, respectively, gives the vertices, midpoints of edges, midpoints of 2-faces, and midpoints of 3-faces of this solid up to scalar factors.

By geometric reasons the elements of

$$\Gamma(\rho_2), \quad \Gamma(\rho_4), \quad \Gamma(\rho_3), \qquad \Gamma(\rho_1)$$

are called

points, lines, planes, symplecta,

for which the letters

a, *b*, *c*, *d*,

respectively, are reserved.

$$\begin{array}{cccc} d & c & b & a \\ \bullet\!\!-\!\!-\!\!\bullet & \!\!=\!\!=\!\! & \bullet\!\!-\!\!-\!\!\bullet, & \\ \rho_1 & \rho_3 & \rho_4 & \rho_2 \end{array}$$

The equivalence classes of pairs $\lambda, \mu \in \Pi$ with the corresponding $\Pi(\lambda, \mu)$ and $\Pi'(\lambda, \mu) = \bigcup_{i=0}^{n} D_i$ are exhibited. Incidence is indicated by a dash.

There is a hierarchy of such incidence figures. If Φ and Φ' are incidence figures for the same kind of pairs, the Φ' is called *at least as weak* as Φ if the existence of Φ' can be derived from that of Φ by the axiomatic rules of 71.6.4. In 73.1–4 the classes of $\ulcorner\lambda, \mu\urcorner$ are arranged from the weakest to the strongest figure.

A subfigure of $\Pi(\lambda, \mu)$ which is as strong as $\Pi(\lambda, \mu)$ itself is said to *determine* $\Pi(\lambda, \mu)$. Minimal determining subfigures are indicated in most cases.

To simplify the figures "trivial" incidence consequences are sometimes left out. (A point and a plane are "trivially" incident if there is a line incident with both; a line and a symplecton are "trivially" incident if there is a plane incident with both.)

Note the duality caused by the exchange of rays through π_1 and π_2, π_3 and π_4. This reduces the task set.

73.1 $x \in \Gamma(\rho_2)$, $y \in \Gamma(\rho_1)$. (Point–symplecton.)

73.1.1 $\lambda = -1100, \quad \mu = 1000.$

$$\xi_1 = \tfrac{1}{2}\lambda + \tfrac{1}{2}\mu = \tfrac{1}{2} \cdot 0100, \qquad \xi_2 = \tfrac{1}{3}\lambda + \tfrac{2}{3}\mu = \tfrac{1}{3} \cdot 1100.$$

$$-1100\text{—}0100\text{—}1100\text{—}1000.$$

$$a\text{—}d\text{—}a\text{—}d.$$

73.1.2 $\lambda = 0110, \quad \mu = 1000.$

$$\xi_1 = \tfrac{1}{2}\lambda + \tfrac{1}{2}\mu = \tfrac{1}{2} \cdot 1110, \qquad \xi_2 = \tfrac{1}{3}\lambda + \tfrac{2}{3}\mu = \tfrac{1}{3} \cdot 2110.$$

$$0110\text{—}1110\text{—}2110\text{—}1000.$$

$$a\text{—}c\text{—}b\text{—}d.$$

73.1.3 $\lambda = 1100, \quad \mu = 1000.$

$$1100\text{—}1000.$$

$$a\text{—}d.$$

73.2 $\qquad\qquad x \in \Gamma(\rho_2), \qquad y \in \Gamma(\rho_3).$ $\qquad$ (Point–plane.)

73.2.1 $\qquad\qquad\qquad \lambda = -1-100, \qquad \mu = 1110.$

$$\xi_1 = \tfrac{2}{3}\lambda + \tfrac{1}{3}\mu = \tfrac{1}{3} \cdot -1-110, \qquad \xi_2 = \tfrac{3}{5}\lambda + \tfrac{2}{5}\mu = \tfrac{1}{5} \cdot -1-120,$$

$$\xi_3 = \tfrac{1}{2}\lambda + \tfrac{1}{2}\mu = \tfrac{1}{2} \cdot 0010, \qquad \xi_4 = \tfrac{1}{3}\lambda + \tfrac{2}{3}\mu = \tfrac{1}{3} \cdot 1120.$$

$$-1-100 \text{---} -1-110 \text{---} -1-120 \text{---} 0010 \text{---} 1120 \text{---} 1110$$

$$a \text{---} c \text{---} b \text{---} d \text{---} b \text{---} c.$$

73.2.2 $\qquad\qquad\qquad \lambda = -1001, \qquad \mu = 1110.$

$$\xi_1 = \tfrac{2}{3}\lambda + \tfrac{1}{3}\mu = \tfrac{1}{3} \cdot (-\tfrac{1111}{2222} + -\tfrac{1113}{2222}), \qquad \xi_2 = \tfrac{3}{5}\lambda + \tfrac{2}{5}\mu = \tfrac{1}{5} \cdot (0112 + 2 \cdot -\tfrac{1111}{2222}),$$

$$\xi_3 = \tfrac{1}{2}\lambda + \tfrac{1}{2}\mu = \tfrac{1}{2} \cdot 0111, \qquad\qquad \xi_4 = \tfrac{1}{3}\lambda + \tfrac{2}{3}\mu = \tfrac{1}{3} \cdot (0110 + 2 \cdot \tfrac{1111}{2222}).$$

See Figs. 8 and 9.

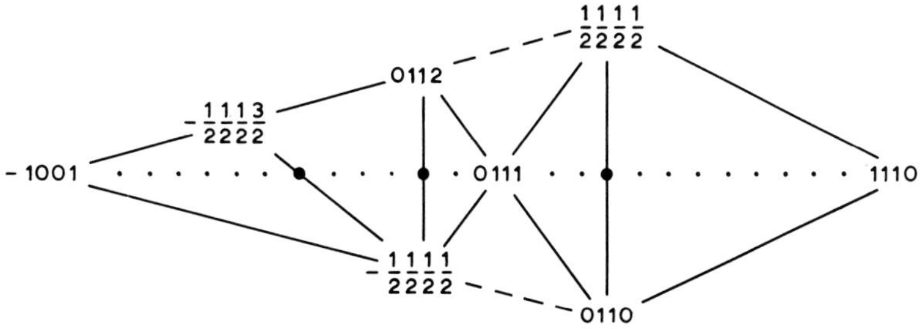

FIG. 8.

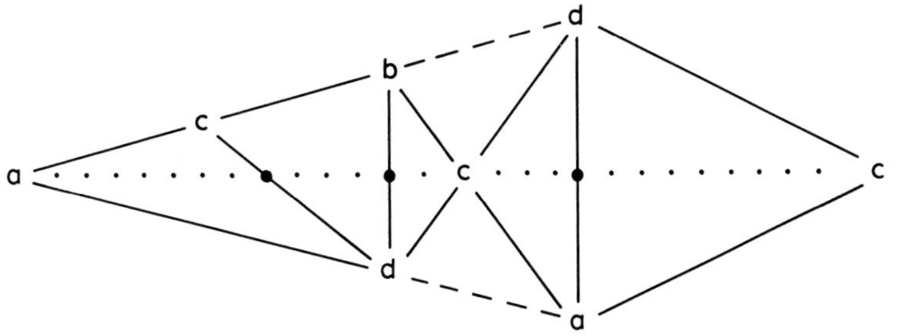

FIG. 9.

The figure is determined by a—d—a—c. Indeed, by 71.6.4(1), d—a—c can be uniquely extended to

$$\begin{array}{c} c_1 \text{---} d_1 \\ /\ \backslash\ /\ \backslash \\ d \text{---} a \text{---} c \end{array}$$

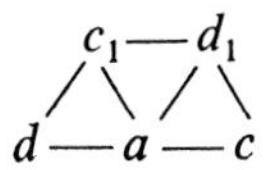

and a—d—c_1 to

$$
\begin{array}{c}
c_2 \!-\! b_2 \\
\diagup\!\diagdown\,\diagup\!\diagdown \\
a\!-\!d\!-\!c_1
\end{array} \quad ;
$$

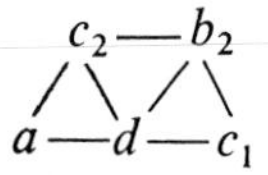

the incidence b_2—d is a trivial consequence.

73.2.3 $\lambda = 1\text{–}100, \qquad \mu = 1110.$

$$\xi_1 = \tfrac{2}{3}\lambda + \tfrac{1}{3}\mu = \tfrac{1}{3} \cdot (1000 + 2\text{–}110), \qquad \xi_2 = \tfrac{1}{2}\lambda + \tfrac{1}{2}\mu = \tfrac{1}{2} \cdot (1010 + 1000),$$

$$\xi_3 = \tfrac{1}{3}\lambda + \tfrac{2}{3}\mu = \tfrac{1}{3} \cdot (1010 + 2110).$$

See Figs. 10 and 11.

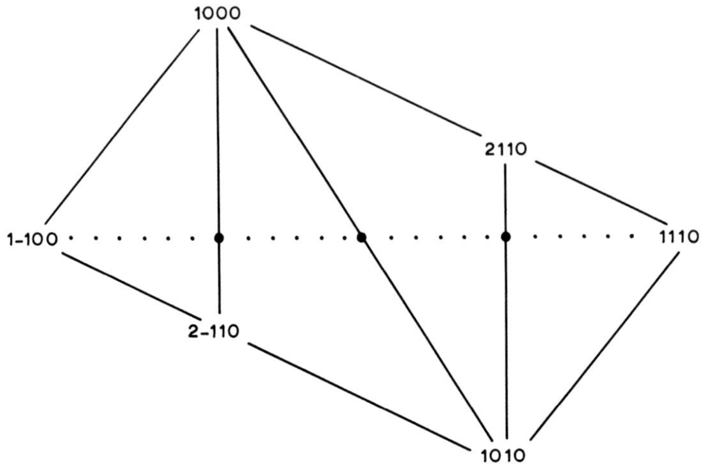

FIG. 10.

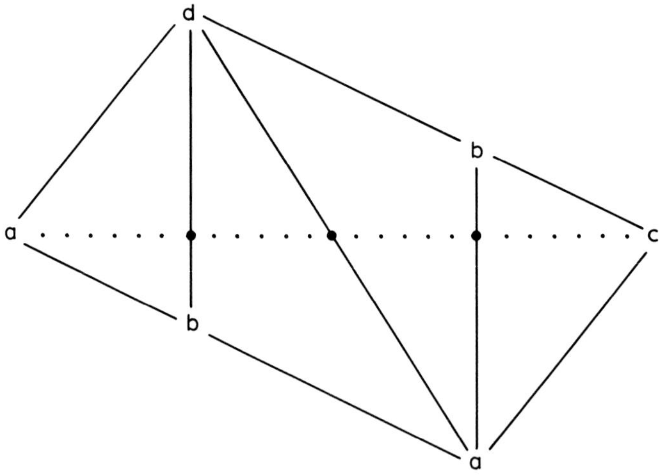

FIG. 11.

The figure is determined by

$$a\text{—}d\text{—}b\text{—}c$$

as well as by

$$a\text{—}b\text{—}a\text{—}c,$$

since the lacking elements can be added by virtue of 71.6.4(1) or (4).

73.2.4 $\lambda = 1001, \qquad \mu = 1110.$

$$\xi_1 = \tfrac{1}{2}\lambda + \tfrac{1}{2}\mu = \tfrac{1}{2}\cdot\left(\tfrac{1}{2}\tfrac{1}{2}\tfrac{1}{2}\tfrac{1}{2} + \tfrac{3}{2}\tfrac{1}{2}\tfrac{1}{2}\tfrac{1}{2}\right), \qquad \xi_2 = \tfrac{1}{3}\lambda + \tfrac{2}{3}\mu = \tfrac{1}{3}\cdot\left(2110 + 2\cdot\tfrac{1}{2}\tfrac{1}{2}\tfrac{1}{2}\tfrac{1}{2}\right).$$

See Figs. 12 and 13.

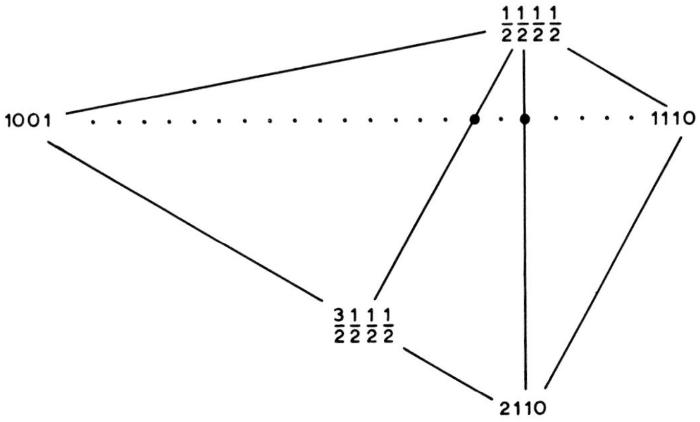

FIG. 12.

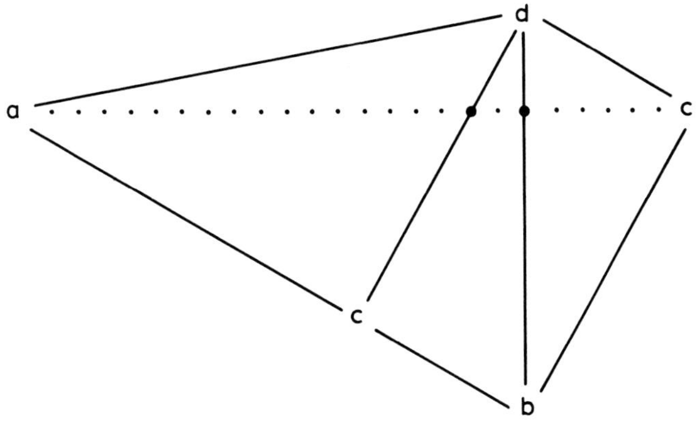

FIG. 13.

The figure is determined by

$$a\text{—}d\text{—}c.$$

73.2.5 $$\lambda = 1100, \qquad \mu = 1110.$$

$$1100—1110.$$

$$a—c.$$

73.3 $$x \in \Gamma(\rho_2), \qquad y \in \Gamma(\rho_4). \qquad \text{(Point–line.)}$$

73.3.1 $$\lambda = -1-100, \qquad \mu = 2110.$$

$$\xi_1 = \tfrac{3}{4}\lambda + \tfrac{1}{4}\mu = \tfrac{1}{4}\cdot -1-2-10, \qquad \xi_2 = \tfrac{2}{3}\lambda + \tfrac{1}{3}\mu = \tfrac{1}{3}\cdot 0-110,$$

$$\xi_3 = \tfrac{3}{5}\lambda + \tfrac{2}{5}\mu = \tfrac{1}{5}\cdot 1-120, \qquad \xi_4 = \tfrac{1}{2}\lambda + \tfrac{1}{2}\mu = \tfrac{1}{2}\cdot 1010.$$

$$-1-100— -1-2-10—0-110—1-120—1010—2110.$$

$$a—b—a—b—a—b.$$

73.3.2 $$\lambda = 0-1-10, \qquad \mu = 2110.$$

$$\xi_1 = \tfrac{3}{4}\lambda + \tfrac{1}{4}\mu = \tfrac{1}{2}\cdot 1-1-10, \qquad \xi_2 = \tfrac{2}{3}\lambda + \tfrac{1}{3}\mu = \tfrac{1}{3}\cdot 2-1-10,$$

$$\xi_3 = \tfrac{1}{2}\lambda + \tfrac{1}{2}\mu = 1000.$$

$$0-1-10—1-1-10—2-1-10—1000—2110.$$

$$a—c—b—d—b.$$

73.3.3 $$\lambda = 0-101, \qquad \mu = 2110.$$

$$\xi_1 = \tfrac{3}{4}\lambda + \tfrac{1}{4}\mu = \tfrac{1}{4}\cdot (1-102 + 2\cdot \tfrac{1}{2} -\tfrac{1}{2}\tfrac{1}{2}\tfrac{1}{2}),$$

$$\xi_2 = \tfrac{2}{3}\lambda + \tfrac{1}{3}\mu = \tfrac{1}{3}\cdot (1001 + 2\cdot \tfrac{1}{2} -\tfrac{1}{2}\tfrac{1}{2}\tfrac{1}{2}),$$

$$\xi_3 = \tfrac{1}{2}\lambda + \tfrac{1}{2}\mu = \tfrac{1}{2}\cdot 2011,$$

$$\xi_4 = \tfrac{1}{3}\lambda + \tfrac{2}{3}\mu = \tfrac{1}{3}\cdot (1010 + 2\cdot \tfrac{3}{2}\tfrac{1}{2}\tfrac{1}{2}\tfrac{1}{2}).$$

See Figs. 14 and 15.

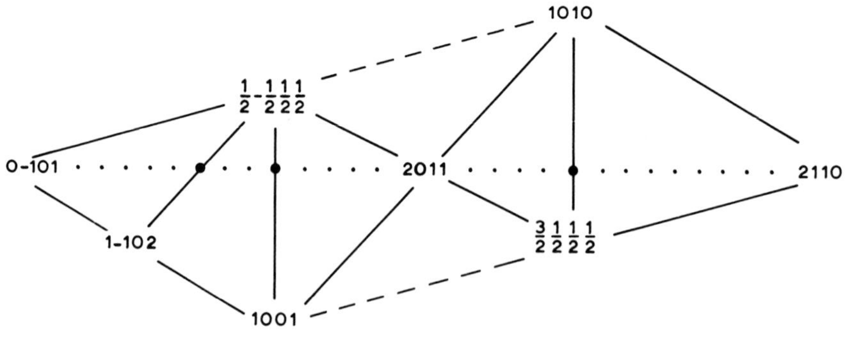

FIG. 14.

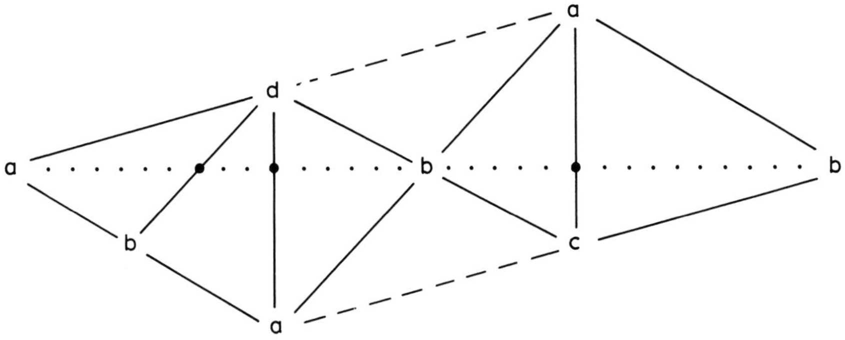

FIG. 15.

The figure is determined by

$$a\text{—}d\text{—}a\text{—}b,$$

as well as by

$$a\text{—}b\text{—}a\text{—}c\text{—}b.$$

In the first case

$$d\text{—}a\text{—}b$$

is filled up to

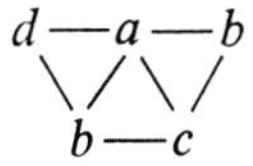

by means of 71.6.4(3) and then

$$a\text{—}d\text{—}b$$

to

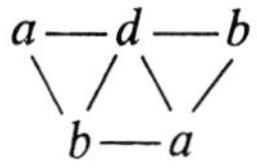

by means of 71.6.4(1). In the second case

$$b\text{—}a\text{—}c$$

is filled up to

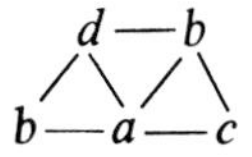

and then, according to 71.6.1,

$$b\text{—}c\text{—}b$$

to

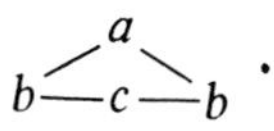

73.3.4 $\lambda = 0\text{–}110, \qquad \mu = 2110.$

$$\xi_1 = \tfrac{3}{4}\lambda + \tfrac{1}{4}\mu = \tfrac{1}{2}\cdot 1\text{–}120, \qquad \xi_2 = \tfrac{1}{2}\lambda + \tfrac{1}{2}\mu = 1010.$$

$$0\text{–}110\text{—}1\text{–}120\text{—}1010\text{—}2110.$$

$$a\text{—}b\text{—}a\text{—}b.$$

73.3.5 $\lambda = 1\text{–}100, \qquad \mu = 2110.$

$$\xi_1 = \tfrac{2}{3}\lambda + \tfrac{1}{3}\mu = \tfrac{1}{3}\cdot(2\cdot 1000 + 2\text{–}110), \qquad \xi_2 = \tfrac{1}{2}\lambda + \tfrac{1}{2}\mu = \tfrac{1}{2}\cdot(2\cdot 1000 + 1010).$$

See Figs. 16 and 17.

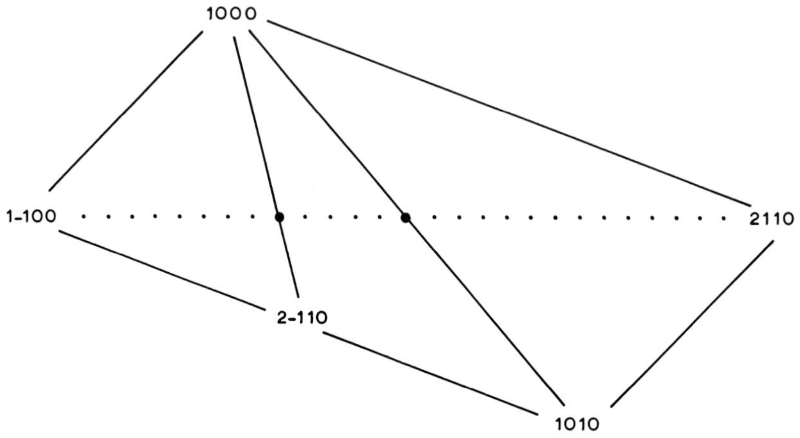

FIG. 16.

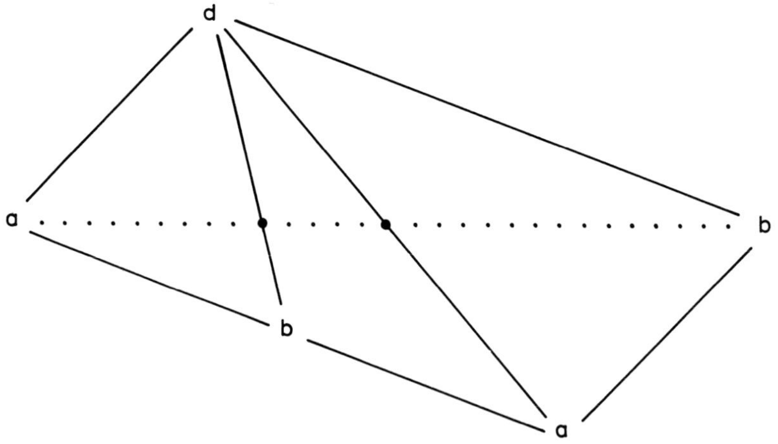

FIG. 17.

The figure is determined by

$$a—d—b.$$

73.3.6

$$\lambda = 0110, \qquad \mu = 2110.$$

$$\xi_1 = \tfrac{1}{2}\lambda + \tfrac{1}{2}\mu = 1110.$$

$$0110—1110—2110.$$

$$a—c—b.$$

73.3.7

$$\lambda = 1100, \qquad \mu = 2110.$$

$$1100—2110.$$

$$a—b.$$

73.4 $x \in \Gamma(\rho_2)$, $y \in \Gamma(\rho_2)$. (Point–point.)

73.4.1

$$\lambda = 1100, \qquad \mu = -1-100.$$

Rank 0.

$$a, a.$$

73.4.2

$$\lambda = 1100, \qquad \mu = -1010.$$

$$\xi_1 = \tfrac{2}{3}\lambda + \tfrac{1}{3}\mu = \tfrac{1}{3}\cdot 1210, \qquad \xi_2 = \tfrac{1}{2}\lambda + \tfrac{1}{2}\mu = \tfrac{1}{2}\cdot 0110.$$

$$\xi_3 = \tfrac{1}{3}\lambda + \tfrac{2}{3}\mu = \tfrac{1}{3}\cdot -1120.$$

$$1100—1210—0110— -1120— -1010.$$

$$a—b—a—b—a.$$

73.4.3

$$\lambda = 1100, \qquad \mu = 1-100.$$

$$\xi_1 = \tfrac{1}{2}\lambda + \tfrac{1}{2}\mu = 1000.$$

$$1100—1000—1-100.$$

$$a—d—a.$$

73.4.4

$$\lambda = 1100, \qquad \mu = 1010.$$

$$\xi_1 = \tfrac{1}{2}\lambda + \tfrac{1}{2}\mu = \tfrac{1}{2}\cdot 2110.$$

$$1100—2110—1010.$$

$$a—b—a.$$

73.4.5 $\lambda = 1100, \qquad \mu = 1100.$

$$1100\text{—}1100.$$

$$a\text{—}a.$$

73.5 $x \in \Gamma(\rho_4), \qquad y \in \Gamma(\rho_3). \qquad$ (Line–plane.)

73.5.1 $\lambda = -2{-1}{-1}0, \qquad \mu = 1110.$

$$\xi_1 = \tfrac{1}{2}\lambda + \tfrac{1}{2}\mu = -1000, \qquad \xi_2 = \tfrac{3}{7}\lambda + \tfrac{4}{7}\mu = \tfrac{1}{7}\cdot -2110,$$

$$\xi_3 = \tfrac{2}{5}\lambda + \tfrac{3}{5}\mu = \tfrac{1}{5}\cdot -1110, \qquad \xi_4 = \tfrac{1}{3}\lambda + \tfrac{2}{3}\mu = \tfrac{1}{3}\cdot 0110.$$

$$-2{-1}{-1}0\text{—}-1000\text{—}-2110\text{—}-1110\text{—}0110\text{—}1110.$$

$$b\text{—}d\text{—}b\text{—}c\text{—}a\text{—}c.$$

73.5.2 $\lambda = -2{-1}01, \qquad \mu = 1110.$

$$\xi_1 = \tfrac{2}{3}\lambda + \tfrac{1}{3}\mu = \tfrac{1}{3}\cdot(-1001 + -\tfrac{1}{2}\,-\tfrac{1}{2}\tfrac{1}{2}\tfrac{1}{2} + -\tfrac{3}{2}\,-\tfrac{1}{2}\tfrac{1}{2}\tfrac{1}{2}),$$

$$\xi_2 = \tfrac{3}{5}\lambda + \tfrac{2}{5}\mu = \tfrac{1}{5}\cdot(-1001 + 2\cdot -\tfrac{1}{2}\,-\tfrac{1}{2}\tfrac{1}{2}\tfrac{1}{2} + -2011),$$

$$\xi_3 = \tfrac{1}{2}\lambda + \tfrac{1}{2}\mu = \tfrac{1}{2}\cdot -1011,$$

$$\xi_4 = \tfrac{3}{7}\lambda + \tfrac{4}{7}\mu = \tfrac{1}{7}\cdot(0011 + 2\cdot -\tfrac{1}{2}\tfrac{1}{2}\tfrac{1}{2}\tfrac{1}{2} + -1021),$$

$$\xi_5 = \tfrac{2}{5}\lambda + \tfrac{3}{5}\mu = \tfrac{1}{5}\cdot(0011 + -\tfrac{1}{2}\tfrac{1}{2}\tfrac{1}{2}\tfrac{1}{2} + -\tfrac{1}{2}\tfrac{1}{2}\tfrac{3}{2}\tfrac{1}{2}),$$

$$\xi_6 = \tfrac{1}{3}\lambda + \tfrac{2}{3}\mu = \tfrac{1}{3}\cdot 0121,$$

$$\xi_7 = \tfrac{1}{4}\lambda + \tfrac{3}{4}\mu = \tfrac{1}{4}\cdot(0110 + \tfrac{1}{2}\tfrac{1}{2}\tfrac{1}{2}\tfrac{1}{2} + \tfrac{1}{2}\tfrac{1}{2}\tfrac{3}{2}\tfrac{1}{2}),$$

$$\xi_8 = \tfrac{1}{5}\lambda + \tfrac{4}{5}\mu = \tfrac{1}{5}\cdot(0110 + 2\cdot\tfrac{1}{2}\tfrac{1}{2}\tfrac{1}{2}\tfrac{1}{2} + 1120).$$

See Figs. 18 and 19.

This is the first case in which $\Pi(\lambda, \mu)$ is larger than $\Pi'(\lambda, \mu)$, namely, by eight elements. This occasion will be used to build up $\Pi(\lambda, \mu)$ formally, starting with a chain which, by virtue of the construction, proves to determine the whole figure.

From Fig. 18 one draws the chain

$$-2{-1}01\text{—}-\tfrac{3}{2}{-\tfrac{1}{2}}\tfrac{1}{2}\tfrac{1}{2}\text{—}-2011\text{—}-1011\text{—}-1021\text{—}-\tfrac{1}{2}\tfrac{1}{2}\tfrac{3}{2}\tfrac{1}{2}\text{—}0121\text{—}\tfrac{1}{2}\tfrac{1}{2}\tfrac{3}{2}\tfrac{1}{2}$$

$$\text{—}1120\text{—}1110,$$

for short,

$$b\text{—}c\text{—}b\text{—}c\text{—}b\text{—}c\text{—}b\text{—}c\text{—}b\text{—}c.$$

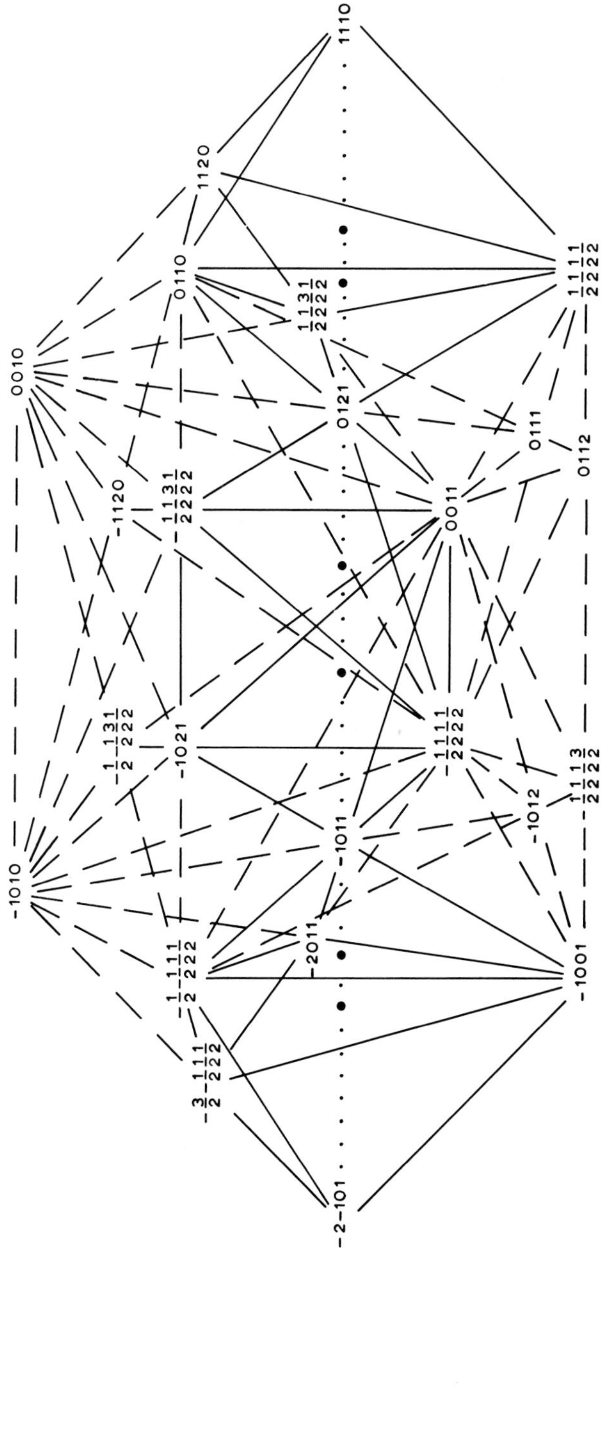
1110
1120
0110
0010
0121
0111
0112
0011
-1120
-1021
-1010
-1011
-1012
-2011
-1001
-2-101

FIG. 18.

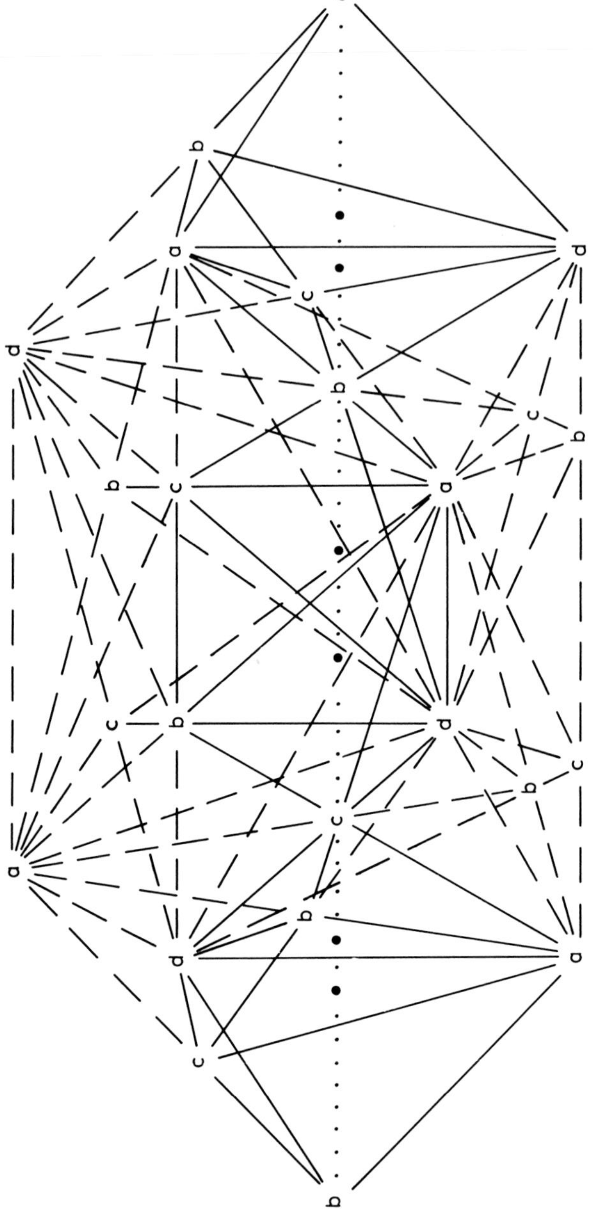

FIG. 19.

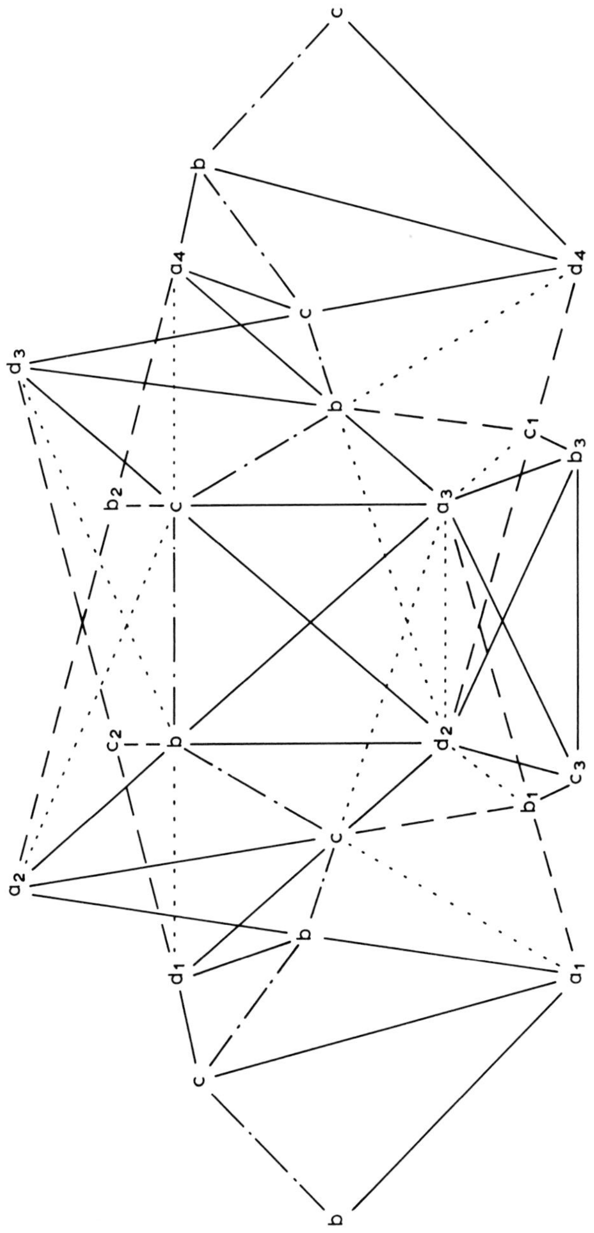

FIG. 20.

This chain is filled up by means of the algorithm in Section 71. (See Fig. 20.) One extends

b—c—b to 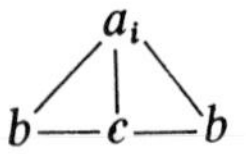

$(i = 1, 2, 3, 4)$,

c—b—c to 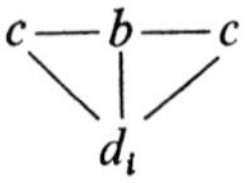

$(i = 1, 2, 3, 4)$,

and after adding some trivial consequences

a—c—a to 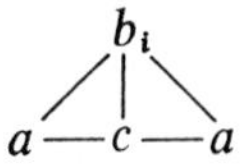

$(i = 1, 2)$,

d—b—d to 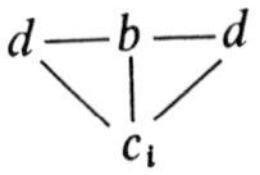

$(i = 1, 2)$;

finally, by virtue of 71.6.4(5), again after having added some trivial consequences, one adds to

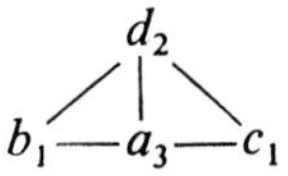

the chain b_1—c_3—b_3—c_1 whose elements are incident with both a_3 and d_2.

All other incidences are trivial consequences and have been omitted in Fig. 20.

The figure is determined by

$$b\text{—}c\text{—}b\text{—}c\text{—}b\text{—}c\text{—}b\text{—}c\text{—}b\text{—}c,$$

but also by

$$b\text{—}d\text{—}a\text{—}d\text{—}c,$$

and by

$$b\text{—}a\text{—}d\text{—}a\text{—}c.$$

73.5.3

$$\lambda = -21{-}10, \qquad \mu = 1110,$$
$$\xi_1 = \tfrac{2}{3}\lambda + \tfrac{1}{3}\mu = \tfrac{1}{3}\cdot(2\cdot -1100 + -11{-}10),$$
$$\xi_2 = \tfrac{3}{5}\lambda + \tfrac{2}{5}\mu = \tfrac{1}{5}\cdot(3\cdot -1100 + -12{-}10),$$
$$\xi_3 = \tfrac{1}{2}\lambda + \tfrac{1}{2}\mu = \tfrac{1}{2}\cdot(-1100 + 0100),$$
$$\xi_4 = \tfrac{2}{5}\lambda + \tfrac{3}{5}\mu = \tfrac{1}{5}\cdot(3\cdot 0100 + -1210),$$
$$\xi_5 = \tfrac{1}{3}\lambda + \tfrac{2}{3}\mu = \tfrac{1}{3}\cdot(2\cdot 0100 + 0110),$$
$$\xi_6 = \tfrac{1}{5}\lambda + \tfrac{4}{5}\mu = \tfrac{1}{5}\cdot(0110 + 2\cdot 1210).$$

See Figs. 21 and 22.

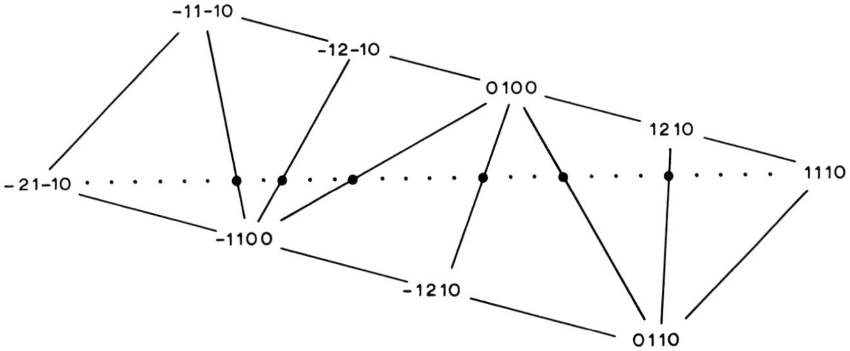

FIG. 21.

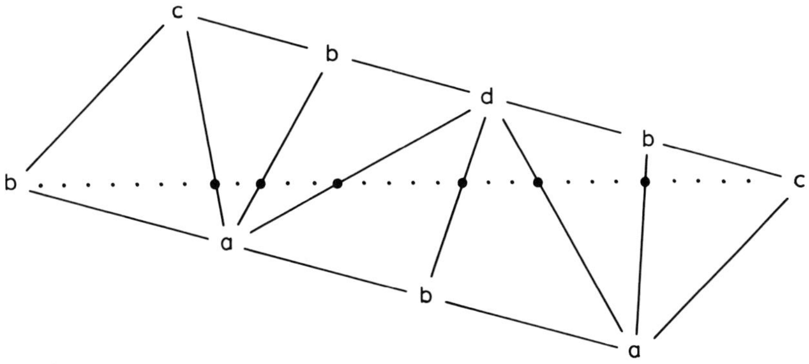

FIG. 22.

The figure is determined by

$$b—a—d—b—c.$$

73.5.3′ $\lambda = -1{-}102, \qquad \mu = 1110.$

$$\xi_1 = \tfrac{2}{3}\lambda + \tfrac{1}{3}\mu = \tfrac{1}{3}\cdot(0001 + 2\cdot -\tfrac{1}{2} -\tfrac{1}{2}\tfrac{1}{2}\tfrac{3}{2}),$$

$$\xi_2 = \tfrac{1}{2}\lambda + \tfrac{1}{2}\mu = \tfrac{1}{2}\cdot(0001 + 0011),$$

$$\xi_3 = \tfrac{3}{7}\lambda + \tfrac{4}{7}\mu = \tfrac{1}{7}\cdot(2\cdot\tfrac{1}{2}\tfrac{1}{2}\tfrac{1}{2}\tfrac{3}{2} + 3\cdot 0011),$$

$$\xi_4 = \tfrac{1}{3}\lambda + \tfrac{2}{3}\mu = \tfrac{1}{3}\cdot(2\cdot\tfrac{1}{2}\tfrac{1}{2}\tfrac{1}{2}\tfrac{1}{2} + 0011),$$

$$\xi_5 = \tfrac{1}{4}\lambda + \tfrac{3}{4}\mu = \tfrac{1}{4}\cdot(3\cdot\tfrac{1}{2}\tfrac{1}{2}\tfrac{1}{2}\tfrac{1}{2} + \tfrac{1}{2}\tfrac{1}{2}\tfrac{3}{2}\tfrac{1}{2}),$$

$$\xi_6 = \tfrac{1}{5}\lambda + \tfrac{4}{5}\mu = \tfrac{1}{5}\cdot(4\cdot\tfrac{1}{2}\tfrac{1}{2}\tfrac{1}{2}\tfrac{1}{2} + 1120).$$

See Figs. 23 and 24.

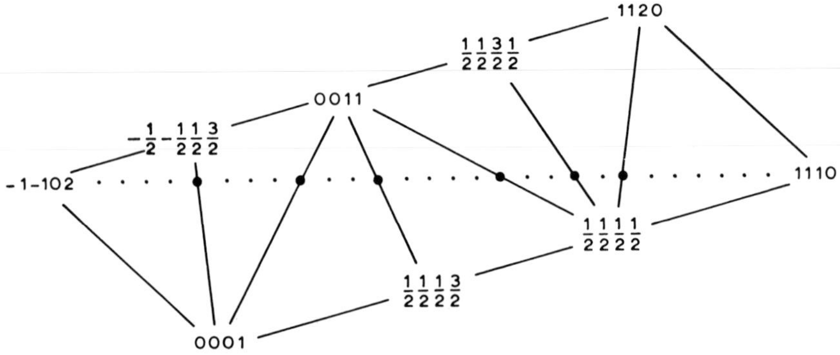

FIG. 23.

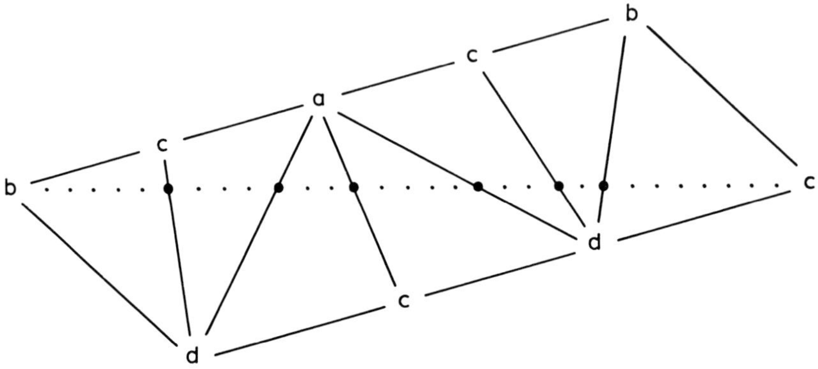

FIG. 24.

The figure is determined by

$$b\text{—}c\text{—}a\text{—}d\text{—}c.$$

It is the dual of 73.5.3.

73.5.4 $\lambda = -2101, \qquad \mu = 1110.$

$$\xi_1 = \tfrac{2}{3}\lambda + \tfrac{1}{3}\mu = \tfrac{1}{3}\cdot(-1101 + -1100 + 2\cdot -\tfrac{1}{2}\tfrac{1}{2}\tfrac{1}{2}\tfrac{1}{2}),$$

$$\xi_2 = \tfrac{3}{5}\lambda + \tfrac{2}{5}\mu = \tfrac{1}{5}\cdot(-1201 + -1100 + 4\cdot -\tfrac{1}{2}\tfrac{1}{2}\tfrac{1}{2}\tfrac{1}{2}),$$

$$\xi_3 = \tfrac{1}{2}\lambda + \tfrac{1}{2}\mu = \tfrac{1}{2}\cdot(-\tfrac{1}{2}\tfrac{1}{2}\tfrac{1}{2}\tfrac{1}{2} + -\tfrac{1}{2}\tfrac{3}{2}\tfrac{1}{2}\tfrac{1}{2}),$$

$$\xi_4 = \tfrac{1}{3}\lambda + \tfrac{2}{3}\mu = \tfrac{1}{3}\cdot(0110 + 0211),$$

$$\xi_5 = \tfrac{1}{4}\lambda + \tfrac{3}{4}\mu = \tfrac{1}{4}\cdot(2\cdot 0110 + \tfrac{1}{2}\tfrac{1}{2}\tfrac{1}{2}\tfrac{1}{2} + \tfrac{1}{2}\tfrac{3}{2}\tfrac{1}{2}\tfrac{1}{2}),$$

$$\xi_6 = \tfrac{1}{5}\lambda + \tfrac{4}{5}\mu = \tfrac{1}{5}\cdot(2\cdot 0110 + 2\cdot\tfrac{1}{2}\tfrac{1}{2}\tfrac{1}{2}\tfrac{1}{2} + 1210).$$

See Figs. 25 and 26.

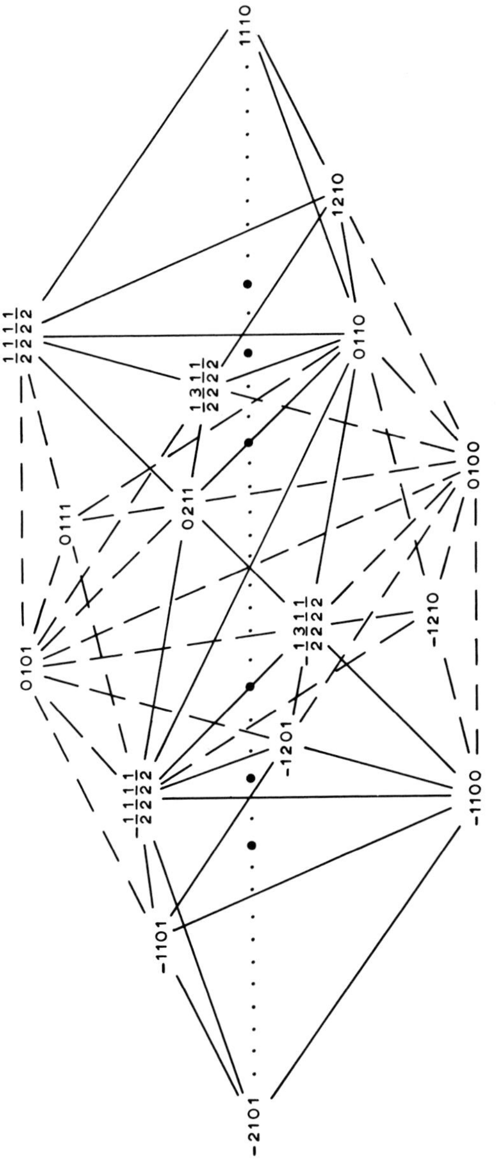

FIG. 25.

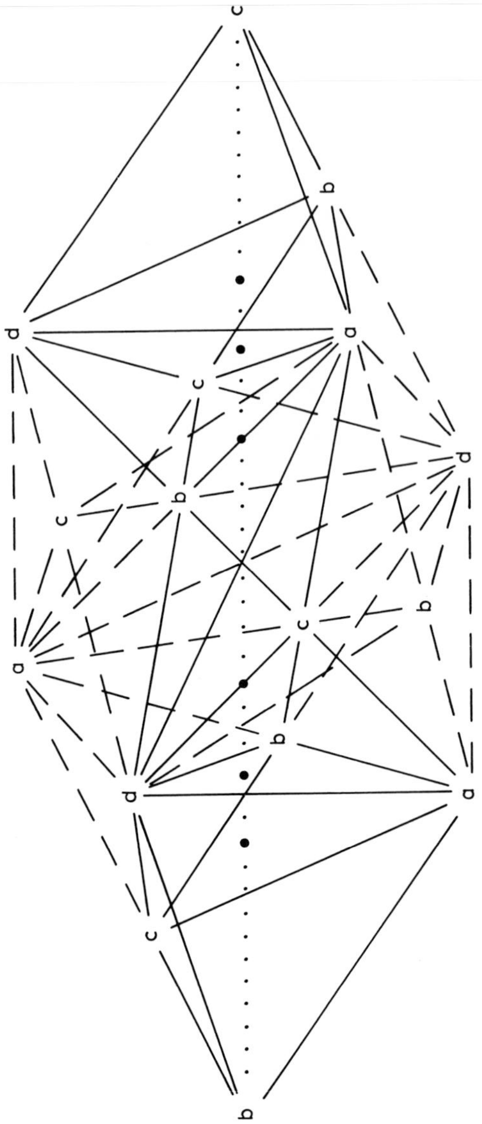

FIG. 26.

Again $\Pi(\lambda,\mu)$ is larger than $\Pi'(\lambda,\mu)$, namely, by four elements.

To find a chain that determines the total number one can start with

$$-2101\text{—}-\tfrac{1}{2}\tfrac{1}{2}\tfrac{1}{2}\tfrac{1}{2}\text{—}0110\text{—}1110.$$

It is denoted by b—d—a—c.

From b—d—a and d—a—c one obtains b—a_1—b_1—a and d—c_1—d_1—c, respectively, together with the obvious incidences, and from b—d—c_1 and b_1—a—c likewise c_2, a_2 and d_2, b_2, respectively (see Fig. 27). After adding some trivial consequences one completes a_1—c_2—a_2, d_1—b_2—d_2, and a—c_1—a_2 with elements b_3, c_3, and b_4, respectively. Now one notes that d is incident with

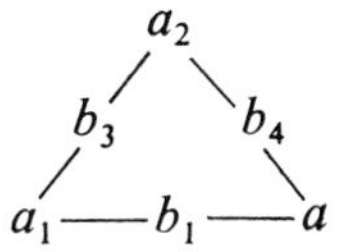
a₂
b₃
b₄
a₁
b₁
a

which implies the existence of

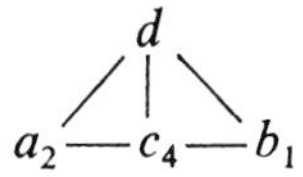
d
a₂
c₄
b₁

by 71.6.4(1); from this b_3—c_4 and b_4—c_4 follow easily. Similarly, if c' is defined by

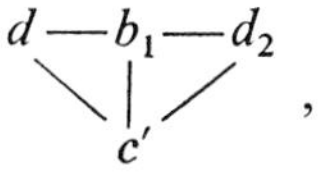
d
b₁
d₂
c′

one finds b' with

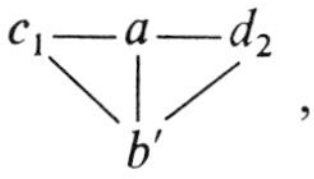
c₁
a
d₂
b′

whence by reduction with respect to d, apart from

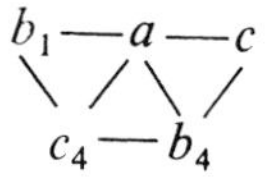
b₁
a
c
c₄
b₄
and
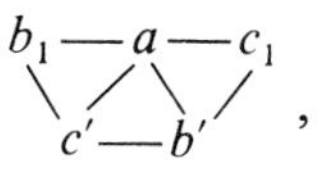
b₁
a
c₁
c′
b′

whence b'—c_1, b'—c_3; therefore $c' = c_4$, $b' = b_4$, by 71.6.4(5). This shows the crucial incidences d_2—c_4, b_4—c_3. The remaining incidences are trivial consequences.

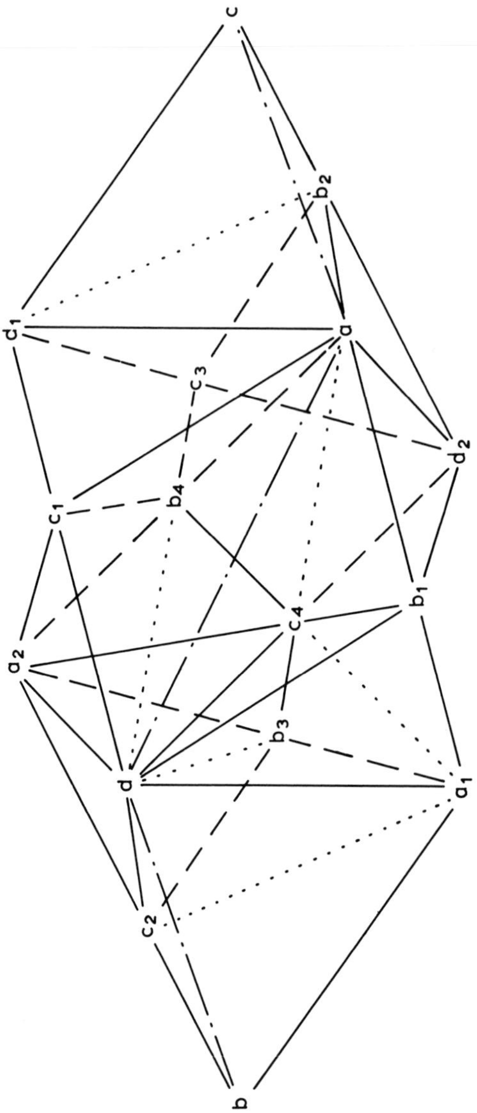

FIG. 27.

The figure is determined by

$$b\text{—}d\text{—}a\text{—}c.$$

73.5.5 $\lambda = 1{-}102, \qquad \mu = 1110.$

$$\xi_1 = \tfrac{2}{3}\lambda + \tfrac{1}{3}\mu = \tfrac{1}{3}\cdot(2\cdot 1001 + \tfrac{1}{2}\,{-\tfrac{1}{2}}\tfrac{1}{2}\tfrac{1}{2} + \tfrac{1}{2}\,{-\tfrac{1}{2}}\tfrac{1}{2}\tfrac{3}{2}),$$
$$\xi_2 = \tfrac{3}{5}\lambda + \tfrac{2}{5}\mu = \tfrac{1}{5}\cdot(3\cdot 1001 + 2\cdot\tfrac{1}{2}\,{-\tfrac{1}{2}}\tfrac{1}{2}\tfrac{1}{2} + 1012),$$
$$\xi_3 = \tfrac{1}{2}\lambda + \tfrac{1}{2}\mu = \tfrac{1}{2}\cdot(1001 + 1011),$$
$$\xi_4 = \tfrac{1}{3}\lambda + \tfrac{2}{3}\mu = \tfrac{1}{3}\cdot(2\cdot\tfrac{1}{2}\tfrac{1}{2}\tfrac{1}{2}\tfrac{1}{2} + 2011),$$
$$\xi_5 = \tfrac{1}{4}\lambda + \tfrac{3}{4}\mu = \tfrac{1}{4}\cdot(3\cdot\tfrac{1}{2}\tfrac{1}{2}\tfrac{1}{2}\tfrac{1}{2} + 1010 + \tfrac{3}{2}\tfrac{1}{2}\tfrac{1}{2}\tfrac{1}{2}),$$
$$\xi_6 = \tfrac{1}{5}\lambda + \tfrac{4}{5}\mu = \tfrac{1}{5}\cdot(4\cdot\tfrac{1}{2}\tfrac{1}{2}\tfrac{1}{2}\tfrac{1}{2} + 1010 + 2110).$$

See Figs. 28 and 29.

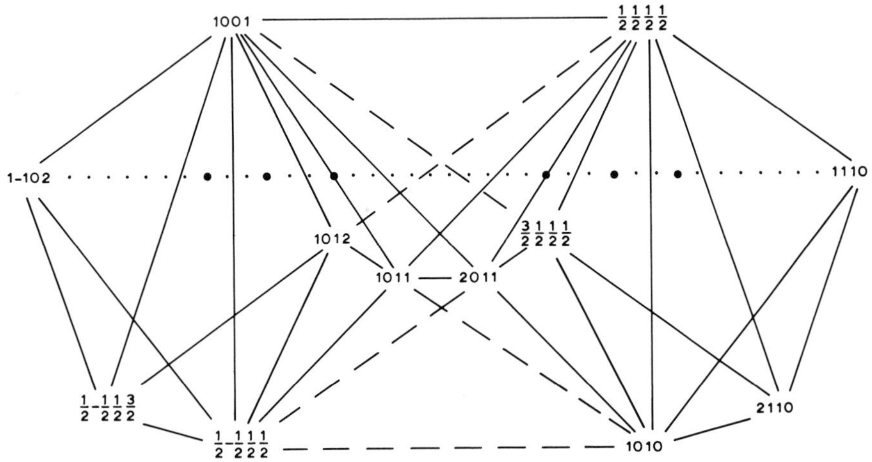

FIG. 28.

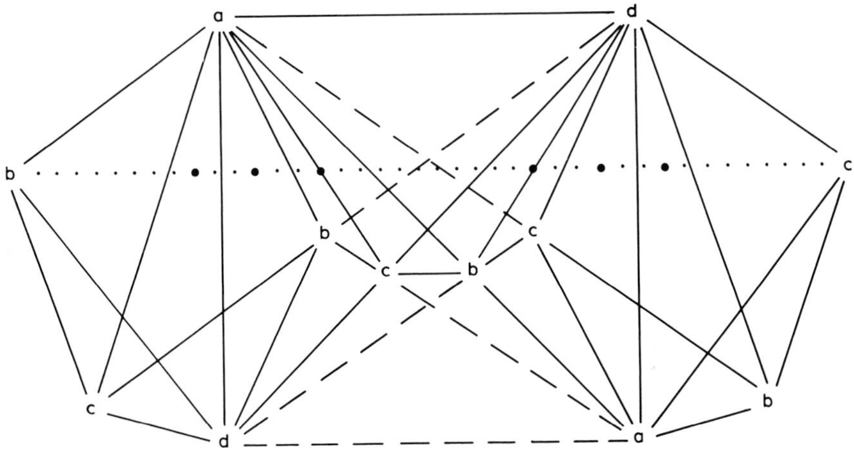

FIG. 29.

Building up from

1–102—1001—$\frac{1}{2}\frac{1}{2}\frac{1}{2}\frac{1}{2}$—1110,

(see Fig. 28), or, for short,

b—*a*—*d*—*c*,

one gets, in Fig. 30, consecutively, the following elements, with incidences as shown:

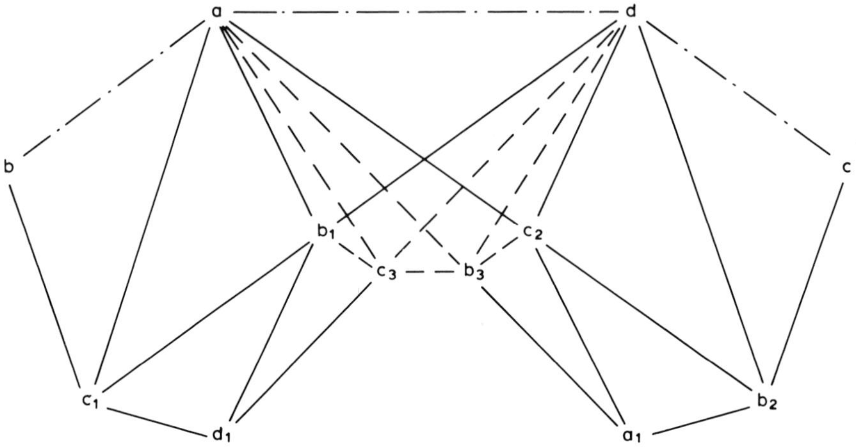

FIG. 30.

by 71.6.4(3) b—c_1—b_1—d in the reduction result of a and a—c_2—b_2—c in the reduction result of d,

by 71.6.4(5)

b_1—c—c_2
\ / \ /
c_3—b_3

in the reduction result of d, and furthermore d_1 and a_1 by means of 71.6.4(6). The incidences not shown in Fig. 30 are trivial consequences.

The figure is determined by

b—*a*—*d*--*c*.

73.5.6 $\lambda = -2110, \qquad \mu = 1110.$

$$\xi_1 = \tfrac{2}{3}\lambda + \tfrac{1}{3}\mu = -1110, \qquad \xi_2 = \tfrac{1}{3}\lambda + \tfrac{2}{3}\mu = 0110.$$

–2110— –1110—0110—1110.

b—*c*—*a*—*c*.

73.5.6′ $\lambda = 2{-}1{-}10, \qquad \mu = 1110.$

$$\xi_1 = \tfrac{1}{2}\lambda + \tfrac{1}{2}\mu = \tfrac{3}{2}\cdot 1000, \qquad \xi_2 = \tfrac{1}{5}\lambda + \tfrac{4}{5}\mu = \tfrac{3}{5}\cdot 2110.$$

$$2{-}1{-}10\text{---}1000\text{---}2110\text{---}1110.$$

$$b\text{---}d\text{---}b\text{---}c.$$

This is the dual of 73.5.6.

73.5.7 $\lambda = 2{-}101, \qquad \mu = 1110.$

$$\xi_1 = \tfrac{2}{3}\lambda + \tfrac{1}{3}\mu = \tfrac{1}{3}\cdot(1000 + 1001 + 2\cdot \tfrac{3}{2}\,{-\tfrac{1}{2}}\tfrac{1}{2}\tfrac{1}{2}),$$
$$\xi_2 = \tfrac{1}{2}\lambda + \tfrac{1}{2}\mu = \tfrac{1}{2}\cdot(1000 + 2011),$$
$$\xi_3 = \tfrac{1}{3}\lambda + \tfrac{2}{3}\mu = \tfrac{1}{3}\cdot(1010 + 2\cdot \tfrac{3}{2}\tfrac{1}{2}\tfrac{1}{2}\tfrac{1}{2}),$$
$$\xi_4 = \tfrac{1}{5}\lambda + \tfrac{4}{5}\mu = \tfrac{1}{5}\cdot(1010 + 2\cdot \tfrac{1}{2}\tfrac{1}{2}\tfrac{1}{2}\tfrac{1}{2} + 2\cdot 2110).$$

See Figs. 31 and 32.

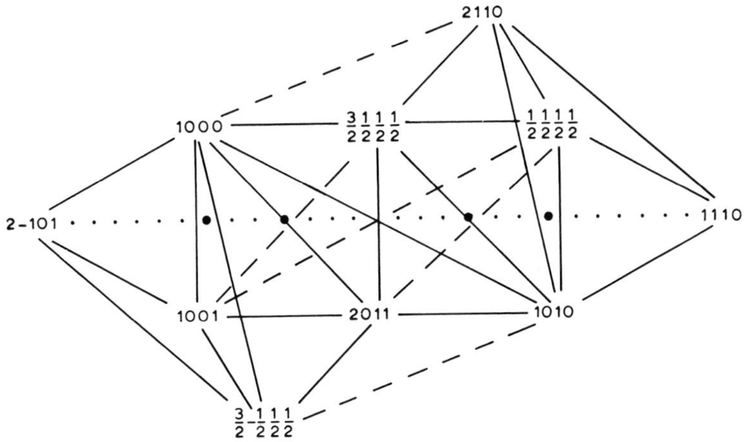

FIG. 31.

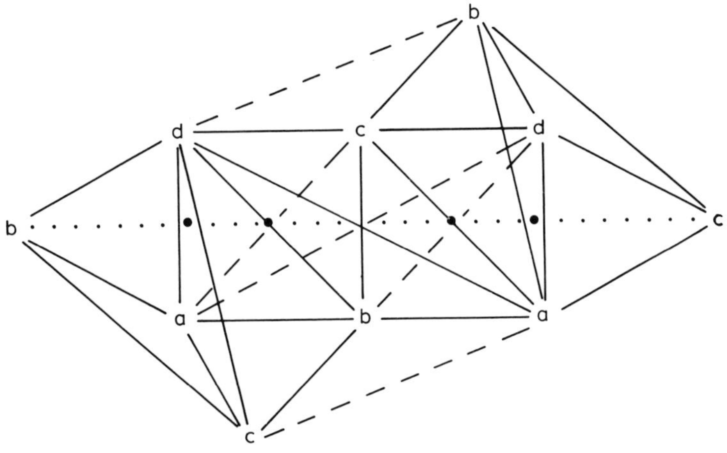

FIG. 32.

The figure is determined by

$$b—c—b—c—b—c.$$

73.5.8

$$\lambda = 1102, \qquad \mu = 1110.$$

$$\xi_1 = \tfrac{1}{2}\lambda + \tfrac{1}{2}\mu = \tfrac{1}{2}(1101 + 2 \cdot \tfrac{1}{2}\tfrac{1}{2}\tfrac{1}{2}\tfrac{1}{2}),$$

$$\xi_2 = \tfrac{1}{3}\lambda + \tfrac{2}{3}\mu = \tfrac{1}{3} \cdot (1100 + 4 \cdot \tfrac{1}{2}\tfrac{1}{2}\tfrac{1}{2}\tfrac{1}{2})$$

See Figs. 33 and 34.

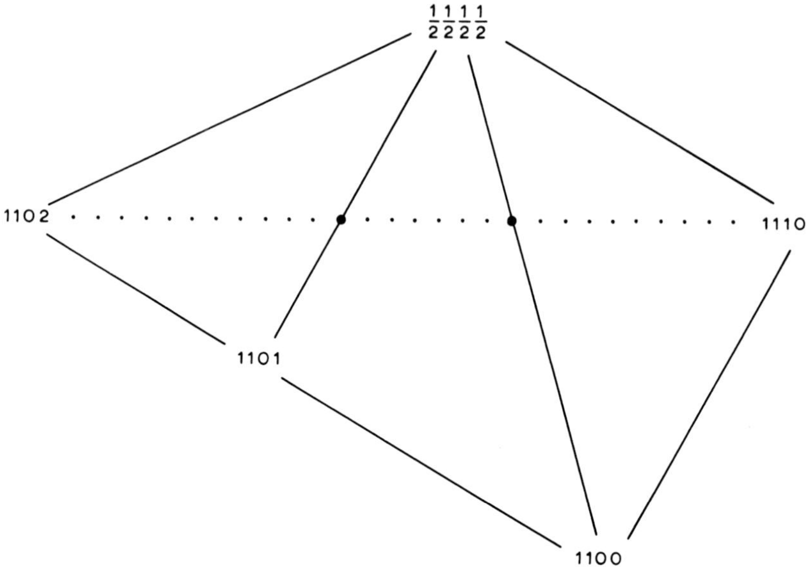

FIG. 33.

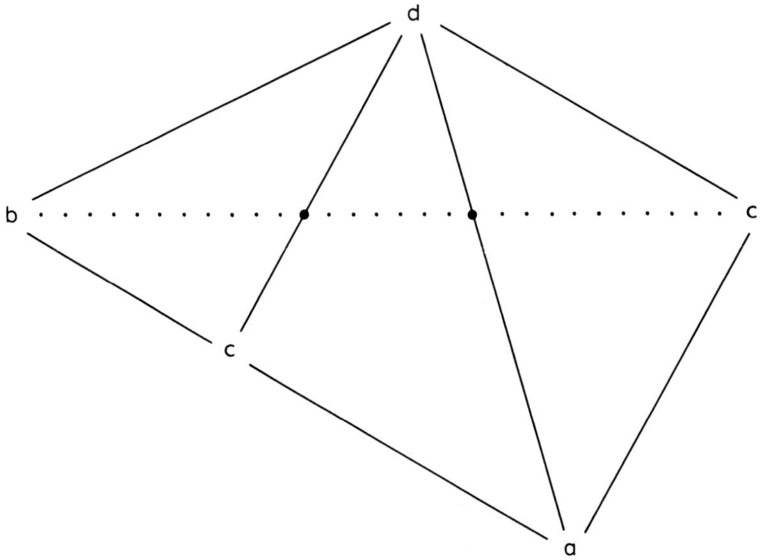

FIG. 34.

The figure is determined by

$$b—d—c.$$

73.5.8′ $\lambda = 21\text{–}10, \qquad \mu = 1110.$

$$\xi_1 = \tfrac{1}{2}\lambda + \tfrac{1}{2}\mu = \tfrac{1}{2}\cdot(2\cdot 1000 + 1100),$$
$$\xi_2 = \tfrac{1}{3}\lambda + \tfrac{2}{3}\mu = \tfrac{1}{3}\cdot(2110 + 2\cdot 1100).$$

See Figs. 35 and 36.

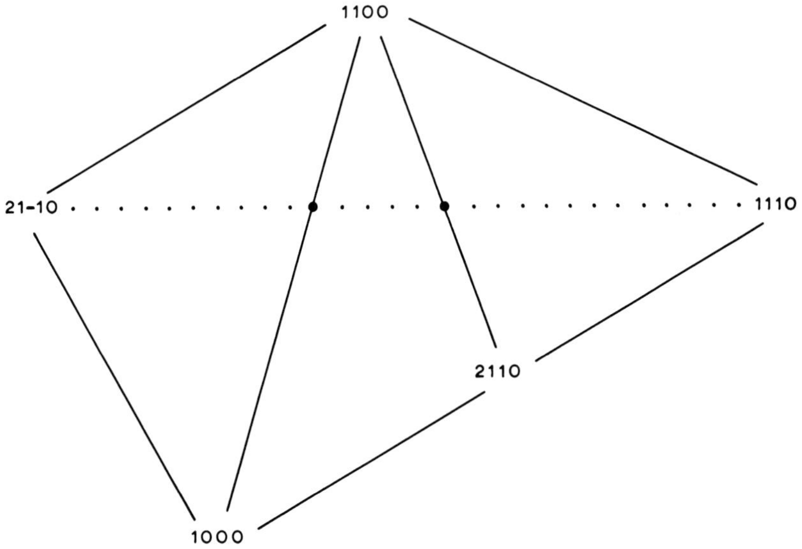

FIG. 35.

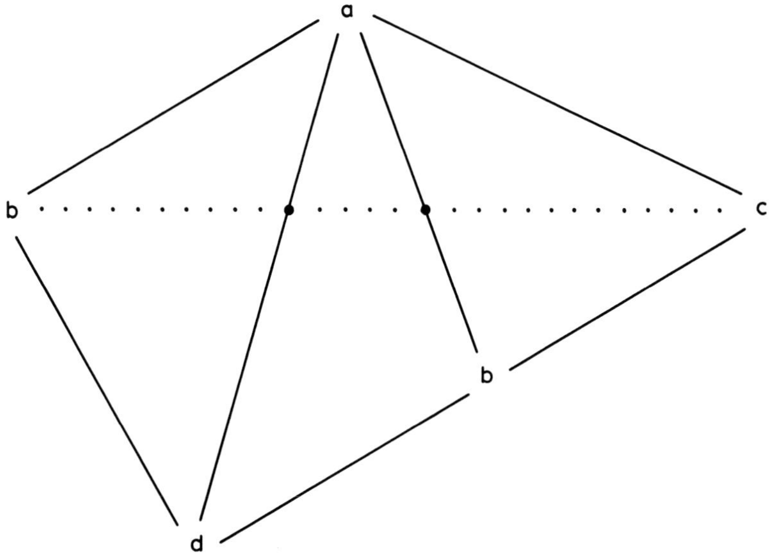

FIG. 36.

The figure is determined by

$$b—a—c.$$

This is the dual of 73.5.8.

73.5.9 $\lambda = 2101, \qquad \mu = 1110.$

$$\xi_1 = \tfrac{1}{2}\lambda + \tfrac{1}{2}\mu = \tfrac{1}{2}\cdot(\tfrac{1}{2}\tfrac{1}{2}\tfrac{1}{2}\tfrac{1}{2} + 1100 + \tfrac{3}{2}\tfrac{1}{2}\tfrac{1}{2}\tfrac{1}{2}),$$

$$\xi_2 = \tfrac{1}{3}\lambda + \tfrac{2}{3}\mu = \tfrac{1}{3}\cdot(2\cdot\tfrac{1}{2}\tfrac{1}{2}\tfrac{1}{2}\tfrac{1}{2} + 1100 + 2110).$$

See Figs. 37 and 38.

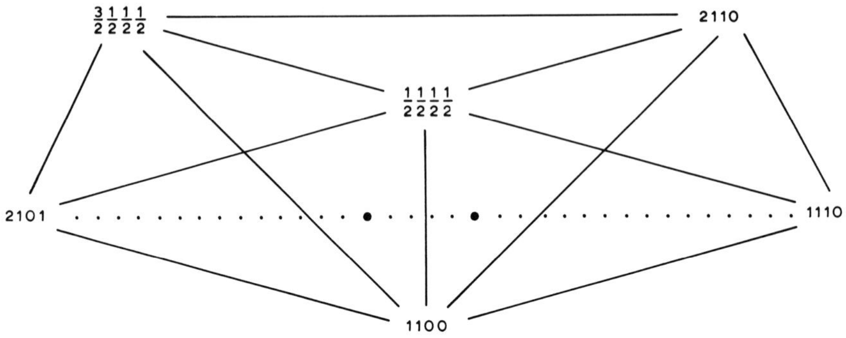

FIG. 37.

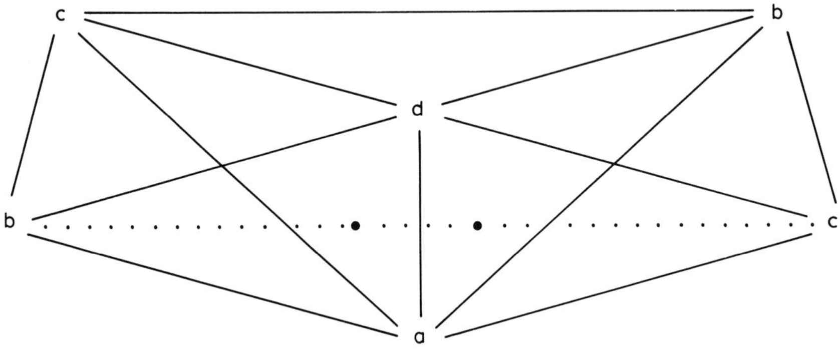

FIG. 38.

The figure is determined by

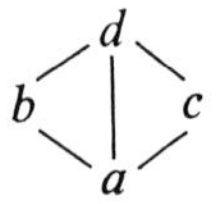

as well as by

$$b—c—b—c.$$

73.5.10 $\lambda = 2110, \quad \mu = 1110.$

$$2110—1110.$$

$$b—c.$$

73.5.1–10 From the weakest to the strongest relation on pairs $\ulcorner b,c \urcorner$ the hierarchy runs:

$$1—2 \bigg\langle {}^{\textstyle 3} _{\textstyle 3'} \bigg\rangle 4 \bigg\langle {}^{\textstyle 5} _{\textstyle 6'}\!\!=\!\!6\bigg\rangle 7 \bigg\langle {}^{\textstyle 8} _{\textstyle 8'} \bigg\rangle 9 —10.$$

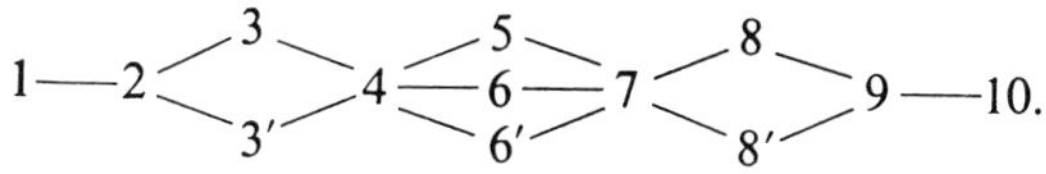

73.6 $x \in \Gamma(\rho_4), \quad y \in \Gamma(\rho_4).$ (Line–line.)

73.6.1 $\lambda = 2110, \quad \mu = -2–1–10.$
                        Rank 0

$$b, b.$$

73.6.2 $\lambda = 2110, \quad \mu = -2–101.$

$$\xi_1 = \tfrac{2}{3}\lambda + \tfrac{1}{3}\mu = \tfrac{1}{3}\cdot(2\cdot\tfrac{1111}{2222} + 1010),$$
$$\xi_2 = \tfrac{3}{5}\lambda + \tfrac{2}{5}\mu = \tfrac{1}{5}\cdot(2\cdot\tfrac{1111}{2222} + 1021),$$
$$\xi_3 = \tfrac{1}{2}\lambda + \tfrac{1}{2}\mu = \tfrac{1}{2}\cdot 0011,$$
$$\xi_4 = \tfrac{2}{5}\lambda + \tfrac{3}{5}\mu = \tfrac{1}{5}\cdot(2\cdot-\tfrac{1}{2}-\tfrac{111}{222} + -1012),$$
$$\xi_5 = \tfrac{1}{3}\lambda + \tfrac{2}{3}\mu = \tfrac{1}{3}\cdot(2\cdot-\tfrac{1}{2}-\tfrac{111}{222} + -1001).$$

See Figs. 39 and 40.

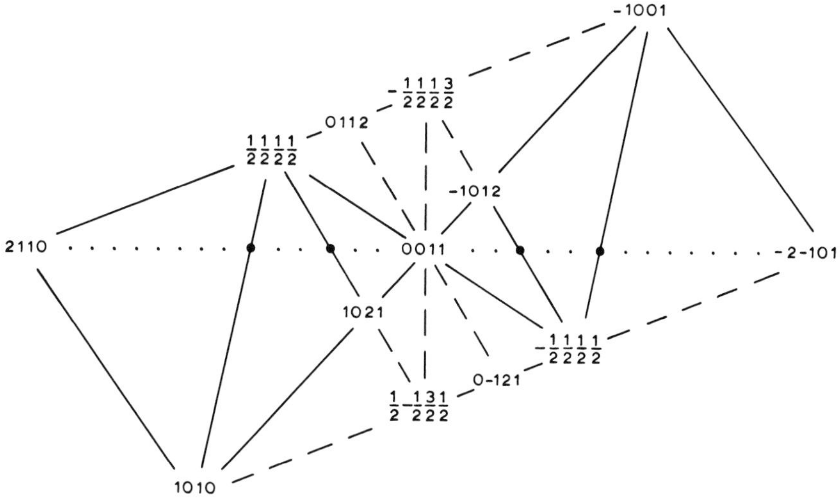

FIG. 39.

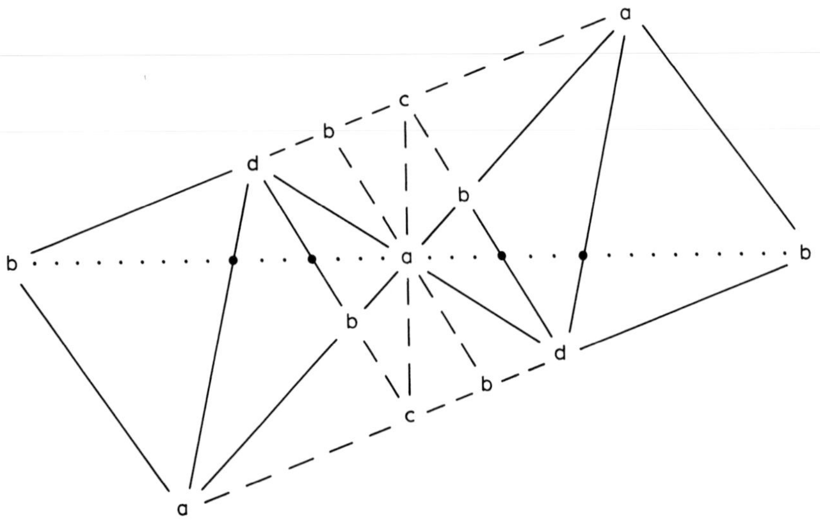

FIG. 40.

$\Pi(\lambda,\mu)$ is four elements larger than $\Pi'(\lambda,\mu)$.

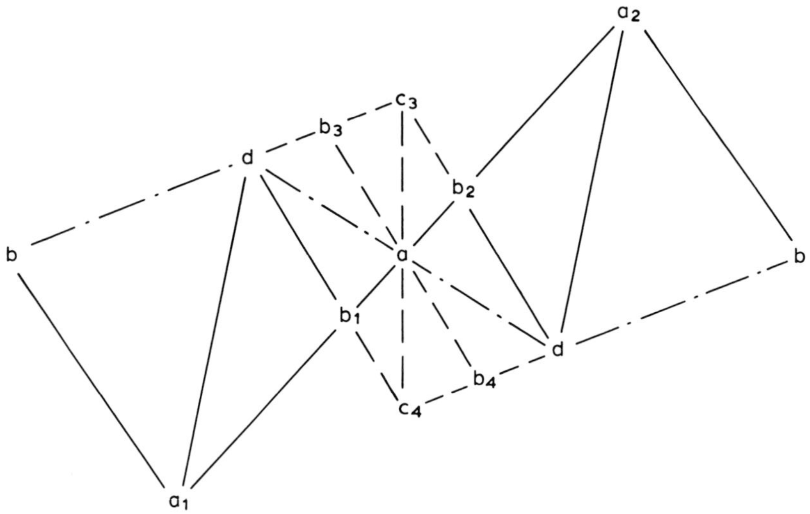

FIG. 41.

Figure 41 shows that the figure is determined by

$$b\text{—}d\text{—}a\text{—}d\text{—}b.$$

73.6.3 $\lambda = 2110, \qquad \mu = -2-110.$

$$\xi_1 = \tfrac{3}{4}\lambda + \tfrac{1}{4}\mu = \tfrac{1}{2}\cdot(1010 + 1110),$$
$$\xi_2 = \tfrac{2}{3}\lambda + \tfrac{1}{3}\mu = \tfrac{1}{3}\cdot(1010 + 1120),$$
$$\xi_3 = \tfrac{1}{2}\lambda + \tfrac{1}{2}\mu = 0010,$$

$$\xi_4 = \tfrac{1}{3}\lambda + \tfrac{2}{3}\mu = \tfrac{1}{3}\cdot(-1010 + -1{-}120),$$
$$\xi_5 = \tfrac{1}{4}\lambda + \tfrac{3}{4}\mu = \tfrac{1}{2}\cdot(-1010 + -1{-}110).$$

See Figs. 42 and 43.

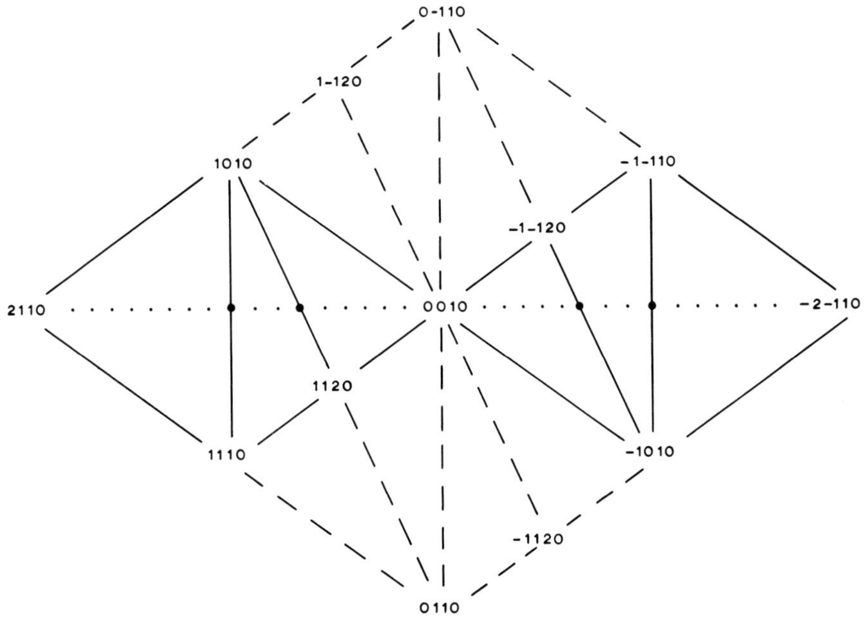

FIG. 42.

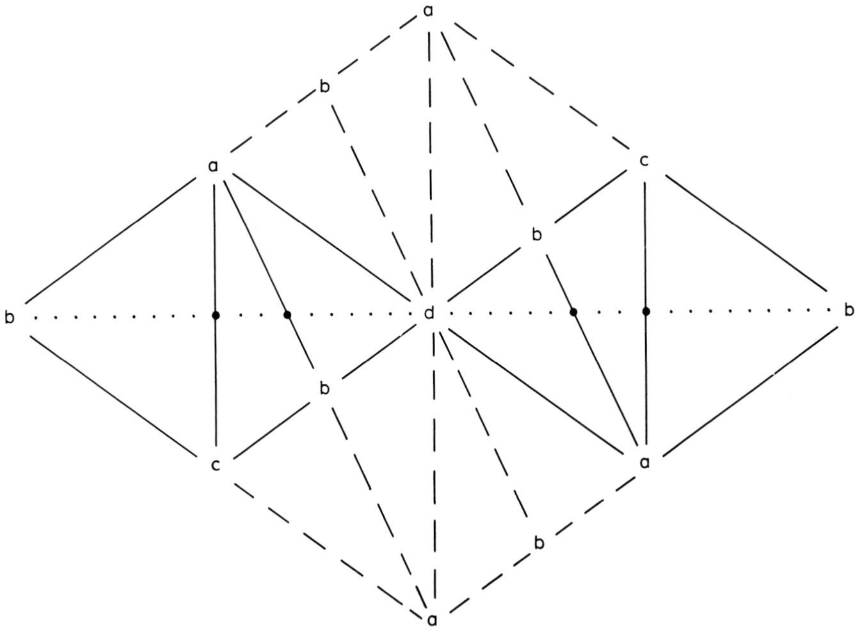

FIG. 43.

$\Pi(\lambda, \mu)$ is four elements larger than $\Pi'(\lambda, \mu)$.

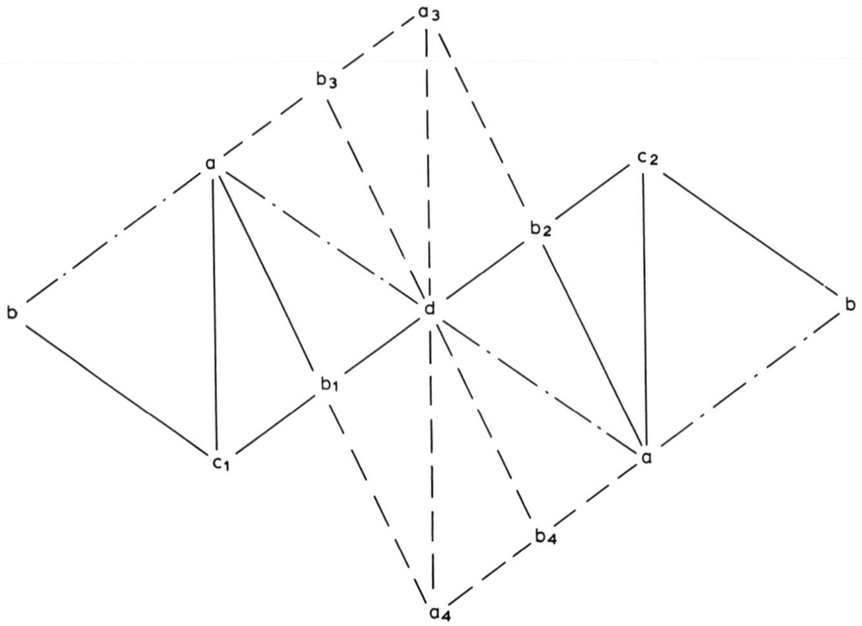

FIG. 44.

Figure 44 shows that the figure is determined by

$$b\text{—}a\text{—}d\text{—}a\text{—}b.$$

As a matter of fact, this is equivalent to

$$b\text{—}a\text{—}c\text{—}\underline{b}\text{—}c\text{—}a\text{—}b$$

because of

$$b\text{—}a\text{—}\underline{c}\text{—}d\text{—}\underline{c}\text{—}a\text{—}b,$$

$$b\text{—}a\text{—}d\text{—}a\text{—}b,$$

$$b\text{—}a\text{—}c\text{—}\underline{d}\text{—}a\text{—}b,$$

$$b\text{—}a\text{—}c\text{—}b\text{—}c\text{—}a\text{—}b$$

Note, however, that this chain cannot be realized in Γ^0.

73.6.4
$$\lambda = 2110, \qquad \mu = -2101.$$
$$\xi_1 = \tfrac{3}{4}\lambda + \tfrac{1}{4}\mu = \tfrac{1}{4}\cdot(2\cdot \tfrac{1}{2}\tfrac{1}{2}\tfrac{1}{2}\tfrac{1}{2} + 2\cdot 1110 + 1100),$$
$$\xi_2 = \tfrac{2}{3}\lambda + \tfrac{1}{3}\mu = \tfrac{1}{3}\cdot(2\cdot \tfrac{1}{2}\tfrac{1}{2}\tfrac{1}{2}\tfrac{1}{2} + 1210),$$
$$\xi_3 = \tfrac{3}{5}\lambda + \tfrac{2}{5}\mu = \tfrac{1}{5}\cdot(2\cdot \tfrac{1}{2}\tfrac{1}{2}\tfrac{1}{2}\tfrac{1}{2} + 2\cdot \tfrac{1}{2}\tfrac{3}{2}\tfrac{1}{2}\tfrac{1}{2} + 0110),$$
$$\xi_4 = \tfrac{1}{2}\lambda + \tfrac{1}{2}\mu = \tfrac{1}{2}\cdot 0211,$$
$$\xi_5 = \tfrac{2}{5}\lambda + \tfrac{3}{5}\mu = \tfrac{1}{5}\cdot(2\cdot -\tfrac{1}{2}\tfrac{1}{2}\tfrac{1}{2}\tfrac{1}{2} + 2\cdot -\tfrac{1}{2}\tfrac{3}{2}\tfrac{1}{2}\tfrac{1}{2} + 0101),$$
$$\xi_6 = \tfrac{1}{3}\lambda + \tfrac{2}{3}\mu = \tfrac{1}{3}\cdot(2\cdot -\tfrac{1}{2}\tfrac{1}{2}\tfrac{1}{2}\tfrac{1}{2} + -1201),$$
$$\xi_7 = \tfrac{1}{4}\lambda + \tfrac{3}{4}\mu = \tfrac{1}{4}\cdot(2\cdot -\tfrac{1}{2}\tfrac{1}{2}\tfrac{1}{2}\tfrac{1}{2} + 2\cdot -1101 + -1100).$$

See Figs. 45 and 46.

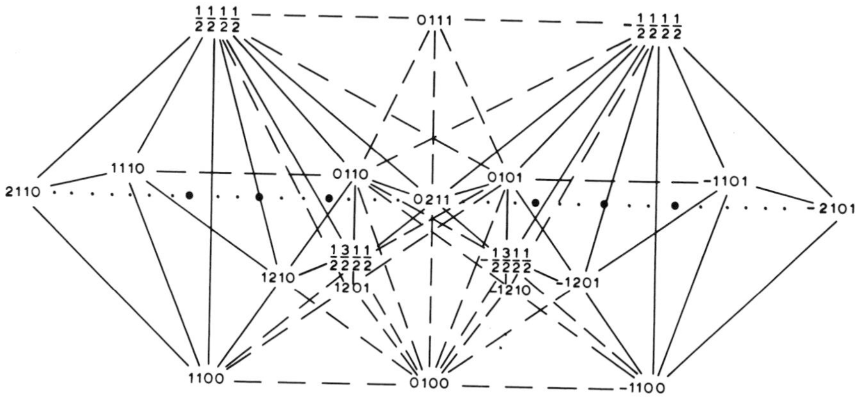

FIG. 45.

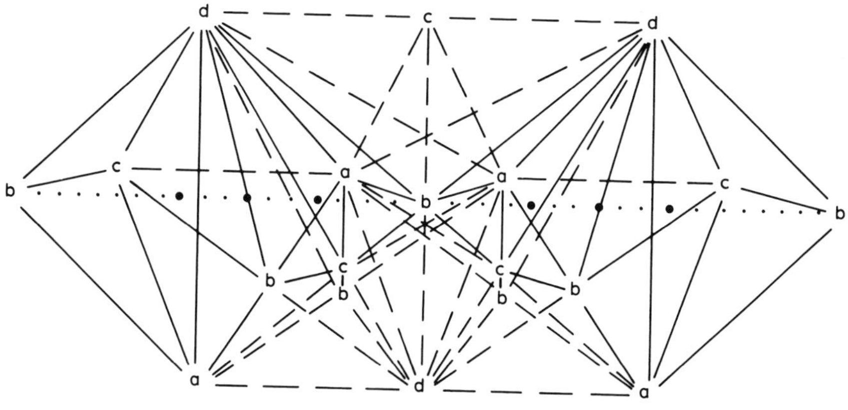

FIG. 46

$\Pi'(\lambda,\mu)$ falls short of $\Pi(\lambda,\mu)$ by four elements. The total figure is also determined by

$$b\text{---}c\text{---}b\text{---}c\text{---}b\text{---}c\text{---}b\text{---}c\text{---}b$$

as well as by

$$b\text{---}d\text{---}c\text{---}d\text{---}b.$$

From the latter figure, the complete figure is reconstructed in Fig. 47, in which the chains b—c_1—a_1—c, c—a_2—c_2—b, a_1—b_1—a_2, c_1—b_2—c_2—b_1, b_1—c_3—b_3—c_2 and b—a_3—b_2, b_3—a_4—b, c_2—d_1—c_3, and finally a_3—b_4—a_2, a_1—b_5—a_4 are retrieved consecutively with the incidences shown. The remaining incidences are trivial consequences.

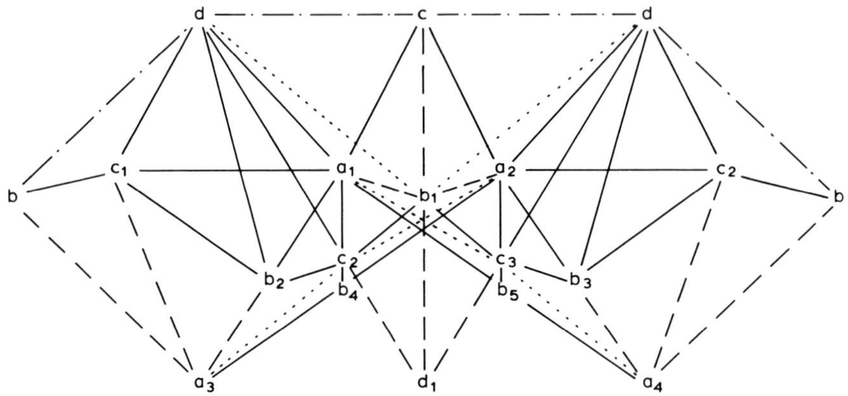

FIG. 47.

73.6.5 $\lambda = 2110, \qquad \mu = -1{-}210.$

$$\xi_1 = \tfrac{2}{3}\lambda + \tfrac{1}{3}\mu = 1010,$$

$$\xi_2 = \tfrac{1}{2}\lambda + \tfrac{1}{2}\mu = \tfrac{1}{2}\cdot 1{-}120,$$

$$\xi_3 = \tfrac{1}{3}\lambda + \tfrac{2}{3}\mu = 0{-}110.$$

$$2110\text{---}1010\text{---}1{-}120\text{---}0{-}110\text{---}{-1}{-}210.$$

$$b\text{---}a\text{---}b\text{---}a\text{---}b.$$

73.6.6 $\lambda = 2110, \qquad \mu = -12{-}10.$

$$\xi_1 = \tfrac{3}{4}\lambda + \tfrac{1}{4}\mu = \tfrac{1}{4}\cdot(3\cdot 1100 + 2\cdot 1110),$$

$$\xi_2 = \tfrac{2}{3}\lambda + \tfrac{1}{3}\mu = \tfrac{1}{3}\cdot(2\cdot 1100 + 1210),$$

$$\xi_3 = \tfrac{1}{2}\lambda + \tfrac{1}{2}\mu = \tfrac{1}{2}\cdot(1100 + 2\cdot 0100),$$
$$\xi_4 = \tfrac{2}{5}\lambda + \tfrac{3}{5}\mu = \tfrac{1}{5}\cdot(12\text{--}10 + 6\cdot 0100),$$
$$\xi_5 = \tfrac{1}{3}\lambda + \tfrac{2}{3}\mu = \tfrac{1}{3}\cdot(01\text{--}10 + 4\cdot 0100).$$

See Figs. 48 and 49.

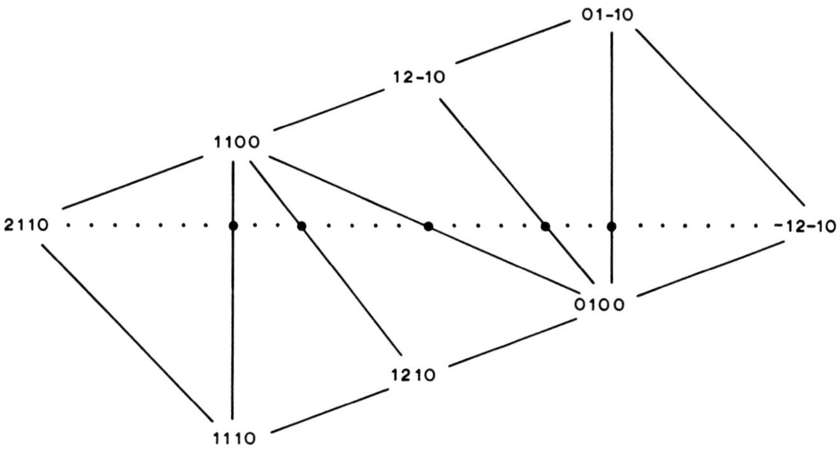

FIG. 48.

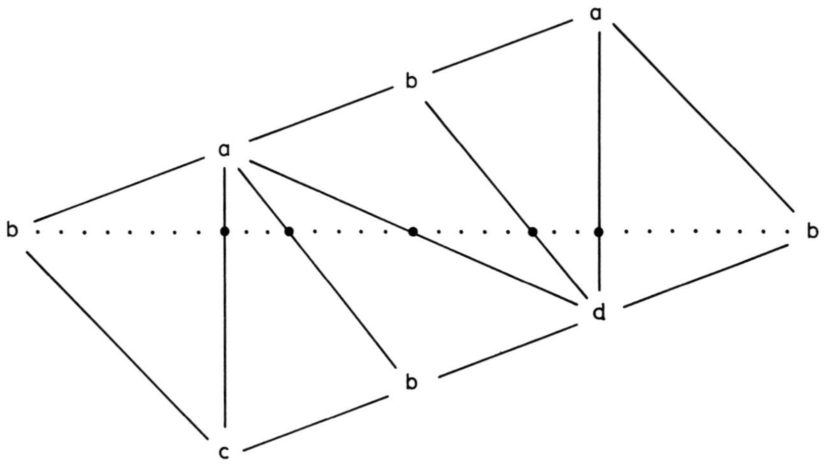

FIG. 49.

The figure is determined by

$$b\text{—}a\text{—}d\text{—}b.$$

73.6.6′ $\lambda = 2110, \qquad \mu = 1{-}2{-}10.$

$$\xi_1 = \tfrac{2}{3}\lambda + \tfrac{1}{3}\mu = \tfrac{1}{3}\cdot(4\cdot 1000 + 1010),$$

$$\xi_2 = \tfrac{3}{5}\lambda + \tfrac{2}{5}\mu = \tfrac{1}{5}\cdot(6\cdot 1000 + 2{-}110),$$

$$\xi_3 = \tfrac{1}{2}\lambda + \tfrac{1}{2}\mu = \tfrac{1}{2}\cdot(2\cdot 1000 + 1{-}100),$$

$$\xi_4 = \tfrac{1}{3}\lambda + \tfrac{2}{3}\mu = \tfrac{1}{3}\cdot(2{-}1{-}10 + 2\cdot 1{-}100),$$

$$\xi_5 = \tfrac{1}{4}\lambda + \tfrac{3}{4}\mu = \tfrac{1}{4}\cdot(2\cdot 1{-}1{-}10 + 3\cdot 1{-}100).$$

See Figs. 50 and 51.

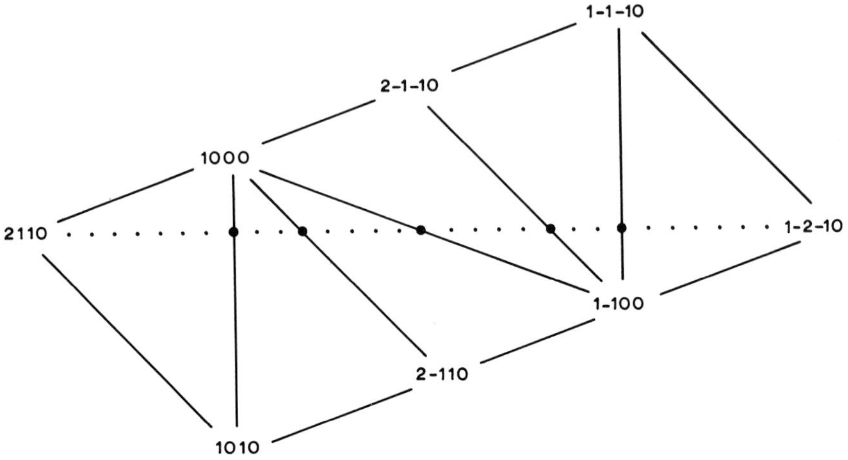

FIG. 50.

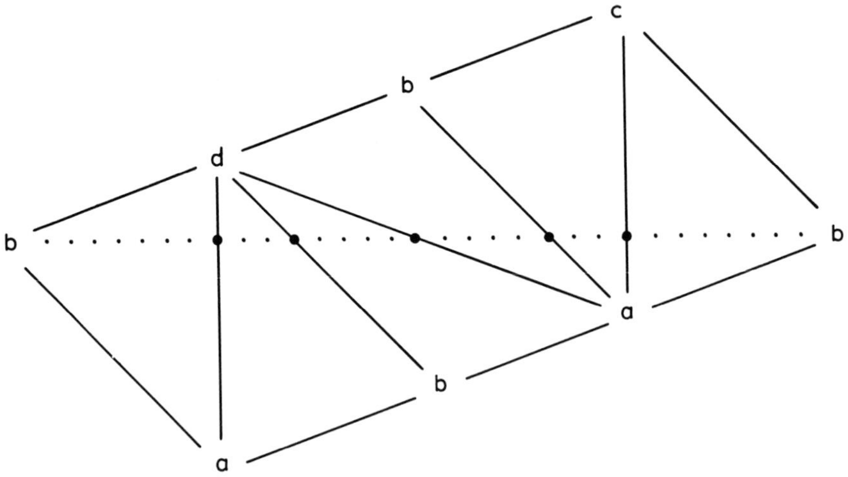

FIG. 51.

The figure is determined by

$$b—d—a—b.$$

73.6.7 $\lambda = 2110, \qquad \mu = -2110.$

$$\xi_1 = \tfrac{3}{4}\lambda + \tfrac{1}{4}\mu = 1110, \qquad \xi_2 = \tfrac{1}{2}\lambda + \tfrac{1}{2}\mu = 0110, \qquad \xi_3 = \tfrac{1}{4}\lambda + \tfrac{3}{4}\mu = -1110.$$

$$2110—1110—0110—-1110—-2110.$$

$$b—c—a—c—b.$$

73.6.8 $\lambda = 2110, \qquad \mu = -1201.$

$$\xi_1 = \tfrac{3}{4}\lambda + \tfrac{1}{4}\mu = \tfrac{1}{2}\cdot(\tfrac{1111}{2222} + 1100 + 1110),$$

$$\xi_2 = \tfrac{2}{3}\lambda + \tfrac{1}{3}\mu = \tfrac{1}{3}\cdot(2\cdot\tfrac{1111}{2222} + 1100 + 1210),$$

$$\xi_3 = \tfrac{1}{2}\lambda + \tfrac{1}{2}\mu = \tfrac{1311}{2222},$$

$$\xi_4 = \tfrac{1}{3}\lambda + \tfrac{2}{3}\mu = \tfrac{1}{3}\cdot(2\cdot 0100 + 0101 + 0211),$$

$$\xi_5 = \tfrac{1}{4}\lambda + \tfrac{3}{4}\mu = \tfrac{1}{2}\cdot(0100 + 0101 + -\tfrac{1311}{2222}).$$

See Figs. 52 and 53.

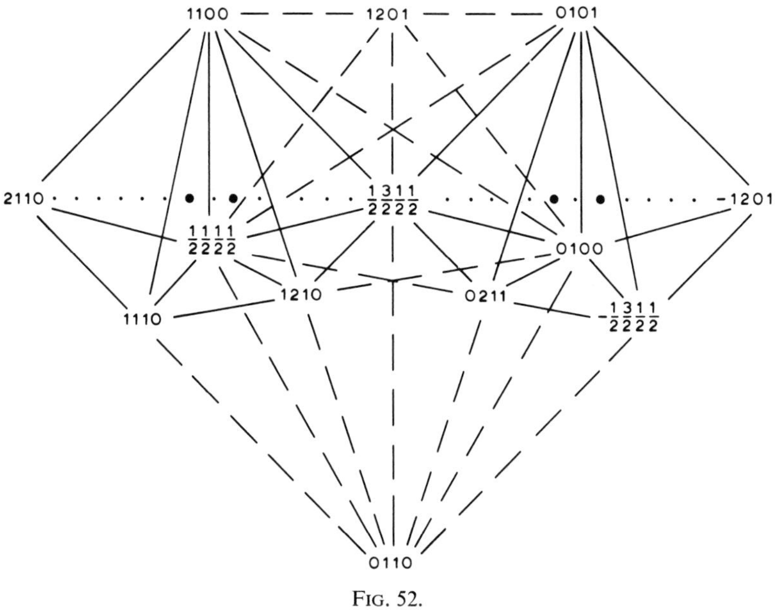

FIG. 52.

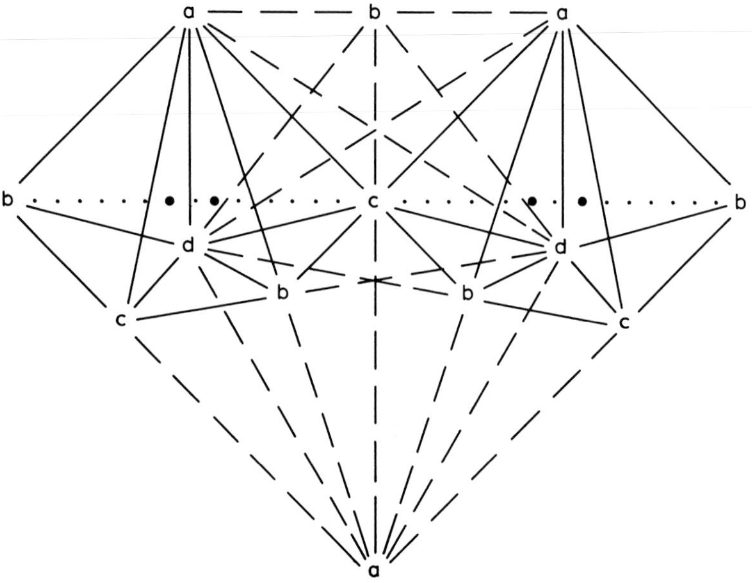

FIG. 53.

The figure is determined by

$$b\text{—}c\text{—}b\text{—}c\text{—}b\text{—}c\text{—}b,$$

as well as by the conjunction of

$$b\text{—}d\text{—}a\text{—}b \qquad \text{and} \qquad b\text{—}a\text{—}d\text{—}b.$$

73.6.9 $\lambda = 2110, \qquad \mu = -1210.$

$$\xi_1 = \tfrac{3}{4}\lambda + \tfrac{1}{4}\mu = \tfrac{1}{4}\cdot(4\cdot 1110 + 1100),$$

$$\xi_2 = \tfrac{2}{3}\lambda + \tfrac{1}{3}\mu = \tfrac{1}{3}\cdot(2\cdot 1110 + 1210),$$

$$\xi_3 = \tfrac{1}{2}\lambda + \tfrac{1}{2}\mu = \tfrac{1}{2}\cdot(0110 + 1210),$$

$$\xi_4 = \tfrac{1}{3}\lambda + \tfrac{2}{3}\mu = \tfrac{1}{3}\cdot(3\cdot 0110 + 2\cdot 0100).$$

See Figs. 54 and 55.

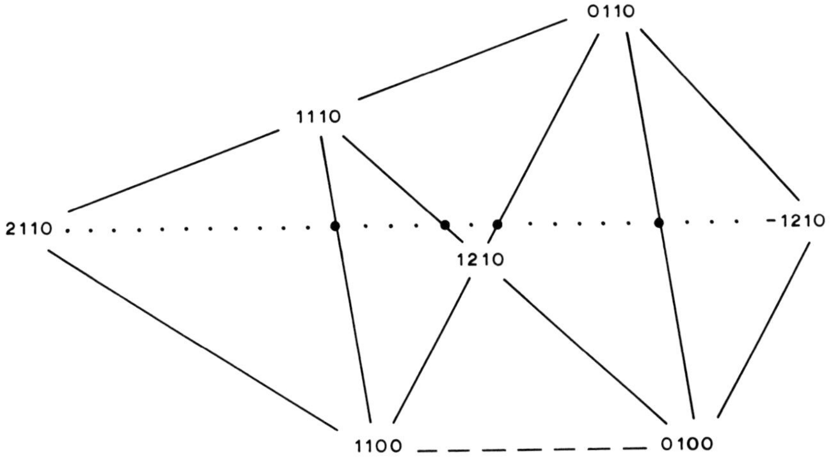

FIG. 54.

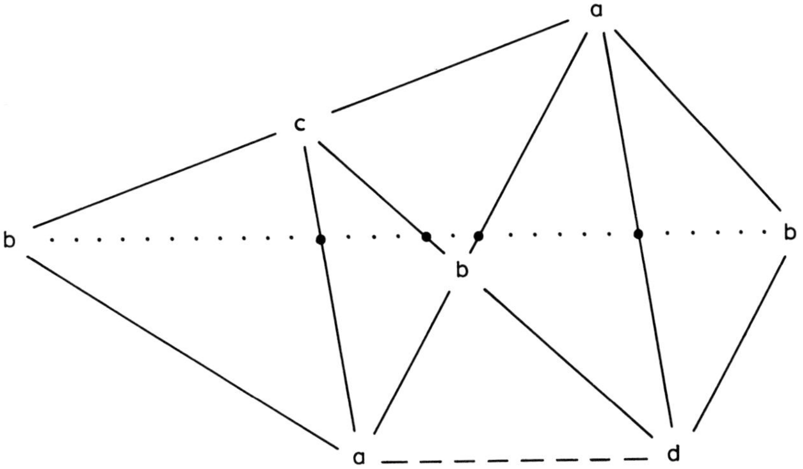

FIG. 55.

The figure is determined by

$$b—c—a—b.$$

73.6.9′ $\lambda = 2110, \qquad \mu = 1\text{–}210.$

$$\xi_1 = \tfrac{2}{3}\lambda + \tfrac{1}{3}\mu = \tfrac{1}{3}\cdot(3\cdot 1010 + 2\cdot 1000),$$
$$\xi_2 = \tfrac{1}{2}\lambda + \tfrac{1}{2}\mu = \tfrac{1}{2}\cdot(1010 + 2\text{–}110),$$
$$\xi_3 = \tfrac{1}{3}\lambda + \tfrac{2}{3}\mu = \tfrac{1}{3}\cdot(2\cdot 1\text{–}110 + 2\text{–}110),$$
$$\xi_4 = \tfrac{1}{4}\lambda + \tfrac{3}{4}\mu = \tfrac{1}{4}\cdot(4\cdot 1\text{–}110 + 1\text{–}100).$$

See Figs. 56 and 57.

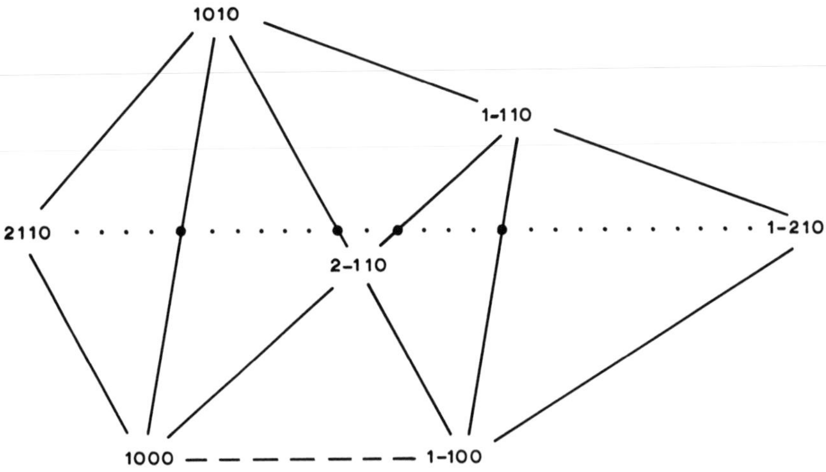

FIG. 56.

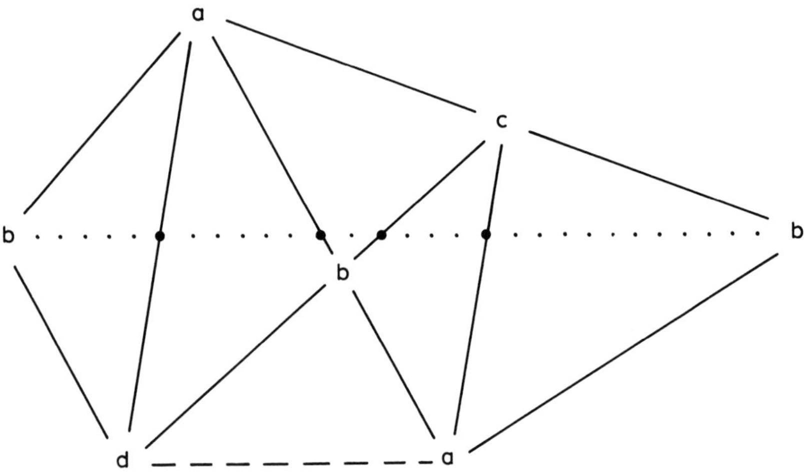

FIG. 57

The figure is determined by

$$b—a—c—b$$

73.6.10

$$\lambda = 2110, \qquad \mu = 2\text{–}1\text{–}10$$

$$\xi_1 = \tfrac{1}{2}\lambda + \tfrac{1}{2}\mu = 2 \cdot 1000.$$

$$2110—1000—2\text{–}1\text{–}10.$$

$$b—d—b.$$

73.6.11 $\lambda = 2110, \qquad \mu = 2{-}101.$

$$\xi_1 = \tfrac{2}{3}\lambda + \tfrac{1}{3}\mu = \tfrac{1}{3}\cdot(2\cdot 1000 + 1010 + 2\cdot \tfrac{3}{2}\tfrac{1}{2}\tfrac{1}{2}\tfrac{1}{2}),$$
$$\xi_2 = \tfrac{1}{2}\lambda + \tfrac{1}{2}\mu = \tfrac{1}{2}\cdot(2\cdot 1000 + 2011),$$
$$\xi_3 = \tfrac{1}{3}\lambda + \tfrac{2}{3}\mu = \tfrac{1}{3}\cdot(2\cdot 1000 + 1001 + 2\cdot \tfrac{3}{2}\,{-\tfrac{1}{2}}\tfrac{1}{2}\tfrac{1}{2}).$$

See Figs. 58 and 59.

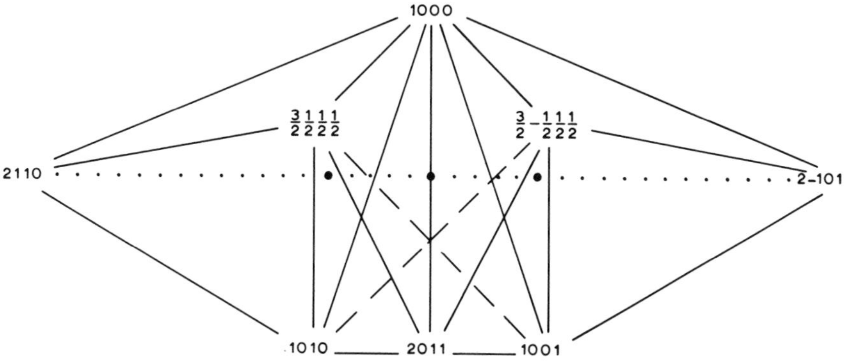

FIG. 58.

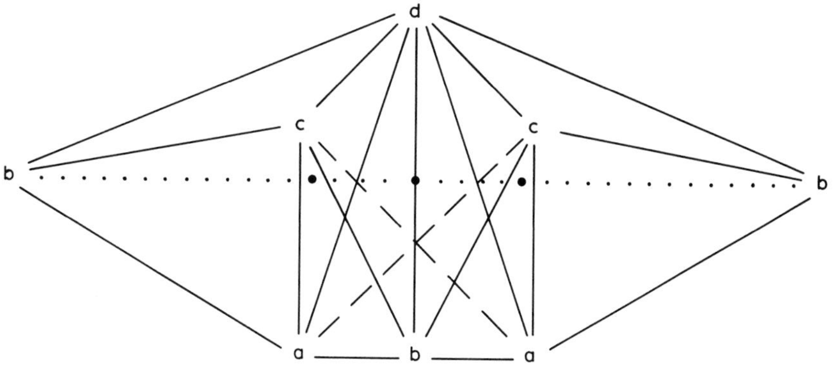

FIG. 59.

This is a special pair of lines in a symplecton. The figure is determined by

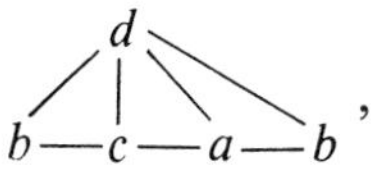

as well as by

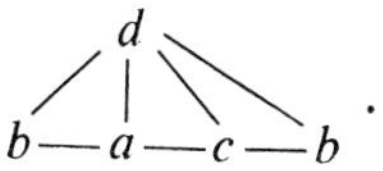

73.6.12 $\lambda = 2110, \qquad \mu = 12\text{–}10$

$$\xi_1 = \tfrac{1}{2}\lambda + \tfrac{1}{2}\mu = \tfrac{1}{2}\cdot(3\cdot 1100)$$

$$2110\text{—}1100\text{—}12\text{–}10.$$

$$b\text{—}a\text{—}b.$$

73.6.13 $\lambda = 2110, \qquad \mu = 21\text{–}10.$

$$\xi_1 = \tfrac{1}{2}\lambda + \tfrac{1}{2}\mu = 1000 + 1100.$$

See Figs. 60 and 61.

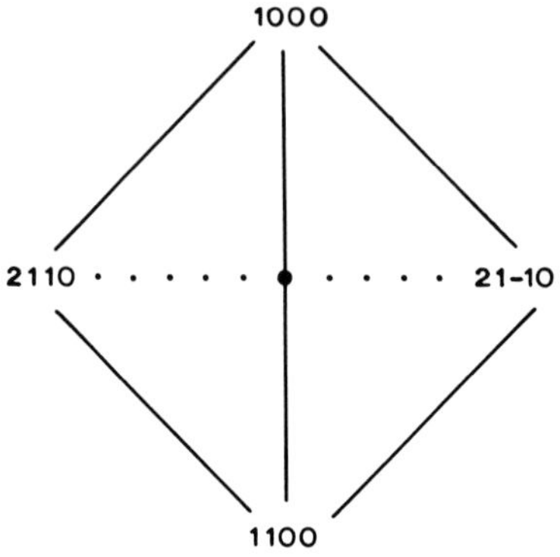

FIG. 60.

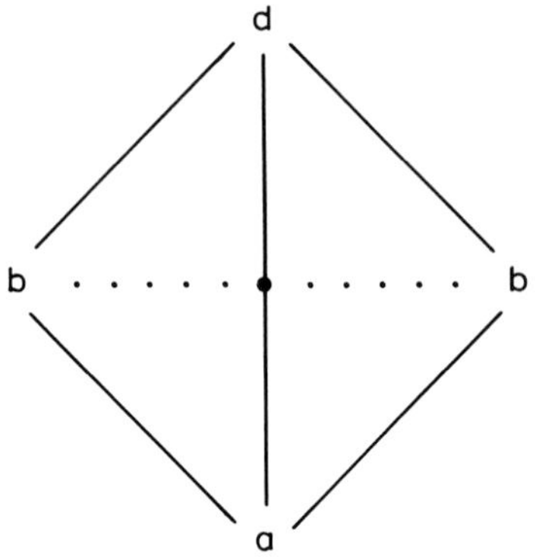

FIG. 61.

73.6.14 $\lambda = 2110, \qquad \mu = 2101.$

$$\xi_1 = \tfrac{1}{2}\lambda + \tfrac{1}{2}\mu = \tfrac{1}{2}\cdot(1100 + 2\cdot\tfrac{3}{2}\tfrac{1}{2}\tfrac{1}{2}\tfrac{1}{2}).$$

See Figs. 62 and 63.

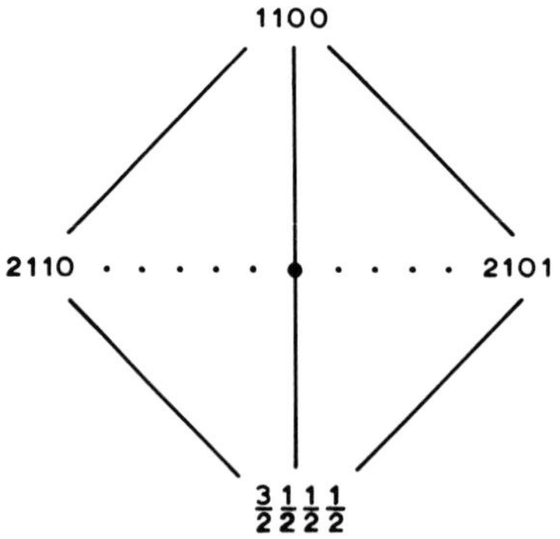

FIG. 62.

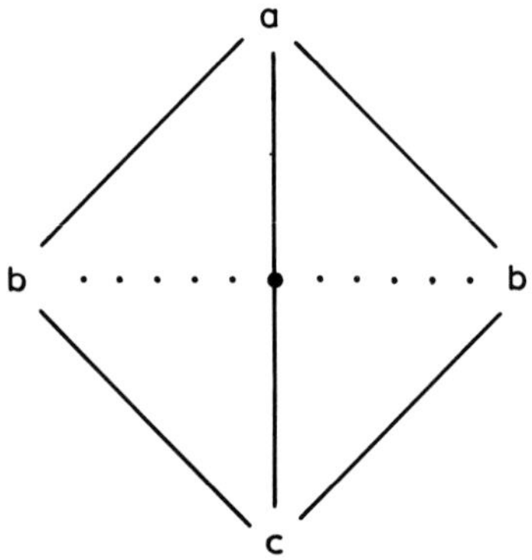

FIG. 63.

73.6.15 $\lambda = 2110, \qquad \mu = 2110.$

$$2110—2110.$$

$$b—b.$$

73.6.1–15 From the weakest to the strongest relation on pairs of lines the hierarchy runs

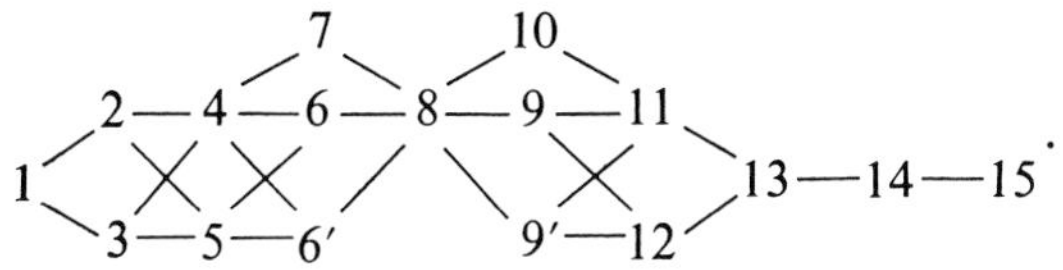

74. THE INCIDENCE GEOMETRIES OF REAL SEMISIMPLE LIE GROUPS

The theory developed in Sections 70 and 71 for complex semisimple Lie groups can be adapted to the real case.

$G \in$ Gru Lie Lin Com SS, $\boldsymbol{G}$ its infinitesimal algebra, C an involutory semimorphism, and $G_C, \boldsymbol{G}_C$ the C-restrictions; other notations as usual.

$\boldsymbol{G}'_C$ sub $\boldsymbol{G}_C$ is the C-restriction of C-invariant $\boldsymbol{G}'$ sub $\boldsymbol{G}$.

74.1. Definition $\boldsymbol{G}'_C$ sub $\boldsymbol{G}_C$ is called *parabolic* if $\boldsymbol{G}'$ sub $\boldsymbol{G}$ is parabolic. The same for G'_C.

Note that parabolic G'_C need not comprise a maximal connected solvable subgroup of G_C, though G' does so with respect to G.

Proposition If $\boldsymbol{G}'_C$ is maximal parabolic sub $\boldsymbol{G}_C$, then $\boldsymbol{G}' = \boldsymbol{M} \cap C\boldsymbol{M}$ for some maximal parabolic $\boldsymbol{M}$ sub $\boldsymbol{G}$.

Proof For $\boldsymbol{M}$ take a maximal parabolic subalgebra of $\boldsymbol{G}$ around $\boldsymbol{G}'$. Then $C\boldsymbol{M}$ is of the same kind, and $\boldsymbol{M} \cap C\boldsymbol{M}$ is C-invariant and thus equals $\boldsymbol{G}'$.

74.2. Theorem If $\boldsymbol{G}'_C$ and $\boldsymbol{G}''_C$ are parabolic sub $\boldsymbol{G}_C$, then $\boldsymbol{G}' \cap \boldsymbol{G}''$ contains a minimally compact C-invariant trunk of $\boldsymbol{G}$.

Proof Let $\boldsymbol{B}', \boldsymbol{B}''$ be maximal solvable sub $\boldsymbol{G}', \boldsymbol{G}''$, respectively. Bruhat's lemma provides a trunk contained in $\boldsymbol{B}' \cap \boldsymbol{B}'' \subset \boldsymbol{G}' \cap \boldsymbol{G}''$, thus a $\boldsymbol{G}$-regular element $\boldsymbol{h}_0$ of $\boldsymbol{G}' \cap \boldsymbol{G}''$. Then $\tau \boldsymbol{h}_0 + \bar{\tau} C\boldsymbol{h}_0$ is still regular for suitable τ and lying in $\boldsymbol{G}' \cap \boldsymbol{G}''$. Moreover, it is C-invariant. Therefore it defines a C-invariant trunk $\boldsymbol{H}$ of $\boldsymbol{G}$ within $\boldsymbol{G}' \cap \boldsymbol{G}''$.

Take C_{un} on the same trunk after C-third dressing, that is, with $CC_{un} = C_{un}C$ (see 51.6). Suppose $\boldsymbol{H}$ is not yet minimally compact. Then for some $\alpha = CC_{un}\alpha$ the condition of 60.9 is not satisfied. Therefore there is some

$$\alpha = CC_{un}\alpha \in W^* \qquad \text{with} \quad CC_{un}\boldsymbol{e}_\alpha = -\boldsymbol{e}_\alpha; \qquad \text{thus} \quad C\boldsymbol{e}_\alpha = \boldsymbol{e}_{-\alpha}.$$

$\boldsymbol{e}_\alpha \in \boldsymbol{G}'$, for otherwise both $\boldsymbol{e}_\alpha$ and $\boldsymbol{e}_{-\alpha} \notin \boldsymbol{G}'$, which contradicts parabolicity. The same is true of $\boldsymbol{G}''$. Therefore $\boldsymbol{e}_\alpha, \boldsymbol{e}_{-\alpha} \in \boldsymbol{G}' \cap \boldsymbol{G}''$. This shows that U_α, as used in 60.15 to transform the trunk $\boldsymbol{H}$, can be formed within Int($\boldsymbol{G}' \cap \boldsymbol{G}''$). The procedure in 60.15 produces a C-invariant trunk of $\boldsymbol{G}$ within $\boldsymbol{G}' \cap \boldsymbol{G}''$, though now with a larger multiplicity of the eigenvalue -1 of CC_{un} on the trunk. This proves the assertion.

74.3 In the sequel the trunk $\boldsymbol{H}$ is supposed to be C-minimally compact. By 60.17 it does not matter which one is chosen. C_{un} is taken with respect to $\boldsymbol{H}$, and with $CC_{un} = C_{un}C$.

Under the aspect of reality the incidence geometry of G_C should be defined as consisting of the maximal parabolic subgroups of G_C. An equivalent and more convenient approach is to use their complex extensions. This explains the following:

Definition Γ_C is the set of C-invariant Lie subgroups of G whose C-restrictions are maximal parabolic sub G_C. The set Γ_C is endowed with the following incidence relation:

a, b are *incident* if $a \cap b$ contains a maximal connected solvable subgroup of G.

Γ_C, the *incidence geometry* of G_C, is considered as acted on by G_C through its adjoint action.

Its transitivity classes are the *sorts* of the geometry.

Γ_C^0 is the set of elements of Γ_C containing the (C-minimally compact) trunk H.

Note that by 74.2 a given pair of elements of Γ_C may be supposed to be in Γ_C^0, thanks to the action of G_C on Γ_C.

74.4 To continue as in 70.6 one must redefine w and Π.

By 74.1 any $a \in \Gamma_C^0$ can be obtained as $x \cap Cx$ with $x \in \Gamma^0$. By 70.6.2 the infinitesimal algebra of x is spanned by $\boldsymbol{H}$ and the $\boldsymbol{e}_\alpha$, with $(wx, \alpha) \geqslant 0$. Clearly $wCx = C^* wx$. Thus the infinitesimal algebra of a is spanned by $\boldsymbol{H}$ and the $\boldsymbol{e}_\alpha$ with

74.4.1 $$(wx, \alpha) \geqslant 0 \quad \text{and} \quad (C^* wx, \alpha) \geqslant 0.$$

Now x and Cx are incident as elements of Γ, for their intersection is still parabolic. Therefore by 70.6.1

$$(wx, \alpha)(C^* wx, \alpha) \geqslant 0 \qquad \text{for all} \quad \alpha \in W^*.$$

In a more compact way the condition 74.4.1 can now be written

$$(wx + C^* wx, \alpha) \geqslant 0$$

or, equivalently,

$$((1 - CC_{\text{un}}) wx, \alpha) \geqslant 0.$$

This suggests the following:

Definition Π_C is the set of $(1 + C^*)\lambda$ with $\lambda \in \Pi$ (i.e., in the set of equivalents of fundamental weights) such that λ is incident with $C^*\lambda$.

w_C is defined by

$$w_C a = (1 - CC_{\text{un}}) wx$$

for $a \in \Gamma_C^0$ with $a = x \cap Cx$ and $x \in \Gamma^0$.

The last part of this definition is still to be justified. A little more will be proved:

Proposition If $x, y \in \Gamma^0$, x incident with Cx, y incident with Cy, and $x \cap Cx \subset y \cap Cy$, then $x = y$ or $x = Cy$.

Proof By 70.10, since $y \supset x \cap Cx$, all parts containing wx and wCx also contain wy. The smallest part, that is, the cell, containing wx and wCx is one- or two-dimensional and its only members of Π are wx and wCx. Therefore $wy = wx$ or $= wCx$, which proves the assertion.

74.5 The following was proved in 74.4:

Proposition w_C maps Γ_C^0 one-to-one onto Π_C such that the infinitesimal algebra of a is spanned by $\boldsymbol{H}$ and the $\boldsymbol{e}_\gamma$, with

$$(w_C a, \gamma) \geqslant 0.$$

Indeed w_C maps Γ_C^0 *onto* Π_C: Given some $\lambda \in \Pi$ incident with $C^*\lambda$, there is an $x \in \Gamma^0$ incident with Cx and such that $\lambda = wx$. Now $x \cap Cx$ is contained in the complex extension $y \cap Cy$ of some maximal parabolic subgroup of G_C so that $x \cap Cx \subset y \cap Cy \in \Gamma_C^0$ with $y \in \Gamma^0$. But then by Proposition 74.4, $x \cap Cx = y \cap Cy$, which proves the assertion.

74.6. Proposition $(1 + CC_{\text{un}})\alpha \in W^*$ for no $\alpha \in W^*$.

Proof CC_{un} multiplies $[e_\alpha, CC_{un} e_\alpha]$ by -1; thus by 60.9 and the minimal compactness of $\boldsymbol{H}$ this expression cannot be a branch and consequently $(1 + CC_{un})\alpha$ cannot be a nonzero rootform.

74.7. Definition The intersections of parts and cells of $\boldsymbol{H}^*_{he}$ with $\boldsymbol{H}^*_C$ are called *C-parts* and *C-cells.* A C-cell of maximal dimension (=real rank) is a *closed C-chamber*, its interior in $\boldsymbol{H}^*_{C,he}$ a *C-chamber.* A *C-edge* is a one-dimensional C-cell.

$\text{Int}_C\, W^*$ is the maximal subgroup of Int W^* leaving $\boldsymbol{H}^*_{C,he}$ invariant, and restricted to $\boldsymbol{H}^*_{C,he}$.

Theorem $\text{Int}_C\, W^*$ is simply transitive on the set of C-chambers. Its elements are induced by inner automorphisms of $\boldsymbol{G}_C$ preserving $\boldsymbol{H}$.

Proof Take two C-chambers with a common wall of codimension 1 in $\boldsymbol{H}^*_{C,he}$. The wall is determined by some $\alpha \in W^*$. Then $\alpha \neq CC_{un}\alpha$, for otherwise $\alpha(\boldsymbol{H}_{C,he}) = \{0\}$. For the transitivity assertion it suffices to show that the reflection in this wall is in $\text{Int}_C\, W^*$. There are three cases with respect to α:

74.7.1 $CC_{un}\alpha = -\alpha$. Then with S_α defined by 20.9, $C^*S_\alpha C^* = S_{C^*\alpha} = S_\alpha$; thus S_α itself induces an element S of $\text{Int}_C\, W^*$ as required.

74.7.2 $(1 - CC_{un})\alpha \in W^*$. Then $C^*S_{(1-CC_{un})\alpha}C^* = S_{(1-CC_{un})\alpha}$. Since the orthoplanes of α and $(1 - CC_{un})\alpha$ have the same intersection with $\boldsymbol{H}^*_{C,he}$, an element S of $\text{Int}_C\, W^*$ as required is furnished by $S_{(1-CC_{un})\alpha}$.

74.7.3 $CC_{un}\alpha \neq -\alpha$, $(1 - CC_{un})\alpha \notin W^*$. Then, as implied by 74.6, $(\alpha, CC_{un}\alpha) = 0$,

$$S_\alpha S_{CC_{un}\alpha} = S_{CC_{un}\alpha} S_\alpha,$$

$$C(S_\alpha S_{CC_{un}\alpha})C = S_{CC_{un}\alpha} S_\alpha = S_\alpha S_{CC_{un}\alpha}.$$

Since $S_\alpha S_{CC_{un}\alpha}\alpha = -\alpha$, $S_\alpha S_{CC_{un}\alpha}$ induces an element S of $\text{Int}_C\, W^*$ as required.

To show that $\text{Int}_C\, W^*$ is *simply* transitive, take an $S \in \text{Int}\, W^*$, leaving $\boldsymbol{H}^*_{C,he}$ and a closed C-chamber K invariant. S causes a permutation in the set D of the closed chambers that contain K. The reflections in the common walls of elements of D produce a subgroup F of Int W^*; the elements of F leave K, hence $\boldsymbol{H}^*_{C,he}$, elementwise invariant, and F acts transitively on D. Thus there is an $S' \in F$ such that $S^{-1}S'$ leaves a certain element of D invariant. Since Int W^* is simply transitive on the set of all chambers, $S^{-1}S' = 1$; thus $S = S'$, and S restricted to $\boldsymbol{H}^*_{C,he}$ is the identity.

To prove the remainder of the theorem, one must extend S as obtained in

74.7.1–3 to the whole of $\boldsymbol{G}$ according to 33.1, and then replace it by some $S' = \tilde{h}S\tilde{h}^{-1}$ such that $h = \exp \boldsymbol{h}$, $\boldsymbol{h} \in \boldsymbol{H}$, and $S' \in \operatorname{Int} \boldsymbol{G}_C$:

74.7.1′ $S = \exp \tau(\tilde{e}_\alpha + \tilde{e}_{-\alpha})$ with a certain imaginary τ.

$$S' = \tilde{h}S\tilde{h}^{-1} = \exp(\tau\tilde{h}(\tilde{e}_\alpha + \tilde{e}_{-\alpha})\tilde{h}^{-1})$$
$$= \exp(\tau(\exp \alpha(\boldsymbol{h})\,\tilde{e}_\alpha + \exp(-\alpha(\boldsymbol{h}))\,\tilde{e}_{-\alpha})).$$
$$Ce_\alpha = \kappa e_\alpha, \qquad Ce_{-\alpha} = \bar{\kappa}e_{-\alpha} \qquad \text{with} \quad \kappa\bar{\kappa} = 1,$$

because of $CC_{\text{un}} = C_{\text{un}}C$. For S' to be real, one gets the condition on $\boldsymbol{h}$:

$$\exp(\alpha(\boldsymbol{h}) - \overline{\alpha(\boldsymbol{h})}) = -\kappa,$$

which can easily be fulfilled.

74.7.2′ The same argument applies to $(1 - CC_{\text{un}}\alpha)$ instead of α.

74.7.3′ Neither $(1 + CC_{\text{un}})\alpha$ nor $(1 - CC_{\text{un}})\alpha$ are rootforms, not even 0. Hence S' is the product of

$$\exp \tau(\exp \alpha(\boldsymbol{h})\,\tilde{e}_\alpha + \exp(C^*\alpha)(\boldsymbol{h})\,\tilde{e}_{C^*\alpha})$$

and

$$\exp \tau(\exp -\alpha(\boldsymbol{h})\,\tilde{e}_{-\alpha} + \exp(-C^*\alpha)(\boldsymbol{h})\,\tilde{e}_{-C^*\alpha}),$$

with a certain imaginary τ. If $Ce_\alpha = \kappa e_{C^*\alpha}$, then $Ce_{C^*\alpha} = \bar{\kappa}^{-1} e_\alpha$, and $Ce_{-\alpha} = \bar{\kappa}e_{-C^*\alpha}$, $Ce_{-C^*\alpha} = \kappa^{-1}e_{-\alpha}$. Furthermore, $\kappa\bar{\kappa} = 1$.

The reality required boils down to

$$\exp((C^*\alpha)(\boldsymbol{h}) - \overline{\alpha(\boldsymbol{h})}) = -\kappa,$$

which can be fulfilled, since α and $C^*\alpha$ are linearly independent.

74.8 If $\lambda \in \Pi$ and $C^*\lambda$ are incident, there is an at most two-dimensional cell that contains both. This cell intersects $\boldsymbol{H}^*_{C,\text{he}}$ in a C-cell which is one-dimensional, that is, a C-edge. $(1 - CC_{\text{un}})\lambda$ lies on this C-edge. The converse is also true:

Proposition The C-edges are the sets of nonnegative multiples of elements of Π_C.

Proof Let d be a C-edge and D the smallest cell that contains d. The C-invariance of d implies that of D. Choose $\lambda \in \Pi$ on D. Then $C^*\lambda$ on D, $\lambda + C^*\lambda \neq 0$, and $\lambda + C^*\lambda$ on D as well as in $\boldsymbol{H}^*_{C,\text{he}}$. This shows that d is spanned by $\lambda + C^*\lambda = (1 - CC_{\text{un}})\lambda$.

74.9. Proposition The following statements are equivalent:

1. $a, b \in \Gamma_C^0$ are incident.
2. There is a C-cell containing $w_C a$ and $w_C b$.
3. $(w_C a, \gamma)(w_C b, \gamma) \geqslant 0$ for all $\gamma \in W^*$.

Proof If $a = x \cap Cx$, $b = y \cap Cy$ with $x, y \in \Gamma^0$, then incidence of a, b means that $x \cap Cx \cap y \cap Cy$ contains a maximal solvable Lie subgroup, thus that x, Cx, y, Cy are mutually incident, and that their w-images are contained in a common cell; this, however, is equivalent to $w_C a$, $w_C b$ being contained in a common C-cell. This proves the equivalence of 1 and 2. The equivalence of 2 and 3 is obvious.

Definition $\lambda_C, \mu_C \in \Pi_C$ are called *incident* if

$$(\lambda_C, \alpha)(\mu_C, \alpha) \geqslant 0 \qquad \text{for all} \quad \alpha \in W^*.$$

74.10. Theorem Every sort of Γ_C intersects Γ_C^0 and even has a member whose w_C-image is in a given closed C-chamber. Two elements of Γ_C^0 belong to the same sort iff they are equivalent under a C-real element of $\mathrm{Int}(\boldsymbol{G}, \boldsymbol{H})$. The number of sorts equals the real rank of G_C.

Proof The infinitesimal algebra of $a \in \Gamma_C$ contains a C-minimally compact trunk $\boldsymbol{H}'$ of $\boldsymbol{G}$ (see 74.2). By 60.17 $\boldsymbol{H}'$ is carried into $\boldsymbol{H}$ by the action of Int $\boldsymbol{G}_C$. The same action carries a into an element of Γ_C^0. This shows the truth of the first sentence. The second follows from theorem 74.7. If $a, b \in \Gamma_C^0$ are equivalent under Int $\boldsymbol{G}_C$, one must show that they are also equivalent under an element of Int $\boldsymbol{G}_C$ that leaves $\boldsymbol{H}$ invariant. By the foregoing $w_C a, w_C b$ may be taken in the same closed C-chamber, that is, incident. Now $a = x \cap Cx$, $b = y \cap Cy$ with $x, y \in \Gamma^0$, x incident with Cx, y with Cy. By Proposition 74.4 and the G_C-equivalence of a, b one may suppose that x, y are equivalent under Int $\boldsymbol{G}$. Thus wx, wy are equivalent under Int W^*. They are also incident, hence equal. This shows that a, b are equal.

Finally, two distinct C-edges of a closed C-chamber cannot be $\mathrm{Int}_C W^*$-equivalent, since otherwise two distinct edges of a closed chamber would be Int W^*-equivalent. This shows that there are exactly as many sorts as there are C-edges of a closed C-chamber.

74.11 A C-chamber can be represented by a graph with dots corresponding to the walls and multiple bonds corresponding to the angles of the walls in the usual way. With due regard to the lengths of the related combinations of rootforms, one can even put arrows in the bonds. It will appear that no new graphs occur except those found in the complex case.

Definition By *C-graph* of G_C one means that of a C-chamber of G_C.

74.12 After this successive reduction of incidence problems in Γ_C to those in Γ_C^0 and Π_C and finally to problems on the C-graph of G_C, one can repeat the analysis of Sections 71–73 with slight changes. The most notable deviation is that arbitrary trunks are restricted to the minimally compact ones. The incidence geometries belonging to real semisimple groups provide a new example of a Tits geometry. In particular, those of real rank 2 give new generalized m-gons ($m = 2,3,4,6$).

75. C-GRAPHS OF INCIDENCE GEOMETRIES OF SIMPLE SEMISIMPLE LIE GROUPS

When studying the incidence geometries of particular real semisimple Lie groups, one can restrict oneself to the simple case. The compact types can be dismissed because then $C^* = -1$ and $\lambda \in \Pi$ can never be incident with $C^*\lambda = -\lambda$, which causes Π_C, hence Γ_C, to be void. Standard type geometries behave as the corresponding complex ones. In the twin case $G_C \in \mathsf{L}_{**}$ there is a trivial isomorphism between Γ(of $G \in \mathsf{L}$) and Γ_C(of $G_C \in \mathsf{L}_{**}$). This justifies the supposition:

G_C noncompact, nonstandard, nontwin, simple.

75.1 $\boldsymbol{H}$ is a minimally compact trunk with a real order (see 60.18). $\boldsymbol{G}$ is in C-third dressing on $\boldsymbol{H}$. Thus,

$$C^*\rho_j = -\rho_j \qquad \text{for } j = 1, \ldots, k,$$

$$C^*\rho_j = \rho_j \bmod \rho_1, \ldots, \rho_k \qquad \text{for } j = k+1, \ldots, m,$$

$$C^*\rho_j = \rho_{l+m+1-j} \bmod \rho_1, \ldots, \rho_k \qquad \text{for } j = m+1, \ldots, l.$$

For the fundamental weights this yields

$$C^*\pi_j = -\pi_j \bmod \pi_{k+1}, \ldots, \pi_l \qquad \text{for } j = 1, \ldots, k,$$

$$C^*\pi_j = \pi_j \qquad \text{for } j = k+1, \ldots, m,$$

$$C^*\pi_j = \pi_{l+m+1-j} \qquad \text{for } j = m+1, \ldots, l.$$

The nonnegative multiples of the

$$\pi_j + C^*\pi_j \qquad \text{with } j = k+1, \ldots, \tfrac{1}{2}(l+m)$$

are elements of the constituting edges of a C-chamber. Its C-graph is constructed in any particular case. At any dot a primitive rootform ρ is placed, together with $C^*\rho$ if they are different. Note that the corresponding wall is $\rho^\perp \cap \boldsymbol{H}^*_{C,\mathrm{he}} = (C^*\rho)^\perp \cap \boldsymbol{H}^*_{C,\mathrm{he}}$.

The real rank l' of G_C is $\frac{1}{2}(l+m) - k$.

75.2 To get more insight into the details by which incidence geometries with the same graph are distinguished from one another more data are added:

Take l' mutually incident elements $a_1, \ldots, a_{l'}$ of Γ_C, a_j from the sort $\Gamma_{C,j}$; for example, those mapped by w_C into $\pi_{k+j} + C^*\pi_{k+j}$, $j = 1, \ldots, l'$. Then for $p \in \{1, \ldots, l'\}$ consider the manifold V_p of all

$$x \in \Gamma_{C,p}, \quad x \text{ incident with all } a_j \, (j \neq p).$$

For $j = 1, \ldots, l'$ let $G_{C,j}$ be the normalizer in G_C of $a_{j,C}$ ($a_{j,C}$ is the group infinitesimally generated by the C-restriction of the infinitesimal algebra of a_j); that is, $G_{C,j}$ is the stabilizer of a_j in G_C as acting on Γ_C. Then $a_{j,C}$ is the 1-component of $G_{C,j}$. Let $x \in \Gamma_{C,p}$. Then both $a_p \cap \bigcap_{j \neq p} a_j$ and $x \cap \bigcap_{j \neq p} a_j$ are parabolic because of Proposition 70.7; hence by Theorem 74.2 their intersection contains a minimally compact C-invariant trunk H' of G. By the G_C-conjugacy of those trunks and by Theorems 74.10 and 74.7 there is an element $g \in G_C$ such that

$$\tilde{g}H' = H, \qquad \tilde{g}a_j = a_j \qquad \text{for} \quad j = 1, \ldots, l';$$

therefore $g \in \bigcap_{j=1}^{l'} G_{C,j}$. Now $w_C \tilde{g}x$ is incident with all $w_C a_j = \pi_{k+j} + C^* \pi_{k+j}$ with $j \neq p$, thus either coincides with $w_C a_p = \pi_{k+p} + C^* \pi_{k+p}$, from which follows, $\tilde{g}x = a_p$ and $x = a_p$, or is the image of $\pi_{k+p} + C^* \pi_{k+p}$ under the reflection in the wall in $H^*_{C,\mathrm{he}}$ determined by ρ_{k+p}; now the element of G_C constructed in the proof of Theorem 74.7 effectuating this reflection is easily seen to lie in the 1-component of $\bigcap_{j \neq p} a_{j,C}$.

Hence V_p is transitively acted on by $\bigcap_{j \neq p} G_{C,j}$, even by its 1-component. Therefore V_p is connected and, as acted on by G_C, isomorphic with the homogeneous space

$$\bigcap_{j \neq p} G_{C,j} / \bigcap_j G_{C,j}.$$

This quotient can be reduced by the maximal normal Lie subgroup of the numerator contained in the denominator. In the complex case this is the radical of the numerator. After this reduction a semisimple group of rank 1 is left in the numerator with a maximal solvable Lie subgroup in the denominator. This means that all V_p in the complex case are essentially complex projective lines.

In the real case, after factoring out the radical of the numerator, the numerator and the denominator may still contain a nontrivial common direct factor, part of the isomorphic image of the C-restriction of the group infinitesimally generated by the $\boldsymbol{e}_{\pm\rho_1}, \ldots, \boldsymbol{e}_{\pm\rho_k}$. This common factor is factored out also. Since V_p is connected, all that finally matters is the 1-component of the numerator, denoted by $G^*_{C,j}$. It is indicated in all particular cases. It is, of course, of real rank 1. V_p is a homogeneous space of $G^*_{C,j}$ with respect to a maximal solvable Lie subgroup.

75.3 The real groups of real rank 1 occurring in this connection and the related manifolds are (cf. also 75.19):

$A_{1,**}$: complex projective line (or quadric in real projective 3-space).
$A_{3,0,*}$: quaternion-projective line (or quadric in real projective 5-space)
$A_{1,1}$: real projective line.
$A_{k,1}$: hermitean quadric in complex projective k-space.
$B_{k,1}$: quadric in real projective $2k$-space.
$C_{k,1}$: hermitean quadric in quaternion-projective $(k-1)$-space.
$D_{k,0,*}$: quadric in real projective $(2k-1)$-space.
$F_{4,1}$: octavian projective line.

(The last statement will not be explained.)
All quadrics are of the type $++\cdots+-$.

75.4 Note that because of the choice of a real order the basis of the (−1)-eigenspace of CC_{un} will be a bit different from that in 60.23. The deviations are:

$A_{l,j}$, $l'=j\leqslant\frac{1}{2}(l+1)$: $\omega_i-\omega_{l+2-i}\,(i=1,\ldots,l')$,

$A_{l,0,*}$, l odd, $l'=\frac{1}{2}(l-1)$: $\omega_{2i-1}+\omega_{2i}\,(i=1,\ldots,l')$,

$B_{l,j}$, $l'=2(j-1)$ for $1<j\leqslant\frac{1}{2}(l+1)$
$=2l-2j+3$ for $j>\frac{1}{2}(l+1)$
$=1$ for $j=1$:
$\omega_i\,(i=1,\ldots,l')$.

$C_{l,j}$, $l'=j\leqslant\frac{1}{2}l$: $\omega_{2i-1}+\omega_{2i}\,(i=1,\ldots,l')$.

$D_{l,j}$, $3\leqslant j\leqslant\frac{1}{2}l+2$, $l'=2j-4$ and

$D_{l,j,*}$, $j=0$, $l'=1$ and $3\leqslant j\leqslant\frac{1}{2}l+2$, $l'=2j-3$:
$\omega_i(i=1,\ldots,l')$.

$D_{l,1}$, $l'=[\frac{1}{2}l]$: $\omega_{2i-1}+\omega_{2i}\,(i=1,\ldots,l')$; however, for l even, $\omega_{l-1}-\omega_l$ instead of $\omega_{l-1}+\omega_l$.

$E_{6,1}$:
```
  2      0
12321  11111
```

$E_{6,0,*}$:
```
  1      1
01222  22210
```

(which are not rootforms).

$F_{4,1}$: $12\Rightarrow 32$.

By use of the kaleidoscope group it is easy to derive from 60.23 that C^* can be assumed to act as above (of course, since C^* is involutory and orthogonal on $\boldsymbol{H}^*_{\text{he}}$, it is now uniquely determined). In 75.5–18 it will be seen that the established order is indeed real with respect to C^*, though the old enumeration of W^{++} is used.

75.5 $\mathsf{A}_{l,j}$, $l' = j \leqslant \frac{1}{2}(l+1)$.

C^* maps:

$$\omega_i \to -\omega_{l+2-i} \quad \text{for} \quad i = 1, \ldots, l'; \quad l+2-l', \ldots, l+1,$$
$$\omega_i \to -\omega_i \quad \text{for} \quad i = l'+1, \ldots, l+1-l';$$

or:

$$\rho_i \to \rho_{l+1-i} \quad \text{for} \quad i = 1, \ldots, l'-1; \quad l+2-l', \ldots, l,$$
$$\rho_{l'} \to \rho_{l'+1} + \rho_{l'+2} + \cdots + \rho_{l+1-l'},$$
$$\rho_i \to -\rho_i \quad \text{for} \quad i = l'+1, \ldots, l-l',$$
$$\rho_{l+1-l'} \to \rho_{l'} + \rho_{l'+1} + \cdots + \rho_{l-l'}.$$

C-graph:

$$\frac{\rho_1}{\rho_l} \text{—} \frac{\rho_2}{\rho_{l-1}} \text{—} \cdots \text{—} \frac{\rho_{l'-1}}{\rho_{l+2-l'}} \Rightarrow \frac{\rho_{l'}}{\rho_{l'+1} + \cdots + \rho_{l+1-l'}}.$$

$$\mathsf{A}_{1**} \text{—} \mathsf{A}_{1**} \text{—} \cdots \text{—} \mathsf{A}_{1**} \Rightarrow \mathsf{A}_{l+2-2l',1}.$$

C-edges:

$$\pi_i + \pi_{l+1-i} \quad \text{for} \quad i = 1, \ldots, l'.$$

75.6 $\mathsf{A}_{2m-1,0,*}$, $l' = m$.

C^* maps:

$$\omega_{2i-1} \leftrightarrow \omega_{2i} \quad \text{for} \quad i = 1, \ldots, l'+1,$$

or:

$$\rho_{2i-1} \to -\rho_{2i-1} \quad \text{for} \quad i = 1, \ldots, l'+1,$$
$$\rho_{2i} \to \rho_{2i-1} + \rho_{2i} + \rho_{2i+1} \quad \text{for} \quad i = 1, \ldots, l'.$$

C-graph:

$$\frac{\rho_2}{\rho_1 + \rho_2 + \rho_3} \text{—} \frac{\rho_4}{\rho_3 + \rho_4 + \rho_5} \text{—} \cdots \text{—} \frac{\rho_{2l'}}{\rho_{2l'-1} + \rho_{2l'} + \rho_{2l'+1}}.$$

$$\mathsf{A}_{3,0,*} \text{—} \mathsf{A}_{3,0,*} \text{—} \cdots \text{—} \mathsf{A}_{3,0,*}.$$

C-edges:

$$2\pi_{2i} \quad \text{for} \quad i = 1, \ldots, l'.$$

75.7 $\mathsf{B}_{l,j}$, $l' = 1$ for $j = 1$, $l' = 2j - 2$ for $1 < j < \frac{1}{2}l + 1$, $l' = 2l - 2j + 3$ for $j > \frac{1}{2}l + 1$.

C^* maps:

$$\omega_i \to \omega_i \quad \text{for} \quad i = 1, \ldots, l',$$
$$\omega_i \to -\omega_i \quad \text{for} \quad i = l' + 1, \ldots, l;$$

or:

$$\rho_i \to \rho_i \quad \text{for} \quad i = 2, 3, \ldots, l',$$
$$\rho_{l'+1} \to \rho_{l'+1} + 2\rho_{l'+2} + \cdots + 2\rho_l + 2\rho_1,$$
$$\rho_i \to -\rho_i \quad \text{for} \quad i = l' + 2, \ldots, l, 1.$$

C-graph:

$$\rho_2 - \rho_3 - \cdots - \rho_{l'} \Rightarrow \begin{matrix} \rho_{l'+1} \\ \rho_{l'+1} + 2\rho_{l'+2} + \cdots + 2\rho_l + 2\rho_1. \end{matrix}$$

$$\mathsf{A}_{1,1} - \mathsf{A}_{1,1} - \cdots - \mathsf{A}_{1,1} \Rightarrow \mathsf{B}_{l-l'+1,1}.$$

C-edges:

$$2\pi_i \quad \text{for} \quad i = 2, \ldots, l' + 1.$$

75.8 $\mathsf{C}_{l,j}$, $l' = j \leqslant \frac{1}{2}l$.

C^* maps:

$$\rho_{2i-1} \to -\rho_{2i-1} \quad \text{for} \quad i = 1, \ldots, l',$$
$$\rho_{2i} \to \rho_{2i-1} + \rho_{2i} + \rho_{2i+1} \quad \text{for} \quad i = 1, \ldots, l' - 1,$$
$$\rho_{2l'} \to \rho_{2l'-1} + \rho_{2l'} + 2\rho_{2l'+1} + \cdots + 2\rho_{l-1} + \rho_l \quad \text{for} \quad 2l' < l,$$
$$2\rho_{l-1} + \rho_l \quad \text{for} \quad 2l' = l;$$

or:

$$\omega_{2i-1} \leftrightarrow \omega_{2i} \quad \text{for} \quad i = 1, \ldots, l',$$
$$\omega_i \to -\omega_i \quad \text{for} \quad i = 2l' + 1, \ldots, l.$$

C-graph:

$$\begin{matrix} \rho_2 \\ \rho_1 + \rho_2 + \rho_3 \end{matrix} - \begin{matrix} \rho_4 \\ \rho_3 + \rho_4 + \rho_5 \end{matrix} - \cdots - \begin{matrix} \rho_{2l'-2} \\ \rho_{2l'-3} + \rho_{2l'-2} + \rho_{2l'-1} \end{matrix} \Rightarrow$$

$$\Rightarrow \begin{matrix} \rho_{2l'} \\ \rho_{2l'-1} + \rho_{2l'} + 2\rho_{2l'+1} + \cdots + \rho_l, \end{matrix}$$

for $2l' = l$:

$$\begin{matrix} \rho_2 & & \rho_4 & & & & \rho_{l-2} & & \rho_l \\ \rho_1+\rho_2+\rho_3 & \text{—} & \rho_3+\rho_4+\rho_5 & \text{—} & \cdots & \text{—} & \rho_{l-3}+\rho_{l-2}+\rho_{l-1} & \Leftarrow & 2\rho_{l-1}+\rho_l \end{matrix}$$

$$\mathsf{A}_{3,0,*}\text{—}\mathsf{A}_{3,0,*}\text{—}\cdots\text{—}\mathsf{A}_{3,0,*} \Rightarrow \mathsf{C}_{l-2l'+2,1},$$

for $2l' = l$:

$$\mathsf{A}_{3,0,*}\text{—}\mathsf{A}_{3,0,*}\text{—}\cdots\text{—}\mathsf{A}_{3,0,*} \Leftarrow \mathsf{C}_{2,1}.$$

C-edges:

$$2\pi_{2i} \quad \text{for} \quad i = 1, \ldots, l'.$$

75.9 $\mathsf{D}_{l,j}$, $3 \leqslant j < \frac{1}{2}l + 2$, $l' = 2j - 4$, and

$\mathsf{D}_{l,0,*}$, $l' = 1$, and

$\mathsf{D}_{l,j,*}$, $3 \leqslant j \leqslant \frac{1}{2}l + 1$, $l' = 2j - 3$.

C^* maps:

$$\omega_i \to \omega_i \quad \text{for} \quad i = 1, \ldots, l',$$

$$\omega_i \to -\omega_i \quad \text{for} \quad i = l'+1, \ldots, l;$$

or:

$$\rho_i \to \rho_i \quad \text{for} \quad i = 3, \ldots, l'+1,$$

$$\rho_{l'+2} \to \rho_{l'+2} + 2\rho_{l'+3} + \cdots + 2\rho_l + \rho_1 + \rho_2,$$

$$\rho_i \to -\rho_i \quad \text{for} \quad i = l'+3, \ldots, l, 1, 2,$$

for $l' = l - 1$, however,

$$\rho_1 \leftrightarrow \rho_2.$$

C-graph:

$$\rho_3\text{—}\rho_4\text{—}\cdots\text{—}\rho_{l'+1} \Rightarrow \begin{matrix}\rho_{l'+2} \\ \rho_{l'+2} + 2\rho_{l'+3} + \cdots + 2\rho_l + \rho_1 + \rho_2\end{matrix}.$$

For $l' = l - 1$:

$$\rho_3\text{—}\rho_4\text{—}\cdots\text{—}\rho_l \Rightarrow \begin{matrix}\rho_1 \\ \rho_2\end{matrix}.$$

$$\mathsf{A}_{1,1}\text{—}\mathsf{A}_{1,1}\text{—}\cdots\text{—}\mathsf{A}_{1,1} \Rightarrow \mathsf{D}_{l-l'+1,0,*},$$

where $\mathsf{D}_{3,0,*}$, $\mathsf{D}_{2,0,*}$ are understood as $\mathsf{A}_{3,0,*}$, $\mathsf{A}_{1,**}$.

C-edges:

$$2\pi_{i+2} \quad \text{for} \quad i = 1, \ldots, l' \quad , \quad \text{with} \quad \pi_1 + \pi_2 \quad \text{for} \quad l' = l - 1$$

75.10 $D_{l,1}$, l odd, $l' = \frac{1}{2}(l-1)$.

C^* maps:

$$\omega_{2i-1} \to \omega_{2i} \qquad \text{for} \quad i = 1, \ldots, l',$$
$$\omega_l \to -\omega_l;$$

or:

$$\rho_{2i+1} \to -\rho_{2i+1} \qquad \text{for} \quad i = 1, \ldots, l',$$
$$\rho_{2i} \to \rho_{2i-1} + \rho_{2i} + \rho_{2i+1} \qquad \text{for} \quad i = 2, \ldots, l',$$
$$\rho_1 \to \rho_2 + \rho_l,$$
$$\rho_2 \to \rho_1 + \rho_l.$$

C-graph:

$$\frac{\rho_4}{\rho_3+\rho_4+\rho_5} - \frac{\rho_6}{\rho_5+\rho_6+\rho_7} - \cdots - \frac{\rho_{l-1}}{\rho_{l-2}+\rho_{l-1}+\rho_l} \Rightarrow \frac{\rho_1}{\rho_2+\rho_l}.$$

$$A_{3,0,*} - A_{3,0,*} - \cdots - A_{3,0,*} \Rightarrow A_{3,1}$$

C-edges:

$$2\pi_{2i} \quad (i = 2, \ldots, l'), \quad \pi_1 + \pi_2.$$

75.11 $D_{l,1}$, l even, $l' = \frac{1}{2}l$.

C^* maps:

$$\omega_{2i-1} \leftrightarrow \omega_{2i} \qquad \text{for} \quad i = 1, \ldots, l'-1,$$
$$\omega_{l-1} \to -\omega_l;$$

or:

$$\rho_{2i+1} \to -\rho_{2i+1} \qquad \text{for} \quad i = 1, \ldots, l'-1,$$
$$\rho_{2i} \to \rho_{2i-1} + \rho_{2i} + \rho_{2i+1} \qquad \text{for} \quad i = 2, \ldots, l'-1,$$
$$\rho_l \to \rho_{l-1} + \rho_l + \rho_2,$$
$$\rho_1 \to \rho_1,$$
$$\rho_2 \to -\rho_2.$$

C-graph:

$$\frac{\rho_4}{\rho_3+\rho_4+\rho_5} - \frac{\rho_6}{\rho_5+\rho_6+\rho_7} - \cdots - \frac{\rho_l}{\rho_{l-1}+\rho_l+\rho_2} \Leftarrow \rho_1.$$

$$A_{3,0,*} - A_{3,0,*} - \cdots - A_{3,0,*} \Leftarrow A_{1,1}.$$

C-edges:

$$2\pi_{2i} \qquad \text{for} \quad i = 2, \ldots, l', \text{ and } \quad 2\pi_1.$$

75.12 $\mathsf{E}_{6,1}$, $l' = 2$.

C^* maps:

$$\rho_2 \to \rho_2 + 2\rho_6 + \rho_4 + \rho_5,$$

$$\rho_1 \to \rho_3 + \rho_4 + \rho_5 + \rho_6,$$

$$\rho_3 \to \rho_1 + \rho_4 + \rho_5 + \rho_6,$$

$$\rho_4 \to -\rho_4, \qquad \rho_5 \to -\rho_5, \qquad \rho_6 \to -\rho_6.$$

C-graph:

$$\frac{\rho_1}{\rho_3 + \rho_4 + \rho_5 + \rho_6} \Leftarrow \frac{\rho_2}{\rho_2 + \rho_4 + \rho_5 + 2\rho_6}.$$

$$\mathsf{A}_{5,1} \Leftarrow \mathsf{D}_{4,0,*}.$$

C-edges:

$$2\pi_2, \quad \pi_1 + \pi_3.$$

75.13 $\mathsf{E}_{6,2}$, $l' = 4$.

C^* maps:

$$\rho_1 \leftrightarrow \rho_3,$$

$$\rho_2 \leftrightarrow \rho_2,$$

$$\rho_4 \leftrightarrow \rho_5,$$

$$\rho_6 \leftrightarrow \rho_6.$$

C-graph:

$$\frac{\rho_1}{\rho_3} \!-\! \frac{\rho_4}{\rho_5} \Leftarrow \rho_6 - \rho_2.$$

$$\mathsf{A}_{1,**} - \mathsf{A}_{1,**} \Leftarrow \mathsf{A}_{1,1} - \mathsf{A}_{1,1}.$$

C-edges:

$$\pi_1 + \pi_3, \quad 2\pi_2, \quad \pi_4 + \pi_5, \quad 2\pi_6.$$

75.14 $\mathsf{E}_{6,0,*}$, $l' = 2$.

C^* maps:

$$\rho_1 \to \rho_1 + 2\rho_4 + 2\rho_6 + \rho_2 + \rho_5,$$

$$\rho_3 \to \rho_3 + 2\rho_5 + 2\rho_6 + \rho_2 + \rho_4,$$

$$\rho_2 \to -\rho_2, \qquad \rho_4 \to -\rho_4, \qquad \rho_5 \to -\rho_5, \qquad \rho_6 \to -\rho_6.$$

C-graph:

$$\overset{\rho_1}{\rho_1 + 2\rho_4 + 2\rho_6 + \rho_2 + \rho_5} \text{—} \overset{\rho_3}{\rho_3 + 2\rho_5 + 2\rho_6 + \rho_2 + \rho_4}.$$

$$\mathsf{D}_{5,0,*} \text{—} \mathsf{D}_{5,0,*}.$$

C-edges:

$$2\pi_1, \quad 2\pi_3.$$

75.15 $\mathsf{E}_{7,1}$, $l' = 4$.

C^* maps:

$$\rho_1 \to \rho_1,$$
$$\rho_5 \to \rho_5,$$
$$\rho_7 \to \rho_7 + \rho_3 + \rho_6,$$
$$\rho_4 \to \rho_4 + \rho_6 + \rho_2,$$
$$\rho_2 \to -\rho_2, \qquad \rho_3 \to -\rho_3, \qquad \rho_6 \to -\rho_6.$$

C-graph:

$$\overset{\rho_4}{\rho_4 + \rho_6 + \rho_2} \text{—} \overset{\rho_7}{\rho_7 + \rho_3 + \rho_6} \Leftarrow \rho_5 \text{—} \rho_1.$$

$$\mathsf{A}_{3,0,*} \text{—} \mathsf{A}_{3,0,*} \Leftarrow \mathsf{A}_{1,1} \text{—} \mathsf{A}_{1,1}.$$

C-edges:

$$2\pi_4, \quad 2\pi_7, \quad 2\pi_5, \quad 2\pi_1.$$

75.16 $\mathsf{E}_{7,2}$, $l' = 3$.

C^* maps:

$$\rho_2 \to \rho_2,$$
$$\rho_4 \to \rho_4 + 2\rho_6 + 2\rho_7 + \rho_3 + \rho_5,$$
$$\rho_1 \to \rho_1 + 2\rho_5 + 2\rho_7 + \rho_3 + \rho_6,$$
$$\rho_3 \to -\rho_3, \qquad \rho_5 \to -\rho_5, \qquad \rho_6 \to -\rho_6 \qquad \rho_7 \to -\rho_7.$$

C-graph:

$$\rho_2 \Rightarrow \overset{\rho_4}{\rho_4 + 2\rho_6 + 2\rho_7 + \rho_3 + \rho_5} \text{—} \overset{\rho_1}{\rho_1 + 2\rho_5 + 2\rho_7 + \rho_3 + \rho_6}.$$

$$\mathsf{A}_{1,1} \Rightarrow \mathsf{D}_{5,0,*} \text{—} \mathsf{D}_{5,0,*}.$$

C-edges:

$$2\pi_2, \quad 2\pi_4, \quad 2\pi_1.$$

75.17 $\mathsf{E}_{8,1}$, $l' = 4$.

C^* maps:

$$\rho_1 \to \rho_1,$$

$$\rho_3 \to \rho_3,$$

$$\rho_5 \to \rho_5 + 2\rho_7 + 2\rho_8 + \rho_4 + \rho_6,$$

$$\rho_2 \to \rho_2 + 2\rho_6 + 2\rho_8 + \rho_7 + \rho_4,$$

$$\rho_4 \to -\rho_4, \quad \rho_6 \to -\rho_6, \quad \rho_7 \to -\rho_7, \quad \rho_8 \to -\rho_8.$$

C-graph:

$$\frac{\rho_2}{\rho_2 + 2\rho_6 + 2\rho_8 + \rho_7 + \rho_4} - \frac{\rho_5}{\rho_5 + 2\rho_7 + 2\rho_8 + \rho_4 + \rho_6} \Leftarrow \rho_3 - \rho_1.$$

$$\mathsf{D}_{5,0,*} - \mathsf{D}_{5,0,*} \Leftarrow \mathsf{A}_{1,1} - \mathsf{A}_{1,1}.$$

C-edges:

$$2\pi_1, \quad 2\pi_3, \quad 2\pi_5, \quad 2\pi_2.$$

75.18 $\mathsf{F}_{4,1}$, $l' = 1$.

$$\rho_1 \to \rho_1 + 3\rho_3 + 2\rho_4 + \rho_2,$$

$$\rho_2 \to -\rho_2, \quad \rho_3 \to -\rho_3, \quad \rho_4 \to -\rho_4.$$

C-graph:

$$\frac{\rho_1}{\rho_1 + \rho_2 + 3\rho_3 + 2\rho_4}.$$

$$\mathsf{F}_{4,1}.$$

C-edge:

$$2\pi_1.$$

75.19. The Geometric Interpretation of the incidence geometries of $G \in \mathsf{A}_l, \mathsf{B}_l, \mathsf{C}_l, \mathsf{D}_l$, as dealt with in 70.1–3, can be extended to the real case. Again the lowest dimensional linear representations of these groups are used. Compare the discussion with that in 59.7, but note that there the trunk was taken maximally compact.

$G_C \in \mathsf{B}_{l,j}$, $\quad \mathsf{D}_{l,j}$ $(j > 2)$, $\quad \mathsf{D}_{l,j,*}$:

The representation with weights $\pm\omega_i$ and possibly 0 is used. The corresponding weight vectors $x_{\pm i}$ and possibly x_0 are orthonormal in the unitary inner product. $C^*\omega_i = \omega_i$, $DD_{\text{un}}x_i$ is a multiple of x_{-i}, Dx_i a multiple $\gamma_i x_i$ of x_i, for $i = 1, \ldots, l'$. Since x_i may be replaced by $\beta_i x_i$, with $\beta_i^2 = \gamma_i$, one may suppose that $Dx_i = x_i$, $i = 1, \ldots, l'$. Now $\langle x_i, DD_{\mathrm{un}} x_j \rangle = 0$, $i, j = 1, 2, \ldots, l'$, and the x_i are real. Therefore the x_i, $i = 1, \ldots, p$, with $1 \leqslant p \leqslant l'$, span a totally isotropic subspace of R_D with respect to the invariant quadratic form; its stability group is the C-restriction of $G(\rho_p)$. By verifying that its stability group in the full orthogonal group of the quadratic form contains elements in each component (cf. 54.1 and note that $l' < l$ is supposed) and by applying Witt's theorem (cf. 70.2) one sees that its sort consists of the totally isotropic p-dimensional subspaces. In projective terms its sort consists of the projective $(p-1)$-dimensional subspaces on the invariant quadric.

$G_C \in \mathsf{A}_{l,j}$:

The representation with weights ω_i ($\sum \omega_\iota = 0$) is used. The weight vectors are correspondingly mutually orthogonal $x_1, \ldots, x_{l+1}$; $C^* \omega_i = -\omega_{l+2-i}$, $i = 1, \ldots, l'$. Hence by 59.4.1 Kx_i is a multiple of x_{l+2-i} for $i = 1, \ldots, l'$. Therefore the span of $x_1, \ldots, x_p$ is a totally isotropic subspace for the invariant hermitean form, for $p = 1, \ldots, l'$. As in the preceding case, one finds that the sorts are the projective $(p-1)$-dimensional subspaces on the hermitean quadric, for $p = 1, 2, \ldots, l'$.

$G_C \in \mathsf{A}_{l,0,*}$, l odd:

The representation with the weights ω_i ($\sum \omega_i = 0$) is used; corresponding weight vectors are $x_1, \ldots, x_{l+1}$; $C^* \omega_{2i-1} = \omega_{2i}$, so Dx_{2i-1} is a multiple of x_{2i}. Now $G(\rho_{2p})$ is characterized by leaving the subspace spanned by $x_1, \ldots, x_{2p}$ invariant, $p = 1, 2, \ldots, (l-1)/2$. The C-restriction of $G(\rho_{2p})$ consists of the volume-preserving quaternion linear mappings in G that leave the p-dimensional quaternion-linear subspace spanned by $x_1, \ldots, x_{2p}$, with complex scalars, invariant. The sorts consist of the quaternion-projective $(p-1)$-subspaces of the quaternion-projective $(l-1)$-space, for $p = 1, \ldots, (l-1)/2$.

$G_C \in \mathsf{C}_{l,j}$, $\mathsf{D}_{l,1}$:

The representation with weights $\pm\omega_i$ is used; weight vectors are $x_{\pm i}$; $C^* \omega_{2i-1} = \omega_{2i}$ for $i = 1, \ldots, l'$. Therefore the situation is similar to that in $\mathsf{A}_{l,0,*}$. There is now, however, an invariant quaternion-hermitean or -anti-hermitean form; $x_1, \ldots, x_{2p}$ span a p-dimensional totally isotropic subspace The pth sort consists of the totally isotropic p-dimensional quaternion-linear subspaces with respect to the invariant form.

75.20. Historical Note The splendid theory dealt with in Sections 70–75 is due to J. Tits. It was gradually developed between 1955–1962. Almost all results were published without proof. The present reconstruction of the proof was made easier by occasional private communications by Tits. The methods are probably not very different from those intended by him. In the present exposition neither the largest generality nor the greatest economy in suppositions was aimed at.

Tits' geometries are particularly important for the understanding of the exceptional groups, which have been extensively studied in the last 10 to 15 years. This theory, which has not been tackled in this book, will be the subject of a monograph.

Tits' most important results on the subject of Sections 70–75 are found in *Mém. Acad. Bruxelles* in 8°, **29** (1955); *Bull. Soc. Math. Belg.* **8**, 48–81 (1955–1957); *Colloque Algèbre Superieure C.B.R.M.* (1956) *Bruxelles* 261–289, and particularly in *Algebraic and Topological Foundations of Geometry, Colloquium* 1959, 175–192.

76–77

BETTI NUMBERS OF SEMISIMPLE LIE GROUPS AND REGULAR SUBALGEBRAS OF SEMISIMPLE LIE ALGEBRAS

76. AD-NILPOTENTS AND SEMISIMPLE SUBALGEBRAS OF RANK 1

Part of the results will be used in Section 77.

76.1–2 $F \in \mathbf{A}_1$.

76.1 If $\boldsymbol{a} \in \boldsymbol{F}$, $\boldsymbol{a} \neq \mathbf{0}$, then

$$\boldsymbol{a}\text{ ad-nilpotent} \leftrightarrow \psi(\boldsymbol{a}, \boldsymbol{a}) = 0,$$
$$\boldsymbol{a}\text{ ad-pure} \leftrightarrow \boldsymbol{a}\text{ regular} \leftrightarrow \psi(\boldsymbol{a}, \boldsymbol{a}) \neq 0.$$

If $\boldsymbol{a}, \boldsymbol{b} \in \boldsymbol{F}$, $\boldsymbol{a} \neq \mathbf{0}$, $\boldsymbol{b} \neq \mathbf{0}$, then

$$\boldsymbol{a}, \boldsymbol{b}\text{ Int }\boldsymbol{F}\text{-equivalent} \leftrightarrow \psi(\boldsymbol{a}, \boldsymbol{a}) = \psi(\boldsymbol{b}, \boldsymbol{b}).$$

This is most easily proved by assuming that $\boldsymbol{F}$ is the infinitesimal algebra of the special linear group of 2-space and applying 19.19 and 69.1.

76.2 The triple $\ulcorner \boldsymbol{h}, \boldsymbol{e}, \boldsymbol{f} \urcorner$ of elements $\neq \mathbf{0}$ of $\boldsymbol{F}$ is called a hef-*triple* iff

$$[\boldsymbol{h}, \boldsymbol{e}] = \boldsymbol{e}, \qquad [\boldsymbol{h}, \boldsymbol{f}] = -\boldsymbol{f}, \qquad [\boldsymbol{e}, \boldsymbol{f}] = \boldsymbol{h}.$$

$\boldsymbol{h}$ is the first member of some hef-triple of $\boldsymbol{F}$ iff $\psi(\boldsymbol{h}, \boldsymbol{h}) = 2$.

$\boldsymbol{e}$ is the second (or third) member of some hef-triple iff it is ad-nilpotent $\neq \mathbf{0}$.

Given such an $\boldsymbol{h}$, the set of its positive multiples is taken as a positive trunk of $\boldsymbol{F}$. Then the (only) positive rootform is called λ. Thus $\lambda(\boldsymbol{h}) = 1$.

The weights of any linear representation of $\boldsymbol{F}$ with respect to this trunk are integral multiples of $\frac{1}{2}\lambda$. If the representation is irreducible with topweight $\frac{1}{2}p\lambda$, then its weights are the $(\frac{1}{2}p - q)\lambda$, with $0 \leqslant q \leqslant p$ (q integral); all are simple; 0 is a weight iff p is even.

76.3–9 $G \in$ Alg Lie Com SS, $\mathbf{A}_1(G)$ is the set of semisimple subalgebras of G of rank 1; $l = \operatorname{rank} \boldsymbol{G}$.

$\boldsymbol{F} \in \mathbf{A}_1(\boldsymbol{G})$; ϑ is the representation of $\boldsymbol{F}$ in $\boldsymbol{G}$ by adjoint action, which is conducible; ϑ_i are the irreducible components of a direct splitting of ϑ, acting on linear sub-spaces $\boldsymbol{R}_i$ ($i = 1, \ldots, m$); dim $\boldsymbol{R}_i = p_i + 1$.

76.3 A hef-triple $\ulcorner \boldsymbol{h}, \boldsymbol{e}, \boldsymbol{f} \urcorner$ and an ordered trunk of $\boldsymbol{F}$ are chosen as in 76.2. Then $\boldsymbol{e}$ is also a $\boldsymbol{G}$-ad-nilpotent. In particular, $\tilde{\boldsymbol{e}}$ takes a vector of weight $(\frac{1}{2}p_i - q)\lambda$ of $\boldsymbol{R}_i$ into one of weight $(\frac{1}{2}p_i - q + 1)\lambda$, or into $\boldsymbol{0}$ iff $q = 0$. Therefore the top-weight vectors of the ϑ_i span the kernel of $\tilde{\boldsymbol{e}}$. The 0-weight vectors span the kernel of $\tilde{\boldsymbol{h}}$.

Proposition dim kernel $\tilde{\boldsymbol{e}} = m(\boldsymbol{F}) =$ number of the $\boldsymbol{R}_i$.

dim kernel $\tilde{\boldsymbol{h}} =$ number of the $\boldsymbol{R}_i$ with even p_i.

$$m(\boldsymbol{F}) \geqslant l,$$

with the equality sign iff $\boldsymbol{h}$ is $\boldsymbol{G}$-regular and all p_i are even.

The last assertion follows from the fact that dim kernel $\tilde{\boldsymbol{h}} \geqslant l$, with the equality sign iff $\boldsymbol{h}$ is regular.

76.4.1. Definition $\boldsymbol{F}_0 \in \mathbf{A}_1(\boldsymbol{G})$ is called *regular* if the number $m(\boldsymbol{F})$ of $\boldsymbol{R}_i$ reaches its minimum for $\boldsymbol{F} = \boldsymbol{F}_0$. An ad-nilpotent $\boldsymbol{e}$ of $\boldsymbol{G}$ is called a *regular* ad-*nilpotent*, if in the set of ad-nilpotents $\boldsymbol{a} \in \boldsymbol{G}$ dim kernel $\tilde{\boldsymbol{a}}$ reaches its minimum for $\boldsymbol{a} = \boldsymbol{e}$.

Clearly, since every ad-nilpotent is in some $\boldsymbol{F} \in \mathbf{A}_1(\boldsymbol{G})$ (see 68.8.3), the following applies:

Proposition An ad-nilpotent $\boldsymbol{e} \neq \boldsymbol{0}$ of $\boldsymbol{G}$ is contained in some regular $\boldsymbol{F} \in \mathbf{A}_1(\boldsymbol{G})$ iff it is regular.

76.4.2 Let $\boldsymbol{H}$ be an ordered trunk of $\boldsymbol{G}$ and $\boldsymbol{u} \in \boldsymbol{H}$ such that

$$\rho(\boldsymbol{u}) = 1 \qquad \text{for all} \quad \rho \in W^{++}(\boldsymbol{G}).$$

Clearly, $\boldsymbol{u}$ is regular and $\boldsymbol{u} \in \boldsymbol{H}_{\mathrm{st}}$. Putting

$$\boldsymbol{e} = \sum_{\rho \in W^{++}} \boldsymbol{e}_\rho, \qquad \boldsymbol{f} = \sum_{\rho \in W^{++}} \tau_\rho \boldsymbol{e}_{-\rho},$$

one can manage that

$$[\boldsymbol{e}, \boldsymbol{f}] = \sum \tau_\rho \boldsymbol{h}_\rho = \boldsymbol{u},$$

since the nodes $\boldsymbol{h}_\rho$ span $\boldsymbol{H}_{\mathrm{st}}$. Then $\boldsymbol{F}_0$ spanned by $\boldsymbol{u}, \boldsymbol{e}, \boldsymbol{f}$ belongs to $\mathbf{A}_1(\boldsymbol{G})$ and $\ulcorner \boldsymbol{u}, \boldsymbol{e}, \boldsymbol{f} \urcorner$ is a hef-triple of $\boldsymbol{F}_0$.

Furthermore, for any $\alpha \in W^*(\boldsymbol{G})$

$$\alpha(\boldsymbol{u}) = a(\alpha) = \text{altitude of } \alpha$$

(see 54.3.2). Therefore all weights of $\vartheta(\boldsymbol{F}_0)$ are integral multiples of λ and all p_i are even. Hence $m(\boldsymbol{F}_0) = l$, and $\boldsymbol{F}_0$ is regular.

This shows:

Theorem For any F the number of R_i is $\geqslant l$; for the regular ones it equals l. For any ad-nilpotent e, dim kernel $\tilde{e} \geqslant l$, with the equality sign for the regular ones.

76.5 Let $\ulcorner h, e, f \urcorner$ be a hef-triple of F. Then h is ad-pure and therefore contained in a trunk H of G (see 17.6). An ordered dressing is assumed on H such that $\alpha(h) > 0 \to \alpha > 0$ for every $\alpha \in W^*(G)$. The branch e_α (with respect to H) is a weight vector of ϑ belonging to the weight $\alpha|_{H \cap F}$.

Proposition $\rho(h) = 0, \frac{1}{2}, 1$ for $\rho \in W^{++}(G)$.

Proof The $\rho(h)$ are integral multiples of $\frac{1}{2}$. Since $\rho > 0$, they are nonnegative. Suppose that $\rho(h) > 1$ for some $\rho \in W^{++}(G)$. Then e_ρ is for ϑ a vector of weight $p\lambda$ with some $p > 1$. Hence $[f, e_\rho]$ is a vector of weight $(p-1)\lambda > 0$. f can be written as

$$\sum \tau_\alpha e_{-\alpha} \qquad \text{with} \quad \alpha(h) = 1, \text{ hence with } \alpha > 0.$$

$$0 \neq [f, e_\rho] = \sum_{\alpha \in W^+} \tau_\alpha [e_{-\alpha}, e_\rho]$$

shows that for some $\alpha \in W^+$ there is a rootform $\rho - \alpha$ with $(\rho - \alpha)(h) > 0$, hence with $\rho - \alpha > 0$, which contradicts the primitivity of ρ.

This disproves $\rho(h) > 1$ and proves the assertion.

An immediate consequence of the foregoing (see 76.3) is the following proposition:

76.6. Proposition For regular $F \in \mathbf{A}_1(G)$ and $h \in F$, with $\psi_F(h, h) = 2$, with respect to any suitably ordered trunk H of G containing h: $\rho(h) = 1$ for all $\rho \in W^{++}(G)$.

All $h \in F$ of all regular $F \in \mathbf{A}_1(G)$ with $\psi_F(h, h) = 2$ are Int G-equivalent.

76.7. Proposition If $\ulcorner h, e, f \urcorner$, $\ulcorner h, e, f' \urcorner$ are hef-triples of F, respectively, $F' \in \mathbf{A}_1(G)$, then $f = f'$.

Proof If $\neq 0$, $f - f'$ would be a weight vector of ϑ of weight $-\lambda$, belonging to the kernel of $\tilde{e}$, which, according to 76.3, should be spanned by vectors of positive weight. This shows $f - f' = 0$.

76.8. Theorem $F, F' \in \mathbf{A}(G)$ are Int G-equivalent

iff the ad-nilpotents $\neq 0$ of the one and the other are Int G-equivalent,

iff $h \in F$, $h' \in F'$, with $\psi_F(h, h) = \psi_{F'}(h', h') = 2$, are Int G-equivalent.

In both cases the "only if" statement is trivial. The first and second "if" statements are proved in 76.8.1 and 76.8.2.

76.8.1 $\boldsymbol{F}, \boldsymbol{F}'$ may be supposed to have an ad-nilpotent $\boldsymbol{e} \neq \boldsymbol{0}$ in common. hef-triples $\ulcorner \boldsymbol{h}, \boldsymbol{e}, \boldsymbol{f} \urcorner$, $\ulcorner \boldsymbol{h}', \boldsymbol{e}, \boldsymbol{f}' \urcorner$ of $\boldsymbol{F}$ and $\boldsymbol{F}'$ may be assumed. Clearly,

$$\boldsymbol{n} = \boldsymbol{h}' - \boldsymbol{h} \in \text{kernel } \tilde{\boldsymbol{e}}, \qquad \boldsymbol{n} = [\boldsymbol{e}, \boldsymbol{f}' - \boldsymbol{f}] \in \tilde{\boldsymbol{e}}\boldsymbol{G}.$$

With respect to the splitting $\boldsymbol{G} = \sum \boldsymbol{R}_i$ under ϑ (associated with $\boldsymbol{F}$),

$$\boldsymbol{n} = \sum \boldsymbol{n}_j, \qquad \text{with } \boldsymbol{n}_j \text{ top-weight vector in } \boldsymbol{R}_j, \text{ or} = \boldsymbol{0}.$$

If $p_j = 0$, then $\boldsymbol{n}_j = \boldsymbol{0}$, since $\boldsymbol{n} \in \tilde{\boldsymbol{e}}\boldsymbol{G}$. Put

$$\boldsymbol{n}' = -2 \sum p_j^{-1} \boldsymbol{n}_j.$$

Then

$$(\exp \tilde{\boldsymbol{n}}')\, \boldsymbol{h} = \boldsymbol{h} + \boldsymbol{n} = \boldsymbol{h}',$$

$$(\exp \tilde{\boldsymbol{n}}')\, \boldsymbol{e} = \boldsymbol{e}.$$

Thus by 76.7

$$(\exp \tilde{\boldsymbol{n}}') \boldsymbol{f} = \boldsymbol{f}',$$

which proves the assertion.

76.8.2 One may suppose $\boldsymbol{h} = \boldsymbol{h}'$ and $\ulcorner \boldsymbol{h}, \boldsymbol{e}, \boldsymbol{f} \urcorner$, $\ulcorner \boldsymbol{h}, \boldsymbol{e}', \boldsymbol{f}' \urcorner$ hef-triples of $\boldsymbol{F}$ and $\boldsymbol{F}'$. Let $\boldsymbol{G}_0, \boldsymbol{G}_1$ be the 0-, respectively, 1-eigenspace of $\tilde{\boldsymbol{h}}$. Then

$$\tilde{\boldsymbol{e}}\boldsymbol{G}_0 = \tilde{\boldsymbol{e}}'\boldsymbol{G}_0 = \boldsymbol{G}_1.$$

In general,

$$\tilde{\boldsymbol{a}}\boldsymbol{G}_0 \subset \boldsymbol{G}_1 \qquad \text{for all} \quad \boldsymbol{a} \in \boldsymbol{G}_1.$$

The $\boldsymbol{a} \in \boldsymbol{G}_1$, with rank $\tilde{\boldsymbol{a}}|_{\boldsymbol{G}_0} < \dim \boldsymbol{G}_1$, form a true algebraic subvariety of $\boldsymbol{G}_1$. Consequently the set $\hat{\boldsymbol{G}}_1$ of

$$\boldsymbol{a} \in \boldsymbol{G}_1 \qquad \text{with} \quad \tilde{\boldsymbol{a}}\boldsymbol{G}_0 = \boldsymbol{G}_1$$

is open and connected. Take $\boldsymbol{a} \in \hat{\boldsymbol{G}}_1$. Then

$$\text{grad}_{\mathbf{0}} \curlyvee_{\boldsymbol{g} \in \boldsymbol{G}_0} (\exp \tilde{\boldsymbol{g}})\, \boldsymbol{a} = -\tilde{\boldsymbol{a}}|_{\boldsymbol{G}_0}$$

maps $\boldsymbol{G}_0$ onto $\boldsymbol{G}_1$. Therefore $\boldsymbol{a}$ is an interior point in $\boldsymbol{G}_1$ of $(\exp \tilde{\boldsymbol{G}}_0)\boldsymbol{a}$ (note also that $\exp \tilde{\boldsymbol{G}}_0$ fixes $\boldsymbol{h}$ and leaves $\boldsymbol{G}_1$ and $\hat{\boldsymbol{G}}_1$ invariant). Consequently $(\exp \tilde{\boldsymbol{G}}_0)\boldsymbol{a}$, contained in $\hat{\boldsymbol{G}}_1$, is open in $\boldsymbol{G}_1$ and because of the connectedness of $\hat{\boldsymbol{G}}_1$ equals $\hat{\boldsymbol{G}}_1$, of which $\boldsymbol{e}, \boldsymbol{e}'$ are members. Together with 76.7 this proves the assertion.

76.9. Theorem Two regular members of $\mathbf{A}_1(\boldsymbol{G})$ are Int $\boldsymbol{G}$-equivalent. Two regular ad-nilpotents of $\boldsymbol{G}$ are Int $\boldsymbol{G}$-equivalent.

The first statement follows from the second statement of 76.6 and the second of 76.8, though it could easily have been proved in a more direct way. By 76.4.1 the second statement is a consequence of the first.

76.10. Historical Note The results of this section belong to B. Kostant [*Amer. J. Math.* **81**, 973–1032 (1959)], though the present proofs are much simpler than his.

77. KILLING–COXETER TOOLS, BETTI NUMBERS

77.1. Introduction In the sequel cohomology is taken over the field of real numbers.

Let G be a compact C^∞-manifold. Its *cohomology algebra* is denoted by $\mathscr{R}(G)$. As a linear space it is the direct sum of the cohomology groups $\mathscr{R}^i$ belonging to the dimension i. It is graded according to the $\mathscr{R}^i$. To any graded linear space $\mathscr{R} = \sum_{i=0}^{\infty} \mathscr{R}^i$ belongs a so-called *Poincaré series*

$$P(t) = \sum (\dim \mathscr{R}^i)\, t^i,$$

a formal power series in the indeterminate t. The coefficient of t^i in the Poincaré series of the cohomology algebra of G (or, for short, of G) is the ith *Betti number* of G.

The degree-graded *algebra of exterior differential forms* on G, denoted by $\mathscr{D}(G)$, also gives rise to a cohomology algebra, denoted by $\mathscr{R}(\mathscr{D}(G))$ as soon as the exterior derivation is interpreted as coboundary operator.

77.1.1. Theorem $\mathscr{R}(G)$ and $\mathscr{R}(\mathscr{D}(G))$ are graded-isomorphic in a canonical way.

This fact was the background of Poincaré's introduction of homology notions and Betti numbers, though no proof was available until G. de Rham's [*J. Math. Pures Appl.* (9) **10**, 115–200 (1931)]. See also J. Leray [*J. Math. Pures Appl.* (9) **24**, 95–248 (1945)].

Now let G be a compact C^∞-group. Then:

77.1.2. Theorem Every cohomology class of $\mathscr{D}(G)$ contains one and only one left and right invariant element.

This is easily proved by invariant-measure-integration over G, as was done by E. Cartan [*Ann. Soc. Polonaise Math.* **8**, 181–225 (1929) = *Œuvres* I_2, 1081–1125]. See also C. Chevalley and S. Eilenberg [*Trans. Amer. Math. Soc.* **63**, 85–124 (1948)].

Let $\mathscr{A}(\mathbf{G})$ be the degree-graded exterior algebra over the real numbers in the tangent space $\mathbf{G}$ of G at 1. Clearly the restriction mapping of $\mathscr{D}(G)$ onto $\mathscr{A}(\mathbf{G})$ maps the algebra of left and right invariants of $\mathscr{D}(G)$ graded-isomorphically onto the algebra of ad-invariants in $\mathscr{A}(\mathbf{G})$, denoted by $\mathscr{A}_{\mathrm{Int}}(\mathbf{G})$.

77.1.3. Theorem $\mathscr{R}(G)$ is canonically graded-isomorphic to the algebra of exterior ad-invariants $\mathscr{A}_{\mathrm{Int}}(\mathbf{G})$.

A classical method in finite groups was adopted by E. Cartan (*loc. cit.*) to obtain an integral expression for the Poincaré series of G:

77.1.4. Theorem With an invariant measure μ such that the total measure of G is 1,

$$P(t) = \int_G \det(1 + t\tilde{a})\, d\mu(a).$$

Proof Let $\mathbf{G}^{[i]}$ be the i-fold skew tensor product of the linear space $\mathbf{G}$ with itself. The action of $a \in G$ on $\mathbf{G}^{[i]}$ according to $\tilde{a}$ is called $\mathrm{ad}^{[i]}(a)$. If the $\alpha_j(a)$ are the eigenvalues of $\tilde{a}$ with due frequencies, then those of $\mathrm{ad}^{[i]}(a)$ are the

$$\alpha_{\nu_1}(a) \cdots \alpha_{\nu_i}(a) \qquad \text{with} \quad \nu_1 < \cdots < \nu_i.$$

The character of $\mathrm{ad}^{[i]}$ takes at a the value

$$(*) \qquad \mathrm{tr}(\mathrm{ad}^{[i]}(a)) = \sum_{\nu_1 < \cdots < \nu_i} \alpha_{\nu_1}(a) \cdots \alpha_{\nu_i}(a).$$

The homogeneous exterior invariants of $\tilde{G}$ of degree i are the $\mathrm{ad}^{[i]}G$-invariant vectors. The restriction of $\mathrm{ad}^{[i]}G$ to the linear subspace spanned by such a vector has a constant character 1. The coefficient of t^i in $P(t)$ equals the multiplicity of this character within the character of $\mathrm{ad}^{[i]}$. By the orthonormality relation for characters (37.1) it is

$$\int_G \mathrm{tr}(\mathrm{ad}^{[i]}(a))\, d\mu(a).$$

Therefore,

$$P(t) = \int_G \sum_i \mathrm{tr}\ \mathrm{ad}^{[i]}(a)\, t^i\, d\mu(a).$$

Together with (*) this leads to the formula stated in the theorem.

Unfortunately, no direct evaluation of this formula is known.

The cohomology algebra of the compact groups in A_l, B_l, C_l, D_l had been computed by R. Brauer, who used the algebra of exterior invariants [*Compt. Rend. Acad. Sci. Paris* **201**, 419–421 (1935)], and by L. Pontrjagin [*Compt. Rend. Acad. Sci. Paris* **200**, 1277–1280 (1935)], and C. Ehresmann [*Compt. Rend. Acad. Sci. Paris* **208**, 321–323, 1263–1265 (1939)] with topological means, when H. Hopf [*Ann. Math.* (2) **42**, 22–52 (1941)], with topological methods, proved the following general theorem:

77.1.5. Theorem $\mathscr{R}(G)$ is graded-isomorphic with the cohomology algebra of a cartesian product of odd-dimensional spheres, that is, an exterior algebra generated by odd-dimensional homogeneous elements. Hence its Poincaré series is a product of factors

$$1 + t^{2k_i+1},$$

with nonnegative integral k_i.

The k_i are arranged in a weakly increasing sequence denoted by k.

The number of factors equals the rank of G if G is semisimple (plus the dimension of the abelian factor in the general case).

Hopf's result has been complemented by H. Samelson [*Ann. Math.* (2) **42**, 1091–1137 (1941)]. Its proof has been refashioned by J. Leray (*loc. cit.*) and translated into the language of exterior algebras over Lie algebras by J.-L. Koszul [*Bull. Soc. Math. France* **78**, 65–127 (1950)].

Yen Chi-Tah [*Compt. Rend. Acad. Sci. Paris* **228**, 628–630 (1949)] determined the sequence k for some exceptional groups by incidental methods before C. Chevalley [*Proc. Int. Congr. Math. Cambridge, Mass.*, 1950, II, 21–24 (1952)] obtained the full result by a more general approach. Chevalley linked the algebra $\mathscr{A}_{\mathrm{Int}}(\boldsymbol{G})$ of exterior invariants on $\boldsymbol{G}$ to the degree-graded algebra of (symmetric) polynomial invariants on $\boldsymbol{G}$, denoted by $\mathscr{P}_{\mathrm{Int}}(\boldsymbol{G})$.

77.1.6. Theorem For semisimple $\boldsymbol{G}$ there is a linear mapping σ of $\mathscr{P}_{\mathrm{Int}}(\boldsymbol{G})$ onto the linear span of the generators of $\mathscr{A}_{\mathrm{Int}}(\boldsymbol{G})$ such that for $p \in \mathscr{P}_{\mathrm{Int}}(\boldsymbol{G})$

$$\text{degree}\, \sigma p = 2\, \text{degree}\, p - 1$$

and the kernel of σ is spanned by 1 and the products of elements of $\mathscr{P}_{\mathrm{Int}}(\boldsymbol{G})$ with more than one factor of positive degree.

This theorem is quoted by Chevalley as a discovery by A. Weil, whereas H. Cartan [*Colloque de Topologie, Bruxelles* 1950, 15–27, 57–71] speaks of a conjecture by Weil. According to H. Cartan, it has been proved by his own and Chevalley's joint efforts, but as far as is known neither Chevalley nor H. Cartan published more than superficial indications of its proof. There can be no doubt, however, of the truth of this theorem, for it follows indirectly from more profound results obtained by A. Borel by topological means [*Ann. Math.* (2) **57**, 115–207 (1953)].

An immediate consequence of 77.1.5–6 is the following theorem:

77.1.7. Theorem $\mathscr{P}_{\mathrm{Int}}(\boldsymbol{G})$ has an algebraically independent system of homogeneous generators of degree $k_i + 1$. The Poincaré series of $\mathscr{R}(G)$ is

$$\prod(1 + t^{2k_i+1})$$

and that of $\mathscr{P}_{\mathrm{Int}}(\boldsymbol{G})$ is

$$\prod(1 - t^{k_i+1})^{-1}.$$

In the same way as in 77.1.4 one proves the following theorem:

77.1.8. Theorem The Poincaré series of $\mathscr{P}_{\mathrm{Int}}(\boldsymbol{G})$ is

$$\int_G \det(1 - t\tilde{a})^{-1}\, d\mu(a).$$

However, neither the evaluation of this integral nor its connection with that of 77.1.5, as stated in 77.1.7, seems accessible by a direct approach.

Let G again be semisimple and $\mathfrak{r}$ the restriction of an element of $\mathscr{P}_{\mathrm{Int}}(\boldsymbol{G})$ to a trunk $\boldsymbol{H}$ of $\boldsymbol{G}$. The image of $\mathfrak{r}$ consists of Int W^*-invariants. The graded algebra of all Int *W^*-invariant polynomial functions on* $\boldsymbol{H}$ is denoted by $\mathscr{P}_{\mathrm{Int}}(\boldsymbol{H})$.

In Chevalley's analysis (*loc. cit.*) the next step is the following theorem:

77.1.9. Theorem $\mathfrak{r}$ is an isomorphism of $\mathscr{P}_{\mathrm{Int}}(\boldsymbol{G})$ onto $\mathscr{P}_{\mathrm{Int}}(\boldsymbol{H})$.

This theorem will be proved in 77.20 and 77.23.

By this step the determination of the symmetric, and finally of the exterior invariants of $\tilde{G}$ and its cohomology, is reduced to those of a finite group. A classical result of Hilbert states that the algebra of invariant polynomials of a finite group of linear mappings of an l-dimensional linear space has a finite generator system. A proof by C. Chevalley [*Amer. J. Math.* **77**, 778–790 (1955)] shows that in the case of a group generated by reflections (as is Int W^*) the (l) generators can be chosen algebraically independent. (See also H. S. M. Coxeter [*Duke Math. J.* **18**, 765–782 (1951)] and G. C. Shephard and J. A. Todd [*Canad. J. Math.* **6**, 274–304 (1954)]).

The method in 77.1.5 also yields the following:

77.1.10. Theorem The Poincaré series of $\mathscr{P}_{\mathrm{Int}}(\boldsymbol{H})$ is

$$\frac{1}{g} \sum_{S \in \mathrm{Int}\, W^*} \det(1 - tS)^{-1},$$

where g is the cardinality of Int W^*.

Theorems like this go back at least as far as Th. Molien [*Sitzber. Preuss. Akad. Wiss.* 1152–1156 (1898)].

Again, there is no direct way of evaluating this formula or of connecting it to the others.

It seems that Chevalley obtained his result on the sequence k for compact simple semisimple groups (*loc. cit.*) by evaluating the $k_i + 1$ of Theorem 77.1.7 in the particular cases of the classification (see also A. Borel and C. Chevalley [*Mem. Amer. Math. Soc.* **14**, 1–9 (1955)]).

Confronted with Chevalley's $k_i + 1$, H. S. M. Coxeter (*loc. cit.*) discovered a similarity to the eigenvalues of a particular element of Int W^*, henceforth called a *Killing–Coxeter tool.* Indeed, its eigenvalues are the ω^{k_i}, where ω is a primitive nth root of unity and n is the order of the Killing–Coxeter tool.

On the other hand, using Morse theory, R. Bott [*Bull. Soc. Math. France* **84**, 251–281 (1956)] succeeded in linking the cohomology of G to the structure of W^* itself. Then A. Shapiro (unpublished) and R. Steinberg [*Trans. Amer. Math. Soc.* **91**, 493–504 (1959)] discovered empirically another way of reading off the sequence k from the structure of W^*, which will be explained in 77.11 and 77.14. Coxeter's and Shapiro–Steinberg's empirical procedures have been justified theoretically and linked to each other by B. Kostant [*Amer. Math. J.* **81**, 973–1032 (1959)]. Greatly simplified as a whole and in many details, Kostant's theory is the subject of the remainder of this section.

In the sequel:

$\boldsymbol{G} \in$ Alg Lie Lin Com SSS, G is centerfree, $r = \dim \boldsymbol{G}$, and $l = \operatorname{rank} \boldsymbol{G}$.

$\boldsymbol{G}$ is in ordered second dressing with respect to the trunk $\boldsymbol{H}$, $\rho_1, \ldots, \rho_l$ the primitive rootforms in a fixed order, $\pi_1, \ldots, \pi_l$ the corresponding fundamental weights, and q the altitude of the top rootform.

77.2–6. Killing–Coxeter Tools

77.2. Definition $T = S_{\rho_l} \cdots S_{\rho_1} (\in \operatorname{Int} W^*)$ is called a *Killing–Coxeter tool.* Its order is denoted by n. The minimal nonvoid T-invariant subsets of W^* are called the *orbits.*

It will become clear that the inner class of T does not depend on the order on $\boldsymbol{H}$ and on the arrangement of the $\rho_1, \ldots, \rho_l$.

Theorem 1 is not an eigenvalue of T. There are precisely l orbits.

Proof

77.2.1. Definition of Γ: $\gamma \in \Gamma \leftrightarrow (\gamma \in W^+ \wedge T\gamma \in W^-)$.

For $\gamma \in \Gamma$ there is a k such that

$$S_{\rho_{k-1}} \cdots S_{\rho_1} \gamma > 0, \qquad S_{\rho_k} S_{\rho_{k-1}} \cdots S_{\rho_1} \gamma < 0.$$

Then

$$S_{\rho_{k-1}} \cdots S_{\rho_1} \gamma = \rho_k$$

and

$$\gamma = S_{\rho_1} \cdots S_{\rho_{k-1}} \rho_k.$$

Conversely, any element of this form clearly belongs to Γ. Therefore Γ consists of the

$$\gamma_k = S_{\rho_1} \cdots S_{\rho_{k-1}} \rho_k \qquad (k = 1, \ldots, l)$$

Now with integral p_{ki}

$$\gamma_k = \rho_k + \sum_{i<k} p_{ki} \rho_i,$$

which shows that the γ_k are linearly independent. Thus,

77.2.2 Γ is a basis of $\boldsymbol{H}^*$.

Since

$$S_{\rho j}\pi_k = \pi_k \qquad \text{for} \quad j \neq k, \qquad S_{\rho j}\pi_j = \pi_j - \rho_j,$$

one gets

$$T^{-1}\pi_k = S_{\rho_1} \cdots S_{\rho l}\pi_k = S_{\rho_1} \cdots S_{\rho k}\pi_k = S_{\rho_1} \cdots S_{\rho k-1}(\pi_k - \rho_k) = \pi_k - \gamma_k;$$

hence

77.2.3 $$(1 - T^{-1})\pi_k = \gamma_k.$$

Now, from the linear independence of the γ_k it follows that $1 - T^{-1}$ is non-degenerate; hence

77.2.4 1 is not an eigenvalue of T.

The sum of an orbit is T-invariant; therefore by 77.2.4 it is 0, and every orbit contains positive as well as negative rootforms. Consequently:

77.2.5 every orbit intersects Γ and there are at most l orbits.

If there were less, some γ_i and γ_j $(i \neq j)$ would belong to the same. Then by 77.2.3 π_i and π_j would be equivalent under some power of T. This, however, is not possible, since both are dominant (see 33.8.1). Hence:

77.2.6 There are exactly l orbits.

77.3. Definition ω is the eigenvalue of T with minimal positive argument and ξ_ω is an eigenvector belonging to ω.

Theorem ω is a primitive nth root of unity (n = order of T). ξ_ω is regular, that is, $(\xi_\omega, \alpha) \neq 0$ for all $\alpha \in W^*$. All orbits have the same length, $n = (r - l)/l$. All primitive nth roots of unity occur as eigenvalues of T with a regular eigenvector.

This theorem rests on the following:

Proposition No coordinate of ξ_ω on the basis W^{++} vanishes.

This proposition will be proved in 77.6.

Proof of the Theorem Suppose that $(\xi_\omega, \alpha) = 0$ for some $\alpha \in W^*$. Then

$$(\xi_\omega, T\alpha) = (T^{-1}\xi_\omega, \alpha) = \omega^{-1}(\xi_\omega, \alpha) = 0.$$

ξ_ω is orthogonal to the orbit of α, hence to some γ_k. Thus by 77.2.3,

$$0 = ((1 - T^{-1})\pi_k, \xi_\omega) = (\pi_k, (1 - T)\xi_\omega) = (\pi_k, (1 - \omega)\xi_\omega);$$

hence $(\pi_k, \xi_\omega) = 0$. This shows that the ρ_k-coordinate of ξ_ω vanishes, which contradicts the preceding proposition. Therefore ξ_ω is regular.

For some m that divides n, ω is some mth primitive root of unity. ξ_ω is T^m-invariant, as are $\operatorname{Re} \xi_\omega|_{\boldsymbol{H}_{st}}$ and $\operatorname{Im} \xi_\omega|_{\boldsymbol{H}_{st}}$. For some real τ, $\operatorname{Re} \xi_\omega|_{\boldsymbol{H}_{st}} + \tau \operatorname{Im} \xi_\omega|_{\boldsymbol{H}_{st}}$ is still regular, thus situated in the interior of a chamber. It is T^m-invariant, but any element of Int W^* leaving an inner point of a chamber invariant is the identity (see 33.8.1). Therefore $T^m = 1$ and, since $T^n = 1$ and m divides n, $m = n$.

Since on a natural basis the coefficients of any S_α, hence of T, are integral, the eigenvalues of T occur in full systems of algebraic conjugates. So any primitive nth root of unity λ, as a conjugate of ω, is an eigenvalue. Under the same conjugation ξ_ω passes into an eigenvector ξ_λ belonging to λ, which is again regular.

Suppose that the orbit of $\alpha \in W^*$ has length k. Then $T^k \alpha = \alpha$, k divides n, and

$$(\alpha, \xi_\omega) = (T^k \alpha, \xi_\omega) = (\alpha, T^{-k} \xi_\omega) = \omega^{-k}(\alpha, \xi_\omega).$$

Since ξ_ω has been proved to be regular, it follows that $\omega^k = 1$. So k is a multiple of n and, since k divides n, $k = n$. Now $n = (r - l)/l$ by 77.2.6.

77.4. Theorem $n = q + 1$, where q is the altitude of the top rootform (see Table D).

Proof (1) Define the operator Z on $\boldsymbol{H}^*$ by

$$Z\xi = \sum_{\alpha \in W^*} \frac{(\xi, \alpha)}{(\alpha, \alpha)} \alpha.$$

Z commutes with every element of Int W^*, which acts irreducibly on $\boldsymbol{H}^*$. Therefore Z is a scalar multiplication.

From

$$Z = \tfrac{1}{2}\sum(1 - S_\alpha),$$

$$\operatorname{tr} Z = \tfrac{1}{2}\sum \operatorname{tr}(1 - S_\alpha) = \tfrac{1}{2}\sum 2 = r - l,$$

it follows that

$$Z = \frac{r - l}{l} \cdot 1 = n \cdot 1.$$

(2) Let μ be the top rootform. Then for $\alpha \in W^+$,

$$2\frac{(\mu, \alpha)}{(\alpha, \alpha)} \geq 0, \qquad \text{thus} \qquad 2\frac{(\mu, \alpha)}{(\mu, \mu)} \geq 0.$$

Now every μ-ladder except $\ulcorner -\mu, 0, \mu \urcorner$ has length 1; thus

$$2\frac{(\mu,\alpha)}{(\mu,\mu)} = 0, 1 \qquad \text{for} \quad 0 < \alpha < \mu.$$

(3) Choose $\boldsymbol{h} \in \boldsymbol{H}_{\mathrm{st}}$ such that $\rho(\boldsymbol{h}) = 1$ for all $\rho \in W^{++}$. Then

$$q = a(\mu) = \mu(\boldsymbol{h}).$$

$$\boldsymbol{h} = \sum_{\alpha \in W^+} (\alpha, \alpha)^{-1} \boldsymbol{h}_\alpha$$

easily follows by the argument used in 41.6. Now

$$q = \sum_{\alpha \in W^+} \frac{(\mu,\alpha)}{(\alpha,\alpha)} = \sum_{0<\alpha<\mu} \frac{(\mu,\alpha)}{(\alpha,\alpha)} + 1 = \sum_{0<\alpha<\mu} \frac{1}{2}\frac{(\mu,\mu)}{(\alpha,\alpha)} 2\frac{(\mu,\alpha)}{(\mu,\mu)} + 1$$

$$= \sum_{0<\alpha<\mu} \frac{1}{2}\frac{(\mu,\mu)}{(\alpha,\alpha)} \cdot 4\frac{(\mu,\alpha)^2}{(\mu,\mu)^2} + 1 \qquad \text{(by 2)}$$

$$= \frac{2}{(\mu,\mu)} \sum_{0<\alpha\leqslant\mu} \frac{(\mu,\alpha)^2}{(\alpha,\alpha)} - 1 = \frac{1}{(\mu,\mu)} \sum_{\alpha \in W^*} \frac{(\mu,\alpha)^2}{(\alpha,\alpha)} - 1$$

$$= \frac{1}{(\mu,\mu)} (Z\mu, \mu) - 1 = n - 1 \qquad \text{(by 1)},$$

which proves the assertion.

77.5 Since $T^{q+1} = 1$, all eigenvalues of T are powers of ω.

Definition k is the weakly increasing sequence of l positive integers $k_i \leqslant q$ such that the ω^{k_i} provide the eigenvalues of the Killing–Coxeter tool T with due multiplicities.

The multiplicity with which a positive integer $x \leqslant q$ occurs in k is called $\varphi(x)$.

As noted in 77.3, the eigenvalues of T occur in full systems of algebraic conjugates. Hence:

Theorem $k_1 = 1$ and, if j occurs in k, then with the same frequency so does every positive integer $\leqslant q$ that has the same greatest common divisor with $q+1$ as j; if j occurs in k, then so does $q+1-j$.

In some cases this settles the structure of k.

E_8: $q+1 = 30$. There are just eight relative prime numbers mod 30; namely,

$$1, 7, 11, 13, 17, 19, 23, 29.$$

This is the sequence k.

E_7: $q+1=18$. The relative primes mod 18 are

$$1, 5, 7, \quad , 11, 13, 17.$$

The element lacking can only be 9.

E_6: $q+1=12$. The relative primes mod 12 are

$$1, \quad , 5, \quad , 7, \quad , 11.$$

Here the two lacking elements might be 3, 9, or 4, 8, or 6, 6.

F_4: $q+1=12$.

$$1, 5, 7, 11.$$

G_2: $q+1=6$.

$$1, 5.$$

To this list one easily adds:

A_l: $q+1=l+1$.

$$1, 2, \ldots, l.$$

77.6. ***Proof of Proposition*** **77.3** A matrix presentation of T is derived by expressing the ρ_i and $T^{-1}\rho_i$ in the γ_k:

$$\gamma_j = S_{\rho 1} \cdots S_{\rho j-1}\, \rho_j,$$

$$\rho_j - \gamma_j = \sum_{k=1}^{j-1} S_{\rho 1} \cdots S_{\rho k-1}(1 - S_{\rho k})\, \rho_j = \sum_{k=1}^{j-1} 2\frac{(\rho_j, \rho_k)}{(\rho_k, \rho_k)}\gamma_k,$$

77.6.1 $$\rho_j = \sum_{k=1}^{j-1} 2\frac{(\rho_j, \rho_k)}{(\rho_k, \rho_k)}\gamma_k + \gamma_j = \sum_{k=1}^{j} 2\frac{(\rho_j, \rho_k)}{(\rho_k, \rho_k)}\gamma_k - \gamma_j.$$

Further,

$$\gamma_j - T^{-1}\rho_j = \sum_{k=j}^{l} S_{\rho 1} \cdots S_{\rho k-1}(1 - S_{\rho k})\, \rho_j = \sum_{k=j}^{l} 2\frac{(\rho_j, \rho_k)}{(\rho_k, \rho_k)}\gamma_k,$$

77.6.2 $$-T^{-1}\rho_j = \sum_{k=j+1}^{l} 2\frac{(\rho_j, \rho_k)}{(\rho_k, \rho_k)}\gamma_k + \gamma_j = \sum_{k=j}^{l} 2\frac{(\rho_j, \rho_k)}{(\rho_k, \rho_k)}\gamma_k - \gamma_j.$$

By 77.6.1–2 T can be written on the ordered basis $\rho_1, \ldots, \rho_l$ as the product of an upper and a lower triangular matrix. Replacing ρ_j, γ_j by

$$\rho'_j = (\rho_j, \rho_j)^{-1/2}\rho_j, \qquad \gamma'_j = (\rho_j, \rho_j)^{-1/2}\gamma_j,$$

one gets a more symmetric expression:

$$\rho'_j = \gamma'_j + \sum_{k=1}^{j-1} 2a_{jk}\gamma'_k, \qquad -T^{-1}\rho'_j = \gamma'_j + \sum_{k=j+1}^{l} 2a_{jk}\gamma'_k,$$

where the

$$a_{jk} = (\rho_j, \rho_j)^{-1/2} (\rho_k, \rho_k)^{-1/2} (\rho_j, \rho_k)$$

are the cosines of the angles of the rootforms. They form a maxtrix $A = \ulcorner a_{jk} \urcorner_{j,k=1}^{l}$ with

$$a_{jj} = 1,$$

$$a_{jk} \leqslant 0 \quad \text{for} \quad j \neq k,$$

$$a_{jk} \neq 0 \quad \text{iff} \quad \rho_j, \rho_k \text{ are connected in the graph.}$$

Let B be the lower triangular matrix arising from A by putting

$$\begin{aligned} b_{jk} &= 2a_{jk} && \text{for} \quad j > k, \\ &= 1 && \text{for} \quad j = k, \\ &= 0 && \text{for} \quad j < k. \end{aligned}$$

Then, on the ordered basis $\rho_1', \ldots, \rho_l'$, the matrix of T^{-1} is

$$-B'^{-1} B$$

(where B' is B transposed), that of T is

$$-B^{-1} B'.$$

Note that

$$A = \tfrac{1}{2}(B + B').$$

The eigenvalues λ of T are determined by the equation

$$\det \tfrac{1}{2}(B' + \lambda B) = 0.$$

The matrix

$$C_\lambda = \tfrac{1}{2}(B' + \lambda B)$$

is real, symmetric, and positive definite for $\lambda = 1$ (since the inner product is so on $\boldsymbol{H}_{\mathrm{st}}^*$). For any λ with $|\lambda| = 1$ the reality and symmetry will now be restored by multiplying

the ith row by $f_i\, g$,

the ith column by f_i^{-1},

such that one gets

$$\begin{aligned} \tfrac{1}{2}\lambda b_{jk}(f_j g) f_k^{-1} &= a_{jk} && \text{for} \quad k < j, \\ \tfrac{1}{2} b_{kj}(f_j g) f_k^{-1} &= a_{jk} && \text{for} \quad k > j, \\ \tfrac{1}{2}(1 + \lambda)(f_j g) f_j^{-1} & && \text{real.} \end{aligned}$$

To reach this goal one must fulfill the conditions

77.6.3 $$f_j f_k^{-1} g = 1 \qquad \text{for} \quad j < k$$
$$= \lambda^{-1} \qquad \text{for} \quad j > k$$

for every pair j, k such that ρ_j, ρ_k are connected in the graph, and

77.6.4 $$\tfrac{1}{2}(1+\lambda)\, g \qquad \text{real.}$$

Instead of 77.6.3 one can write

77.6.5 $f_j f_k^{-1} g = \lambda^{-1}, \qquad f_k f_j^{-1} g = 1 \qquad$ for $\quad j > k$ and ρ_j, ρ_k connected.

Thus one must postulate $g^2 = \lambda^{-1}$. Indicating the square root of λ with a non-negative real part by $\lambda^{1/2}$ and its inverse by $\lambda^{-1/2}$, one puts

$$g = \lambda^{-1/2}.$$

Thus

$$\tfrac{1}{2}(1+\lambda)\, g = \tfrac{1}{2}(\lambda^{1/2} + \lambda^{-1/2})$$

fulfills 77.6.4. Now 77.6.5 takes the form

77.6.6 $$f_j = \lambda^{-1/2} f_k \qquad \text{for} \quad j > k \text{ and } \rho_j, \rho_k \text{ connected.}$$

This can be fulfilled with nonzero numbers, since the graph is a tree.

By this modification a matrix D_λ has arisen from C_λ. It agrees with A outside the main diagonal, whereas in the main diagonal it bears the value $\frac{1}{2}(\lambda^{1/2} + \lambda^{-1/2})$. The condition $\det(T - \lambda) = 0$ is equivalent to $\det C_\lambda = 0$, which is equivalent to $\det D_\lambda = 0$, that is,

$$\det(A - (1 - \tfrac{1}{2}(\lambda^{1/2} + \lambda^{-1/2}))) = 0.$$

The eigenvalues α of A correspond to eigenvalues λ of T by means of

$$\alpha = 1 - \tfrac{1}{2}(\lambda^{1/2} + \lambda^{-1/2}),$$

and the corresponding eigenvectors differ in every coordinate by a factor $\neq 0$. For this one need only look at the construction of D_λ and observe that the kernels of the linear transformations with matrices $\lambda + B^{-1} B'$ and $C_\lambda = B' + \lambda B$ all coincide. The minimal eigenvalue of A, called α_0, corresponds to the eigenvalue of T with a minimal positive argument. Since A is positive definite, $A - \alpha_0$ is still positive semidefinite, which implies that the corresponding eigenvector has no vanishing coordinate, thanks to the following:

Lemma Let Q be a real positive semidefinite quadratic form, $b_1, \ldots, b_l$ a basis that does not admit any proper partition in mutually orthogonal subsets, and $u_{ij} \leqslant 0$ for $i \neq j$ if $\ulcorner u_{ij} \urcorner_{i,j=1}^{l}$ is the matrix of Q on the ordered basis $b_1, \ldots, b_l$. Then no coefficient on this basis of an arbitrary nonzero isotropic element vanishes.

Proof After a rearrangement of the indices it is sufficient to refute the existence of numbers $x_1, \ldots, x_l$ and a positive integer m less than l with

$$\sum_j u_{ij} x_j = 0, \qquad x_1 \cdots x_m \neq 0, \quad x_{m+1} = \cdots = 0.$$

Such a system, if it existed, would imply

$$0 = \sum_{i,j} u_{ij} x_i x_j \geqslant \sum u_{ij} |x_i| \cdot |x_j| \geqslant 0,$$

where the first $\geqslant$ sign is justified by $u_{ij} \leqslant 0$ for $i \neq j$ and the second because of the positive semidefiniteness. Thus,

$$\sum_{i,j} u_{ij} |x_i| \cdot |x_j| = 0;$$

hence, again because of the semidefiniteness,

$$\sum_j u_{ij} |x_j| = 0$$

and

$$\sum_{j \leqslant m} u_{ij} |x_j| = 0.$$

For $i > m$ all summands are $\leqslant 0$, thus $= 0$. Hence $u_{ij} = 0$ for $i > m, j \leqslant m$. But this means that the quadratic form breaks in a way that is excluded by assumption.

It is easily seen from the connectedness of the graph that the lemma applies to the proof of the proposition.

77.7–14. Killing–Coxeter Elements

77.7 According to 33.1 T transferred to $\boldsymbol{H}$ is the restriction on $\boldsymbol{H}$ of some $\tilde{t}$ with $t \in G$. If $\boldsymbol{G}$ is given in third dressing on $\boldsymbol{H}$, t may even be supposed to belong to the corresponding G_{un}. Such a t is called a *Killing–Coxeter element*. More precisely:

Definition For any ordered third dressing of $\boldsymbol{G}$ on any ordered trunk $\boldsymbol{H}$ with, moreover, any ordering of the primitive rootforms, t is called a *Killing–Coxeter element* if $t \in G_{\text{un}}$ and $\tilde{t}|_{\boldsymbol{H}} = T$.

Remember that $\tilde{t}$ is pure.

Definition For any G_{un}, a is called *regular* if $a \in G_{\text{un}}$ and the nullity of $\tilde{a} - 1$ is minimal (hence l).

Theorem Let t be a Killing–Coxeter element inducing T and let $\boldsymbol{L}_i$ be the span of the $\boldsymbol{e}_\alpha$ with α in the orbit of γ_i, $i = 1, \ldots, l$ (see 77.2.1). Then

77.7.1 the eigenvalues of $\tilde{t}|_{L_i}$ are the $q+1$ different powers of ω, each with multiplicity 1,

77.7.2 the eigenvalues of $\tilde{t}$ are the components of the sequence k, and the $q+1$ different powers of ω, each with multiplicity l,

77.7.3 $\tilde{t}$ has order $q+1$,

77.7.4 t is regular,

77.7.5 the Killing–Coxeter elements corresponding to the same T are conjugate.

In 77.10, all Killing–Coxeter elements will be shown to be conjugate.

Proof 77.7.4 is an immediate consequence of 77.7.1 and the fact that $\tilde{t}$ has no eigenvalue 1 on $\boldsymbol{H}$.

77.7.2 follows from 77.7.1.

Let $\boldsymbol{F}$ be the 1-eigenspace of $\tilde{t}$ acting on $\boldsymbol{G}$ and $\boldsymbol{F}_i = \boldsymbol{F} \cap \boldsymbol{L}_i$. Since $\tilde{t}\boldsymbol{e}_\alpha$ is a scalar multiple of $\boldsymbol{e}_{T\alpha}$, the branches can be supposed renormed (in first dressing) such that

$$\tilde{t}^p \boldsymbol{e}_{\gamma_i} = \boldsymbol{e}_{T^p\gamma_i} \qquad \text{for} \quad 0 < p < q.$$

Then $\boldsymbol{F}_i$, if $\neq \{\boldsymbol{0}\}$, is spanned by

$$\sum_{p=0}^{q} \boldsymbol{e}_{T^p\gamma_i},$$

hence

$$\dim \boldsymbol{F}_i \leqslant 1.$$

Clearly

$$\boldsymbol{F} = \sum \boldsymbol{F}_i,$$

and

$$\dim \boldsymbol{F} \geqslant l.$$

Since by 77.2 the number of orbits is l,

$$\dim \boldsymbol{F}_i = 1,$$

which implies

$$\dim \boldsymbol{F} = l,$$

and

$$\tilde{t}^{q+1} \boldsymbol{e}_{\gamma_i} = \boldsymbol{e}_{\gamma_i},$$

so the order of $\tilde{t}$ is $q+1$, which proves 77.7.3.

The eigenvectors of $\tilde{t}$ in $\boldsymbol{L}_i$ are the

$$\sum_{p=0}^{q} \omega^{-kp}\, T^p\, \boldsymbol{e}_{\gamma_J}$$

belonging to the eigenvalues ω^k $(k = 0, 1, \ldots, q)$, respectively. This proves 77.7.1.

If t' is another Killing–Coxeter element, then $\tilde{t}' = \exp \tilde{\boldsymbol{h}} \cdot \tilde{t}$ with some $\boldsymbol{h} \in \boldsymbol{H}$. One must look for an $\boldsymbol{h}_1 \in \boldsymbol{H}$ such that $\exp \tilde{\boldsymbol{h}}_1 \cdot \tilde{t} \cdot \exp(-\tilde{\boldsymbol{h}}_1) = \exp \tilde{\boldsymbol{h}} \cdot \tilde{t}$. This condition is fulfilled by an $\boldsymbol{h}_1$ with $\boldsymbol{h}_1 - T\boldsymbol{h}_1 = \boldsymbol{h}$, which, according to 77.2, exists. This proves 77.7.5.

77.8 In the sequel ordered second dressing on another trunk $\boldsymbol{H}'$ will be needed. One adopts the following convention:

Notation Rootforms, second dressing branches, and so on, with respect to $\boldsymbol{H}'$, are distinguished from those with respect to $\boldsymbol{H}$ by a prime.

77.9 Elements of G of finite order belong to some maximal compact subgroup, hence to some G_{un} with a suitable C_{un}. Up to conjugacy they may be supposed to be in G_{un}.

Theorem All regular elements of G of order $q+1$ are conjugate. No regular element of G has order $\leqslant q$.

Proof The given regular element is of the form $\exp \boldsymbol{u}$ with $\boldsymbol{u}$ in the principal domain (see 31.4) of some suitable suitably ordered trunk $\boldsymbol{H}'_{\mathrm{un}}$.

Thus, if

$$\mu' = \sum q_i \rho'_i$$

is the top rootform,

$$\operatorname{Im} \rho'_i(\boldsymbol{u}) > 0, \qquad \operatorname{Im} \mu'(\boldsymbol{u}) < 2\pi.$$

If $\exp \boldsymbol{u}$ has order $q+1$, all $\alpha'(\boldsymbol{u})$ $(\alpha' \in W^{*\prime})$ are integral multiples of $2\pi i/(q+1)$;

$$\operatorname{Im} \rho'_i(\boldsymbol{u}) = p_i \cdot 2\pi/(q+1) \qquad \text{with positive integers } p_i.$$

$$\operatorname{Im} \mu'(\boldsymbol{u}) = \sum q_i \operatorname{Im} \rho'_i(\boldsymbol{u}) = \sum p_i q_i \cdot 2\pi/(q+1).$$

This must be $<2\pi$, hence

$$p_i > 0, \qquad \sum p_i q_i < q+1;$$

therefore

$$\text{all } p_i = 1.$$

Up to conjugacy $\boldsymbol{u}$ is unique, as is $\exp \boldsymbol{u}$.

The second statement is now obvious.

77.10 A Killing–Coxeter element t is regular and of order $q+1$. Therefore 77.9 applies. The infinitesimal trunk of t, called $\boldsymbol{H}'$, is spanned by the $\boldsymbol{F}_i$ (of Theorem 77.7).

Definition $\boldsymbol{u} \in \boldsymbol{H}'$ is defined by $\rho_i'(\boldsymbol{u}) = 1$ for all $i = 1, \ldots, l$. It is called the *altimeter* (with respect to $\boldsymbol{H}'$).

This terminology derives from the formula

$$\alpha'(\boldsymbol{u}) = a(\alpha')$$

(altitude of α'). From 77.9 it follows:

Theorem A Killing–Coxeter element t can be written as $\exp(2\pi \mathrm{i}/(q+1))\boldsymbol{u}$ with respect to its infinitesimal trunk $\boldsymbol{H}'$.

The inner class of a Killing–Coxeter element depends neither on the arrangement of the ρ_i nor on the choice of $\boldsymbol{H}$.

The inner class of a Killing–Coxeter tool does not depend on the arrangement of the ρ_i.

77.11. Definition $\boldsymbol{G}_j$ is spanned by the $\boldsymbol{e}'_{\alpha'}$, with $a(\alpha') = j$ $(-q \leqslant j \leqslant q)$. For $|j| > q$, $\boldsymbol{G}_j$ is defined as $\{\boldsymbol{0}\}$; furthermore $\boldsymbol{G}_0 = \boldsymbol{H}'$.

$\tilde{\boldsymbol{u}}$ acts on $\boldsymbol{G}_j$ as the multiplication by j. $\boldsymbol{G} = \sum \boldsymbol{G}_j$.

Clearly

$$\dim \boldsymbol{G}_j \text{ is the number of rootforms of altitude } j.$$

As the respective multiplicities of the eigenvalues j of $\tilde{\boldsymbol{u}}$, the $\dim \boldsymbol{G}_j$ are closely connected to the multiplicities of the eigenvalues of $\tilde{t} = \exp(2\pi \mathrm{i}/(q+1))\tilde{\boldsymbol{u}}$. The latter are known from Theorem 77.7. This leads to the

Theorem After reduction mod $q+1$ and with due account to multiplicities the eigenvalues of $\tilde{\boldsymbol{u}}$ are the components of the sequence k and l times each of the numbers $0, 1, \ldots, q$. In other words,

$$\dim \boldsymbol{G}_j + \dim \boldsymbol{G}_{j-q-1} = \dim \boldsymbol{G}_j + \dim \boldsymbol{G}_{q+1-j} = l + \varphi(j) \qquad (j = 0, \ldots, q),$$

if $\varphi(j)$ is the multiplicity of j in the sequence k.

Since the $\dim \boldsymbol{G}_j$ can be read from Table D, this establishes the sequence k.

77.12 The Sequence k

A_l:	$1, 2, \ldots, l$	
B_l:	$1, 3, \ldots, 2l-1$	(the odd numbers)

C_l: $1, 3, \ldots, 2l-1$ (the odd numbers)
D_l (l even): $1, 3, \ldots, l-1, l-1, \ldots, 2l-5, 2l-3$ (the odd numbers, with the multiplicity 2 for $l-1$)
D_l (l odd): $1, 3, \ldots, l-2, l-1, l, \ldots, 2l-5, 2l-3$ (the odd numbers and the number $l-1$)
E_6: 1, 4, 5, 7, 8, 11
E_7: 1, 5, 7, 9, 11, 13, 17
E_8: 1, 7, 11, 13, 17, 19, 23, 29
F_4: 1, 5, 7, 11
G_2: 1, 5

An inspection of this table shows:

77.13 $\dim \boldsymbol{G}_j + \dim \boldsymbol{G}_{q+2-j} = l \quad$ for $\quad j = 0, \ldots, q+2.$

Compared with 77.11, this yields the following:

77.14. Theorem $\varphi(j) = \dim \boldsymbol{G}_j - \dim \boldsymbol{G}_{j+1}$ for $j = 0, \ldots, q$; in other words, $\varphi(j)$ is the drop in the number of rootforms of a given altitude x when passing from $x = j$ to $x = j+1$.

For this formula, which makes the computation of k much easier, one can provide an interesting general proof:

Proof $\boldsymbol{H}_j = \boldsymbol{H} \cap (\boldsymbol{G}_j + \boldsymbol{G}_{j-q-1})$ is the eigenspace in $\boldsymbol{H}$ of $\exp(2\pi i/(q+1))\tilde{\boldsymbol{u}}$ belonging to $\omega^j = \omega^{j-q-1}$. Thus,

(1) $$\dim \boldsymbol{H}_j = \varphi(j),$$

and

$$\boldsymbol{H}_0 = \{0\}$$

by 77.2.

Corresponding to the former ξ_ω in $\boldsymbol{H}^*$ there is a regular $\boldsymbol{x} \in \boldsymbol{H}_1$.

Put

$$\boldsymbol{G}_{>0} = \sum_{j>0} \boldsymbol{G}_j$$

and define $\boldsymbol{G}_{\geqslant 0}$, $\boldsymbol{G}_{<0}$, and $\boldsymbol{G}_{\leqslant 0}$ analogously. Call σ_+ and σ_- the projections onto $\boldsymbol{G}_{>0}$ and $\boldsymbol{G}_{<0}$, respectively, in the direct splitting

$$\boldsymbol{G} = \boldsymbol{G}_{>0} + \boldsymbol{G}_0 + \boldsymbol{G}_{<0}.$$

Then

$$\boldsymbol{x} = \sigma_+ \boldsymbol{x} + \sigma_- \boldsymbol{x}, \qquad \sigma_+ \boldsymbol{x} \in \boldsymbol{G}_1, \qquad \sigma_- \boldsymbol{x} \in \boldsymbol{G}_{-q}.$$

Therefore, with suitable $\tau_{\rho'}$, τ,

$$\sigma_+ \boldsymbol{x} = \sum \tau_{\rho'} \boldsymbol{e}'_{\rho'}, \qquad \sigma_- \boldsymbol{x} = \tau \boldsymbol{e}'_{-\mu'},$$

where μ' is again the top rootform. All $\tau_\rho \neq 0$, for otherwise there would be some (ad-nilpotent) $\boldsymbol{e}'_{-\rho'}$ in the centralizer of $\boldsymbol{x}$, which is $\boldsymbol{H}$. So there is some $\sum \tau^*_{\rho'} \boldsymbol{e}'_{-\rho'}$ such that

$$[\sum \tau_{\rho'} \boldsymbol{e}'_{\rho'}, \sum \tau^*_{\rho'} \boldsymbol{e}'_{-\rho'}]$$

is a given element of $\boldsymbol{G}_0 = \boldsymbol{H}'$.

Put $\boldsymbol{e} = \sigma_+ \boldsymbol{x}$ ($\in \boldsymbol{G}_1$) and take $\boldsymbol{f} \in \boldsymbol{G}_{-1}$ such that

$$[\boldsymbol{e}, \boldsymbol{f}] = \boldsymbol{u};$$

obviously

$$[\boldsymbol{u}, \boldsymbol{e}] = \boldsymbol{e}, \qquad [\boldsymbol{u}, \boldsymbol{f}] = -\boldsymbol{f}.$$

Then $\boldsymbol{u}, \boldsymbol{e}, \boldsymbol{f}$ form a hef-triple (see 76.2) spanning an element of $\mathbf{A}_1(\boldsymbol{G})$, which by the arguments of 76.4.2 is regular.

Under the adjoint action of this element of $\mathbf{A}_1(\boldsymbol{G})$ the linear space $\boldsymbol{G}$ splits into irreducible linear subspaces, denoted by $\boldsymbol{R}_i$ in 76.3.9; all dim $\boldsymbol{R}_i$ are odd and $\boldsymbol{u}$ is regular; by 76.3

$$\text{(2)} \qquad \dim \operatorname{kernel} \tilde{\boldsymbol{e}} = l$$

and $\boldsymbol{e}$ is a regular ad-nilpotent.

Take $\boldsymbol{a} \in \boldsymbol{H}$. Then the $\boldsymbol{G}_0$-component of $\boldsymbol{a}$ vanishes. Since $\boldsymbol{H}$ is the centralizer of $\boldsymbol{x}$,

$$\boldsymbol{0} = [\boldsymbol{x}, \boldsymbol{a}] = [\sigma_+ \boldsymbol{x}, \sigma_+ \boldsymbol{a}] + [\sigma_+ \boldsymbol{x}, \sigma_- \boldsymbol{a}] + [\sigma_- \boldsymbol{x}, \sigma_+ \boldsymbol{a}] + [\sigma_- \boldsymbol{x}, \sigma_- \boldsymbol{a}],$$

with the last three summands belonging to $\boldsymbol{G}_{\leqslant 0}$ and the first to $\boldsymbol{G}_{>0}$, thus vanishing; hence

$$\text{(3)} \qquad \sigma_+ \boldsymbol{H} \subset \operatorname{kernel} \tilde{\boldsymbol{e}}.$$

Now $\sigma_+ \boldsymbol{a} \neq \boldsymbol{0}$ if $\boldsymbol{a} \neq \boldsymbol{0}$, for otherwise $\boldsymbol{a} = \sigma_- \boldsymbol{a}$ would be an ad-nilpotent $\neq \boldsymbol{0}$ in $\boldsymbol{H}$. Thus

$$\text{(4)} \qquad \sigma_+|_{\boldsymbol{H}} \text{ nondegenerate},$$

$$\dim \sigma_+ \boldsymbol{H} = \dim \boldsymbol{H} = 1,$$

and because of (2) and (3)

$$\text{(5)} \qquad \sigma_+ \boldsymbol{H} = \operatorname{kernel} \tilde{\boldsymbol{e}}.$$

Now by (1), (4), (5)

$$\text{(6)} \quad \varphi(j) = \dim \boldsymbol{H}_j = \dim \sigma_+ \boldsymbol{H}_j = \dim(\sigma_+ \boldsymbol{H} \cap \boldsymbol{G}_j) = \dim((\operatorname{kernel} \tilde{\boldsymbol{e}}) \cap \boldsymbol{G}_j).$$

Further, from (2) and

$$\tilde{\boldsymbol{e}} \boldsymbol{G}_{\geqslant 0} \subset \boldsymbol{G}_{>0},$$

$$\dim \boldsymbol{G}_{\geqslant 0} - \dim \boldsymbol{G}_{>0} = l,$$

it follows that

$$\tilde{e}\, G_{\geqslant 0} = G_{>0};$$

hence

$$\tilde{e}\, G_j = G_{j+1},$$

thus

$$\dim((\text{kernel}\, \tilde{e}) \cap G_j) = \dim G_j - \dim G_{j+1},$$

which compared with (6) shows

$$\varphi(j) = \dim G_j - \dim G_{j+1}.$$

77.15–18. Int W^*-Invariants

77.15. Definition $\mathscr{P}_{\mathrm{Int}}(H)$ is the algebra of polynomial functions on H invariant under Int W^*.

It is taken for granted that $\mathscr{P}_{\mathrm{Int}}(H)$ possesses l algebraically independent homogeneous generators [C. Chevalley, *Amer. J. Math.* **77**, 778–790 (1955)]. Then the following will be proved in 77.18.

Theorem The Poincaré series of $\mathscr{P}_{\mathrm{Int}}(H)$ is

$$\prod (1 - t^{k_i+1})^{-1},$$

the k_i being the components of k (see 77.5) with due multiplicities.

In other words, the degrees of the generators of $\mathscr{P}_{\mathrm{Int}}(H)$ are the $k_i + 1$. They are known from 77.12.

Since $\mathscr{P}_{\mathrm{Int}}(H)$ is known to have l algebraically independent homogeneous generators, with degrees m_i, say, the Poincaré series of $\mathscr{P}_{\mathrm{Int}}(H)$ has the form

$$\prod_{i=1}^{l} (1 - t^{m_i})^{-1}.$$

77.16. Proposition $\prod m_i = g$ (= cardinality of Int W^*).

$$\sum (m_i - 1) = \tfrac{1}{2}(r - l).$$

Proof By 77.1.10

$$\prod_i (1 - t^{m_i})^{-1} = (1/g) \sum_{S \in \mathrm{Int}\, W^*} \det(1 - tS)^{-1}.$$

Both members are considered to be developed according to powers of $1 - t$.

$$(1-t)^{-l}\prod_i(1+t+t^2+\cdots+t^{m_i-1})^{-1}$$
$$=(1-t)^{-l}(1/g)(1+(1-t)^l\sum_{S\neq 1}\det(1-tS)^{-1}).$$

In the last sum $1 - t$ occurs in the denominator at most with the exponent $l-1$, and this happens only if S is a reflection in an $(l-1)$-hyperplane, which, necessarily, is the orthoplane of a rootform, since no interior point of a chamber is invariant under S (see 33.4.5).

Multiplying by $(1-t)^l$ and putting $t = 1$, one gets

$$\prod m_i = g.$$

The coefficient of $(1-t)^{-l+1}$ in the left member is the negative of the derivative of

$$\prod_i (1+t+\cdots+t^{m_i-1})^{-1}$$

at $t = 1$, namely,

$$\sum m_i^{-1}\binom{m_i}{2}\cdot\prod m_j^{-1}.$$

In the right member it is $1/2g$ times the number of reflections in orthoplanes of rootforms, namely,

$$\frac{1}{2g}\frac{r-l}{2}.$$

Thus

$$\sum (m_i - 1) = \tfrac{1}{2}(r-l).$$

77.17. Definition $I_1, \ldots, I_l$ is a system of homogeneous generators of $\mathscr{P}_{\mathrm{Int}}(\boldsymbol{H})$ of degrees $m_1, \ldots, m_l$, respectively. J is the functional determinant of

$$\sigma = \curlyvee_{\boldsymbol{h}}\ulcorner I_1(\boldsymbol{h}), \ldots, I_l(\boldsymbol{h})\urcorner,$$

according to an ordered basis of $\boldsymbol{H}$.

Proposition $J(\boldsymbol{h}) = \text{const}\cdot\prod_{\alpha\in W^+}\alpha(\boldsymbol{h})$.

In the proof of this proposition a particular consequence of Hilbert's zeros theorem will be used:

Lemma For polynomials $P, Q \neq 0$ over Com: if Q vanishes in all zeros of P, then every irreducible factor of P is a factor of Q.

Proof of the Proposition J is a polynomial function on $\boldsymbol{H}$ of degree $\Sigma(m_i - 1) = \frac{1}{2}(r - l)$. The mapping σ cannot be homeomorphic in the neighborhood of any $\boldsymbol{h}$ in which some nonzero rootform vanishes, for it takes the same value in points symmetrically situated with respect to the orthoplane of a rootform. Therefore

$$\prod_{\alpha \in W^+} \alpha(\boldsymbol{h}) = 0 \rightarrow J(\boldsymbol{h}) = 0.$$

Since all $\alpha \in W^+$ are different and both polynomial functions have the same degree, they agree up to a constant factor.

77.18. *Proof of Theorem* **77.15** After a basis $\boldsymbol{h}_1, \ldots, \boldsymbol{h}_l$ in $\boldsymbol{H}$ has been chosen, the I_i determine polynomials $\hat{I}_i$ in l variables, say $X_1, \ldots, X_l$, by means of

$$\hat{I}_i(\tau_1, \ldots, \tau_l) = I_i(\Sigma\, \tau_i \boldsymbol{h}_i).$$

The basis is assumed to consist of the eigenvectors of the Killing–Coxeter tool T such that

$$T\boldsymbol{h}_i = \omega^{k_i} \boldsymbol{h}_i,$$

with $k_1 = 1$ and regular $\boldsymbol{h}_1$; thus,

77.18.1 $$J(\boldsymbol{h}_1) \neq 0.$$

Because of the particular choice of the basis, each monomial in $\hat{I}_i$ is T-invariant; that is, if $X_1^{a_1} \cdots X_l^{a_l}$ occurs in $\hat{I}_i$ with nonzero coefficient, then

$$\Sigma\, a_i k_i = 0 \bmod q + 1.$$

Because of 77.18.1, there is a permutation f of $\{1, \ldots, l\}$ such that

$$(\partial_{f(i)} I_i)(\boldsymbol{h}_1) \neq 0.$$

Because of the homogeneity of I_i of degree m_i, this means that $X_1^{m_i - 1} X_{f(i)}$ occurs in $\hat{I}_i$ with nonzero coefficent. Therefore

$$\omega^{m_i - 1}\, \omega^{k_{f(i)}} = 1,$$

$$m_i - 1 + k_{f(i)} = 0 \bmod q + 1 \qquad \text{for} \quad i = 1, 2, \ldots, l.$$

By applying the last part of Theorem 77.5 one finds a rearrangement of the m_i such that

$$m_i - 1 = k_i \bmod q + 1 \qquad \text{for all} \quad i = 1, \ldots, l.$$

Now by Theorem 77.14 and Proposition 77.16

$$\Sigma\, k_i = \sum_{j=1}^{q} \varphi(j) = \dim \boldsymbol{G}_{>0} = \tfrac{1}{2}(r - l) = \Sigma\, (m_i - 1),$$

which proves that

$$m_i = k_i + 1.$$

77.19–23. Int G-Invariants

77.19. Definitions

$\mathscr{P}(\boldsymbol{G})$, $\mathscr{P}(\boldsymbol{H})$ are the algebras of polynomial functions on $\boldsymbol{G}$, $\boldsymbol{H}$.

$\mathscr{P}_{\mathrm{Int}}(\boldsymbol{G})$, $\mathscr{P}_{\mathrm{Int}}(\boldsymbol{H})$ are the subalgebras of those invariant under Int $\boldsymbol{G}$, Int W^*.

$\mathscr{P}_{\mathrm{Aut}}(\boldsymbol{G})$, $\mathscr{P}_{\mathrm{Aut}}(\boldsymbol{H})$ are the subalgebras of those invariant under Aut $\boldsymbol{G}$, Aut W^*.

$\mathscr{P}^*_{\mathrm{Int}}(\boldsymbol{G})$, $\mathscr{P}^*_{\mathrm{Int}}(\boldsymbol{H})$ are the subalgebras generated by the coefficients of all $\curlyvee_{\boldsymbol{a}} \det(f(\boldsymbol{a}) - \lambda)$, where f runs through the linear representations of $\boldsymbol{G}$, and $\boldsymbol{a} \in \boldsymbol{G}, \boldsymbol{H}$.

$\mathscr{P}^*_{\mathrm{Aut}}(\boldsymbol{G})$, $\mathscr{P}^*_{\mathrm{Aut}}(\boldsymbol{H})$ are the subalgebras generated by the coefficients of $\curlyvee_{\boldsymbol{a}} \det(\tilde{\boldsymbol{a}} - \lambda)$, $\boldsymbol{a} \in \boldsymbol{G}, \boldsymbol{H}$.

$\mathfrak{q}$ is the operation of forming the quotient field of such an algebra.

$\mathfrak{r}$ is the operation of restricting elements of $\mathscr{P}(\boldsymbol{G})$ to $\boldsymbol{H}$.

Clearly $\mathfrak{r}$ is an epimorphism.

77.20. Theorem $\mathfrak{r}$ is an isomorphism of $\mathscr{P}_{\mathrm{Int}}(\boldsymbol{G})$ onto $\mathscr{P}_{\mathrm{Int}}(\boldsymbol{H})$ and of $\mathscr{P}_{\mathrm{Aut}}(\boldsymbol{G})$ onto $\mathscr{P}_{\mathrm{Aut}}(\boldsymbol{H})$.

This contains a statement made in 77.1.9.

It is evident that $\mathfrak{r}$ maps $\mathscr{P}_{\mathrm{Int}}(\boldsymbol{G})$, $\mathscr{P}_{\mathrm{Aut}}(\boldsymbol{G})$ into $\mathscr{P}_{\mathrm{Int}}(\boldsymbol{H})$, $\mathscr{P}_{\mathrm{Aut}}(\boldsymbol{H})$, respectively. Since the trunks are Int $\boldsymbol{G}$-equivalent and their union is dense in $\boldsymbol{G}$, any element of $\mathscr{P}_{\mathrm{Int}}(\boldsymbol{G})$ is determined by its restriction to $\boldsymbol{H}$. Therefore $\mathfrak{r}$ maps $\mathscr{P}_{\mathrm{Int}}(\boldsymbol{G})$, $\mathscr{P}_{\mathrm{Aut}}(\boldsymbol{G})$ one-to-one. It remains to show that it maps *onto* $\mathscr{P}_{\mathrm{Int}}(\boldsymbol{H})$, $\mathscr{P}_{\mathrm{Aut}}(\boldsymbol{H})$, respectively. This will be done in 77.23.

Remark The statement about $\mathscr{P}_{\mathrm{Int}}(\boldsymbol{G})$ could also be proved by means of the monodromy theorem of algebraic functions: an element p of $\mathscr{P}_{\mathrm{Int}}(\boldsymbol{H})$ can be expressed in the rootforms; by extending the rootforms to roots one gets an algebraic function on $\boldsymbol{G}$ that extends p and behaves in univalued fashion under analytic continuation; therefore it is a rational invariant and actually a polynomial function.

77.21. Theorem $\mathfrak{q}\mathscr{P}^*_{\cdots}(\cdots) = \mathfrak{q}\mathscr{P}_{\cdots}(\cdots)$.

If $\sigma \in \mathrm{Aut}\, \boldsymbol{G}$, then $\widetilde{\sigma\boldsymbol{a}} = \sigma\tilde{\boldsymbol{a}}\sigma^{-1}$; thus,

$$\det(\widetilde{\sigma\boldsymbol{a}} - \lambda) = \det(\sigma\tilde{\boldsymbol{a}}\sigma^{-1} - \lambda) = \det(\tilde{\boldsymbol{a}} - \lambda),$$

which shows that

$$\mathscr{P}^*_{\mathrm{Aut}}(\boldsymbol{G}) \subset \mathscr{P}_{\mathrm{Aut}}(\boldsymbol{G}).$$

Generally,

77.21.1 $$\mathscr{P}^*_{\ldots}(\cdots) \subset \mathscr{P}_{\ldots}(\cdots).$$

The remainder is proved in 77.22 and 77.23.

77.22 $\mathfrak{q}\mathscr{P}^*_{\ldots}(H) = \mathfrak{q}\mathscr{P}_{\ldots}(H)$.

Proof It suffices to prove the inclusion $\supset$.

Note that $\mathfrak{q}\,\mathscr{P}(H)$ is the splitting field over $\mathfrak{q}\,\mathscr{P}^*_{\mathrm{Aut}}(H)$ of the λ-polynomial $\curlyvee_a \det(\tilde{a} - \lambda)$; indeed, its zeros are the rootforms, which generate $\mathfrak{q}\,\mathscr{P}(H)$ as a field. Therefore $\mathfrak{q}\,\mathscr{P}(H)$ is a Galois extension of finite degree of $\mathfrak{q}\,\mathscr{P}^*_{\mathrm{Aut}}(H)$, as it is of $\mathfrak{q}\,\mathscr{P}^*_{\mathrm{Int}}(H)$, $\mathfrak{q}\,\mathscr{P}_{\mathrm{Aut}}(H)$, and $\mathfrak{q}\,\mathscr{P}_{\mathrm{Int}}(H)$.

Let σ be an automorphism of $\mathfrak{q}\,\mathscr{P}(H)$ that fixes $\mathscr{P}^*_{\mathrm{Aut}}(H)$ elementwise. Then σ leaves $\curlyvee_a \det(\tilde{a} - \lambda)$ invariant. Consequently σ permutes the rootforms while preserving the linear relations among them. Therefore σ is induced by an element of Aut W^*. Thus the Galois group of $\mathfrak{q}\,\mathscr{P}(H)$ over $\mathfrak{q}\,\mathscr{P}^*_{\mathrm{Aut}}(H)$ is contained in that over $\mathfrak{q}\,\mathscr{P}_{\mathrm{Aut}}(H)$. This proves

$$\mathfrak{q}\,\mathscr{P}^*_{\mathrm{Aut}}(H) \supset \mathfrak{q}\,\mathscr{P}_{\mathrm{Aut}}(H).$$

Let σ be an automorphism of $\mathfrak{q}\,\mathscr{P}(H)$ that fixes $\mathscr{P}^*_{\mathrm{Int}}(H)$ elementwise. Then σ also fixes $\mathscr{P}^*_{\mathrm{Aut}}(H)$ elementwise and thus is induced by an element of Aut W^*. Let f be any irreducible linear representation of G and χ its character, both of which restricted to H. Then

$$\chi(h) = \sum \exp \nu(h) = \sum_s (1/s!) \sum_\nu \nu(h)^s,$$

where ν ranges over the weights of f with due multiplicities. In a well-known way the $\sum_\nu \nu(h)^s$ can be expressed in the coefficients of $\curlyvee_h \det(f(h) - \lambda)$. Therefore χ is invariant under σ. An outer automorphism causes a nontrival interchange of some fundamental representations and so does not leave all χ invariant. This shows that σ is induced by an element of Int W^*. Thus the Galois group of $\mathfrak{q}\,\mathscr{P}(H)$ over $\mathfrak{q}\,\mathscr{P}^*_{\mathrm{Int}}(H)$ is contained in that over $\mathfrak{q}\,\mathscr{P}_{\mathrm{Int}}(H)$, which proves

$$\mathfrak{q}\,\mathscr{P}^*_{\mathrm{Int}}(H) \supset \mathfrak{q}\,\mathscr{P}_{\mathrm{Int}}(H).$$

77.23.1 $$\mathfrak{r}\mathscr{P}^*_{\ldots}(G) = \mathscr{P}^*_{\ldots}(H)$$

is obvious. To complete the proof of 77.20 one must show

77.23.2 $$\mathfrak{r}\mathscr{P}_{\ldots}(G) \supset \mathscr{P}_{\ldots}(H).$$

Proof Let $p \in \mathscr{P}_{\mathrm{Int}}(\boldsymbol{H})$. By 77.22 and 77.23.1 p is the quotient of restrictions of elements of $\mathscr{P}^*_{\mathrm{Int}}(\boldsymbol{G})$; thus,

$$p = \frac{\mathfrak{r}(p_1)}{\mathfrak{r}(p_2)} \qquad \text{with} \quad p_i \in \mathscr{P}^*_{\mathrm{Int}}(\boldsymbol{G}).$$

By 77.21 one can suppose that $p_i \in \mathscr{P}_{\mathrm{Int}}(\boldsymbol{G})$. Let d be a greatest common divisor of p_1, p_2. Then so is $\tilde{a}d$; therefore $\tilde{a}d = \kappa(a)d$ for $a \in G$, where $\kappa(a)$ is scalar and κ a linear representation of G; hence $\kappa(a) = 1$ and $d \in \mathscr{P}_{\mathrm{Int}}(\boldsymbol{G})$. After canceling d, one may assume that

$$\mathfrak{r}(p_2)p = \mathfrak{r}(p_1) \qquad \text{with} \quad p_i \in \mathscr{P}_{\mathrm{Int}}(\boldsymbol{G}), \text{ relatively prime in } \mathscr{P}(\boldsymbol{G}).$$

Since p is a polynomial function on $\boldsymbol{H}$, p_1 must vanish in all zeros of $p_2|_{\boldsymbol{H}}$ and even in all zeros of $p_2|_{\tilde{a}\boldsymbol{H}}$ $(a \in \boldsymbol{G})$, since $p_1, p_2 \in \mathscr{P}_{\mathrm{Int}}(\boldsymbol{G})$. Because of the conjugacy of trunks and the density in $\boldsymbol{G}$ of their union, p_1 now vanishes in all zeros of p_2. But this indicates a common divisor of p_1, p_2 unless p_2 is a constant polynomial function. This shows

$$\mathfrak{r}\mathscr{P}_{\mathrm{Int}}(\boldsymbol{G}) = \mathscr{P}_{\mathrm{Int}}(\boldsymbol{H}).$$

Now suppose that $p \in \mathscr{P}_{\mathrm{Aut}}(\boldsymbol{H})$. By the foregoing

$$p = \mathfrak{r}p' \qquad \text{with some} \quad p' \in \mathscr{P}_{\mathrm{Int}}(\boldsymbol{G})$$

as well as

$$p = \sigma p = \mathfrak{r}\sigma p' \qquad \text{for any} \quad \sigma \in \mathrm{Aut}(\boldsymbol{G}, \boldsymbol{H}).$$

Since $\mathfrak{r}$ maps $\mathscr{P}_{\mathrm{Aut}}(\boldsymbol{G})$ injectively, it follows that

$$\sigma p' = p' \qquad \text{for} \quad \sigma \in \mathrm{Aut}(\boldsymbol{G}, \boldsymbol{H});$$

but this also holds for $\sigma \in \mathrm{Int}(\boldsymbol{G})$, hence for $\sigma \in \mathrm{Aut}\,\boldsymbol{G}$, which proves that

$$\mathfrak{r}\mathscr{P}_{\mathrm{Aut}}(\boldsymbol{G}) = \mathscr{P}_{\mathrm{Aut}}(\boldsymbol{H})$$

and completes the proof of Theorem 77.20.

Now the remainder of Theorem 77.21 is a consequence of 77.22 and Theorem 77.20.

77.24. Relating $\mathscr{P}_{\mathrm{Int}}(G)$ to the Center of $\mathscr{E}(G)$

Theorem There is a degree-preserving one-to-one linear mapping of the space of $\boldsymbol{G}$-invariant polynomial functions onto the center of the associative envelope of $\boldsymbol{G}$.

Proof The adjoint action of $\boldsymbol{G}$ induced in $\mathscr{P}(\boldsymbol{G})$ is a linear representation of $\boldsymbol{G}$ called f. The adjoint action of $\boldsymbol{G}$ extended to $\mathscr{E}(\boldsymbol{G})$ (the associative envelope) is a representation of $\boldsymbol{G}$ called g (so $g\boldsymbol{a}$ acts as an inner derivation on the ring $\mathscr{E}(\boldsymbol{G})$).

$\mathscr{P}(\boldsymbol{G})$ splits under f into invariant linear subspaces $\mathscr{P}^n(\boldsymbol{G})$, consisting of 0 and the homogeneous polynomial functions of degree n.

Under g, which is conducible, $\mathscr{E}(\boldsymbol{G})$ splits into invariant linear subspaces $\mathscr{E}^n(\boldsymbol{G})$, such that $\sum_{i=0}^n \mathscr{E}^i(\boldsymbol{G})$ consists of all elements of degree $\leqslant n$.

Obviously f in $\mathscr{P}^n(\boldsymbol{G})$ and g in $\mathscr{E}^n(\boldsymbol{G})$ are equivalent (see 39.3), and under this equivalence invariants and center elements correspond to one another as expressed in the statement.

77.25–27. A Characterization of Killing–Coxeter Elements

77.25. Proposition The classes of Int W^*-equivalent elements of $\boldsymbol{H}$ are separated by the set $\mathscr{P}_{\mathrm{Int}}(\boldsymbol{H})$ and thus even by its homogeneous generators $I_1, \ldots, I_l$.

Proof Let $\{\boldsymbol{h}_1,\ldots,\boldsymbol{h}_a\}$, $\{\boldsymbol{h}_{a+1},\ldots,\boldsymbol{h}_b\}$ be two different equivalence classes. For every $i<b$ take a first-degree function β_i on $\boldsymbol{H}$ with $\beta_i(\boldsymbol{h}_i)=0$, $\beta_i(\boldsymbol{h}_b)=1$, form their product β,

$$\beta(\boldsymbol{h}) = \prod_i \beta_i(\boldsymbol{h}),$$

and β^*, defined by

$$\beta^*(\boldsymbol{h}) = \sum_{S\in \mathrm{Int}W^*} \beta(S\boldsymbol{h}).$$

β^* separates the two classes.

Corollary The homogeneous invariants $I_1,\ldots,I_l$ extended to homogeneous invariants in $\mathscr{P}(\boldsymbol{G})$ separate the inner classes of elements belonging to the same trunk, hence those of ad-pure elements.

77.26. Proposition $\boldsymbol{a}\in\boldsymbol{G}$ ad-nilpotent iff $I_1(\boldsymbol{a}) = \cdots = I_l(\boldsymbol{a}) = 0$.

Proof If $I_1(\boldsymbol{a}) = \cdots = I_l(\boldsymbol{a}) = 0$, then, in particular, all coefficients of $\Upsilon_{\boldsymbol{a}} \det(\tilde{\boldsymbol{a}} - \lambda)$ except the highest vanish, as do all roots of $\boldsymbol{a}$. Then $\boldsymbol{a}$ is ad-nilpotent. If $\boldsymbol{a}$ is ad-nilpotent, then by 69.32 there is an $\boldsymbol{h}\in\boldsymbol{G}$ with $[\boldsymbol{h},\boldsymbol{a}]=\boldsymbol{a}$. Thus $(\exp\tau\tilde{\boldsymbol{h}})\boldsymbol{a} = e^{\tau}\boldsymbol{a}$ for scalar τ, and $I_j(\boldsymbol{a}) = I_j((\exp\tau\tilde{\boldsymbol{h}})\boldsymbol{a}) = I_j(e^{\tau}\boldsymbol{a})$, from which $I_j(\boldsymbol{a})=0$ follows.

77.27 According to Theorem 77.3, the adjoint of a Killing–Coxeter element has in $\boldsymbol{H}$ a regular, hence non-ad-nilpotent, eigenvector belonging to a primitive $(q+1)$th root of unity.

Theorem Let $a \in G$ be such that

$$\tilde{a}\boldsymbol{x} = \lambda \boldsymbol{x},$$

with an $\boldsymbol{x} \neq \boldsymbol{0}$ that is non-ad-nilpotent (equivalently, because of cleaving, ad-pure). Then

$$\lambda^{k_j+1} = 1 \qquad \text{for some } j.$$

If, moreover, λ is a primitive $(q+1)$th root of unity, then a is a Killing–Coxeter element.

Proof By 77.26, since $\boldsymbol{x}$ is not ad-nilpotent, $I_j(\boldsymbol{x}) \neq 0$ for some j. Now $I_j(\boldsymbol{x}) = I_j(\tilde{a}\boldsymbol{x}) = \lambda^{k_j+1} I_j(\boldsymbol{x})$; thus $\lambda^{k_j+1} = 1$.

Now suppose λ is a primitive $(q+1)$th root of unity. Then, of necessity,

$$I_1(\boldsymbol{x}) = \cdots = I_{l-1}(\boldsymbol{x}) = 0, \qquad I_l(\boldsymbol{x}) \neq 0.$$

By Corollary 77.25 all such $\boldsymbol{x}$ are conjugate up to a scalar factor. If t is a Killing–Coxeter element, then by Theorem 77.3 (last statement) there is a regular eigenvector $\boldsymbol{y}$ such that $\tilde{t}\boldsymbol{y} = \lambda \boldsymbol{y}$. By the foregoing $\boldsymbol{x}$ and $\boldsymbol{y}$ are conjugate up to a scalar factor. Therefore t may even be chosen such that, in addition to $\tilde{a}\boldsymbol{x} = \lambda\boldsymbol{x}$, also $\tilde{t}\boldsymbol{x} = \lambda\boldsymbol{x}$; moreover, $\boldsymbol{x}$ has turned out to be regular. Let $\boldsymbol{H}$ be its trunk. Then $\tilde{t}^{-1}\tilde{a}$ leaves $\boldsymbol{x}$ invariant, thus $\boldsymbol{H}$ elementwise invariant. So by the argument in the proof of Theorem 77.7, a is conjugate to t and thus a Killing–Coxeter element itself.

77.28. Historical Note A few remarks are added to the exposition of 77.1.

The proofs in 77.15–18 have been borrowed from A. J. Coleman [*Canad. J. Math.* **10**, 349–356 (1958)] who in turn owed some of these ideas to G. C. Shephard and J. A. Todd (*loc. cit.*).

Some ideas in 77.2–6 also come from Coleman, though the framework and details have been simplified, particularly by a direct proof of the empirically discovered formula 77.4; this proof is due to R. Steinberg (*loc. cit.*). The matrix method in the proof of 77.6 is due to Coxeter (*loc. cit.*). It is the least satisfactory link in the whole procedure. An alternative method is found in Steinberg's paper.

The Killing–Coxeter tool goes back to R. Killing [*Math. Ann.* **33**, 1–48 (1889)]; it was excavated by Coxeter (*loc. cit.*). The Killing–Coxeter element was introduced by Kostant (*loc. cit.*).

The main ideas of 77.9–11 and 77.13–14, as well as the contents of 77.24–26 have come from Kostant (*loc. cit.*).

Theorem 77.24 is usually found in the literature with extremely complicated proofs.

R. Steinberg's proof of $\mathfrak{r}P_{\mathrm{Int}}(G) = P_{\mathrm{Int}}(H)$, found in D.-N. Verma's Yale thesis, 1966, Structure of Certain Induced Representations of Complex Semisimple Lie Algebras, A.5, is shorter than the present one, which, however, shows other interesting perspectives.

APPENDIX

TABLE A

THE GRAPH AND DIMENSION OF $G \in$ Alg Lie Com SSS; THE LENGTH SQUARE OF THE SHORTEST NONZERO ROOTFORM

A$_l$:	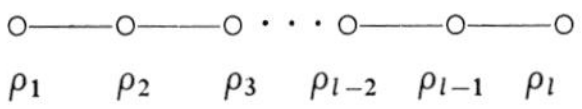	$(l+1)^2 - 1$	$(l+1)^{-1}$
B$_l$:	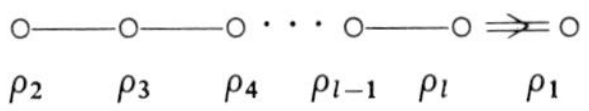	$l(2l+1)$	$(4l-2)^{-1}$
C$_l$:	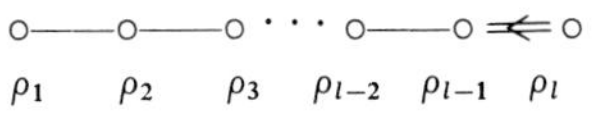	$l(2l+1)$	$(2l+2)^{-1}$
D$_l$:	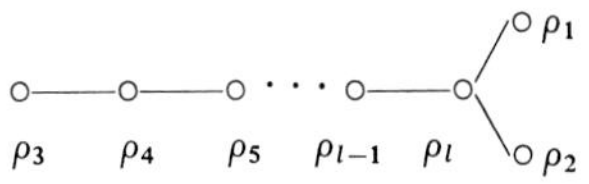	$l(2l-1)$	$(2l-2)^{-1}$
E$_6$:	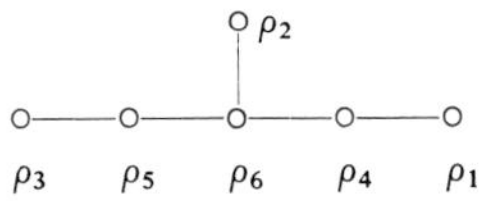	78	$\frac{1}{12}$
E$_7$:	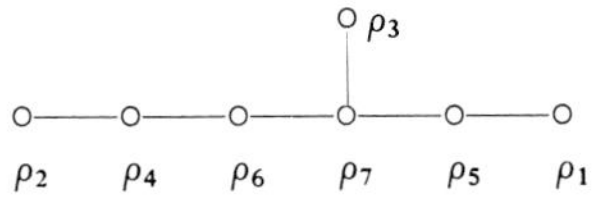	133	$\frac{1}{18}$
E$_8$:	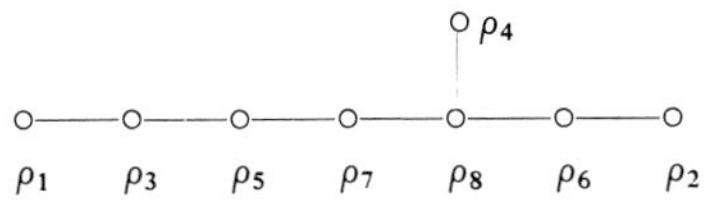	248	$\frac{1}{30}$
F$_4$:	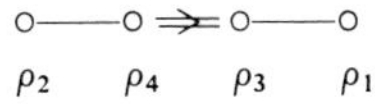	52	$\frac{1}{18}$
G$_2$:	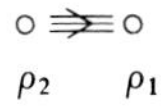	14	$\frac{1}{12}$

TABLE B

The Positive Rootforms on a Natural Basis

Indicated by the distribution of the relative coefficients on the graph.
Obligatory fillings are underlined.
In the case of the exceptional Lie algebras the rootforms are arranged according to their altitudes (sum of coefficients).

A$_l$: 0—0— · · · —0—1—1— · · · —$\underline{1}$—0—0— · · · —0

B$_l$: 0—0— · · · —0—1—1— · · · —$\underline{1}$—0—0— · · · ⇛ 0
0—0— · · · —0—1—1— · · · —1 ⇛ $\underline{1}$
0—0— · · · —0—1—1— · · · —$\underline{1}$—2—2— · · · —2 ⇛ $\underline{2}$

C$_l$: 0—0— · · · —0—1—1— · · · —$\underline{1}$—0—0— · · · —0 ⇚ $\underline{0}$
0—0— · · · —0—1—1— · · · —1—2—2— · · · —2 ⇚ $\underline{1}$

D$_l$: 0—0— · · · —0—1—1— · · · —$\underline{1}$—0—0— · · · —0 ⟨ $\underline{0}$ / $\underline{0}$ ⟩

0—0— · · · —0—1—1— · · · —1 ⟨ $\underline{1}$ / $\underline{0}$ ⟩

0—0— · · · —0—1—1— · · · —1 ⟨ $\underline{0}$ / $\underline{1}$ ⟩

0—0— · · · —0—1—1— · · · —$\underline{1}$—2—2— · · · —2 ⟨ $\underline{1}$ / $\underline{1}$ ⟩

E$_6$:

0	0	0	1	0	0
10000	01000	00100	00000	00010	00001
0	0	1	0	0	
11000	01100	00100	00110	00011	
0	1	0	1	0	
11100	01100	01110	00110	00111	
1	0	1	0	1	
11100	11110	01110	01111	00111	
1	0	1	1		
11110	11111	01111	01210		
1	1	1			
11111	11210	01211			
1	1	1			
11211	12210	01221			
1	1				
12211	11221				
1					
12221					
1					
12321					
2					
12321					

TABLE B—*continued*

$\mathbf{E}_7$:	0	0	0	0	1	0	0
	100000	010000	001000	000100	000000	000010	000001
	0	0	0	1	0	0	
	110000	011000	001100	000100	000110	000011	
	0	0	1	0	1	0	
	111000	011100	001100	001110	000110	000111	
	0	1	0	1	0	1	
	111100	011100	011110	001110	001111	000111	
	1	0	1	0	1	1	
	111100	111110	011110	011111	001111	001210	
	1	0	1	1	1		
	111110	111111	011210	011111	001211		
	1	1	1	1	1		
	111210	111111	012210	011211	001221		
	1	1	1	1			
	112210	111211	012211	011221			
	1	1	1	1			
	122210	112211	111221	012221			
	1	1	1				
	122211	112221	012321				
	1	1	2				
	122221	112321	012321				
	1	2					
	122321	112321					
	1	2					
	123321	122321					
	2						
	123321						
	2						
	123421						
	2						
	123431						
	2						
	123432						

$\mathbf{E}_8$:	0	0	0	0	0	1	0	0
	1000000	0100000	0010000	0001000	0000100	0000000	0000010	0000001
	0	0	0	0	1	0	0	
	1100000	0110000	0011000	0001100	0000100	0000110	0000011	
	0	0	0	1	0	1	0	
	1110000	0111000	0011100	0001100	0001110	0000110	0000111	
	0	0	1	0	1	1	0	
	1111000	0111100	0011100	0011110	0001110	0000111	0001111	
	0	1	0	1	0	1	1	
	1111100	0111100	0111110	0011110	0011111	0001210	0001111	
	1	0	1	0	1	1	1	
	1111100	1111110	0111110	0111111	0011210	0011111	0001211	
	1	0	1	1	1	1	1	
	1111110	1111111	0111210	0111111	0012210	0011211	0001221	

TABLE B—*continued*

E_8 *continued*:

1	1	1	1	1	1
1111210	1111111	0112210	0111211	0012211	0011221
1	1	1	1	1	1
1112210	1111211	0122210	0112211	0111221	0012221
1	1	1	1	1	1
1122210	1112211	1111221	0122211	0112221	0012321
1	1	1	1	1	2
1222210	1122211	1112221	0122221	0112321	0012321
1	1	1	1	2	
1222211	1122221	1112321	0122321	0112321	
1	1	2	1	2	
1222221	1122321	1112321	0123321	0122321	
1	1	2	2		
1222321	1123321	1122321	0123321		
1	2	2	2		
1223321	1222321	1123321	0123421		
1	2	2	2		
1233321	1223321	1123421	0123431		
2	2	2	2		
1233321	1223421	1123431	0123432		
2	2	2			
1233421	1223431	1123432			
2	2	2			
1234421	1233431	1223432			
2	2				
1234431	1233432				
2	2				
1234531	1234432				
3	2				
1234531	1234532				
3	2				
1234532	1234542				
3					
1234542					
3					
1234642					
3					
1235642					
3					
1245642					
3					
1345642					
3					
2345642					

TABLE B—*continued*

$\mathbf{F}_4$:	$10 \Rightarrow 00$	$01 \Rightarrow 00$	$00 \Rightarrow 10$	$00 \Rightarrow 01$
	$11 \Rightarrow 00$	$01 \Rightarrow 10$	$00 \Rightarrow 11$	
	$01 \Rightarrow 20$	$11 \Rightarrow 10$	$01 \Rightarrow 11$	
	$11 \Rightarrow 20$	$11 \Rightarrow 11$	$01 \Rightarrow 21$	
	$12 \Rightarrow 20$	$01 \Rightarrow 22$	$11 \Rightarrow 21$	
	$11 \Rightarrow 22$	$12 \Rightarrow 21$		
	$12 \Rightarrow 22$	$12 \Rightarrow 31$		
	$12 \Rightarrow 32$			
	$12 \Rightarrow 42$			
	$13 \Rightarrow 42$			
	$23 \Rightarrow 42$			
$\mathbf{G}_2$:	$1 \Rrightarrow 0$	$0 \Rrightarrow 1$		
	$1 \Rrightarrow 1$			
	$1 \Rrightarrow 2$			
	$1 \Rrightarrow 3$			
	$2 \Rrightarrow 3$			

TABLE C

The Positive Rootforms on a Symmetric Basis and Their Altitudes

Orthonormality is always meant up to a common factor. The norming factor is indicated. In some cases a redundant orthonormal basis is used, that is, an orthonormal basis of a linear extension of H^*.

A_l: A redundant orthonormal basis $\omega_1, \ldots, \omega_{l+1}$ with $\Sigma\omega_i = 0$.
Norming factor: $(2l+2)^{-1/2}$.
All rootforms $\neq 0$: $\omega_i - \omega_j$, $i \neq j$.
Positive rootforms: $\omega_i - \omega_j = \rho_i + \cdots + \rho_{j-1}$ for $1 \leqslant i < j \leqslant l+1$.
Altitude $\omega_i - \omega_j = j - i$.
Primitive rootforms: $\omega_i - \omega_{i+1}$ for $i = 1, \ldots, l$.

B_l: An orthonormal basis $\omega_1, \ldots, \omega_l$.
Norming factor: $(4l-2)^{-1/2}$.
All rootforms $\neq 0$: $\pm\omega_i, \pm\omega_i \pm \omega_j$ ($i \neq j$, $\pm$ independent).
Positive rootforms:

$$\omega_i = \rho_{i+1} + \rho_{i+2} + \cdots + \rho_l + \rho_1,$$
$$\omega_i - \omega_j = \rho_{i+1} + \cdots + \rho_j, \quad i < j,$$
$$\omega_i + \omega_j = \rho_{i+1} + \cdots + \rho_j + 2\rho_{j+1} + \cdots + 2\rho_l + 2\rho_1, \quad i < j.$$

Altitude $\omega_i = l - i + 1$.
Altitude $\omega_i - \omega_j = j - i$.
Altitude $\omega_i + \omega_j = (l - i + 1) + (l - j + 1)$.
Primitive rootforms: $\omega_i - \omega_{i+1}$ for $i = 1, \ldots, l-1$, and ω_l.

C_l: An orthonormal basis $\omega_1, \ldots, \omega_l$.
Norming factor: $(4l+4)^{-1/2}$.
All rootforms $\neq 0$: $\pm 2\omega_i$, $\pm\omega_i \pm \omega_j$ ($i \neq j$, $\pm$ independent).
Positive rootforms:

$$\omega_i - \omega_j = \rho_i + \cdots + \rho_{j-1}, \quad i < j,$$
$$2\omega_j = 2\rho_j + \cdots + 2\rho_{l-1} + \rho_l,$$
$$\omega_i + \omega_j = \rho_i + \cdots + \rho_{j-1} + 2\rho_j + \cdots + 2\rho_{l-1} + \rho_l, \quad i < j.$$

Altitude $\omega_i - \omega_j = j - i$.
Altitude $2\omega_j = 2(l - j) + 1$.
Altitude $\omega_i + \omega_j = 2l - i - j + 1$.
Primitive rootforms: $\omega_i - \omega_{i+1}$ for $i = 1, \ldots, l-1$, and $2\omega_l$.

D_l: An orthonormal basis $\omega_1, \ldots, \omega_l$.
Norming factor: $(4l-4)^{-1/2}$.
All rootforms $\neq 0$: $\pm\omega_i \pm \omega_j$ ($i \neq j$, $\pm$ independent).
Positive rootforms:

$$\omega_i - \omega_j = \rho_{i+2} + \cdots + \rho_{j+1}, \quad i < j < l,$$
$$\omega_i - \omega_l = \rho_{i+2} + \cdots + \rho_l + \rho_1, \quad i < l,$$
$$\omega_i + \omega_l = \rho_{i+2} + \cdots + \rho_l + \rho_2, \quad i < l,$$
$$\omega_i + \omega_j = \rho_{i+2} + \cdots + \rho_{j+1} + 2\rho_{j+2} + \cdots + 2\rho_l + \rho_1 + \rho_2, \quad i < j < l.$$

Altitude $\omega_i - \omega_j = j - i$.
Altitude $\omega_i + \omega_j = (l - i) + (l - j)$.
Primitive rootforms: $\omega_i - \omega_{i+1}$ for $i = 1, \ldots, l-1$, and $\omega_{l-1} + \omega_l$.

TABLE C—*continued*

E$_6$: A basis $\omega_1, \ldots, \omega_6$ with $(\omega_i, \omega_i) = \frac{4}{9}$, $(\omega_i, \omega_j) = -\frac{1}{18}$ $(i \neq j)$ up to norming.
Norming factor: $12^{-1/2}$.
Rootforms $\neq 0$: $\ulcorner 1, -1, 0, 0, 0, 0 \urcorner$ and all permutation results,
$\pm \ulcorner 1, 1, 1, 0, 0, 0 \urcorner$ and all permutation results,
$\pm \ulcorner 1, 1, 1, 1, 1, 1 \urcorner$.
Primitive rootforms: $\omega_i - \omega_{i+1}$ $(i = 1, \ldots, 6)$ and $\omega_4 + \omega_5 + \omega_6$.

E$_7$: A basis $\omega_1, \ldots, \omega_7$ with $(\omega_i, \omega_i) = \frac{4}{9}$, $(\omega_i, \omega_j) = -\frac{1}{18}$ $(i \neq j)$ up to norming.
Norming factor: $18^{-1/2}$.
Rootforms $\neq 0$: $\ulcorner 1, -1, 0, 0, 0, 0, 0 \urcorner$ and all permutation results,
$\pm \ulcorner 1, 1, 1, 0, 0, 0, 0 \urcorner$ and all permutation results,
$\pm \ulcorner 1, 1, 1, 1, 1, 1, 0 \urcorner$ and all permutation results.
Primitive rootforms: $\omega_i - \omega_{i+1}$ for $i = 1, \ldots, 6$, and $\omega_5 + \omega_6 + \omega_7$.
Another: A redundant orthonormal basis $\omega_1, \ldots, \omega_8$ with $\Sigma\, \omega_i = 0$.
Norming factor: $36^{-1/2}$.
Rootforms $\neq 0$: $\ulcorner 1, -1, 0, 0, 0, 0, 0, 0 \urcorner$ and all permutation results,
$\frac{1}{2} \ulcorner 1, 1, 1, 1, -1, -1, -1, -1 \urcorner$ and all permutation results.
Primitive rootforms: $\omega_i - \omega_{i+1}$ for $i = 1, \ldots, 6$, and
$\frac{1}{2}(\omega_1 + \omega_2 + \omega_3 + \omega_4 - \omega_5 - \omega_6 - \omega_7 - \omega_8)$.

E$_8$: A basis $\omega_1, \ldots, \omega_8$ with $(\omega_i, \omega_i) = \frac{4}{9}$, $(\omega_i, \omega_j) = -\frac{1}{18}$ $(i \neq j)$ up to norming.
Norming factor: $30^{-1/2}$.
Rootforms $\neq 0$: $\ulcorner 1, -1, 0, 0, 0, 0, 0, 0 \urcorner$ and all permutation results,
$\pm \ulcorner 1, 1, 1, 0, 0, 0, 0, 0 \urcorner$ and all permutation results,
$\pm \ulcorner 1, 1, 1, 1, 1, 1, 0, 0 \urcorner$ and all permutation results,
$\pm \ulcorner 2, 1, 1, 1, 1, 1, 1, 1 \urcorner$ and all permutation results.
Primitive rootforms: $\omega_i - \omega_{i+1}$ for $i = 1, \ldots, 7$, and $\omega_6 + \omega_7 + \omega_8$.
Another: An orthonormal basis $\omega_1, \ldots, \omega_8$.
Norming factor: $60^{-1/2}$.
Rootforms $\neq 0$: $\pm \ulcorner 1, 1, 0, 0, 0, 0, 0, 0 \urcorner$ and all permutation results,
$\ulcorner 1, -1, 0, 0, 0, 0, 0, 0 \urcorner$ and all permutation results,
$\pm \frac{1}{2} \ulcorner 1, 1, 1, 1, 1, 1, 1, -1 \urcorner$ and all permutation results,
$\pm \frac{1}{2} \ulcorner 1, 1, 1, 1, 1, -1, -1, -1 \urcorner$ and all permutation results.
Primitive rootforms: $\omega_i - \omega_{i+1}$ for $i = 1, \ldots, 7$, and
$-\frac{1}{2}(\omega_1 + \omega_2 + \omega_3 + \omega_4 + \omega_5 - \omega_6 - \omega_7 - \omega_8)$.

F$_4$: An orthonormal basis $\omega_1, \omega_2, \omega_3, \omega_4$.
Norming factor: $18^{-1/2}$.
Rootforms $\neq 0$: $\pm \omega_i \pm \omega_j$ $(i \neq j)$,
$\pm \omega_i$,
$\pm \frac{1}{2}\omega_1 \pm \frac{1}{2}\omega_2 \pm \frac{1}{2}\omega_3 \pm \frac{1}{2}\omega_4$, with independent signs.
Primitive rootforms: $\omega_2 - \omega_3$, $\omega_3 - \omega_4$, ω_4, $\frac{1}{2}(\omega_1 - \omega_2 - \omega_3 - \omega_4)$.

G$_2$: A redundant basis $\omega_1, \omega_2, \omega_3$ with $\omega_1 + \omega_2 + \omega_3 = 0$.
Norming factor: $12^{-1/2}$.
$(\omega_i, \omega_i) = 1$, $(\omega_i, \omega_j) = -\frac{1}{2}$ $(i \neq j)$.
Rootforms $\neq 0$: $\pm \omega_i$, $\omega_i - \omega_j$ $(i \neq j)$.
Primitive rootforms: $\omega_1 - \omega_2$, $-\omega_1$.

TABLE D

Number of Rootforms of Given Positive Altitude a

A_l: $l-a+1$ for $1 \leqslant a \leqslant l$.
Altitude of the top rootform: l.

B_l: 1 of type ω_i for $a \leqslant l$,
max $(l-a, 0)$ of type $\omega_i - \omega_j$,

$$\min\left(\left[\frac{a-1}{2}\right], \left[\frac{2l+1-a}{2}\right]\right) \text{ of type } \omega_i + \omega_j \quad \text{for} \quad a \leqslant 2l-1;$$

$$\text{together} \quad \left[\frac{2l-a+1}{2}\right] \quad \text{for} \quad a \leqslant 2l-1.$$

Altitude of the top rootform: $2l-1$.

C_l: max $(l-a, 0)$ of type $\omega_i - \omega_j$,
1, 0, respectively, of type $2\omega_j$ for odd, even $a \leqslant 2l-1$,

$$\min\left(\left[\frac{a}{2}\right], \left[\frac{2l-a}{2}\right]\right) \text{ of type } \omega_i + \omega_j \quad \text{for} \quad a \leqslant 2l-1;$$

$$\text{together} \quad \left[\frac{2l-a+1}{2}\right] \quad \text{for} \quad a \leqslant 2l-1.$$

Altitude of the top rootform: $2l-1$.

D_l: max $(l-a, 0)$ of type $\omega_i - \omega_j$,

$$\min\left(\left[\frac{a+1}{2}\right], \left[\frac{2l-a-1}{2}\right]\right) \text{ of type } \omega_i + \omega_j \quad \text{for} \quad a \leqslant 2l-3;$$

$$\text{together} \quad \left[\frac{2l-a+1}{2}\right] \quad \text{for} \quad 1 \leqslant a \leqslant l-1,$$

$$\left[\frac{2l-a-1}{2}\right] \quad \text{for} \quad l \leqslant a \leqslant 2l-3.$$

Altitude of the top rootform: $2l-3$.

E_6: $a = 1, 2, 3, 4, 5, 6, 7, 8, 9, 10, 11, 12$
$\# = 6, 5, 5, 5, 4, 3, 3, 2, 1, 1, 1, 0$

E_7: $a = 1, 2, 3, 4, 5, 6, 7, 8, 9, 10, 11, 12, 13, 14, 15, 16, 17, 18$
$\# = 7, 6, 6, 6, 6, 5, 5, 4, 4, 3, 3, 2, 2, 1, 1, 1, 1, 0$

E_8: $a = 1, 2, 3, 4, 5, 6, 7, 8, 9, 10, 11, 12, 13, 14, 15, 16, 17, 18, 19, 20, 21, 22, 23$
$\# = 8, 7, 7, 7, 7, 7, 7, 7, 6, 6, 6, 6, 5, 5, 4, 4, 4, 4, 3, 3, 2, 2, 2, 2$

$a = 24, 25, 26, 27, 28, 29, 30$
$\# = 1, 1, 1, 1, 1, 1, 0$

F_4: $a = 1, 2, 3, 4, 5, 6, 7, 8, 9, 10, 11, 12$
$\# = 4, 3, 3, 3, 3, 2, 2, 1, 1, 1, 1, 0$

G_2: $a = 1, 2, 3, 4, 5, 6$
$\# = 2, 1, 1, 1, 1, 0$

TABLE E

DOMINANT ROOTFORMS (THE TOP ONE FIRST)

$\mathbf{A}_l$:	$\rho_1 + \cdots + \rho_l$	$= \omega_1 - \omega_{l+1}$
$\mathbf{B}_l$:	$\rho_2 + 2\rho_3 + \cdots + 2\rho_l + 2\rho_1$	$= \omega_1 + \omega_2$
	$\rho_2 + \rho_3 + \cdots + \rho_l + \rho_1$	$= \omega_1$
$\mathbf{C}_l$:	$2\rho_1 + 2\rho_2 + \cdots + 2\rho_{l-1} + \rho_l$	$= 2\omega_1$
	$\rho_1 + 2\rho_2 + \cdots + 2\rho_{l-1} + \rho_l$	$= \omega_1 + \omega_2$
$\mathbf{D}_l$:	$\rho_3 + 2\rho_4 + \cdots + 2\rho_l + \rho_1 + \rho_2$	$= \omega_1 + \omega_2$
$\mathbf{E}_6$:	$\begin{matrix} & & 2 & & \\ 1 & 2 & 3 & 2 & 1 \end{matrix}$	
$\mathbf{E}_7$:	$\begin{matrix} & & & 2 & & \\ 1 & 2 & 3 & 4 & 3 & 2 \end{matrix}$	
$\mathbf{E}_8$:	$\begin{matrix} & & & & & 3 & \\ 2 & 3 & 4 & 5 & 6 & 4 & 2 \end{matrix}$	
$\mathbf{F}_4$:	$23 \Rightarrow 42, \quad 12 \Rightarrow 32$	
$\mathbf{G}_2$:	$2 \Rrightarrow 3, \quad 1 \Rrightarrow 2$	

TABLE F

Fundamental Weights

$\mathbf{A}_l$: $\pi_k = \dfrac{l+1-k}{l+1}(\rho_1 + 2\rho_2 + \cdots + k\rho_k) + \dfrac{k}{l+1}(\rho_l + 2\rho_{l-1} + \cdots + (l-k)\,\rho_{k+1})$

$\quad = \omega_1 + \cdots + \omega_k$

$\mathbf{B}_l$: $\pi_1 = \frac{1}{2}(l\rho_1 + \rho_2 + 2\rho_3 + \cdots + (l-1)\,\rho_l)$

$\pi_k = (k-1)\,\rho_1 + \rho_2 + 2\rho_3 + \cdots + (k-1)(\rho_k + \rho_{k+1} + \cdots + \rho_l)$ for $k \neq 1$

or

$\pi_1 = \frac{1}{2}(\omega_1 + \cdots + \omega_l)$

$\pi_k = \omega_1 + \cdots + \omega_{k-1}$ for $k \neq 1$

$\mathbf{C}_l$: $\pi_k = \rho_1 + 2\rho_2 + \cdots + k(\rho_k + \rho_{k+1} + \cdots + \frac{1}{2}\rho_l)$ for $k < l$

$\pi_l = \rho_1 + 2\rho_2 + \cdots + (l-1)\,\rho_{l-1} + \frac{1}{2}l\rho_l$

or

$\pi_k = \omega_1 + \cdots + \omega_k$

$\mathbf{D}_l$: $\pi_1 = \frac{1}{4}l\rho_1 + \frac{1}{4}(l-2)\,\rho_2 + \frac{1}{2}(\rho_3 + 2\rho_4 + \cdots + (l-2)\,\rho_l)$

$\pi_2 = \frac{1}{4}(l-2)\,\rho_1 + \frac{1}{4}l\rho_2 + \frac{1}{2}(\rho_3 + 2\rho_4 + \cdots + (l-2)\,\rho_l)$

$\pi_k = \frac{1}{2}(k-2)(\rho_1 + \rho_2) + \rho_3 + 2\rho_4 + \cdots + (k-2)(\rho_k + \rho_{k+1} + \cdots + \rho_l)$ for $k \neq 1, 2$

or

$\pi_1 = \frac{1}{2}(\omega_1 + \omega_2 + \cdots - \omega_l)$

$\pi_2 = \frac{1}{2}(\omega_1 + \omega_2 + \cdots + \omega_l)$

$\pi_k = \omega_1 + \cdots + \omega_{k-2}$ for $k \geqslant 3$

$\mathbf{E}_6$: $\pi_1 = \frac{1}{3}\cdot\begin{array}{ccccc} & & 3 & & \\ 2 & 4 & 6 & 5 & 4 \end{array}$

$\pi_2 = \begin{array}{ccccc} & & 2 & & \\ 1 & 2 & 3 & 2 & 1 \end{array}$

$\pi_3 = \frac{1}{3}\cdot\begin{array}{ccccc} & & 3 & & \\ 4 & 5 & 6 & 4 & 2 \end{array}$

$\pi_4 = \frac{1}{3}\cdot\begin{array}{ccccc} & & 6 & & \\ 4 & 8 & 12 & 10 & 5 \end{array}$

$\pi_5 = \frac{1}{3}\cdot\begin{array}{ccccc} & & 6 & & \\ 5 & 10 & 12 & 8 & 4 \end{array}$

$\pi_6 = \begin{array}{ccccc} & & 3 & & \\ 2 & 4 & 6 & 4 & 2 \end{array}$

$\mathbf{E}_7$: $\pi_1 = \begin{array}{cccccc} & & 2 & & & \\ 1 & 2 & 3 & 4 & 3 & 2 \end{array}$

$\pi_2 = \frac{1}{2}\cdot\begin{array}{cccccc} & & 3 & & & \\ 3 & 4 & 5 & 6 & 4 & 2 \end{array}$

$\pi_3 = \frac{1}{2}\cdot\begin{array}{cccccc} & & 7 & & & \\ 3 & 6 & 9 & 12 & 8 & 4 \end{array}$

$\pi_4 = \begin{array}{cccccc} & & 3 & & & \\ 2 & 4 & 5 & 6 & 4 & 2 \end{array}$

$\pi_5 = \begin{array}{cccccc} & & 4 & & & \\ 2 & 4 & 6 & 8 & 6 & 3 \end{array}$

$\pi_6 = \frac{1}{2}\cdot\begin{array}{cccccc} & & 9 & & & \\ 5 & 10 & 15 & 18 & 12 & 6 \end{array}$

$\pi_7 = \begin{array}{cccccc} & & 6 & & & \\ 3 & 6 & 9 & 12 & 8 & 4 \end{array}$

TABLE F—*continued*

$\mathbf{E}_8$:

$$\pi_1 = \begin{array}{ccccccc} & & & & 3 & & \\ 2 & 3 & 4 & 5 & 6 & 4 & 2 \end{array}$$

$$\pi_2 = \begin{array}{ccccccc} & & & & 5 & & \\ 2 & 4 & 6 & 8 & 10 & 7 & 4 \end{array}$$

$$\pi_3 = \begin{array}{ccccccc} & & & & 6 & & \\ 3 & 6 & 8 & 10 & 12 & 8 & 4 \end{array}$$

$$\pi_4 = \begin{array}{ccccccc} & & & & 8 & & \\ 3 & 6 & 9 & 12 & 15 & 10 & 5 \end{array}$$

$$\pi_5 = \begin{array}{ccccccc} & & & & 9 & & \\ 4 & 8 & 12 & 15 & 18 & 12 & 6 \end{array}$$

$$\pi_6 = \begin{array}{ccccccc} & & & & 10 & & \\ 4 & 8 & 12 & 16 & 20 & 14 & 7 \end{array}$$

$$\pi_7 = \begin{array}{ccccccc} & & & & 12 & & \\ 5 & 10 & 15 & 20 & 24 & 16 & 8 \end{array}$$

$$\pi_8 = \begin{array}{ccccccc} & & & & 15 & & \\ 6 & 12 & 18 & 24 & 30 & 20 & 10 \end{array}$$

$\mathbf{F}_4$:

$\pi_1 = 1 - 2 \Rightarrow 3 - 2$
$\pi_2 = 2 - 3 \Rightarrow 4 - 2$
$\pi_3 = 2 - 4 \Rightarrow 6 - 3$
$\pi_4 = 3 - 6 \Rightarrow 8 - 4$

$\mathbf{G}_2$:

$\pi_1 = 1 \Rrightarrow 2$
$\pi_2 = 2 \Rrightarrow 3$

TABLE G

Isomorphisms and Equivalences for Low-Rank Semisimple Lie Algebras (Partly Conventional)

$\mathbf{A}_0 = \mathbf{B}_0 = \mathbf{C}_0 = \mathbf{D}_0 = \mathbf{O}$ = class of null algebras.
$\mathbf{A}_1 = \mathbf{B}_1 = \mathbf{C}_1$.
$\mathbf{D}_1$ = class of the one-dimensional Lie algebras.
$\pi_2(\mathbf{B}_1) = 2\pi_1(\mathbf{A}_1)$.
$\mathbf{B}_2 = \mathbf{C}_2$.
$\pi_1(\mathbf{B}_2) = \pi_2(\mathbf{C}_2)$.
$\pi_2(\mathbf{B}_2) = \pi_1(\mathbf{C}_2)$.
$\mathbf{D}_2 = \mathbf{A}_1 + \mathbf{A}_1$.
$\pi_3(\mathbf{D}_2) = \pi_{1,1}(\mathbf{A}_1 + \mathbf{A}_1)$.
Type of the $\pi_3(\mathbf{D}_2)$-invariant:

real quadratic form

$++++$	$\mathbf{D}_{2,0}$	$\mathbf{A}_{1,0} + \mathbf{A}_{1,0}$
$+++-$	$\mathbf{D}_{2,0,*}$	$\mathbf{A}_{1,**}$
$++--$	$\mathbf{D}_{2,3}$	$\mathbf{A}_{1,1} + \mathbf{A}_{1,1}$

quaternion hermitean form

	$\mathbf{D}_{2,1}$	$\mathbf{A}_{1,0} + \mathbf{A}_{1,1}$

$\mathbf{D}_3 = \mathbf{A}_3$.
$\pi_3(\mathbf{D}_3) = \pi_2(\mathbf{A}_3)$.
Type of the $\pi_3(\mathbf{D}_3)$-invariant:

real quadratic form

$++++++$	$\mathbf{D}_{3,0}$	$\mathbf{A}_{3,0}$
$+++++-$	$\mathbf{D}_{3,0,*}$	$\mathbf{A}_{3,0,*}$
$++++--$	$\mathbf{D}_{3,3}$	$\mathbf{A}_{3,2}$
$+++---$	$\mathbf{D}_{3,3,*}$	$\mathbf{A}_{3,2,*}$

quaternion hermitean form

	$\mathbf{D}_{3,1}$	$\mathbf{A}_{3,1}$

KEY TO DEFINITIONS

Characters with a meaning that remains constant in some substantial part of the book are contained in the present list.

For terms that are not included here, refer to the lists of symbols (0.1–5) and logograms (0.6).

A, 33.3.1, 51.11.1
A_l, $\boldsymbol{\mathsf{A}}_l$, 16.1
$\boldsymbol{\mathsf{A}}_1(\boldsymbol{G})$, 76.3–9
$\mathscr{A}$, 39.2
$\mathscr{A}(\boldsymbol{G})$, $\mathscr{A}_{\mathrm{Int}}(\boldsymbol{G})$, 77.1.2
abelian Lie algebra, 12.6
abelian symmetric space, 64.7.1, 64.10
$\mathrm{ad}_{\boldsymbol{G}}$, 9.8
ad-cleaving, 18.3
ad-closed, 9.12
ad-nilpotent, 17.1
  regular, 76.4.1
ad-pure, 18.3
adjoint (algebra), 9.8
adjoint (group), 9.6
Alg Lie, 7.3
  Rea, 7.3
  Com, 7.3
Alg Lie Lin, 7.4
Alg Lie Lin SS, 19.1
Alg Lie Lin SSS, 19.1
algebra
  abelian Lie, 12.6
  adjoint, 9.8
  Borel, 68.2
  Clifford, 49.2
  commutator, 12.8
  exceptional Lie, 26.24
  exterior, 77.1.2
  Lie, 7.3
  linear Lie, 7.4
  maximal solvable Lie, 68.2
  of exterior differential forms, 77.1
  semisimple Lie, 13.4, 19.1
  simple Lie, 12.10
  solvable Lie, 13.2
altimeter, 77.10
altitude, 54.3.2
analytic manifold, 5.3, 5.6
anticommutative, 7.2
antireal, 57.1
areal, 57.1
associative, Jacobi-, 7.2
associative envelope, 39.2
Aut, 0.6
Aut $\boldsymbol{G}$, 9.2
Aut W^*, 33.2.1
Aut W^{++}, 33.2.1
$\mathrm{Aut}^G(W^{++})$, $\mathrm{Aut}^{\boldsymbol{G}}(W^{++})$, 33.3.2–3
Aut(G, H), Aut$(\boldsymbol{G}, \boldsymbol{H})$, 33.9
Aut$(\boldsymbol{F}, \boldsymbol{J})$, 66.3
Aut$(\boldsymbol{F}, \boldsymbol{J}; J_0)$, 66.3
Aut R, 63.7
autometrism class, 66.3
autometry group, 63.7
automorphism, infinitesimal, 9.2
  inner, 9.5, 33.2.1
  minus-, 23.1
  plus-, 33.11
automorphism classes, 66.3
automorphisms
  group of (inner) . . . of W^*, 33.2.1
average, left, right, 34.3

B_l, $\boldsymbol{\mathsf{B}}_l$, 16.1
ball, smooth, 8.4
basis, natural ... of W^*, 25.2.1
Betti number, 77.1
between, 70.20
boldface type, 7.4
bond, 71.1.4
Borel subalgebra, 68.2
bounded, 36.13
branch, 16.2, 20.7

C, 1.11
C-cell, 74.7
C-chamber, 74.7
C-contravalent, 55.2, 56.2
C-edge, 74.7
C-graph, 74.11
C-part, 74.7
C-restriction, 1.11
C-third dressing, 51.5.1
C-trunk, 24.2
$C(\ldots)$, 13.1.3
$C(\ldots)$, 33.4
C^*, 51.6, 56.1
C^k-curve, 2.3, 5.1
C^k, C^∞, C^{an}, 5.1
C^k, semi-, 5.1
C_r^k-group, 5.5
C_r^k-manifold, 5.3, 5.6

AUTHOR INDEX

[Occurring in notions.] (Occurring in theorems and formulas.)

Pure and Applied Mathematics

A Series of Monographs and Textbooks

Edited by

Paul A. Smith and Samuel Eilenberg

Columbia University, New York

1: Arnold Sommerfeld. Partial Differential Equations in Physics. 1949 (Lectures on Theoretical Physics, Volume VI)

2: Reinhold Baer. Linear Algebra and Projective Geometry. 1952

3: Herbert Busemann and Paul Kelly. Projective Geometry and Projective Metrics. 1953

4: Stefan Bergman and M. Schiffer. Kernel Functions and Elliptic Differential Equations in Mathematical Physics. 1953

5: Ralph Philip Boas, Jr. Entire Functions. 1954

6: Herbert Busemann. The Geometry of Geodesics. 1955

7: Claude Chevalley. Fundamental Concepts of Algebra. 1956

8: Sze-Tsen Hu. Homotopy Theory. 1959

9: A. M. Ostrowski. Solution of Equations and Systems of Equations. Second Edition. 1966

10: J. Dieudonné. Treatise on Analysis. Volume I, Foundations of Modern Analysis, enlarged and corrected printing, 1969. Volume II — in preparation

11: S. I. Goldberg. Curvature and Homology. 1962.

12: Sigurdur Helgason. Differential Geometry and Symmetric Spaces. 1962

13: T. H. Hildebrandt. Introduction to the Theory of Integration. 1963.

14: Shreeram Abhyankar. Local Analytic Geometry. 1964

15: Richard L. Bishop and Richard J. Crittenden. Geometry of Manifolds. 1964

16: Steven A. Gaal. Point Set Topology. 1964

17: Barry Mitchell. Theory of Categories. 1965

18: Anthony P. Morse. A Theory of Sets. 1965

Pure and Applied Mathematics

A Series of Monographs and Textbooks

19: Gustave Choquet. Topology. 1966

20: Z. I. Borevich and I. R. Shafarevich. Number Theory. 1966

21: José Luis Massera and Juan Jorge Schaffer. Linear Differential Equations and Function Spaces. 1966

22: Richard D. Schafer. An Introduction to Nonassociative Algebras. 1966

23: Martin Eichler. Introduction to the Theory of Algebraic Numbers and Functions. 1966

24: Shreeram Abhyankar. Resolution of Singularities of Embedded Algebraic Surfaces. 1966

25: François Treves. Topological Vector Spaces, Distributions, and Kernels. 1967

26: Peter D. Lax and Ralph S. Phillips. Scattering Theory. 1967

27: Oystein Ore. The Four Color Problem. 1967

28: Maurice Heins. Complex Function Theory. 1968

29: R. M. Blumenthal and R. K. Getoor. Markov Processes and Potential Theory. 1968

30: L. J. Mordell. Diophantine Equations. 1969

31: J. Barkley Rosser. Simplified Independence Proofs: Boolean Valued Models of Set Theory. 1969

32: William F. Donoghue, Jr. Distributions and Fourier Transforms. 1969

33: Marston Morse and Stewart S. Cairns. Critical Point Theory in Global Analysis and Differential Topology. 1969

34: Edwin Weiss. Cohomology of Groups. 1969

35: Hans Freudenthal and H. De Vries. Linear Lie Groups. 1969

36: Laszlo Fuchs. Infinite Abelian Groups: Volume I. 1970

In preparation

Keio Nagami. Dimension Theory.

Peter L. Duren. Theory of H^p Spaces.